Neothink®
Superpuzzle

Neothink®
Superpuzzle

Mark Hamilton

NEOTHINK® BOOKS

Published by Integrated Management Associates
850 S. Boulder Highway, Henderson, Nevada 89015, U.S.A.

First published in the United States of America by
Integrated Management Associates

4 6 8 10 9 7 5

LIBRARY OF CONGRESS
CATALOGING-IN-PUBLICATION DATA
Hamilton, Mark
Superpuzzle
ISBN 0-911752-08-0

791112108
Library of Congress #89-85937
Printed in the United States of America
Original Edition
1999 - 2012 over 250,000 copies [MAS]
New Edition

October 2012 [PP-NTIII] [5,228]
May 2013 [PP-NTIII] [11,168]
August 2013 [PP-NTIII] [26,408]
April 2014 [PP-NTIII] [26,619]
March 2015 [PP-NTIII] [25,000]

Table of Contents

Conceiving The Superpuzzle

Book One Of Superpuzzle

1 of 3

The Secret Society Begins

A Word From The Author

It's true: there are now a handful of immortals on Earth, which has been kept secret. They are Earth's first immortals, and they reside deep within the Society of Secrets. Members within the Society of Secrets join Earth's first immortals each year. In fact, that has been the secret mission of the world's most powerful secret society for the past four decades.

The story that follows takes you deep inside the highly-guarded, inner circle of the Society of Secrets, deep into the heart of the secret society — into its secret mission. I tell you the story from the beginning, starting when Earth's first immortals were just children, when the superpuzzle was conceived. In order to communicate this story that involves explicit details deep inside the highly-guarded walls of a secret society, I had to develop a new writing form, which I call faction.

Faction is not a new word, but I am creating a new definition. Faction puts the *fact* into fiction...*fact*ion. But the factional story in your hands does much more than simply blend fact with fiction. It builds an unbroken line of logic based on the facts, which defines faction. Although the story line can cross over into fiction, the line of logic is pure nonfiction.

Faction was the only way I could bring to you the ongoing, greatest kept secret of all time. Indeed, faction was the only way I could bring you the goings-on deep within the world's most powerful secret society and expose the details of its most secret mission: bringing us Earth's first immortals.

CONTENTS

Book One
Conceiving The
Superpuzzle

I.

Miracle Year

CHAPTER
ONE

The fraternity brothers and sorority sisters gathered around the television. "Five, four, three, two, one...Happy New Year!"

The party in the Sigma Chi fraternity house suddenly turned into a kissing free-for-all. Everyone joined in...except Jake. He never looked away from the television as the host recounted the three major discoveries made during the year that just ended.

"Will the magic continue in the new year, after a year that'll go down in history in medicine, economics, and physics?" the host was saying.

"Humanity will forever honor Dr. Sally Salberg for her *miracle molecules* that plug up the receptor sites of the influenza virus, making it unable to attach to and attack our living cells, rendering all strains of the virus harmless to humans. Dr. Salberg's discovery, that will save millions of lives, came by a sort of twist of fate as she was working on a radically different approach to curing cancer. We can only hope that her genius can bring us that cure someday, too. I speak for humanity, and from the bottom of my heart, when I say, *'Thank you, Dr. Salberg.'*

"Shifting to economics, millions of ordinary working men and women are forever grateful to software genius, Theodore Winters, who brought us the internet software called: 'A Company Without a Company/Without a Country'. His groundbreaking software lets people build and run multi-million-dollar companies all over the world...right out of their homes or right on their laptops. Through his controversial phantom-bantam-company method, the company itself seems to vanish as it becomes impossible for governments to determine what country it belongs to in order to tax the corporate profits. His World-Wide-Web software gives entrepreneurs one major advantage: without profits being taxed, the many new companies-without-a-company/without-a-country can pour money back into their businesses. Therefore, they're thriving and growing around the world. In less than two years, millions of new entrepreneurs hiring tens of millions of new employees have nearly eliminated unemployment in some countries, generating trillions of dollars worldwide in annual employee income taxes, a good portion of that going to the IRS itself. A bill in the House of Representatives to outlaw 'A Company Without a Company/Without a Country' seems to be losing support. Too many people want it, and politicians seem afraid to vote against it. So it appears Mr. Winters — the man who never finished high school, the richest man alive — will go down in history as the hero who essentially eliminated unemployment, not as the villain who cheated the government, as Capitol Hill would have it.

"And, of course, shifting to physics, we'll never forget last January when the world watched the proof unfold, right before our very eyes, to Dr. Ian Scott's theory of an ether, otherwise known as an invisible *existence field* made up of the tiniest subatomic particles he calls *gravity units*. Never will we forget the dramatic half-time show that upstaged last year's Super Bowl...as 75,000 fans pushed the buttons installed on their chairs each time they saw one of the sixty green laser lights that flashed during the laser-light show. People around the world watched as the 75,000 fans pushed their buttons sixty different times, causing four-and-a-half million registered impulses. As you know, those four-and-a-half million impulses were being captured and displayed on a big-screen computer terminal. As they were being captured, they dramatically formed into the pattern of the double sine waves:

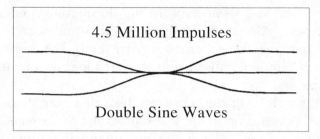

"Before the experiment, Dr. Scott explained why, given the speed of Earth's revolution around the Sun relative to the different locations of the people in the football stadium, the fans' impulses forming the double sine waves could only mean a field of invisible matter — an ether — was affecting the light and the fans' perception of it, relative to where they were sitting. The moment people around the world knew an ether existed, Dr. Scott's exciting follow-up question rose in their minds: could the existence field work like a super-advanced quantum computer, as the circuitry to a Universal Computer into which advanced conscious beings download their knowledge? The theory now abounds among physicists. Tapping into such a Universal Computer would mean tapping into all knowledge in the Universe, unlocking the secrets of the Universe, perhaps Dr. Scott's next great discovery.

"Ladies and gentlemen, let us go now to the three young heroes — the favorites to win the Nobel Prize in medicine, economics, and physics. ...Hello, Dr. Salberg, Mr. Winters, and Dr. Scott!"

The satellite feed went to the three phenoms for a few words. Each of them took a few minutes from their private New Year's Eve parties to answer questions. Jake's eyes widened. The three heroes looked about the same young age...somewhere in their mid-30s. He strained to hear them through the slurred singing of *Auld Lang Syne* in the frat house. Curing the flu, ending unemployment, tapping into universal knowledge...wow, Jake pondered, they represent our first clues of what's to come in the twenty-first century.

Thirty minutes later, Jake wrestled his way through a half-dozen of the fraternity's "little sisters" who hugged him and did not want to let go as he tried to leave. After a 10-yard drive, he broke free and went back to his dorm room and logged onto the Internet. After a few minutes with some search engines, he learned that the three heroes were exactly the same age. That astonished him and caused him to start looking for other common denominators.

At about 1:30 in the morning, Jake discovered something that made his mouth drop open: the sensational three went to the same elementary school! They did not attend the same high school or college. Now, this had Jake thinking. If they had, by chance, gone to the same university, Jake could possibly understand that...but the same elementary school?

*

Jake loved to solve a good mystery. So, with no classes until next semester, and a week off from his part-time job as a waiter at Steaks & Wines, Jake got in his black Grand Cherokee Jeep early in the morning of the third of January and drove to Cheektowaga, New York, 455 miles away, where the three phenoms attended Duncan Elementary School about twenty-five years before.

He arrived at the small town early in the evening and checked into a small motel. He drove around the town that evening wondering: how could the three most sensational accomplishers in the world come out of this little blue-collar town, and all three at the same time? What did they have in common here?

The next day, after having spent the morning on the Internet further researching those three superachievers, Jake walked into Duncan Elementary School around one o'clock in the afternoon. Only two people seemed to be there. Jake started asking the pleasant young receptionist some questions. She was aware that the three big names had gone to school there, but she did not know much more about them other than that.

As Jake asked the young woman a few more questions, the janitor who had been in the room cleaning the floor approached the two of them with mop in hand. He was a kind black man approaching sixty.

"Excuse me, I overheard your questions," he said. Leaning against the handle of his mop, the janitor continued with a hint of pride, "I've worked here for over 30 years, and I personally knew those kids."

Jake felt as though he hit the jackpot, and he started asking the janitor questions, trying to find a clue to perhaps something that might have had an influence over those three great achievers. But the janitor seemed to be a step ahead of Jake's questions, as if he already knew what Jake was looking for and was guiding him to it.

"Those three kids were in the same third-grade class together, you know," the janitor said.

"You mean, they had the same teacher?" Jake asked.

"Yup, they sure did."

"Did they have any other classes together here?"

"Nope, only third grade."

"Do you remember much about their third-grade teacher?"

The janitor motioned for Jake to step outside with him. Outside, the air was crisp, but Jake and the janitor stood in the sun, and there was no wind. It felt good.

"So, do you remember what their third-grade teacher was like?" Jake asked again.

"Oh yes...I'll never forget her," the older man said. He smiled. "And to answer the question you've been searching for, she was the launching pad for those three kids."

Jake felt the skin on the back of his neck crawl. "Can you tell me about her?"

"I can tell you," the janitor said. Then he began telling the story, with unmistakable love in his voice...

"Oh yes...I remember that September morning when I saw Miss Annabelle for the first time. She was standing outside the school, not in her classroom like the other teachers. She was so beautiful, yet so reachable; she was different than anyone I ever met, even to this day...

"She was smiling and saying hello to all the children as they came in. From the moment I saw her, I knew she loved children, and it was almost as if she knew her time here would be limited, so she absorbed every moment right from the start.

"I couldn't help myself; I followed her to her classroom. She went inside and closed the door. I stood next to the door and listened through the glass panel. She...she started singing *The*

Impossible Dream from the play Don Quixote. The kids were laughing. They must've thought she was crazy, until she finished…wow, what she said to those kids. I wish someone said that to me when I was in third grade. I'll never forget it…"

*

"Don Quixote chased after an impossible dream," began the lovely Miss Annabelle, "but he was insane. His golden helmet was a tin shaving cup. His enemies were windmills. He was a crazy old man who lived in a world of illusions. You, too, live in a world of illusions. This world we live in will have you think you're crazy to go after your dreams. But I'm here to show you that you *can* go after and achieve your dreams. Those dreams are NOT impossible, and you are NOT crazy to go after your dreams. In fact, seemingly impossible dreams can be achieved routinely when you have the power to see through appearances to the essence of things. This year, I'll teach you how to do that. Don Quixote was a powerless dream chaser in a world of illusions. You, beautiful children, will grow up to become powerful dream doers in a world of reality. My dream is to be sure you do. This year, I'll: 1) properly educate you in the basics of math, science, literature, and history, and 2) teach you how to think in integrated concepts and to see past all the powerless appearances to the powerful essences. *It is my dream* for you children not to live the normal blasé life that appears before us, but to dig deeper at life to build great achievements and happiness. And because I'll go after my dream, some people around here might start calling me a crazy person. I sort of expect it. But, when you go to the essence of things, which is how I'm going to teach you, then no outside appearances make any difference at all. I'll be focused on the essence of educating you. Sometimes in this world, you must forge ahead when you reach through to the essence, no matter what appearances develop around you. You must forge ahead to do what you know at its essence is right.

"So, how many of you want to grow up and do great things with your lives?" All hands shot up.

"How many want to make things people want to buy, and

14

make a lot of money?" Every hand went up with no depreciation of enthusiasm. Miss Annabelle kept on:

"What is the reason for living?" Such a philosophical question to eight-year-olds would normally silence the group. But, of her twelve students, four hands went up. Miss Annabelle pointed to the boy in the back. "Stand up, state your name, then give me your answer."

"My name is Danny Ward. I want to build tall buildings when I grow up." With that comment, every hand in the class went up within about five seconds or less. Each child wanted to tell what he or she wanted to do when grown up. Miss Annabelle, who cleverly led the class to this charged-up introduction of names and dreams, had each child stand up and tell his or her name followed by his or her dream. From then on, each child's dream took on a new dimension, for the child was using his or her dream to answer the question, "What is the reason for living?"

After all twelve children introduced themselves and their dreams, Miss Annabelle continued the stampede of thoughts: "When you told me your dreams, I saw in the eyes of each and every one of you the sparkle of happiness. *Happiness* is the reason for living. And achieving your dreams is the way to generate happiness. And, as I told you, each one of you will grow up to achieve your dreams. Your journey began when you walked through my door, and it is a journey of no return."

The eight-year-olds sat at attention. Not one child had yawned. They never, not ever in preschool, kindergarten, first or second grade, or at home, had ever been talked to like this. Twelve wonderful children were awestruck; they were falling in love with Miss Annabelle.

"This week and next, we'll work hard on the basics. A week from this Saturday, I'm planning a camp-out at Lake Pinewood for those who want to enjoy a night in the wilderness. I'll need four parents to volunteer to go. Bring me a note by Wednesday signed by a parent if you're going. And let me know if your mom or dad can volunteer to join us."

Over the next two weeks, the children and their teacher grew close.

Superpuzzle

*

The janitor stopped telling the story and started studying Jake's face. For a moment, Jake wondered if the janitor were going to continue.

Finally he said, "When it was all over, she left me her diary, which included her private thoughts during that miracle year."

"When it was all over?" Jake asked.

After another searching look and long pause, the janitor cautiously continued, "I'll tell you the full story, son, from my own observations, from things her students told me, and from her private diary. But you have to promise me something."

"Sure. What's that?" Jake said.

"If you tell others the story, you must tell it like it was, not like the papers told it."

"Yes...I promise," Jake said sincerely.

The tall black man seemed so careful and caring, Jake forgot to ask, "Why? Why did she give you her private diary?" But the janitor anticipated the question and asked it for him:

"Do you know *why* she gave me her diary?" he said.

"She didn't...*die*, did she?" Jake asked.

"No! Well, not physically anyway. She gave me her diary because she wanted my wife and me and her students to know how much she loved us."

"What happened here? What happened to her?" Jake asked.

"To understand, you need to know everything from beginning to end."

Then, the janitor continued telling Jake the story...

*

When Saturday came, it was a beautiful September day for the camping trip. Miss Annabelle felt flattered, for all twelve students showed up by noon at the school with eight parents...quite a turnout for a Saturday overnight excursion!

They loaded two Vans, two Suburbans, and a pickup truck with sleeping bags, blankets, food, and people. They brought tents, but only as a precaution, for Lake Pinewood Campground was famous for the soft beds of fallen pine needles. They had

16

decided to sleep tentless under the stars. The forty-minute drive to Lake Pinewood Campground passed quickly. The children barely noticed the green countryside and farm animals as they played rock, scissors, paper, or sang with the radio or, for most of the drive, told the scary ghost stories they had planned to tell later when it was dark.

When they arrived at Lake Pinewood, the windows came down as cheers trumpeted from the five vehicles, announcing to the campsite the kids had arrived. Miss Annabelle took a deep breath of the fresh air. She loved the minty smell, the green pine trees, the brown bed of soft pine needles, the lake and its cool breeze. Everything here was soft — the soft smells, soft ground, soft sounds of fish jumping, birds chirping, and little waves breaking.

*

That night after roasting marshmallows and telling ghost stories, they lay zipped tight in their sleeping bags. As they lay on their backs and looked above into the cloudless night, their vision seemed to skip right past the invisible sky and into space, filled with big bright stars. The night was still; Miss Annabelle talked in a relaxed voice, "The first day of school you each told me your dreams in life. I wonder if any of you can think of a common denominator beneath those twelve dreams?"

"What's a common denominator?"

"Something in common. What's something in common among your twelve different dreams?"

The parents were a bit surprised by the deep level of the discussion with their eight-year-olds. And they were even more surprised by their children's responses that were perhaps more thought out than the parents' own thoughts about their own dreams:

"They all made us happy," Sally said.

Miss Annabelle smiled in the dark and whispered, "Yes, and what else?"

"They all were valuable to others," Danny added.

"Yes!" Miss Annabelle said, her voice radiating with pride, "I *am* impressed with you children. Those are two common

17

denominators beneath your different dreams. Achieving your dreams involves *building values* for others, which in turn brings pride and *happiness* to you. Now, I want you to know that your specific dream may change someday. Dreams sometimes do that. And sometimes, when we get close to going out on our own after high school and college, we're not sure what we want to do, and no dreams step up to bat as they did for you the first day of school. If that happens to you, I want you to remember that sometimes life gets very complicated. When you are almost grown up and aren't sure what to do with your life, remember back to when you were in Third Grade...you already knew the answer, which I will repeat: *Achieving dreams comes from building values.*

"In whatever you do, put full effort towards *building values* — not just getting the most for doing the least like so many people today. Put your focus on building values to get on the winning path in life. Building values for society, no matter what you're doing, will bring you success, pride, and *happiness*. As your momentum grows, you'll naturally form new dreams; then, as your momentum grows, you'll achieve them."

When Miss Annabelle stopped talking, no one said anything because they were still listening to her words in their minds.

After a stretch of silence occasionally broken by a few young people's yawns, Miss Annabelle read a number of the campers' thoughts when she said, "Isn't it beautiful up there?"

"Have you ever wondered where it all came from?" one mother said.

"From God," another mom softly said.

"Miss Annabelle, would Charles Darwin say that God created the Universe?" Ian asked.

"Yes, Ian, he probably would have," Miss Annabelle answered. "Charles Darwin desperately wanted to keep a place for God and a place for Natural Selection. ...By the way, the kids have been studying Charles Darwin's Theory of Evolution by Natural Selection the past week," she explained to the parents. "But there's something I haven't told you about Natural Selection.

"Before Natural Selection, the whole world believed that the beautiful animal kingdom, including man, was God's creation. Before Darwin and Natural Selection, there simply was no other rational way to explain intelligent man, beautiful animals, and perfectly complex ecosystems. When Darwin released his Theory of Evolution, the world was stunned. There, before them, after thousands of years of thinking a Majestic Creation made man, was overwhelming scientific evidence that told us man, animals, the ecosystem came not from a divine plan, but merely by *chance*. Before Darwin, a scientific explanation for the world around them was simply beyond their scope of knowledge.

"When I look at the stars above, I feel that our knowledge about the Universe is sort of like our knowledge about the world before Darwin. Majestic Creation is perhaps our best possible explanation now, yet I wonder if someday science will explain it all. Throughout all of history, when something goes beyond man's scope of knowledge, humanity always turned to God as the explanation...until science caught up and solved the mystery."

Miss Annabelle had just questioned the existence of God before twelve students and eight parents, but her voice, with traces of English accent picked up from her English nanny while growing up, was so sincere and lovely; even the adults seemed to find solace in her wandering thoughts, and no one objected.

*

Miss Annabelle was singing as the children came into the classroom and sat in their chairs. They enjoyed watching their teacher; she was an image of beauty with a sweet voice. She stopped, which broke the enchantment. "How old are you?" she asked.

"NINE!" Seemed to drown out the eights, although she knew the ratio would certainly favor the eight-year-olds.

"So, you're eight or nine already. You're growing up fast. Who of you have ever thought about love?" Four or five hands went halfway up, but came down quickly in reaction to the snickers and giggles. Miss Annabelle could not hold back her own giggle, delighted by the children's innocence.

"Someday, love will become one of the most important events in your lives. So today, I'd like to talk just a little about love." She looked around at the twelve little blushing faces. After a moment, their nervous giggles turned to curiosity. They want to know, she said to herself; they're ready to hear this, and I'm going to tell them.

"I hear more and more these days that men and women have to be equals at everything they do. But let's see through to the essence of things."

"But shouldn't they be equal, Miss Annabelle?" Nattie asked.

"When talking about life in general, you're absolutely right. But when in love, everything changes."

"Let's go to the essence," wide-eyed Teddy requested. That expression had become a sort of motto in Miss Annabelle's class over the past couple of weeks. When teacher or student wanted to fully understand something, someone usually said, "Let's go to the essence."

"OK, let's do," she said. "What is the essence of love? I know you kids can get this one."

A number of answers filled the room:

"To tell each other secrets."

"No...to have someone to pick out your clothes."

"To be together — like going to the movies."

"Someone to grow old with."

"To have babies."

"To take care of the kids."

"You're all on the right track," said Miss Annabelle, "but go down to the common denominator that makes all those things happen. Remember, common denominators can help us get down to the essence."

Cathy, who silently suffered the toll of witnessing frequent fights between her parents, somberly said, "The essence of love is to be happy."

"Yes!" Miss Annabelle shrieked, startling Cathy, causing a tiny smile to crack her face. "To be happy! Don't ever forget that. Now, I'll tell you what is needed to be happy."

At this moment, the door to the classroom opened, and in walked Mr. Burke, the school's guidance counselor. He walked to the back of the room and sat at an empty desk. The children all got tense, but Miss Annabelle quickly removed their anxieties:

"Are we not talking about the essence of something here?

20

Remember what I've told you: once you get through to the essence of something, then no outside force can be of any influence. No one can change *the essence* of love, no matter what they might say or do."

Mr. Burke looked surprised by the subject matter and ironically became tense himself, while the kids relaxed. A voice then floated through the air, "Miss Annabelle, I want to know what love is."

"Of course, Nattie. Love is your reward in life — your reward for making values. Love is your way *to be* happy. Who remembers how you *make* happiness?"

"Building values for the world!" Teddy shouted.

"Yes, Teddy! And true love is the time two people take together to feel that happiness. Do not fall in love for any other reason than to be happy. No matter what others say about love and what it should be, the essence of love is to be happy. The person you fall in love with must be someone with whom you can celebrate your life and be happy.

"Whereas men and women both make or build values, they sometimes do so differently. A man will be happiest building values for the world through his work. A woman can be happy that way, too, and by making values for her husband, even helping him build his values."

At this moment three hands went up.

"Yes, Sally?"

"Isn't a man happy from helping his wife build her values?"

"Sally, when you grow up, you can go as far as any man in any career you choose. Your mind can do what any man's mind can do. But when you get married, you're going to want a man you can look up to and admire...someone driving on his own value production, not someone who depends on your value production. It has to do with the nature of man and woman, and, no matter what we are told, never deny your nature. You, as a woman, want to fall in love with your hero, not your assistant."

"Yeah," Sally sighed, getting lost in a dreamy fantasy.

In the back of the room, Mr. Burke sat with his arms folded. Miss Annabelle could not help thinking how the boys, at that moment, looked like mature little men while Mr. Burke looked

21

like an immature big boy.

"That's enough about love today," Miss Annabelle announced, but she was surprised by the moans of disappointment among her little audience who obviously wanted more.

"But Miss Annabelle, what about, you know..." Reggie said shyly.

"Yeah, like going all the way," a more confident Danny said.

Miss Annabelle was shocked to see the class looking at her seriously. Some of the kids knew what Danny meant, some did not. But no one was giggling. Things sure have changed since I was a girl, she thought; I didn't even know what getting to first base was for another four or five years. ...Kids grow up so fast these days.

Miss Annabelle studied her students' faces. They really want...and *need*...to know *from me*, she realized. Although romance at any level is several years away, she thought, they need to understand romantic relationships *from me* in order to shape and be ready for their futures and to protect themselves.

The children knew that whatever Miss Annabelle told them was different from what others told them. What she told them cut through appearances to what was real, what was best. After a long pause, she said, "OK, kids..." But before she could continue, an amazed Mr. Burke in the back cleared his throat loudly. His obvious disapproval, however, did not stop Miss Annabelle. One sweeping glance across the twelve sets of eyes transfixed on her told her they were crying out for competent knowledge about future intimacy. They needed to know now to prepare psychologically for their futures.

"Romance. That one word opens a whole new world to you when you're older. Its emotional repercussions and physical consequences throughout your life are major." Miss Annabelle liked to throw big words at her eight and nine-year-olds from time to time. "The older you are, the better you'll handle the vast world of romance. You must always treat romance as important, especially you girls."

"Why?" one little girl named Debbie asked, trying to remain anonymous.

"For one thing, you can become pregnant. But you'll hear a lot about that from others. What you will *not* hear about, I'm going to tell you now: When a woman has romance with a man, she's giving herself to him physically and emotionally, which means she's giving her body and heart to him. She's saying, 'Take me...I'm yours.' The man she chooses must be a man she looks up to and admires...or she is devaluing herself."

"Do men give themselves to their women?" Al asked innocently.

Miss Annabelle smiled affectionately and said, "They do give all of their love to their true love, darling. But a man does not physically and psychologically surrender himself, not like a woman does. For one thing, when they have romance, the man is larger and stronger, and the woman allows herself to be taken and gives her body and heart to that one man who deserves her — that valuable man building important values for society whom she looks up to."

By now, Mr. Burke would not stop writing down notes in the back of the room, but Miss Annabelle would not stop talking until she felt the essence of a romantic relationship was planted. She thought, if I don't do this, no one ever will.

"The man she chooses to give herself to reflects back every day her own self-image and self-worth. Now, maybe you can see why a woman is deeply happy with a man she looks up to," she continued. "And now, maybe you can see why she can be happy helping him build his values. The more *he* accomplishes for the world, the more *her* happiness grows.

"On the other hand, it is very important for you men to find the woman who understands values, for she will love you deeply and devotedly for being a man who builds values. She will look up to you as the real catch."

Of course, Miss Annabelle knew that many of the kids did not understand everything she said and that most probably did not even know the details of lovemaking. But she felt she said enough to plant a sense of man/woman physical/psychological relationships and their life-changing importance. So now, she wrapped up the love discussion and tied it back to where they started today:

"So, back to what I said earlier, do not get confused by what you might hear about how love should be. The mixed-up world around you will take away your nature as man and woman. For instance, do not listen to that women lib talk. That talk is the first to balk at the idea of a woman giving herself to a man in an intimate relationship. Women's lib causes millions of women to deny their nature, which takes away the deepest happiness in a woman's life of being in love with a man she can look up to and admire, a man she can privately surrender to. Of course, girls, remember you can go as far as any man in any career, but your husband must be someone special — that productive man you can look up to.

"Now, boys and girls, I want you to get out your Math books. It's time to get into numbers..."

Mr. Burke got up and left the room.

CHAPTER
TWO

Jake had planned to drive back to Boston that first night. But he knew the janitor's story about Miss Annabelle had just begun. And from what Jake heard so far, the three heroes of the new century had their start right there in the third grade, twenty-seven years ago in Miss Annabelle's classroom. Indeed, the three heroes made radical shifts from grooved-in appearances in their fields; they cut through to the essence in physics, medicine, and business.

Jake asked the janitor if they could spend some time together over the next couple of days.

"Sir, in honor of Miss Annabelle, I'd find it a privilege to tell you the whole story, 'cause if I don't, Lord knows the world will never know what happened here."

"What do you mean?" Jake asked.

The janitor's face seemed to be full of emotions as he gazed at the horizon; he said, "My god, I sometimes imagine what could have been. ...Yeah, we'll spend some time talking; you'll find out soon enough. I'll tell you everything."

"Thank you, Mister..."

"Jessie...call me Jessie."

"Thank you, Jessie. My name's Jake...I'm attending Boston University."

25

"Are you writing a story for the college paper?" Jessie asked.

"You know, Jessie, I'm minoring in journalism, but I came here only out of curiosity. Now, it seems to be more than that...like I'm going to discover powerful ideas about life. But whatever I do with this story, I'll split the credit and, if the story sells, I'll split the money with you. We're partners, OK?"

"Ah, that's not necessary, Jake. I'm happy with my life here. I don't need nothin'. If you sell a story, my only price is that you tell it like it happened."

"You really care about Miss Annabelle, don't you?"

That statement seemed to surprise Jessie. He paused, remembering her, then said, "Yeah, I really do." A somber look came over his honest face. He hesitated as if he were going to say more, but instead gestured for Jake to come along.

They walked back inside the school, down a hallway lined with red lockers to the first door on the right.

"Tomorrow, I'll show you Miss Annabelle's old room," Jessie promised.

"Whatever happened to her?" Jake asked, feeling the urge to meet the former third-grade teacher.

"Ah, you'll find out. But ya gotta hear it in order, my man." Jessie was smiling. "Oh, and Jake, you're staying with me and the Mrs. We're going to need to spend some nights doing lots of talking to get you back to school in time for next semester."

They turned into the little room with the time clock. Jessie said he didn't have to work on January 4th, but he came in for a few hours to wax the floors while no one was in. He walked past the time clock without punching his time card, for he hadn't clocked in. They walked straight through the small room to the back door. Jessie lifted his worn red and black flannel jacket off the only hook on the wall, and they left through the back door. The temperature had fallen, and the condensation from their warm breaths blew back into their faces. They walked through the school's side parking lot to Jessie's old beat-up Plymouth Fury parked alongside three other newer cars.

"I'll drive you around to your car," Jessie said.

Jessie unlocked the passenger door first, saying something about the lock only working with the key, and went around to open his own door. Jake stood next to the car looking at his new friend.

"Jessie, I really appreciate what you're doing."

"No, I appreciate what you're doing, Jake. For twenty-seven years, I've waited for someone like you to come along." Then, Jessie looked down at his hands fumbling with the keys, and added, "I only hope it's not too late for Miss Annabelle."

"What happened to her? What happened to Miss Annabelle?"

But Jessie only smiled and whispered, "You must hear her story, first."

*

Jessie followed Jake to the motel. Jake got his things and checked out. Then he got in his car and followed Jessie. After a five-minute drive through the suburbs, they pulled into Jessie's driveway. Jake looked at the small but nicely manicured house and lawn: new paint, trimmed bushes and trees, a recently raked lawn. Jake could see that Jessie was a proud man.

"Yeah, this is where I've parked it for over 30 years. House and car are paid for. Me and the Mrs. drive to Florida for a week every year. We're happy." As Jessie said the words *we're happy*, Jake felt as if those two words summed up the meaning of Jessie's life. Without a lot of monetary success per se, Jake sensed the summary of Jessie's life, '*we're happy*', had come from a life of honesty.

As they stepped inside, a pleasant lady's voice called out, "Darling, you're home!"

Instinctively, Jessie leaned over and removed his shoes. Jake followed his lead. The house was warm, and taking off the shoes felt cozy.

In a moment, the pleasant female voice was followed by the appearance of Jessie's wife. "Oh, hi there. I'm Angie."

Jake looked up from his shoes at the slim, tall black woman with long straight hair, and he quickly stood up. "Hi, I'm Jake," he said while reaching out his hand to shake hers.

"Honey, Jake's from Boston University," Jessie said. "He's my new friend. He's doing some research, and I asked him to stay with us for a few days."

"Oh? What kind of research?" Angie asked Jake.

As Jake started to answer, he noticed he already felt at home around Jessie and Angie. They were old enough to be his parents. Jessie was an honest, salt-of-the-earth working man. And his wife, who had wrapped one arm around Jessie's waist, struck Jake as the jewel of Jessie's life. She was attractive, loving, and she obviously took good care of Jessie.

"I'm looking into the schooling of Theodore Winters, Dr. Sally Salberg, and Dr. Ian Scott," Jake answered.

"He's the first one to know," Jessie almost whispered to Angie. Jake noticed Angie's expression change.

"He's figuring it out?" Angie quietly said back to Jessie. He nodded.

After a moment of looking at Jake, Angie took a deep breath and smiled. Her face was so smooth and sweet that Jake thought it could outcompete two-thirds of the young girls' faces back at Boston University.

"Yes...we know a lot about them," Angie said to Jake. "I was wondering when someone *out there* would figure it out. Are you writing an article?"

"No...no, I'm just a student," Jake explained, "but I think something big is going to come of this. ...Angie, when you said you wondered when someone out there would figure it out, what did you mean by '*it*'?"

Angie looked at her husband.

"A few of the townsfolk know about the roots of the three heroes," Jessie offered. "I'm glad someone like you is here to find out more. The school has hushed it up. But when the three kids...I mean alumni...had their big breakthroughs, the few of us who remember...we knew it would only be a matter of time before someone would show up here."

"A cover up? What happened here?" Jake was confused.

"Let's have dinner, dear," Angie said. "We can talk then." She turned and took Jessie's hand. From behind, they looked like a couple of teenagers, Jake thought as he followed them into the kitchen and to the adjoining dining room.

*

"The pot roast was delicious, Angie," Jake announced.

"Yes it was, baby," Jessie agreed. "She takes good care of me, always has. I love ya, baby."

Angie, who was cleaning the table, looked at Jessie and moved her mouth, without speaking, in the unmistakable three motions declaring, "I love you."

Feeling right at home, Jake said, "Jessie, do you think Scott, Salberg, and Winters remember Miss Annabelle?"

"They'll never forget her," Jessie said without hesitation. "But I really don't know if they remember each other. Twenty seven years is a long time ago, especially for those giants."

"Well, then," Jake said, "Can I write them each a letter tonight to let them know?"

"No, dear," Angie jumped in, "let Jessie tell you everything first. You need to know everything. ...Why don't you two go into the living room. Jessie darling, light a fire, and you two get comfortable. I'll bring you coffee."

Jessie nodded at her affectionately and then led the young visitor into the living room. Jake rested back in the love seat as Jessie stuffed newspaper under two dry logs in the fireplace.

"Son, I've lived long enough to know that a spectacularly wonderful thing can be too good for this world. If you put a beautiful work of art like a Michelangelo sculpture in front of people, someone will eventually attack it with a hammer."

"What happened?" Jake asked.

"Well, it didn't go bad all at once. It started slowly late one Friday afternoon, but it grew like a cancer. The students had been out of school for about two hours, and the faculty had also gone home. The school was empty, except for Miss Annabelle, preparing lectures for her class. She often stayed late like that, which is how I got to know her. About six o'clock Friday evening, I was cleaning the hallway floor around the corner from her room when I heard Miss Annabelle talking loudly in her room. Something was wrong — she sounded afraid. I rushed to her room and opened the door. Mr. Burke turned around. Miss Annabelle's face looked frightened. 'Is there a problem here?' I asked. 'No, Jessie,' Burke replied. 'We're going over some issues here about the kids. You can go on about your work.'

"But I could see Miss Annabelle didn't want me to leave.

Superpuzzle

So I said, 'Your room's next on the agenda; I'm here to clean.'
Burke then left. While he was leaving, he said to her 'We'll
continue this discussion later,' and he bolted past me."

Jessie paused.

"Go on," Jake urged. "What happened next?"

Jessie continued his story, taking Jake's imagination back to
the time and place twenty-seven years before...

*

Miss Annabelle was speechless after Burke left the room.
She looked shaken and scared.

"Are you okay?" Jessie asked her.

She searched Jessie's genuinely concerned eyes for a moment
then said, "Yes. ...Thank you for showing up."

"I heard you all the way from the other hall; you sounded
upset."

"I was. That man...he was threatening to get me fired if I
didn't...never mind."

"I'll call the police, ma'am."

"No, no...please don't. You stopped him before he could
do anything. No, I'm just in shock over his behavior. Thank
you. Please, tell me your name."

"I'm Jessie. I'm the custodian." But seeing her still
breathing hard from the adrenaline released in her system, Jessie
added, "Miss Annabelle, are you sure we don't need to call the
police?"

"No Jessie. I *am* okay now."

Jessie tried to point out that Burke left saying he would
continue this discussion later, which was a threat. Miss
Annabelle listened to Jessie and thought about what he said,
weighing it heavily against another thought in her mind. After
sorting through her own thoughts, she said, "Jessie, with this kind
of thing, who knows what kind of psychoanalyzing and rumors
can get started. In the end, I might find myself in the middle
of a scandal and not be allowed to continue teaching my class."
Her voice trailed off. She was unaware that she was muttering
her own reaction to that last thought, "I couldn't bear to lose
my kids."

At that moment, the young black man understood, for he saw a look on her face he would never forget: the greatest infliction on Miss Annabelle would be separation from the twelve children she now loved. Her drive in life, he realized, was to educate those children her way — toward a new and limitless mind. Jessie knew that Burke's threats were sexual, which were very difficult for a woman to prove and could backfire and cause the worst kind of scandal for a third-grade teacher. She could not risk something like that, which could interfere with, or worse, end her year with her pupils.

*

The following Monday afternoon, after the children had gone home, Jessie slipped into Mr. Burke's room and shut the door behind him.

"Listen up, Burke: When it comes to Miss Annabelle, I'm your judge and your jury." Jessie's eyes were wide and looking down, his nostrils flared open. "You continue that discussion with her again, and I'll come after you."

Something inside Jessie was driving him to the edge of violence, and Burke could sense it. He was afraid, but he tried to act fraternal, for a moment. "Now Jessie, come on, I'm single; she's single. You know? I was just playing with her. Come on, you're acting like you're her father."

Jessie grabbed Burke's sports jacket and pulled him close, "You threaten her; I hurt you. You hurt her; I cripple you. Do you know what I'm saying?" Jessie stared at Burke who was nodding, too scared to talk. Then Jessie pushed Burke away.

Jessie left Burke crumpled and humiliated. Next Jessie went to Miss Annabelle's room. Her door was open, and he knew the moment he saw her that she was nervous. "Miss Annabelle?" he said as gently as he could. She jumped nonetheless. "I'm sorry, ma'am. May I come in?"

"Please do, Jessie. I've been on edge all day."

"You don't have to worry about him. I've put a scare into him. He'll stay away from you now."

"What did you do?" she asked, genuinely surprised.

"Let's just say he won't touch you if he respects his own

life."

"Thank you, Jessie. Thank you. Now I can get back to developing my lectures."

*

Early October brought cool mornings to this northeastern town...as well as increased absenteeism of the student body. But not a single student had missed a single day in Miss Annabelle's class. She gave more homework than the other teachers, lectured the basics more as a college professor might. But during those lectures, she would go off on important, related subjects, and she would uniquely dig past appearances to the essence of things to reveal startling new ways of looking at things. She showed her students how to begin to dig deeper by seeing common denominators.

Common denominators helped them dig past confusing appearances while pulling information together. Those daily "digs" into life were like delicious treats to the children. Her children loved to learn and understand, so for her students to miss a day of her class would be to *miss out*. Their young minds were putting together the exciting puzzle of life...and they did not want to miss a single piece to the puzzle! They had already learned the meaning of life and love...and there was something exciting about hearing long-standing beliefs, appearances, and the status quo routinely batted down by their teacher. Was she a rebel...or just very smart?

*

By mid October, Miss Annabelle was delivering startling lectures. When the cold and flu season began and some of Miss Annabelle's kids got sick, they argued with their parents to go to school, at least to first period. Parents were amazed at their children's new love for school.

At the parents' request, Miss Annabelle started recording her General Lecture, her first lecture of the day, so sick children who missed school could listen to the lecture at home. The General Lecture snapped exciting new puzzle pieces into the puzzle of life. The children loved those unpredictable morning lectures.

That same month, some parents began asking Miss Annabelle if they could make copies of her General Lectures for themselves. They really enjoyed her first lecture each morning before the specific lectures on math, science, history, and literature. But the parents' enthusiasm, as with all adults in this world in which dreams fade, never reached the level of their eight and nine-year-olds. For, their children, who were learning to see through appearances and illusions to the essence of things, sensed they would someday make their dreams come true.

Some adults had not given up, however. One evening when Miss Annabelle was walking toward her car, she noticed Teddy and his dad in the playground adjacent to the parking lot. They were throwing a football when they spotted Miss Annabelle.

"There she is, dad," Teddy said, giving away his father's ulterior motive for being there.

"Isn't it a little dark for football guys?" Miss Annabelle said with a chuckle, putting him at ease. "Hello, Mr. Winters."

"I'm so pleased to meet you, Miss Annabelle. My son has never loved school like he does now. I want to thank you for that...and for myself, too. I listen to the tapes of your General Lectures. Miss Annabelle, you have a special gift to see things differently."

"Not really," she said. "I just learned how to see through appearances to the essence of things. And your son is learning how to do this, too. My hope is that someday he makes wonderful values for the world and lots of money and happiness for himself."

"He believes in you. I can see your gift growing in my son...growing every day."

Miss Annabelle stopped walking; she turned and looked directly into Mr. Winters' eyes. "I normally don't say this to parents...but, it can happen to you, too."

"Yes...I want more. My life is like a trap of stagnation. My job is a routine rut...year after year. There's got to be more!"

Miss Annabelle studied his eyes further. Then she said, "There is more, and I'll tell you how to get it. I don't know your specific situation, but in general, success in every area of life comes by piercing through whatever appears to be, to *what is* — to the *essence*. Take your job and mine, for example. From what I've learned in my job, I would tell you to look past the stagnant responsibilities of your job, because they're misleading and not, in the end, what makes the business work, not what the business really demands. Forget about the managers, just as I forget about my staffs. They'll lead you either to miserable stagnation...or failure. I ask myself, what does educating a child demand, what's the essence? Let me tell you: it's not what meets the eye or what staffs or managers tell you. When I started teaching, I was told, more or less, to teach the children to integrate effectively in society. Sounded good, like what *appears to be* good education, but the year of my awakening I learned to look past appearances to *what is*...in my case, to what teaching really is: to teach the children how to someday build magnificent values that a lot of people want to buy, which starts by teaching them how to think for themselves, how to see past appearances to the essence of things. By doing that, my students will start integrating substantial thoughts that hold together because they're down past powerless illusions, down to *what is*...where the power is. There, they'll have the power to build clusters of substantial thoughts and ideas to eventually create values for the world and experience the excitement and happiness of their accomplishments, not to mention the wealth from selling their values...just as you can.

"So, just as I asked myself, you must now ask yourself, what does the business demand, what's its essence? You must look past the stagnant responsibilities handed to you, past all that to the essence of the business, which can always be reached in *any* job. What is the essence of the business? I'd say, to make money. How is money made in the business you work for? You must learn and absorb *those* responsibilities, Mr. Winters. Then, you're where the power is. Instead of just doing your boring routine rut and dreaming about a better life, you'll start putting together potent thoughts *that count*, that stick together and grow because they have to do with making money. At the essence of business — where the money is made — you'll feel the excitement of creating values and really living."

Miss Annabelle noticed that both Teddy's father and Teddy, too, listened intensely. Then Mr. Winters spoke in the tone of a man who just experienced an epiphany, "Learn and absorb the *money-making* responsibilities. Why, yes! What I do now at work has nothing to do with making money, nothing at all. ...But how do you suppose I'd take over those money-making responsibilities?"

"Go to where the power is — down to the essence," she said, so simply. "The essence of each money-making responsibility would be the nitty-gritty details it's made of. From my experience, most people don't like doing nitty-gritty details. If some eager, capable person came along, willing to soak up those unpleasant details, I'm sure he wouldn't be stopped. Before long, once he's got the details, he'll soak up the entire responsibility, too. No one even needs to know what's going on as you ferret your way to where the power is."

Mr. Winters and his son both looked as if they were thinking some daring thoughts. Miss Annabelle smiled at the two of them and concluded, "None of this is too difficult to do if you remember to answer to the essences. That's what I answer to, and that's why I am who I am and why Teddy's so motivated in my class."

*

"I feel as though I'm gaining the keys to success and learning the secrets of life," Jake said, interrupting the story being told. "How could anyone have a problem with that!"

"That toad started it all," Angie said in disgust.

"Burke?" Jake guessed.

"Yeah," Jessie said, shaking his head. "While Miss Annabelle was creating little geniuses for the world and helping their parents, one jerk was quietly spreading cancer seeds throughout the staff. Seeds grow, you know. In retrospect, had I known it back then, I would've scared that loser right out of town."

"My husband's right. Being rejected by Miss Annabelle, Burke went on a quiet mission of revenge; none of us knew it. He quietly told a handful of staff members, privately on an individual basis so no one could pinpoint the source that started those rumors, that Miss Annabelle had been talking about the act of sex to her students. He took her valuable discussion out of context and made it seem perverted."

"What a bastard," Jessie said under his breath.

"It's hard to recover from this type of accusation, you know, even if it's completely false," Angie continued. "Soon, the staff started talking among themselves. Miss Annabelle came under suspicion. The principal summoned her class recordings, which unfortunately had not started soon enough to have captured her valuable lecture on love. With tainted, preconceived notions, the principal concluded that the new teacher was strange and needed to be monitored."

"The thought that Miss Annabelle had done something wrong made everything she did that was brilliant with the kids seem as though it did not belong — like something weird, something too different," Jessie said.

"After all, the public school's definition of an education was to prepare the children to *fit in*," Angie said. "And Miss Annabelle *was* different — she was not about to teach her kids to conform."

"Besides, the principal of the school at the time was a mean-spirited woman who seemed to hate kids," Jessie said. "I noticed she didn't like Miss Annabelle. How could she? Miss Annabelle represented the child. She was everything good and wonderful the principal was not. Miss Annabelle was the essence of happiness. The principal was the essence of misery. Miss Annabelle reflected the beauty in life. The principal reflected the ugliness in life."

"So, Ms. Minner was quick to dig into the rumors with 'grave concern'," Angie said. "The rumors now escalated into an investigation and got on the agenda of the school board meeting. The negative thoughts about Miss Annabelle were spreading fast. And envy fanned the flames. Here was an opportunity to tie down her free spirit."

CHAPTER
THREE

Miss Annabelle seemed unfettered. She had no idea, however, of the dangerous sexual theme simmering beneath the gossip.

The more the gossip spread, and the more strange looks she got from staff and faculty, the more she pulled out all the stops and poured her love and free thinking into her lectures and onto her students.

The growing disapproval of her actually freed her to cut the disapprovers out of her constant considerations that tended to make her lectures a bit conservative. Removing them from the equation was like taking the last impurity out of a chemical solution needed to set off the power-reactor explosion. Her lectures now freely blew apart the matrix of illusions that trapped adults in a suppressed anticivilization.

She loved her kids, and they loved her. The bond grew so strong that its positive current swept her students away from anything destructive. The parents were delighted by their children's attitude toward school and life.

Defamed yet unfettered, devoted and determined...that combination of events and emotions brought out the most eloquent Miss Annabelle. Her lectures were stirring for her eight and nine-year-olds, for 39-year-olds, for 69-year-olds. She worked late into the evenings cutting through appearances in this world of illusions created by the media, academia, the Establishment, politicized big business, organized religion, the legal profession, the government...by the many freeloaders, by those who drain or tear down values instead of contributing to or building values. She pierced through to the essence of things, where the real power in life resided. If her students could grow up with their minds focussed not on appearances but on the essences of life, they could build powerful puzzles of ideas that would take them to new levels, to puzzle-pictures never seen before. They would become the power players, the value creators, the money/power giants.

She was not going to let anything in this world suppress those twelve children. Something inside her, something from her past, gave her a keen awareness of the life-destroying world of appearances and illusions — something she would catapult her pupils over and beyond.

*

During the rising controversy at Duncan Elementary School, a situation arose that made all Miss Annabelle's problems shrink by comparison. In early November, a little girl's parents visited Miss Annabelle. The mother was diagnosed with ovarian cancer. The doctors said she had from only a few months up to two years to live.

In Miss Annabelle's classroom that evening, overlooking the empty, little chairs and desks, Sally's mother struggled to talk clearly. "What should we do for poor Sally?" her mother asked as a large tear, then another, escaped her eyes.

Consciously, Miss Annabelle did not know how to answer that, but the answer, to her surprise, came rushing out from her subconscious, "Make every day beautiful. Send her to school so her mind keeps growing. When she gets home, spend as much time together as your energy allows. Make beautiful memories together that will last Sally's entire life. Of course, let her be with friends sometimes, which'll give her some experience of life without you. Gently, consistently prepare her for when the time comes...when she must go on without you.

The love you give Sally these few precious months must last a lifetime."

From that evening onward, Sally's mom spent almost all her afternoons and evenings with Sally, making every day precious. They did everything together and reached a love so special that they, at times, felt almost lucky.

That night Miss Annabelle could not fall asleep. She lay awake, knowing she could not protect Sally from the pain she would endure.

"What is the essence of death?" she sat up in bed, wondering. "Is there something beyond the appearances?"

She got out of bed and went to her desk. "I must break through. I *must* break through..."

*

Miss Annabelle's heart sank when she watched Sally come through the door the next morning. Sally knew; her eyes were wide with fear and lost in pain...a helpless, hopeless burden no one so young and tender should have to bear. Miss Annabelle watched Sally walk to her desk, lost in her pain, unaware of the other children. Sally sat and dropped her head down on her desk. Miss Annabelle saw her shoulders and back bobbing; she was crying. She looked so small, yet her pain was so large. Miss Annabelle, overwhelmed by the sight of the little girl in such grief, put her hand over her mouth as she herself fought to keep from crying. She walked over, knelt beside the little girl and put her hand on Sally's little shoulder. In one quick motion, Sally jerked around and buried her face into Miss Annabelle's shoulder. They hugged tightly for several minutes. The other children behaved like little adults, sat quietly at their desks, knowing their friend was very sad.

The other children silently watched Miss Annabelle and Sally. "Children, Sally's mother has an illness called cancer." Miss Annabelle felt Sally's grip tighten as she spoke. "Who of you here wants to someday discover cures to illnesses and diseases?" Sally eased her grip and lifted her eyes from Miss Annabelle's shoulders to see *all* her classmates raise their hands.

"I want to save Sally's mom," one little girl said.

"Me too." "Me too." "Me too," was said in near harmony by eleven classmates.

The compassion for Sally and her mother removed a little of the fear for Sally, at least for now. She was able to stop crying for now and lift her head off Miss Annabelle. Sally, her face overwhelmed with devastation, looked at her classmates one by one. Her eight and nine-year-old classmates looked back with compassion and love. Each child allowed Sally to look at him or her as long as she needed, without saying a word, as if her soul were being fueled with a little strength from each classmate.

Miss Annabelle noticed how beautiful the children looked during this magical moment. Their eyes all looked so big and round. Their faces looked so sweet, like little angels. She realized that this was how people looked, all people, both children and adults, when they were pure...free of negativity and dishonesty. This was the look of pure honesty and love. People, in their most genuine moment, are beautiful, she thought as this magical moment lasted.

With each look, Sally organized something inside her little head that was in disarray. This is exactly what she needs at this stage, Miss Annabelle realized. Each look into one of her classmates' eyes would warm Miss Annabelle's heart as she saw a little bit more emotional disarray put back into order. As Miss Annabelle watched this phenomenon, she felt so proud of her eight and nine-year-olds. This is my family, she thought. This is my life. I love them so much. I will protect them; I will teach them how to protect themselves to keep their dreams and to turn them into reality. I want them to have these beautiful faces when they are all grown up.

*

Over the next two weeks, Miss Annabelle struggled with the idea of death. What is the essence of death? She could not seem to break through the appearances. She thought about Sally a lot. Sally and her mother had discovered immense joy celebrating life together every day. Sally was doing fine now, but Miss Annabelle wondered how Sally would be once her mother took a turn for the worse.

When thinking about Sally one evening, how to possibly protect her, Miss Annabelle could not get over the hopeless finality of death. She shook her head in dismissal when thinking about the prevalent belief that death is not final, but just the beginning. Miss Annabelle was unsure of afterlife ideas and not sure if she believed in God or if God would someday be a silly ancient idea replaced by scientific explanations. But whether she believed or not did not matter. She emotionally knew, for Sally and her mom, the hopeless finality of death.

In acknowledging to herself the finality of death and its inescapable tragedy, she suddenly realized the *rightness* of happiness when we are alive...the unapologetic *rightness of happiness* during our one special flicker of life.

She never thought of her life that way before: the *rightness of happiness*. In fact, the more she thought about the finality of death, the more she felt this rightness of happiness. Ironically, she realized, the more she thought about death, her own death and Sally's mom, the more determined, even "pumped up" as her students would say, she got to squeeze every drop of happiness out of every day.

What's happening here? she was wondering. I feel like celebrating and savoring each day as a precious gift with my students. Then she thought about Sally and her mother. Those two make each day a celebration together. They savor each moment as a precious gift...even the mundane and minor moments. They have amplified their *rightness of happiness* because of impending death.

Can we all amplify our happiness by acknowledging our imminent deaths? Can we, too?

*

Two days later, Miss Annabelle handed out to each student a copy of a typewritten sheet with 30 rows across and 29 columns down, forming 870 little squares.

"Children, you're just eight or nine years old. You have your whole futures ahead of you. But I must warn you: that future — your everything — goes by *so fast* that it's easy for time to flash by without you getting out of life everything that you should. In this world of illusions, it's so easy to waste so much of our futures.

"In fact, the appearance to eight and nine-year-olds is that you have *so much* time ahead of you. But digging through appearances to the essence of your time ahead, you realize *how little* time we have. For instance, look at the Life Chart in front of you. That represents how little time we have to experience everything and to create everything we ever will in all eternity.

LIFE CHART

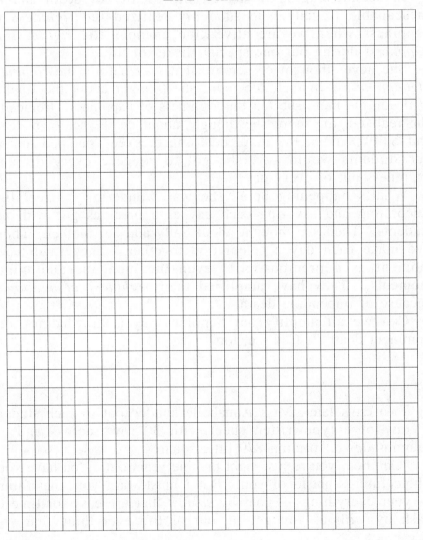

Each square represents one month of our lives. I invite each of you to put an "X" through about a hundred squares, leaving you with just about 770 left. Those 770 open squares represent your future — 770 months left. As you can see, it's not some huge, vast space for adventures untold. No, it's a confined and pressing finite period of time. The limited nature of that time is *why* our futures seem to fly by us so fast and why it is so easy to waste those precious months.

"The Life Chart is designed for you to not be fooled by appearances, but for you to see through to the essence of your future — just 770 months left! By seeing your future this way, you'll squeeze so much more out of life."

"Excuse me, Miss Annabelle," Teddy was saying, raising his hand. "Why 870 squares?"

"Good question, Teddy. Now in the 1970s in America, life expectancy has risen to 72 and 1/2 years. What's $72^{1/2}$ years multiplied by 12 months?"

After some pencil work, Teddy said, "Oh yeah, 870 months."

"And you kids are eight or nine years old. Eight times twelve is 96. Nine times twelve is 108. Put an 'X' through how many months old you are now.

"By doing this, you'll become acutely aware of the preciousness of life. It's a limited commodity, and that limited commodity is *your everything*. I do not expect Sally to do this because she and her mother know the preciousness of life. They know it so much more than we do, and they do not need to be reminded. But we do — we need to be reminded of *how little* life we have to experience everything we will ever know in all eternity.

"How many of you think about or at least feel, on a daily basis, how *precious* your life is and the lives of your loved ones?" One hand went up, Sally's hand. The expression on her face was one of awe for Miss Annabelle seeing through to what she and her mother had discovered.

"All of you will feel the preciousness of life when you start your Life Charts. I know, because I've started my own. I have a lot more squares 'X'd' off than you. In fact, about *half* of mine are gone! Every morning when I get up, I think about how precious my life is. Everything I do now, even routine things, I savor. I get so much enjoyment now out of things that before either I never stopped to notice or felt indifference for. I now celebrate my days. I really feel the excitement in life. For example, when coming to school in the mornings, I get all happy inside like I'm going to a big celebration. I celebrate life every day now. By seeing through to the essence of our futures — how little time we really have — I'm getting every bit out of life. I've become so focussed and so determined to educate you to be able to cut through illusory appearances and obstacles in order to build your dreams and happiness. ...I want to accomplish more. I want to love more. I want to share meaningful time together with loved ones. In short, I have amplified my existence, and I savor it.

"You'll find yourselves enjoying your parents and siblings more, loving them more while you're still together. Life together, and life in general, is precious. You'll find yourself, as you 'X' off those open squares, wanting to learn more, wanting to learn how to start building values for the world. You'll find yourself thinking that every value you ever make is limited to those open squares, and you'll find yourself wanting to make more and more values as you grow older. One thing is for sure: you'll *never* waste a portion of your precious life with the Life Chart."

Fortunately, Miss Annabelle was recording her lectures now. When parents first saw their children's Life Charts, they did not know what to think. But, Miss Annabelle made twelve copies of her General Lecture and sent the tapes home with her students. Hearing the lecture of the Life Charts warmed parents' feelings for Miss Annabelle.

The children responded with mature thought and insight into their lives. They began pondering their futures and their dreams, which was very advanced for eight and nine-year-olds. A few days later Danny said in class, "I started Life Charts for my parents." Before the week was over, all the children had started Life Charts for their parents. Seeing firsthand so many squares were "X'd" off on their parents' Life Charts, they grew closer to their parents. Over the next seven months of the school year, Miss Annabelle would get comments, phone calls, and mail from parents explaining how thoughtful and loving their children had become. The most common remark from parents was how their children were saying "I love you, mom and dad" for the first time in years...and saying it daily.

Whereas the children's love for their parents and siblings grew, so did their love for Miss Annabelle. Her sense of life seemed to mirror that of the children. She was always seeing through the gloomy appearances to the uplifting essence of things.

*

The effect Miss Annabelle had on her students was like a positive, powerful current. A child could swim against the positive current in rebellion, perhaps, but her omnipresent positive flow would soon wash the child further toward good than his or her struggle against it.

Rico, a nine-year-old boy, exemplified the effect of her powerful current of good. He was born into an unscrupulous line of male criminals. His father, uncles, and grandfather had notorious reputations and several years of prison time among them. Rico was not particularly attracted to crime. He got no thrill from the idea of stealing, like some other criminals. But the philosophy he was exposed to ever since he could think and talk filled his head with the criminal mind: *others owe me a living*. Therefore, guilt was removed from crime, greasing the way to a life of easy money through acts of crime.

But when Rico listened to Miss Annabelle one cold November morning, he was deeply moved. He was moved along in her current of good. Perhaps...perhaps he was experiencing his first love, his first crush...for the wonderful woman.

She was saying, "When we're young, like you children are now, life at times seems bigger than life. I want you to think of something you've done that, at the time, was so exciting that it almost didn't feel real. At the time, you knew it was a special experience, and today it might be in your memory as something spectacular, like a dream. Or, I'd like you to think about something you have not done but seems bigger than life to you, something you only dream about, but if you ever did it...wow!"

Rico found himself thinking about being on the big blue ocean in a beautiful yacht with his brother and Miss Annabelle, deep sea fishing. He could see a sailfish way out in the distance

Superpuzzle

jumping out of the water as Rico's brother and Miss Annabelle cheered Rico on...to reel it in. As this image teased his thoughts, he continued listening to the pretty teacher who was gracefully moving her arms like a ballerina in dance as she talked to the class:

"Right now, some fancy thoughts must be in those heads of yours. ...Anybody care to give us a peek inside?"

Sally was the first to raise her hand, which pleased Miss Annabelle. She knew today's lecture would be an important link to Sally's future, perhaps a masterlink to help Sally make the transition when the time came from life with mother to life without mother. Coincidently, Sally was also thinking about the ocean, but Sally's thoughts were a real memory from a few weeks before:

"Oh, I'm thinking about my trip to Hawaii with my mom and dad. It's like you say...it's like a dream in my head. The ocean. The beach. The fields. The mountains. I remember the motor-raft journey on the ocean to some little island and snorkeling there with dad and seeing all those tropical fish! Mom went with us and stayed on the raft. But we took lots of underwater pictures for her. And you know what, a whole school of dolphins came to the raft, and Daddy and I and the other people jumped in, and we swam with the dolphins!"

The room was filled with "wows" and questions for Sally like, "Did you touch one?" "What did it feel like?" "How many?" "Were you scared?"

After Sally answered her curious admirers, Miss Annabelle saw a twinkle in Cathy's eyes. Her hand was not raised, but Miss Annabelle had been wanting to reach this quiet student who sat away from others in class and in the lunchroom. "Cathy, will you share with us your thoughts? ...What seems bigger than life to you?"

Cathy's twinkle quickly retreated in fear. Her private world suddenly had eleven kids and her teacher trying to look inside. Then, for a brief moment, a flash of courage emerged in her eyes. It seemed she would open the door, but at that same moment she turned the lock to close out her classmates.

"No," she said with much effort; her eyes then darted nervously around the room at her classmates as her mouth sank back into her rotund face. Ever since she was a baby, she had always been obese. Years before her peers would know what self-consciousness was, Cathy struggled with being self-conscious and retreated to a life of self-chosen ostracization. ...Not since the first day of school, when Cathy announced she wanted to be a beautician, had she participated in class.

In the meantime, Rico was lost in his fantasy of pulling in the sailfish. In his daydream, he now was face to face with his oversized catch, waving the fragile Miss Annabelle back from the dangerous ferocity of his catch. Completely caught up in his daydream, he suddenly cried out, "...stand back, Miss Annabelle!" Of course, he startled himself along with the whole class and his teacher.

"Rico, what's wrong?" Miss Annabelle said.

"Nothing...umm...I didn't want you to trip over that chair." He was trying to recover; he did not want to reveal his private fantasy.

"I had a bigger-than-life experience with my dad," Teddy Winters offered. When he got Miss Annabelle's nod of approval, he told of his fascinating tour with his father of the General Motors car assembly plant. "Everything was *so big,* like those big metal arms that moved around and put the cars together! It was so cool to see the cars form right before you — so *many* cars. They told us that every single movement was studied so as not to waste even a split second."

Miss Annabelle nodded knowingly and said, "I've also visited a car production line. It was awesome, Teddy. Someday, I'll tell you about Henry Ford and his creation of the assembly line."

Hands were still up, and Miss Annabelle knew she must not leave any story untold. She pointed to Ian Scott.

"I can't forget the Observatory. We drove up the side of this mountain at night to the very top. Up there was a building and inside was a huge telescope. We looked at planets. The best one was Saturn. We could even see the rings around it. When I looked at the planets through the telescope, they seemed so clear and so close. I wonder when we'll travel to those planets."

After the last raised hand was chosen and the last story was told, Miss Annabelle was ready to continue her lecture. But Rico suddenly spoke, "I was dreaming I was on a big yacht, and I was reeling in a monster of a sailfish, and that you were there looking over the side at the big fish flapping against the boat. That's why I told you to stand back."

Miss Annabelle laughed in her sweet way, and Rico relaxed and smiled. She laughed some more and said, "Thank you for protecting me!" And with that, she continued her lecture:

"Those bigger-than-life experiences have a common denominator: they're all something new to you, never before experienced. Brand new experiences spark stimulating new sensations and carve powerful impressions and permanent places in your memories. Adults, however, have experienced most of those things already. So adults go through life deflated, flat, not feeling the bigger-than-life excitement that children do. But that boring life does not have to happen for you when you grow up. Let's look through appearances that make people believe that when grown up, we must settle into a boring rut. Tell me, what is the essence of happiness? Remember back to the first day of school...and to our camping trip. Do you remember? What is the essence of happiness? Yell it out...anyone."

"Making values," several students said out loud.

"Yes! Making values. And building something never seen or known before makes adults feel the bigger-than-life excitement like a child again. Children feel bigger-than-life excitement when they experience something new; adults feel bigger-than-life excitement when they build something new."

As Rico admired Miss Annabelle, he could feel his orientation to life changing. Does the world really owe him a living? If so, he thought, then he would miss out on the bigger-than-life excitement of building something new. He would miss out on the excitement he sees in his teacher every day. Yes, he wanted to be excited by life like his teacher, not in misery like his father. ...Later that afternoon, Rico returned an astronaut pen he had taken from Ian's desk. And for the first time in Rico's life, he apologized to a peer for wrongdoing.

*

At noon, the third-grade and fourth-grade students and

teachers filed into the school's cafeteria. Miss Annabelle was grateful that Mr. Burke, one of the school's two guidance counselors, ate during the later lunch period.

The teachers ate in a small break room next to the large cafeteria. The teachers' lunch room had two oblong tables with three chairs on each side and one on each end. And there were two smaller square tables with four chairs around them.

Miss Annabelle felt increasingly uncomfortable in the teachers' lunch room, especially since the rumors started. At first, she was welcomed by the other teachers. But even before the rumors started, she noticed a gradual change in attitude. The women started deliberately sitting at a different table. But because of Miss Annabelle's attractiveness that made men want to be near her, the male teachers would all sit at Miss Annabelle's table. But she was not interested in any of those men, and she was in no mood for men after being terrorized by Burke a few weeks before. So she was not responsive to their macho overtures or constant comedy.

Without Miss Annabelle applauding their efforts, the men slowly joined the women in characterizing Miss Annabelle as someone who "has problems", someone "strange", "different", and, eventually, as "that introvert child-woman who'll never find a husband."

Moreover, unbeknown to Miss Annabelle, the rumors about her "sexual discussions" with her third-grade students grew like a cancer. The other teachers, some subconsciously motivated by jealousies, began to ask rhetorical questions about Miss Annabelle. "I wonder if she's weird or has a thing for kids; maybe that's why she's not married?"

Today, Miss Annabelle could feel the tension as she walked into the teachers' lunch room. As she sat at one of the smaller square tables, alone, she suddenly thought, what am I doing here? I don't care about these people who eagerly entertain illusions without any effort or care to know *what is*.

Without wasting another moment of her life, Miss Annabelle stood up and almost ran out of the room. She went to the student cafeteria and scouted for a seat. The tables were oblong with attached benches, filled with about eight children per table. There were a few spaces open at the table where Cathy was sitting. Perfect! Miss Annabelle thought.

The cafeteria quieted down as Miss Annabelle entered. The children were surprised to see her. To their memory, a teacher had never eaten here with the kids. The hush, however, was not because the children felt tension in front of this teacher. The majority, those not in Miss Annabelle's class, were curious about the pretty lady who stood outside and greeted them the first day of school. They were merely observing her and enjoying the contagious smile that lit up her face as she joined the children. Unlike other teachers who looked tense and unhappy when approaching a crowd of children, Miss Annabelle was genuinely happy. This was where she belonged — with the children. And the children sensed this kinship with the pretty teacher who always looked so happy.

Her twelve students did not look away as they would with any other teacher. Instead, they said proudly to those around them, "Look, that's my teacher!"

When Miss Annabelle joined them that day — the first time a teacher at that school had eaten with the kids — her students' love for her grew even deeper. She was becoming their soul mate. From that day on, her twelve students wanted to sit with her at lunch. Within a week, all the children during lunch period wanted to sit with Miss Annabelle. One of the favorite lunch activities was for Miss Annabelle to tell a mystery story, and the kids at the table would try to solve it. She soon had to make a rotating seating arrangement so she could share her time somewhat evenly among the children, slightly favoring her twelve students.

That first day she came into the student cafeteria was a special moment. She went to the cafeteria line and got a student lunch while the children watched. She then sat at the table next to Cathy, the overweight, quiet girl in class. In less than a minute, the other four spaces at the table were filled with other students from her class. The table came to life with talk and laughter. This is where I belong, with these happy people, Miss Annabelle thought. Cathy stayed quiet, but Miss Annabelle noticed Cathy observing her. Miss Annabelle looked at the lunch before her: an open-face hot turkey sandwich with gravy, mashed potatoes, a dinner roll, and a dessert. Knowing Cathy was watching, Miss Annabelle matter-of-factly moved the dessert and the dinner roll to the top right corner of her tray, obviously with no intention of eating them. Out of the corner of her right eye, she saw Cathy do the same thing. Then, Miss Annabelle proceeded to slowly eat the sandwich and potatoes. Cathy kept pace with her. Without warning, Miss Annabelle turned and gave Cathy a hug. Cathy was shocked — she could not remember being hugged. She tilted her head down, her chin sinking into her fleshy neck. But inside, Cathy had taken flight with joy. Someone had noticed her! ...I will free this little girl from her prison, Miss Annabelle thought.

CHAPTER
FOUR

The holiday season was approaching, but Miss Annabelle no longer noticed the other adults at the school except for Jessie.

By now, all the children in the third and fourth grades knew her from lunch period. Miss Annabelle's recordings of her General Lectures now went to a cassette duplication service as the other third and fourth graders and several of their parents now listened to those lectures. The positive interest in Miss Annabelle among the students surged at about the same rate as the negative interest among the adults at Duncan Elementary School. But Miss Annabelle did not care. She shut herself off from the adults and devoted herself to the children.

On a chilly morning the week of Thanksgiving, Miss Annabelle's spirits rose when the handle to her door turned, a half hour before class. Someone's here for extra help, she thought. The class had been hard at work on the basics of math, science, literature, history, and two or three times a week someone would come in early for a little boost, which Miss Annabelle always enjoyed. But Miss Annabelle's spirits sank when she saw two adults at her door. One she recognized — Ms. Minner, the gloomy principal with a cold corpse-like look. The other pleasant lady, Miss Annabelle did not know.

"Miss Annabelle," the unsmiling principal said, skipping past common courtesies such as a pleasant greeting, "This is Mrs. Shaffer. She'll substitute for you today."

"I don't understand?" Miss Annabelle said.

"We'll talk in my office in fifteen minutes. Right now, please brief Mrs. Shaffer on what she'll be teaching today."

Twenty minutes later, Miss Annabelle walked into Ms. Minner's office without knocking. The principal was about to get a preview of the Miss Annabelle none of the adults at Duncan Elementary School knew: She was more courageous and emotionally stronger than most men...and her students were her treasure of love whom no one was to bother.

"Ms. Minner, don't you *ever* walk into my room thirty minutes before the day starts and yank me away from my kids. Unlike other yahoos you have here who call themselves teachers, I *lecture* my class — or have you forgotten about the old-fashioned lecture method that actually puts knowledge into young minds? I can't possibly turn a lecture over to a substitute in fifteen minutes. So you know what that means? My students do not get an education today! But that's probably okay with you, anyway. Now tell me, just what the hell is going on?"

Ms. Minner, who thought she could intimidate and easily handle Miss Annabelle, knew she was outmatched. Miss Annabelle not only was fearless — she was deeply knowledgeable on teaching. That made the principal nervous, especially when sensing the inseparable love this lioness standing before her had for her twelve students.

Miss Annabelle's gentle looks certainly were deceiving, and the principal was caught off guard. At this moment she had to make an instant decision: to sanctimoniously lecture Miss Annabelle as she had planned...or to just give her the facts. Overwhelmed by Miss Annabelle's fearlessness, the principal retreated and just relayed the facts, "The school board is having an emergency meeting tonight regarding you being able to continue teaching here. Until a decision is made, Mrs. Shaffer will teach your class."

"Continue teaching? What are you talking about!" Miss Annabelle was angry...and scared. She put her hands on the principal's desk and leaned close, seeing eye to eye. Ms. Minner sensed she'd better talk.

Superpuzzle

"There's been talk of sexual misconduct with your students," Ms. Minner said. She had not planned to reveal that to Miss Annabelle, not until surprising her with it in the evening's emergency meeting.

Miss Annabelle felt as though lightning had just discharged from her mind, attacking her heart, burning away everything in between. Then came the thunderclap behind her bosom, rocking all her internal organs, making it hard to breathe.

The comment was quick and deadly, like a gunshot in the heart. The impact was so great and left Miss Annabelle in such pain, that Ms. Minner, for an honest moment, felt sorry for the woman. At that moment, Ms. Minner knew Miss Annabelle was a victim of vicious rumors.

Miss Annabelle turned all white and felt faint. The thought that someone could even entertain the accusations that she could be a child molester, *and with these children who were like her own,* repulsed her to the verge of being sick.

But then, her repulsion shifted to the adults themselves who were *spreading* this rumor — those humanoids in the teachers' lunchroom who were either women filled with jealousy or men filled with spite for her constant rejections of their hidden desires to bed her. Of course, she now knew the humanoid who was behind this whole thing — Burke!

Without saying a word, Miss Annabelle left the principal's office. Ms. Minner was no longer an issue. The school board was.

Miss Annabelle had a sinking feeling inside her as she walked through the empty halls; classes had already begun. My god...I hope the kids don't hear any of this, she thought. But she knew they would. And that thought hurt her more than anything else. How rotten those adults were who put these ugly thoughts out there that'll violate innocent children! My accusers, she thought, *they're* the child molesters!

Her color returned now that she was thinking again. She thought: Do I tell the school board about Burke's threats? Will that solve this, or make things worse? Do I get a lawyer, or will that drag everything out? ...One thing she knew for sure, she had to get back to teaching her students. She loved them, and she knew that within the one school year, she could plant

54

the seeds that would grow into exciting creation-driven lives filled with wealth, happiness, and love. She knew that nowhere else in public or private education could they get those seeds. Nowhere else would they learn to see through the matrix of illusions to the essence of things — to the world of building never-before-seen puzzle-pictures, creating awesome values for the world and making lots of money, happiness, and love for themselves.

Miss Annabelle loved her twelve students as a mother loves her children. Yet, a mother usually has two decades to raise her child. Miss Annabelle had just the nine months of a school year. She had no children of her own. Her love really was maternal, protective, *everything*. Her love for her students, especially now that she could lose them, was all-embracing. She could neither feel nor think about anything else. Nothing else mattered. As she walked down the empty hall, she felt as though she were going to panic. She knew she needed a clear head to deal with this. But she couldn't get a clear head.

Although reason told her to stay away, she was pulled to her classroom door from a force beyond her control. She looked through the narrow vertical window at her children. Their faces looked worried. What did Mrs. Shaffer tell them about her? Her fighting spirit swelled up within. She turned away from the window and turned inward and did battle with her emotions to stop herself from entering the classroom and taking over the lecture to her children. She knew that rash act could get her fired, and she had to use discipline.

After a moment, she looked through the window again; the darkness on the children's faces was unbearable to her. She would not — she could not — let them worry.

She quietly opened the door. At first, only a couple of faces looked her way. Those two faces suddenly brightened as if a brilliant light shown on them. Then another child turned then about half the children turned to see her standing there. The faces that were turned toward her were bright and brilliant; the faces that were still forward toward Mrs. Shaffer were dark, blending into the background and the shadows. At this moment, the dark and light contrast of faces was striking — like a Rembrandt painting. As each new face turned toward Miss

Annabelle, it glowed as if Miss Annabelle were the Sun itself, lighting and warming those wonderful faces. By the look on their faces, she knew she had done the right thing. She stepped inside the room, but stayed by the door.

"Children, I'll be away for a few days," she said, concealing her fears and anxieties. "I'm okay, but I must tend to something very important. There was a sudden situation that came up this morning beyond my control. Mrs. Shaffer will be your substitute until I'm back." Miss Annabelle hesitated, then added, "Until then, remember what you have learned about life — always see past the appearances to *what is*."

Mrs. Shaffer did not understand that last comment, but she noticed the kids obviously did.

"When will you be back?" Cathy, the quiet overweight girl called out, surprising everyone including Miss Annabelle, yet asking the question every other child wanted to know.

"Darling," Miss Annabelle said, looking back at Cathy and then the others, "I'll be gone as short a time as is in my power. I should be back in a few days. ...I love you all too much to be gone for long! Bye, bye."

"Bye, Miss Annabelle," the twelve children called out as she slipped out the door. Standing outside her room, Miss Annabelle stood with her back against the wall, next to the door. She sighed deeply and leaned toward the door and peeked through the window. They'll be OK, she told herself, but her eyes welled up with tears.

"They *will* be OK," a deep, wonderfully understanding voice said, as if reading her doubts. Its paternal quality was so comforting that Miss Annabelle's fears seemed to momentarily vanish. She turned around to find Jessie smiling at her.

"Oh Jessie, I've got to talk to you!"

"I already know. Talk is everywhere." Then he purposely changed the subject. "Thanksgiving is in two days. Do you have plans? If not, Angie and I want you to have dinner with us."

"Oh..." The change of subject in the midst of a crisis felt refreshing.

"Miss Annabelle, spend the afternoon with us. My wife's making a big dinner and baking two pies, and there's just the two of us. We want you to join us. Angie is looking forward to meeting you. She's a wonderful woman. If you feel comfortable, we can talk some about things with Angie. She's also been through a lot."

"I'd love to Jessie." Miss Annabelle just realized that Jessie was her only adult friend here, and for the first time since moving to this town, she was looking forward to meeting a woman friend. "I really would like that." They turned and walked in the empty hall toward the janitor's room.

"You're here early today," Miss Annabelle said to Jessie, who normally started work in late morning.

"I'm cleaning the bleachers today, so I wanted to get an early start."

Miss Annabelle nodded and looked down. Jessie knew she was hurting inside. In a moment, she looked up again. Squinting as though squeezing out thoughts and trying to get some understanding, she said, "I see something very different in children. They're able to see *what is,* not what *appears to be.* Children absorb reality like a sponge. But I can point out *what is* to an adult over and over again, yet months or years later, he or she will never get it."

Jessie was a good listener; they were now both sitting in his "office" as Miss Annabelle continued, "In a couple of weeks, for example, I'll tell my kids that no person should tell another person how to live his or her life. The person who tries to rule over others, no matter what the appearances are or how good the reasons may sound, is wrong for doing so. My kids will see right through to the essence...to the fundamental wrong of politicians and regulatory bureaucrats. But if I try to explain that fundamental wrong to an adult, explain that politicians and regulatory bureaucrats are all about ruling over people and that role is fundamentally wrong, he or she will say, 'But what about all the good things they do for us? After all, we elect them!' So, for centuries, adults keep putting a ruling class over themselves. But my children, when they grow up, they'll never be controlled by others."

Ever since the first day of school when she sang *The Impossible Dream* and he listened outside her room, he'd wished someone had talked to him like that when he was a boy. Miss

57

Annabelle did not know that Jessie had listened to the tapes of every General Lecture and loved to hear her insights.

"Looking back over my life," she continued, "I realize how little power and control over life I had before I saw through appearances to the essence of things. The children's uncanny ability to see past the matrix of illusions in this world to the essence of things lets me move quickly. I must get them past the entire matrix of illusions before I leave. It'll take me the *full* nine months of the school year. I cannot afford to be away from them for long. Every day, every lecture counts. I *cannot* be fired. I must just get back to teaching my kids."

Jessie understood. He sat quietly thinking.

"If I don't get back to teach my students, they'll go on to live mediocre lives, sinking in silent frustration like most others. If I get back and teach them, they'll go on to live the way people were meant to live...with power, freedom, wealth and love. They'll go on to be spectacularly happy. They'll go on to three levels of happiness that adults today don't have, which I call the celebrations of love *every day,* the preciousness of *every moment,* and a bigger-than-life excitement throughout their *entire lives.*"

Suddenly Miss Annabelle's voice deepened and strengthened, "Jessie, I must get back to teaching those kids."

Her love for her children sent a rush through him and made him long again to have children of his own. For a moment, Jessie drifted into the unhappy memory of why he and Angie would never have children: Down in urban Philadelphia thirteen years ago, when Angie was 17 years old and still living at home, she was kidnapped and raped by a gang. The internal damage and resulting infection of her uterus made her unable to have children. Jessie, two years older and deeply embittered about his helplessness to do anything about that crime, vowed to take his childhood sweetheart out of that gang-infested hell swarming with white, black, and Puerto Rican gang members taking revenge upon one another through racial attacks on anyone of opposing color — even girls such as Angie who never associated with gangs. When he got his job in Cheektowaga, a rural town almost four hundred miles North, a whole world away from their violent past, Jessie and Angie had discovered "heaven". They lived with a freedom they never knew existed. Their favorite activity was long walks together after dark. Like children discovering a new sensation, they discovered the night and its peacefulness — something they never knew existed. Their only empty moments came when they thought about children and the life with children they would never have. And now Miss Annabelle brought that buried longing back to the surface. And it was the depth of his longing for something he could never have that made him genuinely understand Miss Annabelle's crisis. Suddenly, Jessie wanted to punish Burke. None of this would have happened if not for that pip-squeak. Burke started the fires that could burn down the fantastic futures of twelve children and their teacher, and Burke just walked away from the damage carefree or laughing. Jessie's thoughts jumped to the gang members who, because of their life threats on Angie and her family, walked away from justice. Burke too, Jessie realized, was walking away from justice. And whereas the gang members diminished the futures of Jessie and Angie and erased the two or three children who never were conceived...Burke potentially diminished the futures of twelve children and their teacher, even more when considering *their* children who would have also grown up with the life-lifting power of building never-before-seen puzzle-pictures, and *their* children and so on.

Knowing the pain of having to live his entire life without experiencing a daughter and a son to love and to develop...he could relate to the loss Miss Annabelle would feel if this class — her children — were taken away from her. He slowly shifted his eyes back toward her and looked straight into her eyes.

"I understand," he said, simply. A wave of relief washed through Miss Annabelle's purple eyes, and she smiled, forgetting for a moment her battle just a few hours away. For once, another adult understood the meaning behind her new life and the importance of her teaching those children...an importance that, to her, went beyond her own wants and emotions. As Jessie watched her smile, he wondered what she had been through in her past. It must have been a struggle, he thought, something she broke free of. His own past and Angie's past were struggles, which they broke free of. The past, somehow, made the three of them different from those around them...and was now bringing them together.

*

Miss Annabelle was nervous when she arrived at seven o'clock that November evening. Seeing the unnatural sight of a dozen or so cars in the parking lot in the dark added to her nervousness. Those are my prosecutors, she thought.

She felt a gush of cold air when she opened her car door, and she started shivering. The cold night unfairly teamed up with her nervousness to send this little warrior into waves of shivers. I hope I'll stop shivering when I'm inside, she thought.

She walked toward the school, which for the first time looked imposing. All she could think about was that she hoped she could stop this uncontrollable shivering. When she entered the school, she quickly walked into the girls' room, partly because she needed to use the rest room and partly to gain composure. As she warmed up, her shivering calmed down, but it still came in waves, particularly when she saw in her mind's eye a table of twelve school board members questioning her sexual behavior. She wondered if she would be able to answer their questions if she were shivering like this. The more she thought about it, the more nervous she got. What if I can't even talk? she thought.

She wished she had worn warmer clothes. She started running in place in the empty rest room. That helped. She was thawing out, and the exercise caused her to breathe more deeply and evenly. She started feeling better, and headed out the door, toward the battlefield.

When she approached the teachers' lunch room, where the emergency meeting would be held, she could hear the congregation of adults talking. Suddenly, she was nervous again, the cold feeling and butterflies returned. When she saw the strangers filling two of the oblong tables pushed together into one extra-long table, she started shivering again. The adults all seemed excited. After all, they had never been summoned for a sex scandal, especially involving a beautiful woman. They held the power of her future in their hands. She never liked this room; now she hated it.

"Miss Annabelle," she heard Ms. Minner snap, "You will sit

there." Miss Annabelle spotted the freshly revived principal who was feeling confident in this den of male wolves. She was gesturing to the chair at the far end of the stretched table. As Miss Annabelle walked toward the chair, she could feel some of the men checking out her body, which made her more uncomfortable. She noticed how *big* the men seemed. Maybe they were posturing like a rooster, but they seemed unusually wide as they turned their heads to look at her. And the women seemed to be checking out her body and dress too. They also seemed big, wide, broad at the shoulders. Ms. Minner could not help feeling powerful now — the lioness looked caged and afraid.

As Miss Annabelle turned to face her prosecutors from the far end of the table, her heart jumped in delight as she saw an oasis, sitting behind the crowd of prosecutors: Jessie and Angie were there! They both looked fearless and strong — two calm black folks who had gone through tough times in the big city, sitting in a room of sheltered, excited rural white folks who never experienced really tough times. Jessie and Angie looked confidently at Miss Annabelle. Before arriving, Ms. Minner had tried to make Jessie and Angie leave, declaring that this was a closed meeting. But it was Angie who, with a voice not to be reckoned with, declared that a public school's school board was exactly what the name implied: *public*. She declared that she and her husband had every right to be there, to observe, to witness...and that they were not leaving. ...No one in the room challenged her.

Miss Annabelle looked back at Jessie and Angie. The eye contact was like a fuel-line between them, and Miss Annabelle felt their strength being pumped straight into her. As strength filled her little body, the warmth returned and the shivering stopped. The little warrior sat down, ready to battle.

"Miss Annabelle, sitting before you are the school board members for the school district by which you are employed," bellowed a thick-boned man of German descent, standing at the opposite end of the table. The tone of his voice made it clear that she was on trial here. This was not an inquiry; it was an inquisition. "Facing us are several complaints against you. The nature of some of those complaints forced us to leave our families this evening to call together this emergency meeting."

Superpuzzle

Ms. Minner seemed to settle into a cozy spot, watching her powerful school-board head, the superintendent, overpower this righteous little sharp-tongued lioness. He continued, his voice growing louder, in a barking crescendo, "Do you have any idea of what those complaints are, Miss Annabelle?"

Perhaps from surviving hard times in her past, the little lady instinctively knew she needed control right from the start. The lioness roared back, "You practically yell my name at me and, what? Do you expect me to address you now as — Sir? If you want to continue with your intimidation tactics, I can make this a very public event to get you a bigger audience. Or, you can cut the show and start by introducing yourselves."

Jessie and Angie leapt for joy, inside of course. Ms. Minner and her allies were shaken from their smug seats. The white folk at the table were looking around, clearing their throats, and then all fixed their eyes nervously at their leader. He was embarrassed. He now hated that woman, and she knew it. But that did not matter. Only getting back to her children mattered, and she knew this was the only way.

"Please excuse me for that oversight." He hated to say those words. "I'm Mr. Hammerschmidt, the superintendent." The other school board representatives introduced themselves one by one, going around the table counterclockwise.

"Thank you. Of course, you all know I'm Miss Annabelle. Now, Mr. Hammerschmidt, before answering your question, I have a legal right to know who my accuser is. Who's making these complaints against me?"

Mr. Hammerschmidt did not expect this. In fact, he really did not know the answer since the allegations just sort of swirled up from a tornado of gossip. He sat, looking at his papers, stumped.

"Let me ask you another question, Mr. Hammerschmidt. Did a single complaint come from one of my students or from one of their parents?" Miss Annabelle had him beaten, and she was ready to make a swift kill of it. "Since you're not answering, I can answer that question: The answer is NO, not a single student, not a single parent made a single complaint, which means, Mr. Hammerschmidt, you're walking on thin ice, about to fall into a pool of defamation. Your so-called allegations come from schoolhouse, lunchroom rumors. You people have no idea how much your giving credibility to such rumors by putting in a substitute teacher and holding this meeting has cost me emotionally and professionally. Let me warn you not to jerk around someone's life, like you have mine. Next time, you'll have a defamation lawsuit to contend with — each of you personally *and* the state. Let this be a warning to you. I'll be in my room teaching my children in the morning. Good night."

Miss Annabelle walked out of the room unscathed, mission accomplished. She had shocked everyone there, including herself. She could hear Hammerschmidt arguing with Ms. Minner. That's good, she thought, that's perfect. She would be back with her children the next day — gone for only one day! She was delighted and wanted to be with Jessie and Angie. They wanted to be with her. But they stayed behind, for the three of them knew not to be seen together as allies. As Miss Annabelle walked from the room, Jessie watched her and wondered from where did this archangel come? He kept hearing her words in his head, "Once you see through appearances to the essence of things, then you have honest power in life." Power, indeed.

The next morning felt like heaven — the preciousness of being reunited with the children reverberated throughout her body all day long. The kids felt it too. Just one day apart — yet threatened with eternity — brought them closer together and lifted them together to a new level. The children sensed by now that Miss Annabelle was a precious gift. They did not take her for granted. As each child walked into the room, his or her face lit up upon seeing Miss Annabelle, and so did Miss Annabelle's heart as she enjoyed celebration after celebration with each child who arrived.

All was wonderful on the day before Thanksgiving.

CHAPTER
FIVE

As Jake listened to Jessie and Angie tell the story of Miss Annabelle, the college student began to imagine this attractive couple twenty-seven years ago.

"What did you and Jessie do for fun in those days?" Jake asked, looking at Angie. She laughed.

"We loved to go dancing," she said. "We still do. We'd go to movies, drive to the ocean. But mostly, we had fun every day just experiencing freedom. Growing up trapped in poverty, surrounded by crime and danger, lets you *feel* your freedom once you have it. And it feels good. We loved going on walks and bike rides. We still do. Memories of growing up in poverty and crime never leave you. Enjoying our freedom never stops." Angie reached over and held Jessie's hand. Jessie and Angie were genuinely happy. Jake smiled at the irony: their stressed-out childhoods caused them to enjoy life more as adults.

Jake had led a somewhat sheltered life, and he knew it. But he felt close to Jessie and Angie, unusually close for having known them for just a few hours. Why? he wondered. Then he thought maybe he knew why: although he had always been insulated from hard times, he was nevertheless always a bit of a rebel...and very independent. He grew up in a nice, middle-class home, but ever since he was a teenager, he always had a job; he paid his own way through college; he was very honest, made his own decisions, and did not particularly follow the trend. Jake had a tendency to resist authority. These seemed to be some common traits in Jessie and Angie...and certainly Miss Annabelle.

"What did *she* do for fun?" Jake asked.

"Teach," Jessie said. "That was her greatest fun, which included developing her lectures — those masterpieces. I'm a wiser man today because of her. She would spend hours after school preparing her lectures — polishing those for the next day, developing bits and pieces for future lectures. She was consumed by those twelve children. And, I believe, she did a lot of deep thinking about those kids' personal lives...like helping Sally, Rico, and Cathy, and encouraging budding talent in other kids like Ian and Teddy. ...It's amazing how I still remember the names of those kids. I guess Angie and I got pretty attached to them through Miss Annabelle."

"And she became our best friend," Angie added. "We were her only adult friends at first. The three of us would occasionally go bike riding, have dinner and long talks, and the three of us would even go dancing sometimes. She loved her freedom, like us. She had a hard life before coming to Cheektowaga."

Jake suddenly had lots of questions. He wanted to know about Miss Annabelle's past before she taught at Duncan Elementary School. He wanted to know what happened to her after teaching there. Also, he wanted to know why this pretty lady did not have a man in her life.

But, as the questions were growing in his head, Angie said, "It's late guys. We'll continue this tomorrow. Come on, Jake, I'll show you your room. ...Oh, wait a minute, I almost forgot...stay here." In a minute Angie returned with a photo album. "We'll look through this tomorrow, but I just wanted to show you what she looked like."

As Jake looked at a 5 X 7 photo, the world around him went silent. He immediately noticed her gentle features. He studied her — first her pretty face, her expression, *her eyes*. They were vibrant, beyond blue...they were lavender. She looked so full of life...and so feminine. Her soft auburn hair amplified her eyes. Now that he knew about her, the picture meant much more. He tried to imagine her having lunch every day with the children...and then shutting down the school board. Her body was small, small bones, but with very appealing proportions. Most striking of all, however, was looking at her *not* feature by feature, but as a whole: *she looked happy.* ...As Jake studied the picture closely, Angie smiled. Few men could resist the attraction to that little package called Miss Annabelle.

*

Jake woke the next morning in the little guest room feeling refreshed. He got up in time to see Angie and Jessie walking around the house gathering a house key, a water bottle, and some other gadget. They were wearing matching sweats, and they looked like a couple of teenagers raring to go.

"Good morning, Jake," Angie said, spotting him first. There's some scrambled eggs and bacon on the stove, and raisin bread in the fridge."

"Thank you," Jake said, wondering what the lovebirds were up to.

"We're going riding," Jessie said. His job did not start until 11:00 a.m. at the school. Every morning Jessie and Angie went for long bicycle rides through the suburbs and out into the country. They loved their mornings...and their nights. They loved their time together.

"Now I know how you two stay so fit and trim," Jake yelled after them as they bounced out the door.

He noticed Angie had left the photo album on the kitchen table for him along with breakfast. He went straight to the photo album, his curiosity overflowing, and he started at the beginning. There they were, Jessie and Angie, in their early 30s, looking just as they did now except Jessie's hair was a shade darker in those days and their skin was a little smoother. Otherwise, they looked almost the same this morning as they did back then. As Jake turned the pages, he noticed in all the pictures of Jessie and Angie, they looked happy together, as they did this morning.

After turning a few pages, he saw *her* again — Miss Annabelle — standing with Angie, arms around each other like schoolgirl friends. Right away, he was studying the petite fair-skinned woman. She held the secret to life, he thought. This beautiful woman knew the secret so few people ever know. She had discovered the key to power over life, which every human being seeks, but so few attain. He thought about her passing that key on to her students. Now, I'll discover that key, too, he realized.

He wanted to track down the other nine children in that class to see what became of them. Were they living average lives? he wondered. Or did they have a little of the magic that caused their three classmates to become living legends?

When Jessie and Angie returned, Jake asked them, "What about the other nine kids in her class, do you know what happened to them?"

"Ambitious people tend to move out of this little town," Jessie said. "None of them live here anymore."

*

At 10:40, Jake jumped in the car with Jessie. He wanted to spend the day with him at the school and brought along some books to study while Jessie worked. On the way, Jake said, "I noticed the pictures of Miss Annabelle with you and Angie stopped after about a year. What happened to her?"

"Annabelle Barclays," Jessie said.

"What?"

"Her name's Annabelle Barclays, but the kids called her Miss Annabelle. I always addressed her as Miss Annabelle around the school."

"Did she teach another class the next year?"

"No, the school board finally got her. They fired her. It was a mess. She was devastated. But, on the other hand, she was able to fight them back until the end of the school year. She loved her twelve students. All she hoped for was to finish the year, and she got it."

One teacher, twelve kids, three of whom became the biggest phenoms of the decade. Jake wondered what dynamos would have risen and what discoveries the world might have seen if she were teaching these past twenty-seven years.

"Where is she now?" Jake asked.

"I don't know. No one does. The court put a restraining

order on her—"

"A restraining order!"

"Yup. She couldn't visit the school or any of the kids. To her, that was like her own children were taken from her. She couldn't take it emotionally and eventually had to leave. We got a postcard from her a few weeks later saying she was okay, but that she couldn't come back. She said she painfully missed us and the kids, but it would be best not to see Angie and me. There was no return address. Angie tried to track her down with no luck."

"But why not at least keep in touch?"

"You'll understand why she could no longer have contact with us once you hear the whole story. I don't know...her world died here, Jake. She had to go. She was a wonderful part of our lives. We still miss her."

The tragedy seemed huge to Jake. "But she handled the school board so well."

"Oh yes she did! She was good; man she was good. She was a *fighter*. And her fearlessness was the only reason she lasted the school year."

"What happened after the emergency school-board meeting?" Jake asked.

Jessie continued the story, "It all started the Monday morning after Thanksgiving..."

*

"Good morning, everyone," Miss Annabelle said, feeling extra cheerful after having found two adult friends in Jessie and Angie over the long four-day weekend. "Did you all have a happy Thanksgiving?"

The twelve children looked different from the other children at Duncan Elementary School. These twelve children looked *glad* to be back to school. Not one child came in late. And in the hallways, Miss Annabelle's students could be seen rushing straight to class, more interested in the lectures in the classroom than the chatter in the halls.

Miss Annabelle's students always did their homework and did it well. After three months of school, parents still could barely believe their children's enthusiasm. Her first lecture of each day was always on a general topic, and the kids were encouraged to interact during this lecture. This was the prize lecture many parents and kids *not* in her class listened to loyally.

The four other lectures that followed each day were science, math, literature, and history. Although those lectures were more specialized to the subject, they too were fascinating and sparkling with broad-sweeping integrations. She designed her lectures weeks, even months in advance. And it was one of those future-planned science lectures, which she was preparing for delivery on the last week of school, that was unexpectedly prompted this Monday morning during her first lecture. She started her first lecture simply enough. The topic was, fittingly, about rumors and gossip.

"How many of you know what rumors are?" About a third of the hands went up.

"How about gossip?" About half the hands went up.

She went on to explain that rumors and gossip caused appearances that we must see through…to *what is*. "Rumors and gossip build a big scenario about something, but they offer no evidence," she said.

Ian Scott, who had taken a growing interest in the cosmos ever since his father took him to the observatory, raised his hand. He shocked the class and Miss Annabelle when he said, "That means God must be a rumor."

Miss Annabelle was in a predicament. She knew that any more controversy could cause her to get fired and lose these children. And she knew that Ian, a budding scientist, was right — there was no evidence but lots of talk, just as she had defined rumors. All eyes stared at her, waiting for her answer.

She knew that her answer had to be honest, yet an honest answer that questioned the existence of God could be used by the school board to stir up discontent and eventually to get her fired. Yet, she knew she couldn't effectively *not* answer the question.

Without a choice, she started into the science lecture she was preparing for the last week of school, just before the summer break when the resulting controversy could not easily build momentum.

Superpuzzle

"I will answer that question as honestly as I can. First, who in here believes that intelligent life exists out there on other planets?" Most if not all the children raised their hands. "When you consider the size and mass of our universe, and the ease for lower life forms to develop and start the process of evolution, it becomes statistically overwhelming that the Universe is full of intelligent beings like us. Now, I want you to consider where we are now with space travel and exploration." Suddenly Ian's hand went up and Miss Annabelle nodded to him.

"Oh, it's nothing compared to what is being planned for the future. We've walked on the moon, but now they're talking about commercial flights to the moon and resorts on the moon."

"Imagine that!" Miss Annabelle said. "Look how fast progress happens, especially once businesses get involved. In 1936, we completed the technology to control nature on a grand scale: we completed Hoover Dam to control the Colorado River. That accomplishment, to control nature on a grand scale, took man thousands of years — from the dawn of human consciousness to 1936. But then, it took just another thirty-three years to travel to the moon. And, as Ian opened our eyes to: when space development becomes commercial and businesses learn to profit from it, especially if left free from political agendas and if able to pursue profits that make capitalism work, then what was not long ago 'one giant leap for mankind' will become commonplace. ...In other words, knowledge and progress when free of political forces, increase not linearly but geometrically." Miss Annabelle went to the chalkboard and drew both the straight-line incline of a linear increase and the upward-curving incline of a geometrical increase.

"If businesses are left alone by regulatory bureaucrats, and in several years we are vacationing on the moon, where will we be in several decades or, with geometrical increases in knowledge, even a few years after lunar vacations?"

"Vacationing on Mars!" Ian shouted out, sitting on the edge of his seat.

"Or, businesses might be corralling and harvesting asteroids for our needs — perhaps mining raw materials or setting up orbiting cities for an expanding civilization. Now, I want you to stretch your minds a bit: What will we be doing with space development a few hundred years ahead? What do you think Ian?"

Ian thought for a moment, then he said, "We'd probably control everything in our solar system."

"Goodness yes, Ian...I'd say at least everything in our solar system. Now, Ian, try this question: What would we be doing with space development a few *thousand* years ahead?"

"We'd probably control everything in our galaxy...or maybe even sooner because of that geometric curve you drew on the board," he said without hesitation.

"Now, Ian, what would we — or any intelligent being, for that matter — be doing with space development a few *million* years ahead?"

"Wow, would they control everything in our Universe?" Ian asked.

"Yes, they would," Miss Annabelle said matter-of-factly. And when considering how big and how old our Universe is, there's intelligent life out there not just a few years into computer-driven high technology and space exploration, but millions of years."

"Do those super-advanced beings control the Universe?" Ian asked.

"It stands to reason, doesn't it?" Miss Annabelle said. "They would have the technology to corral matter and create big-bang explosions, perhaps creating a galaxy for some beneficial purpose to balance gravitational forces or for other unimagined reasons. As far out as I can think, logic seems to dictate that intelligent beings like us control the cosmos."

"Wouldn't there be some bad star wars?" Danny asked.

"Actually, no," Miss Annabelle said, smiling. "Every planet inhabited with intelligent beings reaches a point called the Nuclear Decision Threshold. We have reached that point on Earth. We have the nuclear power to destroy civilization. Now, we either learn how to end irrationality and war, or we will eventually destroy ourselves. To advance significantly beyond this Nuclear Threshold, our civilization must discover how to end irrational political power and its wars and terrorism. Once this is figured out, and only if it is, an intelligent civilization advances limitlessly and eternally. Those super-advanced beings then join the pure, benevolent Civilization of the Universe. In that

71

civilization free of irrationality and war, everything and everyone is focused on building values for others. And those values grow geometrically to become enormous values such as eliminating disease...even death."

Ian, always so astute, finally voiced it: "So, intelligent beings like us control the cosmos — not a mystical spirit called God."

After a pause, Miss Annabelle answered: "It would seem so." She felt anxious acknowledging his comment. She was worried what the school board would do with this lecture. "When you pierce through to the essence of the Universe, intelligent beings rather obviously control the cosmos. But if we back down to the appearances of things, then we could say that God controls the cosmos."

"Is there a God?" a little girl named Debbie asked.

"In thinking over and over again about what I lectured today, I realized that perhaps there is no more need for God. At first, man needed God to explain things we didn't know like our existence and our superior intelligence, our beautiful animals and our sophisticated ecosystems. Then, Charles Darwin came along. Remember I mentioned this on our camping trip? His Theory of Evolution through Natural Selection ended the need to explain man and animals in terms of a Majestic Creation or a divine plan. Everything was easily explainable through science. As scientists prove that intelligent beings take over nature and control the cosmos on a grand scale, the need for God creating and controlling the Universe will subside. Something even better and even more secure will replace the idea of God and heaven."

"God is man," Jeremiah said.

"Yes, Jeremiah," Miss Annabelle concurred.

"Man controls the cosmos," Jeremiah continued.

"God-Man," Miss Annabelle added.

Ian sat on the edge of his chair, eyes big, brain busy. The other children were fascinated by the lecture. Like the first day of school, never had anyone talked to them like this. They felt alive, exhilarated, and they understood what their teacher was saying. In fact, they all had an extraordinarily easy time grasping that the size, mass, and age of the Universe meant that intelligent beings long ago took complete control of the cosmos. And as these children gained more and more control of life, the thought that their cosmic cousins controlled the heavens stimulated their desire to learn.

"Someday I want to say, 'let there be light!' and create a galaxy," Ian said.

It's just phenomenal, Miss Annabelle thought, how in thirty minutes children can see through to the essence of things, whereas adults would require years or decades...if they'd ever see through to the essence at all.

*

Jessie and Jake had arrived at the school. The car was noisy and in need of repair, but Jake was in a space that no sound could interrupt; he was deep in thought about Miss Annabelle's breakthrough-thinking about the cosmos. Jake felt his skin crawling as he realized that every major cosmological discovery in the past twenty-seven years pointed strongly to her hypothesis: the discovery of abundant water throughout the Universe, the ease within a planetary system for naturally occurring chemical reactions that start life and its process of evolution through natural selection, the older age of the Universe than suspected as we see further and further into it. Jake knew that her lecture, as told to him by Jessie twenty-seven years later, was having an impact on his view of himself and his role in life.

When he and Jessie were walking from the car across the parking lot, Jake broke the silence:

"What happened to her tapes? They weren't destroyed were they?" Jake asked, almost feeling panic.

"No, I have a copy of every lecture," Jessie answered with a big smile. Jake stopped Jessie and put his hands on both of Jessie's broad shoulders and practically shouted, "That's wonderful! Jessie, you're sitting on a gold mine of knowledge!"

"I know it, Jake. I've known it for twenty-seven years."

"I've got to go back to the house. I've got to start listening to her lectures!"

"Be back by seven," Jessie said with a smile, handing Jake the keys.

*

Superpuzzle

Angie and Jake pulled the boxes out of the closet. They were full of hundreds of tapes. The lectures were all labeled and in immaculate order. The tapes were old, but Jake could hear her voice. He fell in love with her voice. It was gentle yet strong, just as she looked in her pictures. What a gift those children had, Jake kept thinking as he listened to complex insights into life and human nature, communicated so simply and so coherently to her class. ...Now Jake understood why Miss Annabelle spent hours each day preparing those lectures, breaking through to the essences of life and breaking them down into easy-to-chew bites for her students. Listening to tape after tape, Jake had no idea that her lectures would cover such a wide range of subjects, piercing each one, going down, down, down to the essence, which usually revealed a whole new way of looking at something. The breadth and depth of her lectures captivated Jake as the hours slipped by. Angie had left him alone.

Jake listened to lecture after lecture as Miss Annabelle systemically broke down illusion after illusion. Then, while listening to his ninth lecture, it hit him: he knew why she *must* finish her year with her students. The sun had gone down and the lecture Jake was listening to was about false authority when suddenly he stopped hearing the important words Miss Annabelle spoke...words he had hung onto, every one of them, for the past few hours as she knocked down the matrix of illusions. His thumb pushed the "stop" button on his audio cassette player. Looking straight ahead, but seeing images from another place and time, Jake uttered, "Wow...she's building something huge."

Each major illusion that was vanished, in turn, revealed and snapped into place a new puzzle piece to the growing puzzle-picture that would reveal a world of *what is*, not ruled by a matrix of illusions...a world never seen before in which ordinary people had enormous power. "For, they see only *what is*," Jake muttered, "causing a completely different mentality." That new mentality, he thought, that next evolution of man can build mental puzzles to reveal never-before-seen puzzle-pictures for the world. In other words, that new mentality enables the ordinary person to create magnificent values for the world. The mind sees *what is*, so its ideas and concepts are real and powerful and can be interlocked with other real concepts to begin the process of

74

building mental puzzles that either take values to the next level or create magnificent new values.

Miss Annabelle was building the never-before-seen picture of the illusion-free world of *what is* that flourished with a new mentality — the next evolution of man, the God-Man. A whole new world, a whole new way of thinking, a whole new way of seeing everything...my god, Jake realized, that's it! That's why three of her students have gone on to change the world! Although the new world is not here yet, Miss Annabelle showed it to them, and their minds had jumped to the next mentality, the mentality of the new world. With that new mentality, they created magnificent values for the world.

Jake now knew that Miss Annabelle was building that puzzle-picture of the new world with each lecture. She was painstakingly fitting each piece into place to give her students the picture — the jumping off point — to the next evolutionary leap of man. That puzzle-picture was the secret key to their life of creation, wealth, and love. And Miss Annabelle knew that if she could not finish the year, she could not complete the puzzle.

She knew what she had to do. No one but she knew what she had to do. She was all alone.

*

"There you are, buddy!" Jessie boomed across the room at Jake.

"What?" Jake said, pulling off his earphones, looking up at Jessie who was feigning a crossed look. "Oh...Jessie, what time is it?"

Jake looked at his watch that displayed 8:55 p.m. "I...I'm sorry! I lost track of time. ...How'd you get home? How long were you waiting?" Jake really felt bad; he felt he was now intruding on Jessie and Angie. But then Jessie laughed like a father who had his son worried.

"I knew when I sent you home to those tapes you wouldn't be back to pick me up. So Angie and I planned to make an evening of it." Jessie was laughing.

"We went to Berticini's for an Italian dinner," Angie said,

smiling at Jake. "You needed your time with her."

Jake felt immediately relieved. "Thank you, guys," he said sheepishly.

"Here, honey. Come over here and have some of this delicious lasagna we ordered for you," Angie said. She set him a place at the dining room table.

"I don't know how I'm going to repay you for what you're doing, but I will," Jake said.

"You're repaying us by what you're doing for our friend," Jessie said, and Angie nodded. "She was something, wasn't she?"

"Yes, she was," Jake said, his thoughts drifting back to her lectures, "...yes, she was."

Seeing the distant look in Jake's eyes, Angie said, "We'll leave you alone tonight, dear." Angie and Jessie went upstairs to retire for the night. When Jessie yawned, his wife pinched him on the cheek, and they giggled like adolescents.

Jake, on the other hand, was full of energy. He would be awake listening and pondering for another five hours or so. After saying "good-night" to Angie and Jessie, he started thinking about this puzzle-picture Miss Annabelle was building.

As Jake listened to lecture after lecture, as illusion after illusion fell, he watched the puzzle-picture coming together and growing piece by piece. Miss Annabelle was building the puzzle-picture that would show her students the world of no illusions in which the next level of the human mind existed — the God-Man.

Late into the night when Jake's eyes got heavy, he felt a release of happiness go through his body. The euphoria woke him up, and no longer felt tired. Then another release of happiness rushed through him. He had never felt these "happiness attacks" before. He was alone, but he had never felt so *happy*. For the first time, he knew that life had much more meaning than he or his parents had ever known. Another whole world existed, an entirely new level of being. The knowledge that something so much better awaits us sent these releases of happiness through Jake. The heretofore hidden meaning of life at the next level would show itself as Miss Annabelle's puzzle grew and revealed man's true potential that had eluded humanity.

Jake was young, but during the past year, he was beginning to sense the stagnation that life had in store for him. But tonight, he knew the secrets to an exciting life lay in those tapes.

"Man, this is how Miss Annabelle felt — *so happy*," Jake whispered to himself, unaware of the lingering smile on his face. "She was not lonely or sad. She didn't feel like a punished outcast. No, she was experiencing these bursts of happiness every day as she built her puzzle that would release man's limitless potential to those she loved most. She had found that elusive 'something more to life', which humanity searched for, generation after generation since the dawn of consciousness, but never found. Now I know that every day, as she enlightened her students, she would feel and collect the rewards." Despite the painful moments, Jake now realized, her life was beautiful.

CHAPTER
SIX

The logs in the fireplace were crackling; the room was warm. Miss Annabelle stood in the middle of her living room. She looked through the big bay window. Her front yard, driveway, and the street were covered in a white blanket of snow. The snow was still falling, and the snowflakes seemed unusually large. It was Christmas Day.

She opened the front door and stepped outside. The roads were empty, and she loved peaceful times like this. She looked at the branches of the pine trees covered with their own blankets of snow. "It's so beautiful out here," she thought. The little blankets of snow on the branches of trees and on the mail boxes and on the cars, and the thick blankets on the houses and over the ground seemed to absorb the normal sounds right out of the air. ...Under growing pressures from the school board and faculty at school, Miss Annabelle derived great pleasure from this peaceful moment.

The neighbors' two boys suddenly cracked the silence with yelps of joy as they ran outside and instinctively started a snowball fight.

"Hi, Miss Annabelle!" they yelled when they saw her. Lee and Todd knew about her enormous popularity among the students at school. And although they were in the second and fifth grades, they felt as though they lived next to a celebrity. And Todd had high hopes of having Miss Annabelle for his teacher the next year.

"Merry Christmas, boys!" she said. She loved to hear those two happy children playing in the yard on weekends and holidays. "I have something for you two."

The boys came running over, and she invited them in to give them their presents. When she handed them the wrapped gifts, she said they could open them now. They tore off the wrapping paper and, at about the same moment, both said, "Cool!" when they saw their new walkie-talkies.

Miss Annabelle put batteries in their new toys; Lee and Todd could be seen the rest of the day, running around the yards, talking to each other through their walkie-talkies.

Back in her house, she was excited to start working on her lectures that day. Today was about to become her most exciting Christmas ever. A few weeks before, Miss Annabelle noticed her lectures were starting to, unexpectedly, snap together like a puzzle, building a picture bigger than the sum total of themselves.

What's happening? she wondered, at first, not yet understanding the nature of Neothink.

She thought about how hard she worked on her lectures, how deeply she thought about things and how honest she must be to cut through what appears to be to *what is*. The common denominator snapping together this synergistic puzzle-picture, she realized, was *pure honesty*. It was hard work to be fully honest and get down to the essence of things — past the appearances to *what is*.

But what would this growing puzzle-picture of her lectures eventually reveal? What would it lead to? Today she would learn the answer.

She knew she was knocking down the complex matrix of illusions for her students, one by one. But that was all she was aware of doing — knocking down illusions. But each time she knocked down an illusion, she was left with something tangible and valuable — a real piece of a whole new world. Today she would explicitly realize that a whole new world exists, a world without illusions, and she was building the puzzle-picture to that new world. Each illusion she knocked down, she was left with another piece to the puzzle. Today she would also learn that in that new world man lives with a different way of thinking, powerful thinking that yields power and wealth. In that world, we become the God-Man — the next evolution of man with a new mentality. Today she would learn that the growing puzzle-picture her lectures would reveal is that new world, and that revelation would show her students the way to make the evolutionary leap into the *new think*.

Honesty is the common denominator building this puzzle, she thought. Can I see enough of the picture, before I know all the pieces, to suddenly see what the whole picture will look like when complete and know what I'm striving to show my students? That'll help me know what the missing pieces look like to form my lectures faster.

Suddenly she knew she needed help from the creative part of her brain. Excited by her challenge, Miss Annabelle twirled across her living room like a ballerina, over to her stereo. She placed two albums on her record player, then the beauty of Tchaikovsky filled her house.

"That's better," she sighed. She filled her bathtub with hot water and bath oils. Just before she stepped in, she remembered to light her scented candles. Then, she slid her fair, sleek body into the liquid warmth as her mind slid into an imaginative, wonderful world.

I'll visit the world of pure honesty, where there are no illusions. Everything is *what is*...a totally honest world. What's it like?

Swan Lake filled the air; vanilla-cinnamon did too as the warm water wrapped itself around her every mound and filled her every dip. Her mind slid toward another place and time, somewhere in the future:

She asked herself, what causes the matrix of illusions all around us? Why do the illusions exist? In many cases, she realized, the illusions originated from politics. What appears good by those who control us is really, at the essence, bad. The common denominator beneath those illusions? The illusions support people who do not contribute tradable values to society. The illusions support politicians and freeloaders. At the same time, the illusions hurt everyone else, but the people don't

80

know it.

What if there were a place, a world of no politicians? As absurd as that seems, Miss Annabelle closed her eyes, slid deeper into her warm bath, and tried to imagine such a place: There, everyone was happy. Letting her imagination flow, without trying to figure out the logic behind it, Miss Annabelle noticed major differences immediately: everyone was wealthy, everyone was healthy, everyone had a livelihood they loved, couples were mutually, madly in love, they were all slim and sexy, and everyone was like a genius building exciting values for the world.

The more the people built their creations, the happier they were and the wealthier society became. Everyone's job was like an entrepreneurial adventure; they thrived in the careers of their dreams. They were so happy, they would celebrate their happiness every day with their spouses of their dreams and their children. And, with so many breakthrough values coming into society, the medical field was no exception. The people lived with near-perfect health.

Somehow, Miss Annabelle knew her beautiful vision of the future, free of the matrix of illusions, was valid. All the pieces fit together perfectly. Her vision had everything to do with the people finally seeing through what appears to be — the illusions — to *what is*.

Unexpectedly, she started remembering her past, which was full of illusions that were impossible to see through. She remembered her ex-husband who obsessively told her that he loved her. And she believed him. One day, he hit her in a jealous rage. But the next day he apologized so genuinely and articulated how he loved her with such passion, she continued to believe him.

But things got worse. She believed him...until one day he battered her so badly that she lay unconscious on the kitchen floor. When she regained consciousness, the last thing she remembered was her husband pointing a knife at her, telling her he would kill her.

Perhaps for self-preservation, at that moment her mind saw straight through the illusions in her marriage. And her mind did not stop there. As if the trauma had altered her brain's thought patterns, she started seeing through the illusions in society all around her. No one else seemed able to break through the spell...until her students.

She had survived a horrible physical beating and severe emotional trauma. Suddenly, though, she started seeing through it all — to the essence of things...where the power in life awaits ordinary, powerless people. For, at the essence, they can take actions that will change their lives for the better.

Like rising from the dead, Miss Annabelle turned all her meekness into the strength of ten people. She ran her husband out of her life, moved to a new state and new life, and started her year at Duncan Elementary.

As she soaked her body in the tub, she smiled at herself. A year ago, she was not able to see through the illusions that had made her a powerless prisoner...not until survival pressures forced her to. ...Survival pressures.

"Ah ha!" she shrieked. "That's it: *survival pressures!*" Suddenly, the mystery started coming together. Could this be how to cross over from today's world controlled by a dishonest matrix of illusions...to the completely honest world of individual power and prosperity...through survival pressures?

For some time, she had likened politicians and regulatory bureaucracies to wife beaters. Indeed, they continually battered down society's potential progress, which suppressed the people's standard of living, and politicians did this harm while telling us they love us with their "compassionate" programs for the "public good".

Like me with my ex-husband, she thought, the people are powerless prisoners to the politicians' illusions. And, like me, the people cannot break free until society suffers enough that the people face survival pressures. But that won't happen because the politicians will not suppress the collective society to that low point where people will break through the illusions.

I ran my husband and his sweet-talk out of my life, she thought. But will the people run the career politicians and their programs for the "social good" out of their lives? Will the people someday elect value producers instead who'll remove the debilitating regulatory bureaucracies that block rapid progress? Without that regulatory web holding everything down, more and more tender youth would rise into entrepreneurial geniuses who would bring great new values to the world, especially exciting new technologies. The computer chips in the new microcomputers, for instance, have been advancing very fast, she thought. Politicians and bureaucrats have no idea yet how to regulate that new technology. Without the regulatory web, thoroughly spun throughout every other industry, technology would advance really fast in *every field,* which would start driving up our buying power, she realized, just as what was starting to happen to the microcomputers. At that moment, an image of Sally's mom flashed in Miss Annabelle's mind. She sighed and then muttered, "Technological breakthroughs in the medical field, especially, would soar when we depoliticize that industry. Sally's mom could be cured."

What a beautiful world that would be, she thought. Buying power would soar in all industries, making ordinary people wealthy. Disease after disease would be cured. And to keep up in that rapidly advancing society, business structures would have to change to survive, she realized. The typical routine rut would become a thing of the past as the wealthy people would no longer need to work from paycheck to paycheck. Instead, they would search for and discover what they really loved to do and, therefore, be highly motivated to build their competitive creations for the world. To encourage that widespread motivation, the job structure itself would have to change, under survival pressures, beyond today's routine ruts. Perhaps jobs would become little entrepreneurial units to encourage and reward people's greatest asset — their buried creativity.

And with such stimulating new jobs, people would become ever more creative thinkers, just as she had herself since switching off her former following mode. Moreover, people would fall in love with their work and goals...just as she had. And, being so happy, their love and family relationships would flourish. Like her own wonderful life since cutting through the illusions and dumping her oppressive ex-husband, the lives of ordinary people would soar once they cut through the illusions and dumped their oppressive politicians and bureaucrats.

With nothing holding back civilization and technology, it would be a new world with super technologies and super standards of living, she thought. Then, she leaned back in the tub and scooped the warm water over her breasts. She suddenly stopped and stared straight ahead. ...But how do we get there...to that new world? How will the people ever dump the politicians and bureaucrats, for Americans are not fighting for survival?

That question tormented her; it also helped her understand the nature of her growing puzzle-picture. The puzzle-picture she was building for her students through her lectures was what she had just been imagining — a new world free of the matrix of illusions. In that new world of *what is*, there would be no more ruling class of politicians and regulatory bureaucrats who drain the people through a matrix of illusions, because the matrix of illusions would not exist. As she imagined that illusion-free world, she realized that a paradigm shift in the human perspective occurred: man saw himself as the supreme value — the *God-Man*. Nothing was above the individual, not government, not God.

The matrix of illusions was today too powerful in the minds of adults to see this fundamental shift in the human perspective. ...But as I break down the illusions, she thought, the children...they'll see it. They'll see that as the supreme value — the God-Man — they don't need anyone telling them how to live...they don't need politicians or regulatory bureaucrats suppressing them anymore. In that new world, the ordinary person, seeing *what is*, has the power to be a self-leader. He needs no external leaders. He jumps to a new mentality that integrates knowledge and builds, through mental puzzles, new knowledge and new values.

As I show them the new world, my students will make the shift...and it'll be my twelve children who bring the paradigm shift in the human perspective to the world.

Over and over, the thought kept going through her head: my twelve students will bring the paradigm shift in the human perspective to the world. But how will they do it? She pondered that question as the album changed and the music of Mozart filled her house. How will the masses make the shift in the human perspective *without* survival pressures? Without the fear of *death*, as I experienced with my ex-husband, what could possibly shatter the matrix of illusions that controls humanity?

Then it hit her: maybe our *deaths* will be what my students will eventually use to create the survival pressures needed to shift the whole human perspective. If my students can show the world that our "natural" deaths really are not natural — not for conscious beings — then humanity would feel immense survival pressures to make the paradigm shift in the human perspective: to feeling the supreme value of the human life. Human consciousness is too valuable to fall into the death cycle of nature, trapped there by government and religion. Human consciousness is supreme. That shift in perspective would quickly dump oppressive politicization off the nation's back and bring about the freedom, demand, and then supply of: biological immortality.

The shift in perspective to the supreme value of man — God-Man — would end politicians and regulatory bureaucrats as we know them. The government could no longer hold back rapid technological progress in any field, especially the medical field; the resulting wealthy and healthy people would discover such rewarding love and happiness they would desire to live eternally; entrepreneurial businessmen and women would have the freedom and motivation to rise and respond to the huge demand to cure the ultimate disease of aging and death. ...That all will happen when humanity shifts its perspective...to the God-Man. Fulfilling her vision of that future world would begin in her classroom, with her growing puzzle-picture of the new world populated with the God-Man.

"Perhaps that's it," she whispered, *"death.* Death certainly is the ultimate consequence for what's wrong with humanity. Human life is the supreme value — not government, not God — and must not be allowed to perish."

She paused and thought to herself, I must create this puzzle-picture for my students. They're the ones who'll change the world. With my puzzle-picture completed, they'll have seen and will permanently know the supreme value of human life, forever in their souls. With that perspective, they'll always avoid destructive activities. They'll never do drugs or drift into other self-destructive activities; they'll even take precautions such as never riding with a reckless driver or someone who's been drinking. They'll simply value their lives too much.

Miss Annabelle knew this puzzle-picture of the other world and its supreme value of human life would permanently stay in her students' minds. Every decision they would hence make would be positively influenced by the immense value of their limited supply of life. Her remaining general lectures would become the puzzle pieces to complete the puzzle-picture of the new world and its supreme value of life.

Upon understanding this puzzle-picture about the world of the God-Man she was creating for her students, Miss Annabelle realized that the God-Man had an entirely different mentality. He needed no outside forces guiding him. By seeing the essence of things, he had the power to guide himself. Moreover, he could integrate concepts to build puzzle-pictures of his future — puzzle-pictures in which he could see the puzzle pieces he must still accomplish to fulfill that future picture. So, she realized, God-Man creates his future and guides himself to fulfill that future; "just as my students will do," she whispered.

Miss Annabelle finished her bath and wrapped a bathrobe tightly around her small torso. She was supposed to go over to Jessie and Angie's place for Christmas dinner, but the roads were not plowed. As Miss Annabelle called them, a unique insight flashed through her head about her general lectures...from a historical perspective.

"Hello?"

"Oh, hi Angie," said Miss Annabelle, bringing her back from her insight, "I guess you've seen the roads."

"I know. I'm so disappointed they're not clearing them. I don't want you to be all alone on Christmas."

"I'm actually excited about working on my general lectures today. I just realized how to shape them to instill in my students the supreme value of life. Honestly, Angie, I can't wait to get to work on the lectures."

"Can you tell me some of your ideas?" Angie asked.

"Sure!" Miss Annabelle loved to share her ideas with Angie. So, she sat down on the couch next to the phone and continued, "I now understand the power of my general lectures. In fact, I just had an insight while calling you as to why there aren't true Renaissance men today or great thinkers such as the ground-breaking Greeks 2300 years ago. Those superachievers had what I'm giving my students in my general lectures. Outside of their strict academic programs, those greats also got general tutelage, often from great thinkers themselves — as did Plato from Socrates, Aristotle from Plato, Alexander the Great from Aristotle. Those tutors would undoubtedly deliver unique insights into life that would shock their young students into different ways of thinking about things, teaching their young minds how to break through boundaries and cut through traditional dogma to the essence and power in life."

"Your general lectures do exactly the same thing for your students," Angie said.

"That's right! Outside the fundamental academic training I give them all day long, they also get my general lecture in the morning, teaching their minds to cut through the matrix of illusions to the essence of life. I know now this type of tutelage was the secret behind the great minds of the famous Greeks and Renaissance men. My students, with that same boundary-breaking power, can become great thinkers on par with anyone in history!" She laughed with delight; a *happiness attack* rushed through her body.

"Oh honey, you're a godsend to those children."

"You know, for years I've known that a person's deep motivational drive, or lack of it, determined that person's eventual success or failure in life. Breaking through boundaries to new insights on life is exciting and motivating to children. They see a whole new world — the world of *what is*, which is a beautiful world of happiness and value creation, the world in which human beings were meant to live. By experiencing boundary-breaking insights during my general lectures, my students gain the ability to do the same. They see through illusions to the essence of things. I see their control and confidence grow every day. They know that they'll someday make major breakthroughs for the world. So, their motivation grows. And it is that growing, deep motivational drive that eventually generates legendary value creators."

Miss Annabelle and Angie talked for nearly an hour. When

they finished, and Miss Annabelle put the phone down, she heard Lee and Todd's mother calling them to come inside for Christmas Dinner. Those two playful boys, she thought, if tutored properly, could grow up to be legendary value creators. What if I could give my general lectures to the entire student body? she wondered. What if I could spread my teaching method across the globe?

*

Now, twenty-seven years later, Jake was listening to the tapes of her general lectures and lamenting over a thought Jessie had first brought up: what if she had taught these past twenty-seven years…how many legendary value producers would have risen from her teachings? Three legendary value producers came from her one year of teaching at Duncan Elementary.

Jake slipped in tape after tape. Miss Annabelle routinely made boundary-breaking insights and snapped together the most compelling picture on the supreme value of life ever presented to nine-year-olds. Once people experience the shift in perspective to the supreme value and power of themselves as the God-Man, Jake thought, this deep-rooted motivational drive will belong to them. With that natural drive and power, they will steadily develop into major value producers…no, something even better, he realized: they will steadily develop into major value *creators*, even if they have no advanced education or particular skills.

As Jake listened to the general lectures late into the night, he knew he was witnessing a different mentality than his own. In college, he had studied Julian Jaynes and his classic work called *The Origin of Consciousness in the Breakdown of the Bicameral Mind*. The renowned Dr. Jaynes of Princeton University presented scientifically sound evidence that humanity existed with a different mentality 3000 years ago. Man lived through automatic, mimicked or learned reactions, without the internal mind space needed *to think* as we do today. Then around 1000 BC, under enormous *survival pressures* as the bicameral mind grew increasingly inadequate to handle the mounting complexities of growing civilizations, mankind started its "jump" to the self-controlling, self-determining mentality we experience today with the internal mind space *to think* and make decisions.

But the God-Man's puzzle-building ability created even greater internal mind space to "jump" yet again, 3000 years later, to another mentality, something Jake heard Miss Annabelle call, during a science lecture, *Neothink* (for New Think). He realized that with puzzle-building Neothink, Miss Annabelle created new mind space and reached new levels previously unreachable within our mind space now, beyond all our thinking tools today such as metaphors and analog models of our current mentality. With the God-Man mentality called Neothink, ordinary people could take every field of knowledge and every value to the next level; they could create entirely new fields of knowledge and magnificent new values.

"Where is this woman taking us?" he wondered as he fell asleep at the kitchen table while listening to her lectures.

CHAPTER
SEVEN

During the holiday break, Miss Annabelle planned to make a visit to each of her students' homes. She wanted to meet the other parents she had not yet met and, most of all, she wanted to know her students' environments at home.

She wanted to visit Rico's home first, for she worried most about Rico's home life and exposure to the criminal mind around him. But she could not get ahold of his parents. When she called, kids always answered the phone and said their parents were not home. Twice Rico himself answered and said the same thing.

So, Miss Annabelle made visits and brought little Christmas presents to the other students. She visited the homes of Teddy, Sally, Ian, Danny, Natasha, and Debbie...half her students. At this point, she analyzed what she had seen, and she was pleased. Their home life, for the most part, seemed normal. Their parents, overall, seemed positive and supportive of their children. Miss Annabelle received compliments from their parents, mostly about how much they appreciated their children's enthusiasm for school.

Because of her treatment from the adults at school and the rumors, Miss Annabelle had been anxious about meeting her students' parents. But whenever she feared doing something in life that she knew was good to do, she made herself go through with it. Now, she felt glad she was going through with this.

Still unable to talk to Rico's parents, however, her next visit was Cathy's house. Miss Annabelle spent a little extra money on Cathy's Christmas present, getting her an elegant jumpsuit...something to feel beautiful in.

When Miss Annabelle went inside, she was at once struck by the obese size of everyone there. Miss Annabelle had seen fat before, but not in this way. Every being in that house was hugely fat; the four-year-old, the eight-year-old, the teenager, the mom and the dad. They all carried the same ratio of fat too, just at different ages. For instance, the fat four-year-old looked like the fat mom, just a shorter version. Usually, Miss Annabelle thought, the fat doesn't start showing up until the third or fourth grade in school, and then the weight gain would be gradual. But in this house, the preschool child was just as fat as the mom.

This scene made Miss Annabelle very sad. Although the house seemed neat and clean, Miss Annabelle immediately noticed two outstanding problems:

First, she could see that the parents continuously pushed food on their children. In the sweetest voice, Cathy's mom several times asked her three girls if they'd like something to eat. The four-year-old and the teenager ate two substantial snacks during the thirty minutes Miss Annabelle was there. When Cathy would not snack, her mother shook her head and said, "I don't know what's wrong with her. Lately, she won't eat anything, it seems."

Being as polite as she knew how, Miss Annabelle said, "Mrs. Solomon, I don't think anything is wrong with your daughter. I think she's trying to cut out snacking, which would actually be healthy for her. ...Maybe she can help lead an example for her sisters, too."

"Impossible!" Cathy's mom said with a smile. "Us Solomons come from big stock. We've been big like this for generations. It's just the way we are. It's in the genes, you know."

Miss Annabelle looked for a moment at Mrs. Solomon's face, then sincerely said, "You have beautiful features. So does Cathy. I'd, for one, love to see her features come out. I bet she'd be the most beautiful girl at Duncan Elementary."

"Do you really think so?" Mrs. Solomon said, her imagination drifting off for a moment. After a brief escape, though, she shook off the thought and answered her own question. "No way, José! The Solomons were born to be large." With that, she automatically performed an ingrained habit and yelled out, "Cathy, come get your ice cream sandwich dear. Eat up!"

The other outstanding problem Miss Annabelle detected was the tension between Cathy's mother and father. Miss Annabelle could feel it the moment she met them. From deciding where to sit and talk to answering Miss Annabelle's questions, the parents constantly went off into little sidebar arguments with each other. A sense of hatred between mom and dad hung heavy in the air.

It seemed to Miss Annabelle that the parents saw in each other what they hated about themselves: out-of-control obesity. Therefore, they seemed almost as if they wanted to hurt each other. Even during the thirty minutes Miss Annabelle visited, they could not stop themselves from taking out their frustrations on each other.

The tension got so thick, Miss Annabelle could just imagine what yelling must occur when they are not restrained by the presence of adult company. Such yelling would frighten little girls, she thought. Seeing the four-year-old watching television and eating sugar pop cereal right out of the box, Miss Annabelle realized that eating, beginning as little toddlers, probably provided comfort to help soothe their frazzled nerves. As she looked at the obese teenager watching TV and eating two pop tarts, Miss Annabelle realized that eating for these girls started as an escape from tension but turned into a way of life that would haunt these beautiful children for their entire lives.

Her visit with Cathy's folks saddened Miss Annabelle. That poor little girl and her sisters are trapped in such a hopeless situation, she thought. How can Cathy possibly lose weight, Miss Annabelle wondered, if she's constantly surrounded by people eating, with parents encouraging her to eat, too?

*

Reggie lived in a home of poverty. His father abandoned Reggie and his older twin sisters just before Reggie was born.

He never saw his father. His mother was a proud black woman who believed in earning a living. Although she qualified, Reggie's mom refused welfare. Instead, she worked full time cleaning homes.

Reggie did not have the same financial advantages of other children. He had no father to speak of, and he saw his mom much less than other children. Reggie's circumstances saddened Miss Annabelle. However, she felt his mother set a powerful example of morals and ethics. In some ways, Reggie's mom reminded Miss Annabelle of Angie — a strong, honest woman who has lived through hard times.

Despite a hard life, Reggie's mom was one of the kindest, most loving human beings. Given the luxury of time, Miss Annabelle knew that she and this woman could be good friends. Reggie would grow up without material things, but he had a solid example of productivity and lots of love from his mom.

*

When Miss Annabelle walked into Jeremiah's home, she was startled by a lifesize statue of Jesus on the Cross in the small entryway where a coat rack might otherwise go. The statue was a hint of what the next 30 minutes would be like. When Miss Annabelle left, she was not sure if Jeremiah's mother was just extremely religious...or what's been called a "Jesus freak".

*

Miss Annabelle's next two visits went well. Both Bobby and Alan lived in perfectly normal homes with kind and supportive parents.

She still could not get through to Rico's parents, though. Finally, on the last day of the holidays, Miss Annabelle went to Rico's home and knocked. Rico opened the door.

"M...Miss Annabelle!" he stammered.

"Rico, why can't I get hold of your parents?"

"They're...they're out."

"Well, can I come in?"

"No! ...Um, my folks don't let anyone in the house unless

they're here."

"Ric, who da fuck's dere!" his father boomed.

"Nobody!" Rico shouted back with the same irritation in his voice.

"Nobody?" Miss Annabelle said in a tone that demanded an explanation, although she was still a bit dazed by his father's vocabulary.

"Miss Annabelle, please leave," Rico desperately whispered.

"Are you in some sort of danger?" she whispered back.

"No…I just want you to go."

"But I want to meet your parents. Rico, let me meet your parents. It won't be so bad."

She noticed when she mentioned Rico's parents, she saw panic in his face. But why?

"Rico," she continued, "I must see your parents. I must come in."

But Rico continued protesting. As he did, it gradually dawned on Miss Annabelle that Rico was ashamed of his parents and did not want his teacher to see how he lived, as if he were silently saying, "Don't worry about me, Miss Annabelle; I can handle it." As she stood in the doorway and looked down at little Rico trying to keep her from this criminal-minded world, she suddenly realized he was trying to protect her. He did not want her exposed to the disgust within his home.

Miss Annabelle all at once felt touched, and she felt sorry for Rico; she knelt down to one knee so she could look straight in his eyes, and said, "Sweetie, I have gone through some very bad times in my life. I don't think anything I see in there is going to frighten me. I really want to come inside because I love you, Rico. I just want to know more about you and your life away from school. However, I'll give you the decision here. I want to come inside because of my love and concern for you. But if you still ask me to leave, I will."

Rico was moved. Out of both frustration and love, Rico could not say anything. His eyes still pleaded with Miss Annabelle to leave. He knew all he had to do was say "Please leave," and she would. But he did not say those two words. Instead, he hung his head toward the floor and stepped aside to let Miss Annabelle come in. As she walked past the devastated little boy, she hated doing it, but she knew she needed to. She put her hand on his shoulder and said, "It's okay, Rico. It's really okay."

Inside, she saw similarities to both Reggie's situation, especially the poverty, and Cathy's situation, especially the tension. But one trait made Rico's situation far worse: the laziness and its manifestations! The house was a pig pen deep in dirt and junk everywhere. It looked like a filthy repair shop.

"I pick up the garbage, but my dad won't let me throw out this stuff," Rico said.

Suddenly a deep voice startled Miss Annabelle. "What do you want?" It was Rico's father who had walked in from the living room. Miss Annabelle noticed the body odor that followed this large man.

"Hello, Mr. Rodriguez. I'm Miss Annabelle, Rico's teacher at Duncan Elementary School."

"Is he in trouble?" he snarled, giving Rico a threatening look. Obviously, this man, who had been in and out of prison more than once, did not have a concern morally speaking. He just resented the inconvenience to himself if Rico had been bad.

"No, to the contrary. Rico is a bright child. He has a promising future."

That comment shocked Rico. Right then, he felt a transformation come over him. *Never* had anyone noticed him as someone with *promise*! All he had ever heard is what "a pain in the ass" he was or how stupid he was. Now, here was this beautiful woman, whom Rico idolized, telling his father that Rico was a bright child with a promising future! I'm *bright*, he thought. That comment opened an excitement about himself and his future he never felt before. He relived her comment over and over again in his head for weeks thereafter.

"Rico's bright?" his father asked, not sure if he heard her right.

"He's more than bright — he's *very bright*, Mr. Rodriguez."

"No shit?" his father laughed, "Imagine dat! ...Do you dink he'll be rich someday?" He was joking.

"Yes, I'm certain he will be," Miss Annabelle said, dead seriously. Rico's heart was pounding.

"You're not here to tell me I need to start saving money to

send him to college, are you? Because I can tell you right now lady, dat ain't gonna happen..."

Miss Annabelle cut him off, "You don't need to do a thing. Rico can do it all himself. I just want you to know that he'll make it legitimately. He's that smart. Don't, please don't influence him down a wrong path in life. Don't let him be around people who are bad influences. He's got too much ahead to waste it."

If someone talked to Rico's father this way — telling him what to do — that person would normally lose a few teeth. But his father stood quiet for a moment as Rico watched him closely.

"OK," he finally said, "I'll respect my boy's mind. ...His smarts come from me, you know." That was the only semi-compliment Rico had ever received from his father. But what made the moment unforgettable for Rico was how Miss Annabelle felt about him. She turned to her handsome little protector and handed him his wrapped present. He immediately opened it to find three books inside: *Martin Eden* by Jack London, *Calumet K* by Merwin Webster, and *Fire Hunter* by Jim Kjelgaard.

"You'll like those," Miss Annabelle said.

"Thank you!" Rico said. He was in awe, not by the present per se, but by the idea that he was smart enough now to be considered *a reader!*

Years later, with his library filled with books, Rico remembered this home visit from Miss Annabelle as the turning point in his life. He kept those three books as long as he lived.

*

That evening, Miss Annabelle reflected upon her holiday visits. Six of her twelve students had quite normal home lives and supportive parents.

One of her students, Teddy, had a home life that was financially fragile, that could slip into poverty but was barely hanging on to "normal". However, since her talk with Teddy's father in the parking lot of the school a couple months ago, he said he had gotten two promotions and was, for the first time in his life, moving up into management and paying off his debts. He said since he was paying off debt he could not improve their standard of living yet, but he was doing much, much better financially. Also, he and Teddy said they had a secret project they wanted to surprise her with later. ...Teddy's father had turned the corner on a life of stagnation and near poverty and was on the rise.

Four of her students, however, had serious problems. Reggie lived in poverty with minimal parental contact; Cathy lived in constant tension with food as the outlet; Rico lived around the criminal mind steeped in laziness. And, of course, Sally's situation was far from normal, knowing that at any time she could lose her mother. Four of my twelve students have serious burdens they carry around, she thought; and they're just children! She worried about their fragile existence. ...She was not sure, besides a smothering environment, to what degree Jeremiah's homelife was detrimental to a child.

She worked on her lectures that evening, glad she made the visits to their homes.

CHAPTER
EIGHT

Miss Annabelle enjoyed the precious moments of watching each of her students enter her room the day after the holidays. She was glad to be back with her students. She was loaded with lectures to start the second half of the school year.

One moment seemed to stand still. Cathy came through the door. She was a good fifteen pounds lighter and was wearing the cute jumper. Cathy shyly looked at her classmates, then at her adoring teacher. Miss Annabelle silently mouthed the word, "Wow!" Cathy smiled for the first time all school year. She *is* a beautiful girl, Miss Annabelle thought.

Her celebration was cut short when she watched Sally come in quietly, not smiling. Miss Annabelle went over and knelt down by her, fearing that her mother's condition took a turn for the worse.

"Sally, how is everything at home?"

"My mom's doing OK. But she told me that this Christmas might have been our last one together." Sally talked in a low and controlled voice. Then she gasped and rushed her words, in a high uncontrolled voice, "I just can't go through Christmas without my mom!"

Miss Annabelle hugged Sally and held her until Sally regained control. Then Miss Annabelle told her, "I'm going to talk about the value of *your* life today, darling. And I think it might help. Okay?" Sally nodded.

"Boys and girls, I'm so happy to be back. Are you ready for your most important lecture so far this school year?"

"Yes!" they cheered. Ian scooted to the edge of his seat, which he did when he was especially excited about a lecture. Sally's eyes looked like two black holes ready to pull in all the hope that came from Miss Annabelle's lecture. Rico looked neat and studious and attentive, quite a metamorphosis from the unkempt appearance when he started the year. Cathy, surprisingly, no longer sat in the back; she sat at a desk close to the front of the room; she's becoming beautiful, Miss Annabelle thought. Teddy closed the book he had been reading and looked charged up and ready to go. Miss Annabelle noticed he was reading a book on Henry Ford.

What a group, Miss Annabelle thought as she took a moment to admire the nine-year-olds. They're still pure and honest, she thought. I mustn't hold anything back...not anything. So, here goes...

"So often have I heard, murmured in a voice of hopelessness, '*Everyone dies.*' How many of you have heard that haunting comment?" About half the kids raised their hands in acknowledgment.

"I'm here today to tell you that human dying is completely *unnatural*. It is wrong. And it must be stopped."

Sally gasped. Miss Annabelle had just encapsulated every feeling and thought that permeated the little girl's soul since learning about her mom's illness.

"Instead of just accepting that we die, let's turn it around and ask, 'Why do we die in the first place?' The answer sheds light on just how bizarre human dying really is.

"So, children, why do we die?"

Ian thought furiously. "I know!" he shouted.

"Yes, Ian?"

"Well, I'm convinced there's no God or other gossipy rumor like that ruling the cosmos. I think it's people like us who have been around a lot longer than us. So, I don't believe we die to go to heaven or anything."

"You're a very smart young man," Miss Annabelle said. "So,

why do you think we die?"

"Evolution," he said, content with his one-word answer. But when the rest of the kids looked confused, he added, "You know, Darwin's Natural Selection...propagation of the species. Every living thing dies to allow the species to evolve and get stronger."

He *really* is smart, Miss Annabelle kept thinking. Then she said, "You're absolutely right, Ian. Mother Nature included aging and death as her mechanism to make the species progress. But let me ask you, Ian, how long do you think it would take for a major positive change to occur through evolution?"

"Thousands of years," Ian answered.

"Now I'll ask you, class, how long does it take *mankind* to make major positive changes?"

"They happen all the time," Teddy said. "Every day my dad tells me something exciting that he's read in the paper or magazine."

"Oh yeah," Alan added. "You should see some of the new technologies I read about in my magazine."

"Every day," Miss Annabelle echoed. "Mankind progresses infinitely faster than Mother Nature. The original purpose for dying no longer applies to humans."

Miss Annabelle looked around her classroom in amazement. All twelve eight and nine-year-olds were watching her every gesture. Not one set of eyes was drowsy. The kids were thinking hard, and Miss Annabelle decided not to say anything at this point. She was curious who would be the first to ask her a question and what the question would be.

Sally asked the first question, "Doesn't that make aging a fatal disease to humans, just like cancer? I mean, aging kills us, and we don't need to die."

What fascinated Miss Annabelle was the speed at which Sally had absorbed and fully integrated Miss Annabelle's concept that death is unnatural to humans. Sally had already seen the logic and was using that concept to build further concepts. Adults, on the other hand, would have to wrestle with the idea of obsoleting death for their entire lifetimes and still not see the logic. Sally, however, saw the logic, snapped it into place, and immediately started building upon it.

"I'd call aging nothing other than a fatal disease, too, Sally," the eloquent teacher agreed. "And it's man's moral duty to cure and eradicate humanity's harmful diseases. It's man's moral duty to cure and eradicate human aging and death."

"Why can't that be done?" Sally asked innocently. Obviously, she had wondered the same thing about her mother's cancer.

"Let's back up and ask, why can't we cure other fatal diseases that are much more simple than curing human aging?" Miss Annabelle looked across the room, then added, "Let me give you a clue: the computer industry versus the medical industry."

The class was silent. Teddy, who had recently read an article about the developing computers, slowly raised his hand.

"Computers are getting cheaper; medical care is getting more expensive?" he said. He looked unsure.

"Yes, Teddy!" Miss Annabelle said. "And there's a reason for that. The computer industry advances very rapidly at cheaper and cheaper costs because it's mostly unregulated. The medical industry is heavily regulated by the FDA and advances slowly at huge costs. Those prohibitive costs cut out the millions of small entrepreneurs working out of their garages, like what's starting to happen in the computer industry. Great computer dynamics are rising from the 'garage entrepreneurs'. If the medical industry were self-regulated like computers and not held down by the FDA, then rapid progress by both the 'garage entrepreneurs' and the huge drug companies would quickly eradicate most fatal diseases, and eventually aging and death."

"You mean, without the FDA, then fatal diseases like cancer would quickly be cured?" Sally asked. Then, she grimaced.

"Yes, darling," Miss Annabelle answered. She could feel Sally's pain.

The room was quiet for several seconds as the kids, who had already snapped the logic into their minds, tried to comprehend why the FDA was allowed to exist. Then Sally broke the silence.

"They're murderers...right?" she asked angrily.

"Yes, they are," Miss Annabelle answered. She knew this would get her in trouble with the school board. She already knew the God discussion before the holidays would get her in trouble. But she knew today's talk was the necessary puzzle piece on which to build the rest of the year's lectures. After her vision on Christmas Day of the beautiful future world and

101

the puzzle-picture that would bring these children into that beautiful world, she knew the key puzzle piece was this lecture to integrate them with the infinite value of their own lives. To successfully do this, Miss Annabelle could not hold anything back, including the destruction caused by politicians and regulatory bureaucrats, no matter what the consequences.

"They're murdering my mom?" Sally continued.

"Yes, they are, darling," Miss Annabelle answered. Her heart was hurting for Sally, who had tears welling up in her eyes.

"Around Thanksgiving, I asked who in here wanted to someday find cures to fatal diseases like cancer. All of you raised your hands. I want you to remember to look through to the essence of what you're doing in life — in this case, saving lives. If there are obstacles that block you here in America because of certain people in the FDA or Congress who want to rule over the medical or drug industry, then you take your life's work and move to a country where you can continue. If that were being done today, then Sally's mom would not be dying."

Sally started crying, and Miss Annabelle walked over to comfort her.

"The value of human life is immeasurable. If we have to go against what bureaucrats deem 'legal research' in order to save human life, then we are morally free to break the law or to go around it."

Miss Annabelle stopped to hug Sally. The class was stunned. No adult had ever told them to *break the law*. But the children were deeply moved. Miss Annabelle talked to them at a level they had never known — the level of *fully integrated honesty*. She went beyond "truth" or "legality". And, having matured decades during the past quarter hour, the children felt the responsibility of this level of communication.

"The value of human life is...*it is everything*. There is nothing more valuable in the Universe. As we talked about before the holidays, we are the Gods of the Universe. The value of each one of your lives is infinite — it is the value of God. In the world with no matrix of illusions, people never die. Like Gods, each of you and your loved ones should live eternally. I want you to start thinking about your right, as an infinitely valuable human being, as a God-Man, to never die. Dying is bizarre. It is unnatural."

Miss Annabelle stopped there. The infinite value of life was now seeded in her students. She knew that seed would grow and the children would grow up with a whole different perspective about human life. She also knew they would now forever scorn anything harmful...from the FDA to cigarettes or drugs. They would take no foolish chances with life such as riding in cars driven by reckless drivers or with someone who has been drinking alcohol.

The longer they live, she thought, the greater their chances of making it to the future world where people don't die anymore.

Still standing next to Sally, Miss Annabelle looked down and put her hand on the little girl's head and patted it gently, and said, "The extraordinary value of our lives is why we must go on and live life to the fullest, even after we lose a loved one."

"But, Miss Annabelle, if there's no God, then there's no Heaven, and I'll never see my mom again!"

Miss Annabelle was not surprised by Sally's comment and said, "Maybe we don't *need* to believe in God and Heaven anymore. Maybe there's something better — something real."

Sally's deep brown eyes, which were scared and puzzled, relaxed a little and became hopeful as she looked up at her teacher.

"Let me tell you a little story first, a true story, then I'll explain why something even better than God and Heaven *and something real* may await your mother."

All the children were now sitting on the edge of their seats and leaning forward like a bed of flowers growing toward their precious sun. Miss Annabelle had their attention, and she would nourish their minds. Whether she was right or wrong with what she was about to say, she knew their minds would forever grow free of status quo and traditional thinking. She was about to give them the gift to break outside of boundaries to explore powerful new thoughts.

"During your history lessons, I've lectured about World War II and the Holocaust. Millions of innocent people died on the battlefields and in the concentration camps. There was a wealthy German businessman named Oskar Schindler who acquired as many Jews as he could to work in his factories in order to keep them out of the concentration camps and save their lives.

"Schindler was a producer of values, an entrepreneurial businessman. As such, he valued values. He, and others like him, could not let the ultimate value — human life — perish. ...Could you?"

Sally and the rest of the class shook their heads right away. They were following Miss Annabelle's monologue word for word.

"You are the future value producers. Value producers would do everything possible to never let the supreme value — human life — perish." Miss Annabelle noticed Teddy look away, as though his mind had just taken off and raced ahead of Miss Annabelle's speech. She gave him a moment, then asked him, "Teddy, I just saw a light go on in your eyes. Can you shed some of that light on us?"

Several children smiled and looked at him. He lifted his eyes and brushed back his thick brown hair, and calmly said, "Everyone out there is a value producer. Remember what you said? To survive beyond their nuclear power that could wipe out civilization, everyone would have to become a value producer. So, they're all value producers out there." ...Teddy was referring to the lecture just before the holidays that suggested that advanced humanlike consciousness controlled the cosmos. The logic was scientifically solid, and these children interlocked solid logic into their brains in a matter of minutes, whereas adults might take months or years...if ever.

Ian's eyes were now sparkling. He turned his chair around to face Teddy. Sally turned too, blinking her soft brown eyes more frequently with all the excitement in the air.

"And those value producers have been there for millions or billions of years," Miss Annabelle prompted. "Think of the technology they would have created in all that time."

Like a levee holding back tons of water, Ian burst: "They would have learned how to keep people from aging and dying!"

"Very quickly," Miss Annabelle added. "Even right here on Earth, we're but a few years away from some early stages of averting death, particularly if the medical industry could progress without the FDA. We've had our modern, conscious minds for only a few thousand years, and we're close to outsmarting death itself once we experience unhampered, advancing technologies.

What about modern minds that have been around for millions or billions of years? We have to ask ourselves, what levels of advanced technologies have they reached?

"Of course, we have no way of knowing their technologies, but there is one thing we can know for sure. Does anyone want to venture what that one thing is?" Miss Annabelle looked around the room. From behind her came a voice so confident, it sounded almost omnipotent:

"They would not let *anyone* perish...not even my mom," Sally said.

Miss Annabelle's heart skipped a beat. She twirled around and locked eyes with Sally.

"How could they?" the teacher happily cried out. "Just as Oskar Schindler could not let the helpless, innocent Jews perish, how could those Gods of the Universe let your helpless, innocent mother perish?"

Sally rose from her chair as though she were pulled from above. She knew now that some technology existed that saved our consciousness after our bodies died. She started walking toward her teacher, then she ran to her and jumped into her receiving arms. "Oh, Miss Annabelle," she cried as euphoria filled her, "mommy's going to be OK...my mommy's going to be OK!"

CHAPTER
NINE

The second week into the new year, Miss Annabelle was summoned to the principal's office. The contents in the sealed envelope centered on her desk when she came in early that morning was no mystery. In fact, she had been expecting it ever since her lecture that challenged the existence of God, and especially since her lecture that challenged the authority of the government.

There it is, she thought, as she removed her camel colored coat that reflected the subtle blonde highlights in her auburn hair. There it is.

*

The first thing Jessie noticed when Miss Annabelle told him about the summons on her way out that afternoon, was how different she seemed than the first time. She appeared neither scared of the confrontation nor overly anxious that she might lose her teaching position before the school year was over. Quite worried himself, he asked her how she felt so calm.

"Because now I know my kids can't be fooled," she said, smiling. Then she turned very serious, "I'm not afraid of those vengeful adults making me look like some kind of monster. My students will pierce right through that illusion, and that thought is very comforting."

"If last time was any indication, they *are* going to try to make you out to be a monster," Jessie said, shaking his head.

"Oh, I know. Just listen to this," she said, pulling the summons from her purse and reading it: "The Duncan Elementary School Board will hold an emergency meeting this Thursday, 7:30 p.m., to investigate the recent actions of Miss Annabelle Barclays, a Duncan Elementary School, Third Grade teacher. Agenda of topics: 1) teaching hatred toward government, 2) teaching hatred toward God."

"Yeah, they're going to do their best to make you look like a hatemonger, all right," Jessie said. Then he grimaced and added, "After the Burke-induced episode, why do they still go after you, anyway?"

"Because I threaten their world, Jessie. A year ago, I broke free from that world of illusions. As I told you and Angie, one day I saw through illusions not just within my marriage, but everywhere. Most adults still live in that stagnant world of illusions. Some, the leaders like Hammerschmidt, live *off of* the matrix of illusions. I'm going to end that matrix of illusions, so I threaten his livelihood."

"You threaten his smug world," Jessie said, fully relating to her explanation. Jessie and Angie were outsiders. They lived through very hard times and lived outside the Establishment's influences. They never got caught up in the world of illusions. They were deeply honest people who got into each other and were happy together in their own world. Therefore, they were the only adults Miss Annabelle knew who were able to honestly appreciate Miss Annabelle's work and like her as a friend.

The students' parents, on the other hand, faced a paradox. They were very impressed by their children's new love for school and for their families. The parents were just as impressed by their children's academic achievements, which went noticeably up two grades in most cases. And their children seemed so happy all week long. That was quite a smooth-sailing boat to now have to rock.

For, unbeknownst to Miss Annabelle, the school board sent its summons for the emergency meeting to the parents of Miss

Annabelle's students. Upon reading that summons, the idea of Miss Annabelle spreading hate was planted in the parents' minds and started growing into uneasiness and concern. Several parents went back to their tapes and listened to the last couple of months of general lectures. Some of the parents started worrying, and some of them started calling each other to ask if Miss Annabelle seemed a little bit weird.

*

During her science lecture on Wednesday, Miss Annabelle noticed that Cathy seemed unusually distracted. She fidgeted continuously in her chair. Finally, Miss Annabelle asked Cathy if everything was OK.

"I think so," the trimmed-down little girl said. She talked louder and with more confidence than the previous semester. "I just want to come to that special meeting about you."

"Me too!" four or five other kids added.

Miss Annabelle had to sit down on the corner of her desk. I'll be damned, she thought. They notified the parents, too. For a moment, her thoughts were trapped in a state of shock.

"Are you OK, Miss Annabelle?" Cathy asked, reviving her teacher from her shock.

"Yes...yes, I'm quite all right," Miss Annabelle answered, feigning normalcy. Miss Annabelle remained seated on her desk and witnessed a half dozen or so children asking each other what meeting was Cathy talking about. As the teacher let the children sort out that question, she began to realize that she did not have to fear the confrontation. For, the two topics on the agenda merely came about as a result of her piercing through illusions to *what is*. As long as she continued to cut through illusions, she would do fine. She remembered the accusations that originated from Burke. Although a volatile situation back then, she came through unscathed. Of course, that time no parents were involved.

"Children," she said to the class, "Cathy is referring to a meeting this Thursday evening here at 7:30 in the evening. The school board will be reviewing what I have been teaching you. Some of them seem to be nervous about my recent talks with you, especially about God and government. Of course, you know that I'm cutting through the matrix of illusions in this world to show you *what is*. I'm also teaching you how to, on your own, use your minds to cut through the matrix of illusions to see *what is*. By doing this, you'll gain the power of God-Man and the motivation to build wonderful values for the world, someday. You will not live trapped in boring, stagnant ruts like most of our parents. You'll instead live with power, growing riches, and happiness. You'll soar beyond the suppression and resignation that results from God and government. By seeing *what is*, you'll become the God-Man and lead yourselves to greatness."

The students only half understood, but they loved and trusted their teacher. Although only nine years old, they increasingly sensed that she was their life preserver who was holding up their spirits and enthusiasm for life in the stormy sea of life into which others sink…into its darkness.

*

When Miss Annabelle pulled into the school parking lot at about twenty minutes past seven on Thursday evening, she was surprised to see it nearly full. Is there a parent/teacher meeting tonight for one of the other grades, she wondered, or maybe a chess tournament?

She walked up the stairs and entered the front entrance to Duncan Elementary School. She walked past the restrooms this time, not needing to stop to calm herself down. In fact, she was aware that she was surprisingly calm.

When she turned the corner to go to the lunch room, she saw a small crowd standing outside the room.

There are the parents who showed up, she thought. But when she walked toward them, she noticed they turned away from the lunch room and walked away, down the hall away from her. When she got to the lunch room, it was deserted. A sign taped on one of the two doors to the room read:

SCHOOL-BOARD MEETING
MOVED TO THE GYM

That's peculiar, Miss Annabelle thought as she continued down the corridor toward the gym. When she reached the gym, she peeked through the small oblong window on the closed door. She did not expect the sight before her: sitting on beige folding chairs were about forty people, facing her from across the gym. Miss Annabelle immediately recognized her students...all twelve came here to support her, she realized. Of course, most parents were there, too. Obviously, they were concerned by the idea of "spreading hate". The chairs were lined up about ten across, four rows deep. Miss Annabelle took a deep breath, then entered.

Twelve little hands instantly started waving at her. Twelve little faces broke into endearing smiles. Miss Annabelle imagined what battles these children must have gone through to convince their parents to bring them here, too. The sight of the children warmed the teacher's heart.

The fuel Miss Annabelle got from Jessie and Angie in her first emergency meeting with the school board now came from her twelve little soul mates. "Hi children," she said as she walked toward the center of the gym where an empty chair awaited her.

"Hi, Miss Annabelle," they said in harmony.

"Thank you all for coming. I can feel your love and support. Thank you," she said so sweetly that, for a moment, everyone present had to ask themselves why they were here.

The stocky Mr. Hammerschmidt, superintendent of the school district, politely asked Miss Annabelle to take her seat and gestured to the lone empty chair that sat perpendicular to her students and faced a smaller group of nine chairs lined up behind three oblong lunch tables where the school board and principal were to sit. About half of those chairs were occupied. They were now waiting for the rest to show.

As Miss Annabelle sat down, she noticed Jessie and Angie come into the gym. They smiled at her comfortingly. Jessie picked up two more folding chairs from the corner of the gym and placed them alongside the audience section, where Miss Annabelle could see them.

At 7:45, the last school board member walked in, and the emergency meeting began:

"Good evening, ladies and gentlemen," Mr. Hammerschmidt

began. "I'm a bit surprised to see all these children at this emergency meeting. May the parents be aware that we will cover two sensitive topics here that may not be appropriate for children. Therefore, I've called in Mrs. Shaffer, a substitute teacher here, to watch your children in the classroom next door while we conduct this sensitive meeting." The children's mouths dropped in dissapointment...after what they had gone through to be here! Mr. Hammerschmidt looked directly at the parents and paused. He was obviously uneasy about the children. But, to his surprise, the parents were not. They seemed to have accepted Miss Annabelle's candid relationship with their children. They seemed to realize that, because of her, their children were no longer at the maturity level of children. The parents had been listening to several of Miss Annabelle's lectures on tape. Although she was different, they admired her. Furthermore, they deeply appreciated what she had done for their children. ...And, deep within each parent was a child of the past full of wonder and motivation who begged to be free again. Free of what? Free of the matrix of illusions. At their subconscious level, Miss Annabelle was a bridge back to their childhood before they had lost their potential in life to resignation. Miss Annabelle represented a way out of the matrix and back to their natural, deep motivational drives. Of course, all those hopes were on a subconscious level.

The superintendent pressed on with a hard stare at the parents and, after a tense moment, he said, louder this time, "Parents, are you going to do the decent thing and remove these children? Mrs. Shaffer is waiting." He gestured to the substitute teacher standing by the door. To the surprise of every school board member, the parents either defiantly shook their heads or sat in stone silence.

Miss Annabelle's heart beat faster. She loved the children so deeply, and to see their parents respect the children's needs over someone's authoritative voice filled Miss Annabelle with hope. Tonight, she would learn something uplifting about adults, something that she never realized before. Tonight, she would learn about adults who have innocently succumbed to resignation, but are good people without envy. Such adults can someday make the journey back to recapture their deep motivational drive

111

and the success and happiness that will come from it. ...Could it be, she wondered, the children who will help their parents get back home to the *real* self before the matrix took over? Could it be *the children* who will save the adults?

Her provocative thought was broken. "Alright then," Mr. Hammerschmidt said. "Let's get started." He then looked at the attractive, petite woman sitting about 15 feet directly before him. "As you know, Miss Annabelle, my name is Mr. Hammerschmidt, and I'm the superintendent of the school district." He went on to introduce the members of the school board. "Today we must investigate two topics regarding you, Miss Annabelle: 1) your attacks on government, and 2) your attacks on God in a classroom of third graders. ...So, let us begin. I have two basic questions I will ask Miss Annabelle on behalf of the school, students, and parents, and we will let her answer these questions.

"First question: I'm sure all parents here share this troublesome concern as to why, Miss Annabelle, do you encourage these children during your lectures to do illegal acts?"

Oh, what a spin doctor, Miss Annabelle said to herself. Then she said out loud, "Mr. Hammerschmidt, I'll gladly answer your question." The audience turned their eyes toward her. "But first, I'll clear up some false impressions you've managed to create. I'll do this in order to answer within the proper context."

"Miss Annabelle, no one here is creating false impressions," Mr. Hammerschmidt snapped back defensively.

"Oh, I'm not so sure about that," the petite woman said, holding her ground. Then, she surprised him by saying, "Aren't you running for lieutenant governor in November?"

"That has nothing to do with this," he answered, obviously ruffled and not able to fully cover up his hatred toward the pretty woman directly before him. But about half the audience was nodding. She was the very image of a woman he could never approach in the real world, but he now had false power over this competitive woman with beauty and brains. Of course, that false power over competitive women and men was the impetus behind this uncompetitive man's aspirations to enter politics.

"As I said, I'll start by clearing up two false impressions," Miss Annabelle said courageously, locking eyes with Hammerschmidt. His eyes darted away, unable to handle the direct confrontation.

"First, I don't think that *all* these parents here shared a troubled concern about my lectures," she said as she turned her head to look at the parents. Most were shaking their heads to confirm Miss Annabelle's statement, "...at least not until you put the thought in their heads in the way that you did. That's a leveraging technique called: forced teaming."

Suddenly the burly body before her, unable to take anymore, moved his hand through the air to indicate he had enough and, in a tantrum, he cried out, "That's not true! Now answer the question, why do you encourage these children to do illegal acts?"

Not the least bit intimidated, Miss Annabelle rolled on, "Well now, that gets us to the second false impression. You ask me, why do I encourage these children to do illegal acts? Mr. Hammerschmidt, every parent would become alarmed if a teacher were, as you put it, encouraging his or her child to do illegal acts. You make me sound like a criminal ring leader. That's an effective impression, though, that would look good in the local papers for a would-be politician: *Hammerschmidt Hammers Out Criminal-Minded 3rd-Grade Teacher.*"

"Now wait a minute, missy," he started to raise his voice but caught himself.

"No, you wait a minute, sir," Miss Annabelle said, sitting straight up and then leaning forward in her chair. "I said I'll answer your questions, and I'm sure that would be helpful to these good parents. But you stop your grandstanding, sir, or I'll take this whole thing to the press as an example of the destruction that can be whipped up from illusions created by agenda-minded, aspiring politicians."

Overwhelmed by the little woman's grit, Jessie shouted, "Yeah!" as he and Angie started clapping, followed by the parents and the children. Once again, Hammerschmidt had been beaten and beaten badly by his nemesis.

"Now, to help alleviate genuine concerns for parents, it would be unconscionable for me to encourage children to blatantly do illegal acts. I do, however, teach your children to do *what is right*." Miss Annabelle turned her chair and body toward the parents, talking directly to them and their children. Neither Hammerschmidt nor the school board was important any longer.

Superpuzzle

The parents and children could feel Miss Annabelle's genuine, heartfelt words.

"To teach your children to do *what is right* requires teaching them to have a mind of their own. They must learn to think for themselves and NOT to rely on others telling them what is right or wrong, including politicians, which I'm sure we agree on. The scribe of history has shown us that prosperity, freedom, and happiness depended on people using their own minds, at times questioning or challenging the world and laws around them.

"I invite everyone to listen to the lecture in question, which I have on tape. Just let me know, and I'll be happy to make you each a copy."

"So, you're promoting vigilantism," Hammerschmidt said slyly.

Rotating herself forward to face her accuser, Miss Annabelle said, "You, sir, are lost in your political world, desperately formulating your out-of-context attacks in order to make someone a villain and yourself the rescuer — the hero. But I'm not here to please your world of appearances or the politicians' world of illusions. I'm here to teach these children's minds to work for themselves. If something is wrongfully illegal, then they can know it and, if necessary, do the right thing. Let's ask the parents, do you want your children to someday be self-thinking adults or a flock of sheep?"

Since the meeting began, the principal Ms. Minner had been looking for an opportunity to fire a shot at Miss Annabelle. At this moment the eerie woman, who was much younger than she looked, shouted in her enthusiasm, "What about calling politicians wife beaters — isn't that spreading hate against our government? Your students might grow up to be Lee Harvey Oswalds."

Miss Annabelle could not believe what she had just heard. But she knew the principal's technique of using emotionally charged non sequiturs was very effective. And she knew she must deal with the non sequitur before answering the question.

"The word non sequitur," Miss Annabelle began, "is Latin and means 'it does not follow'. It does not follow that my lecture articulating the problem with politicians, which I'll address in a moment, leads children into murderous acts. The criminal mind is dominated by the belief that 'others owe me a living'.

114

My lecture, teaching children to always question the status quo, to always use their own minds in order to build important values for the human race, is certainly moving in the opposite direction of the criminal mind.

"Perhaps the biggest force moving children toward the criminal mind is the huge welfare class created by the government, moving welfare families into the mentality that they are owed a living."

Reggie's mother clapped her hands and called out, as one does in a prayer meeting, "Amen!" Miss Annabelle looked over at her, and they nodded to each other. Then the teacher looked back to the principal and continued: "I'm teaching these children to someday build great values for the world and a great life for themselves. For example, the lecture in question, I was encouraging these children to someday develop cures to life threatening diseases, such as cancer. The comments I made against the government referred to those politically ambitious bureaucrats and politicians with vote-gathering, ego-gathering agendas that block lifesaving progress. For example, everyone knows that the FDA retards, even prevents progress on lifesaving drugs. Now, when a close loved one is dying from a disease like cancer, and some politically ambitious bureaucrat is retarding or killing progress through his portfolio-building political agenda, that makes such a bureaucrat not human. When you realize that people like that are why Sally will lose her mother, that makes them worse than wife beaters. That makes them murderers." Miss Annabelle's voice broke, obviously emotionally moved.

Sally and her mother hugged each other as the other mothers looked at them and felt great compassion. Sally's mother and Miss Annabelle's eyes met. Sally's mother let go of Sally, sat up straight, and began to clap. Her clapping was slow and meaningful. She looked deep into Miss Annabelle's eyes as she stood up and continued her ovation. Jessie and Angie stood up and joined her. The other mothers joined them. Sally and all the children sprang out of their seats, smiling and clapping fast. Then, the dads joined the standing ovation.

What is happening here? Miss Annabelle wondered. Those adults are really behind me and my educational ideas that challenge the Establishment.

Superpuzzle

Her face grew full of wonder as she looked at the applauding parents and children. Her eyes moved from Sally's mom to Sally, then across the row, making contact with each adult and child. When her eyes met the last person on her far right, Teddy's father, Mr. Winters, she knew. As she looked at his innocent face, she saw something different than before. She saw a small fire of hope still kindling as he looked back at her.

These adults are innocent people caught in the matrix of illusions, she thought to herself, genuinely amazed at this discovery. The child of the past still lives somewhere deep within them, and perhaps I offer them hope. They're completely different than the dishonest adults who've killed that child of the past. That child within Teddy's dad, she thought while still looking into his eyes, strives to live the way man was meant to live. He still wants to make a difference in this world; he still wants to build magnificent values for society and extraordinary happiness, success, and wealth for himself.

Miss Annabelle could not identify what she was feeling at that moment while realizing those adults were behind her. She felt goosebumps running up her back and down her arms as she suddenly realized she was feeling hope, too...hope for the future, for the new world. She looked for what seemed like a long time at the parents and children, and they at her; they were like mirrors reflecting her deepest emotion of hope back to her. ...If not for the change in these children, she thought, I don't think I'd see this hope in these parents' eyes. What does that mean?

In the meantime, the school board was in a quandary. Miss Annabelle had just gotten a standing ovation from the parents. The school board superintendent wondered, what do I do now? Do I call the end to this meeting...or is there still a way to save the school from this awful threat? ...Even after the parents' confirmation of approval for Miss Annabelle, the politically ambitious school board president searched for ways to attack and perhaps destroy this value in hopes to add to his portfolio of "accomplishments". He knew that he really could become, through the voice of the media, the hero who rescued the school from an awful villain. So he pressed on...

"Thank you parents for your enthusiasm," he said with feigned sincerity, "but we must now consider something together on a more spiritual realm. I know we are all good God-fearing people...all of us but one person here." His roundish head rolled from the parents toward Miss Annabelle. To emphasize his point, he looked at her with exaggerated scorn. "It seems you parents have an atheist teaching your kids to abandon their faith in God."

Miss Annabelle knew this would be a tough subject to discuss with adults, even the innocent ones. The God concept was just too embedded in their thinking from childhood. But she was prepared...

"I believe in a creator, and I believe in God," Miss Annabelle said confidently.

"Not according to your lecture last November," the principal squealed.

"Oh yes I do," Miss Annabelle said without yielding, "only I believe in a creator or God that is closer to our own consciousness. Ms. Minner, listen to my lecture again, and you'll agree.

"And remember, Ms. Minner, different religions have different beliefs and different Gods to worship. I'm no different. My God rises from a scientific hypothesis. However, anyone who goes back and listens again to my lecture last November will see that I wasn't pushing a belief upon the children, rather I was teaching the children how to use their own minds and not follow blindly. My dialogue with Ian during that lecture was a powerful example on how to use logic to challenge tradition and, perhaps, dispel illusions that surround us."

The arrogant school-board leader blurted, "So is that what you think of God — as some illusion?"

"No, I believe God is very real," Miss Annabelle said calmly, "But let me ask you this: If my God is different from your God, and your God is different from a Japanese man's God, and his God is different from an Arab man's God...then which Gods are the illusions?"

"Are you saying your God is real and mine is not?" Mr. Hammerschmidt said, not looking very bright.

"That's not the point," Miss Annabelle said, obviously more intellectually endowed than the wannabe politician before her. "The point is that children's minds must be shown how to challenge another person's ideas in order to become strong enough to form their own thought-through ideas. Too many children grow up just adopting the belief system given to them by society. But I believe children must be equipped with the ability to challenge and think through any belief system instead of just blindly accepting it. These children challenging *your* personal belief system, Mr. Hammerschmidt, is not a bad thing."

That last comment moved through the room like an emotional tidal wave, for the parents did not like the arrogant bully. No, they did not want *his* beliefs pushed on their children. Jessie and Angie had to control themselves from laughing.

"And I don't push my personal beliefs on those children," Miss Annabelle added. "Instead, I teach them how to use their minds to develop their own beliefs."

"And when do you teach them all that? We have a curriculum here teachers must follow, you know."

"And I do. In fact, we'll be done with the curriculum by Valentine's Day. Remember, I told you I use the lecture method. My kids not only will have completed the curriculum, they are, if you'd notice, getting all A's."

"Amen," Jeremiah's mother called out. "My boy never took home A's before. ...Does she believe in Jesus Christ our Savior?"

"I do believe in Jesus Christ. He's the only true Christian," Miss Annabelle answered.

"Amen to that!" Jeremiah's mother cried out. "That's all that matters," she added, looking at Mr. Hammerschmidt.

Frustrated, with nothing left to say, Mr. Hammerschmidt asked point blank, "Do you or do you not believe in God?"

Miss Annabelle answered calmly, "Yes, I do believe in God. As I said before, my God is not the same as your God."

"Tell me about *your* God," he said sarcastically.

"My God is called Zon." Her students looked at her curiously. They had never heard that word before. "Zon is the creator of the Universe. He rises from very advanced consciousness called God-Man. However, as I said, I do not push my God on my students. But I will engage in a flow of logic, as I did in my lecture last November."

Miss Annabelle was purposefully avoiding a philosophical discussion on the 2000-year manipulative use of guilt by

Christianity. Such a discussion would be counter productive. So she kept her answers light, sticking only on the point of not pushing her beliefs on her students. The parents were a bit confused by Miss Annabelle's sort of New Age sounding spiritual preference, but they also felt her spiritual leanings were harmless. What impressed the parents was her dogged determination to teach their children how to use their own minds. The parents liked that, and they were not about to let the school-board superintendent have his way with her.

"May I make a suggestion?" Teddy's father injected fearlessly, directing his powerful workingman's voice at Mr. Hammerschmidt. The protocol of school-board meetings normally would not allow for outside comments like this, but Mr. Hammerschmidt was up against the wall. He knew he could not afford to make any enemies among the parents.

"Sure," he said, surprising the rest of the school board members.

"Let's call it a night," Mr. Winters said with an air of finality. He stood up and added, "I want *this* woman to teach my son, and I'd probably look into some kind of class-action lawsuit along with the other like-minded parents here if you pulled any shenanigans to get her fired."

Like a daytime talk show, the audience clapped immediately. Miss Annabelle sat in stunned silence, her mind processing this new data that innocent adults exist who are still searching for honesty. She was pleased by the parents' reaction; she was ecstatic about her discovery of the innocent adult.

Mr. Hammerschmidt felt rage rising within. But like a smooth politician, he simply smiled and said, "Ladies and gentlemen, if you feel comfortable with the job Miss Annabelle is performing for your kids, then the school board sees no reason to take any further action." Then, turning his head to his right, he said to his fellow members, "All in favor of taking no further action, say 'Aye'." The school board members, some reluctantly, said, "Aye."

*

That night Miss Annabelle reflected on the progress of her

Superpuzzle

grand puzzle for the children. I'm behind schedule, she confessed to herself. But now that I have the support and trust of the parents, I can snap together the puzzle-picture of the new world and its supreme value of human life more quickly, starting tomorrow.

She felt overwhelming relief as she thought over this evening's meeting at the gym.

CHAPTER
TEN

Miss Annabelle noticed exciting changes occurring in her classroom. One by one, her students were becoming self-perpetuating puzzle builders of knowledge. That meant, at just nine years of age, they were already evolving into the new mentality, *Neothink!* This new mentality belonged to the next evolution of man, to the God-Man.

Three of her nine-year-olds, in particular, showed signs of this new mentality. Ted, Sally, and Ian could see through appearances to the essence of things so clearly now they regularly formed unique and powerful insights. As their often startling insights grew in numbers, the three little God-Men began spotting common denominators and snapping their unique insights together into powerful, expanding puzzles of new knowledge.

Miss Annabelle had never before felt such euphoria as on the three separate occasions she knew for sure that each of these three nine-year olds was building, through Neothink, a never-before-seen puzzle-picture of new knowledge. She sat at her desk one morning, studying the three wonders. She silently prophesied: with this new Neothink mentality, these three children will someday catapult civilization as dramatically as their forerunners Nicolaus Copernicus, Henry Ford, and Alexander Fleming.

Superpuzzle

*

The first of the three nine-year olds to show signs of the Neothink mentality was Teddy Winters. A few months before, Miss Annabelle had talked to his father. She knew their family had been financially strapped, and she worried about Teddy who would come to school in the snow with old sneakers, his socks showing through the worn-and-torn holes.

But for the past few weeks, Miss Annabelle had noticed a steady improvement in Teddy's clothes, culminating this week with expensive new black leather shoes, new black slacks and black leather belt *and* expensive new brown leather shoes, new brown slacks and brown leather belt.

"How's your father doing?" Miss Annabelle asked him one morning before class.

"He's doing great. He's been promoted three times and is now a manager," Teddy said proudly. "He says that in his previous seven years he wasn't promoted once. But now that he sees through to the essence of things and uses what we call a mini-day schedule with power-thinking, he's becoming very valuable at work."

Miss Annabelle felt relieved. She would no longer have to worry about Teddy's monetary well-being. "I guess that's why you've been looking so debonair lately in your new clothes."

"Oh, actually *I'm* buying these new clothes with my own profits," he said, trying to hold back a smile.

Miss Annabelle knew that your basic morning paper route could not generate the money to buy the shoes, slacks, and belts he wore that week *and* the new three-speed bicycle he rode to school that morning. She had thought his father was spoiling Teddy a little after a long period of hardship. But she was in for a surprise.

"I started my own business a few days after you and my dad talked that one night when we were playing football," Teddy said, with his mouth now hopelessly locked in a proud smile.

"What?" Miss Annabelle exclaimed, her eyes wide with surprise and excitement.

Teddy laughed. "It's true, I started selling two products door-to-door. I got so good at selling them, my dad would drive me to different neighborhoods and pick me up before dark. Then I ran out of neighborhoods, and at this point I would have gone out of business. But I came up with a plan." Teddy stopped when he noticed about a half dozen classmates had come in and were standing behind him, fascinated with his enterprising story.

"Teddy, you're amazing. I have got to hear *everything*...if you're willing to tell me," Miss Annabelle said.

"Oh, sure," Teddy said full of pride.

"Can we hear, too?" Cathy asked while smiling dreamily at Teddy.

"Sure," Teddy said.

"Great!" Miss Annabelle said. "Everyone please take your seats...except for Teddy. He's going to tell us how he's making lots of money by providing lots of values to others!"

"Alright!" someone yelled. The children scurried to their desks and pivoted into their seats. The excitement in the air was thick, like an arena before a championship prize fight. Miss Annabelle noticed the children's spontaneous response, and she thought: business, feeling your power to make a difference in this world providing values to others, all while making money, pride, and happiness for oneself, is the *natural* state of conscious man...just look at these kids' enthusiasm. Their faces looked to the front like they were about to be entertained by a Disney movie.

"Class, I've asked Teddy if he would share with us his road to success. Teddy has become a successful businessman, and he's going to tell us how he's done it." Miss Annabelle then turned the floor over to the nine-year-old entrepreneur and sat down at her desk. When she looked at Teddy, she could not help thinking what a shy little boy he used to be, yet now he seemed like a powerful little *man*.

"A few months ago, I was looking through my dad's magazines. One of them was showing lots of different things people can sell to make money. I wanted to start making money, so I studied the magazine...there were *so many* products that could be sold.

"So I started thinking of our town and what everyone might want to buy. And I came up with a common denominator: just about every adult I knew, from my mom and dad to my friends' parents, seemed to be always concerned about their kids' safety. So, I looked through the magazine again to pick something that offered safety, and I picked inexpensive smoke alarms that stick to the ceiling and warn you if there's a fire in your house, especially when you're sleeping.

"At first it was hard for me to sell the smoke alarms. Everyone seemed to start closing their doors before I started telling them about the alarms. It was really embarrassing. I got stressed out and thought about quitting.

"But before I quit, I remembered Miss Annabelle telling my dad, when he was down and out, to pierce through to the essence of things, right in your job. And that was the start of my success.

"You see, on the surface I was selling smoke alarms and was just another salesman at their door. But going to *the essence,* I was selling them their own lives and their loved ones' lives, which no other salesman could do. Realizing *the essence* of the value I offered, everything changed. I started selling, and selling fast. At first I played a little game with myself to see how many words it took me before a person would take a serious interest in what I was selling."

Cathy's hand went up. "How many words does it take you now?" she asked him.

Teddy turned somber and said, "Zero."

"How do you do that?" Danny asked.

"Here, I'll show you," Teddy said. He pulled a neatly folded magazine picture from his pocket. He unfolded it and held it up for the class to see. The two students closest to Teddy in the front row gasped when they made out what the picture was showing: two beautiful little girls ages five and three and their one-year-old baby brother, three little darlings sleeping peacefully in their beds and crib, or so it seemed; the caption read: **Siblings Die In Sleep From Smoke Asphyxiation**. Teddy's classmates wanted him to pass the picture around to take a closer look.

"I get really sad when I look at that picture," he said. "When people open their doors, I show them this photo. The unspoken message brings them immediately to the essence of why I am there: I plead with them, 'Never let this happen to you or your loved ones.' It makes me feel good to know that I'm stopping this from ever happening to my customers.

"I'm selling smoke alarms so fast I can't get them fast enough from the manufacturer. My success came because I cut through surface perceptions to the essence of my business — *the value of life.*

"I realized I bring my customers a value that taps into a common denominator among all people — the value of their lives. I believe in my product. I believe in saving lives.

"I started selling so many that I called the president of the manufacturing company. He was able to knock down my wholesale purchase price by nearly two thirds, which meant I was now really starting to make money!"

"How much did you make?" Danny blurted. He forgot to raise his hand first.

"Oh, in just twelve days I was able to buy the go-cart I had always dreamed of driving! Before starting this, I always thought I'd grow up and never once ride that go-cart. That go-cart was everything I wanted to get from working, but now I have only just begun. I'm figuring out bigger and bigger ways to grow my business."

Miss Annabelle's heart jumped with Teddy's last comment that he was "figuring out bigger and bigger ways to grow my business." With that comment, she knew he was discovering integrated thinking and was snapping together a success puzzle. As her heart pounded with joy, she contained herself to calmly say, "Teddy, go on and tell us the bigger and bigger ways to grow your business. I'm very proud of you and want to hear more."

"Okay, Miss Annabelle," Teddy said innocently. "I sold the smoke alarms so fast, that I soon ran out of houses to sell to. My dad drove me to nearby towns, but I sold to every house there, too. I thought my glorious business days were over."

"What happened?" Ian blurted out.

"I went nationwide," Teddy said like a grown tycoon.

Miss Annabelle nearly fell out of her chair. She involuntarily sat up and leaned forward and nearly tipped over.

"Here's what happened: I'd lie in bed at night thinking, 'I figured out how to be successful; I could keep going and going...if only I could get to more homes...if only I could clone myself and be all over the country!'

"Then, one day, it hit me: I had already figured out the common denominator and perfected the formula to sell my product successfully. Why couldn't I, in a sense, clone my secret formula in others around the country to sell in their neighborhoods? Everyone would win because those I replicated my secret formula to would make money that perhaps they could not make before, the customer would get a safer home, the manufacturer would get more orders, and I would make more money. All that good for everyone would happen the more I reached out to more homes."

Miss Annabelle could not believe what she was hearing. Euphoria filled her whole existence, but she tried to remain calm and quiet as Teddy told his story.

"So I ran a classified ad in the Buffalo News. I got eight replies from people who were interested in selling the smoke alarms. They were pretty spread apart from each other, especially the five who were serious enough to meet with me.

"I cloned my secret. I explained to the five sellers the essence of the smoke alarms: we were not mere salesmen at peoples' door; we were compassionate people interested in saving lives...*their* lives and loved ones. Then I explained the common-denominator demand for the product was — *safety*, and I gave them my formula starting with holding up the picture of the three siblings in bed who died in their sleep. Then, I took all five out with me for a couple of days. I did all the talking and selling. They just watched and picked up how I did it.

"Pretty soon, I had five people in Buffalo selling for me. Then I tried the same thing in Hartford, Connecticut. But my dad would not drive me or let me take the train to go out selling with my four sellers there. So that forced me to put it all together into a kit. I audio recorded about four hours of me selling door-to-door. I included those cassette tapes with each kit, along with the pictures of the siblings. I wrote down the essence of the product and the powerful common-denominator demand for the product.

"The start-up kits were enough, and I had four people selling in Hartford.

"I was still trying to figure out how much money I should

get and how much my sellers should get when my dad suggested I call the president of the manufacturer and discuss what I was doing with him. I did, and he sounded amazed at what I was doing. I told him I planned to go national, and he flew my dad and me to his headquarters in St. Petersburg, Florida, three days after Christmas. I told him my numbers and my plans to increase my business city by city.

"But I saw a flaw in my plan: My sellers could go straight to the manufacturer cheaper than through me as a middleman. But, without my secret marketing approach, they would not sell so many.

"When I told my plan to the president of the manufacturer, he said he could fix that problem. He lowered my purchase price so low that I could sell my smoke alarms to my sellers for less than they could get them at their numbers from the manufacturer. And if I could scale up even more, the manufacturer would lower my cost even more.

"In fact, if my numbers are right, by the time I have sellers in one third of the country, the manufacturer will, at that quantity, provide the alarms to me *for free*."

At this point Danny could not restrain himself and cried out, "How can he *give* them away?"

Teddy started laughing when he answered, "That's what I asked him, too. Here's how it works: His company manufactures a lot of products. The smoke alarms cost him less than a couple dollars to make. But if I give him the name and address of every buyer, they will buy, on average, ten dollars of products from his company in the future. He just sends them a catalog or other advertisements through the mail. So, he gives me a two-dollar smoke alarm for free, and I give him a ten-dollar name and address."

"Wow," Cathy said. "You're the main man!"

Teddy's speech here floored Miss Annabelle. He *really is a man*, she thought. He is integrating a major success puzzle, and he's only nine years old! And Cathy, the shy, withdrawn girl is twenty pounds lighter and boldly crying out her affection for Teddy across the room. The other ten children sat at the edge of their seats, more into Teddy's success story than anything before in their lives. Teddy made super success real and achievable — to the kids! Their pulses were racing, too. Their dreams were confirmed and motivation was soaring.

"Thank you," Teddy said, blushing a little, looking Cathy in the eye. "But I've just begun. I have so much more to build. At this time, I have sellers in eleven cities. I think I can expand to about a hundred cities by summer." Looking back at Miss Annabelle, he added "This was my secret when you came to our house after Christmas. But, I wanted to tell you when I had a hundred cities…"

Miss Annabelle was speechless. She smiled with utter admiration and nodded.

"But let me tell you about the greatest thing in the world: it really is making values like Miss Annabelle told us. Something happened that I'll never forget: Over the holidays, a house burned in Buffalo. It was on the news and in the newspapers. The father said his new smoke alarms woke him up, and he was able to get his family out. One of my sellers sold him those smoke alarms. He called the president of the manufacturer, and he asked to speak to me. He came to our house and thanked me for bringing the smoke alarms to his home. He told me that they saved his family's lives. He brought with him his daughter who was about my age and his son who was five. Seeing their faces, alive, happy, and grateful gave me the greatest feeling I've ever had, and I'll always carry that feeling inside me. Anytime, for the rest of my life, I can stop whatever I'm doing and know that that girl and that little boy are still alive because of me. I really know the value of what I'm doing. I'm really making a difference out there. I really know where *happiness* comes from."

A sea of admiring faces let out waves of "wow's" and "gosh's". After a few moments of stunned stillness, Danny raised his hand slowly and asked, "What happens when your sellers run out of houses?"

"Great question," Teddy answered, shifting gears. "I thought about that and realized that once I figured out one successful marketing program to replicate across the country, I needed to develop another. I've already done that. I have another product called The Defender. It's a tear-gas spray that stops attackers. To develop a successful marketing program, I hit the streets myself and sell to my home town. I learn the essence of the value I'm selling, and I learn the common-denominator demand. From there, I perfect the sales formula. Then I replicate it to my sellers. I've already done this with the second product, and I've already replicated it to my five Buffalo sellers."

"What will you think of next?" an admiring Cathy asked.

"Actually, I'm very excited by that ten-dollar per name and address," Teddy answered, amazing Miss Annabelle and everyone else in the class. "Lately I've gotten to thinking, since I'm learning how to sell directly to people, why can't I transfer that formula to paper and sell through the mail? I called the president of the smoke alarm manufacturer and asked him some questions. He said that for every name and address I have, I will sell to about fifteen percent another product through the mail at the same price that I sold them their original smoke alarm. But, from my own data, well over half will buy a second product from the same salesman who sold them the original smoke alarm.

"So I'm transferring my sales formula for my second product — The Defender — onto paper. Next I'll send that solicitation through the mail to all the names and addresses who bought the smoke alarms.

"I'll have to see what happens. Here's what I suspect might happen: First, before I replicate The Defender to my sellers, I send my offer through the mail and, hopefully, I make a profit through the mail. Second, I replicate The Defender to my sellers and, hopefully, my sellers get a better rate of sales because my mailing piece already introduced their potential buyers to the idea. When a person stands before them with product in hand, the near-buyers from my mailing piece will now convert to buyers.

"I'm so excited to get my first test mailing out. It's costing me some money to get everything printed and for the postage. But I like taking a lot of my profit and putting it back into my business. ...I guess that's about it for now."

All eleven classmates burst into a mighty applause. As Miss Annabelle clapped too, she realized that Teddy was moving too fast to be held back by a slow education, particularly once he left her class. She predicted, in her mind, that Teddy would never finish school. He'll leave school early, she thought, to put all his energy into his burgeoning success puzzle. He'll leave school somewhere between eighth and eleventh grade, she silently predicted. Then she asked, "How do you have time for all this?"

"I'm busy," Teddy said, "but I learned how to break down my day by mini-days. I get a lot done that way."

"What are mini-days?" his teacher inquired.

"Oh, I was reading a book on Henry Ford. He developed the assembly line by breaking labor into physical movements. Production soared. I decided to break my day into physical movements, and my production soared. I have a numbers mini-day where I go over the data, costs, profits, and inventories. I have a sales-writing mini-day where I work on my sales pitch or sales piece or classified ad. I have a quick phone call mini-day. I have a selling mini-day for the periods I go door to door. Each mini-day is a physical movement, and I allot a strict 'time-station' to each movement. I get *so much* done this way, you'd hardly believe it!"

Miss Annabelle could hardly believe it. Witnessing Teddy's forward leap into Neothink was overwhelming. Danny raised his hand and asked, "How do you figure out all these ideas as you go along?"

Flattered, Teddy answered, "I do power-thinking...that's what I call it. I think into the future to the finished image of my program, like taking my sales program to all houses in America and maybe beyond, and then I figure out the steps I need to take to get there. I write down those steps. Then I put those steps straight into my mini-days. That's how I move forward so fast. Before I started power-thinking, I had reached the end; I was stuck with no more houses to sell to. Then I broke through to the next level through power-thinking."

Miss Annabelle listened to this amazing success story unfolding before her from her nine-year-old student, and she wondered, could geniuses like this be in all children, waiting to be sprung free? With proper, boundary-breaking education, would geniuses like this rise up in nine-year-olds regularly?

"I've started tracking my sellers now. I have them send me weekly reports on how many houses attempted, how many sold. I closely watch their ratios and call anyone who starts slipping. I also just started a motivational letter with tips and figures and congratulations that I'll send my sellers once a month."

Conceiving the Superpuzzle

As she listened, Miss Annabelle was aware of two things going on inside her: First, this was the greatest reward in her life. This was what she lived for — to send her students into this new mentality of integrated thinking and Neothink. She could feel her body trembling from an adrenaline rush, and her skin was tingling. Second, she could see by the look in her other students' eyes that they would break through to Neothink and rise to the next level of life and happiness soon. ...This is what I live for, she thought.

*

Thank goodness she turned on the tape recorder to get that presentation by Teddy, Jake thought as he switched off the audio cassette player. Listening to the great Theodore Winters, now the world's richest man, as a nine-year-old first discovering the limitless power of his mind, had given Jake a body full of goose bumps. Man, that gave me a rush, he thought, I hope there's more of Theodore on these tapes. With Miss Annabelle, Theodore Winters, Sally Salberg, and Ian Scott in the same room, there's going to be a lot of secrets to success told on these tapes, Jake realized. There's a treasure in here, for me...for everyone.

He knew he would have to dig out that treasure and bring it to the world. His trip here to Duncan Elementary started because of his curiosity. Now, it was turning into an adventure of self-discovery...if not a mission for humanity.

Lying in bed that night, Jake felt a growing, burning desire to find out what happened to the other nine children in that amazing class.

CHAPTER
ELEVEN

As Jake listened to more tapes, he seemed to be pulled into another world, a world that seemed so natural yet so different from the world he had always lived in.

By any outside measure, this world would seem strange: kids going national in business, kids questioning the validity of God and sitting on the edge of their seats in discussions about the Universe, politics, medicine, and love. Kids running to get to class and not wanting to leave. Kids compassionate to each other's feelings. ...Even adults cannot begin to exist at this level, he thought.

Yet, when Jake listened to the tapes, it all seemed so natural. When he turned off the tapes and thought about it, however, that other world seemed bizarre, for his mind would try to measure it against this world's standards.

Using Miss Annabelle's technique to see through to the essence of things, he tried to grasp what constituted that different world where he felt so at home as he listened in on it. He really felt he belonged there.

He remembered Miss Annabelle saying to search for common denominators to help see the essence. What is the common denominator in that third-grade classroom, he pondered over and over.

He noticed how alive and motivated the twelve students became as the year went on. He also noticed that their minds did not seem at all like children — not one of them. Their voices were high and sweet like nine-year-olds. But their minds worked in concepts that reached out far beyond most adults and made clear understandings of complex ideas. Their young minds worked much better than adults' minds. No, Jake thought, those children's minds worked *beyond* adults' minds; those children are in some other world.

*

Angie was calling Jessie and Jake to the kitchen table. She always fixed a substantial breakfast. She believed that breakfast was the most functional meal of the day and was put to good use, so she never skimped.

She scooped three poached eggs, several sausages, and cut cantaloupe onto their plates. Jessie buttered a piece of toast. Jake took a biscuit and poured some white gravy over it.

Angie and Jessie wanted to ask Jake what he had heard thus far. But Jake stared at his plate as he slowly ate. He was trying to figure out what constituted that other world. The breakfast was quiet for about three minutes. Then Jake looked up. Seeing Angie and Jessie looking at him, he smiled and apologized for his absentmindedness.

"What are you wrestling with inside your head?" Jessie asked.

Jake, suddenly buoyed by the thought that Jessie and Angie had listened to the tapes too, said, "When you listened to the tapes, one after the next, did you get, uh...a feeling like some other type of life exists...that everyone is missing out?"

Angie and Jessie looked at each other and Angie sighed.

"It's like, when I listen to those tapes..." Jake continued, grasping for an analogy, "...it's like going through some kind of space-time jump to another place, a special, secret place very few have ever been, but everyone belongs."

"Yes," Angie said. Then reaching over to hold her husband's hand, she added, "We've talked about that many times. It's like, in that world, everyone is learning. They just keep building those amazing thoughts."

"Everyone is doing the *right thing* during that one year," Jessie said emphatically. "Life out here is just not like that."

"But why not?" Jake asked, never so sincere before in his life.

"Honey, we don't know how to make it like that," Angie said with noticeable maternal feelings for Jake. "I wish…I really wish we did."

"I think I do," Jessie said, surprising Angie and Jake. "My head's been spinning with memories ever since the day before yesterday when Jake arrived," he said looking at Angie. "And I think I've spotted the common denominator behind every moment in that classroom that year, especially after the holidays when things really started happening fast."

Then Jessie turned his gaze to Jake and his voice dropped into the most serious tone Jake had yet witnessed: "Jake, have you heard the talks by Theodore Winters, Ian Scott, Sally Salberg, and Danny Ward?"

"Only the talk by Ted," Jake said.

Jessie continued, holding Angie's hand while bouncing his eyes back and forth from Jake to Angie, "Those amazing learning curves and those amazing thoughts you refer to…and everyone doing the right thing…it seems so miraculous, so impossible. But what is it we witness when we hear those kids putting together those amazing thoughts? We witness people who, as far as their knowledge reaches, are completely *honest* with reality. Those kids become incapable of hedging on honesty. They could not rationalize away *what is*, regardless of what anyone else said, regardless of what *everyone* else said."

"Yes!" cried Jake. "Remember what Ian started saying about God being a rumor. When he had enough knowledge to see God as an illusion, he did. Nothing held him back, not a thing."

"And that's why they always did the *right thing*," Jessie added.

"They became so loyal to honesty, they couldn't be held back by the many illusions in this world built on a dishonest matrix of illusions," Jake added enthusiastically. "Therefore, they soared."

"It's because of their profound honesty that they so rapidly cut through to those huge insights," Jessie continued. "I remember Miss Annabelle telling me how she could explain a very complex idea to her children, an idea that cut through illusions to the essence of things. She told me that her children could immediately get it, whereas adults would take much longer, if they would ever see through the illusions at all. ...Well, now I know, that's because the children used profound honesty in dealing with logic and reality."

"That's it!" cried Jake. "That's it. Those kids and their teacher had a powerful but elusive tool: they were able to see reality — see through the many illusions to the essence of things, which takes profound honesty in dealing with reality. Like you said, Jessie, as the year went on, they seemed to actually become incapable of being dishonest in any way. Therefore, they always did the right thing."

"Yeah, they really soared. Just wait till you get to Danny's talk," Jessie said while nodding.

"What about Danny's talk?" Jake asked.

"You don't know who he is yet, do you?" Jessie asked; his eyes were smiling.

"Should I?"

"Yeah, if you follow the news."

After a moment of thought, Jake blurted, "No...not Daniel Ward. I love him! ...He's not the same person as Miss Annabelle's Danny...is he?"

"Yup, that's him," Jessie said laughing, "and you thought there were just three greats. Nope, there's at least four."

Jake was stunned. Daniel Ward had surprised the nation with his figures in polls as a third-party presidential candidate who came out of nowhere running under his new political party called the Twelve Visions Party! He did not lead in any poll, and he was not second. But he had captured the attention of the nation and his numbers were rising.

"My God," Jake said. He shook his head in disbelief. More missing pieces to the puzzle inside Jake's mind were snapping together. "Daniel Ward today represents that other world of profound honesty. That man blasts through all the political illusions that have existed since the beginning of civilization. He opens my eyes to illusion after illusion that even I couldn't see through."

Superpuzzle

*

Jake had been interested in the Twelve Visions Party after hearing Daniel Ward deliver a campaign speech at Boston University a month before. Jake had never been interested in politics before Daniel's speech and his new Twelve Visions Party.

Daniel Ward, who never held public office before, was a wealthy self-made businessman. He was a developer who revolutionized luxurious yet affordable planned communities throughout the western United States. He personally designed the homes and the tall condominium buildings. He was known for his enormous conceptual reach and, paradoxically, for his enormous capacity for tracking the details of his sprawling empire. He possessed a rare dynamism that let him smoothly handle huge situations. He was a lover of life; he knew how to succeed, and he had enormous energy.

He financed his own presidential campaign. His platform was simple: depoliticize America. His platform was built on two premises: 1) He would free the existing geniuses and the many more potential geniuses of society by ending most government regulations, 2) in turn, new technology would soar in all industries as already happened in the mostly unregulated computer industry, sending consumer costs to fractions...making the consumers — the people — wealthy.

He honed Six Visions from his Twelve Neothink Visions. Those stimulating Six Neothink Visions drew standing ovations at his campaign stops. His Six-Visions Campaign attracted the man in the street and caused escalating support. Daniel packed auditoriums wherever he spoke; he had become a rising star. Jake could not get a seat in Boston University's overflowing auditorium, so he stood with others along the back wall and listened closely to Daniel:

"In my First Vision, I saw all people's needs taken care of by the geniuses of society, rising by the many millions as I removed most government regulations. Those freed geniuses rapidly drove technologies into new dimensions that brought undreamed of values to the people.

"My Second Vision showed me that those soaring new technologies, in turn, plunged toward zero costs like the computer revolution. That Great Technological Revolution made ordinary people more and more wealthy, like millionaires, as costs in all industries kept plunging to fractions.

"In my Third Vision, I saw that the new technologies racing ahead in all industries also raced ahead in the medical industry without the destructive FDA regulations holding the geniuses back. The geniuses eradicated disease after disease, and their soaring new technologies drove down medical costs. People lived with nearly perfect health well into their hundreds.

"In my Fourth Vision, businesses strove to keep up with the rapid progress of the Great Technological Revolution. So everything changed as businesses, to stay competitive, concentrated on bringing out their greatest asset — the unique creativity of their employees. Ordinary people experienced extraordinary entrepreneurial-like jobs; they loved going to work, and they shared in the profits they created.

"My Fifth Vision showed me that the wonderful falling-in-love feelings in the early weeks of romantic relationships did not fade over time. Why? People were no longer sinking in stagnation. Instead, they were successful and soaring in the livelihoods of their dreams. With that ongoing source of happiness inside, filling them and overflowing into their romantic relationships, they could forever feel the power of love.

"My Sixth Vision showed me ordinary people becoming smarter than today's richest people. Heretofore, ordinary people awaited their instructions in life from work, from the media, from the government, the church, the Establishment. In the new Twelve-Visions World, however, instead of being told how to live, ordinary people began integrating knowledge to lead themselves. They began snapping together knowledge into growing success puzzles at work and life in general. They could see through the matrix of illusions and no longer needed or wanted to be led by false authorities. The need and desire for a government ruling class and its regulations became repulsive. The old structure of government could not exist with that new mentality.

"In total, I had Twelve Visions that showed me a new world of wealth, health, and peace. I am here to take you into that new world — the Twelve-Visions World."

Superpuzzle

The large crowd of college students burst into applause. The intensity of the applause forced Daniel to stop talking. Someone in the overflowing room yelled out, "Why does your political campaign keep rising in the polls while the other third parties remain just a small percentage of likely voters?"

Jake listened in awe as Daniel described a new political structure for a new mentality:

"I'm becoming a contender in this political race because my campaign has nothing to do with political ideas," he proclaimed, befuddling his college audience. "I'm becoming a contender because I represent the next evolution of man, which has already begun. Political structures, ironically, are not based on political ideas; they're fundamentally based on man's mentality. Heretofore, our political structure along with the other basic structures of civilization like religion, education, marriage, enterprise were based on mankind's mentality from the past, known as the bicameral mentality. The bicameral mentality goes back to over 3000 years ago when people's minds regularly hallucinated the voices of the gods emanating from statues, tombs, pyramids or other awe-inspiring objects of worship, telling man what to do and how to live his life.

"Today's mentality still functions in that bicameral fashion. Instead of voices of the gods, however, people let the voices of the politicians and regulatory bureaucrats tell them what to do and how to live their lives. In short, the current and past mentalities seek to be told how to live by some outside authority.

"But the next evolution of man has begun. The dawn of a completely new mentality has arrived. That new mentality seeks no further than one's own mind for direction on how to live. Man's new mentality no longer looks toward external authorities. He needs no authorization from outside. The mentality of the future looks inside to one's own honest, integrating mind for authority.

"All those government programs for the so-called 'public good', with politicians telling us how to spend our money, and all those regulatory programs with bureaucrats telling us how to run our businesses...none of those programs could survive in the new mentality that no longer accepts being told what to do. ...Perhaps now you can understand that the Twelve-Visions Platform of 1) removing all government programs that are on the *offense* telling people how to live their lives, and 2) reducing government to programs of *defense* only, protecting individuals from physical aggression...is *not* a platform based on political ideas per se. The platform is simply a new political structure based on the new God-Man mentality of no external authorities telling us how to live our lives. Therefore, as mankind makes its next evolution, the Twelve Visions Party will be the only political survivor."

Jake joined the thunderous applause. Holding his hand up to quiet the crowd, Daniel Ward continued.

"That, my friends, is the secret to this campaign. Our next evolution into the new mentality has begun. Now you can really understand where the issues of my campaign are coming from: *the Solar-Eclipse Budget* that eclipses over half of the typical budget in order to eliminate the solar-high spending programs for the 'public good' and to eliminate the regulatory bureaucracies, leaving money for national defense and paying off the debt...well, now you can see that such issues are much more than mere political ideas; they represent a new political structure for the new mentality of no external authorities telling us how to live.

"The results of eliminating a government of offense and all its burdensome regulations will be *spectacular wealth* for the people as the freed geniuses of society rise up. In this day and age of high technology, they'll drive technologies through the next level to create spectacular new values for us, and the cost of those spectacular new values will plunge toward zero as we've already seen with the computers and communications. Ordinary people will live like millionaires — healthy millionaires who rarely get sick as the geniuses eradicate disease through soaring new medical technologies.

"Businessmen and women who have no interest in political careers are joining my Twelve Visions Party across the country. I call this phenomenon the *Great Replacement Program* as we'll say good-bye forever to the career politician. There'll be no such thing as career politicians telling us how to live our lives in the new mentality of no external authorities.

"Government programs for the 'public good', including the regulatory bureaucracies, will now go to the private sector. Now, instead of politicians serving themselves and their political agendas, millions of geniuses of society will be serving *you* — the consumer. I call this phenomenon the *Great Displacement Program* as we say good-bye forever to so-called political 'public good'. There'll be no such thing as bureaucrats telling us how to spend our monies or run our businesses in the new mentality of no external authorities.

"As we displace those programs and services to the private sector, the Federal government will have a huge sale — selling off everything that has nothing to do with defense. The trillions of dollars generated from the sale of big government will repay every American's past contributions toward Social Security *with interest*. Then, when everyone is repaid with interest, the Social Security program for the so-called 'public good' will be terminated. Social Security telling us how to save our monies could never survive in the new mentality of no external authorities.

"The only government that could survive the rapidly approaching new mentality is a protection service, a government of defense protecting individual and property rights from physical aggression. A Protection-Only Budget less than half the typical budget is all that is needed to do that. The other money that goes to government on the offense, telling individuals how to live, will not survive the new mentality of no external authorities.

"Of course, the budget today is bound by existing law that needs to be weeded out with new law. That won't actually happen until the Great Replacement Program sweeps through the mid-term elections. Then, Congress will appropriate funds for physical protection only.

"The new government structure of defense will serve one *Prime Law* of Protection. In fact, it's so short, clear, and indivisible, anyone can memorize it as his or her anchor to freedom and can recite it in about two minutes anytime, anywhere to uphold it and forever protect it:

The Prime Law

(The Fundamental of Protection)

Preamble

*The *purpose* of human life is to prosper and live happily.

*The function of government is to **provide the conditions** that let individuals fulfill that *purpose*.

*The Prime Law **guarantees those conditions** by forbidding the use of initiatory force, fraud, or coercion by any person or group against any individual, property, or contract.

Article 1

No person, group of persons, or government shall initiate force, threat of force, or fraud against any individual's self, property, or contract.

Article 2

Force is morally-and-legally justified only for protection from those who violate Article 1.

Article 3

No exceptions shall exist for Articles 1 and 2.

Daniel Ward slowly emphasized every word of Article 3 of the Prime Law. The crowd broke into whistles, clapping, and loud young men shouting, "Yeah!" and "ou! ou! ou! ou!" with their arms gyrating. Jake's face turned red as he felt his blood throbbing through his neck. He was moved and thought he might get involved with the Twelve Visions Party. ...This all happened a month before Jake knew anything about Miss Annabelle.

Daniel Ward waved to the roaring crowd and left the platform, thinking to himself that someday soon the idea of campaign rallies will seem weird, like ancient history, as government of defense will fairly quickly run like a business based on people's performances, not elections.

Superpuzzle

*

Returning to the present from his memory of the moving campaign speech, Jake said to Jessie and Angie, "I'm still in shock. But it makes so much sense now. Daniel Ward is driving for a fully honest society. That society provides the ultimate conditions for happiness for everyone."

"Doesn't it fit Miss Annabelle's classroom?" Angie said. "Daniel is using widescope honesty to blast through illusions like political 'good intentions' for the 'public good'."

"Yes, yes it does all fit together," Jake echoed.

"Yeah," Jessie said. Then his voice trailed off as he mumbled a tormenting, unanswerable question, "What could have been if that woman had been teaching over the past 27 years?"

That thought, indeed, haunted Jessie, Angie, and Jake. What could have been? Jake kept hearing, in his head, the word he had heard Miss Annabelle mention a handful of times on her tapes — *God-Man*.

CHAPTER
TWELVE

The winter weeks following Miss Annabelle's second school board confrontation were not only good weeks for her, but surprising ones as well. Each week, more teachers at Duncan Elementary School approached her to offer their support. Furthermore, more and more teachers showed genuine interest in her successful teaching methods and even complimented her lectures.

Miss Annabelle was deeply surprised by this support. In fact, she had no idea that teachers were actually listening to her tapes. She knew some of the progressive general lectures were too much for those adults to begin to comprehend after exposure to a lifetime of illusions. But, they obviously sensed something wonderful.

During these winter weeks, Miss Annabelle learned more about adults than in her previous thirty-five years. She observed these supportive adults trying to comprehend some of her radically different ideas. They tried hard to cut through illusions to the essence...to *what is*. ...They're good people, Miss Annabelle thought, but they're guided along by the matrix of illusions created by the small minority of bad people.

That observation would, of course, prove to be her fate at Duncan Elementary School. She pondered how just one person with power, in her case, Hammerschmidt, could create and successfully carry forth illusions that would have destroyed her career if she were not so unusually effective at defending herself.

She thought how just *one* person with power can cause extensive damage, for ordinary good people cannot pierce through the matrix of illusions *on their own* to the essence of things...*because they put authority outside their own minds*. That's the problem, she thought. Until the ordinary person learns how to become a self-leader and no longer looks outside himself for leadership and guidance...and instead turns inward to his own mind for self-leadership and self-guidance by seeing *what is*...until his jump to that God-Man mentality, he will ultimately give his power away and blindly follow his leaders. Those leaders, like Hammerschmidt and like most politicians, are generally dishonest people who thrive on usurping people's power.

Miss Annabelle also thought about her students "jumping" one by one to that new mentality, the God-Man mentality where the authority resides in one's own integrating mind. She sensed the change could someday come to society, for she observed a small but growing core of people rebelling against authority, particularly against the politician. Those people, she noticed, were not just complaining about specific politicians. Instead, those people were rebelling against the idea of the agenda-driven politician, period. Slowly, one by one, people were beginning to turn down the idea of external authorities directing human life beyond the basic laws of protection.

Of course, the basis of her educational program was to teach her students to seek no further for authorization than their own minds honestly integrating reality to see the essence of things and know *what is*. She thought about how the majority of people, on the other hand, inherently know they do not see through to the essence of things and cannot integrate knowledge needed to guide their lives with any degree of power. Therefore, they turn their guidance system and broadest decision making over to the authorities — the external "authorities". Her students would never do that. They saw through to the essence of things and were beginning to integrate knowledge needed to guide their lives with power. Indeed, they had *the power* and would never turn it over to someone else. They would never be dependent upon and would never accept external "authorities", for her students were already jumping to the God-Man mentality.

But, she wondered, why are my peers showing interest and support? They have sunk so deeply into the beds of quicksand hidden by illusions. ...Why do they seem to want this?

*

About a half dozen teachers actually started joining Miss Annabelle with the students for lunch. It was during one of these lunches when Miss Annabelle got her second glimpse since the parents' support at the second school board meeting at why these adults were drawn to her and her ideas. Ian Scott was talking when she got this second clue.

"All that enormous data that's been collected on our Universe has always been studied while assuming mass and energy were the controlling factors," Ian said to the amazement of the group of teachers. "But, what if we look at all that enormous data while asking another set of questions based on: 'What if human-like consciousness controls the Universe?' Physicists might find a whole new set of answers."

Miss Annabelle felt that same jolt of euphoria that she had when Teddy told his story about his burgeoning fire-alarm business. Ian has started building his knowledge-puzzle, too, she realized. ...The fascinating thing about this God-Man mentality, she thought, is that a person, using his *own mind* as his guide, can build these knowledge puzzles; he or she can see out further and further by piercing through illusions to the essence, lassoing and pulling together common denominators into growing success puzzles...a new way of thinking that she witnessed in Teddy and now in Ian, which she called Neothink.

One of the teachers, Mr. Melbourne, a healthy-looking man originally from Australia, had a strong interest in physics; he turned to Ian and asked him what made him, in the first place, think intelligent life controlled the cosmos. Ian elaborated on the talk he and Miss Annabelle had during the year before about how intelligent life naturally and very quickly takes control of nature and then reaches out into space exploration and space colonization, cultivation, and control of the cosmos. Ian explained how, given the logistics of the Universe, intelligent life has existed for millions or billions of years before earthlings. Rapid technological progress would tend to intercept the cosmos and, a long, long time ago, taken control of the dynamics that control the Universe.

Mr. Melbourne became fascinated with this hypothesis. The two of them talked the entire half-hour left to the lunch period. As Miss Annabelle watched them, she noticed how Mr. Melbourne seemed like an excited kid again — full of enthusiasm and wonder. He seemed to have rekindled his child of the past. That child of the past so full of life and wonder has died long ago in most adults, killed by the adult world of lost dreams and stagnant routine ruts. But here she saw the beautiful wonder of the child fill Mr. Melbourne's expression, and she knew this *wonder* is what draws these adults to her.

"It's that child of the past within," she thought, answering why these teachers were drawn to her. "Those adults see me as their bridge to the child of the past buried within every adult. I'm their hope; their bridge to that lost child of wonder and happiness."

While Miss Annabelle was making this observation, suddenly Mr. Melbourne turned to her and asked, "Can I get a copy of that lecture of you and Ian last year? I want to listen to it and talk to Ian some more on this."

"Why, sure you can," she said. And for that brief moment, his eyes and hers locked; they both felt something urgent inside, like a tugging feeling. A wave of energy from some unknown source swooped through Miss Annabelle.

*

That evening, Miss Annabelle went for a walk just before dusk. During her walk, she saw in her mind's eye that moment again...his eyes. Whatever was drawing him to me, she thought, was drawing me to him. What is it about him? Is it his good looks? she wondered. No, she realized quite to the contrary, she had become very suspicious of good-looking men since she broke away from her abusive ex-husband, who had exceptional looks.

If anything, John Melbourne's healthy outdoorsman looks backed her off. So, what was it, she wondered, that tugged at me during that moment when I looked into his eyes?

She relived the moment in her mind. She gazed into his blue eyes, again. Yes, it has to do with his *eyes*. Oh, the innocence in those eyes, she thought; they're like a child's eyes. But, then again, his eyes carry the strength of a man who's been around the world, figured it out, and has no fear. Then, all over again, the feeling of attraction rushed through her.

She stopped walking. "I like his innocence and strength," she confessed out loud. "I see in him beautiful life; he hasn't been pulled under by the negative forces around him. He's too strong."

Suddenly she laughed at herself, thinking about a man. She was still too wary of romantic relationships to acknowledge the romantic feelings stirring within her. On the surface, she thought she was simply admiring his character.

"Why did I just laugh?" she asked out loud, amused at herself. She didn't admit it, but it felt good. She involuntarily laughed again, and as she laughed, she saw John Melbourne's face smiling at her.

*

Another blissful week passed; Miss Annabelle arrived to school early Thursday morning. It was an unusually cold day, but she forgot about her chill when she approached her desk and saw the envelope with her name on it.

Many thoughts raced through her mind: Sally's mother, another summons, a private note from one of her students. ...She took a deep breath and opened it.

What she saw made her gasp and place the note back on the table. John Melbourne had listened to the lecture about the cosmos. He wrote,

"Miss Annabelle, I was intrigued by your lecture. I have a thousand questions. Will you be my guest for dinner Saturday?"

Her heart was pounding; her palms were sweating. She felt

147

nervous. She was gathering her thoughts when she heard a light knock on her door. Before she could answer, her door cracked open and John Melbourne poked his head in and said in his soft-spoken Australian accent, "Good-day, ma'am."

Not knowing what to say, she managed to echo his greeting, "Good day," she said gently.

"Well, will you have dinner with me?" he asked, flashing a handsome smile that, like his eyes, carried innocence and strength.

Miss Annabelle decided to say "no". Besides, she thought, my life is devoted to my twelve students and to preparing my lectures for them. She had no time for distractions, particularly with the growing possibility that this could be her last and only year as a teacher here. She had to equip her students with the ability to forever, without her future help, see through the matrix of illusions to the new world of *what is*.

Her mind was made up that she would not join Mr. Melbourne for dinner; she looked directly in his eyes and said, simply, "Yes."

*

Moments later the click of the door handle turning brought Miss Annabelle out of her daze. The door opened, Miss Annabelle saw a beautiful girl and realized it was Cathy. Cathy was still a little chubby, but beautiful and headed toward gorgeous.

"Come here, you pretty thing," Miss Annabelle commanded in an elated voice. "Look at you!"

Cathy grinned with poise and confidence. Miss Annabelle could hardly believe her eyes. She remembered how just a few months ago Cathy couldn't even smile. Now she smiled effortlessly.

"Miss Annabelle," Cathy said, her smile not yielding, "Is it possible to be, you know...*in love* at my age?"

"By the way you're glowing, I'd say it must be possible!" They both laughed and talked for twenty minutes. Miss Annabelle loved this moment with Cathy. The little girl had become alive and interested in life. Miss Annabelle soaked up the little girl's giggles as precious gifts.

Cathy, too, had been starving for conversation with someone who cared about her. Her parents were not interested in happy subjects. They got excited over long-winded complaints.

After the twenty-minute chitchat, Cathy gave Miss Annabelle a hug. Just then the door opened. The stern faced principal stared at Miss Annabelle as if she were caught doing something wrong.

"Yes, may I help you?" Miss Annabelle asked.

"Certainly you can, Miss Annabelle, by following school policy. You keep your door open when you have a child in there with you, henceforth!"

"Oh? I didn't realize that was a school policy," Miss Annabelle said.

"It is now!" Ms. Minner snapped back.

*

The sun had gone down; it was Saturday evening, and Miss Annabelle noticed she was getting nervous. Her date would arrive in less than fifteen minutes, and she had tried on four different outfits and was still trying to decide what to wear.

While putting on makeup, she stopped and looked in the mirror into her own eyes and, for the first time, asked herself, do I like him?

She confessed to herself that she was attracted to him. Yet, wise from her first marriage, she knew her feelings were but an initial attraction.

She calmed down a little and looked forward to their dinner together...just in time, for the doorbell was ringing. She put her lipstick on in three smooth strokes and went to the door.

"You look stunning," John Melbourne said. His comment was a genuine, knee-jerk reaction upon seeing Miss Annabelle. She was wearing a one-piece red sweater-dress that contoured her small, curvaceous frame. He was helpless to stop his eyes from roaming over her body. Her auburn hair belonged with this dress; her purple eyes radiated with feminine mystique. The dress seemed to shrink around her tiny waist. Then, looking down, he saw the dress stop about four inches above her knees, revealing just a peek at her slim thighs.

"Miss Annabelle, it's just that I've never seen you so...so ravishing." He was speaking in all sincerity of a man taken aback by a woman's beauty.

"Thank you, Mr. Melbourne..."

"Please, call me John," he said, not sure whether to be embarrassed by his reaction or whether she took it as a compliment.

"Thank you, John," she said, "and call me Anna."

She gestured for John to come inside and went to get her purse. When she pulled her coat from the closet, John took the long white overcoat and helped slip it over her shoulders. Outside on the steps Miss Annabelle nearly slipped on the ice. John grasped her arm firmly to keep her from falling. They both laughed, which broke the nervous tension, and enabled them to relax.

They drove about twenty minutes to a restaurant with a "down-under" theme. When they walked through the front door, two pleasing sensations greeted them: the relief of warmth from an open, circular fireplace crackling right in the middle of the restaurant, and the sweet smell of fresh baked bread. The dark wood tables and walls glowed with reddish reflections from the big fireplace and the individual candles on each table. It was rustic and romantic inside. She was excited to sit down and get to know him better.

The hostess sat them at a table close to the fire. Miss Annabelle looked radiant in her red dress, the red sequins sparkling in the fire's glow, her auburn hair blending with the warm wood furnishings, her purple eyes reflecting the fire itself. They ordered steaks and a bottle of cabernet.

"I was so impressed with your lecture, Annabelle," he said. "I'm going to listen to all of them, and I'm compelled to tell you something I've never told anyone but one other person. First, I've done a *lot* of reading, research, and writing over the years..." Miss Annabelle loved his intense eyes and sexy accent. "And I've concluded that everything we do originates from one of two fundamental minds: from man's mind functioning as it did in the distant past or from early glimpses into man's mind functioning as it will in the future."

Miss Annabelle's eyes suddenly ignited. She knew exactly what he was saying.

"In fact, the basic structures of civilization today like education, religion, politics, business, science, marriage, and the arts were built by our mind of the past, but I can see that all changing over the next few years."

Miss Annabelle leaned forward in her chair and rested both arms on the lacquered wood table. The flame from the candle illuminated the beauty of this woman's face when interested in a man. For the first time, she sensed that this man saw the world from a much wider perspective than she ever suspected, possibly surpassing her own perspective.

"You're the first, Annabelle, from all that I've read and seen, who's taking education to the next structure...for the mind of the future."

He stopped talking, catching Miss Annabelle off guard. She was just starting to let herself feel her physical attraction for him and was noticing his full lips, masculine jaw line, sandy hair and matching whiskers, and soft blue eyes...when he suddenly stopped talking. She had to momentarily gather herself and her thoughts.

Miss Annabelle pulled back a little and said, "Tell me, John, what is this mind of the future like?"

He leaned forward and looked into her eyes. "Annabelle, you know what it's like. Humanity never stopped looking for a voice to guide us. All structures of civilization today are set up that way — for us to be guided. But you teach children to guide themselves. They use their own minds to pull together and structure knowledge like structuring a map. They build a knowledge map and use that mental map to guide themselves. They sidestep outside guidance. They see, as you say, *what is*. They guide themselves. Outside voices can never control your students now...or ever."

If a man could ever get Miss Annabelle's attention, he had just done it perfectly, but sincerely. Miss Annabelle felt pure joy in hearing this reflection. "That's why they've begun building new ideas that will affect the world," she said proudly.

"Yes, I know," Mr. Melbourne said, "like Ian and the amazing hypothesis he's putting together. He's advancing into the mind of the future that integrates and builds knowledge to lead himself and create new knowledge, which is what happens with the mind of the future. Most people don't know how to lead themselves or create *new* knowledge, but I believe the day is coming when everyone will shift to that mind of the future, and we'll live to see the day. All the structures of civilization will change."

Miss Annabelle could not believe what she was hearing. First, here was someone who knew, as she did, that a new mentality existed. Second, here was someone who possibly could see even beyond herself into what this new mentality would mean to humanity. And here he was, living in Cheektowaga and teaching at Duncan Elementary!

"How will the structures of civilization change?" she asked as calmly as she could.

"Politics, religion, business are fundamental structures of civilization, and currently they tell us what to do and how to live. Imagine politics *not* telling us how to spend our money and run our businesses. With us running our own lives, the government would reduce to one of protection only. Progress and prosperity would be phenomenal.

"Imagine religions without a 'higher' authority, a guiding voice telling you how to live. Instead, your own mind becomes your guide and god by efficiently integrating knowledge together into pictures of the future. Suddenly, religion would focus on the greatest value in the Universe — *human life* in the here-and-now.

"Imagine businesses without external 'authorities' dictating our work day, such as one's routine-rut delegated down from management above. Instead, with integrating minds like Teddy, the entire business structure would have to change to something radically different to accommodate so many self-thinking entrepreneurs.

"I don't have clear answers to how those new structures will function, but I know they'll be far superior to what they are today. In fact, I predict your students will discover some of those new structures. For example, Ian's ideas about the Universe, at nine years of age, are the most exciting ideas I've heard or read in years. And his ideas are very sound. His whole concept of humanlike consciousness controlling the Universe and intercepting the course of nature is fascinating and logical. In fact, I can't find a flaw in the logic. All the existing and new data will have to be looked at again, as he said, asking a different set of questions. Some completely new understandings will come out of that data, a superior understanding than we have today...because of that one *little boy* using this new mentality, bringing us a whole new structure of the cosmos."

When Mr. Melbourne brought her here, she just thought he was going to ask some questions about the lecture she and Ian had about God. She had no idea...

"And there are other things on the horizon like your discussion about medicine and the plight of poor Sally's mother. A superior structure of the medical world will come when the external 'authorities' like the FDA are gone.

"Annabelle, your students are starting to make absolutely startling breakthroughs. Ian and Teddy have gone beyond any nine-year-olds I've ever been aware of. They both, frankly, shocked me with their reach of concepts...and it takes a lot to shock me. ...I would not be at all surprised to see others in your class break through, too, to the mind of the future."

Miss Annabelle knew all along he was right, but it felt so good hearing it from him.

"I see the media structure changing from power in the elite few external 'authorities' to power in the hands of everybody." Mr. Melbourne continued. "I even see the arts changing from power in the hands of a few key players or external 'authorities' to the marketplace of consumers. Again, I can't tell you *how* it's all going to change. I just know that the mind of the future will no longer let external 'authorities' guide our lives. Therefore, everything *has to* change."

"And what about love?" Miss Annabelle asked. Her eyes softened. She had never had a conversation like this with a man, and she never thought she would.

"Ah, love," he said. "I've read that only a beautiful woman really understands love. So, please, you tell me."

Miss Annabelle felt her heart pounding. "I...I'll tell you. But...I love listening to you talk." She suddenly felt vulnerable, "Please, go on."

"Well, I know people will be much happier with the mind

153

of the future, in its new world," he said. Then he added, slowly, "And I know happy people are the most romantic people...and the best lovers." He stopped. He looked into her eyes. She felt that rush of energy go through her again.

"Are you a happy person?" she asked sensuously. Her eyes involuntarily looked down slightly at his lips then back to his blue eyes. He leaned forward and kissed her gently, yet with a firmness that gave away his desire for her.

CHAPTER THIRTEEN

The children in Miss Annabelle's class were changing fast. They were changing from little children to powerful thinkers. And they *loved* it!

She asked Mr. Melbourne to speak to her class. She wanted him to reveal to her students what he had told her at the romantic restaurant. She wanted him to compare their open-ended future through the new mind versus the dead-end future through the "normal" mind. She felt he would enlighten her students to the major breakthroughs they could someday enjoy using the new puzzle-building Neothink mentality.

The very next day, Mr. Melbourne delivered his lecture: "A few of you have advanced to the mind of the future. Oh, what power you possess. Let me tell you about it." All twelve students sat up and listened closely. They liked what they heard, and they would discover that Mr. Melbourne was one of them.

*

That night, Miss Annabelle whispered in his ear, "You were beautiful today with the kids."

Like a proud father, he asked if she saw the look in their faces. For an hour, they talked about the looks and reactions on each child's face.

"Talking to your students today was an honor," he told her. "I've never, *never* experienced an atmosphere like that. ...Thank you."

Miss Annabelle melted when she heard those words of admiration.

"John, I want you to know...I've never known real love before," she heard herself saying. She felt her eyes fill with tears. "I haven't known you long, I know. But I've never felt like this before with anyone."

They talked late into the night. They shared their dreams and ambitions. Miss Annabelle, of course, was focused on a very near-term goal: to make it through the school year and equip her twelve students with the power to see the essence of things, to see through the matrix of illusions to *what is*. She was achieving startling success, but she was terrified that any day the school board could issue an emergency substitute teacher for the remainder of the school year. Such a measure would destroy everything. Miss Annabelle knew she would not be teaching here again.

She told John everything, from the incident with Burke to the showdown with Hammerschmidt. She also told John that she feared people at the school discovering their romantic relationship.

"The school board will use it against me, and against you, too," she insisted.

John Melbourne had a strong, fearless personality. He was also sweet and supportive. "I'll do this any way you wish," he assured her. "But, I want you to know that I'll step up to your defense instantly when it'll help you, no matter what. It's not something that can be controlled. ...Yes, we'll be smart and play our cards to outsmart those dishonest people. But when the time comes, I'll be there and will be a force to deal with."

Just listening to his strong voice made her feel better about things. She knew the school board would not leave her alone as long as Hammerschmidt was in charge. She lived with anxiety every day, dreading another summons...particularly now that some of her students were articulating extraordinary ideas. She feared that some of those brilliant ideas could, ironically, grow into more accusations against her such as teaching blasphemy and

156

hatred toward the government.

But she felt strength in John Melbourne. He was a remarkably bright man who had spent the past sixteen years teaching by day, researching and writing by night. He told her about his goals, too, which were broad and long range.

He was the son of a self-made entrepreneur who invented products that made people's lives more efficient. At first, his dad sold his inventions through direct mail. His products sold well, and his business eventually grew into a chain of retail stores. He searched the world for inventions that made life more convenient. He would advance promising inventions into commercial products that sold only in his stores.

John Melbourne developed a deep appreciation of the effort that went into creating and providing affordable values to others, known as business. He admired self-made businessmen.

He told Miss Annabelle that eighteen years ago he was sitting in the University of Sydney, Australia listening to his economic professor when his whole life changed.

"There I was, a nineteen-year-old kid listening to the esteemed Professor Rosewall," he said, "when I leapt from my chair, ran to the front of the class and started putting big black X's through his stack of overhead transparencies! One after the other, I'd place a transparency on the overhead projector, put a big X through it, and loudly proclaim, 'Bullshit!'"

Miss Annabelle laughed. "Whatever inspired you to do that?" she queried, very interested in the rebel she was seeing in him.

"Professor Rosewall seemed to have a relentless dislike for business — especially the self-made businessman. I put up with his attacks for awhile, but that particular day, I looked around at my classmates while he lectured. I remember their faces — openly watching and listening...innocently absorbing his envy. Then I looked back at Rosewall. He looked so worn and sinister as he put up one overhead after the other showing facts and graphs that were out of context, building toward some conclusion that self-made businessmen were greedy people who were out to hurt society. Day after day, he made his way through his career sanctimoniously denouncing people like my dad. All those students absorbed his attacks without the victims able to raise their voices. In the stream of young minds that passed through his class year after year, he destroyed in their minds people like my father who worked his tail off to bring a lot of values to a lot of people. Even worse, he destroyed their desire to be like my dad...he destroyed their dreams. I just couldn't sit there any longer and let him so dishonestly destroy good people. So, I X'd off every overhead image and got suspended for one week. But I know that I brought a few of those kids out of Rosewall's spell. Their lives could be totally different today."

"I like what you did, John," Miss Annabelle said, putting her hand on his. "I like to see people do what is honest and courageous."

"That moment was the turning point in my life," he said. "During my week out of school, I started reading like I never read before. I wanted to figure out exactly how civilization prospered. I started reading history to learn about the prosperous civilizations versus the poor ones. I started reading economic theories. I even started reading different philosophies. And you know what? In the end, the answer was elegantly simple: the businessman creating and efficiently distributing values and employing people makes society prosperous. Now I was explicitly understanding what I implicitly knew before.

"So when I returned in one week, instead of humbly apologizing for my actions, I boldly challenged Dr. Rosewall to a debate! You should've seen the look on his face! 'Me for the businessman, you for the politician,' I said. He was shaken, but he couldn't back down in front of his students. So we set the date two weeks from my challenge.

"The debate quickly became the buzz. The next day I saw posters everywhere with a headline that read: Challenger Johnny 'Badboy' Melbourne versus Reigning Champ Dr. Kelvin Rosewall. The debate became a major event at the University; everyone was talking about it, like a championship prize fight. The magnitude of it spurred great motivation within me to dig into the books as I never have before. For the first time, I was putting in sixteen-hour days of intense research studying economics for theory...and history for proof. I was determined to defeat that dishonest academic who was destroying young people's minds.

"As it turned out, I really enjoyed those two intense weeks

of research so much that I didn't stop after that. I gained so much knowledge and power in such a short time that I decided to keep going. I just kept on studying and pulling together more and more information from all subjects on economics, history, philosophy, psychology, biology, physics. All that knowledge kept building, and I kept integrating it all together into a giant 3-D picture about life, which is what I've been doing ever since, researching and writing around my teaching job. I'm nearly ready to publish my work."

The more Miss Annabelle learned about Mr. Melbourne, the more fascinated she became. There was so much more to him than she ever imagined.

"I had no idea you've been developing this," she said.

"No one does. Well, of course my ex-wife knew about it," he answered, suddenly realizing he brought his ex into the new relationship.

"You mean, you've been putting this enormous energy into this book for eighteen years and no one, besides your ex-wife, even knows it?" Miss Annabelle said, not affected by his previous marital status, although inwardly curious about it.

"That's right," he said matter-of-factly.

Miss Annabelle's appreciation of this man soared again. Here was a man so dedicated to a goal and yet so modest that he rarely talked about it. She was also flattered that he was telling her. "What is the underlying theme to your work?" she asked.

"Prosperity," he simply answered, "prosperity in every way: financially, personally, romantically. The final three chapters of my work fell into place as I listened to your lectures. Witnessing the state of your students gave me the living proof of the naturalness of the new mind, which I've been hypothesizing. I'll always be grateful to you, as you'll see when you read my book."

Miss Annabelle felt a floating sensation inside as she realized she contributed to her lover's lifetime work. She also felt a burning curiosity. She wanted to read his book, starting *now*. It was the fastest and deepest way into the heart, mind, and soul of this man she loved.

"Can I start reading it tonight?" she asked.

"In about three months it'll be ready for you to read," he answered. As the author, he was not ready to release it, even to his lover, until he was satisfied.

"Did your ex-wife read it?" Miss Annabelle asked, feeling a little jealous.

"No, not a page," he said. "In fact, I never even discussed it with her. She was a nice person, but she was never interested in my work."

"But this project is *you*. It's your life and what you're all about. What could be more exciting to your woman?"

John Melbourne wanted to take her and make love to her right then and there; he wanted to make her *his woman*. But he stopped himself. That would come later. Right now, this beautiful woman before him wanted to know more about *him*, and he let her ask her questions:

"Can you tell me more about your book?"

"I could, but it would be best if you read it first, because it's so different and built on so many years of foundation. I can tell you this much: no publisher will touch it. It's too anti-Establishment for them."

"So, how are you going to get it out there?"

"I learned the direct mail business inside and out, growing up in my father's company. I'm going to publish and market the book myself."

"Oh John, that's exciting. ...Will you still teach?"

He hesitated, then answered, "I'm really not there yet to try to answer that. I love teaching; I'd miss it if I had to leave."

Miss Annabelle snuggled up against her man and said, "I'd really love to stay up and talk all night about your book if you'd let me! ...But since you won't talk about it yet, tell me what happened in your debate with Dr. Rosewall."

"Oh, what a night!" he laughed. "Looking back at it now, I was like a young and tender amateur boxer stepping into the ring to fight a ferocious professional prizefighter. I was the underdog who trained for this 'fight' beyond human expectations. My mouth dropped open when so many people showed up that we had to move the debate from the student union to the University's theater, which delayed the start for about 45 minutes. A number of students shouted out things like, 'Clean him out, mate!' Some were chanting, 'No more bull...no more bull!' I remember someone, I think he was a professor, yelling in my face, 'Now you'll know what it feels like in the slaughterhouse!' I just tried to stay calm and focused.

"When things finally settled down and the audience was seated, Rosewall and I took our places behind two podiums on the stage with microphones hooked into the PA system. This debate had no rules, unlike those you see on college deate teams. So it got interesting right from the start. Rosewall came out swinging. He put on a forceful, lawyer-like voice that seemed to rock the building: 'Businessmen, if left unattended and unregulated by government, will rip you blind!'

"I was shocked when a huge cheer boomed back at us. What's this? I thought to myself. I *was* intimidated, but I refused to show it. In the middle of the cheer, I bellowed back, 'Yes, businessmen will rip you blind. In fact, I'll show you how they'll drive you into poverty!'

"The crowd went silent. Even my supporters didn't know what to do; they couldn't very well cheer for what I had just said. They must have thought I cracked. Astonished faces stared back at me or looked to their neighbors for some answer. Was I here to support...or to *bash* the businessman? Even Dr. Rosewall looked bewildered. At that moment, I said calmly into a stone-silent room that gave me its full attention, 'Don't you know, two types of businessmen exist: 1) market businessmen who survive by creating and marketing increasing values at decreasing prices, and 2) political businessmen who survive by aligning themselves with political clout to receive advantages and special rights of way over competition. Those political businessman are the greedy money-mad sleaze who rip you blind. They flourish because of the laws and regulations Dr. Rosewall will try to tell you are needed to protect you! Dr. Rosewall's argument today is an ironic joke. The very regulations he argues for create advantages for the big-business political businessmen who, in turn, line the politicians' pockets. It's a nice relationship. The politicians' litigation and resulting regulations choke off competition from the value-producing market businessmen, especially the smaller entrepreneurs. I urge all students to keep their own minds working in overtime as Dr. Rosewall serves up his hodgepodge of socialism. And that goes for you who take his class, because his class is, put politely, a sucker trap!'

161

"Rosewall snapped, 'Now that's enough, young man!' I could hear him on the stage's sound monitors, but the crowd cheered so loudly for me that I don't think they heard him. He had no choice but to let them quiet down some, which took a good minute or so. Then he said, 'Alright, Mr. Melbourne. You used a very clever debate technique. My hat's off to you. But while they applaud you, I laugh at you. You argue in the face of centuries of philosophers and economists who devoted entire lifetimes to their studies. You, at your young age, speak in sophomoric simplicities. You're a novice at how things work in the complex world of economics and politics. You have a lot to learn still, and your argument can be dismissed as simply too naive.'

"Rosewall was a skilled debater. By taking away my credibility, he could take away my entire argument in one fell swoop, no matter how sound. I was inexperienced, and his approach caught me off guard. I stood there with nothing to say. I thought, how do I answer him? Everything he said about me being young and naive was true, although I still knew I was right. But how would I continue? Everything I'd say would now seem naive and too simplistic. While I stood there wondering, he took advantage of my uncertain state and said in a rich, paternal voice, 'It's only natural at your age, to think you can come along and change the world for the better. I only commend you for your brave effort, Mr. Melbourne. But life is so much more complicated than that, as you'll discover, unfortunately, with age. Remember, there must always be a balance of power between business and government. I'm not saying business is bad or that government is good. I'm just saying, like anything, you must have *balance*. Without balance, you'll have unregulated drug companies putting out drugs that could hurt people. And, to the other extreme, you'll have excessive regulation with no life-saving drugs reaching those who need them. ...Johnny, you need balance.'

"He was good, as good as any politician I'd ever heard. He sounded fair and objective, but I knew he was creating an illusion of objectivity to block, as you would say, the essence of things or *what is*."

"I'm getting goose bumps listening to you," Miss Annabelle

injected. "I wish I had been there! Whatever did you do now?"

"I remember struggling with the illusion. I could feel drops of sweat breaking free and running down my back and down my sides over my ribs. I started thinking, the world *really is* complicated, and I *really am* young and inexperienced. My confidence started to wither as Rosewall kept working his spell, 'Come back to my class, Johnny, and give me another chance. You're free to disagree at anytime, but let's discover together the faults that make this an imperfect world we live in. I understand you hold businessmen on a pedestal. And I know you genuinely believe that in your own mind. I was once like you, Johnny, but then over the years I learned reality versus my own fantasies. Businessmen are people. They're not perfect. They succumb to temptation. And officials elected by the people are needed to keep them in line. That's reality, son.'

"The veteran professor had broken my spirit, and he knew it. Now, with no resistance from me, he really poured it on, saying, 'Johnny, come back to my class. When I look at you, I see myself thirty years ago. I'll show you the real world, son. Let it be known, you won here, tonight, Johnny. You won the battle to journey forth from the innocence of childhood into the harsh real world. Come back to my class, and we'll journey that road together. Let me shake your hand and welcome you to your future.' He started walking toward me with his hand out, wearing a warm, infectious grin. The students, overwhelmed by the niceness of it all, started to clap. I didn't know what to do as he stood before me with his hand out while the students clapped for us. I didn't know what to say. I felt overwhelming pressure to reach out and shake his hand. I raised my hand toward his and looked once more out into the audience. The young men and women seemed to be clapping almost robotically. Their faces seemed eerie...blank. I flashed back to the sea of innocent faces in his classroom three weeks before that sent me rushing to his overhead projector. I looked back at Rosewall, and suddenly his gracious smile seemed like a mask. It was covering a monster, and I knew it! All at once, my confusion and anxiety evaporated.

"I dropped my hand that I had half raised toward his in my weak moment, then I turned away from him and addressed the crowd, 'Thank you, Dr. Rosewall, very much for everything you've done here tonight.' He was still smiling. 'You have created a real-world anecdote for everyone in here to observe and to learn our lesson.' He still wore his smile, but it was getting stiff. 'You, sir, in your support of politicians and bureaucrats, represent the politician. I, teenage son of a well-known self-made entrepreneur, represent the up-and-coming businessman. Like the other students here, I'm at a young and naïve age, as you yourself put it. You graciously approach me with your hand out, your mouth grinning, your voice hypnotically endearing, and you encourage me to join you on a journey. You and me together. You the politician and me the young businessman, we team up and tacitly become partners in this complicated real world...made complicated by people like you — by agenda-driven politicians and regulatory buraucrats! Sure, I can surrender my innocence and my drive to create greater values at cheaper prices like my dad, and I can come into your world of dishonest collaboration between politicians and political businessmen. The politician gets his monetary connections and unearned power; the political businessman gets his political connections and unearned advantages. And together we could reap easy money and power and make the world a very, very complicated place for everyone else with all those regulations and taxes that choke off the real competition. A nice and happy team we'd surely make, politician and businessman. But through our joint journey of feel-good smiles and seemingly compassionate regulations, we're the bloodsuckers! Let there be no mistake! Dr. Rosewall is right: the real world *is* very complicated. The more complicated, in fact, the more opportunity for politicians, bureaucrats, and political businessmen to multiply and flourish. All I ever wanted to do was to get out there and work my tail off to create exciting values and to figure out ways to get more and more of my creations around the world through creative marketing and price reductions. But you come along and seductively say, come with me innocent youth; there's an easier way to go through this harsh, complicated world. To make it out there, you must join with me. Then you reach out to me.'

"By now Rosewall had gone back to his podium. He lashed out, 'You're putting words into my mouth, mister!' His mask of niceness was off and the monster was out; he lost his cool and snapped, 'You try your sophomoric thinking in the real world, and you'll be sunk you little punk...er, I mean, society will be sucked dry by you bloodsucking businessmen.'

"I said, 'That's right, millions of tender youth do sink or never even get started, especially the lone entrepreneur who is the seed of all future jobs and values. He or she cannot make it against you and your parasitical collusion of politicians and regulatory bureaucrats and political businessmen. Furthermore, you scare everyone into believing that the politicians and regulatory bureaucrats are needed to keep those so-called bloodsucking market businessmen in line. That way, with a willing public, you'll always have your bogus jobs, easy money, and unearned power. You'll always have your parasitical ruling class.'

"Rosewall was mad. He was also scared. He cried, 'You're just a kid — you don't know what you're talking about. I'm a tenured Professor, and I've spent my whole life studying this!'

"I saw his hands were shaking as I said, 'And how many thousands of innocent spirits have you broken?' He turned toward the audience and, recovering from his outburst, said, 'It's obvious Mr. Melbourne is stuck on a fantasy about the almighty businessman. It's very understandable, for his father is a famous businessman, and Mr. Melbourne obviously idolizes his father and stands to inherit his fortune. It's obvious I can't enlighten this young man. But let me tell you, without your public servants, you would be the subjects of a world of greed. Respect your elected officials. They, not the businessmen, are your true friends.'

"When he finished, I said, 'Earlier I warned you to think for yourselves. Less than five minutes later, Dr. Rosewall overcame your minds with his generous offer to take me on a journey with him...a journey, it turns out, into dishonesty and parasitism. Yet, you felt his embracing grin, as did I, and you clapped for his emotional generosity. He's a politician; he's one of them. And he's taking all of you for a ride into his world of envy and dishonesty against those who are good, honest, hard-working people. Don't go on his journey. Abandon him. Without you, his usurped power dries up. His soul mates — the politicians and regulatory bureaucrats — lose their unearned power. They'll become powerless to live off of us, the producers. See him for who he is — a man seething with envy against innocent value producers. If you can't see through his smiles and charm, hear his envy. Every day in class he attacks the businessman — the good — as someone evil who needs to be supervised. He attacks the successful person you once hoped to become. Journey with this man, and he'll destroy your spirit to succeed and replace it with envy to destroy those who succeed. To rekindle that spirit to succeed is why I'm standing before you tonight—'

"Rosewall cut me off and said, 'Knowing the way businessmen think, I wouldn't doubt that your father put you up to this to drum up some sales.'

"I snapped back, 'When you talk like that, you demonstrate that *you* are the naive one. It takes a lot more than a mere debate to, as you put it, drum up sales. I grew up in my father's business and know the enormous effort that goes into creating and marketing values. You certainly would never make it as an honest market businessman, and you know it. That's why you envy businessmen so.'

"Rosewall laughed nervously and said, 'Son, I've studied, in depth, everything from Plato to Kant. Who have you studied? I could have argued their works, but I knew you'd be lost. Do you want to try me?'

"I responded, 'You're the academic; you're not the market businessman. In many ways, you're the one who's lost, not me. I grew up as a first-hand witness of the market businessman. I saw how hard my father worked to create wonderful values and to find ways to cut costs to bring those values to more people. In the ways that count, I'm not so lost. People like me, like my classmates — we're young. We're just starting our lives. We want to go out there and make values for the world that people want. That'd make us successful financially and emotionally. But before we get our chance, you pollute our minds by making us think the very person we dream of becoming is someone bad — that greedy businessman who's destroying society. So, you break our spirit, Dr. Rosewall. Year after year, you break hundreds of young adults. You fill these young adults with shame for those people they strive to become.' Rosewall started categorically denying everything I was saying, but I turned

166

to the students and raised my voice over his and shouted, 'Even if you cannot see through Dr. Rosewall's clever tactics, ask yourself if he's attacking or putting down the value producer. If he is, then no matter how convincing he is, say one word silently in your head: *envy*. If that word seems a little too academic, then when Dr. Rosewall puts down the creator of values and jobs, say one other word silently in your head: *bullshit*. ...That's all I have to say on this matter. I hope I've helped rekindle some snuffed-out spirits in here tonight. Thank you for coming. Thank you!'

"I was prepared for an applause, but not for the thunderous ovation that rocked the theater. Rosewall was trying to object, but the power of the students overwhelmed him. He suddenly looked like a nervous, guilty little man. About five students rushed onto the stage carrying a tall trophy. One of them rushed to my microphone and blurted out that he was the captain of the University's debate team and that I had performed one of the most convincing debates he'd ever witnessed. The debate team unanimously declared me the winner and, to my surprise, presented me with the four-foot victory trophy. Dr. Rosewall stormed off the stage and out of the building. I accepted the trophy, but explained to the crowd that the key to my strength was not a focus on winning, but a focus on honesty. I said, 'Even if it means losing the debate or embarrassing myself, I would not hesitate to change if I realized I was out of focus with reality.' The crowd gave me a standing ovation. I was a hero. I never again attended Rosewall's class, and about half his students dropped his class. The next year, he transferred to another, smaller, city college."

Miss Annabelle had been curled up next to him on the couch, listening and imagining herself as a college girl in the audience that night. She smiled at him and asked, "Why didn't you ever sit near me when I used to eat in the teacher's lunch room?"

"Because you're so beautiful," he answered smoothly, sincerely.

"Oh? You avoid beautiful women?" she said, laughing.

"Beauty and emotional maturity never seemed to go together, until I met you. Wow, had I any idea who you were!"

"Make love to me, my darling," she whispered.

CHAPTER
FOURTEEN

It was the fourth day Jake had spent at Jessie and Angie's home when Angie told him about Miss Annabelle's romantic relationship with John Melbourne.

"When John came into her life, of course, we didn't see her as much then, but we were so happy for her. She was really, really happy."

"But then?" Jake said. He was anticipating the irrational world they lived in.

"But then...just when her students and her romance — her *life* — started soaring, her world started tumbling toward something terrible," Angie said. She looked away, deep in reflection, and she added, "I don't know if she ever fully recovered."

"It all started at Sally's birthday party..." Jessie said, continuing the story...

*

Everyone was singing "Happy birthday to you! Happy birthday to you! Happy birthday, dear Sally! Happy birthday to you!"

The dark haired little girl leaned forward and blew out the

nine candles on her cake in one gallant breath. February 12th was Sally's birthday...her favorite day. Her eleven classmates were all there. So was Miss Annabelle; she would not miss it for the world. They all felt extra close to Sally and her mom, and they wanted to be with them on this special day. There was so much love in Sally's home; everyone was hugging everyone. They were soul mates. They all felt deeply for Sally and her mother's fate. But this was a day for happiness and love.

Sally's mom was filled with warmth at the sight of these special little friends together with Sally. Each birthday card Sally read from her classmates went so much deeper than the usual happy-birthday greeting. The children wrote things like, "I feel like you are a sister to me," and "Let's always be friends, wherever we might go," and "I admire your strength and your positive attitude; I want to be your friend forever". Those were powerful messages from these little children, Sally's mom thought. She'll have a lot of support when I'm gone.

While Sally laughed and played the games at her party, Miss Annabelle noticed that Sally's mom was right there next to Sally, but sitting most of the time. Her energy was going, Miss Annabelle realized.

*

The next two weeks at school were the two best weeks of Miss Annabelle's life. Sally's party seemed to have pulled everyone closer. They seemed more like a family than a class. Instead of the usual "hi" and "good-bye", the girls would greet each other with a hug when they arrived and a hug when they left school. They'd do the same to Miss Annabelle, who happily obliged. Some of the boys started to give Miss Annabelle a hug, too. The class always sat together at lunch. Miss Annabelle liked it most when she sat with her class during lunch hour. They would arrange the table so all twelve of them could be around Miss Annabelle, John Melbourne, and the other "cool" teachers.

Miss Annabelle would always fondly remember those last two weeks in February, for she never knew such pure love and

169

happiness as during those winter days. Her life was fulfilled in every way. She had found the love of her life. For years she had given up on the idea of falling in love, yet now she felt like a teenager again. And, she was beside herself in her passion to develop her students' minds to efficiently see and integrate reality so they could always rule their own lives and never be ruled by the illusions of politicians, regulatory bureaucrats, journalists, professors, idols, Hollywood producers, clergymen, the crowd, the Establishment. Miss Annabelle knew that most people, including her students' innocent parents, did not know how to efficiently see through the matrix of illusions. Therefore, they could not integrate reality to rely on the authority of their own minds. So, they turned that authority over to the "experts". Those "experts" fleeced an easy, prestigious living from the innocent working person, leaving him suppressed and stagnant. Life could be so much more for these children than it was for their parents, she thought. For, her twelve students would never turn their power over to others.

The final two weeks in February confirmed their developing self-leadership and growing power, which boosted Miss Annabelle's happiness beyond anything she had ever known.

She heard mouth-dropping integrations of new knowledge coming from her students, particularly during the lunch hour, which had become her students' *discussion* hour as well. A couple days after Sally's birthday party, Miss Annabelle, Mr. Melbourne, and the handful of other teachers sat amongst her twelve students and listened in amazement to their lunch-hour discussion. The other teachers either implicitly or explicitly knew that these twelve children were entering a new mentality of puzzle-building, self-leading authority. Moreover, with their ability to see and integrate reality on their own into these growing puzzles, they were already, at nine years old, developing puzzle-pictures seen by no one before. Both Miss Annabelle and Mr. Melbourne, in particular, knew this group of children would produce the next great scientist, businessman, doctor, psychologist. Mr. Melbourne smiled knowingly at Miss Annabelle as she basked in the children's lunch hour discussions this particular winter afternoon:

"Remember when Miss Annabelle explained to us that our

lives are the greatest value in the Universe, and therefore the super smart people out there would not let us perish?" Ian started.

"Yes!" Sally answered. "I believe in that. My mom's going to be all right."

"I believe in that too," Ian responded. "I really do. I've been reading lots of books about our Universe. Scientific theory has it that our Universe started from a big bang, and is moving outward. Eventually, though, it will run out of energy...and someday the Universe will reach something called entropy death, which means there is no more energy, no more life. But I've been thinking...I don't think any Universe ever reaches entropy death for the very reason your mother will be OK, Sally. The super advanced people out there wouldn't let entropy death happen. In theory, every Universe moves toward eventual entropy death. But in practice, I don't think it's ever happened."

Mr. Melbourne looked at Miss Annabelle, his eyes as big as quarters. His mouth dropped, and he wanted to yell out, "Jesus Christ, Annabelle...what geniuses you've brought out of your kids!" But he said nothing because he did not want to disturb the amazing discussion.

"You know what, Ian," Jeremiah, a quiet, tall boy in Miss Annabelle's class said, "Talking about not dying, I'm tired of going to church with my folks. They're always talking about after you die...like I'm living to die. And the preacher's always talking about how we sin, like we're bad people or something. I mean, what's the deal with that? My mom and dad are good people; I'm a good person; all of you guys are good people. I don't know, my brother and I call that place the Church of Death. Maybe someday I'll change all that and create the Church of Life. Yeah, we'll talk about immortality...but not *after* you die. We'll join up with the scientists and doctors who are trying to make us stop aging and dying."

Miss Annabelle felt that jolt of joy again in her heart. Jeremiah was thinking completely on his own now. Illusions and external influence did not stop him from using the authority of his own mind to see and integrate reality.

"All right, Jer!" Sally said. "I go to the library a lot with my mom; I've been learning as much as I can about her cancer. It seems so simple: cells multiplying too fast. Can't they be shut off somehow?"

"They could be," Danny said, "if the FDA were stopped. Then the drug companies and entrepreneurs could really advance fast. They'd figure out how to shut off those cancer cells in no time."

A new boy at Duncan Elementary, who was a year or two older than Danny, sitting at the next table, snickered at Danny's comment.

"You doubt that?" the confident younger boy challenged.

The older boy turned around and said, "Yeah. My dad works for the EPA, and without him, your businessmen would end up killing our beautiful Earth. And without the FDA, your businessmen would end up killing people for a buck. Next thing you know, more and more people would get sick and die from some new drug or something."

"Have you ever had a paper route?" Danny asked the older boy.

"Yeah, why?" he answered, puzzled.

"Did you go so fast on your bike that you broke the windows on several houses every day because you wanted to get done quickly?"

"Of course not!" the bigger boy said, agitated at Danny.

"You didn't because you wouldn't have lasted; you would've been fired. That's not to say that you didn't break a window, once maybe, by accident. But you would've learned from your accident and learned your limitations and stayed within them."

"So, what's your point?"

Seeing the older boy was confused, Danny said, "What about cutting grass? Have you ever done that for money?"

"Yeah, I cut three lawns; one of them has expensive flower beds overlapping the lawn, so I take extra care of that, too," the older boy said. He shook his head at Danny's line of questioning.

"OK then, do you just mow right over those expensive flowers that overlap the lawn because you want to spend as little time to make the most amount of money?"

"Of course not, they'd never let me come back!"

"I'm not saying you didn't once, maybe, run over a flower by accident. But you learned and corrected your technique, right?" Danny winked.

"Yeah, right...why?" The older boy was lost.

"Because when you deliver your papers and when you cut your grass, *you're* a businessman...and you sound like a good one, too! See *what is* with your own eyes — not through your dad's stories. Businessmen have to do good jobs at what they do, or they lose the business! They can and will make mistakes. This is not a risk-free world. But they quickly learn and correct their mistakes...you're living proof."

Several kids at the older boy's table made acknowledging sounds like "hummmm...yeah ...he's right". The older boy shrugged his shoulders and turned back around. Miss Annabelle and Mr. Melbourne saw a special skill in Danny Ward. His mind was so fast...and at nine years old. This speed of thinking was possible because he, too, now efficiently burned through illusions to see reality. Miss Annabelle sat back and enjoyed the metamorphosis occurring among her students.

"I have a little real-world experience on what you're saying, Danny," Ted offered. "I never think of ways to make more money by sticking it to my customers. It just doesn't work that way. Instead, I think in the total opposite. Remember when I told the class how I want to learn to sell several products to my customers? I have to make them feel they got a great value so I can sell more to them in the future, which is where the real profit is. So, the more value my customer gets, the more money I can make from him. Every businessman *has to* work that way — or he'll go bust!"

"How's your business doing?" Cathy asked Ted with an admiring look.

"Oh, Cathy, I keep improving it. I've improved my data tracking reports. I get so much more control now, I'm going to bring in two more products to sell."

Mr. Melbourne and Miss Annabelle looked at each other, amazed. Teddy was always going to the next level.

"I've been reading a lot about the greatest businessmen who've ever lived," he continued. "The latest book I'm reading is about Henry Ford. He's my hero. He invented the assembly line, which enabled mass production and much higher standards of living for everyone because suddenly costs went so much lower. Henry Ford mastered something called the division of labor with this assembly line. Labor was cut to its shortest and fastest possible movements by the assembly line that brought the work to the employee and not the other way around. Perfecting the division of labor and mass production was wonderful then, but I think it's all going to change again to something even better."

Mr. Melbourne leaned forward. He could not imagine what Teddy was about to say.

"In all that we've been learning in class lately about the supreme value of human life, doesn't the idea of physical labor seem a little like being short-changed? We are the greatest value in the Universe, for what? To drive a rivet into the rim? No, our whole business structure is going to change."

Mr. Melbourne couldn't wait to hear what this little genius would say next. "What, Teddy...what do you see coming?"

"I see all jobs of labor changing to jobs of the mind. I've experimented with this idea in my own business, and I've proved it. At first, I trained my sellers, then paid them on a per house basis, no more, no less. They did the labor, and my company like most others functioned through this division of labor. Then I tried something different. I wanted to bring out the creative powers of my sellers' minds. So I replicated what I knew, then I set them up as their own entrepreneurs within my company. They built their mini-companies within my company and shared in the profits they made. Suddenly, they started thinking creatively to sell more...and sell more they did — *they nearly tripled sales!*

"The next evolution of business will be businesses restructuring from jobs of labor into jobs of the mind. Our workers will no longer be so stagnant like our parents. They'll become the value they're meant to be. I call it the Division of Essence."

"Teddy," Mr. Melbourne said with both hands raised, knowing he was about to hear something precious, "Why do you call the next paradigm of business the Division of Essence?"

"The essence of business is to make money. I remember you

telling my Dad that, Miss Annabelle. By setting up workers in profit-making entrepreneurial jobs of the mind like I have, you're no longer dividing business by labor...you're dividing it by essence. I believe the reason I'm doing so well is because I'm using the Division of Essence, a leap beyond the Division of Labor."

"Brilliant!" Mr. Melbourne shouted, unable to contain himself. He knew these kids had normal IQ's, but they were making breakthroughs that went beyond other child geniuses with the highest IQ's. ...He knew he was witnessing the next mentality of man — Neothink. He silenced his mouth because he did not want to disrupt this discussion.

"I wish there were some way to bring people to those new jobs of the mind, *right now*," Bobby Chapman said passionately. "I'd love to see my dad and mom doing something they love to do. They hate their work. They have most of their lives — all day long, all week long...what a waste!"

"Teddy, I have a question for you," Debbie Kirkland said. "My mom and dad own Kirkland Burger. But they've never been able to expand beyond their two small restaurants. I know they want to, but they're stuck. They run the restaurants well, but they say there's just not enough profits to expand. I don't think they make enough money to even think about franchising. What do you think they should do?"

"I really can't say, Debbie," Teddy answered. "I've eaten there a few times, and they seem to run well. ...Maybe the problem is not the management. Maybe they need a creative new product or marketing idea. I know that no matter how well-run my business is, I need to introduce fresh products or fresh marketing ideas."

"Man, I love cutting-edge products," Al Patterson chimed in, "especially now with so much new stuff coming out with all the new technologies. Did you read about those microprocessors they're coming out with?"

"I'm really excited about what they might be able to do for my business," Teddy said. "My tracking reports, my data...I can't wait!"

"You'd love my father's stores in Australia and New York City," Mr. Melbourne said. "He always sells new inventions."

"Oh, I love that stuff!" Al said. "I really love new stuff, especially the new products that I could use someday. I love reading about new breakthroughs, anything from new medicines to new cars. I really wish there were some paper or magazine where I could find all the new stuff coming out. I think business is cool...I mean, it keeps pumping out these great new products that'll save our lives or make life better."

Miss Annabelle observed a genuine love growing in Al...a love for *business*. As she sat there, the realization struck her that one could emotionally *love* a business for the values it gives us.

"I'll tell you guys something strange, OK?" Rico said, a little nervously. "OK, my uncle's spending some time in prison. I go with my dad to visit him. In the visiting room, there's lots of prisoners walking around. I like to study a prisoner, then ask my uncle why they're there. I can see something very clearly about these prisoners now, after all these months. I can tell the ones who did something really bad like rob someone or worse. But there's those other guys who are there but didn't hurt nobody."

Miss Annabelle was fascinated by his story and did not dare interrupt to correct his double negative.

"What'd they do?" Danny asked.

"They hurt nobody. I don't know...maybe they didn't pay some taxes or maybe they were smoking some weed — you know, something like that. They hurt nobody, and after awhile, you can see they don't belong in prison just because some fuckin' politician or judge says they should."

Miss Annabelle jumped at Rico's use of the "f" word, but down deep she knew she jumped because Rico's mind was now its own authority. He, too, could now see through illusions to *what is*.

"Sorry, Miss Annabelle," Rico said immediately after he finished, realizing he had startled everyone with the "f" word. Using the "f" word was part of Rico's vocabulary all his life. Every male in his house and neighborhood used the "f" word in nearly every sentence. But Rico had been determined to break that habit, and the "f" word now slipped out only occasionally when he felt angry.

176

"If I was stuck in prison," Reggie, the black boy in Miss Annabelle's class who lived in poverty, said, "I'd spend my time inventing a new kind of music."

"What do you mean — a new kind of music?" Natalie asked.

"I *love* music. I read that classical music is the best music ever written. But when I listen to the classical radio station, it puts me to sleep. Then I found out those guys who wrote classical music lived 200 years ago. Well, no wonder their music puts me to sleep...they had no technology back then! They had no electric guitars or amplifiers. So I checked out a Beethoven album from the library and put it on my mom's record player — then I cranked it really loud. I started hitting my drum behind it. I'll tell you, I started getting goosebumps! I think that classical music should be modernized with drums, electric guitars, and electric violins...amplified like rock 'n roll. Man, that'd be the hottest sound out there!"

Suddenly the lunch bell rang, signalling the end of lunch.

"We need to talk about this amazing phenomenon!" Mr. Melbourne whispered to Miss Annabelle.

The leap in self-thinking among her students *really was* phenomenal. But to the students, it seemed completely natural now. They were all moving ahead toward becoming geniuses of a different kind...not IQ geniuses, but creative puzzle-building or Neothink geniuses.

As Miss Annabelle turned to stand, she saw an ugly sight in stark contrast to the beauty she had just witnessed. She saw the corpse-like Ms. Minner standing in the lunchroom, looking directly at her. That's odd, Miss Annabelle thought. I've seen her a lot lately, now in here. She never comes in here; why now?

*

That night Mr. Melbourne and Miss Annabelle were like two excited partners who'd struck it rich. Everything Miss Annabelle had hoped for was coming true. She knew her students would make it now, on their own...even if she could never return.

Furthermore, her students were providing immeasurably valuable confirmation of Mr. Melbourne's lifetime work on the

Superpuzzle

mind and mans' coming "evolutionary jump" into a new mind of the future.

CHAPTER
FIFTEEN

Ms. Minner sat up tall and proud as her visitor looked over the dozens of photos across her desk. She felt deep satisfaction knowing the "evidence" she had manufactured. She had grown up in the Bible Belt and was a deeply religious woman, a mystic, who actually hallucinated conversations with angels. She was convinced that the lovely Miss Annabelle was the work of Satan himself, for an angel had sent her that message from God, and she took personal responsibility to do whatever it took to get Miss Annabelle removed from her school...and from ever teaching children again if possible.

"You've got some extraordinary pictures here," her visitor said in a deep voice, taking his time looking at each one. He obviously took great pleasure in the pile of pictures. "How did you get them?"

"With this," she answered, putting her new hard purse on the desk. "It's a camera that looks like a pocketbook."

"Good work!" he cried out in the little office, taking his eyes off the pictures for just a second to see the purse. Then his eyes turned right back to the pictures of Miss Annabelle affectionately hugging and, in some cases, kissing her students. "Maybe we've discovered why this pretty young thing has nothing to do with men. Once again, good work!"

Superpuzzle

"Thank you, Mr. Hammerschmidt."

*

Mr. Hammerschmidt privately, personally hired a private investigator to find out as much as he could about Miss Annabelle's past. He discovered that this pretty woman was the victim of domestic violence. Hammerschmidt read the hospital report and the brief article in the Buffalo News on the beating from her husband that nearly killed her.

The image of that little fearless lioness, being beaten into submission by a man, went around and around in Hammerschmidt's mind. The image terribly aroused him, and for days he repeatedly relieved himself. He couldn't stop thinking about her in uncompromising positions; his private name for her was now, "my little bitch".

A week later he was back in the principal's office with several of the school board members and an attorney, reviewing Ms. Minner's pictures.

"Do you feel this is grounds to hold a school board meeting on dismissing this teacher on grounds of too much touching and kissing…too much fondling her students?" Hammerschmidt asked the attorney. The attorney told them they could go ahead; the pictures caused enough suspicion to hold a hearing and a vote on whether Miss Annabelle could continue teaching.

During this informal meeting in Ms. Minner's office, Hammerschmidt gave the child-molestation theory traction; he inflamed the school board members. Hammerschmidt, who had inwardly gone to the point of perversion with his sexual fantasies of physically beating Miss Annabelle, suggested she might be a pervert, which would explain why she had no interest in men.

After the meeting, Hammerschmidt coincidentally passed Miss Annabelle in the hall going back to her room after lunch. She saw him a good 15 yards away and decided to ignore him. Unless he addressed her, she would just keep walking.

Because of this plan, she was extra aware of his every move…in case he did greet her politely, she would want to respond. She watched him closely in her peripheral vision.

Hammerschmidt got very excited as they walked closer to

each other, seeing her tiny body while imagining it being hit by a man. Just before he was next to her, he quietly closed his hand closest to her into a fist. It was a subtle, almost disregardable event. But Miss Annabelle quietly gasped. Hammerschmidt detected her quiet yet unmistakable reaction. He turned into the next boys' room, locked himself in a stall, and almost instantly relieved himself at the touch of his hand. As his own perversion grew to a new level, he cursed beneath his breath how this "little bitch" must not inflict her perversions on innocent children.

*

"The final two weeks in February, twenty-seven years ago, were the finest in Miss Annabelle's teaching career," Jessie said, continuing the story. "From then on, everything fell into disarray and then disaster."

Looking directly at Jake, Angie began telling him the beginning of the end:

"Midday, the first of March, Miss Annabelle missed the lunch hour for the first time since her tradition with the kids began. In the halls, she told John Melbourne she wouldn't be there. Instead, she went to see my husband..."

*

"Hi Jessie," the pretty lady said at the same instance she tapped the busy custodian on his shoulder.

"Whoa!" Jessie shouted as he turned around. "Anna...I mean Miss Annabelle, you startled me!"

"Sorry Jessie. Didn't mean to sneak up on you. I guess I kinda feel like I need to be sneaky right now."

"Why, what's wrong?" Jessie asked. He could see that Miss Annabelle was disturbed about something.

"This," she said. She handed him another summons for another emergency school board meeting. "I just want to know if you've come across anything that can help me...maybe some clue or some papers on her desk or in her trash."

Miss Annabelle was visibly upset. Jessie suddenly felt

181

fatherly feelings toward her as he saw how vulnerable she looked. He put his arm around her and took her to his little room, sat her down, and closed the door.

"Does John know yet?" he asked her.

"Not yet," she said, wiping her eyes. Jessie handed her a box of tissues. She dabbed her eyes with a tissue, then continued, "I haven't had a private moment with him yet to tell him, and I don't want anyone seeing us alone together."

"OK. Let me read this," Jessie said calmly. The summons said:

A Closed-Door
Emergency School-Board Meeting
Wednesday, March 3rd at 5:15 p.m.
To All Parties: Please note that a closed-door meeting is in
    best interest of all parties involved.
Subject: Miss Annabelle's Employment

Jessie looked at Miss Annabelle. He felt sorry for her for having to even deal with these attacks.

"What do you think it is this time?" he asked her.

"I don't know," she said. She looked lost. "We haven't gotten into anything about God or government since the last meeting in January. ...That's what's bothering me so much — I don't know what this meeting is about."

"Neither do I," Jessie said. He dropped his eyes. "I haven't seen anything about it, but I'll be looking, you can bet on it."

"Hammerschmidt scares me," Miss Annabelle said in a moment of weakness.

"What!" Jessie was surprised. "You handled that creep both times; you made a fool of him. And the parents like you."

"Why do I feel that won't matter this time?" Miss Annabelle softly asked. "They've got something on me...but what could it be? What could it be? And why do I keep seeing those creepy people?"

"Who?" Jessie asked.

"Minner and Hammerschmidt!"

"Anna, how are your students coming along?" he asked.

She looked up slowly and her face brightened, "Oh, they're

amazing. They're going to new levels, Jessie. Even if I weren't allowed back to class, my students give new meaning to having minds of their own. They're going to live with a different mentality than their peers. My students will build *new* knowledge for the world through building never-before-seen puzzle-pictures."

"I know," Jessie said. "I listen to all the general lectures. Some of the projects some of those kids are building just blow my mind. Some of them are becoming geniuses!"

"Jessie, you know what? You've just cheered me up," Miss Annabelle looked up and smiled. "Thank you."

"Annabelle...Angie and I, we love you. You're our best friend, and we believe in what you're doing."

"I know," she said. She stood up. She leaned forward and gave Jessie a kiss on the cheek and said, "I can feel you and Angie giving me strength at these school-board meetings. I wish you could be there this time."

"We'll be there," Jessie said.

"But the note specifically said it's a CLOSED meeting."

"Do you think they'll be able to stop my wife?" They both laughed.

"I'd better get back to class," Miss Annabelle said, looking at her watch and feeling much better.

"Before you go, tell me, how are things going with you and John?" Jessie whispered. No one at Duncan Elementary knew about their romantic relationship except Jessie.

"Oh, it's beautiful...he's beautiful!" she whispered back.

"Angie says your eyes tell her everything...you're in love!" They both laughed again. "Anna...Angie and I've been wanting to spend a little time with you and John. Let's all get together tomorrow; it'll be good for us to feel like a team going into the meeting Wednesday."

"I'd love that, Jessie."

"See if you and John can come over around seven o'clock. We'll have dinner at our place, and we'll talk."

"I'm glad I talked to you. Thank you. You and Angie are special. ...See you tomorrow."

"See you tomorrow."

*

Superpuzzle

John Melbourne stayed at Miss Annabelle's home most nights now. Their schedules were very compatible. After completing their school papers, he worked on his book and she worked on her lectures. But the three hours immediately after they left school belonged to enjoying each other. They could do anything they wanted in their fun-time together. They always ate dinner together, and they did a number of other things that included working out together at the gym, going to the mall together, going to art shows, craft festivals, going to movies, to the theater, to the park, jogging together, riding bikes, picnics, playing tennis, visiting Jessie and Angie, grocery shopping...anything to be together. When they got back home, they'd get into their evening work.

Tonight they were going to Jessie and Angie's house to have dinner and talk. Of course, their minds were on the school-board meeting the next day. As they were changing to casual clothes, John said, "I'm coming to the meeting."

"But they'll figure out about us if you come," Miss Annabelle said. She wanted him there; she *needed* him there. But she also wanted to protect him. She did not want him to become a target, too.

"That doesn't matter anymore," he said calmly. "It really doesn't. You're my woman, and I want to be there."

"And you're my Prince Charming," she said, jumping playfully into his arms. They laughed. ...He was right. To hell with trying to keep their romance a secret. It felt so good to be able to laugh with him, even when she faced the worst crisis of her life. They left the house with high spirits. Outside on the steps, Miss Annabelle slipped, and he grabbed her arm. "Just like our first date," she said, and they laughed some more. They felt good; they were excited to visit Jessie and Angie.

They arrived at the bright little house feeling full of fun and games. Jessie and Angie came out on the doorsteps to greet them. Immediately all four were laughing about something. God, I love this sound of us all laughing, Miss Annabelle thought. I hope it always stays like this.

That night, Jessie, Angie, and John decided to be at the meeting no matter what was said to them. Miss Annabelle felt they were a team, a strong team. With them there, my lover and my two best friends, she thought, I will not lose.

*

The next morning Miss Annabelle woke up nervous. What are they investigating? she wondered. Her nervousness subsided when she was with her class. But it came back after school let out. Jessie and John came to her room to be with her. They, too, felt nervous but tried not to show it.

"What's the worst that can happen?" she said. "They could fire me, which would end my teaching career. But at least my students are past the point of no return. I have pushed them into the Neothink mentality." That thought, and that thought alone, relaxed Miss Annabelle. She explained her confidence in her students to John and Jessie. They relaxed some, too.

The meeting would start in two hours in the school auditorium, which Miss Annabelle thought was a large location considering it was a closed meeting. John stayed with Miss Annabelle, and soon Jessie returned with Angie. They sat around talking about her students and the progress they've made.

After about thirty minutes of this, Angie said, "Anna, you're a hero. You *are* a hero! What they're doing to you is so upside-down!"

"That's because Anna's a hero," John said while nodding. "Albert Einstein said, 'Great spirits have always encountered violent opposition from mediocre minds.' Annabelle," John looked into her eyes, "in that meeting, you remember what you've done for those twelve kids. You've led them to the new mind of the future!"

*

At five o'clock, Annabelle Barclays, John Melbourne, Jessie and Angie Attison walked into the auditorium together. Tension filled the large room. Miss Annabelle looked to the front and saw Hammerschmidt and Minner looking over some papers. Most of the school board had arrived and were already seated.

The four walked down the aisle together; their hearts were beating fast. Ms. Minner glanced up at them and tapped

Hammerschmidt's arm. He looked up and saw the four approaching the front. He instinctively attacked, "I'm sorry, you three will have to leave. This is a closed meeting."

John answered politely, "Sir, we're just going to quietly observe the proceedings here today. My name is John Melbourne, and I teach here. Jessie Attison is the school's custodian and this is his wife, Angie. Honestly, sir, Miss Annabelle is entitled to a little support, isn't she?"

Although a rhetorical question, Hammerschmidt snapped, "No, I'm sorry. This is a closed meeting." He did not know Miss Annabelle had a man in her life, and the possibility that this handsome Melbourne was romantically connected to Miss Annabelle sent waves of envy and anger through the stocky superintendent.

"You have your little closed-door meeting, mister," Angie said, "But when those doors close, we'll be right here." Angie leaned over and gave Miss Annabelle a kiss on the cheek, whispered something in her ear, then sat down in the front row. Jessie and John smiled warmly at Miss Annabelle, and they sat down too. Hammerschmidt looked at them for a moment. Before he had a chance to object, John Melbourne said, "You can have us watch — and we're harmless — or you can have her attorney accompany her. It's your choice."

Hammerschmidt thought about it for a moment, then gave up the fight. Miss Annabelle took her seat at the solo chair and small table facing the school board, still without a clue as to what this was about. As she sat there, she noticed a man sitting in the vacant audience seats toward the very back, in the shadows. She strained to see who it was, but it was too dark. She put a hand over her eyes to block the glare of the lights. Still, she could not make him out.

"Let's get started!" Hammerschmidt shouted. "Miss Annabelle, we all know each other now. So, the best way to handle this is to start the meeting with a slide show. As they say, a picture's worth a thousand words. We'll talk after the show. Lights please!"

Someone dimmed the lights and the slide projector illuminated the screen at the front of the room. Miss Annabelle looked to her left and smiled as she saw a picture of Sally and herself puckering up for big hug and kiss. Although a close-up, Miss Annabelle knew by the dress, the picture was taken at Sally's birthday party.

After a moment, the slide changed, and there was Miss Annabelle again in a tight embrace with Cathy. The next slide showed her hugging Teddy in the lunchroom. Then another showing her hugging Ian at the school's science fair. ...What is this? she wondered. Who took all those pictures? After a dozen more pictures of her hugging her students, the slide show ended and the lights came on.

"Miss Annabelle, you're the only teacher here who does that," Hammerschmidt said.

"Does what?" she asked, quite confused.

"Miss Annabelle, do you realize, you're the only teacher here who physically touches, hugs, even kisses these nine-year-olds."

"I really do love them. I've got no children of my own, and I've become very attached to them. ...What are you saying, anyway?"

"After seeing the complete library of pictures, the school board must review and decide the terms of your employment," Hammerschmidt said, trying to sound diplomatic.

"We must also review the conditions, as they pertain to your teaching license, under these circumstances," Ms. Minner added.

"What circumstances?" Miss Annabelle asked emphatically. Visibly upset and shaking, she said, "This is the most disgusting show of vindictiveness; I couldn't have thought of this line of attack, even in my worst fears of what was going to take place here today! Tell me, how does one defend oneself against *this* sort of accusation? You have pictures of me hugging these children. I hug them because *I care*...I LOVE THEM! Everything I do, I'm thinking about them. I feel their pains; I share their victories. Sally's mother is dying, which has brought us all closer together. Since Sally's birthday party, the hugging began. ...What do you want from me? Why can't you just leave me alone to teach these children?" Miss Annabelle knew she was going to cry as her eyes filled with tears. She looked at Hammerschmidt. She could not know that Hammerschmidt was aroused while watching her little body quivering, broken, and about to cry...secretly imagining her this way during "a good beating". But her subconscious picked up something overwhelmingly eerie at the way he was looking back at her. A woman's instinct instructed her from within to get out of there. She stood up and ran out of the room. Crying and disoriented, she could not see well and the entire right side of her torso hit the doorway hard and knocked her back and spun her halfway around. Her line of sight landed directly on the mysterious figure who was sitting in the shadows. She was close enough to see his face, smiling victoriously. It was Burke!

John was running after her and calling her, but she staggered out. Just before John left the auditorium exit, he turned around and shouted at Hammerschmidt, "You'll pay for this, you bastard! I'll *personally* make sure of that!"

Outside, John caught up with Miss Annabelle. She was leaning face forward against his car, crying uncontrollably. He turned her around and hugged her. She leaned into him and buried her face into his chest. Her hands were shaking severely as she grabbed him and hysterically gasped, "Oh John, oh John, what have they done! What have they done!"

He hugged her tightly. Her whole body was shivering. What *have* they done? he wondered. Jessie and Angie came out. "Oh, baby," Angie said as she reached over and rubbed Miss Annabelle's back. Jessie was hot with anger, but he stayed calm. Miss Annabelle could not stop crying. "Let it out, let it all out," Angie urged in a gentle, maternal voice.

All four got in John's Chrysler. Angie and Miss Annabelle sat in the back. Angie put her arm around Miss Annabelle who was leaning forward, still crying into a tissue pressed against her face.

"Please, take me home, John." Miss Annabelle said in a terribly sad voice.

When they arrived, all four went into the living room. Miss Annabelle had regained some of her composure and sat down. Angie went into the kitchen and made coffee. John sat on the arm of the chair next to Miss Annabelle and held her hand. Jessie sat across from them on the couch.

"Is this it? Am I fired?" Miss Annabelle blurted, still in a state of shock.

"No, darling," John said reassuringly, "there's protocol to

follow. It'll take three months before anything like that could happen. That would get you through the end of the school year."

Miss Annabelle immediately relaxed. She even managed a slight smile. She had told herself before the meeting that her students had their own minds now, but from the moment she ran out of the meeting, she had the horrifying thought that she would not be able to teach her students again. The most wonderful music to her ears was what John had just said: *she would be able to finish out the school year.*

He knew she wanted to hear those words, too. But he said those words with sincerity. In fact, the past two days he did a lot of research on protocol and talked in depth with his lawyer, preparing for the worst. He did not tell Miss Annabelle of his research so as not to worry her. He also had no clue on what the meeting would be about, but he suspected it would be significant as she had twice previously battled and beaten the school board, and they were not going to be embarrassed again.

He let go of Miss Annabelle's hand and stood up. He walked over and put his hand on the mantle over the fireplace and leaned his weight forward. Looking at the ground, he thought for a moment and then said, "We must throw a log on their tracks to slow them down."

He hesitated because he knew what he was going to say next would upset her. After a moment, he turned around and said, "Anna, we must reveal our love affair to show that you're a normal, heterosexual woman."

Her face crumbled, revealing the pain again that was eating away inside her. Two tears raced down her mascara-stained cheeks, and she struggled to speak. Her words came out in slow motion. Her voice was filled with the devastation of a violated soul; a devastation only a woman knows. She had to fight with her mouth to speak and pronounce these words, "I have to be sleeping with a man to be sexually normal?"

John walked over, knelt before her, and took her hand. "My love," he said, "they're going to create this horrible illusion about you. We need to slow them down. It's an unfair, rotten thing to have to prove your innocence, but you have little choice. You must fight back, Anna."

Miss Annabelle was quiet.

"He's right, Anna," Jessie said. "This is a war. Your kids can't lose you. If you do what John's saying, there's no way they could take you away from the kids before the school year ends."

Angie walked in with the coffee. They all sat down and sipped, their minds hard at work.

"What about filing a lawsuit for defamation of character?" Angie asked.

Miss Annabelle looked up and quietly said, "A lawsuit centered on child molestation." She paused, gathering her thoughts, then continued, "That'd bring my kids under the type of questioning that'd undermine the one person who must have complete credibility in their eyes — *me*. I don't want to undo what I've done for those kids. ...Oh, that Hammerschmidt is a sick man!"

Her pain was turning to anger. "I wish I could make him feel the hurt he's put in me! God, I feel violated!" John sat next to her and rubbed his hand down her hair. "We'll fix this," he assured her.

"I've got an idea," Jessie said, lifting his eyes from the floor to look at John and Miss Annabelle. Angie, who was sitting next to him, put her coffee on the end table, then turned and put her hand on Jessie's lap, giving him her undivided attention as he said, "I think we *should* hurt him."

"What do you mean?" John asked.

"A man like that has done some awful things; he's proven that by what he's doing to Anna. He's got no principles. Now, I heard something on the radio today, just before the school board meeting, and it shouldn't surprise you: Brian Petersen announced his democratic candidacy for governor, and guess who's his running mate for lieutenant governor?"

"Hammerschmidt?" John responded instantly, in an *I-knew-it* tone of voice.

"You got it," Jessie said, "and he's going to put his wrath on Anna to get some media attention and win some votes. We must stop him. We need to dig up some dirt on this scum and make a private little offer: he drops his investigation of Anna, and we don't take our dirt to the local media."

"I like it Jessie," John said. "He's darn clever, but if we

can find a skeleton or two in his closet, I'll personally handle it. I'll start tomorrow; I'll meet with a private investigator. I'll also put together an affidavit detailing our romantic relationship. ...How do you feel about all this, Love?"

Miss Annabelle looked up at John. "I'll do anything to keep teaching through the end of the school year," she said, obviously worn out emotionally and physically. "And I'm all for finding out whatever we can about Hammerschmidt's past." She looked at John, Jessie, and Angie and said, "Thank you, so much, for all that you're doing for me. I think what I need right now is to think about my kids and how this might affect them. I need to really concentrate for a couple of hours...alone."

"We understand, dear," Angie said, getting up and gathering the coffee cups. When she returned from depositing the cups in the kitchen sink, she asked Miss Annabelle if she could fix her something to eat.

"I'll make a sandwich or something later," Miss Annabelle said, smiling. "Thank you for being here."

John said he'd take Jessie and Angie back to their car at the school, then go home for a couple of hours. He wanted to work on the affidavit. He hugged her and said he'd be back around ten o'clock.

"I love you," Miss Annabelle whispered, and she hugged him tight.

CHAPTER
SIXTEEN

March was a painful and humiliating time for Miss Annabelle. She was allowed to continue teaching, but a member of the faculty had to sit in her room and observe at all times.

At first, the children did not talk much. They inherently knew the stranger sitting in their world did not belong there. After a couple of days, however, the children forgot she was even there.

While the world around Miss Annabelle seemed insane, she found peace and sanity in her classroom and in her private world with John. In fact, for most of her day, she was in a world of rationality — surrounded by her students during the day and by John in the evenings and nights. She kept enormously busy after school developing her lectures around her paperwork. If not for the looming threat of losing her students to these trumped-up charges, she realized her life would be wonderful. So, she determined not to let the insane charges drag her down. She decided to, instead, enjoy every precious moment with her students as if it were the last. Every morning she prepared herself mentally to feel and enjoy the *preciousness* of rational, happy life. Caught in this topsy-turvy world, she discovered the *rightness* of happiness.

Conceiving the Superpuzzle

*

When she arrived at school Thursday morning after the emergency meeting, Miss Annabelle opened the envelope on her desk. It was from Ms. Minner, and it read:

"We understand that you left the meeting due to the sensitive topic. However, we must proceed with this matter. The school board must meet with you to get your story. That's the American way. We will meet again next Wednesday, same place and time. Again, it is a private meeting, but you may bring Mr. Melbourne and Mr. and Mrs. Attison if you so desire."

Miss Annabelle realized this nightmare would not go away. As she put the summons down, an eerie thought rushed through her: What if my students and their parents hear about these accusations? The thought made her shudder.

*

The next morning, Cathy walked into the classroom first, about 10 minutes before the others. Only a little fluffy and round, but certainly no longer fat, one could see her pretty features. She walked directly to Miss Annabelle. Her bright blue eyes looked concerned, and she was not smiling. Her expression revealed the natural beauty of her face that, not long ago, was diluted by fat. She has high cheek bones, Miss Annabelle noticed.

"Good morning Cathy," Miss Annabelle said smiling. But she knew something was wrong.

"Hi," Cathy said. But her full pink lips frowned. "Why is my mom calling people on the phone and talking bad about you?"

"Oh, what's she saying?" Miss Annabelle managed to say cheerfully, yet fearing what she would hear.

"I don't know. Something about you being in the paper."

Just then Teddy walked in.

"Hi Teddy," Cathy said in a low voice.

Teddy walked to the front of the room. "Hi Cathy," he said. Then he looked at his teacher and said, "I read the article about you in this morning's paper. I know it's a bunch of lies and so does my dad."

Miss Annabelle's heart dropped. An article in the paper?

"What does the article say?" she asked Teddy, then wishing she hadn't.

"It says you're being questioned by the school board for misconduct — for possible child molestation. One man says that if it's true, he would remove you from teaching here, and that scared me."

Miss Annabelle felt enormous pain inside but tried not to show it. The evil was catching up to her and now seemed bigger than her. These children do not even understand sex, she thought, yet here they're going to be introduced to the idea of child molestation!

"Yeah, that's what my mom was telling her friends. What do they mean by that, anyway?" Cathy asked innocently. Miss Annabelle was suddenly confronted with her greatest fear: to have to present this horrific thought to her students.

"Cathy, I don't know how to explain it to you yet," Miss Annabelle said honestly. "But I will answer that question for you and maybe for the whole class tomorrow after I've had time to think about it."

When the other students came in, there was a lot of talk among each other, which made it clear that talk was everywhere. "Class," Miss Annabelle began, introducing some control, "I'm going to make the same deal with you that I made with Cathy earlier. A lot of people have read or been told about an article about me in this morning's paper. I have not seen it yet, but I hear some pretty bad things were written about me. Tomorrow I'll talk about it with you after I've had some time to look at the paper and think things over."

"Miss Annabelle, are they going to make you leave?" Rico asked in such a sad voice from such a macho little man that he almost made Miss Annabelle cry.

"The good news, Rico, is that I was able to teach you wonderful children for six months, and you are already, on your own, seeing through illusions to the essence of things...to *what is*. And by doing that, you're starting to build new knowledge and real power. That was my goal when we started this school year."

"Are you going to keep on teaching us?" Jeremiah asked very sadly.

"I'm certainly going to do everything in my power," Miss Annabelle said, feeling a lump growing in her throat.

"Can we still get a hug from you sometimes?" Sally asked slowly.

Miss Annabelle's eyes flooded with emotions. She looked over at the woman sitting in her room whose name Miss Annabelle did not even remember, then Miss Annabelle looked back at Sally and said, "Yes, Sally. Whenever you need a hug, I'd love one. I love our hugs, too."

*

John Melbourne gave Miss Annabelle the paper at lunch. The article was on the front page of the local section with a picture of her hugging and kissing an unidentified student. Of course, Miss Annabelle immediately recognized the student was Alan, and she knew it happened at Sally's birthday party.

*

Later that evening Sally's mother called and said she had sent Ms. Minner pictures of the party for the school's yearbook. She said she knew these accusations were ridiculous. With her terminal condition, Sally's mom saw the bigger picture of life now and talked to Miss Annabelle for about forty-five minutes. She also told Miss Annabelle how indebted she felt toward her for shaping Sally's mind so dramatically...and for helping Sally prepare for her loss.

The call was exactly what Miss Annabelle needed after seeing the article. The villain was Hammerschmidt. He was behind the article. As is the case in the world of politics, the villain came across looking like the hero. Hammerschmidt, pressing for public exposure to gear up his race for Lieutenant Governor of New York, repeatedly made a point to assure the people of New York that "...if something insidious is occurring in *my* school system, I personally will not stop until that filth is removed and the school is restored to a wholesome environment." Also

195

accompanying the article was a picture of Hammerschmidt with a caption that read, "Wholesome minded: School Board Superintendent, Charlie Hammerschmidt, will run for Lieutenant Governor on the Brian Petersen ticket this November."

*

Miss Annabelle's answering machine had seven messages when she had arrived home. Six were from the media: three calls from the local newspaper, two from New York radio stations, and one from the television news! She took her phone off the hook and got to work on her explanation for her class. They needed to understand.

*

Miss Annabelle looked closely at her twelve students. They look like little adults, she thought. Their eyes show me the strength of human beings in control. And that control over life comes from efficiently seeing *what is*. This Friday morning, my innocent children will learn a lesson about the irrational world that awaits them.

Today, Miss Annabelle would turn the calamity that surrounded her into an opportunity to further develop her students' defenses against imminent irrationality in their futures. She began with a metaphor:

"Forty thousand years ago, animals of all kinds would come to the ponds to drink and cool off. When they waded in certain ponds, however, the animals got stuck, unable to leave. You see, some ponds were illusions. They were actually tar pits, and the poor animals that got stuck would slowly sink in the tar to their deaths.

"That man, Mr. Hammerschmidt, is like one of those tar pits, and I'm caught. He seems like an oasis of fresh water. You saw his picture in the paper. Like any politician, he looks for any opportunity to create an illusion that'll give him an advantage. But his illusion pulls good people down. Put another way, to push himself up falsely, he must push good people down...down into his tar pit. I'm one of those good persons being pushed down, and, I'm sorry to say, so are you.

"In general, when politicians look like they're doing public good, it's a vote-gathering illusion. Good people get stuck. In the end, everyone is stuck in limited economies.

"Hammerschmidt is a politician and a tar pit. But your parents and most others will see him as an oasis. He will pull people down on his way up in politics. We're the first of many to come.

"I was forced into contact with Hammerschmidt in our school-board meetings and became caught in his deceptive pit. The article in yesterday's paper was his illusion — the oasis the public will see."

"Why is he so bad?" a disturbed Natasha asked.

"I can answer that," Danny said, looking at Miss Annabelle, who nodded permission. "Remember when we all went camping at the beginning of the year?" Several of the children smiled while recalling that fun time. "I remember Miss Annabelle telling us what makes people happy."

"Yeah, making values," Teddy contributed. "It sure makes me happy!"

"What would happen if grown ups did *not* make values?" Danny continued. "They'd become unhappy people. I now read the newspapers a lot, and I don't think politicians are really making any values. I think they're unhappy people, and that's why they're so bad."

Miss Annabelle smiled inside at the profound insight into the human psyche.

"It's called self-esteem, Danny," Miss Annabelle said, adding the final touches to his observation. "Self-esteem is how a person feels about himself. If he feels bad about himself, he'll often do bad things. If he feels a lacking self-esteem, he'll often create illusions so people will like him and give him a sense of importance. But, since he's not making values for the people, he'll have to steal his sense of importance from those who earned it — namely from good working people, especially those important entrepreneurs and market businessmen. Politicians will make the biggest value producers, the best of the good people, look like bad people who must be controlled by 'public servants'...the politicians...the 'good' people. Controlling truly good people is how politicians get their power and sense of importance, which they substitute for self-esteem."

"You're a good person, a value producer, and Mr. Hammerschmidt is a bad person, a lying politician. He's making you look bad and himself look good, right?" Danny asked.

"Right," Miss Annabelle said.

"That makes him a value destroyer," Danny said with conviction.

*

Later that afternoon when the kids were outside for recess, Natasha bolted through Miss Annabelle's classroom door.

"Miss Annabelle," Natasha cried, "Danny's in a fight!"

Miss Annabelle and Natasha ran out to the schoolyard. Mr. Kenny, a fifth grade teacher, had the two boys separated. Miss Annabelle ran over and saw a lot of blood coming out of Danny's badly battered nose. She recognized the other boy, who seemed unhurt. He was the older boy from the lunchroom whose father worked for the EPA.

"I need to take Danny to the nurse," Miss Annabelle said. She took his arm and acted quickly. She was nervous about how profusely he was bleeding. Mr. Kenny nodded as Miss Annabelle took Danny's arm. She rushed Danny into the restroom and wetted a number of paper towels and pressed them against his nose.

"Hold these here, sweetheart," she said. Then off they rushed to the school nurse.

A few minutes later, the nurse had stopped his nosebleed. His nose was not broken, but it was badly bruised.

"What happened out there?" Miss Annabelle asked Danny.

"Oh...well...um...I slugged that big kid. Then he beat me up. But I hit him pretty good, too, you know."

Miss Annabelle could not believe what she was hearing. She could not imagine Danny hauling off and slugging anybody...and that boy looked like he was two years older, six inches taller, and at least fifteen pounds heavier.

"Why did you slug him?" Miss Annabelle asked.

"Well...I don't think I should tell you," Danny said

protectively.

"Tell me," his teacher said firmly. She looked straight into his eyes.

"He...he called you a pervert. Damn, I hate that punk!"

Miss Annabelle could not help feeling touched by Danny's courage and passion. He's my little knight in shining armor, she thought, smiling inwardly.

At the end of the schoolday, Miss Annabelle had a private talk with Danny. As they were looked upon by the school observer, Miss Annabelle quietly explained why we must never cross the line and physically strike someone, no matter how powerful our emotions get. Danny looked so humble and sweet as she talked to him, like a little warrior with his face all bruised from his gallant defense of her honor. She couldn't take it anymore and leaned over and hugged him. "Thank you," she said. "But don't do that again, okay?"

"I won't, Miss Annabelle," he said innocently. He turned his head and gave Miss Annabelle a kiss on her cheek, then turned his little body around and walked out of the room.

Miss Annabelle watched her little hero, her eyes filling with tears of love. A moment or two after Danny was gone, a noise made Miss Annabelle suddenly remember the school observer who was looking at her. Feeling vulnerable and violated, Miss Annabelle snapped, "To hell with you and your superiors!"

The school observer got up to leave. On her way out she said, "I for one have seen nothing to report...nothing at all." The middle-aged woman then flashed a kind smile at Miss Annabelle.

Surprised by this woman's decency in the indecent setting brought more sensitive feelings rushing to the surface. Miss Annabelle could not speak, but her teary eyes said, "Thank you!"

The kind woman nodded knowingly and left the classroom. Miss Annabelle dropped her face into her hands, and wept.

CHAPTER
SEVENTEEN

The private investigator who Mr. Melbourne hired came through with gold. He dug up three assault arrests in domestic disputes — one with Hammerschmidt's former girlfriend and two with his ex-wife. Moreover, the P.I. learned that Hammerschmidt, a former IRS auditor, had tried to pay off some officials to get these assaults removed from his record. Miss Annabelle's lawyer, a professional poker strategist, said to *not* use this to control Hammerschmidt until *after* the meeting later that month. "The train is too much in motion to stop," her lawyer said. "So we'll control it later, when we see everything they have to use."

Another good thing happened for Miss Annabelle. The yearly aptitude tests had come back, and Miss Annabelle's students scored phenomenally beyond their years, even beyond nearly all of the sixth graders! Natasha had the highest score in the school — the first time a third grader held that honor at Duncan Elementary School. Moreover, the local media picked up the story. Mr. Melbourne knew the national media would be interested, too. But Miss Annabelle and Mr. Melbourne decided not to submit the story when one editor in the local paper opened his article with, "Miss Annabelle: a Miracle or a Monster?"

National media attention on the molestation charges would

disintegrate her class. Nevertheless, the local coverage on the tests was mostly positive, which put pressure against the school board from dismissing the teacher responsible for those record-shattering grades.

Politically savvy, Hammerschmidt postponed the school board meeting to the end of the month. By then, the wave of positive coverage would have washed over. The delay, however, actually played into Miss Annabelle's hands, allowing her team to pick up strength.

Angie, very privately, went to each child's house and asked each child to write an essay describing their teacher. They could say anything they wanted to — anything at all.

By the third week in March, Angie had collected all twelve essays. Reading the essays would move even the most hardened and worldly man. They were by far the most powerful evidence in existence of Miss Annabelle's innocence. When Mr. Melbourne read the essays, he said they sent him into a whole new emotional realm he never knew existed. Miss Annabelle, well, she now saw, reflected back to her, what she meant to these children. It was the greatest gift she ever encountered.

John Melbourne developed an affidavit describing Miss Annabelle as a normal, healthy heterosexual with absolutely no such neurotic yearnings for child sex.

Upon advice from Mr. Melbourne's lawyer, Jessie secretly took pictures of other teachers touching students, too, holding hands, putting their arms around the children, and football coaches patting a boy's butt for a good play.

By the time the end of March arrived, Miss Annabelle had some solid ammunition going into the private school board meeting.

*

Ostensibly for Miss Annabelle's sake, Mr. Hammerschmidt closed the meeting to the press. He maintained its private status. In reality, always the politician, he was worried about what this unpredictable little lady might spring on him. He did not want anything to surprise him that could hurt his forthcoming political run.

Superpuzzle

Before this past month, Miss Annabelle did not know much about Hammerschmidt. She was not surprised to learn he was once an IRS accountant and agent for the Criminal Investigation Division. He liked to go along on raids "for the sport of it". And although a senior accountant, he loved carrying a gun and had been known to use his fists during a CID raid. He was a heartless yet intelligent man, a prime combination for politics. Void of principles and a skilled, automatic liar for whatever pragmatic advantage he could gain, this man represented the epitome of a political animal. His serious political career was just beginning with his run for Lieutenant Governor of New York. He was forty-one years old.

Now, the night of the school board meeting, the press waited outside the school, which was perfect for Hammerschmidt who was becoming an effective spin doctor. He arrived early and stopped to talk to the press and pose for pictures.

"Crimes on children will not be tolerated under my jurisdiction in the great state of New York," he proclaimed. "Having served as superintendent of the school board, the children will always come first and foremost in my heart. I'll remain their guardian angel as your lieutenant governor."

Someone from the press murmured, "Oh, he's good."

Miss Annabelle and her small team arrived. She commented to John how surreal it all seemed — like a Hollywood event, walking past reporters and TV cameras. John kept Miss Annabelle moving through the small crowd. Miss Annabelle heard a few people in the back jeering her, while a few others were clapping. I wonder who's clapping, she wondered.

Inside, she did not feel so nervous this time. Instead, she felt well prepared. She reminded herself that Hammerschmidt and his sidekick Minner were her enemies, not the entire school board. The others will be objective, she said to herself; they're the ones I'm addressing with my evidence of innocence.

The meeting started. Mr. Hammerschmidt started the proceedings, then Ms. Minner said, "Today, Miss Annabelle, we are here to see your side of the situation. This meeting is merely a continuation of the last meeting. You know what our concerns and suspicions are. What do you offer in response to all those photographs of you being overly intimate with your students?"

Miss Annabelle looked at Ms. Minner. This all seemed too fair: they're giving me a chance to show my side? These people don't do that, she thought. They have something up their sleeves.

"Let's start with a few pictures of my own," Miss Annabelle finally said. "John, would you dim the lights please?"

Hammerschmidt did not look too happy to see the first slide illuminated on the screen: the football coach with his hand on one of his player's behind.

"If those photos were supposed to incriminate me for child molestation, then the next few photos will incriminate Coach Norton for molesting boys," she said bluntly. The next slide showed the coach hugging a boy, and the next showed him picking up a boy in an elated bear hug. "Of course, these photos are nothing more than the coach celebrating with his players after a big play, but my point is: by taking the photos out of context, unjust conclusions can be construed. I hugged Alan at a birthday party; Coach hugged his quarterback after a touchdown. But neither one of us is a child molester."

Miss Annabelle went through a whole slide show of teachers on the playground, coaches on the field, faculty in the classrooms touching the students.

She noticed Hammerschmidt was not happy. But he did not look at all defeated, which concerned her. ...She knew she and her team were in a prize fight with Hammerschmidt and Minner. The rest of the school board were the judges. Her photos hit him hard, but not hard enough. She wondered, what kind of rabbit punch is he waiting to deliver?

Next, Miss Annabelle read John Melbourne's affidavit. It was well done and left little doubt that she was no manless, child pervert. It hit Hammerschmidt hard, but he was not down and out. He had concocted something big, a big knockout blow, and Miss Annabelle decided she had better save the children's essays for a counter punch if she was going to stand a chance.

"That's it," she said, surprising everyone on her team. "I'm a normal woman who has been misjudged and misrepresented to the media, putting me under a lot of unnecessary pain. You should stop now this investigation that is so unjust. No one should have to live through this."

Miss Annabelle sat down. Angie leaned forward to ask her

203

about the essays, but Miss Annabelle nodded that she knew she had not revealed them. Her instincts proved right on.

"Thank you, Miss Annabelle," her stocky foe said. "We'll deeply consider everything you presented here today. Before we adjourn, however, I feel we must hear from *your* very own students. Their words outweigh anything else we can bring to this meeting. Those children are the innocent. They pay the price. This afternoon, during your students' last period — at art class — Ms. Minner called them all to the office and asked each one the same two questions: 'Does your teacher, Miss Annabelle, hug or kiss you?' 'Does she like it?' We recorded their answers, and here is what they said. Please, run the tape!"

Miss Annabelle had a sinking feeling in her stomach as she heard her students' innocent answers paraded before the school board. Miss Annabelle and most of the parents had chosen not to get into explaining "child molestation" to the children, so most of them did not really know what it was. So, when they answered Ms. Minner, they thought they were helping their teacher by emphasizing how sweet and loving and affectionate she was with them and how she was so much more affectionate than any other teacher.

"Oh yes, she loves hugs and kisses," Debbie said.

"One time, she even got all mushy and wet!" Danny said, referring to her teary eyed moment when he defended her honor.

"She holds me tight, sometimes for a long time. I think she really likes it!" Sally said proudly.

"Once when I came to school early, I sat in her lap and talked to her. She's so loving to me."

"I was crying one day when I fell at recess. I didn't want anyone to see me crying, so we went into the classroom, and she hugged me until I was all better."

"She *loves* to hug us. Sometimes, I think she doesn't want to let go!"

This dishonest display went on and on. Miss Annabelle thought, however, that she could break the spell Hammerschmidt was putting on the school board using a similar technique that she used for the photos. She would explain that Hammerschmidt took facts out of context, and she could do the same for any other teacher as she did with the photos.

But she did not count on what was to come next.

Hammerschmidt introduced a psychologist who specialized in sexual child abuse and who worked for the state as one of its top social psychologists. Hammerschmidt went to work:

"Please introduce yourself, doctor," he said.

"My name is Dr. Michael Masterson. I have a Ph.D. in Psychology. I work for the state of New York specializing in sexual child abuse."

"How long have you been practicing, sir?"

"Fifteen years. I've written three books on the subject," the doctor said.

"Can you give us your thoughts on what you just heard from these children?"

"From what I heard, in my professional opinion, something is going on here."

"But why do none of the children seem upset?" Hammerschmidt asked, feigning objectivity.

"Often I see cases where the child is not even aware that he or she is a victim of sexual molestation. The predator is sometimes gentle and quite subtle."

"In such a case, does the child have little to worry about?" Hammerschmidt continued.

"Actually, there's always reason for concern," the doctor responded. "A subtle molester usually escalates his or her habit over time, just as a drug addict or alcoholic does. The subtle inflictions become a little more aggressive with time."

"What eventually happens?" Hammerschmidt asked. He was a master at creating illusions.

"You never know for sure. I've seen cases begin innocently but end with rape or uncontrollable groping and fondling. Now, may I ask you a question, sir?"

"Certainly," Hammerschmidt said.

"Has anyone noticed this teacher hug her students in any increased frequency since, say, the beginning of school?"

"Why, yes," Ms. Minner said eagerly. "These past six weeks, it seems she is always hugging her kids."

"OK, that's a classic signal that the neurosis is taking over. Next, she'll become more bold with her contact with those children."

"Sir, what do you recommend our action to be?" Hammerschmidt tried to sound diplomatic.

"Once a child becomes aware that he or she has been molested, a trauma could occur at a deep level that's never fully reversed. That child will carry that with him for the rest of his or her life. Because the consequences are so severe, I suggest you remove a teacher if you have good reason to suspect a pattern indicative of sexual molestation."

"Does good reason to suspect sexual molestation exist in this case?" Hammerschmidt asked, concluding his masterful illusion.

"In my professional opinion: YES."

Watching Hammerschmidt play this doctor like a movie script seemed unreal to Miss Annabelle, like she was watching a movie. She did not know how to jump into this motion picture to save herself. She just sat there and watched. She wondered, how can someone so absolutely innocent be made to look so convincingly guilty? It's like a nightmare that I can't get out of. As she sat there, not knowing what to do, she was startled by a full, deep voice behind her.

"Excuse me, my name is Bruce Salinski. I'm Miss Annabelle's attorney."

She turned around to see a well-dressed, slim man coming down the aisle, coming to her rescue. He sat down behind her, next to Angie.

"This is a private school board hearing, not a legal hearing," Hammerschmidt interrupted. "We're not open to lawyers."

"OK, what I have to say here is—"

"We're not open to lawyers, Mr. Salinski," Hammerschmidt interrupted again.

"Mr. Hammerschmidt, you ambushed her with your expert doctor, which in legal terms is called a hostile expert witness. I think Miss Annabelle is entitled to a little representation here. Of course, I could give my personal opinion of this talented, agenda-driven orchestration to the media, but I think you'd prefer if I addressed the school board."

Mr. Hammerschmidt stayed quiet. Miss Annabelle realized by that exchange that she had a slick lawyer.

"Ladies and gentlemen," her lawyer began, "in the justice

system, the prosecution and the defense are not permitted to spring surprises on each other as we witnessed here today. All evidence, which is called discovery, is presented to both sides. That is the only fair thing to do so the other side can give its side, too. Bringing in this esteemed doctor as a surprise was totally unfair."

"We're not in your justice system here," Hammerschmidt growled.

"Not technically," Salinski, unaffected, replied, "but ethically you are. You are dealing with SOMEONE'S LIVELIHOOD and ENTIRE FUTURE. Ethically, you *are* in the justice system, and the way you did this today was insidiously unfair. If you want to include witnesses, we could go out and find our own expert witness who would show Miss Annabelle is completely normal with absolutely no threat to her students. I officially insist, for the sake of honesty, that the school board members strike that hostile expert witness from your consideration. ...Shame on you, Hammerschmidt."

Hammerschmidt was livid. "What did you say your name was?"

"Bruce Salinski," the lawyer said, knowing full well he would soon be hit with an IRS audit.

Miss Annabelle, John Melbourne, Jessie and Angie felt a fondness for Bruce Salinski. He demonstrated solid legal competence and charisma, yet he had a moderate practice. Mr. Melbourne believed he was one of the rare lawyers who did not thrive on creating problems where none existed.

After Salinski talked, Miss Annabelle had new hope. She stood up and said she had something she wanted each school board member to read. She handed out her photocopied collection of essays. When she got to Hammerschmidt and Minner, she stopped.

"You two do not need these," she said. "No, you already have your agenda. These are very loving reflections my students wrote about me, without my knowledge, on the request of Angie Attison. You two are agenda driven and do not deserve to see my students' private thoughts. We already know you two are voting me out."

Hammerschmidt wanted to use his fists on her. But he just

said, "Ah, do whatever you want." The board members looked surprised by his surly reaction, obviously full of hatred and temper.

The board members were left with the essays, and the meeting was adjourned. No one noticed Hammerschmidt gritting his teeth while staring at Miss Annabelle as she was leaving.

*

Angie and Jessie, Bruce Salinski, John, and Miss Annabelle decided to meet at her house to review the meeting.

The gathering was very different from last time. Miss Annabelle was shaken, but not destroyed. Now, accepting Hammerschmidt for who he was — a liar with an agenda — nothing came as a surprise, no matter how low. Instead of feeling defeated, she was very much on her feet and still fighting. And the team felt new strength with Bruce Salinski.

"I guess the strategy now amounts to: how and when do we use Hammerschmidt's skeletons," she said looking straight at Salinski.

Miss Annabelle and John Melbourne sat together on the couch. Angie and Jessie sat across on the love seat, and Bruce Salinski sat on the chair next to the fireplace.

"You're right," he said. "He's the leader all right. And he's out to make a name for himself at your expense. We need to get to him by the weekend. He'll control the outcome of the school board's decision. We'll control him."

"Who should confront him?" John asked, ready to do the deed.

"I will," Salinski said confidently. "I'm experienced at dealing with scum."

The atmosphere was relaxed, and everyone felt justice in the plan. Miss Annabelle felt the children were still mostly unscathed by the whole thing. In fact, she rather looked forward to making Hammerschmidt squirm, and she felt confident in Salinski. They talked for another forty minutes, then got up to leave. The team looked forward to the next play, and they had a pro carrying the ball.

John had to run home to get some school papers to grade

and left with the others. He also knew Miss Annabelle needed and wanted a little time to herself. He'd be back in about an hour, he told her, and he kissed her.

"I'm proud of you, darling," he said as he was leaving.

Exhausted, she lay down on the couch after everyone left.

*

Miss Annabelle was asleep on her living room couch when she was awakened by knocking on her front door. Disoriented on seeing it was night time, she looked at the grandfather clock. It was 9:50 p.m. It must be John, she thought. Sometimes he knocked when he felt she needed some warning, respecting her privacy.

She missed him and eagerly opened the door. Staring back at her was Hammerschmidt! She gasped; her little body noticeably jumped, which pleased her nemesis.

"I have to give you these papers," he said, sounding official as he walked past her into the house without asking. "It's policy that you fill these out and return them. We'll hold another meeting soon."

As the large man walked past her, she smelled alcohol on his breath. She got cold and clammy all over, for that odor brought back memories of her ex-husband coming home after drinking, sometimes turning those difficult nights into violent physical abuse.

Miss Annabelle was trembling terribly. "Thank you," she said. She managed to keep her tone steady, for she knew she must not show fear to this sadistic drunk before her who was quite aroused after the evening's dramatic event earlier.

Unbeknownst to everyone in the meeting, Hammerschmidt had gotten quite aroused watching her facial reactions to the audio footage of her students. To see agony in her face brought ecstasy to this man. He got easily turned on by seeing this brave little lady break down and appear vulnerable. In fact, that arousing thought would not leave his head. After the school board meeting, he went to a bar. Building more and more desire with each drink to see her broken down, he decided to look in her school file for her address and head to her home. Now he stood in her house, alone with her, and the desire to further break her made his pulse race and his mouth salivate.

When he didn't leave after placing the papers on the coffee table, Miss Annabelle felt something bad was about to happen.

"Thank you, Mr. Hammerschmidt," she said as evenly as she could, while walking to the front door. "I'll review them tonight and return them tomorrow."

She opened the door for him to leave. He followed her and, calming down inside when confronted by her in-control voice that showed no fear, he appeared to be leaving.

In the doorway, however, he saw her hand trembling as she let go of the door knob.

"Wait!" he said, putting his hand up to stop the door from being pushed closed.

Instinctively, Miss Annabelle put both hands on the back of the door and tried to push it shut. But Hammerschmidt pushed it open with one hand, throwing Miss Annabelle back several steps.

The scuffle broke the ice for Hammerschmidt to act on his desire, which now overtook him.

"YOU'VE BEEN A BAD GIRL!" he bellowed loudly, breaking all boundaries between them. Then he lost his head, as a whirl of emotions swooshed through him. He started walking toward the helplessly petrified woman. With every step, the terror in her face intensified, causing greater and greater sensations in him. He was going to dominate her and put her through sheer horror.

"You little bitch!" he screamed while smacking her with a right cross and adjusting his groin with his left hand.

She screamed for help, but he took his left hand off his pants and wrapped it around her neck so hard that she couldn't make a sound. Then he pushed her to the ground. She coughed and tried to breathe again.

"Who the FUCK do you think you are?" He leaned over and hit her hard twice on the side of her head. "Hummm? Answer me, bitch!"

He jumped on her and started shaking her violently. Each shake forced air out of her lungs, making an eerie repetitive sound of terror being squeezed out of her. He was extremely strong, much stronger than her ex-husband, and she could do nothing to fight back to save herself.

He stopped shaking her and pushed her hard, back against the floor. He rubbed his big hand up and down her torso then ripped her blouse back.

He leaned forward and started rapidly unbuckling his belt. "Oh...you're gonna pay now," he mumbled. But Miss Annabelle could only think of how she could not breathe. His entire body weight was resting on her ribs. She could not breathe, and she started to black out.

As she was fading, she suddenly started breathing again and realized the stocky German man had been knocked off her. He must have been hit hard, she thought, as she saw him staggering to his feet. She looked up and saw John with both hands clasped together. Like swinging a club, he swung his clasped fists again and battered Hammerschmidt so hard the thick man spun back to the floor. Blood was coming out of his left ear and dripping from his mouth.

But Hammerschmidt was like a machine. He got back up and yelled at John, "You gonna die, nigger lover!" Then he charged with his balding head down, like a bull, screaming the whole time, straight into John's stomach, which drove him against the wall. Hammerschmidt was obviously heavier and stronger than John, but the Australian kept a cool head. He walked away from the wall, doubled over trying to catch his wind.

Hammerschmidt stumbled backwards a few steps. He was catching his breath, too. For a moment, both men stood looking at each other, and everything seemed calm. For that one moment, Hammerschmidt could make a choice — to stop or to continue his crime. After a pause, Hammerschmidt could not let the reality and consequences of what he was doing set in; so he went berserk.

His face turned deep red as he released a horrifying yell so hard that the skin in the back of his throat could be heard scraping off. He charged John again, head down. This time, John, who was leaning back against the fireplace, sidestepped Hammerschmidt at the last instant. The madman smashed into the stone mantle head first at full force. He staggered backward from the sheer impact, then collapsed face first onto the floor.

John limped over to Miss Annabelle.

"Are you hurt badly anywhere?" he asked, looking at her closely for the first time. Seeing her swollen face made him so sad...and so angry he wanted to go beat Hammerschmidt to death. But he just hugged her, instead.

"I don't know," she was sobbing and desperately hugging back. "I think I'm hurt. I couldn't breathe."

"I'm taking you to the hospital," he said while picking her up like a baby.

"What about him?" she asked, still sobbing.

On the way out, Mr. Melbourne put Miss Annabelle on a chair and quickly phoned the police. He reported the crime and said they should send an ambulance to treat Hammerschmidt. Mr. Melbourne gave them the address and said he would leave the door unlocked. He stopped their questions and said they would need to get the details later because he was taking the victim to the hospital.

*

In the emergency room, while waiting to be seen by a doctor, two plainclothes policemen came to talk to Mr. Melbourne and Miss Annabelle.

"Hello, are you Miss Annabelle Barclay?" the taller man asked.

"Yes, I am," she said, holding an ice pack against the side of her head.

"And you, sir," the taller policeman said politely, "are you Mr. John Melbourne?"

"Yes, I'm John Melbourne," he answered.

"I'm Detective Steve McClennahan, and this is my partner, Detective Joe Sicolli, homicide," he said.

"Homicide?" John said, puzzled.

"Charles Hammerschmidt is dead," the shorter detective said.

Miss Annabelle and Mr. Melbourne looked at each other and held each other's hand.

"I explained what happened to the dispatcher," Mr. Melbourne said. "We had no idea he died from running into the wall."

"We just need to ask you some questions," the shorter Italian

212

detective said.

"Here?" Miss Annabelle asked, in obvious pain.

"Just a few, for now," the taller detective said.

Then Detective Sicolli said, "Please move over there, Mr. Melbourne." He was pointing to the adjoining waiting room. "We need to talk to you separately, and let's get Miss Annabelle's statement out of the way first before the doctor calls her in."

"Honey, are you OK to talk right now?" Mr. Melbourne said. "I'd better ask the doctor."

"Sweetheart, I'm OK to answer questions," she said. She stopped him from going to get a doctor. "I just want to get it over with."

"Okay, okay," he said, but he looked uneasy.

"I'm feeling much better now. I'll be fine," she said, "honestly."

They kissed, and Mr. Melbourne walked into the adjoining waiting room.

*

After nearly an hour wait they called Miss Annabelle and Mr. Melbourne in to be seen by a doctor. Mr. Melbourne said he was not seriously hurt and did not need to be looked over. He wanted to be with her, but the detectives asked him to stay with them. Miss Annabelle followed the nurse, and the homicide detectives continued questioning Mr. Melbourne in the waiting room.

The examination went well. Besides some bruising and a one-inch surface cut on the left side of Miss Annabelle's face, she was OK. But when she came back out to the waiting area just after midnight, the detectives were still there, still talking with John.

When John saw her come out, he nearly jumped out of his chair and rushed over to her. She told him everything was fine, which removed the anxieties that had been growing in him for the past forty-five minutes. "But why are they still here?" she asked.

"Excuse me, ma'am," Detective McClennahan said. "I

apologize for the inconvenience, but you both must come with us to the station."

"Why?" she asked bluntly.

"A man was found dead in your house tonight. Approximately four hours before he died, you sat in a tumultuous school board meeting over which he presided. In the previous meeting less than a month before, witnesses say he upset you so much you had to run out. We also have witnesses saying that after that meeting, John Melbourne threatened Mr. Hammerschmidt."

Miss Annabelle looked at John. "I was angry," he said. "I told him he was going to pay for this. ...Of course, how was I to know all this would happen?"

"But he ATTACKED me," Miss Annabelle said, in shock at the implications. "He tried to rape me and might've killed me if John hadn't shown up! What is this? We're *the victims* here!"

"Ma'am, we're not arresting you," Detective Sicolli said reassuringly, then added firmly, "We just need to get more information."

*

Things did not go well at the station. Both a motive and what could be construed as a life threat gave the police too much probable cause not to consider Mr. Melbourne and Miss Annabelle suspects.

They were arrested and held overnight in separate holding cells. They appeared the next day before a magistrate. Bruce Salinski represented them. He did a good job derailing the theory that Mr. Melbourne and Miss Annabelle conspired to kill Hammerschmidt.

"If that were a plausible possibility, why was Mr. Hammerschmidt in Miss Annabelle's house? Why would he have come there? He wouldn't. He was there for a dark agenda. He'd been drinking at the town's pub before he showed up. My client was attacked by this man."

Of course, the District Attorney argued that Hammerschmidt had his way in the school board meeting earlier in the evening and had no reason to attack her.

Salinski countered that Hammerschmidt was attacking Miss Annabelle sexually, which could be set off by a major confrontation as occurred earlier that day.

In the end, the judge set bail at $100,000 each and ordered them to turn in their passports. Salinski began preparing for trial.

CHAPTER
EIGHTEEN

The news and photos of Hammerschmidt's gruesome death covered the front page of Thursday's morning paper. By the time school started, all twelve students knew what had happened. They sat in silence, staring at the substitute teacher, frightened for their beloved teacher.

*

The school board members convened for an emergency meeting the day after Hammerschmidt's death. They all agreed that the logical course of action would be to remove Miss Annabelle from teaching the rest of the year, irregardless of her yet-to-be-determined guilt or innocence on her child molestation case or her role in Hammerschmidt's death. Her twelve students could be split among the other third-grade teachers for the final nine weeks of school.

That was the obvious course of action to handle this bizarre situation...several of the school board members were moved deeply by the children's essays about their teacher. Never had those adults seen such love expressed for a teacher. Several of those school board members admitted in the meeting that they were moved to tears while reading the essays the night before.

Miss Annabelle was more than a teacher to these children...she was a hero and a mother. Although the school board members knew the logical thing to do, the easy thing to do, the question was asked, "Is there another way?"

*

By Friday morning, it was the rumor of upstate New York: a beautiful woman and her foreign lover colluded to take revenge on a wholesome school board superintendent who had stopped the nymph from her sexual yearnings for her students. The beautiful siren lured the helpless school board superintendent to her home and to his death, the rumor went. She and her foreign lover ambushed the school board superintendent and bludgeoned him nearly to death. Then, they left him to die alone.

The rumors, media, accusations were just too much. The school board, with Ms. Minner now the acting superintendent, ruled on Monday against Miss Annabelle in the child molestation case. Of course, Miss Annabelle being a murder suspect overwhelmed their decision. Now she would never teach again.

Ms. Minner got what she wanted. But several of the school board members, still deeply moved by the children's essays, felt horrible about their ruling. Those members, in a strange move, fought with Ms. Minner to give the students and their parents the choice to keep Miss Annabelle as their teacher for the final eight-and-a-half weeks left of school. Those school board members who still had the innocent child of the past within them, knew that this move would forever mean so much to the children and would be a precious gift to Miss Annabelle. These adults knew their child molestation ruling was wrong, but to keep Miss Annabelle and her students together...that would be justice.

The school board drafted a letter that same day and sent it home on Tuesday with Miss Annabelle's students to their parents. The letter explained the permanent dismissal of Miss Annabelle based on the child molestation ruling. The letter also explained the bizarre string of events, climaxing in Hammerschmidt's death, for which Miss Annabelle had been indicted as a suspect and would stand trial this coming summer. Each parent was given the option to have his or her child switched to another teacher...or, "because of the rare personal and academic success of this student/teacher combination, parents may elect to have their child finish out the year with Miss Annabelle." Of course, Ms. Minner figured all parents would want their children moved to another class, and Miss Annabelle's year would be effectively over.

In a stunning display of belief in Miss Annabelle's innocence, all parents, under great pressure from their children, let their children stay in Miss Annabelle's class. That totally unexpected reaction shocked Ms. Minner and some members of the school board. But that unanimous decision did not surprise the school board members who fought for this option.

*

Mr. Melbourne's father posted bail for his son and Miss Annabelle. The school board assigned a substitute to finish the school year teaching Mr. Melbourne's students.

Thursday morning, however, one very long week and one day after her darkest day, Miss Annabelle re-entered the rational world again. Miss Annabelle looked at her twelve little unsung heroes and knew they had fought hard to remain here. Who knows what horrible things they heard about me, she thought. Yet, here they sit, all twelve. ...Miss Annabelle could feel how much these little ones loved her. And, oh how she loved them! The pure love all around her and in her nearly overwhelmed her.

"I want to thank you," Miss Annabelle began, "for honestly seeing through the illusions that surround me. Each and every one of you are using *your own* thinking. I know it's not easy, but you're struggling to see past other people's thinking to *what is*. I'll reward you with the best two months of the whole year."

Miss Annabelle really meant that, for now she could get very focused. She knew where things stood. After this school year, she would not teach again, but now it was certain that she would have until the end of the school year with her students. She felt enormous relief and peace. At the same time, she felt sadness that she would be kept out of their futures and would not see their development in the years to come.

"May I say something?" Ian asked, making Miss Annabelle

realize she had drifted off momentarily in her thoughts.

"Yes, Ian," she said, smiling.

"You're a genius, Miss Annabelle. No, I really mean it. You've seen our test scores. Nattie was the highest, and most of us beat the sixth graders. Talk about values — look at what you're doing for us." Ian was very serious, and his voice was shaking because it meant a lot to him to be able to express this to his teacher. "So when I heard what happened last week, I knew it wasn't true — not like I heard about it. I asked my dad what Hammerschmidt did for a living. He said he was a tax collector. I read the paper. It said he was a *tough* tax collector. I thought, 'What values has he brought to people?' You know, I couldn't think of anything. Then I realized what makes the world nice — it's geniuses like you who bring lots of values to people. And good people who devote their whole lives to bringing values to others cannot turn around and do bad things like those rumors say about you. So when my mom and dad read the letter to me, I told them nothing in the world can get me to leave your class, not even Hammerschmidt's death. *Nothing* could stop me from being right here with you!"

Miss Annabelle was so moved she could not manage to say more than, "Thank you, Ian, from the bottom of my heart." But the children could see how deeply Ian's explanation affected her.

Next, Teddy talked. Then Sally. Then Cathy. Then Jeremiah. ...Miss Annabelle let them talk, all twelve of them, as long as they wanted, all along thinking how glad she was to have all this on tape to keep as her fond memories in the years ahead.

*

Salinski called Miss Annabelle to tell her that the earliest the trial would happen was mid-summer, which pleased her. She wanted to devote herself to her students the next two months with few distractions.

Knowing she had just eight weeks left brought on the nostalgia. She felt as if she had shared a lifetime with her students. She decided to offer a voluntary hour after school each day for open discussion. She saw it as a way, for those who wanted to attend, to socialize...yet socialize through good discussions. The extra hour meant that those who stayed would have to arrange rides from school or take a long walk home since they would miss their school bus. Miss Annabelle wanted to give them all rides home, but her lawyer told her she could not do that, for the school had a faculty member in the classroom at all times, and the ride home would give Ms. Minner grounds to terminate Miss Annabelle *before* the end of the school year.

In yet another testimony to Miss Annabelle, all twelve students attended the extra discussion hour. The discussions were, in fact, so interesting and so full of puzzle-building neothinking in action, Miss Annabelle started to record them. She could see the seeds of greatness being planted during these discussion sessions.

As Miss Annabelle had hoped, the class grew closer and closer from the discussion hour. Most of them rode home together in car pools. During these final weeks, the twelve children were discovering a whole new dimension to friendship. Together, they were discovering who they were meant to be.

Together, they were in another world never seen here on Earth, a fully honest world. A world of pure love. A world with powerful meaning and drive. The motivation in Miss Annabelle's class broke new dimensions in schooling. They shared a love for life that would, twenty-seven years later, bring these Neothinkers together once again to lead the greatest project ever endeavored by mankind.

*

As a consequence of their neothinking, several of her students were getting involved in a hobby, business, experiment, or research of some kind in a major way. Their projects brought exciting discussions to the discussion hour, which helped generate ideas that benefited those projects. Also, the discussion hour brought the little Neothinkers positive reflections and peer interest in their projects. They were soul mates, independently blazing ahead on their own success puzzles in life, yet coming together and sharing and admiring each others' accomplishments.

Teddy, at nine years old, ran a million-dollar company now.

He was able to handle it through revolutionary new time-management and business concepts. He managed his busy schedule through the mini-day schedule where he scheduled his *physical movements* to time slots instead of scheduling his tasks to time slots as in the traditional schedule. He explained that by doing this, he set up his schedule like a production line, driving through tasks like a rivet man driving through rivet after rivet on the assembly line.

"The traditional schedule that attaches tasks to time is like the old way of building cars at the turn of the century," he said in the discussion hour. "They used to bring over and put the seat in, then they would change all their tools to put the steering wheel in. Then they'd have lunch. It'd take all day to put together one car that way. When Henry Ford completely changed production from doing whole tasks to doing simple movements with the production line, no one wasted time walking around or changing tools. Soon, the same factories were putting out a hundred cars a day!

"I could never do what I'm doing now without breaking my work day into physical movements. Like the work stations on an assembly line, I start and end each mini-day right on the time allotted. I can get more done in an hour than in a whole day the other way I used to work.

"Also, I discovered the mini-company. Setting up those in-house entrepreneurs, as I told you before, makes others drive their portions of the business with entrepreneurial energy. I couldn't have grown to this level of revenues any other way.

"Miss Annabelle's talk with my dad and me at the beginning of the school year always stayed with me. That talk, and being taught in class how to seek common denominators to get down to the essence of things, let me spot the crucial common denominators in business: For example, I could see, after I read a book on Henry Ford, that the common denominator behind mass production was scheduling work by the physical movements and *not* by tasks, sending production through a major leap. Why not set up *my* production that way, I eventually realized, setting up my mini-day schedule, which sent my production through a major leap. And let's not forget, the common denominator behind *every* business is making money. Why not set up *every job* that way, I eventually realized, setting up my mini-companies."

Teddy always seemed to be on the go, but he attended *every* discussion hour those last two months. He, along with the other students, inherently knew this gathering was something special, something they would never have again. The children and their teacher cherished *the preciousness* of this time together.

*

Cathy, becoming more beautiful by the day, always sat next to Teddy. She liked him a lot and loved to hear his stories about his business. She, too, talked openly now. Three weeks into the discussion period, she revealed the most unique diet Miss Annabelle had ever heard about. Cathy figured it out on her own — and it worked!

"The idea is very simple, and that's why it works so well," Cathy said proudly. "I always had cravings like my mom, my dad, and my sisters. I'd try, on my own, to diet. But the cravings always won in the end. My mom always has a book or article around the house on some diet she is trying. Through all the fancy diets, though, I knew the essence of what would cure my weight problem was: get rid of my *cravings*. If those went away, I'd be slim and beautiful. But I had no control over my cravings. They could hit me at any time and in many different ways. I fought them, but the cravings always won out in the end. Dieting just made it worse."

Then Cathy looked down, perhaps a little embarrassed, and said, "Of course, I noticed how beautiful Miss Annabelle was the first day of class. And when she sat next to me at lunch that one day and hugged me...well, I really liked it. No one ever noticed me before. And that made me want to become like her. ...So I watched how she ate, every day. I noticed she always got the same thing — a turkey sandwich. And she always ate the same amount and never bothered with the dessert or roll. I used to think, doesn't she get bored with the same food every day? But I wanted to be like her, so I tried it too. Every day, I'd get the turkey sandwich. And after about three weeks, something weird happened: I found myself *craving* that hot turkey sandwich! I no longer craved all those other items sitting on the lunch line...for the first time, I only craved my hot turkey sandwich! That's when I realized I might have discovered the golden key to curing my weight problem, because I realized I might be able to *control* my cravings! Instead of having dozens of cravings every day, maybe I could have just three or four."

"Cool," Teddy said, a whole step ahead of the rest of the class, "What a great breakthrough."

"Thank you," Cathy said, looking up and blushing. "So, I started eating the same breakfast and the same dinner too. I also picked out an evening snack and had the same snack each evening. My mom yelled at me at first, but I didn't care. Maybe I could help her, too, I used to think. Sure enough, in about three weeks, I *craved* those breakfast and dinner foods too. In turn, the dozens of other cravings I fought against every day were gone! That's because I already had my craving in place. What's more, my four cravings now actually occurred like clockwork at their times of the day. For the first time in my life, I had control."

"Wow," Natasha said, thoroughly absorbed in Cathy's story.

"Right away, I started losing weight. I lost about eleven pounds because I no longer snacked. Then, I stopped losing. Now I knew I had to do the dreaded thing: eat less food. Boy, was I in for a surprise! When I cut my evening snack in half, I still just craved the same thing...my strawberries and whipped cream. But because it was just *one* craving and not fifteen or more, it was *easy* to handle and overcome. And when I had my strawberries and cream, although half the amount, I still serviced my craving. It was really easy. I cut down my dinner the same way. It was easy to do. And that is how I got to where I am today!"

"You're beautiful, Cathy," Teddy said.

"I admire you for what you've done," Natasha said.

"Yeah, me too!" Sally said.

Cathy turned red. Miss Annabelle walked over and said, "I knew you would be slim and beautiful someday, darling. I'm very proud of you."

Cathy had never been so happy. She had conquered the nemesis in her life, an enemy that had destroyed many branches of her family tree in the past. For weeks to come, she replayed in her head those compliments given to her today. The one compliment she heard over and over in her head was Teddy telling her not that she looked beautiful, but that she *was* beautiful.

Miss Annabelle realized the creation of the discussion hour late in the school year was crucial. She saw the seeds of greatness begin to grow. This was a way for her students to start articulating and crystallizing their beginnings. Miss Annabelle encouraged Cathy to write her complete diet onto paper. Teddy said he could probably sell the diet through his business!

When Teddy made that comment to Cathy, something wonderful happened in Alan's mind. He was passionately interested in new technological breakthroughs. He could not seem to read enough about technology. His father got him his own subscription to a magazine called *Tomorrow*. Alan would scour the magazine to get a glimpse of new technologies of any kind. He knew his dad paid good money for his subscription. ...Sitting in this discussion, he thought, "Just as I love to read about new technologies, a lot of people out there would love to read about Cathy's new diet...or about Teddy's new business ideas...or about Ian's new theories."

Alan loved to read, and he enjoyed writing, too. The idea of selling valuable information excited him.

"Who else has got a breakthrough — something really different like Cathy?" he said out loud.

"I might," Natasha answered. "Mine has to do with love."

"Oh yeah?" Cathy said, eyes wide and smiling.

"Well, my mom and dad never seemed to get along. They even went to counseling, and they did two of those retreats together. But they always seemed to get back into arguing. Therapy didn't help much. I used to avoid them when they argued, but one morning over breakfast, I started to listen to them. I listened to every argument for the next couple weeks. It always seemed that when they started to get agitated, Mom would say some comment that began with, 'Maybe if you were around a little more...'. Every time, this would make my dad furious, and the argument would quickly escalate. My dad is a very successful general contractor. He designs and builds expensive custom homes. I know he takes enormous pride in his work. His work is his accomplishment in life, and each home is like his personal trophy. He works hard to do such great work, *and* he works hard so our family can live in one of those beautiful homes. He's also saving money so my brother, sisters, and I can all go to college. So, I talked to my mom. I think she was worried that my dad would meet another woman like her father did when he left her mother. But I told her how much dad's creations meant to him...they were a part of him; I know this because he always takes me to every new house he's building, and he walks me through every room and tells me why it's that way. He gets really excited, and I used to wonder why mom wasn't with us. Each custom home he's created and built was like a part of him, all his creations that together make up the whole man. I explained this to my mom. I told her she needs to become interested instead of antagonized by dad's creations. 'Go with him and let him get excited and show you, too,' I told her. 'Compliment him and admire his work — it's beautiful!' I told her. 'Get behind his life's work, not against it.' As the bait, I told her the closeness would make him fall in love with her again. So, she did exactly what I suggested. Now, mom spends a lot more time with him, going around with him in the day from site to site. They even discuss ideas and look at blueprints together in the evenings. They're both so happy now. I even see them kissing and hugging now, which I could not remember ever seeing before. And they laugh together. I love their laughter. ...I don't know, I just knew it would work if Mom could get into his accomplishments. And Dad gets so inspired now by my mom. It's beautiful."

"Wow, that's sweet," Sally said. "They've discovered what my mom and I call *the celebration*."

"I wish my parents were like yours," Cathy said.

"Man, that's really good, Nattie," Alan said. "Do you think you could write down the reasons why you think it worked so well for your mom and dad?"

"I think so," Natasha answered.

"Great! Who else has something unique like Nattie and

Cathy...and Teddy?"

Miss Annabelle looked at Alan curiously. He was really pumped up. What idea does he have? she wondered.

"I've got a lot of ideas on physics and metaphysics," Ian said.

"Oh, yeah...I love your ideas," Alan said, smiling wide. "Can you write a paper on your theory?"

Ian nodded.

"I've been getting into politics and why it's not working," Danny said. "I can surely write a paper about it."

"I go to the library and do a lot of research on cancer and health with my mom," Sally said. "I already have lots of research notes."

"I don't like what I hear at church. I've come up with some new ideas, some of them based on Miss Annabelle and Ian's ideas," Jeremiah said.

"Oh, I've got some different approaches to music I've been experimenting with," Reggie said.

Alan looked around the room at everybody. His eyes were big. He was about to burst with a big idea, but he remained calm and calculating and said, "During these discussion periods, I've heard some of the most innovative ideas I've ever heard or read about. You know, I love to read about new developments in technology. But I love *anything* new that goes beyond what exists now...to the next level. These things you all talk about like Teddy's business techniques, Cathy's diet, Nattie's love advice, Ian's cosmos, Reggie's music, Jeremiah's religion, Sally's medical ideas, Danny's politics...these are fantastic advancements of knowledge!"

Miss Annabelle could not have said it better herself.

"What," continued Alan, "should we do about that? I say we should get this knowledge down on paper and *spread it* to hundreds or thousands of people. Let *your* special knowledge spread to many others. Nattie, what if you could save a thousand marriages?"

"Wouldn't that be cool!" she answered.

"Cathy, what if you helped thousands of people get slim and happy like you?" he said, on a roll.

"Yeah, I'd love that!" she said. She also loved being officially considered *slim* now.

226

"And you, Danny...what if your political ideas started to get others interested out there?"

"Awesome," Danny said, throwing an air high-five across the room to Alan's reciprocating air high-five.

Now the kids were pumped up, too. Miss Annabelle was moved by Alan's charisma and his ability to create a big idea.

"Think about it — hundreds of people seeing our breakthroughs," Alan rolled on. "I want to put together a booklet called *Breakthrough News: Fresh Money, Power, Love, and Health Ideas!* Teddy, you're the businessman. You said you could sell Cathy's diet...how about a whole information package covering all these breakthroughs?"

"You're a genius, Alan. I could sell a lot of those — I know it. Are you kidding, with a title like that...coming from kids? The curiosity will be fantastic. When can this be done?"

"Let's set a deadline," Alan said. "We've still got five weeks of school left. Let's get *Breakthrough News* finished in three weeks. That gives us two weeks to work on it together in the discussion hour with Miss Annabelle before I get the final copy printed for you and your salesmen."

"Deal!" Teddy yelled.

The other kids applauded and cheered. As it would turn out, *Breakthrough News* would be the legacy of the puzzle-building Neothink mentality Miss Annabelle achieved with her third graders. Twenty seven years later, the seeds of their greatness could be found in this historic publication.

*

All year, Miss Annabelle had three main objectives: 1) teach the children fundamental academics in an integrated conceptual fashion as opposed to a disintegrated perceptual fashion as did most educators. Instead of simply teaching the dates and events in history, she tied each historic event back to the larger concept of freedom versus tyranny, which shaped history and its events. That integrated, conceptual thinking, integrating endless, scattered events (i.e., percepts) to larger, timeless common denominators (i.e., concepts), enabled her students to see deeper than others — to the deeper logic behind events. 2) Her second main goal was to prompt her students' minds into integrated thinking and onto puzzle-building Neothink. 3) Her third goal was to inject supreme love for life into the hearts and souls of her students. She did this by bringing them into the exhilarating life of value creation, happiness, and love during their special year together. She introduced them to the way they could feel and live for the rest of their lives. By feeling supreme love for life, they emotionally knew their lives — conscious lives — were the supreme value in the Universe. Their lives were wonderfully indispensable. ...She wanted her children to leave her class superbly educated, with Neothink in their minds and supreme love for life in their hearts.

She had spent seven months developing their minds. Now, over the last two months, they had become self-perpetuating integrated thinkers or *self-leaders* as Mr. Melbourne called them. With their ability to efficiently see through appearances to the essence of things — to *what is* — in this world of many illusions, they were competent to make their own decisions, be their own authorities, and lead themselves through life. They would not need "higher" authorities or leaders telling them how to think or live.

The final two months became a rewarding time for Miss Annabelle as she watched her beloved students' minds take off with Neothink as they began building their success puzzles in life. Miss Annabelle helped them integrate and coordinate their launching pad — their *Breakthrough News*. During the final five weeks, their discussion group resembled a publishing house as they discussed, developed, read and edited their breakthroughs. Here, at nine years old, these children experienced the meaning of life: the happiness that comes from creating important values that benefit society.

"Oh, what a feeling..." Alan muttered two weeks before the end of the school year as he handed out the first draft to his soul mates.

CHAPTER
NINETEEN

Less than two weeks before the last day of school, John Melbourne stopped by Duncan Elementary in the evening after the children had gone home. He found Jessie in the halls, and they walked into Jessie's little janitor's "office", closing the door behind them.

"In two weeks," John said, "the single most important part of Annabelle's life ends, perhaps forever. It's going to be rough for her, especially with the added pressure of this trial."

"I know," Jessie said. "I feel so rotten about all this. How do you think she's going to be?"

"I don't know. Teaching was everything to her."

"Do you ever think about just getting away from all this — just you and her?" Jessie asked.

"I may not have much of a choice."

"What do you mean, John?"

"We'll have to see what happens in the trial. I'm just an alien, you know. If I'm convicted of a felony, they'll take away my green card."

Neither Jessie nor Angie ever thought about that. Jessie was quiet and sad.

"That's why I'm looking toward you and Angie to be there for her if I'm not. I know you will be; I just wanted you to know I'm not a citizen. I don't know what could happen. I haven't told Anna yet; she's just got too much to think about, so I probably won't say anything. I can't change my status now."

"I understand," Jessie said, sadly. He stood up and shook John's hand. "If you get through this trial OK, I hope we get to know each other a lot more."

"We will, Jessie," John said, putting his free hand on Jessie's shoulder.

*

The school days were counting down. The days were warm and long. Early June was a beautiful time of year in upstate New York. Just four days to go, and Miss Annabelle took her class on an all-day picnic/hiking/fishing expedition in the country. Many years later, this outing would still be a lasting memory in all twelve students and in Miss Annabelle herself, not because of any one outstanding event that day, but because of the overall quality of feelings these thirteen people shared. This happy feeling together is how life should always be, yet they inherently sensed *the preciousness* of that one day.

The children still liked to fill in their Life Charts, and they had come to realize that life was *not* permanent. Their lives were but their string of experiences. And the overall quality of those experiences, in the end, would rate the quality of their lives. The children sensed that this day was one of those special experiences that raised the overall quality of their lives.

They told serious and funny stories during their picnic, they reminisced, played games, hiked, learned about the land, admired their final printed *Breakthrough News*, and fished. Although the school's observer was present, she happened to be the same decent lady who never saw anything to report. Miss Annabelle and the kids laughed like they had never laughed before. An onlooker would have said their laughter sounded like an ensemble of happiness.

During these past two months, it seemed whenever these twelve students and their teacher got together, especially during the discussion period, they were always on the verge of some breakthrough. The atmosphere seemed full of creativity at the picnic. The kids were all sitting or lying on the picnic blankets after a long day out in the country when Mr. Melbourne showed up by surprise at 4:00. He lay down on a blanket next to Miss Annabelle and listened to the third graders.

After hearing some of their creative talk, Mr. Melbourne raised his eyebrows and nodded. He said something he'd been storing up for weeks: "You kids are going to be more successful than any group of children I've ever faced. I know that, and I've been planning to tell you that for some time now." He looked around at the little geniuses and thought, I've never felt such camaraderie with *anyone* as I do with these *children* and their teacher.

He smiled at their potential and continued, "The *cause* of success and happiness comes from something very deep within. Some people just *seem* to be born with it, but that special something can be identified and developed. You kids are developing that special something. Everyone can. In fact, people around you — maybe your brothers and sisters or parents — might sort of 'catch' that special something from you.

"That elusive, something special that super successful people have is a deep-rooted *motivational drive*. That deep-rooted motivational drive that *appears* to be inborn keeps pushing them forward for all their lives. As a result, they steadily rise above the multitudes around them who do not have that rare, seemingly inborn drive.

"The key here, once we've identified the most fundamental cause of success, is to understand *what causes* that cause of success, that deep-rooted motivational drive. Once we do that, then we realize the deep motivational drive to success and happiness is *not* something we are either luckily born with or not. Then, we realize we can acquire it and control it. We can turn it on! In other words, we — anyone — can control his or her life and make it successful and happy!"

Unable to stand the suspense, Teddy said, "What causes that deep motivational drive?"

"Oh, I think you know, Teddy," Mr. Melbourne said, smiling.

Teddy just looked at him, blinking without a clue.

"Okay, tell me how you felt when you put together the division of essence, which took your business to the next level?"

"Wow, I felt excited. I almost couldn't get to sleep because I was so excited. Man, I was..."

"Motivated?" Mr. Melbourne queried.

A smile broke open on Teddy's face. "Yeah," he said. "I got really motivated."

The other kids broke into the same contagious smile.

"Your excitement over your accomplishment fired up your deep motivation, which in turn drove you into further accomplishments, which in turn fueled your motivation...and so on like a cylinder driving the engine. That excitement, by the way, is the same thrill for life that toddlers experience. Toddlers are also in that upward spiral of happiness as they get extremely excited over their accomplishments in learning to talk and becoming conscious, for example. That's why they learn to talk and become conscious beings so rapidly, in about a year, from two to three. But around six or seven years old, their geometric learning curves slow way down to gradual learning curves. Their aggressive upward spiral is increasingly broken by the so-called 'normal' world around them. You children know what I mean — the 'normal' world around you cannot relate to what you're like. A quick read through your awesome *Breakthrough News* demonstrates that!"

The children looked around at each other with huge smiles. They were very, very proud of their booklet.

"Now, you do feel different from other nine-year-olds, right?" Mr. Melbourne asked.

"Right...yes." the kids echoed back.

"I said your deep motivational drives work sort of like a cylinder engine. Now, the world's most important question is: how do people *start* their engines? If they only knew how to *start* their engines, they could drive themselves into success and happiness."

Ian, insatiable for knowledge, jumped in and said, "What is it? What's the secret?"

"You started your engine," Mr. Melbourne replied. "Now, think back to the beginning of the year. Were you different then, different than now?"

Conceiving the Superpuzzle

Ian paused. He was recalling how he used to be; a look of shock came over his face. "I used to be what we're calling 'normal'. I mean, I had no drive at all and never thought about things like I do now."

"So, tell us how you started your engine. What happened?" Mr. Melbourne asked him.

Ian thought about it for awhile. Then he smiled slowly and said, "It was when I started putting together thoughts about the Universe. I started sensing that maybe I was seeing something not seen before…"

"Stop right there," Mr. Melbourne said, putting up his hand in the stop position. "To get to that point where you started seeing a puzzle-picture never seen before, you had to start snapping together the puzzle pieces. You started integrating together facts and concepts as you learned them…until a new puzzle-picture started forming."

"Yes!" Ian confirmed. "That's *exactly* what happened."

"Mr. Melbourne," Teddy said with a distant look on his face as if he were recalling a different place and time, "I think that's what happened to me, too. I was learning every day, just a little bit at a time, it seemed. Then one day, it all just seemed to come together into this division of essence."

Mr. Melbourne looked around at the twelve attentive nine-year-olds and said, "Toddlers naturally enjoy the thrill for life and its deep motivational drive. All others have to get it back. And as Ian and Teddy demonstrated, people get it back when they discover integrated thinking."

"Why?" Ian asked.

"Because," Mr. Melbourne answered, "the human mind was designed for dynamic integrated thinking, not static routine thinking. People get in routine ruts because their integrated thinking and motivational drives — their upward spirals — got disintegrated by the world around them dominated with resignation and routine or specialized thinking. It all goes back to our mind of the past that was a follower and not a self-leader like our mind of the future, which I explain in my book. The reason integrated thinking brings back your motivational drive is that it opens up your future and removes stagnation — the way human beings are supposed to live their lives. Through

233

integrated thinking and only through integrated thinking, the puzzle pieces of knowledge start coming together to build a puzzle-picture, which, as Teddy and Ian learned, is when the motivation kicks in."

"How do my parents get into this positive spiral to success?" Bobby asked.

"They need to start their engines of motivation by learning how to do integrated thinking as you have done. They need to start small at work or on a goal. Here's exactly what they need to do: they must start integrating percepts into concepts at work. By doing this, they'll make little breakthroughs that'll be potent contributions to the company. This is how the engine of motivation always starts in adults...this is how *anyone* can get back the drive to success."

"What are percepts and concepts?" Reggie asked.

"Percepts are what your five senses perceive — what you see, hear, feel, taste, or smell. You hear thunder; you look up and see lightning and dark clouds in the Eastern sky; you feel a gust of wind against your face followed by a steady wind coming from the direction of those dark clouds. Pulling together those three percepts — sound, sight, feel — you can jump to the concept that a storm is coming. Of course, that is the most simple example of forming a concept. But all concepts come from percepts, and that's where adults need to start, and a good place to start is at work. They must observe recurring problems, for example, and then through their perceptual observations, jump to concepts that will *solve* those problems."

"I think I know what you're saying," Teddy said. "I saw my numbers drop way down with my sellers; I could hear the lack of enthusiasm in their voices; I could really feel my frustration with them...and from pulling together those percepts letting me know I had a problem and from really thinking hard about it, I jumped to the whole new concept of setting up my sellers as their own entrepreneurs on performance pay, as little companies within my company."

"There's an example of observing percepts to discover a powerful concept that solved a serious problem," Mr. Melbourne said as Teddy nodded. "*That's* integrated thinking, Teddy. ...Now, you're taking your *concepts* and snapping them together into a *puzzle*. This is where adults will advance to soon enough: snapping together concepts into growing success puzzles. Eventually, never-before-seen puzzle-pictures will form such as Teddy's division of essence and Ian's God-Man Universe."

"That's right," Teddy said, "I did snap together several big concepts like my mini-companies instead of routine-rut jobs, mini-days instead of traditional schedules, power-thinking instead of no thinking, replicating instead of delegating, tracking reports instead of letting go of details, essence meetings to cover my every expectation from my entrepreneurial employees. By snapping together those concepts one by one, I built my success puzzle piece by piece. Then the new puzzle-picture formed — the division-of-essence company structure, outperforming the traditional division-of-labor structure."

"Yeah," Ian said, "I kind of went through a similar step-by-step, concept-by-concept process to build my picture of the eternal universe controlled by immortal conscious minds."

"Both of you have major breakthroughs, one in business and one in physics," Mr. Melbourne said. "Those are what Miss Annabelle and I call *Neothink* breakthroughs that take your fields of knowledge to the next level. Neothink happened by snapping together your success puzzles to reveal your new pictures of future business and physics. But it all started with pulling together percepts to jump to concepts. That is what adults must do first. That restarts their engines of deep motivational drive. In time, they too will snap together concepts into success puzzles and eventually go to the next level through Neothink."

Miss Annabelle sat up and put her arm around Mr. Melbourne and said lovingly, "You've just described the process for tens of millions of *adults* to break out of their stagnation-traps to live the lives they've always dreamed of." She admired her lover and expressed that she wished she had brought the tape recorder to have captured this immense value.

"Don't worry about that," he said. "It's all in my book, and more."

The evening shadows grew longer and the temperature dropped a few degrees. This group of people reluctantly made their way back to the small school bus. They really loved their

world together, but now they had to make their way back into
the 'normal' world around them.

CHAPTER
TWENTY

"It seems just like yesterday," Miss Annabelle said gently as she sat alone in her classroom an hour before school would start. Today was the last day of school, and Miss Annabelle felt as if she had *just begun* spending time with these twelve children whom she loved. It seemed like just *a couple of weeks ago* she was singing *The Impossible Dream* to twelve curious onlookers. She started remembering back over the school year, week by week, and she felt overwhelming nostalgia. She did not want it to end. Her nostalgia was amplified because she would not be back. If she were here to watch them develop and have contact with them, she would feel different.

Yet, Miss Annabelle always turned the negatives in her life around into positives, and she had a plan. Today, she said to herself, I will start...

Her thoughts were interrupted. With still a half hour before school was to start, Sally came through the door. Rico was right behind her.

"Good morning, you two," Miss Annabelle said, smiling.

"Are you going to teach summer school?" Rico asked, sounding dejected. Sally nodded her confirmation of the same question, biting her bottom lip.

Miss Annabelle was touched by their feelings for her. "This

will *not* be good-bye," she said cheerfully. Immediately Rico and Sally smiled. Soon, they were joined by their ten classmates.

As Miss Annabelle looked over her classroom, she was remembering when she did this the first day of school. How far they've come, she thought.

Today, her students looked different from the other students in Duncan Elementary. Parties and laughter filled the other classrooms, and the faces of other students beamed with excitement for summer vacation. But this classroom was different. The air was somber, and the students looked sad.

"Can I fix those long faces?" Miss Annabelle asked them.

"Miss Annabelle," Alan burst, "our parents let you down! They *know* you're innocent. They *know* you're the reason for our high test scores. They *know* you're why we're doing things we're really proud of. But they didn't complain to the school. If our parents didn't complain, then who would? Who could save you?"

Miss Annabelle knew Alan was right. So did the other students. Before she could talk, however, Reggie spoke, "My mom likes you, I know that. But she's scared to stand up to the authorities, even after I begged her to. She let me come back to finish the year with you; she was able to see through to *what is* enough to know the great value you are to me, but in the end she would not stand up for you. Damn it, that makes me so mad. It's like she's helpless to act on her own mind. She let the minds of others — people like Ms. Minner and that politician who died — make her decision for her!"

Miss Annabelle saw how upset Reggie was. The right course of action seemed so painfully obvious to him and to the other students, she realized, because their minds worked completely on their own now. Their passion for what so obviously was right, and their frustrations with their parents were wonderful signs that these nine-year-olds now lived in the world of *what is*. Therefore, as Miss Annabelle had set out the year to do, they now had *the power*.

Reggie's strong words expressed what others in the class wanted to say. Again, before Miss Annabelle could talk, someone beat her to it. She realized the children needed to express themselves and vent their frustrations.

"Most of our parents are good people," Danny said directly to Reggie, "and they all have the facts to see through the illusions. But, good as they are, they don't stop the firing of Miss Annabelle. They default at the deepest level of honesty and turn their power over to authorities."

Again, Miss Annabelle knew he was right. She knew that the reason their parents were afraid to act on their own authority stemmed from their lifelong inability to effectively see through to the essence of things — to *what is*. She knew that many things caused their inefficiency at seeing and acting on reality. And by not being effective at seeing reality, they turned over their decisions to the so-called "experts" or "authorities" who, in turn, obscured reality and manipulated the good people for selfish ends, just as Hammerschmidt and Minner did. Those "authorities" were everywhere, including politicians, clergymen, the media, the Establishment. Good people, she thought, still had to look outside their own minds for guidance. But not her students. She knew now, they saw through appearances to *what is* so efficiently that they could never accept being told how to think or act. And that was what bothered them so about their parents accepting the school firing their innocent and beloved teacher.

"Unlike you, your parents for the most part do not see reality efficiently enough to be their own authorities. So, in the end, they turn their authority over to the leaders," Miss Annabelle explained. "You're equipped to efficiently see and integrate reality, so you don't turn over your decision making to the so-called authorities. Most people, including your own parents, are not able to be their own authorities all the time, like you. However, two parents did call and fight for me — Sally's mom did and Teddy's dad."

The twelve students clapped, and Sally and Teddy grinned from ear to ear, feeling very proud of their special parents.

"As you know," Miss Annabelle continued, "in today's world *what is best* oftentimes is not what *appears to be* best. When I started here, I was told that my job was to 'teach the children how to integrate effectively into society'. That sounded good, like the best thing to do. But, this being the year of my own awakening, I learned to look beyond appearances to what teaching

239

really is: 'teach the children how to someday build magnificent values that a lot of people want to buy'. Now, look at you...you have *already* begun to experience the real excitement of life — creating values like your *Breakthrough News* masterpiece. You feel the excitement and happiness inside and have discovered the meaning of life. Remember our camping trip? I told you the meaning of life was the happiness you would feel by making values for society. And all of you will someday become wealthy from selling your competitive values. Teddy already is becoming wealthy, which makes me so proud."

She stopped to take a moment to absorb those beautiful faces beaming back at her. During this memory, Bobby raised his hand.

"Yes, dear?" she said.

"Can I request something?" he asked.

"Sure, Bobby."

"Okay," Bobby said, then looked at Teddy. "I was wondering if Teddy could tell us how our parents can break out of their stagnant traps?" Bobby loved his parents and knew they wanted more out of life.

"Sure, I can," Teddy said.

Bobby smiled gratefully and asked, "Miss Annabelle, could you record Teddy?"

"I'd love to," she said, taking the audiocassette over to Teddy's desk and pushing the record button.

"First of all," Teddy began, "it's so true what you've taught us about seeing through what *appears to be* to the *what is* — to the essence of things. It applies everywhere. A couple of months ago, my uncle showed me his schedule at work. In about two minutes, I saw he was trapped in a routine rut. I knew he would quadruple his effectiveness if he set up his schedule *not* task by task, but by the few *physical movements* he must perform each day — by *mini-days* like me. For instance, phone calls are one physical movement. So I told him to write down a list of three days of tasks *as he did the tasks*. From that list, together we figured out his handful of physical movements and set up his mini-day schedule. His productivity multiplied four or fivefold, immediately. He got a bonus and promotion three weeks later. That happened by looking past what appears to be efficient...to the essence of efficiency. After he got his bonus and promotion, I started to wonder about something. You see, I multiplied the profitability of my business four or fivefold by dividing my workers into entrepreneurial mini-companies. Of course, I'm the owner of my company, so I could do that. But what about my uncle? Well, my dad has risen rapidly in his company ever since that talk with you that one evening after school. He started looking past what *appears to be* best. My dad has essentially become an entrepreneurial unit with his own mini-company in his place of work. He absorbed the money-making responsibilities by enthusiastically taking over their nitty-gritty details as you told him. He's now called a project manager with a team of people under him. ...Well, we asked my uncle to write down his job responsibilities. At first glance, they *appeared to* represent a definitive job. But as we thought about *the essence* of business, which is *making money*, we realized how stagnant his job responsibilities were. They had nothing at all to do with making money. They amounted to nothing more than maintaining the business, not moving it forward and making money. My dad said this was exactly the trap he was in just a few months ago. As I looked at my uncle's job responsibilities, I could not stop from feeling his job was a terrible waste of the company's greatest asset — *the mind*. So, I looked at the company my uncle worked for as if it were mine. Then, with both my dad's and my uncle's help, we figured out every way in which the company made money. Therein lay the secret to breaking this company down into jobs of essence — into the 21st-century division-of-essence business. For each way the company made money, I asked my uncle what responsibilities were needed, and I listed those responsibilities under their corresponding money-making essence. When we finished that, we realized that we were looking at the company from a completely different dimension — the division of essence. As I stared at the different ways the company made its money and the list of responsibilities under them, I knew that the company my uncle works for could be divided differently — into profit-making jobs just like my little company. His company makes money in six basic ways. In my little company, six ways of making money might result in only six money-making or entrepreneurial employees with their mini-companies. In the big company my uncle works for, you could have several mini-companies in each money-making area with the same set of responsibilities, and each would have his or her own money-making project. Changing them from dead-end routine ruts of labor to exciting money-making jobs of the mind, well...you should see the change in my uncle. Like my dad, he absorbed the money-making responsibilities and is now his own mini-company at his place of work. It's like he's alive and young again, just like my dad!"

"Yes!" Bobby shouted, "That's exactly what I want for my parents, too!"

"Teddy, how long did it take your dad and uncle to get from their routine ruts as you call them to those exciting entrepreneurial jobs?" Miss Annabelle asked. She knew the parents would love to know this secret and was glad she was recording him.

"Oh, it was a very exciting process that lasted a couple of months," Teddy explained. "They selected the money-making area they wanted to move into, and they targeted the corresponding responsibilities. They didn't tell anyone what they were doing, but they started aggressively taking over, one by one, the nitty-gritty details that made up those responsibilities. They found that nitty-gritty details are open for the taking, just as you told my dad. People will easily let go of them and allow someone eager to take over those tough details. By taking over those essential details, they gradually absorbed the bigger responsibilities, one by one. Within two months, they both created their mini-companies at work. Both my father and my uncle and, of course, *I* got so much success by being able to see past what *appears to be* best to *what is* best."

"That's a great story, Teddy." Miss Annabelle said. She felt the most incredible pride for this young man. His classmates clapped. Most of them planned to bring the idea home to their folks.

"The power behind Teddy's story," Miss Annabelle continued, "is that he can efficiently see through to the essence of things and therefore, uses the authority of his own mind and does not turn his authority over to 'the way it is'. This is how breakthroughs are made. This is how society progresses. Through this process of seeing through what *appears to be* best to *what is* best, you can take things in life to the *next level* never seen before as Teddy is doing in business. I liken Teddy to Henry Ford, being able to cut through 'the way it is' to something altogether different and better."

Teddy's eyes opened big and he blinked several times. He was just compared to his hero.

"Mr. Melbourne and I think Teddy is building piece by logical piece the world's next business paradigm. Henry Ford did this in the 1920s as he developed the assemblyline, which perfected the division of labor and brought mass production to the world. Before that, everything was more or less handmade in limited supply. Whereas Ford perfected labor's role in business, Teddy is perfecting the mind's role in business. Mr. Melbourne and I believe most businesses will shift to the division of essence in the next few years."

Teddy was blushing and bursting with pride.

"And I see comparisons between Ian and Copernicus," Miss Annabelle continued. Ian sat up to the edge of his seat when he heard his name mentioned next to his hero; his teacher explained why, "Copernicus completely changed the way we looked at the Universe. Until he came along, we thought Earth was at the center of the Universe and the Sun, planets, and stars circled us. Looking up at the sky, that geocentric or 'earth centered' explanation seemed quite logical. But Copernicus saw through that appearance to *what is*. He built that breakthrough piece by logical piece until he saw a brand new puzzle-picture forming, taking the cosmos to the next level — the heliocentric or 'sun centered' perspective of our solar system. I also see Ian building a breakthrough, piece by logical piece, and I see a puzzle-picture forming not seen before — the God-Man Universe. Until now, everyone looked at the Universe as controlled by mass and energy. Ian sees through that appearance to *what is* — the Universe is controlled by consciousness millions of years more advanced than earthlings. Mr. Melbourne and I both believe Ian is developing a profound, Neothink breakthrough."

Now Ian was blushing and bursting with pride.

"Remember this as you leave my class and go forward: do

not glide through life — pierce through appearances! The other day at recess, I heard two older boys arguing who would be better for the country — a white president or a black president. Then I was so proud when Danny interrupted and showed them that anything or anyone who rules over us is wrong. The things Danny said sounded like pieces to yet another success puzzle that could lead to a powerful political breakthrough. For example, one of the boys started arguing that we owe a living to some unfortunate people trapped at the bottom of society. He said we historically suppressed blacks, and now we 'owe them'. Welfare and other handouts by the government were good and necessary, he said. A black president would assure such public good, he concluded. Danny then, very benevolently, said, 'You will become a slave all over again, this time to the government, with that kind of thinking. Freedom comes from producing values — producing your own way is how you get independence.' Danny went on to turn this eleven-year-old's thinking around. Danny finished his mission by saying, 'Politicians are political animals. Their talk about the *public good* is like a wife beater saying *baby, I love you*. It sounds good, but when you see through it, you realize it keeps you sticking around for more abuse.' ...Danny, you were magnificent."

Danny was blushing. "I got the wife beater idea from one of your lectures," he said.

Miss Annabelle smiled and continued, "I see several success puzzles starting to form in your *Breakthrough News*. I see Neothink working in all of you; it's exciting and rewarding!"

Miss Annabelle's gaze focused on Sally. Her emotional maturity, displayed in her contribution to *Breakthrough News*, was breathtaking. Sally saw through appearances to *what is* the meaning of life and death. Her depth of the value of human life went beyond anything Miss Annabelle had seen before. The *only* thing wrong with life, as Sally so well demonstrated, was death. Everything else could be corrected. Death could not. Sally vowed to someday cure cancer and work toward the elimination of human death itself.

"Nothing I've ever seen even came close to expressing the value of human life the way you have, Sally. I see a couple of possible success puzzles forming for you. One is medical research to cure cancer, aging, and death. The other is emotional research into why people do not resist death as the worst natural disaster and aging as man's worst plague...a disease that is 100% fatal that must be cured. In either case, you're on your way."

Miss Annabelle savored the moments...their last precious moments together as a class. She knew she had accomplished what she had set out to do. In fact, she now realized she never had a completely clear focus on what she was hoping to accomplish because she had never witnessed the Neothink mentality before her twelve students showed her. So, on this day, the results of her goal were fresh and exciting. Those results were concretized and forever captured in the *Breakthrough News* publication. For Miss Annabelle, that publication was *the* final exam from her students. And in it, she witnessed her students go to the next level beyond people today.

Filled with pride, filled with nostalgia, she continued her talk, "All of you are using common denominators to form concepts, and then using those concepts like puzzle pieces to form success puzzles. ...Rico, who would have ever thought to separate criminals by two different common denominators — by those who committed a crime through force or fraud versus those who committed a crime *not* through force or fraud, but through breaking some political-policy law or regulation."

Rico was smiling. He had spent many days in the prison's visiting room the past five years. His father was imprisoned three of those years and his uncle the past two years. While visiting the prison, Rico began to notice a clear distinction in looks between those who committed a crime of force or fraud versus those who committed a crime *not* through force, but through breaking a law or regulation created by politicians or bureaucrats. The distinction became so evident to Rico that he would play a little game when he visited: he would observe a man for about an hour, then decide in his head what category he fell into. Then he would ask his father why the man was in prison. Rico was right most of the time.

Rico came to realize the men who were in prison because of political reasons were different — they were *good* people for the most part. They shouldn't be in here, he'd conclude.

Rico sat quietly but proudly after Miss Annabelle complimented him. But Danny spun around in his chair and said to Rico, "Yeah, Riccy. I wanted to tell you what a great piece you wrote about those two concepts of law and regulations. You're right on about that."

"Thanks," Rico said modestly. He was quiet, but he felt a wonderful power within. He now easily saw through illusions and perceptions that had trapped his family for generations before him and had previously begun to trap him, too. He could not get over how good he felt now. Seeing reality for *what it is* feels spectacular, he thought.

"I want to thank you, Miss Annabelle," Rico said, overcoming his shyness. "Anyone could have shown me another path than I was on before — the good path. But it would have never changed me. But you showed me how *to think*...how to see through illusions to *what is,* and *that* changed me because I was able to discover, through *my own* thinking, the good path. Thank you."

Rico's words were said with sincerity and sensitivity. Coming from this little nine-year-old tough guy, they slammed into Miss Annabelle's heart and stuck on it like a heavy plunger. God, I'll miss him, she thought. But, she knew his life would be a good one now. ...With a heavy but happy heart, she continued.

"Each of you demonstrated signs of Neothink in your *Breakthrough News*," she said glancing around the room. "Jeremiah, that was a powerful common denominator you identified that keeps churches going today despite their growing problems with scientific facts. You're absolutely right: churches do offer substantial life advantages because of their social networkings. I love your idea of starting a new, scientifically sound church someday, emphasizing that common denominator of great social networking as the building block while working toward a common goal of achieving biological immortality *before*, not after, you die."

"I love that idea too," Sally said.

"What an exciting set of concepts you have, Jeremiah, from the value of such a church to the marketing ideas of such a church," Miss Annabelle continued, still impressed by Jeremiah's conception of an entirely new church to outcompete the waning religions today.

Jeremiah, a humble fellow on the outside but stirring thinker within, was quick to give credit where it was due. "My idea came off of the God-Man theory of the Universe, in which we would never die," he said. "Also, your lecture on life being the highest value in the Universe made me realize that biological immortality is the most important goal, and religion should be focussed that way. Also, Mr. Melbourne taught me about how religions, including today's religions, came out of the past, primitive mind."

"And you took all those concepts and began snapping them together into a completely new puzzle-picture never seen before," Miss Annabelle said. "You'll succeed with the new church, Jeremiah, because you know how to go down to the common denominators of people's needs. I started the school year by saying that you children would learn how to make values that a lot of people want to pay money for. Well, you have learned how to do that...by going down to the common denominators of many people's common needs. That's where the greatest values await to be discovered and the greatest marketing ideas, too. You've got a nice start, Jeremiah."

Miss Annabelle glanced around again, then stopped, spotting her next subject. "There's the master synthesizer, Alan Patterson. He organized and narrated this diverse set of subjects into one integrated publication. He tied all those subjects together under one common denominator: breakthroughs that jump to the next level, a common denominator of great interest to a lot of people."

"That's right," Teddy added. "That's proving out, too, with the number of the *Breakthrough News* that I'm selling. I tell people it's the next evolution of money, power, and love."

"Congratulations Alan. Congratulations Teddy. Congratulations every one of you!" Miss Annabelle said. She could have said that a hundred times and not grown tired of saying it. It was like congratulating her own children for doing something no one has done before. Looking over her class of little geniuses, she stopped when she saw Reggie.

"And what a breakthrough you're onto, Reggie," she said. "You saw through to the essence of music, through the way things are set up today. Is the essence of music what we see

today? Is the *essence* of music to be decided by an elite
Establishment? As you point out, Reggie, ultimately the
consumers and artists must hold the power in a mutual, supply-
and-demand value exchange. You say the music industry is like
a big balloon waiting to be popped by piercing through to a
direct consumer/artist exchange that eliminates the enormous but
unnatural power held by the brokers. I think you're right on
with your point that the music industry still needs to be run
through business, but through a new business format set up more
like an indifferent supplier bringing endless choices to the people
instead of feeding the market with its relatively select few
choices. That way, the consumer, not the elite, make their own
choices. You pierced through powerful illusions to the essence
of music. And you're absolutely right: if you figure out the right
business format that is true to the essence of music — the
consumer/artist value exchange — the whole industry would
change to that consumer/artist value exchange you talk about, and
there would be no more Establishment controlling the music
industry or any of the arts for that matter."

Miss Annabelle knew that Reggie was on to something
powerful that could change the world of art once some
entrepreneur figured out the right business format. She wondered:
would that someone be Reggie himself someday?

Miss Annabelle looked around the room to savor these
geniuses before her. They were geniuses because during the year
they had advanced into the new mentality that saw through
appearances to *what is*. By being able to know reality
effectively, they did not need to turn their authority over to the
"experts" such as politicians, clergy, and others who tell people
how to live. Because these children so effectively saw the
essence of things, they became their own authorities as they
efficiently, naturally integrated reality into broad puzzle-picture
understandings that others could not reach. These children were,
at nine years old, going to the next level of living.

Miss Annabelle rested her eyes on the slim beauty who
represented physically the metamorphosis the students went
through psychologically. As with Cathy, their minds went from
uncompetitive and out of shape to potent beauties. Miss
Annabelle continued, "Cathy, dear, you pierced through all the

illusory diets out there and went to the essence of dieting. You showed us in *Breakthrough News* a diet based on the three forces of nature: hunger, cravings, and fullness. Once you got past all the illusionary diets...down to the essence of dieting at this biological level, you developed the most effective diet I've ever seen. As you so clearly showed us, the essence of dieting is removing hunger and cravings while adjusting fullness levels downward, which you proved! I think your diet can help millions of people, just like it helped you. Congratulations, beautiful!"

The class gave Cathy an ovation. Cathy smiled and blushed. These days, she was always smiling.

"Another breakthrough came from you, Nattie," Miss Annabelle said, looking across the room at the attractive brown-eyed blonde. "You cut through to the essence of what happiness is made of. But how obvious you make that age-old mystery: Man *is* a social animal, as you say, and he gets his pride and happiness by putting values into society. Your short story about the scientist who is the only survivor on the planet after a cataclysmic event is powerfully moving. With no society, he can't feel happiness. That anecdote underscores that *value production* for society is the essence of happiness, for your poor survivor has no society to produce values for, thus can feel no happiness. Without a society for which to inject one's value production, there can be no value reflection...no pride or happiness. Nattie, you really pierced through a very difficult subject that has befuddled humanity through all ages: what is the meaning of life? Once you answer *happiness*, then you must ask: what is happiness? You, Nattie, answered that elusive question once and for all, clearly and convincingly, with your short story *Sole Survivor*."

Ian turned around to talk to Natasha. "I love that story about Sergio," he said. "I like the part where he was so unhappy he was about to take his own life when that last-second survival pressure, just as he squeezed the trigger, made him break through to realizing the existence of the Civilization of the Universe. That was thrilling. Suddenly, he had a civilization. Now he had to figure out how to create values for it."

"But how?" Reggie joined in. "Finally, he realized how: He spent his life learning and developing magnificent classical music.

He then sent his beautiful creations — his music — into the Universe through continuously running radio beams. He thought, someday, other civilizations would discover his music, and it would live on as an eternal value in distant planets. I thought that was thrilling. ...My favorite part was his passion to learn how to create great music, knowing his valuable creations would someday live on in the Civilization of the Universe. I can see why that made Sergio a very happy man, even though he was all alone."

"That was so emotional," Sally added, "when Sergio was old and dying. I cried when he went around and turned the speakers all the way up on all the radio stations in the valley where he lived, all alone. He was beaming his music into the Universe while also listening to it for the last time. That was so sad when he lay down on the comfortable grass that night to die. It was like I could see him lying on his back, all alone, looking into the cosmos above him, listening to his beautiful creations boldly filling the valley, from mountainside to mountainside. That was just so sad as he lay with a smile on his face, immensely proud and happy, sharing his last moments with his greatest creations."

"I cried too," Cathy said, "as his favorite piece played proudly across the valley floor, and Sergio yelled out, 'I wish I could travel with you, my love! You must journey to distant civilizations and live *forever* in the Civilization of the Universe. You will be loved by many. You make me so very, very proud. But my time has come; I must say good-bye. Tonight I will leave you, my companion, my love. You must find other ears to listen to you, to admire you, to *love* you as I have. Go now on your journey. Go now, my love, and find a new home. Make millions of people happy. You are free!'"

Everyone in the classroom took a deep breath, and then Danny continued Natasha's short story:

"When the morning light rose over the valley, it found Sergio's lifeless body lying on the bed of grass. His face still had a smile on it. Conscious life no longer existed on Earth, but his wonderful music proudly played on and filled the lonely land with its final triumphant sounds of human consciousness. ...That was really moving."

"It was a stunning story," Miss Annabelle said. And, she

thought, it was also a beautiful metaphor of the lonely yet happy God-Man on Earth who was not as fortunate as herself to be surrounded by soulmates, instead left all alone, surrounded by the anticivilization. ...What *value* that *Breakthrough News* brings its reader! These are just nine-year-olds, she thought, and they're answering centuries-old mysteries about the meaning of life, love, religion, politics, physics, wealth and power! Miss Annabelle could not stop wondering: what would these dozen children be like as adults? I mean, she said to herself while shaking her head, Natasha knows more about happiness and love than any woman or mother I've ever known! How can that be? ...Yet, Miss Annabelle knew the answer to her own question: these twelve children had gone to the next level...they were now her twelve God-Men.

"Natasha," Miss Annabelle continued, "your puzzle-picture kept on growing to reveal the answers to love that could save marriages. More and more marriages today end in divorce. People don't understand the essence of love. You continued expanding your puzzle about happiness and showed us that happiness is needed first in order to feel and sustain romantic love. Value *production* is the essence of happiness, and you showed us a *man's* value production comes through his livelihood. Value *reflection* is the essence of love, and you showed us a man's value *reflection* comes most through his wife and children. You're so right that a person must know and admire and reflect his or her spouse's value production in order to have value reflection. That, in fact, keeps the love alive and burning, like your mom and dad's renewed love affair. I love your true story about saving your mom and dad's marriage by understanding this value production/value reflection dynamic. ...Your piece on the essence of love helps me in my relationship!"

The twelve children laughed. ...What a shame I didn't have more students than just twelve, Miss Annabelle thought, for she knew that the natural competitive pressures pushed all twelve students to the next level of Neothink and would have pushed thirty students to the next level if her class would have been that big.

Next, she looked at Debbie. She wrote a remarkable article

about her parents' restaurants and her first taste of Neothink. For the past two and a half months, she spent evenings and weekends in her parents' two hamburger restaurants. She learned every imaginable detail and searched for common denominators. She was determined to make the breakthrough that would let her parents achieve their dream of expanding their business, which seemed stuck at this level for years.

Debbie made a number of little breakthroughs among the details that improved efficiency. But she came to learn that the problem of not being able to expand was not an operations or personnel problem. As Teddy had once suggested, she learned the problem had to be either in marketing or in the product. Both the product and marketing were satisfactory, but something was needed, something not known to her parents before, in order to go to the next level. So, Debbie started studying the customers' eating habits, searching for common denominators. She had to break through the way things were now to something new. She also sat for long periods of time in McDonald's. There, she spotted a common denominator: almost everyone, regardless of their order, also got the golden fries. The more she watched, the more convinced she became that the fries caused an "addiction" that brought people back, over and over again. Debbie thought the people did not themselves realize that the fries (not the hamburgers) were behind their trips to McDonald's. The children, too, ate their fries and ate them first. It all happened on a subconscious level, Debbie believed. But McDonald's had to be aware of the secret of the fries, for the combo meals with fries costs about the same as ordering the burger and drink separately, without fries. In other words, the fries were given out, more or less, for free.

So, she talked about her observations with her parents. They decided to give fries away, free of charge, with a purchase of any hamburger and drink. One month later, sales were up 40%. Based on those results, her parents were in the process of changing the name of the restaurants from Kirkland Burgers to Debbie's French Fry City with the marketing hooks: "free fries with every order" and "fresh fries cooked every 180 seconds". They were planning to open a third restaurant in Buffalo. And they were remodeling the two existing restaurants and purchasing new equipment to display, in plain view, clean stainless steel french fry cookers, with fresh fries cooked every three minutes and "old" fries discarded. They were perfecting the art of the perfect, tasty, crispy fry that was "addicting". Debbie kept close track of the customers. She recorded a threefold increase in frequency of repeat customers and scores of new customers. She knew she had taken the product and the marketing to the next level.

"Your story of Debbie's French Fry City was fascinating," Miss Annabelle said. "Debbie's French Fry City is on its way to the next level because of your Neothinking. Do you think your parents will start franchising them?"

Debbie really was excited about her family business and its growing success that she was now part of. "Yes, we've even been talking about it! And my parents are studying Teddy's article about mini-companies, replicating, tracking reports, and division of essence. Daddy says the division of essence is exactly how he will set up his franchising!"

Bobby turned to Debbie and said, "Cool! That's a franchise I'd suggest people getting into." All his life, Bobby witnessed his father and mother stuck in stagnation — despite their natural ambitions. Bobby helplessly witnessed their dreams fade away. He remembered them talking with enthusiasm about their goals when he was still very young. Now, at nine years old, he never heard them mention those goals. He could never forget their enthusiasm from the past. They were so happy then, he remembered. During the last few weeks as Bobby felt his power to make a difference grow, he became more and more interested in the idea of finding the right employer for the right people. Bobby absorbed Teddy's division of essence concept and was convinced the division of essence was the answer to so many people's stagnation traps. He was convinced that the division of labor — *jobs of labor* — was the reason for stagnation traps. He was also convinced that Teddy's division of essence, with its mini-companies creating entrepreneurial jobs, gave people *jobs of the mind*. The mind — thinking — was the essence of man and opened a whole new exciting world to the employee. Bobby became convinced that the division of essence with its jobs of the mind was the future of business and jobs. He became obsessed with the idea of bringing ambitious people, like his parents, to those new businesses set up that way. It was the way back to enthusiasm and happiness for adults, he wrote in *Breakthrough News*.

Bobby did not have a specific breakthrough, for he was working off Teddy's breakthrough. Nevertheless, Bobby was searching for common denominators that would let him start building a success puzzle that would someday take him to the next level with his passion.

First, Bobby identified that the essence of business was making money by creating and effectively marketing values, which meant the essence of business depended on man's *creativity*. Then he demonstrated that the essence of man was his mind, thinking, *creativity*. Thus, the most competitive business structure in the future had to be the division of essence where the employees — *all* employees — used their minds creatively. The employees' *thinking minds* were the greatest assets to any business that previously were wasted in the old division of labor structure.

He demonstrated how the division-of-essence business would be quickly filled with ambitious, creative people who would get as close to filling the business with clones of the original entrepreneur as can be. Both the business and the employee would break through to the next level.

"You have become so motivated, Bobby, to bring ambitious working people together with the new division of essence business," Miss Annabelle said. She was delighted to see such passion take root. Bobby had seen that Teddy's new business paradigm was the answer to his parents' stagnation traps and to all stagnation traps. As far as Bobby was concerned, the whole business world had to change. And he wanted to bring together ambitious people with those businesses as they changed.

"I haven't figured out *how* to bring them together yet," Bobby said, "but I will. I know it can be done. There must be some way to find the right companies for the right people."

Miss Annabelle marveled at the intellect of her students. They had gone to the next level of integrated thinking, and onto Neothink. Their mentality was different than others. They had, at nine years old, evolved into our next evolution: God-Man. As

God-Man, they did not think in percepts, one thought, one perception at a time as most people. Instead, they thought in pictures. Their minds sought common denominators, pulling together percepts into powerful concepts and then snapping together those concepts as pieces of growing puzzles to reveal never-before-seen puzzle-pictures.

As Teddy and Bobby exchanged some ideas, Mr. Melbourne walked into the classroom. He was the other person who really belonged with this group of people. The children smiled, waved, and said, "hi!" They loved him.

"Class," Miss Annabelle said, "As you know, Mr. Melbourne has worked on a book for over a decade — since before you were even born! Today, he wanted to reveal a bit of it for the first time — to us..."

"Whoa! Yeah! Wahoo! Alright!" shouted several students. Their reaction was impulsive and genuine. They felt this was a treat and felt honored. Mr. Melbourne raised an eyebrow and smiled.

"Hi kids!" he said to the applauding class. "You twelve children have impressed me over and over again since I've known you. Your teacher has impressed me, too." The kids laughed, catching the second meaning to that comment. Mr. Melbourne smiled and continued, "You're a unique group, a unique little society, that has advanced to the next level — into a new mind of the future that I've spent over ten years identifying in my book. You're the manifestation or the evidence of my hypothesis."

He paused to gather his bearings of where to begin. After some thought, he said, "Last night, your lovely teacher talked to me for a long time. She was proudly telling me all the many different success puzzles you're building. I also read about those growing success puzzles in your stunning *Breakthrough News*. But the surprising thing is, of the wide diversity you present, all of it is tied together by a common denominator: all twelve of your very different success puzzles do the same thing in their respective areas — they *get rid of the external authorities*. Think about it: the mind of nearly everyone else outside this room is ultimately controlled by external authorities. But you represent the next mentality — everything you wrote in your *Breakthrough News* eliminates the external authority. What is the new mentality, the mind of the future? It's putting authority from 'out there' to inside yourself. You can do that only if you effectively see through illusions to *what is*. You children can do this, so you're dumping external authorities left and right in every area that interests you and making breakthroughs that take those areas to the next level. You are your own authority integrating *what is*, free of external guidance. You build your own mental maps for guidance. You represent the next evolution of man!"

The children were very proud of themselves. The amazing thing was: they knew exactly what Mr. Melbourne was talking about. They looked up to him and respected him. His impression of them was very important to them.

"Let's quickly go back and see this common trait among the twelve of you: Bobby, you're not accepting the status quo in the way almost all jobs are set up. You're dumping that external authority for a better way based on your own authority of seeing *what is* — Teddy's division of essence, in particular. And Teddy didn't accept jobs of labor and their routines dictating the unthinking human being. He went to the next level, dumping the external authority in the form of a routine dictating us...doing our work in an unthinking, following mode. He replaced that external authority, that we blindly follow, with the internal authority of our thinking minds — jobs of the mind — the entrepreneurial mini-companies where we think for ourselves to build values. Danny wants to end politicians and bureaucrats telling us how to live — needless external authority — and limit their power to protection only. Jeremiah wants to jump past religion and the clergy demanding blind faith — destructive external authority — and replace it with the integrating, scientific mind. Sally wants to remove the corrupt FDA — destructive external authority — and free up research for the hard thinking, entrepreneurial mind. Reggie wants to rid the elite control — the external authority — over the music industry. Ian breaks through staid scientific Establishment perspectives like the point of origin and the mass/energy view of the Universe and breaks through religious external authority to bring our understanding to the next level where God-Man uses his internal authority —

his mind — to control the cosmos. Rico differentiates bad law based on force versus good law based on protection from force. He wants to eliminate bad laws under gun-backed external authority created by image-seeking politicians. Debbie simply does not accept the common external authority that one reaches his or her limit and levels off and must passively accept stagnation. Natasha does not accept similar external authorities — the emotional norms of limited happiness and lost love — for she broke through to God-Man's *natural* state of intense happiness and intense love, forever. Cathy broke through her external authorities — her parents — trying to convince her to overeat. And Alan, you orchestrated a publication that breaks through the views of the two external authorities that envelop everyone in this country — *the media* and the Establishment with their agenda-driven illusions."

The children looked a bit surprised. Mr. Melbourne was right — a very simple common denominator did tie all their success stories together. Their successes seemed to grow from the same seed: dumping external authority for internal authority. How elegantly simple, they thought. ...What exactly is this external authority thing, anyway? They wondered.

"Outside this room, almost everyone is guided by external authorities," Mr. Melbourne continued, and as if reading their minds, he said, "What is external authority, where did it come from, and why does almost everyone follow it? Before Ancient Greece, man was not like man today. His entire existence was guided by oracles and god-kings who 'heard' the gods telling man what to do, especially in stressful situations. The oracles and the god-kings and even the common man himself hallucinated the 'voices' of the gods. Of course, we now know that those 'voices' of the gods were audio hallucinations. But 3000 years ago, important decisions were made by those external authorities — by those 'voices of the gods'.

"As civilizations evolved and man left behind those audio hallucinations, he still sought external authority. He simply switched from the 'voices' of the gods and god-kings to the voices of the church fathers and politicians. But today, such religious and political leaders are unnecessary because man has the ability to integrate reality to know *what is* and to act on his

257

own authority as a self-leader. However, today man still looks to leaders to guide him. You are the first group of people I've witnessed who naturally turn inward to your own, integrating minds for guidance. Always seeing through to the essence of things, you rely on your own minds to see *what is* as the authority, not what 'experts' or leaders tell you per se. Therefore, illusions used by leaders for easy power and money do not affect you. You represent a new mentality altogether. People around you still function under a modern-day format of the ancient mentality — seeking external authority for guidance. You function under the brand-new God-Man mentality: broadly and honestly integrating knowledge to know *what is*, then using the authority of your own minds to lead your lives."

"Why do you and Miss Annabelle call it God-Man?" Ian asked.

"The reason I think God-Man is a good description goes back to the hallucinated 'voices' of the gods. I have been in communication with a psychology professor at Princeton University who is doing some amazing work on our ancient mentality over 3000 years ago. He's demonstrated that human nature was split in two: an executive part called a god and a follower part called a man. The imagined god was the authority, and the man was the follower. A few hundred years later, the two parts of the mind — the executive part and the follower part — were starting to integrate together as one powerful mind, which gave rise to history's most powerful minds: the great Greeks during Ancient Greece. The authority or the god part of human nature became part of *man's* mentality — the God-Man mentality of that ancient time. But master neocheaters of the Western World figured out how to return man to a follower so those neocheaters could rule over civilization. Those self-serving educated elites — the scholars of the Church — split the god part or the authority off to a God in heaven. Man was now nothing more than a follower to be led by the leaders of the Church in the name of God. That reversed humanity for a thousand years, now known as the Dark Ages. Mankind was caught in some kind of weird mutation of the ancient mentality. Once again, man sought to be led by external authorities, and those external authorities became our leaders who used illusions to rule over us for easy money and power.

"Today, you twelve children represent the modern pioneers breaking free from that mutation of the ancient mentality. *You* are integrating the executive part or god-part of human nature with the man-part. You are the first — at least since the great Greeks — to advance into the God-Man mentality. There's no telling how far you will go in your lifetimes."

Miss Annabelle's heart was pounding with pride as her lover described what was happening to her students. Her students' eyes were opened wide with wonder. Their eyes were glued to Mr. Melbourne. She knew he was right. They knew he was right, for they could feel their power to cut through the leaders' illusions to the essence of things and to make their own decisions. They really were different from those around them, and they knew it. Yes, they were the God-Man. ...Ian had a special feeling going on inside him, for he had been calling the advanced beings who control the cosmos the *God-Man* because they were men with the control and power of God. Now, Mr. Melbourne was calling Ian and his classmates the God-Man. "I really am one of them," he thought.

"Thank you, Mr. Melbourne," Miss Annabelle said into the silent room. Her voice brought her children back from the depths of their thoughts, and they clapped and smiled. They loved Mr. Melbourne. His value reflection and articulation of who they were gave them pride and confidence for the years ahead.

The kids sat peacefully. "We live for happiness," Miss Annabelle continued. "As Natasha so well demonstrated in *Breakthrough News*, happiness comes to man — a social animal — by putting values into society. That's how human beings earn pride and happiness. They *feel* large doses of their earned happiness from reflections of admiration and love from their spouses and children and fellowman. The meaning of life — happiness — comes from value production and is felt through value reflection. In other words, happiness comes from producing values and is felt during time celebrated together with loved ones and friends.

"There's also room in our hearts to feel love for those individuals who bring great values to society. Those geniuses of society are raising our standards of living. Of course, I know you'll cut through the illusions of our variety of leaders in the media, in the government, and in law who orchestrate class envy against those geniuses of society. You'll never fall into that trap that builds resentment against success. We've had a taste of this envy with our own battles with the principal and the school-district superintendent."

The nine-year-olds knew exactly what she was talking about. They looked up to the geniuses of society, the great value-and-job creators now and in the past, with great admiration. Miss Annabelle knew they did, but she wanted to *state it* to help counteract what will be drummed into their heads in the years to come, for resentment toward success would hurt their own deep motivation to be successful.

"Now that you know the meaning of life is *happiness*, and now that you know how to create and experience happiness, I'll tell you how to someday *multiply* your happiness! That'll bring you the greatest feeling life offers. ...Someday, you'll have children, and seeing your children become happy value producers making their dreams come true will *multiply* your own happiness. I know because I felt my happiness multiply many times over as I watched you advance toward happy value producers. Or, maybe I should say, value *creators*, for you're creating values that never existed before. Watching you children do this...well, it's the greatest joy a grown-up can feel."

Her comment sparked curiosity among her students. She was talking about *their* children. The students did not recognize the pleasant feeling that filled them; they had never felt this way before. They felt unusually warm and special. Without knowing what it was, they felt good that their teacher thought about their well-being...so far into the future.

Rico raised his hand. His teacher nodded toward him, and he said, "But how would we do that? You're a professional teacher, and I don't know if any of us will be teachers. So, how can we do for our kids what you did for us?"

Miss Annabelle knew that Rico seldom saw his father while growing up. She said, "You can bring your children into the new God-Man mentality in less than five minutes a day. You don't need to educate them; they can even go to public schools for that — as long as you show them one thing: show them how

260

to penetrate *what appears to be* to *what is*. You want to break through traditional ways of looking at things, just as you did in *Breakthrough News*. Your example teaches their young minds to cut through illusions to *what is*. From there, as you know, mental puzzles of powerful knowledge grow, and eventually your children will create new values for the world. Also, from the emotional side, tell them bedtime stories about the great value producers who brought our many values to the world. All this can be done in a daily bedtime story — in a five-minute story each day.

"Let me take you back in history to demonstrate this secret to bringing your future children into little God-Men. I figured this out, believe it or not, on Christmas Day five months ago. During the Age of the Greeks, the great minds — the ancient God-Men — got a good education, yes, but they also had exposure to an accomplished philosopher or scientist. Sometimes that philosopher or scientist was hired to live with the pupil. Aristotle, for example, lived with and was mentor of Alexander the Great. Aristotle's mentor was Plato. Plato's mentor was Socrates. The same format took place during the Renaissance: the great Renaissance men studied under accomplished or renowned artists, inventors, philosophers, or scientists. Those great minds grew not out of the many hours of good education, per se. They grew from Neothink seeds planted in, perhaps, five minutes a day. Those seeds were the stories told by the mentors that broke through the normal way of thinking. Those boundary-breaking talks taught the student's mind, at a young age, to break through boundaries, go through appearances to *what is*. With reality, they could start integrated thinking and eventually Neothink to go to the next level. The general lectures I gave you each morning were examples of this type of talk that pushed your minds through the traditional boundaries of thinking created by external authorities. Now you use your own minds; you see through illusions; you see *what is*; you see common denominators, and you build success puzzles. You never look toward external authorities on how to live; instead your own mind honestly integrates reality and has become the authority. To get to this point, I talked to you for about forty-five minutes a day, and that was enough for you to make the jump out of the ancient-mentality mutation to the new God-Man mentality. But we only had nine months together. If you spread that time over fifteen years, you're well under five minutes a day. So, you bring your children into this happy new world with you, and your happiness will soar. I know, because my happiness has soared this past year, seeing you come into this new world with me."

Sally raised her hand slowly.

"Yes, Sally?" Miss Annabelle said.

"But...well...are we going to be together anymore?"

Sally had asked a powerful question, for this group was its own civilization, different from the rest of the world. How could it end now?

"It would be a crime to split us up," Miss Annabelle said, and she could feel the tension leave the room. Twelve sets of little shoulders relaxed and dropped an inch or two. "I'll hold a class every Thursday afternoon at my house from 3:30 to 5:00. I'll lecture for 45 minutes to an hour, and we'll have our discussion group for the remaining 30 to 45 minutes. We'll always keep this class going and our group together."

This good news put smiles on her twelve little God-Men. Now, they could enjoy themselves again and feel the celebration of life. For, this was another beautiful day full of precious, bigger-than-life memories.

II.

Separation

CHAPTER
TWENTY-ONE

The ominous storm cloud had finally blown in: the trial date had arrived.

Salinski's case was well prepared. He had subpoenaed Hammerschmidt's ex-wife and former girlfriend as witnesses. In depositions, they both told of Hammerschmidt's violent side inspired by perverse, sexual satisfaction. Both women got out of their relationships with Hammerschmidt because of his neurotic behavior.

Salinski felt their testimonies were powerful for his case, but he also knew that both witnesses had some character issues that the prosecution would exploit to discredit their testimonies.

While studying the prosecution's discovery (i.e., material the prosecution planned to introduce as evidence), Salinski came across an official looking affidavit on Duncan Elementary stationery. This was the paper Hammerschmidt brought to Miss Annabelle that evening as an excuse to get into her house. From that piece of evidence, Salinski suspected the prosecution would submit a theory that Miss Annabelle and Mr. Melbourne attacked the unsuspecting Hammerschmidt out of rage or revenge. The prosecution charged Mr. Melbourne and Miss Annabelle with voluntary manslaughter. The prosecution offered, during plea bargaining, to reduce the charges to involuntary manslaughter, which Salinski rejected. He believed he could get an acquittal.

Salinski could have delayed the trial for months, perhaps a full year or longer, with a number of motions. But he and his clients wanted to get it over with and felt confident and ready. So, they opted to go straight to trial. Thus, the day after Independence Day, the trial date had arrived.

Jury selection lasted just one afternoon. Opening arguments were delivered the next morning.

"We will prove beyond a reasonable doubt that Mr. Melbourne and Miss Annabelle ambushed an innocent, unsuspecting Mr. Hammerschmidt who was merely following his civic duty by delivering an affidavit to Miss Annabelle for her side of the story in a school inquisition," the prosecuting attorney said to conclude his opening argument.

Salinski felt he had the key puzzle parts to snap together the honest picture, however, that would hold together. "I will show that Hammerschmidt planned to batter and rape Miss Annabelle. As he executed his plan, he was surprised by Mr. Melbourne; a fight ensued, during which Hammerschmidt accidentally inflicted a fatal wound upon himself that killed him quickly. Mr. Melbourne immediately called the authorities to help Mr. Hammerschmidt. Mr. Melbourne and Miss Annabelle acted in self-defense in exercising their most basic right of protecting themselves."

The prosecution called its first witness.

"Your honor, the prosecution calls Ms. Rosemary Minner to the witness stand."

"Please state your full name for the record."

"Ms. Rosemary Minner."

"Place your left hand on the Bible and raise your right hand. ...Do you solemnly swear that the testimony you are about to give in the case pending before this court will be the truth, the whole truth and nothing but the truth, so help you God?"

"I do."

"Please be seated."

"Ms. Minner," the prosecutor said, "what was your relationship to Mr. Hammerschmidt?"

"He was the superintendent of the school board, of which I

am a member."

"Ms. Minner, tell me what you thought of your school district's superintendent."

"Oh, he was a good man," Ms. Minner said. "He was a God-fearing Christian. The things the man over there says about Mr. Hammerschmidt are lies!" She pointed straight at Salinski.

"Are you saying the defense attorney is a liar?"

"Objection your honor!" Salinski said. "The prosecution is—"

"Overruled."

"Ms. Minner," continued the prosecutor, "did Mr. Hammerschmidt ever give you reason to believe he could do these things the defense attorney is accusing him of?"

"It's not possible. I know for a fact it's not possible."

"Objection."

"Overruled!"

Miss Annabelle noticed something strange: the judge seemed to favor the prosecuting attorney over Salinski. She was not sure, but the judge's tone of voice and disposition seemed more tolerant with the prosecution. She wondered if she were just being paranoid or if her observation could be true. She also noticed how the judge sat so high in his courtroom, towering over everyone else. He's supposed to be an indifferent third party moderating the trial, she thought. Why would he want to interfere with the search for justice? But as the day progressed, she became convinced that the judge was taking the side of the prosecution. He was also befriending the jurors in the paternal way he talked to them. Therefore, she thought, his opinion would carry more weight on his "adopted" jury members.

At an afternoon break, Miss Annabelle asked Salinski, "Why does the judge rule in the prosecution's favor almost unanimously? It seems almost like he's taking their side."

Salinski was quiet, not sure how to answer. Mr. Melbourne looked at Salinski curiously, for Mr. Melbourne had come to the same conclusion about the judge.

*

The next day, the defense would get their answer. The

prosecution called its witnesses first. At the last minute before the trial, the prosecution had added three more witnesses to its list of witnesses. Salinski observed that they were prominent members of the community: the mayor of Buffalo, the former lieutenant governor of New York, the district's congressman. Salinski knew these witnesses were summoned as character witnesses on behalf of Hammerschmidt. But he never expected the judge to become influenced by witnesses — political or otherwise. Salinski was a good courtroom lawyer, but he was young. He was about to learn a lesson in *ego justice.*

The prosecution spent most of the day building its theory that Hammerschmidt was innocently delivering official school papers following Miss Annabelle's upsetting school board meeting. Salinski felt confident, however, sure he could tear down that theory. He cross examined the prosecution's witnesses and nearly destroyed the theory on cross examination alone. But, in mid-afternoon, the prosecutor called forth one of the three witnesses who were added last to the witness list.

He called to the witness stand Congressman Adams. After being sworn in, the seasoned prosecutor began,

"How long did you know Charles Hammerschmidt, sir?"

"Oh, I've known Charlie...excuse me...I *knew* Charlie for over 20 years," the Congressman said in his warmest, trained voice. "Twenty one years ago, when my daughter was a few months old, I was a struggling lawyer just out of law school. It was tight rationing for awhile. Once, when it got too bad for my family, he loaned me two thousand dollars. He was an assistant accountant at the time. Two thousand dollars was a lot of money to him. But that was the kind of man Charlie was. He'd loan his next paycheck to a person in need."

Salinski felt sick. His gut legal sense knew this was just fantasy rhetoric, so he objected on grounds that there was no evidence of this so-called $2000 loan. But he was caught off guard with the judge's seemingly uncharacteristic response:

"Overruled! Mr. Salinski, the honorable Congressman Peter Adams has been our district's esteemed congressman for over ten years. His word is respected in New York, and it's respected in this courtroom."

Salinski sat down, in shock. What a subjective statement,

he thought, right in a court of law! He had not yet run into this sort of thing in which the judge took a position and then worked his agenda into his court.

The next day, more would follow. Salinski was helpless at stopping the prosecution, the political witnesses, and the judge. That political team had an agenda and was creating a fraudulent fantasy about Hammerschmidt's character. Obviously, Hammerschmidt was politically well connected. Moreover, most politicians were his soul mates and would do whatever it took to support him, regardless of lies or injustice, especially if they could personally look good doing so.

By the third day of the trial, the prosecution had completed its case. Salinski felt ambushed by a political agenda. Hammerschmidt's character had been built up beyond harm. He was like a legendary philanthropist in the eyes of the vulnerable jury. The judge not only allowed, but saw to it that the jury was dazzled by the three political witnesses. For Salinski to try to cut down to size Hammerschmidt's character with his four lowly witnesses by comparison would be ineffectual now, particularly after cross examination. It mattered not what reality was. The prosecution, led by the judge himself, had created an illusion that could not be vanished.

Salinski tried his best, but he was fighting a fraud and had no way to overcome the judge-led prosecution. The judge had decided it would be best for his political future to tacitly join the prosecution. It was a tough lesson for Salinski, even tougher for Miss Annabelle and Mr. Melbourne.

Salinski certainly had powerful witnesses of his own: the bartender who testified that on the night of his death, Hammerschmidt was drinking a lot and telling people he was going to go teach some "little bitch" a lesson after he left the bar; Hammerschmidt's ex-wife who testified that Hammerschmidt did have a drinking problem and that he did physically abuse her, especially when he was drinking; his ex-girlfriend who confirmed his ex-wife's story. But it didn't matter. Aggressive cross examination by the prosecutor made these three witnesses appear either incompetent to give testimony or driven by vengeance. Although Salinski was able to demonstrate that his witnesses had no such motives other than to state the truth and that, indeed, his ex-wife and former girlfriend were genuinely saddened by his accidental death, the damage had been done.

*

"I remember one night on a flight to Washington D.C., while we were still married, Charlie had too much to drink," his ex-wife testified. "Charlie started getting loud and unruly as he often did when drinking. A stewardess came by and politely asked Charlie to please keep his voice down. Charlie snapped, 'Shut up and get me another coke'n rum!' The small woman quietly said she couldn't do that because he had too much to drink."

"What happened then?" Salinski asked.

"He went ballistic. He stood up and grabbed shots of rum from her cart. When she tried to stop him, he pushed her and she fell down in the aisle of the plane. Instead of sitting back down, Charlie stumbled toward her and *kicked* her. Three men jumped out of their seats and wrestled Charlie back into his seat. One of those men was big and very tough. He threatened Charlie pretty harshly. Charlie didn't get up again after that, but for weeks he kept telling me how he 'should've beat the daylights out of that little bitch'. Charlie could hold a grudge for years."

"Did he ever beat the daylights out of you?"

"Yes," Hammerschmidt's ex-wife said. She looked down. "It'd start after he'd been drinking." She looked back up at Salinski.

"Did it happen often?"

She looked down again. "Yes."

"How severely would he beat you?"

"I'd have bruises, it was pretty bad."

"Is that why you left him?"

"Yes."

"No more questions, your honor."

The prosecution seemed anxious to go after the witness. Springing to his feet, the prosecutor bellowed, "That's not what I hear. I have depositions from several credible witnesses who say Charlie left you because of *your* drinking problem. ...Do *you* have a drinking problem, Miss Kimble?"

"I did." Murmurs spread through the courtroom. "I did while I was with Charlie."

"What's your job now, Miss Kimble?"

"I work at...a club."

"A club? Is that what you call it — *a club?* Some people would call it...*a topless bar."*

"I'm raising two children on my own. It pays the bills."

"And you're surrounded by low-lifes all day...excuse me...*all night* long? Tell me, Miss Kimble, to pay your bills, do you ever do sexual favors for money?"

"Objection!" Salinski yelled, jumping to his feet in disbelief. "The prosecution has drifted off the relevant points of the trial, and into a personal character assassination of the witness."

"Overruled!"

*

With the help of the judge, the trial became something of a character-judgment contest between the prosecution's esteemed witnesses versus the defense's lowly witnesses. The point of the trial seemed to get lost. With outright adulation from the judge, the prosecution's witnesses shone as pillars of society who should be trusted. With implicit disdain from the judge, the defense's witnesses sank as lowly alcoholics and irresponsible menaces to society who should not be trusted. Influenced by the judge, the jury associated Hammerschmidt to the esteemed witnesses; the jury associated Miss Annabelle and Mr. Melbourne to the "low-lifes". Trapped in the court of ego justice, Salinski did not stand a chance.

That night, Salinski hoped for a breakthrough. The trial had slipped between his fingers, and he knew it. The next day would be the closing arguments. *I need to bring everyone back to the facts,* he thought. But he knew that even getting back to the facts would not be enough, for the credibility behind the witnesses presenting those facts had been dishonestly destroyed by the judge. "Is there something even *more powerful* than the facts?" he wondered.

That night, the team gathered at Salinski's home: Miss

271

Annabelle, Mr. Melbourne, Jessie and Angie. As the young lawyer faced his two clients, he was overcome with remorse. "I'm so sorry," he said. "I didn't expect the trial to go this way. I've never seen anything like this and could've never anticipated it, not even in my darkest imagination."

"Anticipated what, exactly?" Miss Annabelle asked.

"The *judge*...it's like he's best friends with the prosecution and those three political witnesses. It almost feels like some kind of conspiracy. It's so *wrong*."

"We can appeal if we lose," John Melbourne said.

"Yes, we could. But I get the feeling higher courts would not call for a new trial. There's something tacitly going on, something tacitly accepted."

"Like a soul mate thing," Jessie said.

"I'm sorry to do this, but I must ask all of you to leave," Salinski said abruptly. "I've got a lot to do...a lot to sort out before tomorrow. Things look bad right now, and I have to see if there's anything in my power that can change that." Then he looked directly into Miss Annabelle's eyes, then Mr. Melbourne's eyes. He knew their futures were in his hands.

Miss Annabelle looked scared. For the first time, she wondered what it would mean to lose the trial.

*

At 8:00 am, the fifth and final day of trial, the defense team gathered outside the courtroom. Miss Annabelle and Mr. Melbourne searched Salinski's eyes to read if he had some sort of breakthrough. Salinski looked as though he had not slept. He looked exhausted and distraught. Only his nervous energy kept him going. Neither Miss Annabelle nor Mr. Melbourne could read him. But they did not want to ask him, either. He looked too preoccupied...as though he were wrestling with thoughts. Miss Annabelle observed that this trial deeply affected the young Salinski and changed his outlook as a lawyer. He was not the same man now, not who he was a week earlier.

"I'm going to do something in there today no other lawyer would do," Salinski said with no warning. He jumped out of his tormented thoughts to talk to his two clients and their dear friends, Jessie and Angie. "Being around you four people these past two months has done something to me. This past week made me realize I don't like the path I'm on. And only by realizing this could I do what I'm going to do today. It goes beyond the facts I've presented. It's the most powerful course to take today and offers you the best chance. I'm...I'm going to expose the judge."

Miss Annabelle, Mr. Melbourne, Jessie and Angie felt their bond for each other reach out and embrace the young lawyer before them. They knew this could be career suicide, but he was a rare lawyer who chose honesty as his course.

"No matter what happens, we're proud of you," Miss Annabelle said, looking into his eyes. He looked scared, but he squared his jaw and headed into the courtroom.

"All rise!" cried the court officer.

Here we go, Salinski said to himself.

Closing arguments started with the prosecution: "Ladies and gentlemen of the jury, as so clearly demonstrated these past few days — and so thoroughly confirmed by your honorable mayor, your respected congressman, your..." so the prosecutor began. For the next hour and fifteen minutes, he would repeat just about everything said by his three political witnesses. The jurors were all wide-eyed and alert.

But Salinski was not listening. He already knew what would be said. Instead, he was still trying to put together the puzzle in his head to rise to the next level. What...oh what switched the judge into the leading member of the prosecution? Aside from the obvious political advantages, what was the hidden force that transmogrified him into a monster who could rob major portions of innocent people's lives? For, if Miss Annabelle and Mr. Melbourne are found guilty, Salinski thought, they'd lose years of their lives in prison. For what? No career advantages could be *that* important!

As he searched for an answer, he realized how much precious time he spent the night before, tormented, trying to decide whether or not to expose the judge. A crushing realization the night before paralyzed him for hours: this behavior was not isolated to this judge. He realized with great pain that this subjective, political-agenda court was malignant and happening everywhere. If he rebelled, he knew this judge and others would punish him, losing future cases for him, harming innocent future clients. He knew his career and future clients would suffer. Moreover, if he did *not* expose the judge, he would sail smoothly along in a promising career. He was bright and hard working. He knew he could be at the top someday.

But what shamed him today was that he spent two *additional* hours the night before, tempting himself to do what he knew was *not* the honest path. As he sat there not listening to the prosecutor, still struggling to grasp the bigger picture, he could not help but wonder if those two unnecessary additional hours wasted the night before could cost him the case for two innocent people, for he needed every moment to figure out his finalé that would expose the judge so the jurors could see the injustice, too.

The prosecutor was coming to a close: "May God be our witness: you owe it to your mayor, to your congressman, to your lieutenant governor, to your schools, to your children, *to your country* to send these dangerous killers to prison!" the prosecutor yelled in righteous ecstasy.

What, oh what, Salinski struggled to know, drove the judge to tacitly take a side? Salinski still did not have a definitive answer when he heard the judge calling out his name.

"Mr. Salinski. Mr. Salinski, the court is ready for your closing arguments."

"Thank…thank you, your honor," Salinski stammered as he stood up. He was so close to putting it all together…so close to why judges perpetuate this dark cloud over their courtrooms that obscures the clarifying light of justice. As he stood, facing the jury, all Salinski could think of at that moment was: *Damn! Those two additional hours last night!*

"Mr. Salinski!" snapped the judge.

*Damn! If only I hadn't wasted those two hours last night — all because of my goddamned **ego**!*

"Mr. Salinski, I've had just about enough of you and your bumbling—" the judge said, but Salinski cut in.

"Ego! That's it — *ego!*" Salinski shouted involuntarily. He might as well have shouted "eureka!" the way the words exploded from his mouth. Disgusted with the path he almost chose —

274

ego over honesty — and disgusted with the precious time he wasted the night before, which could have cost an irreplaceable portion of his clients' lives, he broke through. He realized that unearned *ego* was the driving force behind the path many lawyers took, and unearned *ego* was behind the judge taking a similar path that offered him unearned, easy career advantages upon tacitly entering the politicians' club for dishonest soul mates. Realizing he had blurted out his thoughts, Salinski continued talking spontaneously as the puzzle snapped together in his head. He focussed on the jurors:

"Let me ask you some rhetorical questions: you *like* the prosecutor, don't you? …You *like* his witnesses, don't you? You don't really *like* me, do you? …You certainly don't *like* my witnesses, right? …And, most important of all, you *really like* our judge, am I right?"

"Mr. Salinski," the judge abruptly interrupted, scowling down at the young lawyer. "You keep your questions focused on the people on trial here. Do you understand me?"

Salinski knew he was in a tight spot and decided to play along with the judge. "Yes, your honor, I'm sorry. No more such questions."

The judge relaxed, and Salinski continued, "I must make one point for the sake of justice itself, and is that not what all members of this court ultimately seek: *justice*?" Salinski looked straight at the judge, who looked away. "When a juror takes an emotional position that is based not on specific facts, but general feelings based on vague stories, then that juror is no longer wearing blindfolds — the very symbol of justice itself." Salinski reached behind his desk and pulled out a drawing of the blindfolded Lady of Justice. He held it up to the jurors and continued. "Instead, the blindfolds are off and the juror is trying his friend…or enemy. In jury selection, we try to eliminate bias. But now, you must ask yourself, 'Am I now biased?' Do you *like* the prosecutor and his witnesses? Is there somehow *a feeling of friendship?*"

The judge was becoming irritated and said, "Get to your point, Mr. Salinski, or I'll stop this nonsense!" Interestingly, Salinski observed, the majority of objections throughout this trail did not come from the prosecutor, but from the judge.

275

Superpuzzle

"Yes, your honor," Salinski said obediently, "I'll get to my point." He put down the drawing, turned back to the jurors, and said, "When you go into deliberations, I ask you to put aside all those feelings that have been, with great calculation, steadily pumped into you the past five days; you're all like big floats filled with these emotions of like and dislike. Your feet are not on the ground, and you can be easily pushed this way and that. But, if you get real honest with yourselves and come back down to earth, you'll realize that those feelings inside you are not based on the facts of this case, but on the special connection you've gained these past few days with some prominent personalities in our society, which would have to feel good to just about anybody's ego. Those personalities are graciously respected by the prosecutor, by the audience, by you, and by your leader...the judge himself. Who can possibly go against all that?" Salinski shrugged his shoulders and looked around as if in search of anyone who could defy that question. If the audience was not unanimously in agreement with him, his point sure was thought-provoking, for every eye was wide-open, every mind contemplating and every ear hanging on his every word. Then he turned back to the jury and spoke with contagious passion, "But that feel-good connection is not *the* point here! Almost everyone here has motivation to go along with those prominent personalities for different reasons. You do, the judge does, even I do. Those reasons all come back to our egos. But our egos cannot come between us and justice. Our egos must not cause innocent people to lose the most important years of their lives, which is what will happen to my clients. Salt-of-the-earth people who had no agendas to fill, and who were not clever enough to create illusions, told you *the facts*. *The cold, hard facts* must override warm, pleasant feelings — no matter *who* is creating those feelings. When you go in that room to deliberate, you remember the Lady of Justice. You put your blindfolds back on and you forget about all this feel-good friendship between you and the mayor, you and the congressman, you and the lieutenant governor, you and the judge. Your job in that deliberation room is to look at *the facts*. That is the only way justice can be served. *You* — not the mayor, not the congressman, not the lieutenant governor, not the judge, not your

276

ego, not their egos — *you alone* with the *bare facts* have *full responsibility* to *serve justice.* Do not come back here to deliver ego justice. Come back here to deliver objective justice."

Salinski sat down and held up his 14x17 drawing of the historical symbol of justice. He knew, regardless of the outcome, he had just soared to a new level of law and justice. He realized he had soared to the next level by being brutally honest with himself and the world around him. He felt powerful and proud. Without knowing the words, he had jumped into using Neothink. Miss Annabelle, Mr. Melbourne, Jessie and Angie looked at the young Salinski sitting tall and strong, boldly holding up the Lady of Justice, and they wanted to cheer. Their hearts welcomed this newcomer to their little civilization growing on planet Earth...consisting of them and the twelve students...the little Neothink World of profound honesty forming on planet Earth. The prosecution could not respond. The judge nervously adjourned the court for lunch.

*

As the court resumed for the afternoon session, Miss Annabelle was thinking about her students. She had asked them in the last weekly summer class to please not attend the trial. She said there was no reason to, since it would be full of falsities flung at her and Mr. Melbourne. She told them she knew they would be thinking of her and were with her in spirit. Now, as she sat at the defense table as the prosecuting attorney and Salinski and the judge reviewed the jury instructions, she had mixed feelings. She would have loved for her students to have witnessed Salinski's closing argument...and to have welcomed him into their world of honesty.

"Bring in the jurors," the judge was saying.

The judge delivered the agreed-upon jury instructions, which took about fifteen or twenty minutes. Miss Annabelle studied the jurors, several of them looked directly back at her with pleasant expressions. Three women jurors even smiled at her. *Salinski did it*, she thought, *he turned this whole thing around!*

Unfortunately, the judge felt the sea change, too. In a completely unexpected and unethical move, which surprised even the prosecuting attorneys, the judge did not stop talking after delivering the jury instructions. He continued talking for another five minutes in a speech he obviously prepared during the lunch break to counter the unprecedented closing argument and stunning turnaround by Salinski.

The judge's unethical ego-instructions seemed, to the unsuspecting jurors, to be simply more jury instructions. Instead, his extended monologue was his own, *personal* agenda to instruct the jurors to deliver a guilty verdict, regardless of the facts.

For nearly five minutes, he assured the jurors that the trial was done the way trials have been done "many thousands of times for hundreds of years". He assured the jurors they should not be persuaded from their original conclusions that they had reached on their own.

"Trust the feelings from your heart," he concluded in his unethical ego-instructions. "You're good people with good hearts. Of course you'll feel compassion, even love, toward a good man who may have needlessly died! And you'll naturally feel respect for his friends. You'll feel many things. From my thirty-two years as a judge, I urge you to seriously weigh those feelings. They're often telling you the right thing to do. The blindfolded Lady of Justice does not see, but she *feels*. So do you. Go place your verdict from your hearts."

Miss Annabelle looked at the jurors again. Not a single juror would look back at her. Their leader had spoken, and he told them to vote *guilty*. He controlled their bicameral minds.

They were sent into deliberations. The judge told all parties to stay nearby. It was 3:10 p.m.

Sitting in the courthouse cafeteria, at 4:25 p.m., the court runner came and told Salinski and his clients that the jury had reached a decision. Back in the courtroom, Miss Annabelle and Mr. Melbourne held hands as the jury entered. Not one juror looked at them.

"Have you reached a verdict?"

"We have, your honor," the jurors' foreman said, handing the decision to the court officer, who took it over to the judge.

"What is your verdict?" the judge asked, after looking at the written decision.

"*Guilty* on the felony count of voluntary manslaughter."

Miss Annabelle gasped; Mr. Melbourne hugged her. One of the women jurors who had earlier smiled at Miss Annabelle started sobbing. Suddenly, the powerful voice of a child filled the courtroom.

"The judge is a fraud! The judge is a fraud! The judge is a fraud!"

The loud voice of a child said it over and over. Everyone in the courtroom looked to where that powerful voice was coming from. In the back, there stood Teddy Winters, red with passion and ready to battle. It was quite a moving moment to see such a young child so passionate, so fearless, so deep-thinking.

"Stop that yelling, young man!" the judge bellowed through his microphone. His loud voice invoked fear in everyone in that room...except Teddy.

"The judge is a fraud. I do not recognize your authority, sir! You're a fraud. The judge is a political animal. The judge is a fraud!"

The people in the court suddenly felt moved by this boy who so clearly saw through the judge's agenda. Two other women jurors who had earlier smiled at Miss Annabelle, started crying, too. Teddy was piercing the illusion and awakening people to the idea that they were hoaxed by a judge who cared only about his own political career and ego. The judge instinctively reacted.

"Settle down your son, there," the angry judge warned Teddy's father who was standing next to the boy. "Stop him, or I'll have the court officer escort you both out of here!"

Teddy's dad looked at his son, who momentarily stopped, not sure what his father would say to him. Then his father looked back at the judge and said, "I won't stop him from speaking the truth, your honor."

"Officer!" the judge roared, "get them out of here!"

What a sight it was: a man with a uniform and gun holding a nine-year-old boy, whose voice was years away from changing, and his gentle father by their arms, forcing them out of the room of fraudulent justice. Anger and sadness swelled at the sight.

As the jurors left the courtroom, an elderly man was the first juror since the verdict to look at Miss Annabelle and Mr. Melbourne, who were still hugging each other. The old man looked very sad, and his mouth shaped the words, "I'm sorry."

Superpuzzle

The jurors are like my students' parents, Miss Annabelle sadly realized as she watched them shuffle forward, in line, heads bent down, forever subservient to their external authorities. They're good people; they know I'm innocent, but in the end they cannot go against the authority...trapped in the bicameral mentality.

*

The trial went by in a blur for Miss Annabelle; how very much a life can change forever in one week! She and her love were going to prison.

Three weeks later they gathered again before the judge to be sentenced. The judge seemed different on this day than he did during the trial. Salinski asked the judge to pass the minimum sentence allowed by law. The prosecuting attorney asked the judge to pass the maximum sentence, saying the judge must be tough and make an example of people who use brutal violence against dedicated public servants. But the judge seemed impatient with the prosecuting attorney. He asked Miss Annabelle and Mr. Melbourne if they had any statements to make. They did not.

So, the judge proceeded with his sentence. To Salinski's surprise, the judge passed the minimum sentence allowed by law.

*

Miss Annabelle stared at a picture on her fireplace mantle. It was taken at the picnic, the last class outing. She studied the expressions of each of her students and her fiancé. *They're so beautiful*, she thought.

I can't believe it, John and I must report to prison in five weeks. She rubbed her thumb lovingly across John's face on the photo. *We won't see each other for three years.* She rubbed her thumb slowly across the face of each student. *I won't see you, my precious darlings, for three years. What will that mean? I can't imagine it...not yet.*

As the days passed one by one, she was never so aware of how wonderful *freedom* was. She never had any idea how exhilarating it was to go where she wanted to go, when she wanted to go there. Not until her freedom would soon be taken away did she realize how wonderful it was. ...Ironically, that made her realize how wonderful Sally and her mother's time together must be.

What is a human life, my life, made of? Miss Annabelle pondered that question as her final five weeks of freedom passed. *My life is made from my experiences,* she finally concluded; *those experiences that turn into memories are the substance of my life...permanent chunks of my life, even as memories. Prison will take away my freedom to have experiences. Three years without experiences is the same as irreplaceably killing three years of my life. The judge murdered three years of my life and John's life!*

*

When she gathered her students for the last time before leaving for at least three years, Miss Annabelle knew she had to hold her feelings back, or she would lose control and break down. The next time I see them, she thought, they'll be at least twelve years old. Three years is a lot of time at their age...I'll miss so much of their development. The judge committed a sick crime on us! ...The tragedy of being put away for three or more years was beginning to sink in.

The children were terribly in need of understanding how the jury could do this to their innocent teacher. Miss Annabelle explained that not until the mentality out there changes from the ancient mentality to the God-Man mentality could the jurors have thought for themselves, as self-leaders, free of external leaders.

Then, Miss Annabelle gave her last speech to her students. They listened sadly to her words on how to remain in their honest God-Man world without her. As she looked at their sad faces, she remembered that same gloom when Ms. Minner put the substitute teacher in her class early in the school year. My God, Miss Annabelle thought, how I wish I could turn this situation around as I did last time they tried to separate us!

But this time, she was helpless. She could not light up those twelve beautiful faces.

Superpuzzle

The painful hour arrived. It was time to say their final good-byes. The doorbell rang; it was Cathy's mother. In a desperate reflex, Cathy looked at Miss Annabelle; the little girl's forehead crinkled into a knot.

"Oh...good-bye, my beautiful girl," Miss Annabelle said. Her voice was shaking. She reached out to hug Cathy; they embraced; the little girl began to cry. Miss Annabelle closed her eyes and thought, I'm *so glad* I was able to free this little girl from her prison...so glad. "I'm so proud of you," Miss Annabelle whispered into Cathy's ear. Cathy hugged her teacher tighter. It was hard for Cathy to let go; her beautiful teacher had saved her future and meant so much to her! Even Cathy's mother was overcome by the love and value flowing between her daughter and Miss Annabelle. The child of the past in Mrs. Solomon was touched, and she was moved to tears. "Good-bye, my darling," Miss Annabelle whispered, wiping the tears from Cathy's cheeks with her thumbs. Miss Annabelle smiled peacefully. But inside, her heart was being torn apart as she watched the little beauty walk out the door.

As Cathy walked toward the street, Mr. Winters passed her on the way to the house. Miss Annabelle turned to Teddy. "Oh, my Teddy," she said. "You keep expanding, you brilliant entrepreneur," she said. He nodded, but he could not smile. They hugged. "Thank you for standing up to that evil judge for me," she whispered into his ear. "You're *very brave.*"

"Remember, you always told us that when you go to the essence of things, you don't have to be afraid of anyone or anything," Teddy said. Miss Annabelle leaned back to look at him, and she smiled. His eyes were full of tears and his lips were twitching. "Yes, I remember, Teddy." she said softly. Teddy nodded, but he was sadly frowning. Such pain, Miss Annabelle thought, needlessly inflicted on these innocent children by evil people.

Teddy knew Miss Annabelle had also saved his dad from sinking into a life of miserable stagnation. Teddy could not imagine his life now without Miss Annabelle. Suddenly, the impact was too great and Teddy sniffled, then started crying. There was nothing Miss Annabelle could do but give him one last loving hug.

"Thank you," Teddy's father said in a very sad, deep workingman's voice. Then he put his arm around his son's shoulder. Miss Annabelle watched them walk away, Teddy's head hanging forward, his spirit shattered.

"I'm so sorry this has happened." The gentle voice was filled with compassion. Miss Annabelle's eyes were drawn to that caring voice of Sally's mother standing next to her. When Miss Annabelle saw her, love and understanding were radiating from her eyes. Miss Annabelle could not stop herself from frowning. She looked down, next to Sally's mother, at Sally. Miss Annabelle saw fear in Sally's eyes. All along, Miss Annabelle, Sally, and her mother tacitly believed Miss Annabelle would be there to help Sally when her mom died. But now, the three of them feared Sally would go through the loss of her mom without Miss Annabelle.

Looking at Sally's pained expression brought back a memory...to the beginning of the school year...when Sally was devastated with fear about her mom's fatal illness. Miss Annabelle knelt down and looked into Sally's eyes. So much fragility exists in my little Sally's life, Miss Annabelle thought...so much love to be so easily, so swiftly lost.

"Sweetie," Miss Annabelle said while putting her hands on Sally's little shoulders, "you must be strong." Sally nodded, but her big brown eyes looked more scared than ever. Miss Annabelle knew while looking into Sally's frightened eyes that the little girl could emotionally get through her mother's imminent death because of having Miss Annabelle here to turn to. Now, that would no longer be the case, which caused great fear in the little girl. "Sally, listen to me. The fear can rob you of the love and joy you and your mom have left. Don't let that happen, darling. Okay? Live each precious day without dreading the future. When the time comes...it comes. Live and love in the present, my precious. Do not live in fear of the future. Live and love in the present."

An unmistakable understanding came over Sally's expression and filled her eyes. Miss Annabelle pulled her against her. "I love you," Miss Annabelle said.

Sally sobbed into Miss Annabelle's shoulder. "I just can't believe you're going to prison," she cried.

Superpuzzle

Miss Annabelle squeezed her eyes shut to stop herself from releasing the enormous pain of parting with Sally. "Oh Sally, don't you for a minute worry about me and bring yourself down over this. This is *your* time to *enjoy life* with your mother. Darling, please don't worry about me. And to help put you at ease, I'm going to write you at least once a week."

Sally pulled her head back. "You mean, we can send each other letters?" Miss Annabelle smiled and nodded. Sally hugged her tightly and said, "I'm going to write you all the time, Miss Annabelle!"

Sally's mother, her eyes filled with tears, smiled and shook her head at the beautiful way Miss Annabelle always cleared the devastating obstacles from Sally's path in life and filled that path with exhilaration, love, and happiness.

As the parents arrived for their children, one by one each child and their beloved teacher would say a special good-bye. Each child hugged her with all of his or her might. She whispered something loving and memorable into each child's ear. When she and each of her little loved ones released their embraces, the little ones would leave in despair, devastated and sobbing, even the boys. She trembled in pain as she watched Danny, Alan, Nattie, Bobby, Jeremiah, Debbie, Reggie, and then Ian walk out of her life. "I'll miss you," she'd helplessly whisper as they left in tears.

Finally, one child remained. He had no parents coming for him; he had ridden his bike. Rico, the little macho man, looked at Miss Annabelle. The room was painfully quiet. "I've read them, you know," he said. "All three...I loved them so much; I don't know which one was my favorite. Maybe...*Martin Eden.* I also bought and read another one of his books called *The Sea Wolf.*"

For the first time, Miss Annabelle discovered Rico was a prolific reader — four major novels since Christmas. That discovery put a glow on her face again, as only her students could do. "*You,* my darling, *are* Martin Eden. But you won't get pulled under by contradictions in the end as he did...because you see through the illusions to *what is*." Her unexpected comment filled Rico with pride, which put a glow on his face.

She stopped and enjoyed the moment, looking at this boy

from a family of hard criminals, choosing a different path in life. She saw before her a *real* tough guy, tough enough to stand up against his father and his way of life...tough enough to blaze his own path as a child. She saw man-size courage in the boy before her. "God, I'll miss you," she said under her breath.

The glow on Rico's face changed to a look of pain...greater and greater pain. Time closed in on him. He couldn't stop the separation from happening. His dreaded fear of this unstoppable moment sent a flash of panic through his eyes. The little tough guy could take no more. "Bye," he said, bursting into tears. He could say nothing more.

"Bye," Miss Annabelle whispered, bursting into tears, unable to say more. Rico ran over and hugged her.

During the moment of their hug, that precious moment when he buried his face into her shoulder and she closed her eyes, she could feel him crying. She could feel the little boy — the vulnerable sweet child — in her arms. The next moment, not wanting her to see him crying, not looking at her, he turned away and ran out of her house, down the stairs, and he rode away. She stood in her doorway, watching him, wishing beyond wish for a peaceful life in his violent home.

Rico sped down the street; he kept looking back for one last glance.

"God, I'll miss you," Miss Annabelle cried. She felt her strength leaving her body as quickly as Rico rode away, as though a string to her soul were snagged on Rico's bike, and her soul was being unraveled and pulled out of her as Rico sped away. The moment she could not see Rico, a severe pain tore through her body. The last connections of her soul burst from their sockets and ripped clear from her heart.

She had nothing left inside her — no strength — to mask the pain. She closed the door and walked into her house. She got no further than the middle of her living room. The pain rushing up from within, rushing up from her lungs and through her mouth, released a primal wail of a mother separated from her young. She collapsed onto the floor and cried so hard her stomach cramped up. Mr. Melbourne picked her up and carried her to bed, where her cramp forced her to curl up like a baby, and she cried herself to sleep.

CHAPTER
TWENTY-TWO

They made their last full day together something memorable. That memory would help keep them motivated throughout their time away from each other.

Miss Annabelle and Mr. Melbourne spent the previous five weeks, since being sentenced, busily putting their affairs in order for a three to five-year absence. Now, the day before they were to report to prison, they were prepared to go. So, they spent the last day absorbing each other's love.

Around ten o'clock in the morning, they spontaneously thought about getting married that last day together. But, they realized they would be busily running around all day to get their marriage license, their blood test, and to find a justice of the peace. Instead, on this day, they wanted to celebrate their love for each other and decided to get married after they were free again. This day was the first time they discussed marriage. It left a wonderful feeling inside them both. Because of this inescapable separation, their love went to a new level that last day together, where their love, she believed, would always stay.

Their last night together, they slept in each others' arms.

*

Conceiving the Superpuzzle

The next morning seemed unreal. To be apart for so long would have been nearly impossible. But the previous day together, with their decision to marry upon getting back their freedom, would carry their spirits until they were together again.

Jessie drove Mr. Melbourne; Angie drove Miss Annabelle. Saying good-bye was hard, but it was possible because, ironically, they were still celebrating the new romantic heights they had reached. They both inherently knew their higher love would get them through the next few years.

It was a beautiful September morning; the sun was shining, the birds were singing. It almost felt as though the world was celebrating their discovery of a higher love.

With smiles on their faces, Miss Annabelle and Mr. Melbourne let go of each other and said good-bye.

*

A week inside prison and Mr. Melbourne was tired. He had no idea how hard prisoners worked. He dropped another tray of dishes onto the dishwasher rack and leaned back against the counter for a breather. He was on cleanup duty.

The dishwasher, a tall black man everyone called Ace, noticed Mr. Melbourne was hurting and said in a mock Australian accent, "Don't worry, mate, you'll adjust, and the work'll go by quickly."

Mr. Melbourne laughed at Ace's attempt at an Australian accent that sounded more Irish than Australian. Ace reminded him of Jessie.

"Thanks. I hope I adjust 'cause I'm worthless after I get done my shift."

"Ah, before you know it, you'll be in the gym pumping iron after them tables are cleared and cleaned," Ace promised. He wisely gave up his attempt at an Australian accent.

"I worry about my fiancé. Dishes weigh the same in women's prisons as they do here." Mr. Melbourne said, shaking his head. Worrying about Miss Annabelle was making his condition worse.

"She'll get used to it too," Ace said reassuringly. "You're young. She's young. In a couple of weeks, she'll be OK. She'll even get that toned up body every woman dreams of!"

"You're sure?" Mr. Melbourne asked.

"Yeah, I know women who've been in prison," Ace answered, seriously and honestly. "They *can* physically handle it."

It was what Mr. Melbourne needed to hear. All of a sudden, his fatigue seemed to be gone. For the rest of his shift, Mr. Melbourne, for the first time since being there, moved with ease through his job and even wondered, for a moment, if he felt *good*. He stopped and thought, for an instant, do I feel a little bit happy?

That evening before lights out, Mr. Melbourne began working on his book again. Suddenly, without a doubt this time, he felt a surge of happiness. He wrote until lights out.

Lying on his back, his body was in a small room with five other men. But as he lay on his top bunk, his mind was free and racing through a universe of thoughts. His experience here, he realized for the first time, was giving him profound insights about man, society, and our mentality. He was also discovering how *free* he still was.

*

Mr. Melbourne's discovery was a godsend: the experience of being in prison as a political prisoner brought unique angles to everything he had written in his book. In bizarre irony, he was discovering that a man is not wholly free in the anticivilization until he goes into the abyss of captivity. When his freedom is taken away, he discovers the power and freedom of his mind. Now, Mr. Melbourne spent every spare moment working on his book. He now knew his life would still move forward. Like a sick man who just got better, he felt really good.

A little over an hour away in the state prison for women, Miss Annabelle had been discovering the same phenomenon. Her nonwork time now all went to developing a weekly lecture that she taped and mailed to her twelve little God-Men each Wednesday. They continued their weekly classes together at Sally's house or Teddy's house. They would listen to Miss Annabelle's lecture on tape and then discuss it among themselves.

Miss Annabelle, like her lover, had discovered *life* in prison. Her lectures now had a dimension and added value she could not reach without this experience. She felt happy again, and her love started flowing from her heart again, which started a stream of perhaps some of the most beautiful love letters ever written. Her nonwork time now consisted of a perfect balance of developing logical left-brain lectures and emotional right-brain love letters.

The stream of love letters flowing back and forth between the imprisoned lovers fueled them and motivated their creations. Their lives, suppressed in routine physical labor and loneliness, were also full of adventure and love. Their minds soared toward new creations...and their hearts beat with love for each other. And Ace was right: the labor was exhausting, but their bodies got used to it.

Miss Annabelle also received a tape each week from her students' discussion session. After they listened to her lecture, they turned on the cassette to record their discussion. The prison gave her permission to listen to those tapes. Her students wrote her personal letters, too. Miss Annabelle was busy from the moment she woke up till the moment she fell asleep. Even after lights out, she would often lie awake in bed, sometimes up to an hour or longer, thinking about the next part to the puzzle-picture she was building for her students...or thinking about her love.

*

At Duncan Elementary School, the third week of the new school year had begun. The whole school attended a special announcement in the school auditorium that Monday afternoon at 2:00 p.m.

No one knew what the announcement would be about. The teachers were surprised when Ms. Minner started to talk about Miss Annabelle and Mr. Melbourne being in prison for the manslaughter of Mr. Hammerschmidt.

Then, what particularly surprised the faculty, was the principal's religious references.

"Let there be no mistake: anyone who commits such a crime will have blood on their hands when they meet God and will be sent to the fire below for eternity." Her voice, filled with bitterness, rang through the auditorium in her thick southern accent, sounding like a leap-of-faith healer.

Ms. Minner was born in Atlanta, Georgia into a devoutly religious family, notched for generations in the Bible Belt. Ms. Minner was physically unattractive all her life with beady black eyes, thick glasses, thin greasy hair, and a splotchy complexion. She never married. She never even went on a date. She never kissed a man romantically. She resented men and hated pretty women. She disliked children, especially young children. She physically tensed up when children laughed and played around her. She avoided places visited by children such as McDonald's and carnivals. At home, she used to refer to the neighborhood children as little brats. Over time, that changed to little *rats*.

When she got together with her two friends — two older ladies who also never married — their talk was negative, always. But they seemed to enjoy their nonstop, negative talk. Their topic of discussion lately often turned to Miss Annabelle and Mr. Melbourne. The three of them would whip themselves into a frenzy, convinced that the attractive couple was the work of the devil himself.

Hammerschmidt had used Miss Annabelle to create an illusion that would boost his political career. Ms. Minner, on the other hand, was not interested in politics. She believed she was the heroine who saved the school, the children, and the town from the devil's work. With her two friends cheering her on, Ms. Minner became obsessed with the mission to get Miss Annabelle out of her twelve students' lives forever.

Moreover, in a euphoric moment, the three ladies agreed that Ms. Minner would be doing God's work by separating the two lovers, for the strength of the devil in Cheektowaga would be broken. Thus, the topic of discussion with the only two friends Ms. Minner had in this world became her mission from God: separate Miss Annabelle from the two things she deeply loved — her students and her man.

Two days later, Ms. Minner searched through Miss Annabelle's and Mr. Melbourne's files at school, and the principal's beady eyes widened at the discovery that Mr. Melbourne was not a citizen of the United States.

Conceiving the Superpuzzle

*

The only contact Miss Annabelle had with the outside world, besides her cherished letters from John, was her weekly audio-cassette tape and the personal letters from her students. She saved every letter and tape and noticed how rapidly her twelve little God-Men were advancing. They all used Neothink now, building puzzle-pictures piece by piece. Teddy was on his way to becoming a millionaire before he turned ten years old. He and Cathy went on their first "date" together. Ian had an article published in the *Buffalo News,* and his ideas on the cosmos were attracting the attention of some prominent physicists. Sally's mom seemed surprisingly strong and the relationship had taken an interesting turn: Sally and her mom were spending hours together after school learning about the disease. Sally was beginning to form some very interesting insights about controlling the disease.

Miss Annabelle knew, during those final weeks in third grade when her students started integrating knowledge and building Neothink puzzles, they would become self-perpetuating creators who would someday create great values for the world. But the speed at which this was happening amazed her.

A few days before Christmas, Miss Annabelle listened to her students' latest tape. A discussion broke out among Teddy, Danny, and Sally that astounded Miss Annabelle. She got permission to send the tape to Mr. Melbourne. It contained a prophetic picture of the future of microprocessors, the economy, and medicine. As she handed the tape over to the prison guard to send to Mr. Melbourne, Miss Annabelle could not stop smiling. For, she could see in her thoughts her fiancé's face, his wide-eyed expressions of astonishment as he listened to her students' breakthrough thinking.

God, I wish I could be there to see John's face, she thought. She lived each day longing to be together with her students and her John again.

*

Christmas Day arrived. Miss Annabelle awakened before the

291

6:00 a.m. bugle sounded. On holidays, she liked to think back to the same day the year before, which she did as she lay in her bunk. She remembered that on Christmas Day last year she had broken through to grasping the immense value of human life and tragedy of human death. She also remembered spreading that God-Man perspective to her students, who were still young enough to genuinely never want to die. That immortal perspective amplified the value of their own lives so greatly that, she believed, their young minds reached for more — reached for Neothink.

At breakfast, Miss Annabelle sat at the table, unaware that she had not eaten a thing. She was feeling down. She had been in this place for just four months, and she had at least two and a half more years to go. Two and a half more years! That's seven times longer than I've been in here, she thought. I miss John; I miss my students. I just miss them too much.

"Merry Christmas, Anna," a cheerful voice said. Miss Annabelle looked up to see one of her roommates, Megan, sitting down next to her. "You haven't touched your food, sweetie. Do you feel okay?"

"Oh...yes. I'm...I'm just..." Miss Annabelle paused, not sure what to say.

"Holidays in here are hard." Megan's voice had so much compassion that Miss Annabelle's eyes involuntarily filled with tears. Megan saw the reaction and said, "Oh...honey, come here." Megan put her fork down, reached around, and hugged Miss Annabelle.

Megan had become a genuine friend. She was a sincere person, forty years old, and a pillar of positivity. Miss Annabelle really enjoyed Megan's sense of life.

"It's going to be so long before I see John again and my students," Miss Annabelle said, her voice shaking. Megan hugged her tighter.

"In here, Anna, time goes by so slowly. But I want you to consider something, dear. Out there, time goes by so quickly. In here, I have a lot of time to think about what I want out of life. I already know that when I get out, the rest of my life will go by in a blink. But, because of my time in here, I'll know what I want. I'll go hard after what I want. I'll be

292

focused and not on an aimless journey that ends before it begins."

Miss Annabelle sat up to look into Megan's eyes. Her friend had expressed a wisdom that surpassed Miss Annabelle. She looked at her vivacious friend who grew up in Rochester, New York in a blue-collar neighborhood. Megan looked cute with her short blonde hair and long spit curls that framed her face. As almost always, she wore a beautiful smile.

"You've turned this negative — your five precious years in here — into a positive. I admire that, Megan."

Megan smiled, and so did Miss Annabelle.

"You're always so positive...so happy!" Miss Annabelle said through a tearful chuckle, obviously feeling better. "What...how..."

"There's really nothing special about it," Megan said. She was not being flippant. In fact, she became very serious and said, "Would you like me to tell you how I got this way?" Miss Annabelle nodded and gave her undivided attention to the story Megan was about to tell.

"Okay...you're the only one I've told this to: When I was 15, I fell in love. His name was Joseph, and he was 20 years old. He landed a good job as an apprentice train mechanic for the railroad, and three months later I was pregnant. At 16, I had a beautiful baby boy...little Joey. Joseph and I got married. At 18, I gave birth to Meg and Peg, our twin daughters. But we weren't like so many teenage marriages...we were *really happy*, and we *stayed* happy. He was a hard-working man and worked his way up to line manager. I was so proud of him! Even though we struggled at first, we were *happy*. He'd rush home from work to play with the children. Throughout the week, he'd announce to the kids that his day off was *family day*, and we'd spend the entire day together, going on picnics, riding bicycles, going to a movie, taking a drive to the shore. When he became line manager, he had weekends off, and we'd spend them together as a family. Now and then, Joe would facetiously fret about the day our kids moved out, but I think he really kinda meant it."

Megan hesitated and looked into Miss Annabelle's gentle eyes, then Megan smiled, but it was a sad smile. "He never did see that day when Joey moved out. My sweetheart died one icy winter evening on his way home from work. A van going in the other direction lost control and spun directly into his car." Megan dropped her gaze to the floor. Miss Annabelle had never seen Megan sad, defeated. She barely could say more, but she continued, "I...I often try to imagine what Joe was thinking about during that last drive home. I know he was excited to see us. He'd always come in through the garage door and yell 'Daddy's home!' The kids would drop whatever they were doing and run to him. He did that for seventeen beautiful years."

Miss Annabelle knew what it was like to lose a loved one suddenly, violently. Eleven years before, when she was in her mid-twenties, she lost her only sibling, her brother, to a freak boating accident.

As Miss Annabelle looked at her friend, she realized that when you lose a loved one to early death, especially to a violent ending during that loved one's prime, your inner world of emotions is mercilessly and permanently defeated. You can grow new emotions, but those emotions in you from the past that revolved around your lost loved one are forever defeated. That look of defeat covered Megan's face.

"I'm so sorry," Miss Annabelle said, her own eyes filling with tears of sorrow for her friend.

Megan nodded and tried to smile. She struggled to say, "Joey, Meg and Peg...oh, they were devastated; they got so skinny after their daddy died. They wouldn't eat. Our world orbited around Joe, and then he was gone ...instantly...forever. Through all our pain and depression, what stood out most in my mind was *how fast* those seventeen years we had together had passed. These days, seventeen years is considered a marathon marriage. But after the accident, those seventeen years seemed like six months. They had gone by in a flash...*they really had*.

"The kids and I barely managed. Two years later, Joey moved out. The year after that, Meg and Peg moved into the dormitory of the local college. For the first time in my life, I was alone. It was really hard. I kept living in the past, and I couldn't get out of my head *how fast* those seventeen beautiful years went by. It felt like my life was over now...over so fast.

"Four years after Joe died, a year after my girls moved out, I couldn't stand the loneliness. I started dating for the first time.

Stanley had worked with Joe; he was a very nice and caring person. He was educated, a college graduate, and had always been part of railroad management. I didn't love Stan; I didn't think I could love again, but I did like him…and he was good to me. So, he moved in. It wasn't until after Stan moved in with me that I discovered he had a cocaine habit. He convinced me that it was only a stimulant for when he was working long hours. He said it did less harm than smoking cigarettes or drinking coffee. He said he'd always used cocaine. I really didn't know anything about it other than what he told me.

"One night, about a month after Stan moved in, six federal agents stormed my home and found his cocaine. Since I knew about it, I was charged with possession and was sentenced to eleven years.

"Well, Anna, that was about as much as I could take. I wanted to die and thought about killing myself, but I kept going because I knew what the suicide option would do to my precious children.

"Months passed in here; I didn't smile, not once. Then, one morning when I woke up, for one beautiful moment I felt like I was with Joe and the kids again. It was the first time I felt really good inside since Joe died. Lying in bed that morning before the wake up call, I smiled for the first time in here."

Megan had a hard time getting through her personal story, but now she seemed to gain strength as she remembered that morning:

"I realized I was letting go. I was telling myself it was okay to let go of those beautiful years and that my life with Joe was an everlasting part of me…a permanent place I could visit in my heart whenever I wanted to, just as I was doing that morning. By that afternoon I realized I had lived one life, which included my fairy tale with Joe and my children. And now, I had one more life to live again. All afternoon, I kept thinking how fast my first life went by in a blink. If I kept frowning, my second life would be over in a blink, and all I would have done was feel miserable. I could either frown…or smile. *Either way*, my life would go by in a flash, but it could be a flash full of frowns or a flash full of smiles. I chose to smile.

"At first, it took discipline to pursue a positive life. After a while, it came naturally. Now, I know that my second life will be over fast, like my first life, so I'm going to make every moment as positive and happy as I can."

Suddenly Megan put both her hands on Miss Annabelle's shoulders and said, "Anna, people don't know, until it's all ending, how fast our lives pass by. I know because I've had one life that already ended. Once you know it, then to be less than positive and energetic is such a waste of your one brief moment alive."

Miss Annabelle shook her head and managed to say, "I so admire you, Megan." ...She doesn't belong here, Miss Annabelle could not stop saying in her thoughts. Why is this good woman in prison? She's not *a criminal*. Yet, she's being stripped of anywhere from eight to eleven years of her prime...aging in here.

Miss Annabelle remembered what Rico had told the class: there are many people in prison who are *not* criminals. They committed no real crimes of force. Instead, they violated the sound-good, vote-gathering laws created by politicians. Megan, a beautiful person who would never hurt anyone, violated one of those political-policy laws. Miss Annabelle agonized over this. How many Megans are trapped in here? The innocence of Megan's face really moved Miss Annabelle as she heard a voice in her head saying, over and over, "I'm so sorry you're in here, Megan!"

Megan smiled. She did not know Miss Annabelle was feeling sorry for her. Megan said, "I'll tell you, Anna, our lives go by in a hurry. When you get out of here, don't waste any time, don't hesitate to do whatever it is that's going to bring you happiness. And let yourself...no, *make* yourself *feel it!* Figure out your path, and then run along it. I've already figured out what I'm going to do. Now, I just can't wait to get out of here! Just four years to go if I get out early."

Four more years murdered by politicians, Miss Annabelle thought.

*

Megan's attitude lifted Miss Annabelle. Why frown when I can smile? Miss Annabelle never forgot those words, and she

296

realized she had *a lot* to smile about. She was deeply in love; she thought a lot about the wedding that would happen when she and Mr. Melbourne were free again. In fact, she started planning the wedding, right from prison, ordering catalogues and brochures. She wanted a wedding and reception so she and Mr. Melbourne could celebrate the special memory with the other people they loved: her students, Sally's parents, Teddy's parents, Jessie and Angie, John's family. With both her parents and her brother gone, Miss Annabelle had no family. These people she loved and wanted at her wedding had become her family. The wedding had become a symbol of freedom for Miss Annabelle and Mr. Melbourne. Thinking about it kept them both very positive.

Miss Annabelle led a busy life in prison. She kept her weekly class going from prison, which made her feel as if she were out there in the free world. She and Megan had become close friends. And every other Saturday on visiting day, Jessie and Angie visited her for a couple of hours. Those visits were like shots of adrenaline. Moreover, Jessie and Angie visited Mr. Melbourne, too, once a month. Miss Annabelle would get so excited hearing everything about him and vice versa. Angie and Jessie really enjoyed it, too. Miss Annabelle was forever grateful for the value and effort Angie and Jessie gave to her.

Her students had asked her on the first discussion tape if they could come to visit her. Rico said that they could and told them how. Miss Annabelle's heart melted as she listened to their euphoria when they thought they could come to see her. But children were not allowed to visit unless they were related to the inmate and accompanied by a parent or guardian. So, they had to settle for the recorded weekly lecture and discussion period, which was very rewarding nonetheless.

Every night now, she lay in bed after lights out and thought: With all these wonderful people and values in my life...why frown when I can smile?

CHAPTER
TWENTY-THREE

During the week between Christmas and New Year's Day, Mr. Melbourne was pleasantly surprised when he was notified that an audio-cassette tape awaited him in the prison library. It was the tape Miss Annabelle sent him, and it was the best Christmas present he could have hoped for. Indeed, the tape of his fiancé's students meant new knowledge!

First thing, before he had to report for his daily duties, he rushed to the prison library and eagerly popped the tape into the cassette player.

He listened closely and gratefully, for the students' sweeping picture helped Mr. Melbourne snap a major puzzle piece into his own growing Neothink puzzle for eventually marketing his own book.

As the tape played, Mr. Melbourne was surprised at how mature Teddy's voice sounded and how articulate he was. Teddy, Danny, and Sally now talked with the vocabulary of middle-aged executives:

"I've been watching a fascinating phenomenon in the new microprocessor industry," Teddy said. "Cofounder of Intel, Gordon Moore, best described this phenomenon nearly nine years ago when he predicted the complexity of the integrated circuit would double every eighteen months, which has held up.

"I know there's more to the geometrical increase of the power and speed of the microprocessor than the advancing technology itself, something that Gordon Moore himself might not understand. I know that the geometrical phenomenon is possible because the microprocessor and brand-new microcomputer industry *isn't regulated*. The industry is too new and different and is advancing too fast to have deep-rooted regulatory control woven throughout it.

"Now, let me ask the question: in the integrated-circuit world, what would the continuation of *unregulated* technology mean? As long as the politicians and regulators don't get a stranglehold on the microprocessors, then I predict that before the turn of the millennium, small inexpensive computers will exist with the power and speed of the huge IBM mainframes. Using Moore's Law, the computing power will soar while costs plunge. Those personal 'mainframes' will sit in ordinary people's homes, helping ordinary people run their personal lives and entrepreneurial businesses. Let me say it again: Ordinary families will have small inexpensive computers at home with the computing power of large expensive IBM mainframes. Think of it: little personal 'mainframes' for everyone, what an exciting thought! In that future world of computers, you would become computer-rich because your computer buying power would multiply a thousand times."

After a long pause, Danny picked up the conversation:

"Now, let me ask a question: in the world *beyond* computers, what would a continuation of unregulated technology mean? Without the regulatory web restricting every other industry, technology would advance geometrically in *every field*, just like the microcomputers. Just as Teddy predicted for the microprocessors, buying power would eventually multiply a thousand times, everywhere in every technological industry."

Suddenly, Sally spoke up, "You know, the medical industry would soar without the external authorities holding it back. I know now, you guys are right about that. I can see it in my research."

"The microprocessor computers are demonstrating the proof to the world," Danny said. He nodded at Sally. "If politicians and regulators — the external authorities — were pulled off of every industry, particularly the technology industries, those industries would advance geometrically. Values would soar; buying power would, too."

"Cancer would be cured," Sally added, sadly.

Mr. Melbourne shut off the cassette player. Although there was more, he was late for his duties and would have to hear the rest later. As he rushed out of the prison library, his eyes were still wide with astonishment over the students' Neothink picture, just as Miss Annabelle had imagined. Mr. Melbourne walked quickly for the cafeteria, oblivious to the world around him, wishing he could talk to his woman about her incredible students.

His head was spinning with his imagination of that nonpoliticized world, where everyone was rich. I have confidence in those kids' vision, he thought. The only valid future tellers are the rare people who see through the matrix of illusions to *what is*, for only they have the widely integrated insights, the puzzle pieces, to most accurately snap together a puzzle-picture of the future.

*

Over the next few months, Mr. Melbourne maximized his values in prison, just as his fiancé had done. After he finished his kitchen duties one evening, as he did often, he told her about his progress in a letter. He hurried into his room, grabbed a pad of paper and a pencil. He kicked off his shoes and climbed onto his bunk. He leaned his back against the wall and pulled his knees up, putting his feet onto the side of the bunk. He rested the pad on his raised knees and started writing his letter:

My Dearest Anna,

I've discovered that, unlike in the free world, in here I can talk to prisoners about the ideas in my book. They listen, and in some cases they actually integrate an understanding of the Civilization of God-Man. Several of the prisoners are part of my work studies. They often see through to the essence and grasp things that would be ungraspable out there in the free world...in the anticivilization filled with political illusions and dishonesties. I ask myself, why? Why can some of these prisoners see reality when free citizens cannot? I've realized that out there, society's political leaders and the media actually calibrate everything to support the political illusions and dishonesties. In here, the prison leaders calibrate nothing, for no illusions exist. In here, people wake up from the spell of external authorities and simply think on their own. Amazingly, in here, several of the prisoners grasp the next evolution of man — God-Man and his Civilization of the Universe. I'm very excited about pursuing what all this means and where it's leading me.

God, I miss you Anna.

Love Forever,
John

*

Two years into his sentence...

My Dearest Anna,

I've extracted lots of information from my extensive 'laboratory' experiments. I could have gotten this information nowhere else. The results really strengthen my work! I've learned that the driving force behind the illusions and dishonesties of the anticivilization is *laziness*. The illusions and dishonesties, for example, bring unearned power to the perpetrators...the ruling class. And that anticivilization trait of seeking something for nothing runs through most people in this suppressed anticivilization. With that insight, I've developed a marketing approach for my book that will embrace the most powerful force of the anticivilization instead of fighting it. With most people's desires dominated by a get-something-for-nothing attraction, I'll market my work as the ultimate route to *easy* success and well-being. When you take in the whole picture, becoming the God-man is the easy route to success. I've now woven that theme throughout my book. My literary and marketing approach is extremely attractive in the anticivilization.

Yet, my new get-something-for-nothing angle is not hype; it is for real once humanity evolves into the new God-Man mentality and ends its dependency on political leaders. I see the first clue: without lifting a finger, consumers' buying power for personal computers has been increasing geometrically for a few years with no end in sight, just as Teddy predicted two years ago. The personal computer industry is new and different; it is the least regulated industry. Therefore, the personal computer industry is the least hindered industry, and it is soaring. Once we enter the age of the God-Man mentality, which will end the reign of political leaders and their regulatory bureaucracies, society will undergo geometrical increases of buying power in nearly all industries, just as Danny predicted two years ago. The people will, in essence, become rich without having to do a thing. I call it: the coming *millionaire phenomenon*, for the people will quickly enjoy the buying power of millionaires and, eventually, billionaires.

Needless to say, the prisoners love this anti-authority, get-rich philosophy. Get rid of the ruling class and get rich. I realize that the general population will be drawn to this philosophy as well because, ironically, it appeals to the pervasive mind-set of the anticivilization: *get something for nothing*.

Two years in prison, and I am discovering the value and power of marketing. In here, I witness a microcosm of what I can accomplish out there through marketing my life's work.

Darling, I cannot wait to be with you again. Every night and every morning I think about you; I see you in my head, and I dream of holding you in my arms. I love you...

Forever,
John

*

A few months later...

My Dearest Anna,

I continue testing marketing ideas in my "lab". I have proven that the get-rich-quick approach is much more effective than an intellectual approach. I keep detailed notes and have started building my puzzle pieces to a Neothink marketing program that I will pursue upon my release.

I know that I will have to market my book myself, for no Establishment publisher could handle its anti-Establishment message. I have my eye on some of the prisoners who were never criminals. Rico was absolutely right: in here I have discovered two different categories of prisoners — those criminals here because of a crime of force versus those innocent people here because of a political-policy 'crime'. Those innocent prisoners' anti-authority mind-set, after being burned by the Establishment, will generate motivated employees for my new anti-authority business. I am thinking business, marketing, personnel, and I am scouting for good employees.

I can't stand, though, being separated from you. I count the days until we're together again. My mind is strong, but my heart is weak.

Love You,
John

Mr. Melbourne was building a plan to advance the world through business and his book. He would leave the academic world behind when he got out. He formed his vision and knew what he needed to do. His business would disseminate his book — his map into Neothink — by the millions.

One evening after his hard labor was done, while studying his notes and data on his marketing approaches, he saw the big picture: a Neothink picture for a powerful brochure for his book. A whole new world was opening up to him. He wrote to the love of his life about it:

My Dearest Anna,

I subscribe to several trade magazines on publishing, advertising, and direct-response marketing. I study the ads in those publications. I also receive several advertisements through the mail, for now I am on several mailing lists.

I learn from those advertisements. I also feel that either they miss the most powerful common denominator of this anticivilization — the desire to get something for nothing — or, if they do appeal to that get-rich-quick desire in people, the product is not valid.

I realize I have *both* the valid get-rich-quick advertising concept and the only valid product that would deliver on such a promise. As I work on my brochure, I know I'm sitting on a powerful marketing concept that'll get my book out to lots of people. I'll press the most urgent buttons in people and get many books out there.

My book is nearly done; now the marketing has just begun. I know this whole new world of marketing is the way to advance the world. Therefore, these days I work fervently on my brochure until lights out. I then slide my folder of notes into my locker and get into bed. I usually slip into dreams of the future, my eyes wide open, staring into the black. My mind's eye sees my future office filled with hard-working people, marketing and shipping my book. If gotten out in large enough numbers, my book will start advancing humanity toward the next, superior mentality. Adults will become like your children...your twelve little God-Men.

Like you, darling, I am feeling good about myself. When I get out of here, I'll be 40 years old. I'll be entering my power years. I'll have completed my book of fifteen years. I'll go into business for myself and market this to the world.

Well, that is my dream of the future. My dreams of the future always wind up seeing *you*...my lovely wife-to-be...*with me*. That beautiful day is not so far away.

> I Love You,
> John

He put down his pencil and climbed into bed. A cool breeze blew in through the one rectangular window in the small room and brushed across his face. He smiled. He liked the wind, for it came from *out there* — from beyond the fence. ...He longed to be free as the wind, again.

CHAPTER
TWENTY-FOUR

Miss Annabelle and Mr. Melbourne qualified for the early release program. They both would get out after three years and one month. They would, of course, be on probation until the full five-year term was served. And, although felons are not allowed to associate by law until the full term of probation is up, an exception had been made in their case because of their romantic relationship. The big day was almost here.

*

Angie planned a surprise welcome-home party. She would pick up Miss Annabelle at noon on Friday, release day. At the exact same time, Jessie would pick up Mr. Melbourne. They would drive to the small house Angie had been asked to rent for Miss Annabelle and her fiancé. Upon arrival at their new home, the couple would be greeted by Miss Annabelle's twelve students and any of the parents who wanted to stay, too. The parents had arranged to pick up their children an hour and a half early from school to be at the party.

Sally's mom would be there. She had amazed doctors by living far longer than they predicted. Teddy's father would also be there. He was now president of the company. Yet, despite his success, he would always get a kick out of telling people that he makes less money than his 12-year-old son. In fact, he would always say he's considering working for his son.

Angie spent all day Thursday decorating the house for the party. She did not want any signs of a party on the outside. But when they would open the front door, they would be greeted by a hundred colorful balloons floating overhead against the ceiling with their multicolor, shiny ribbons dangling in the air. Right in the middle of the floating artscape would be a huge red and white banner, reaching from the left wall to the right wall, declaring "Welcome Home, Mr. & Mrs. Melbourne!" Angie thought it was only fitting, for she knew the thought of the wedding gave them both fuel and was an important emotional dimension they carried with them through the prison years.

The counselors for the prison system had met with Miss Annabelle the week of her release and coached her about readjusting to civilization. They explained to her a common reaction called "overstimulation". It was easy for a person confined in the uneventful prison life to become overstimulated and overwhelmed physically and emotionally. The counselor told Miss Annabelle the signs to watch out for and what to do to handle herself if overstimulation happened to her.

Miss Annabelle called Angie Thursday evening. They were both excited about the big day to follow. Miss Annabelle told Angie about the meeting she had with the prison counselors about overstimulation. So, Angie realized she had to tell her about the party so she would be prepared physically and emotionally.

"Oh, Angie...you and Jessie have stood by me and done so much for me...for years. You've meant so much to me. I just don't know how to repay you."

"Listen to me, honey," Angie said, "we *love* you, and that's all that matters. You and John — you're our best friends."

"We love you, too. Thank you, Angie."

*

Twelve children lay wide awake in bed Thursday night. They were tossing and turning with excitement to be with their beloved teacher again. Over and over, they kept seeing their teacher in their mind's eye. They were twelve years old now, and they were physically maturing.

Miss Annabelle also lay in bed, wide awake, her mind shuffling through images of her students and of John. Excitement dominated her emotions. Yet, she wondered why she felt a little scared. "To touch John again, *wow*," she quietly whispered. "To teach my kids again, *wow!*"

She had lived every day the past three years for tomorrow — to be together again.

*

The bugle sounded at 6:00 a.m. Miss Annabelle smiled. That's the last time I'll ever hear that, she thought as she sat on the side of the bed. Already standing directly before her was Megan. They had become close friends. Miss Annabelle stood up and gave Megan a hug.

"You'll be out in eleven months. I'm going to get permission to visit you!" Miss Annabelle said.

"I'm so happy for you, Anna," Megan said. She took a deep breath and added, "Next time I see you, you'll be Mrs. Annabelle Melbourne!" They both laughed. "Remember what I told you about how life goes by in a blink. Grab what is good for you out there."

"I'll never forget, Meg. You gave me a precious gift. I'll *never* forget."

As they stood there, they knew their feelings for each other were going to a special, permanent place in their hearts. They had gone through a struggle together that they now forever shared. This was their last moment together in this struggle. From now on, they would be a special memory to each other. They looked deeply at each other, for that one last moment. Then, the next moment, they were pulled apart by the morning protocols, blending right back into the bustle of a prison morning. This morning, however, Miss Annabelle did not report for duty. Instead, she reported to the warden's office where the release procedures and paperwork began.

A few hours later, Miss Annabelle was given the clothes she had arrived in. As she looked at her clothes, she couldn't get over the feeling that time stopped when she took off those clothes three years and one month ago. When she put them on and looked at herself in the mirror, she couldn't get over the feeling that whereas the world out there may go on, time in here stops for prisoners.

Deep in that eerie thought, she did not notice the counselor in the room. In a gentle voice, so as not to startle Miss Annabelle, the female counselor said, "Remember Annabelle...take it slowly at first."

"Oh...oh, yes. Thank you." Miss Annabelle said, turning around. She could already feel emotions crawling around her skin, and she knew the kind counselor knew it too.

"Good-bye, Annabelle. God bless."

*

At noon, she walked out the front gate. When she stepped past the gate, a wave of euphoria rushed up from her feet, up through her heart and into her mind. She felt a great weight leave her body. She ran over and hugged Angie, who was waiting for her with open arms.

"I'm free."

They walked around the wall toward the parking lot. In the middle of the parking lot was a long, shiny black limo. "There's our ride," Angie said. Angie had rented the limo and driver to escort Miss Annabelle home in style.

"What! Angie...you're spoiling me!" Miss Annabelle was laughing as she looked over to the hill where the prisoners stood at the front fence and cheered — a tradition whenever one of them was released. Miss Annabelle waved to the ladies; they cheered louder. Miss Annabelle was well liked by all who knew her in there.

As the chauffeur got out to open her door, the ladies cheered even louder. Miss Annabelle walked over to the car, then stopped for one last look at the place she had spent the past three years of her life. She felt an odd fondness for that simple place and bade it farewell in her thoughts. As she took this one last look, she saw Megan, smiling at her. Miss Annabelle nodded. She blew Megan a kiss and got in the limo. As they drove away,

Megan's words filled her thoughts, "Why frown when you can smile?"

*

Miss Annabelle braced herself for the happiest day of her life. She imagined this day over and over for three years...this was the day she had lived for.

She lowered the window and felt the wind brush the side of her face at 50 miles per hour. She enjoyed that sensation because it was something only a free person outside the prison gate could feel. She savored the sights of the countryside. Even the sight of a cow grazing in the pasture was a symbol of freedom, for those poor souls behind the gates go for years, even in some cases for their remaining lives without seeing a cow grazing on the dull green October grass. ...John is seeing this too, she thought.

The drive home was like the first feeding of a sight-starved soul. The images of freedom are beautiful, Miss Annabelle thought as they neared her hometown. The details of freedom that go unnoticed for a lifetime in the ordinary person were now amplified in her consciousness and filled her soul with extraordinary joy. For my remaining years, she thought, I'll find joy in freedom for its own sake, a joy I never knew before. She realized, for the first time, the joy Jessie and Angie felt every day in their freedom from the inner city. This new sensation of freedom made her aware of another form of freedom taken for granted — the freedom of good health, a freedom Sally's mom will never have.

The big limousine cruised quietly along the small streets lined with colorful trees about to drop their leaves. The limousine turned left, then right, then right again. Then the car slowed down.

"Third house on the right," Angie said to the driver.

Miss Annabelle started trembling. In a minute, she would be in John's arms. She had not seen him for over three years. She had not been in his arms. She had not made love to him. What will it be like? She wondered nervously. Yet, she was excited beyond words.

Superpuzzle

"Here's the little love shack I told you about, for you and your man," Angie said while sweeping her arm toward the little white house.

"It's perfect," Miss Annabelle said. Her eyes were wide. She stared at the little white house lined with flower beds. Her soul was absorbing this beautiful symbol of freedom, and it felt wonderful that this beautiful sight would now include her and the love of her life. "Here's where all my dreams will come true," she whispered.

Miss Annabelle held Angie's hand as they walked along the sidewalk to the front steps of Miss Annabelle's new home. She was breathing rapidly from excitement and nervousness. "Are my students inside?" she asked Angie.

"They're here," Angie said. Originally, this was going to be a mighty surprise party. But when Angie learned not to overstimulate Miss Annabelle or Mr. Melbourne after their release, she told them both about the party so they could prepare themselves.

"Are you OK?" Angie asked. Miss Annabelle shivered and then nodded.

Angie opened the door slowly. Miss Annabelle stood behind her. Suddenly, she could not wait another moment to hug John and see her students. Oh, I hope he's already here, she thought as she and Angie walked through the door.

"What?" Angie said; her mouth dropped. Miss Annabelle squeezed in to see one lady inside. It was Teddy's mother.

"Jessie and John aren't here yet," Angie said to Miss Annabelle. Then Angie turned to Teddy's mom and asked, "But where are the children?" Miss Annabelle looked at Teddy's mom, and noticed her eyes were bloodshot, as though she had been crying.

"I have some sad news to tell you, Miss Annabelle", she said. A tear dropped out of her eye and splattered on her cheek; she took a deep breath, then continued, "Today at school, your twelve students were called to Ms. Minner's office. She told them that a judge issued a restraining order against you coming from within 300 yards of them."

Miss Annabelle was stunned. She had just spent three years in prison, and now she was told she could not see her students.

Lost in a fuzz of confusion, she sat down, right where she stood, onto the tile floor.

"Teddy told me the girls cried and the boys angrily cursed Ms. Minner. She had to leave her office."

But Miss Annabelle was lost. "What's going on?" she asked Angie. "Where's John...where's my John?" Miss Annabelle was beginning to panic. Just then, the phone rang.

Miss Annabelle was frightened. Something was terribly wrong. She looked at Angie and wanted to speak, but nothing would come out. Angie was on the phone saying, "Who are they? What do they want? Call me as soon as you know anything". She hung up and knelt down face-to-face with Miss Annabelle.

"John and Jessie are still there," Angie said. "Jessie says there are some authorities in a room talking to John right now. Jessie will call as soon as they clear John."

Miss Annabelle nodded, but she was scared. Who are those authorities, and what do they want? Sixty seconds later the phone rang again. Miss Annabelle shrieked; she was scared and not familiar yet with a phone ring. Angie picked up the phone on the first ring.

"Jessie?" Angie's face went blank, "No...no...no!" Angie dropped the phone. "Oh, baby," she said, looking at Miss Annabelle, "they're the INS, and they're deporting John!"

"Oh my God, Angie. I must get to him...I must see him...I must be with him..." Miss Annabelle was panicking. This was the day she fantasized about for three years that kept her sanity while in prison. Now the day that gave her rationale to keep going was vanishing like a mirage of an oasis.

"Anna, they won't let anyone see him, not even Jessie."

"No, goddamn it, nooo!" Miss Annabelle's wretched cry could be heard outside. She started to sink emotionally and sobbed so hard her torso sank to the floor. There was no John to hold; there was not one of her students to get to know again. Angie felt helpless as she watched her best friend cry so hard that her body pulled itself into the fetal position.

For three years Miss Annabelle held onto an image of this day when she would reunite with her precious loved ones. That image kept her sane. But that wonderful image would never

311

happen. Now, she had to face the horror that for three years, she was living for a nonreality — a mirage. Her sanity was for naught, which now caused her to lose her sanity. The torture of losing the two great values in her life — her students and her John — was launched and could not be retrieved and extinguished. Losing them was too much for her. The three years of coping now, in a sense, turned inside out, and all the pain she suppressed came gushing out as she lay on the floor physically out of control, not coping, overstimulated with agony, crying like an injured baby. Angie and Teddy's mom were frightened as they watched their friend sink deeper and deeper…into a nervous breakdown.

The doorbell rang; Teddy's mom turned around, barely cracked open the door and peeked outside. There stood Ms. Minner escorted by a policeman.

"Mrs. Winters, what's going on in there?" Ms. Minner demanded. Teddy's mom wanted to shut the door and not let this evil woman see her victim like this, but the policeman firmly said, "Ma'am, open this door."

Teddy's mom slowly opened the door, revealing Miss Annabelle during this tragic moment.

"Mercy me!" Ms. Minner exclaimed upon seeing Miss Annabelle curled up and crying on the floor.

The policeman asked if she needed medical help. Angie's maternal instincts knew that Miss Annabelle needed some sense of control and that being carted off by strangers would worsen the situation.

"No sir. She just lost the most precious people in her life," Angie said, glaring at Ms. Minner. "She needs to be left alone right now. Your being here — especially *that woman* — is making the situation worse."

The policeman was a decent person and told Ms. Minner they should leave.

"This is God's work, you know," Ms. Minner said, caught up in the moment. "Can't you see? She's possessed by evil spirits. Look at her! Separating the forces of evil, separating this woman and her lover will exorcise the demons, believe you me! …I'd be not a bit surprised if John Melbourne is in the same condition right now!"

"What!" Angie looked up at Ms. Minner. "How do you know about John?"

Ms. Minner looked startled and realized she had said too much.

"I asked you a question," Angie continued. "How do you know about John?"

Ms. Minner turned to the policeman and said, "Yes, we should leave." She quickly thrust some papers into the hands of Teddy's mom and said, "This is for her." Then she turned and rushed away.

Angie was fuming at Ms. Minner, but she had to devote her attention to Miss Annabelle. Angie sat on the floor and placed Miss Annabelle's head on her lap and said, "Go ahead and let it out, honey, let it all out. John's okay. He's okay, darling. He's okay."

*

The next day was spent gathering information...as much as could be gathered on a Saturday. Getting information brought a sense of control into Miss Annabelle's life, which helped her cope again the day after the darkest moment of her life.

The INS had deported Mr. Melbourne, and Salinski was proceeding to understand the legal reason and to spring free a copy of an affidavit that was, perhaps, behind the deportation.

As the day progressed, however, the news got worse. "The problem with the INS," Salinski explained to Miss Annabelle in frustration during an early afternoon phone call, "is that they can decide the fate of any noncitizen at any time for any reason — even for no real reason or, although they're not supposed to, for an agent's own personal reasons. An INS agent can play God with a noncitizen. A noncitizen is, in a sense, always on probation. He has no rights whatsoever in relation to the INS."

Another ominous fact Miss Annabelle learned as the day went on was that once deported, it was nearly impossible to get back to the United States. What does that mean? she pondered. She also learned she could not go to live with him until her sentence and probation was over — another two years! And what about her students?

Superpuzzle

The paper Ms. Minner gave to Teddy's mom was the official restraining order. Miss Annabelle could not see her students *and* could neither send them information through the mail nor otherwise communicate with them until her probation was over.

She would be in a sort of prison for the next two years without access to the greatest values in her life. And after that, she would have to choose between her students and her fiancé.

The conflicts were piling up and starting to jeopardize her emotional stability. She was emotionally fragile after her nervous breakdown the day before. She was staying with Angie and Jessie, and Angie could see the strain starting to add up.

The phone rang again as it had been all day. But it was now 9:00 p.m. — too late for Salinski to still be getting information. Let it be good news this time, Angie pleaded.

"John!" Jessie shouted in an elated voice. "She's right here!" He no less finished the sentence as Miss Annabelle ran over and took the phone.

"Darling!" Miss Annabelle said...then she smiled. It was the first time she heard his voice in three years. The sound of his voice immediately removed the strain in her face and body. Angie and Jessie looked at each other and breathed a sigh of relief. This was the first sign of life in their guest since the breakdown.

John was back in Australia. He had just arrived and was in his parents' home. To hear his voice brought strength back to the little lady. Angie and Jessie knew this was the best medicine for their friend.

"Now, she can talk through all the conflicts with the love of her life," Angie said to Jessie as they went upstairs to let her talk and cry and laugh, for this was the lovers' first moment together in "freedom".

CHAPTER
TWENTY-FIVE

Salinski handed Miss Annabelle the sealed affidavit, two weeks later. It had been sealed by the federal government for ten working days. As suspected, the affidavit was written by Ms. Minner warning the INS that Miss Annabelle and Mr. Melbourne would get married soon after their release.

"If you want to remove a violent threat to society — the work of the devil himself — before his marriage to a U. S. citizen, you'd better move fast," she wrote.

Miss Annabelle had been weighing her options over and over those past two weeks. There was no good answer. But tonight, after seeing Minner's affidavit, Miss Annabelle began reviewing her options again. She was searching for a clear choice, but there was none.

She had, with her lawyer, discussed three options. The first two options were illegal and carried great risks and grave consequences. The third option was the safe choice, but it was an unbearable thought: to not be with John for two more years, not until probation concluded and she would be free to leave the country.

The first option was high risk. The day John got to Australia and called Miss Annabelle, they talked for hours and figured out what their three options were. Like her, he did not want to wait

315

Superpuzzle

two more years for the third option, although he knew the third option was safe and would mean that he might return to the United States in ten years or perhaps less — to become a U. S. citizen.

He started researching their first option: sneaking back into the country either through Mexico or Canada. The idea seemed drastic to Miss Annabelle, and the thought of the love of her life risking his health or freedom worried Miss Annabelle. She called Bruce Salinski for his input.

"A Caucasian with blond hair and blue eyes coming through a high-traffic, tourist point such as Niagara Falls from the North or San Ysidro from the South carries good odds," Salinski explained.

"But what if he were caught by the Border Police?"

"Then he would be permanently blocked for life from ever returning to the United States. But the odds are good, maybe a 90% chance of getting through. Once here, he could live a low-profile life indefinitely. When your probation is over in two years, he could quietly slip back to Australia where you could go to get him. You could marry, and start working on getting him back to this country legally."

"What if we were caught living together?"

"Disaster would strike. You could both go back to prison for your full original sentences of five years each, *plus* added time — perhaps substantial added time for a second felony offense — for criminal acts of illegally entering the country and you illegally harboring him. Moreover, two felons on probation seeing and talking to one another is prohibited by law."

"What about the second option — me going to Australia?" she asked.

"That'd be relatively easy to do, but the consequences would be immediate. Upon missing your weekly probation meeting, you'd be in violation. Upon coming back to the U.S., you'd have to go back to prison for your full five-year term. Time done already would *not* count against those five years. Plus, you'd get more time for fleeing the country. In short, if you leave to be with him, you could *never* come back."

Miss Annabelle sighed, overwhelmed by the harsh consequences.

"But I have an idea that could help you reach a decision," Salinski continued. "After talking to different immigration experts, I feel confident you would be permitted three one-week trips to Australia per year for the remainder of your probation."

"I love the idea," she said immediately. "Being together for a full week every four months will work wonderfully. Two years will zoom by, and we'll marry. ...Yes, I like it!"

So, Salinski prepared a reasonable proposal to present to the authorities.

*

A sense of control was jelling around Miss Annabelle. The proposal for travel permission had been presented. She had moved into her little home, and though she could not contact her students in any way, she started working on the next weekly lecture, just as if she would send it to them on audio tape as she did in prison. She did not know if her students would ever hear it, but she knew she needed to continue developing her program. Someday, she knew, it would be an immense value to many children.

One afternoon while working on an invaluable lecture about developing the power of a curious mind, Salinski called Miss Annabelle.

"I'm coming over, Anna. We've got an answer. I'll be there in fifteen minutes." Salinski sounded rushed, so Miss Annabelle did not probe for the answer.

Ten minutes later the doorbell rang. Miss Annabelle was pleasantly surprised to see Angie.

"Hi Angie! Bruce Salinski is on his way over. They gave him our answer. ...Oh, I can't wait!"

"I know, he called me and told me, too. He asked me to come over."

While they were still standing in the doorway, Salinski pulled up to the curb and seemed to hurry out of his car toward the house.

"Let's go inside, and I'll read their response," he said.

Inside, he pulled a piece of paper from an envelope and read: "Based on additional information learned about Annabelle

Barclays, permission to travel to Australia is denied."

Miss Annabelle gasped as he read the response.

"What additional information?" Angie asked, in shock herself.

"I don't know, but I'll find out," Salinski said.

Miss Annabelle sat down. "Will I be able to get permission to travel to him *at all* over the next two years?"

"I don't know. I don't know the nature of the additional information they've found about you. My suspicion is that someone who doesn't like you — Ms. Minner — is providing the authorities with something damaging to your credibility."

"That bitch!" Angie cursed.

"Right now, I can't say, but if I had to lay odds, I doubt if you'll get to see John before your probation is up."

*

"How are you holding up, baby?" Angie asked Miss Annabelle. Angie and Jessie were visiting.

"I don't know," Miss Annabelle said. "I'm scared to death for John. If he's caught...I can't even think about it."

"He's made his decision; don't think about the what-ifs," Jessie said. "The odds of getting through are really good."

Mr. Melbourn decided to slip back into America and secretly live with Miss Annabelle. Only Angie and Jessie, Bruce Salinski, and Miss Annabelle knew.

"I know," Miss Annabelle answered, "But the penalty, if he *is* caught, is unacceptable."

Jessie and Angie looked at each other. Jessie sighed then said, "Yeah, I know. I've gotta say, I'm a nervous wreck myself."

"Me too," Angie said. They looked at Miss Annabelle.

Miss Annabelle looked back at her two best friends and smiled. The admission of their nervousness, for some reason, helped her to relax some.

"He called me and told me he couldn't communicate with you until he's here," Jessie said.

"He called you?"

"Yeah. He explained that he can't call you because that could incriminate you if he's caught."

Miss Annabelle looked down and said, "I know, he told me."

"John said he'll call Angie and me every day to tell us how he's doing."

"And we'll tell you everything," Angie added.

"Thank you," Miss Annabelle said. She smiled and added, "I'd sure like that."

"Try to relax, honey," Angie said. "He should be here in a few days."

*

Before Miss Annabelle could offer her guests anything, Jessie said, "I've got bad news. John was stopped at the U.S.-Canadian border. They didn't apprehend him, thank goodness."

Miss Annabelle stared at Jessie; she was frozen. She did not know what to say.

"Honey," Angie said, putting her arm around Miss Annabelle, "They let him go."

Miss Annabelle nodded.

"There's more," Jessie said. "Let's all sit down."

Angie sat on the couch with Miss Annabelle. Jessie sat on the chair and continued, "John didn't want me to tell you this until he was in."

"Tell me what?"

"He crossed the Mexican border on foot."

"What!"

"Upon being stopped at the U.S.-Canadian border," Jessie continued, "his picture was automatically posted at all entry points. He decided to make a run for it."

"Oh my god!" cried Miss Annabelle. She looked at Jessie in horror.

"The hard part's over. He's in the country, and he's going to call me every other night or so. He had a pretty rough first night, but that's behind him now." Jessie paused to think of where to start his story. Miss Annabelle's eyes were begging for him to continue.

"He befriended a wonderful Mexican family," Angie said.

"Yes," Jessie continued, "and there's this wonderful little boy who's going to cross the country with John. His name is

319

Oscar..."

"Why doesn't John just get on a plane and fly here?" Miss Annabelle asked.

"It's complicated," said Jessie. "He can't fly here, so I offered to fly to San Diego, rent a car, and drive him here, but he won't allow it."

Jessie and Angie stayed for over an hour relaying to their best friend the detail-by-detail story of John's first night crossing the border.

As they were leaving, Miss Annabelle said, "Thanks for all this. I really appreciate you two."

Angie hugged Miss Annabelle and said, "You and John are our best friends; we'd do anything for you."

*

"John and the little boy, Oscar, are riding on a large semi with this great guy named Chuck," Jessie reported to Miss Annabelle two days later. "If everything goes smoothly, John will be here in a little over a week."

"Where's he sleeping, what's he eating? Is he warm enough?" Miss Annabelle had many questions. "Why don't they just get on a plane?"

Angie looked at Jessie and frowned.

"What is it?" Miss Annabelle said. "Something's wrong!"

Angie nodded and said, "He's okay, but he got in a terrible fight—"

"A fight? A fight! Oh my god, is he hurt?"

"He's pretty sore, but he'll live," Jessie said.

"What happened? Tell me, Jessie!"

"Some white-trash racist tried to hurt Oscar, the little boy who's travelling across the country with John."

"John wouldn't let that happen," Miss Annabelle said.

"No, he sure wouldn't," Jessie said. "He and the racist got into it pretty seriously. I guess John's a lucky man to walk away from it."

Jessie and Angie told Miss Annabelle everything. Miss Annabelle cried when she heard how violent the fight had been.

"But he's all right now," Angie said in conclusion, "except

he really misses you and the kids."

Miss Annabelle smiled.

"Oh, yes," Angie continued, "during every call he asks us to tell him about you...and he asks us to tell him everything about what's going on in the lives of your former students."

"I think our stories give him peace...and strength," Jessie said. "It's a taxing journey, but John's a strong man. After his fight, I told him about what's going on with Ian. That story really lifted John. I could feel it in his voice."

Miss Annabelle smiled again and said, "But why don't they just get on a plane?"

"The evening news in California carried the story of the fight," said Jessie, "and they showed John's picture on television. And worse, when we called Bruce Salinski to tell him about the fight, he told us he already knew and that several states had picked up, over the wire, the local paper's article about the fight, using it as an example of growing racial tensions building in California and throughout America. John's picture is in the papers; he has to stay out of sight."

*

"Hi Anna," Jessie said over the phone. "Everything's going well. John and Oscar are about halfway across the country."

Miss Annabelle closed her eyes and took a deep breath. She reopened her eyes and said, "I just can't wait to see him and hold him again."

*

Miss Annabelle arrived at Jessie and Angie's house for dinner. Angie opened the door wearing a large smile. "Tonight they'll arrive in Savannah, Georgia," she said. "Tomorrow they'll take a bus to Miami to drop off the little boy. And the next day — the day after tomorrow — John will be on a bus for Buffalo. In just three days, he'll be knocking at your door!"

Miss Annabelle could not stop her grin from going too wide — the smile of a little girl.

"Come in, honey," Angie said. "Let's celebrate John's

homecoming!"

"Hi Anna!" Jessie called out from the kitchen. "I was thinking, if John calls while you're here, what's the harm of you talking to him tonight? No one'll ever know."

"Oh, thank you. You two—" Miss Annabelle suddenly burst into tears. She covered her face with her hands. The anxiety had caught up to her.

"Oh, honey," Angie said, "it's almost over. It's almost all over."

Miss Annabelle nodded and removed her hands to look at her friends. Her face was oscillating between crying and smiling. "I know...I know," she said in a worn, sad voice, "I just need him in my arms again."

CHAPTER
TWENTY-SIX

A light knock on the front door caused Miss Annabelle's heart to jump for joy. "It's John," she whispered. This was the day he would arrive. She ran for the door; her heart pounded wildly. She pulled back her door with arms wide open...

Instead of her John, she faced Bruce Salinski and Angie.

"Anna, I need you to be strong," Angie said.

Immediately, Salinski followed with, "The INS took John into custody earlier this morning in Florida, waiting to load a Greyhound Bus for Buffalo."

Miss Annabelle felt a numb buzzing fill her head. "Oh no, Bruce...he can't go back to prison! Oh no! No!"

"Anna, wait, wait..." Salinski interrupted, "John's on a plane right now heading back to Australia."

"He's...he's free to leave?" She was breathing very fast from fright, and she was staring at Salinski for answers.

"I'm told he's safely on his way back to Australia."

"Oh...thank goodness!" Miss Annabelle breathed deeply from relief. She was so relieved that John Melbourne was going back home instead of going back to prison that the letdown of not seeing him did not register.

"Come in, come in...oh, I was so afraid he'd be going back to prison to serve out the rest of his sentence."

Superpuzzle

Angie breathed a sigh of relief upon seeing that Miss Annabelle was handling this well. "How do you feel, honey?" Angie asked her.

"I'm okay. I'm actually feeling good now that I know John's safe, and he's free."

"Good," said Salinski, "because you're going to need a clear head to make a decision that's going to have lifelong consequences. Anna, the INS here was contacted about John being apprehended in Florida. Your probation officer called me at home a short while ago. He asked that you turn in your passport first thing in the morning. I'm your lawyer and can't be telling you otherwise. But if you ever considered any other option, you'd have to move on it *now*. Tomorrow by noon, your probation officer will be at your door looking for you."

Miss Annabelle sat down and, in a strained voice backed by many hours of previously agonizing over this consideration, she asked, "What would it mean if I left the country?"

Angie gasped.

"You'd never come back. The odds are against Australia extraditing you. You'd live the rest of your life with John in Australia; you'd never be here again." Salinski paused. He took a deep breath and said, "If you go within the hour, you can drive through Niagara during the busy dinner rush and be in Toronto with your passport by eight o'clock. You can be in Australia by the time your probation officer notifies his superiors that you're missing. But remember, when you say good-bye to Angie, you'll never be back here again. You'll never see your students again."

Miss Annabelle's head dropped. She stared at the floor for what seemed like a long time in the hurried atmosphere, then slowly said, "If I stay?"

"If you stay, you must turn in your passport tomorrow morning. I find out what negative information Ms. Minner has given them and work to reverse the damage. There's a slight chance you'll get travel permission, but these decisions against you are hard to reverse, especially now. ...You certainly would not get to go three times a year and, most likely, not at all. ...In short, plan on not seeing John for two years. If you and John can live with that, it's the choice that would allow you to return

324

to or visit America whenever you wanted to."

"I should stay," she said. An immediate wave of relief went through Angie and a lot of tension left Salinski. "But I don't know if I can stay," Miss Annabelle said after a pause. She looked up at Salinski helplessly.

"You must realize," Salinski said, "John will never step foot here again unless they change the laws."

The anxiety returned. "Oh God, I need to really think about this. I need an hour," she said, looking at Salinski and then at her best friend. "Angie, could you come back in an hour? I'll know my decision then."

Angie nodded, too emotional to talk. She walked over and hugged her best friend. She and Salinski turned to leave. At the door, Salinski turned around and said, "If you don't know in one hour, then you'll have no choice but to stay. You need to be out of the Sydney Airport before the authorities here figure out what's going on."

Miss Annabelle nodded.

"If you go, I'll drive you to Toronto. You'll pose as my wife. One lightly packed suitcase is all you can take in case they check. It must look like we're going up for the weekend."

"Thank you," Miss Annabelle said, realizing Salinski was risking his livelihood and even criminal exposure.

When the front door closed behind her friends, Miss Annabelle closed off her emotions. She knew she did not have the luxury of time to feel the pain. She had to think and think hard to make the decision that would result in entirely different futures.

How could I ever leave my students? she asked herself. If I stay, I'll see them in *two years*. If I go, I'll never see them again. I couldn't bear that.

But she realized that if she stayed, in reality she would see her students just briefly again. For, she would soon thereafter be off to Australia to be with John, who could never come back to the States now. She would then see her students maybe three times after that, taking a trip alone back home to visit them once a year. But after three trips, her students would be off to college. With their superior Neothink minds, they would be leaving little Cheektowaga to attend different universities and to create values all over the grand globe.

I was thirty-six years old, she reflected, when I left my students and kissed John good-bye. If I stay, I'll be almost forty-two years old when I see him again. That's too long...that's a whole phase of life we'll never share.

She remembered Megan in prison telling her how life goes by in a blink...then is gone. "Go after what makes you happy," Megan said from a life of experience. If she were here now, Miss Annabelle thought, Megan would say, "When something is good for you, don't hesitate. Go for it, or you might miss everything. Your journey could end before it begins."

Miss Annabelle knew what to do. She had known all along. She knew before Angie and Salinski had left.

*

The knock on the door was tentative.

"Come in!" Miss Annabelle called out.

Angie and Jessie walked in. They both dropped their heads as they saw their best friend standing with a small suitcase. Angie nearly cried.

"Oh, Anna," Jessie said in a sad, deep voice. "You're going."

The depth of feeling in Jessie's voice broke open the dam Miss Annabelle had placed before her emotions. She dropped her suitcase and cried. In a high voice, she said, "I've been such a pain to both of you for four years. I don't want to leave you. You're the most wonderful friends I've ever had. I have to go, but I don't know how I can possibly leave you. ...This is so hard!"

Miss Annabelle was trembling as she was in that first school-board meeting when she entered the lunch room. Angie gathered herself and walked over and hugged her.

"Listen to me, Anna," Angie said. "You *never*, not *ever* were a pain to Jessie and me. You're the only person we've met since moving out of our nightmare in Philly who is like us at heart. We love you and always will."

Jessie bit his bottom lip and added, "We fought for what was right down in Philly, and now we're living our dream together. You fought for what was right in Cheektowaga, and now you

must go, Anna. You'll live your dream, a new dream in a new
life, with John. You gave all that you could to your students
— and it was enough. It was enough."

"You must go," Angie repeated, putting her hands on Miss
Annabelle's shoulders and looking into her eyes.

Here Angie and Jessie were, right to the end, giving her that
priceless value they gave her from the beginning: strength. As
in that first school board meeting, Miss Annabelle could feel
strength coming from Angie and Jessie, calming her nerves. The
trembling left.

"Good-bye," she said, hugging Angie and then Jessie. They
knew it was their last embrace, their last look. She whispered,
"I'll always treasure our friendship...it's so rare...so special."
Then she slipped a book into Jessie's hand, turned around and
walked away.

Jessie and Angie watched their friend walk to Salinski's car,
out of their lives forever.

*

Salinski did not speak for twenty minutes, giving his client
time to feel the impact of what she was forever leaving
behind...and to give her the freedom to change her mind. Once
she passed the border, there would be no turning back. Her life
would be forever dramatically different.

Miss Annabelle welcomed the silence. Her mind went back
to her students. She knew Jessie was right: *it was enough.* She
had planted the seed of Neothink — and that's all she needed
to do. She felt grateful she had the full year to plant the seed
in her twelve students and grateful that their seeds were growing.

A sad, sad thought tormented her though — that she would
not be there for Sally when her mom died.

"When we get to the border," Salinski said, breaking the long
silence, "they'll just wave us through. If they stop us, it won't
be the U. S. Border Patrol; it'll be the Canadian Border Patrol.
In thinking it through further, we should not pose as spouses on
a holiday. It'll be easiest, especially on you, if we tell them
true facts and still accomplish our goal, instead of telling lies.
They're professionals at catching lies. So, if they ask, we'll tell

them our real names. If they ask the nature of our stay, we'll say we're going to Toronto on business. If they ask for more details, I'm your lawyer, and we have a meeting with William Davenport, a retired appeal-lawyer specialist who practiced in New York before retiring to Mississauga, a suburb about 25 kilometers south of Toronto. I actually set up an appointment with him tomorrow at eleven o'clock. Everything will check out, and we'll be confident telling true facts. Your passport record will not yet have a flag on it...it's too soon."

His plan relieved the growing anxieties in Miss Annabelle. Now, she felt completely relaxed. When they got to the border, the border patrol waved them through without asking any questions.

"When we get to the airport, you'll get on the first plane to Australia, even if it's double the cost of the following flight," he said, wanting her cleared at the Sydney Airport before the authorities here sounded the alarm.

At the airport, Miss Annabelle managed to get a quick call to John to tell him she would be there tomorrow. He was shocked and elated. She had no time to explain what was happening to her. That would have to wait.

At 8:50 p.m., Miss Annabelle thanked Salinski and shook his hand. "I wish we had some time to talk about *you*," she said. "I'll never forget your honesty three years ago when you stood up to ego justice in our trial."

"I'll talk to you on the phone and will let you know what I've gone through," he answered. "Until then, let me just say, it's been a hard path, but it's the honest path, and I would never change that."

They were both living in a different world than most everyone else — the fully honest world. They were both enduring the attacks from those who built their lives on dishonest illusions.

"By the way," Salinski added, "don't call anyone in the States, no one but me. The authorities can trace any other phone line but mine since I'm your lawyer. And don't write to anyone...not even Angie, not even your students — no one. The authorities can and will track you down. Call only me."

Those last comments by Salinski made the reality of what she was permanently leaving behind sink in for the first time.

This was it; she was going for good. The reality of leaving her loved ones made her go numb. She nodded to Salinski, turned and boarded the plane. She would be in Australia, in John's arms, sometime tomorrow.

*

Miss Annabelle cried for hours during the flight. People sitting around her assumed she had suffered a death in the family. But the pain went even deeper. She felt the pain of a mother permanently separated from her children.

*

She saw him before he saw her. She stopped to admire him. She always knew he was a good-looking man, but she never realized how he stood out as so handsome among the people around him.

He looked big and strong, yet slim. He filled out his camel colored short-sleeved, pullover wool shirt. His chest, shoulders, and arms looked broad and well-defined. His legs looked long in his white slacks. Most of all, his face, with those piercing blue eyes, radiated a sexy strength that came from years of constant hard thinking and penetrating breakthroughs. She studied him; she felt herself overflowing with beautiful emotions. She stood there, tingling and warm inside. Being here, she thought, is oh, so right...so very right.

He spotted her and ran toward her. This amazing man is running *to me*, she thought, which tickled her inside and made her laugh out loud. He wrapped his arms around her and scooped her off her feet. "God, I've missed that laugh, my darling," he said, his voice coming from somewhere deep within. "Anna, I forgot how beautiful you are! Oh...you feel so *good*!"

He was saying everything she was feeling.

"My John," she said looking into his sweet blue eyes. "I've missed you more than I could bear."

"Everything is okay now," he whispered into her ear while hugging her tightly.

"Everything is beautiful," she said. She hugged him as tightly as she could. She was afraid to let go. "I could never be away from you again."

Somewhere in the back of their minds, they knew the option of "waiting it out" would have never worked, for they knew they could not ever be apart for any length of time, not ever again.

Still, very deep within, Miss Annabelle's soul was weeping and asking, "Where are my students?"

CHAPTER
TWENTY-SEVEN

"That is, sadly, where our story ends," a generation-older Jessie was saying to Jake.

Jake had been staying with Angie and Jessie for a week and had to be getting back to campus soon. He felt as if he were uncovering a valuable part of history here. He was making an important discovery and was part of something bigger than himself. He was also building a deep friendship with Angie and Jessie, and he felt as if his lifelong friends would be found through forging ahead with this project.

"What happened to her?" Jake asked, hoping he would somehow hear more about Miss Annabelle.

Angie, as slim and healthy as she was the day her best friend left twenty-three years before, said, "We left out a piece of information; it was too early to tell you before." Angie looked at Jessie. He nodded, and she continued, "Ms. Minner was writing authorities to extradite Miss Annabelle. She knew Annabelle went to Australia to be with John. So, Anna took on a new identity."

Angie hesitated, then said, "She wrote us occasionally, Jake. We're sorry we told you we didn't have any contact with her, but in essence we didn't because she never included her address...or name."

Superpuzzle

"She'd sign every letter 'Your friend'," Jessie said.

"Why?" Jake interrupted. "Do you have those letters — can I see them?"

"Yes, we have them," Angie said, looking at Jessie. "And I'll let you read them because I think Anna would want that."

"Yes, I agree," Jessie said, nodding.

"She didn't give us her address," Angie continued, "because she didn't want to incriminate us. The District Attorney's office asked us on three different occasions if we knew her whereabouts. ...But, as you'll read in those letters, she was dying to hear from us."

"But, wouldn't the statute of limitations be long over by now?" Jake asked.

"John and Anna and their lawyer were too smart for that trick," Jessie said.

"What trick?" Jake looked puzzled.

"First of all, the IRS twice questioned us about her whereabouts years after she left." Angie answered.

"Anna warned us in her letters that would happen," Jessie added. "Salinski told her the IRS was the government's best resource to get people it wants."

"And there's NO statute of limitations for not filing with the IRS," Angie said. She shook her head.

"Even if you're not here in this country?" Jake asked.

"It doesn't matter," Jessie said. "If you're a U.S. citizen and in Australia making money, you need to file. Of course, Anna couldn't file because of the extradition proceedings against her."

"And this is why she couldn't contact her students all this time," Angie said. "The U.S. authorities could not know where she was, and they were looking."

"That's right," said Jessie, "by contacting people here who loved her and would protect her and would never reveal her whereabouts could bring them problems with the law. She wouldn't do anything that could hurt her students, so she decided she wouldn't write to them."

"What happened to her students after she left?"

"It was very sad," Angie said. "Anna broke the rule just once. Two weeks after she left I received a letter for her students. She asked if Jessie and I could somehow get them together and read it to them."

"I told them one by one in the halls at school that Miss Annabelle sent us a letter to read to them," Jessie said. "We would all meet at Sally's house Friday after school. I think most of the kids' parents knew, but no one said anything. I'll always remember how each child's face lit up when I told him about receiving the letter. ...But every last one of them cried as Angie read the letter. I think they thought it was the start of contact again with their beloved teacher. As Angie read the letter, they realized it was her good-bye."

"Everyone was crying, even me." Angie said.

"Wow, I can imagine that," Jake said, realizing the power that little lady had on his own emotions even though he never met her. "Do you still have that letter?"

"No," Angie and Jessie said in harmony. Then Jessie continued, "It was hard evidence of breaking the restraining order. Annabelle was afraid a parent would tell Ms. Minner and the authorities would come to us for it. She asked us to destroy it after we read it to the children."

"It really felt as if Anna herself were there, though, talking to the kids...then she was gone...gone from their lives, forever."

*

Later that Saturday afternoon, Jake asked Angie, "Did Miss Annabelle ever have children of her own?"

Angie dropped her eyes towards the floor. Jake suddenly realized this was a very sensitive topic for her.

"No," she said. "Like Jessie and me, Anna wanted children with John more than anything else in the world after she left here. But mother nature played a cruel trick on her. A few months after she left her twelve 'adopted children', she could not have children of her own. She told us about it in a letter. She said she now knew the emptiness of not ever being able to have a child, as Jessie and I expressed to her once. The physical and psychological trauma of Hammerschmidt, prison, and then permanent separation from her students added up against her system and brought on early menopause, shortly after she moved to Australia. When I read her letter, I kept thinking how I wanted to save her from the emptiness Jessie and I have lived with...especially Anna of all people."

"What about adoption?" Jake asked.

"She couldn't. They'd discover her true identity. She was a woman with so much love to give and yet, she could never be a mom."

*

Later that evening, Jake asked Jessie, "What was the book she put in your hand when she was leaving?"

"Her diary," Jessie said.

Her diary! Jake had forgotten all about that.

"Her diary, starting with that one, beautiful year...until the day she slipped it in my hand," Jessie continued. "She left a note inside that said: 'Jessie and Angie, the memories are special. The memories are permanent pictures in my mind that I'll never forget; they're even more visually vivid and permanent in my mind than the words here on paper. So, I give my diary to you because I think it will show you how deeply I feel for you...and for those beautiful children I'm leaving behind. You may read it to them, too. I love you, forever. Anna.' ...Let me tell you something, Jake, even twenty-seven years later, reading her diary of that year still takes my breath away."

"Jessie and I got together with the kids a few times after Anna left," Angie added. "Every time we did, they'd ask me to read to them from her diary...sometimes a specific part, sometimes just at random. The kids loved hearing her thoughts. Sometimes they'd laugh...sometimes they'd cry because they missed her so."

"May I read it?" Jake asked.

"Yes," Jessie said, "Now that you know the story, you may read it."

Jessie went to get the diary. He returned and gave it to Jake. Jessie and Angie knew Jake wanted to read it right away, so they said good-night.

Jake opened the diary and looked into Miss Annabelle's soul. And although the story Jessie and Angie had told Jake had prepared him, still what he read sent an emotional impact through him that shook him from his head to his feet. Had he *not* been told the story by Jessie and Angie, he would have been frozen like a deer looking directly into the blinding lights of an oncoming truck; he would have been helpless to brace himself for the emotional impact.

But with the story behind him, he could handle the emotional impact, her breathtaking connection with and love for the children in her class. Her descriptions of her students' expressions, their growing thrill for life, and the incomprehensible trap of the anticivilization they were heading into...shook up Jake's emotional constitution and drew to a head the tragedy of the anticivilization. Her revelations of *pure love* and its power went an entire leap beyond Jesus or Buddha. Jake knew he was inside the soul of the next evolution of man.

After fifteen minutes, Jake closed the diary to calm down. As he rested, he could not think of one parallel experience...not one in his life.

Jake reopened the diary. He was emotionally shaken as he read her entries about the lives, the love, the togetherness and happiness of her students. Jake never knew those levels of emotions even existed. He knew those new emotions came from the soul of the God-Man. Jake read every page of the miracle year and then collapsed on his bed, immediately falling into an exhausted sleep.

*

Jake woke the next morning with a start.

"Of course!" he called out as he stumbled out of his room looking for Angie or Jessie, but they were still sleeping. Oh right, he remembered, it's Sunday. That's okay, I'll surprise them later.

Jake went back into his room; he knew how to find Miss Annabelle. In fact, the more he thought about it, the more obvious it became. He chuckled under his breath: isn't that the way so many discoveries are made? Seeing the obvious?

He remembered, from one of her lectures, the meaning of life was happiness, and the real source of happiness came from putting values into society. The more values, the more happiness. Miss Annabelle lived her life for happiness, so it followed that her great values — her lectures — would be put into society to reach as many people as possible. When he woke up this morning and saw his laptop, the idea clicked: she would have put her lectures out there — on the Internet!

But Jake had just recently bought his laptop and only used it for writing school papers. He was not yet set up to log onto the Internet. His desktop back in his dorm room used DSL service for high-speed Internet access, which required a special modem. He thought about how he also went to his University's library sometimes to do Internet research.

I wonder where I can find a community college around here, he thought. "Then again," he said to himself, "it's probably too early on a Sunday morning."

He looked at the phone in his guest room and mumbled, "I bet I can figure out how to get set up on the Internet with my laptop before I can get to a library that's open."

He pulled out his laptop and placed it on the little table in his bedroom and plugged it in. He pushed the phone line into its receptor. "I hope I can get a dial-up connection," he said. Then, he called directory service on his cell phone.

Ten minutes passed. "Yes!" he hissed. He was on-line.

Now, he went to his search engines and entered several key words from one of his favorite lectures — the one where Miss Annabelle explained why Sally's mom might be saved by advanced God-Man. He got a listing of 147 possibilities. Barely able to breathe, he scrolled through those, linking to those that looked like possibilities.

He came upon one listing by a Darlene Belle. He clicked to its web site, read a few lines, then shouted, "Oh my God, I found her! I found her!"

Jake leapt from his chair and rushed out of the room to get Jessie and Angie. He didn't realize Jessie had gotten up and heard Jake yelling. Jessie rushed toward Jake's room to see what was going on. They nearly crashed into each other in the doorway, startling Jake and causing him to holler, which, in turn, startled Jessie and caused him to holler. After the two men settled down, Jake said, "Jessie...I found her. Here! She's Darlene Belle! This is her lecture to the class about God-Man saving Sally's mom!"

Jessie leaned over and squinted at the laptop. "I'll be doggone! I always knew I should learn how to work these computers! Angie!" Jessie ran out of the room to get his wife.

By the time Jessie and Angie returned a moment later, Jake had nearly a full history on Darlene Belle.

"This is Miss Annabelle, all right," Jake said. He scrolled down a long page of accomplishments. "She's famous, you know. She's the author of that bestseller *How To Raise A Genius Through Five-Minute Bedtime Stories!*"

Jessie whistled as Jake scrolled down her many lectures, articles, books, and links.

"Hi Anna. It's been a long time, baby," Angie said. "Oh, I'm so proud of her!"

"I can email her, you know," Jake said, "or at least her secretary."

"Oh my Lord, I don't know what to say!" Angie said. She looked at Jessie. Her eyes were full of uncertainty as emotions started to overwhelm her. Jessie put his big arm around her and said, "Tell her, we miss her very much."

*

That evening, the floodgates broke. Miss Annabelle read her email first thing at work Monday morning, which was Sunday evening in New York. Miss Annabelle, now world-renowned as Darlene Belle, and Angie and Jessie exchanged two long letters each, via email, by midnight, New York time.

Jake had asked them if he should leave, but Angie and Jessie did not mind that Jake was there, reading the exchange of letters. They actually liked having him there. He was turning into their first close friend since Miss Annabelle and Mr. Melbourne left.

What stood out to Jake was the love among these people. Success and separation did not make Miss Annabelle emotionally distant. It seemed to Jake that her success made her emotionally closer, for Angie and Jessie were her *real* friends.

As Jake watched the excitement and passion in their letters, he began to wonder what it would be like to see Miss Annabelle and her husband together again with her former students, with Angie and Jessie, and with that honest lawyer who represented her and helped her leave the country to have a happy life with Mr. Melbourne.

*

Now that Jake had found Miss Annabelle, he knew he must locate her twelve former students. Of course, he already knew about Ian, Sally, Theodore, and Daniel Ward. They were internationally famous people taking science, medicine, business, and politics to the next level.

What were the other eight doing now? That question beat like a drum, over and over again, in Jake's mind. Were they God-Men, too? Under any other circumstances, four of the world's most known persons coming out of the same third-grade class of twelve students would be statistically unbelievable. But under these circumstances, Jake realized Miss Annabelle had taken her students through an evolution into the next mentality of man. Jake began to think that the other eight students *must* be very creative and successful.

He told Angie and Jessie of his idea to locate each former student. They got excited about the idea, too. By god, Jake asked himself, why does Miss Annabelle have to be separated from her students any longer? Then he got lost in the possibilities as he asked himself, what would it be like to have a reunion? The threat of the IRS, however, was too great to bring Miss Annabelle to America...or to reveal her pseudo identity. Jake knew she could never lose her freedom again.

Jake was not sure how it would all work out, but he knew he must proceed. For, he knew he had found his "calling", his historic role in bringing humanity into the fully honest civilization.

*

The next morning, Jake drove into Buffalo. He met with a private investigator. For $1600, he would find the location of and provide a profile on the other eight members of the class.

While leaving the small office that looked as if it came directly off a movie set complete with the unshaven, private investigator in suspenders wrapped tightly over his white shirt,

338

Jake turned and put his hand to his chin, his eyes not fixed on any object as if deep in thought. Then he fixed his eyes on his private investigator and said, "Look in high places for these eight people."

"Wait a minute, kid," the PI said, looking down the list of eight. "Grab my newspaper, will you?"

"Why?" Jake asked, not sure what he was looking for.

"Just pick it up," the PI retorted. Jake picked it up and started to hand it to the PI, but the PI stopped him.

"What's it say at the very top?"

"Uh...Patterson Press."

"Yeah, Patterson Press. I think that's one of your guys — the owner of Patterson Press. Huge paper group, huge. But I'll do a full report to be sure."

Jake knew about the unique thrust of the daily Patterson Papers that made them grow into a national powerhouse. The Patterson Papers, in a daring move, shifted their format from political coverage to coverage of up-and-coming important technological progress that people loved to read about, just as Alan talked about in third grade and actually started with *Breakthrough News!*

"Do you know the owner's name?" Jake asked, swallowing hard.

"Al Patterson."

The PI did not notice Jake's reaction. The owner of Patterson Press was considered a maverick who was changing the look of daily print through shifting his readers' interest from the boring world of politics to the exciting world of technological progress, bringing both science and business to the forefront. Jake was speechless, once again. This now made five great accomplishers taking their fields of knowledge to the next level. ...The story was just beginning to unfold.

"I'll track 'em all down and have the report for you by the end of the month," the confident PI said. The end of the month was less than two weeks away. What, oh what, Jake wondered, will his report reveal?

CHAPTER
TWENTY-EIGHT

Jake had to get back to Boston to register for his classes for the second semester and to get back to work. During his stay with Angie and Jessie, they had become lifelong friends and helped Jake open the door to another life he never knew existed — the life he was meant to live.

On the drive back to Boston, he smiled over and over in disbelief at what he had done. He thought about the profundity of what he was involved in. Here he was barely old enough to buy beer, and he would be contacting and, hopefully, bringing together some of the world's most powerful people. Not only that, he said to himself shaking his head in disbelief, but I'll meet those people and be part of that crowd. I'll be surrounded by and communicating with those geniuses!

When he asked himself how this could be happening, he realized it all started because of spotting a common denominator — seeing that Ian Scott, Sally Salberg, and Theodore Winters all attended the same school at about the same time, which led to the discovery that they all sat in the same classroom together, taught by the amazing Miss Annabelle.

Jake drove home, watching the scenery go by, daydreaming how his life would now change. How is it, he asked himself, that I'm the person who'll bring those powerful giants together?

When he realized he was bringing a powerful value to *their* lives by reuniting those soul mates, a rush of pride and happiness filled him beyond what other twenty-one-year-olds know.

"Life is beautiful," he sighed.

*

Back at school, everything seemed to move so unbelievably slow. Jake had not started classes yet, but he pulled out his books from last semester. After having listened to Miss Annabelle's lectures and having witnessed her eight and nine-year-old students leap so dramatically throughout the school year, his college learning schedule for twenty and twenty-one-year-olds seemed to move at a snail's pace. Yet, how could their studies, he wondered, really move any faster? The college students in their fourth year were flat out studying each night and on weekends.

That riddle monopolized his thoughts. What exactly enabled Miss Annabelle's class to consume knowledge and cover so much ground? What was it in her technique that created those geniuses?

He knew he would find the answer in her book *How To Raise A Genius Through Five-Minute Bedtime Stories.* He had ordered the book through Amazon Books over the Internet the day he first discovered Miss Annabelle's alias, and today it had arrived.

Jake felt as if he were opening a lost treasure as he opened the cover of the book. In essence, he was. And there, in the first chapter, he understood the clear difference why Miss Annabelle created geniuses out of little children and why his college professors merely created knowledgeable young adults.

Her first chapter selected some of history's great geniuses who broke through to the next level of thinking. Jake remembered her lecture the last day of school when she told this to her students: In many cases, history's great minds had, while growing up, a mentor. This mentor did not necessarily teach the child scholastic lessons of literature, history, writing, math, and science. Instead, this mentor would, starting at a young age, talk to the child about life: how and why things were the way they were. By showing the impressionable young mind broader thinking patterns, the mentor gave the child so much more than the knowledge in the lesson itself. The mentor was showing the child the power of his mind to integrate sensory percepts into structured concepts and, eventually, to integrate concepts into growing mental puzzles that would reveal breakthrough puzzle-pictures.

In some cases, the mentors routinely used Neothink, such as Socrates who mentored Plato...Plato who mentored Aristotle...Aristotle who mentored Alexander the Great. The child would naturally go into Neothinking himself.

Telling the child broadly integrated stories about life leaves deep impressions on a child's early psyche, her book explained. Those children inevitably start pulling together information as their method of thinking to take startling leaps in thought beyond their peers. At first, a parent will think his child is forming mature thoughts beyond his age. Soon, the parent will realize the child's thoughts go well beyond a function of maturity. The child's thoughts are a function of creativity, the parent realizes. Miss Annabelle's book explained that the child's creative thoughts often come from seemingly nowhere — out of thin air — yet carry a wallop of insight.

Jake realized that Miss Annabelle's general lectures at the start of each day were those broadly integrated stories about life, pulling together raw percepts into potent concepts, and potent concepts into powerful Neothink puzzles from which new puzzle-pictures would form and radiate new knowledge to her students. Each morning her stories would send warm new knowledge into their receptive minds.

Miss Annabelle's book went on to say that, whereas parents are obviously not mentors like those great scholars throughout history, ordinary parents can have a similar effect and outcome. She gave them effective techniques to ignite the new way of thinking — building Neothink puzzles — in their children's minds. She told parents to go outside of normal boundaries, to talk about unlikely topics for young children — like how asphalt roads are like little pebbles pressed and held together and that sidewalks are like sand pressed and held together. By bringing up unexpected subjects, their young minds learn from the beginning how to stretch and reach beyond the average child's world.

She also emphasized that, in these five-minute bedtime stories, for parents to explain the *why, how,* and *what* behind things: what they are made of, how they work, and why they work that way. The combination of unusual, unexpected topics with the how, why, what behind them both expands the child's mind to broader thought patterns and starts their minds going down to the essence of things where the child could best understand them and, later on, bypass illusions. Over time, as the child absorbs more and more knowledge at its essence through these five-minute bedtime stories, he will start to see common denominators and begin to link together the world around him into growing concepts and, eventually, growing puzzles.

Whereas the parent himself may not know how to do Neothinking, the child will rather quickly evolve into that next level of thinking, for that is the natural way of thinking for very young children up to the age of six or seven, her book explained, showing substantial evidence to support her hypothesis. The sign of the child's mind making the jump into puzzle-building Neothink is when he becomes curious and starts asking a lot of questions about things around him. His mind is searching for common denominators to snap together or, in more advanced cases, for puzzle pieces to snap into a growing Neothink puzzle.

Reading Miss Annabelle's book let Jake understand why her twelve students covered so much more ground of new knowledge than he and his peers in college. Her third graders were pulling together thoughts from every conceivable corner of life as they snapped together growing puzzles of knowledge in their minds.

"Wow," Jake said as he put down Miss Annabelle's book to think. The idea hit him that, with the widespread simple techniques in her book, the next generation could be the civilization of God-Man. What would the world be like, he wondered, with hundreds of millions of geniuses such as disease-curing research doctors like Sally and cost-vanishing value producers like Theodore? A world of millionaire wealth and perfect health for everybody...what a life that would be!

He lay back on his pull-out couch in his dorm room. Down near the end of the hall, Amad's party was heating up. Soon, there was a loud knock on Jake's door. It was Amad.

Superpuzzle

"Come on, Jake," Amad said. He sounded like he'd been drinking for awhile. "Three girls at my room are new this semester, and they want to meet you!"

Jake liked Amad, his Saudi Arabian friend. Jake had been really deep into his discovery of Miss Annabelle since New Year's day. Although he wanted to finish Miss Annabelle's book, he decided to take a break and visit Amad and meet those mysterious girls. Although Jake was a serious minded young man, he loved girls.

Jake's room was next to the lobby on the fourth floor, across from the elevator. He left with Amad and walked to the end of the hall where people were coming and going from Amad's room, using the stairway just outside Amad's room at the end of the hall. Amad led Jake into his crowded party room.

Jake instantly caught the eye of the young women. Jake was a good-looking and confident guy. His light brown hair and blue eyes were especially attractive to Middle Eastern gals. Tonight, though, Jake's mind was preoccupied with the chapter he had just read by Miss Annabelle.

His preoccupation with his thoughts made him even more mysterious and appealing to the ladies. When Amad introduced him to three attractive young ladies, Jake felt an immediate attraction for the one in the middle. She had a mature look that seemed to put a protective layer between her, with her natural good looks, and the party guys. But that serious aura is what caught Jake's attention.

The initial attraction was mutual. She had been watching Jake since he entered the room. She liked men who were thinkers.

"Hello," Jake said to the three young ladies, his eyes settling on the mature one.

Amad was saying something silly to the three ladies about "My main white-man, Jake". Two of them were giggling.

"Hi. I'm Jasmine," the mature one in the middle said, holding Jake's eye contact as she put out her hand to shake his. As Jake introduced himself, his mind visually absorbed her. She was very slender with long, sleek curves. She must have been no taller than five foot one, but her long features made her look taller. Lots of noise and activity surrounded them, but they heard

344

and saw only each other.

"What's your major?" she asked.

"Economics," Jake said. He had always dreamed of being very successful in business, but as he answered this beautiful woman, he wondered for the first time where his education stood with his goal. He was discovering a path he knew he must travel — a path he knew would lead to the life he was meant to live. Does an economics degree fit into that journey?

"Are you still with me?" the lovely Jasmine said, smiling beautifully.

"Oh, I'm sorry...my mind's really been preoccupied lately," Jake said, realizing with some embarrassment that he started wrestling with thoughts in the middle of meeting Jasmine. "What's your major?"

"English literature and journalism," she said. "And the journalist part of me is just a little curious about those serious thoughts I'm competing with."

Jake looked at her and laughed. She was a beautiful sloe-eyed Middle Eastern girl. He knew that his array of thoughts would bore most college girls, especially those he met at parties. But this beauty was asking, and she seemed to perk up when he said, "Oh, well, it's a long story."

"I'd love to hear your story," she said, standing up straight from the wall she was leaning against.

Her gesture, her serious interest in his goal, really attracted him to her. "I'll tell you if you'll tell me your story of why you're getting into journalism," Jake offered.

"Well, you'd be the first," she said, not hiding her attraction for him.

"I'd like that. Have you had dinner, yet?" Jake felt a little nervous about officially asking her out.

"I know the perfect place," Jasmine said. A shy smile escaped from her lips.

Amad spotted Jake and Jasmine leaving the party. "What's this?" he said in his Saudi Arabian accent. "No, don't tell me...yes, it's true...I see that glow...I see that glow in your eyes. It's got to be love!"

Jake and Jasmine laughed. Amad was funny and disarming, and...down deep...they hoped he was right.

Superpuzzle

*

"What a quaint little place," Jake said facetiously as they squeezed into the corner cafe and pub. It was packed with college kids, back from the holidays and in the cafes at night, socializing with old friends and meeting new ones just before the new semester. It was a crowded, cozy place full of warmth and spirits. The windows were covered with a thick layer of condensation, adding to the toasty aura inside.

Jake led Jasmine through the crowded bar — and through a chorus of greetings, hugs, and handshakes from his friends — toward a small empty table in the corner. Jasmine was surprised by how many people knew Jake. She knew that a number of them wanted to talk with him but gave him his space because they did not know his date.

Jake and Jasmine made it to the corner table before anyone else and sat down.

"How do you know all those people?" Jasmine asked.

"Oh, you'll know 'em too within a month."

"Oh yeah?" She gave him a peculiar smile. "I'm a sophomore here, you know."

"You transferred?" Jake asked.

"No. I've been attending here for a year and a half."

"Really! Why haven't I seen you before?"

"I don't go out much," Jasmine said, not sure whether to be a little ashamed or a little proud. "I'm usually too busy studying...or too picky."

"Too picky? But you're out with me."

Jasmine blushed. "You got me really curious back there, you know. What is it that's got your mind so preoccupied?"

"Not so fast," Jake said playfully. "We had a deal, remember? What made you want to become a journalist?"

Jasmine looked intensely at Jake, searching his eyes, deciding if she could trust him. Within his eyes, she saw strength and compassion, qualities she could trust.

"By the way," Jake said, interrupting her thoughts, "I'm minoring in journalism, and we haven't had a class together yet. But I plan to fix that problem this semester." He smiled.

She smiled back. The thought of taking a class with him

pleased her.

"Tell me why you picked journalism," Jake said, seriously.

She decided to trust him and tell him something very personal.

"I got into journalism for what I believe is the opposite reason than most," Jasmine began. She noticed she felt comfortable telling Jake her secret. "When I was a little girl, my dad was like Hercules — so big, strong, confident, successful. He was a developer, always building his next small empire a little bigger than he'd ever done before. He was a proud and happy man.

"One night when I was about 10 years old, I woke up and walked downstairs because I thought I heard him. There he was, crying like a little boy. I didn't know what to do, but I wanted to help him. I brought him a tissue and hugged him. He didn't want anyone to see him like that, but at least he knew I loved him with all my soul.

"That month, we moved out of our beautiful custom home into a small tract home, and I left my private school for public school. The change didn't in itself bother me in the least. But what did bother me was how my dad didn't laugh anymore. He didn't walk around like a proud man anymore. I didn't understand it then, but his spirit was broken."

Jake listened. What had happened to her father? "Did he ever get his spirit back?" he asked.

Jasmine dropped her eyes and said, "No. I always hoped to see his pride and happiness return, but it never did. ...I remember looking across at him at the dinner table. When his eyes met mine, I'd smile, hoping to see that infectious happiness erupt again in his smile. He'd always smile back, but it was empty — a shell of what once filled that man."

Jasmine stopped talking and looked down, sad, shaking her head, sighing. Jake hung on her every word, watching her every breath. He noticed her pained expression relax a little; then she smiled and said, "There was one time every year, though, I'd see pure happiness in his eyes. Every year on my birthday, he'd take me camping." Jasmine took a deep breath and tilted her head back, smiling, remembering. "Oh, I'd lie in the tent with daddy at night, making little animal shadows on the side of the tent, laughing, talking. When it got late, I'd tell him I didn't want to turn off the lights yet because I didn't want that day to ever end. So, he'd keep the lights on till we could barely keep our eyes open. He'd tell me stories, we'd tell jokes, we'd visit, we'd talk until we were falling asleep. I'd see that happiness in his eyes, and although I never told him, that's why I didn't want the day to ever end. When I was falling asleep, he'd always softly sing *Happy Birthday To You,* like it was a lullaby. Then, he'd kiss me and say, *'Being with you is beautiful.'* That was always the last thing I'd hear before falling asleep. I could feel in his voice that his soul was, at that moment, *happy* and at peace."

She stopped talking and frowned. Reluctantly, as though she did not want her memory of the camping trips to end yet, she continued:

"Years later I learned what had extinguished his spirit. I stumbled upon it while doing a report for high school. My father had invested every dime of his life savings to go for yet the next level in his self-made growing empire. He invested every dime he had into developing a beautiful shopping mall.

"The local media wrote inflammatory articles that stirred up environmental activists, neighborhood protesters, and zoning officials. The media wouldn't let up. Some journalists decided they'd make heroes out of themselves by 'rescuing society from this business scrooge who would destroy their planet and their neighborhoods.'

"The momentum against my father got out of hand because of the dishonest media attacks until finally, after he invested every dime he had, he couldn't do anything more. Because of the bad publicity, the big retailers stayed out of his mall. He drowned in a tidal wave of manufactured envy."

Jasmine stopped herself from saying any more, before she lost her composure.

"I'm so sorry," Jake said. During his four-week journey discovering Miss Annabelle, his emotions had matured and expanded, and he really felt sympathy from his heart for Jasmine's father. Jake had learned a lot about values, effort, and justice. Jasmine's father risked everything and put out a lot of effort to build beautiful values for society. But, in the end, that same society turned on him and destroyed him. It

348

genuinely bothered Jake that her father was a victim of manufactured envy and ego-justice.

"I'm sorry for asking this: is your father still living?" Jake did not know *why* he asked that from a college-age girl, but felt compelled to know. Jake hoped her father was alive and well, because Jake felt as if justice needed to and might still be served.

"Yes," Jasmine said, a little surprised. "Oh...I'd just curl up and die if anything happened to him."

Jasmine felt vulnerable. Yet, she could feel Jake's genuine pain for her father, and she asked him, "I saw relief in your eyes that my father is still living. Why?"

"Maybe you really can understand what I've discovered these past few weeks," Jake said, realizing that Jasmine was coming from a different world than other young women he'd met. Jasmine lived in a world searching for justice.

"Jasmine, you're becoming a journalist to make things right out there, aren't you?"

"Yes...you're the first person who understands me." Jasmine felt her emotions swept up into Jake's warm eyes. "I want to help wonderful people like my dad, not punish them. I want to show the world what good exists in them and the beauty in what they create."

"Where can you be a journalist like that?" Jake asked. He swallowed in anticipation.

"There's only one group of papers I'd ever write for. It's the Patterson Group. The owner, Al Patterson, is my hero."

Jake swallowed again, then said, "Now, I must tell you my story..."

Jasmine cried and laughed as she listened to Jake's story. She was overwhelmed. Her hero was one of the students of Jake's Miss Annabelle. Jasmine also sensed her father belonged with this unique group of people. Maybe his internal light could glow again.

III.

Reunion

CHAPTER
TWENTY-NINE

Jake's sixteen-hundred-dollar investment in the PI from Buffalo paid off. He was competent at his job. Two days before schedule, Jake pulled from his mailbox the report on the "other eight" students. He rushed to his room and opened the PI's report.

The first of the 'other eight', Jake already knew about: Al Patterson owned a chain of twenty-eight daily papers and a cable TV station under the Patterson Media Group. Each daily paper was called the *Patterson Press*. The chain of daily papers was referred to as the Patterson Papers. He said he wanted to be in fifty markets within the next five years.

The Patterson Papers was the fastest growing chain of daily papers in the country. It was based on a new concept of seeking out and tracking the development of new values, especially new technologies, that would dramatically benefit the general population. His papers would follow the development of a new technology, covering its progress, sharing the hopes, the visions, the obstacles, the victories...reporting with the passion of an exciting television drama. People started to turn to that section first, *before* sports or political news, because that section directly notified the reader of exciting, upcoming values and technologies that would benefit him. This section called *New Technologies and Other Values* was stimulating and became addicting to read. Developers of new technologies cooperated with an open-arm policy to intense reporting, for Patterson's coverage built a large following and a ready market for the new technology.

The shift in format happened gradually. Over the years, he learned his *New Technologies and Other Values* section became more widely read than the political news on the front page. So, the Patterson Papers gradually blended new-value news into the front page along with other newsworthy items and gradually moved political news off the front page, back to a *Political News* section of its own. Now, the only political news that Al Patterson allowed on the front page was the rise of Daniel Ward, for Patterson Group viewed Daniel Ward's platform of ending government regulations, to free the country's businesses and entrepreneurial geniuses, as the catalyst to bringing us spectacular *new values*. Daniel referred to his campaign for president as the launching pad for a new political party he named the Twelve Visions Party. The Patterson Group picked up on that name and started referring to Daniel's *Twelve-Visions World* as "a world of soaring standards of living after Daniel gets elected and frees businesses and entrepreneurial geniuses". Al Patterson's papers extrapolated the image of that Twelve-Visions World, an attractive image more and more people began to believe in.

In every market his *Patterson Press* appeared, he would steadily take more and more of the market share from the traditional daily paper. In every market entered thus far, the traditional daily paper eventually sold out to the Patterson Media Group. The Patterson Media Group was currently planning to enter eight new markets.

That plan for expansion ended the first page of the PI's report and the description of Al Patterson's empire. Jake could not wait to turn through the rest of the pages in the PI's report. What became of Miss Annabelle's other seven students? Jake hopped off the couch and locked the door of his small dorm room. This way, he would not answer his door if one of his fraternity brothers stopped by. He sat at the desk built into the wall and turned the page to reveal…Reggie Tucker.

"I didn't know that!" Jake said out loud as he read the first line of the page: Reggie Tucker, Grassroots Charts, Inc., CEO, owner.

Grassroots Charts was the six-year-old national cable station that took America by storm, spanking the other music stations in the ratings. Moreover, the Grassroots Charts' 24-hour show pulled ratings not only from the music cable stations, but from the radio stations as well. Teenagers at home, it was discovered, preferred leaving Grassroots Charts on instead of their radios.

Grassroots Charts began as a novel idea, destined to success from the beginning. Grassroots Charts took the power of selecting musical tastes out of the hands of the industry-elite power brokers and put it in the hands of the people. That shift in power not only appealed to the viewing audience, but multiplied the entertainment value beyond anything seen before in the music industry, for the depth of quality and breadth of variety exploded with the new phenomenon.

Here's how Grassroots Charts worked: Local musicians, singers, bands *of any type* from around the country were encouraged to send in a complete 40-minute CD of their own original music, which could include some creatively done remakes. Reggie had learned as a teenager that there were thousands upon thousands of exceptional bands and singers that the people never heard because the elite few power brokers in the recording industry selected only a handful of artists to market. Logistics, not quality, kept brilliant and entertaining values from the people.

Reggie made a Neothink breakthrough that changed the way the music industry had always been run. His company received hundreds of CDs a month by small-time but serious musicians and bands. A local band serious enough to produce a CD was a good sorting mechanism. With its 24-hour format, Grassroots Charts actually aired over half of the bands that sent in CDs. It truly was a grass roots dynamic.

The bands chosen to go on the air (actually, televised via cable) were notified and asked to send in a homemade video of the band performing. They would, of course, send in their very best performance. The video was introduced between midnight and seven in the morning. Up to a hundred new groups could be introduced during this time. Each new group or artist would be scored...by the viewing audience. Now, here was the genius behind Reggie's concept: the score was, simply, how many CDs were sold.

His station functioned sort of like a hybrid of MTV and the Home Shopping Network...with the stimulating tension of those live COPS type shows. He would televise the videos shot on location, jumping from back-street clubs to high society...from swank to sleaze. On the left bottom side of the screen was a telephone number to call and order the CD and a live tally of how many sold — the score. Next to that live tally of number sold on the bottom left side of the screen was another small box with a live tally of the number sold of the previous video. (90% of orders came in within four minutes after the televised video.) The viewing audience enjoyed this relentless competition and became familiar with the records set and the exciting consequences when a new band broke the existing record (usually meant million-dollar recording deals).

The viewing audience from midnight to 7:00 a.m. loved the feeling of "going into" uncensored nightlife scenes. Many people watched late-night Grassroots just for that purpose: to "visit" the sometimes "dangerous" nightlife scenes. Between midnight and seven in the morning, all CDs sold for the bargain introductory price of $6.95. If fifty or more sold, that video was guaranteed to stay on the next night and the next, as long as the score stayed at fifty or more.

Those videos with the highest scores for the week moved on to rotation in the better time slot between 7:00 a.m. to 4:00 p.m. Grassroots Charts would send their recording crew to professionally video those winners of the week from the introductory time slot. Grassroots produced a professional quality video for the more prominent daytime slot.

At this new time slot, a score of 200 — that meant 200 CDs sold — guaranteed continuing airing the next night as long as sales stayed above 200. During that time slot, the selling price of the same CD jumped to $9.95. The increasing cost of the CDs toward a retail store's price as the airing time improved actually kept a solid viewing audience tuned into the introductory time slot between midnight and 7:00 am, for those were the increasing number of bargain hunters. Those bargain hunters made the whole system work.

Reggie learned early on that his company would manufacture and store the CDs. He developed a formula that gave him a good idea of how many CDs would sell based on the introductory results. By producing all the CDs himself, his huge quantity got the price down to rock bottom costs, even if manufacturing only a couple hundred of any one artist.

Grassroots Charts kept the revenues of sales and paid the artists a 10% royalty for each CD sold. Of course, by far the greatest value to the artists was the opportunity at national exposure. In fact, a metamorphosis occurred in the music industry over the six years Grassroots Charts entered the music scene. The major retail stores were filling their shelves with the top artists on the Grassroots Charts.

It was inevitable that the big retail stores stopped listening to the elite power brokers from the record labels and started listening to the people — the voters for the Grassroots Charts. It was inevitable because the leading artists on Grassroots Charts were already demonstrated in the marketplace as the best sellers. The retail stores' improved net profits using this indicator — the leading Grassroots artists — broke down the control of the elite few power brokers in the music industry and put the control in the hands of the consumers and the artists.

That meant: doing well and moving up to the prime time rotation from 4:00 p.m. to midnight on Grassroots Charts could put an artist in the big leagues. Doing among the best of the artists on Grassroots Charts would attract lucrative, multi-million-dollar record deals with the established record labels. Artists who would have never reached the ears of a music power broker could now get their shot at marketability by recording a CD and sending it to Grassroots Charts. Nearly every artist would get a fair shot at the marketplace. If his or her musical creation was marketable — a value to the people — it would rise to the next level. If his or her musical creation was marketable at that next level to a broader viewing audience, it would rise to the prime-time audience.

At prime time, the CD would sell for $12.95. As long as it scored/sold 500, it would be guaranteed to run the next night. In some cases, an extremely marketable group or solo act could have a run of several weeks in prime time, which guaranteed the artists would become multimillionaires with a major record label.

The major record labels also benefited from Grassroots Charts, because it took the risk out of signing artists. Those artists, by way of Grassroots Charts, already demonstrated their marketability. That demonstration enabled the record labels to aggressively, without risks, market their newly signed artists.

The most talented and marketable artists, as determined by the marketplace, aired during prime time, creating the best musical entertainment on television. Grassroots Charts not only offered the most creative and quality entertainment in America, but also the greatest variety with artists in so many different settings. The viewer never got bored as Grassroots Charts took the viewer into backstreet clubs all across the country for unique and fresh entertainment. For his advertisers, Reggie Tucker even took numerous polls that demonstrated the viewer never felt bored watching his station.

The PI's report on Reggie ended by saying that Grassroots Charts announced it will launch its own record label that "will sign and market its own star artists instead of giving them away to the record labels that once made it impossible for the majority of artists to succeed." ...Reggie Tucker, a black child from a poor family, now sitting on top of the world...wow, Jake thought...thank you, Miss Annabelle, for giving these kids the keys to Neothink.

Who, Jake wondered, is on the next page of this report? What surprise am I in for next? He flipped the page and read: Rico Rodriguez, Rico Steaks, President and Owner. Ah, yes...Rico, Jake remembered, the shy Mexican boy from a family line of criminals. He owned Rico Steaks, the largest consumer-direct steak retailer in the East with outlets all along the East Coast. Also, three years ago, Rico expanded nationally, selling his steaks through direct mail, and in that time, he was already the third largest mail-order steak retailer in the country.

What, Jake wondered, was his breakthrough? Jake had seen a trend in Miss Annabelle's students: They rose to the top because of breaking through to the *next level* at something. But on the private investigator's well-done and thorough report, there was nothing that indicated a specific breakthrough about Rico

Steaks.

Jake could not wait to find out, because he knew Rico had done something different than had ever been done before. So, Jake impulsively picked up the phone and called Rico Steaks. He was surprised when he asked to speak to Rico Rodriguez, and the receptionist said, "Just one moment, please."

Jake almost hung up. Where, he wondered, would I begin? How do I start my questions? He realized he really needed to prepare for this call.

"This is Rico." It was such a deep and friendly voice, which helped Jake's frozen mind to thaw out a little.

"Oh, yes sir," Jake stammered.

"How can I help you?" Rico asked.

It was so strange to hear this mature man after having heard Rico's high, prepubescent voice on the lecture tapes. Jake felt as though he had gone through a time warp into the future. Just the other day he was listening to this person who was then a little boy less than half of Jake's age and now that little boy was Jake's senior, nearly twice his age.

"Rico...I mean, Mr. Rodriguez, my name is Jake Catchings. I'm calling from Boston. I'm doing a report for college, and I wanted to ask you if you could shed some light on your company's success." Jake realized he could have kept the bigger picture from Rico for now, for Rico was genuinely glad to help ambitious students toward a successful future. But as Rico started revealing the breakthrough Jake was looking for, he knew he would go ahead during this phone call and tell Rico the whole story.

"My success story is a story about my workers, son," Rico answered. "I did something no one else would have dared. Two out of every three people who work for Rico Steaks are ex-cons."

Rico paused, expecting a knee-jerk reaction of surprise out of Jake. But Rico did not know that Jake knew all about his roots. When Rico heard no reaction, he went on to tell Jake about his breakthrough, "I've become quite famous in these parts for hiring ex-cons for high wages. My secret is that I hire ex-cons of political-policy crimes and NOT objective crimes of force and fraud. So-called criminals of laws of some politician's claim to fame are not really criminals. Instead, they're innocent people caught in the illusion of that politician's rise to power...their lives used and stepped on for his ladder to the top of politics. Those decent people who should've never gone to prison have a hard time getting good jobs with good pay when they get out. So, when I hire them and pay them nearly twice the industry norm, they become highly motivated, loyal, and protective. I have the highest morale and productivity in my industry, anywhere in the country. ...Now, other companies throughout other industries are looking into my unique personnel program."

"Your breakthrough in business came through *personnel*?" Jake asked, suddenly realizing breakthroughs in business are not limited to product, marketing, or operations.

"That's right, son," Rico said. And, as if reading Jake's mind, he added, "My business is labor intensive. A breakthrough in my workers' productivity can be as effective as a breakthrough in marketing."

Jake sat at his little desk and stared at the PI's report, opened to the page about Rico Rodriguez. These people live at a different level than everyone else, Jake thought. He wanted to talk to this benevolent man on the phone about all this. Jake had no preparation but felt he wanted to open up.

"Sir, can you remember your childhood?" Jake asked.

"Yes, sure I can. ...Why?"

"I know a time in your past, when you were just eight or nine years old," Jake said. Rico was surprised. How does this young man know about that?

"You know about my past?" he asked.

"Mr. Rodriguez, can you remember when you were eight years old...can you remember when you went to third grade?"

Still confused, Rico said, "Can you refresh my memory?"

"Can you remember Ian? Or how about Teddy...or Danny...or how about Sally and her mom who had cancer?"

"Oh yes, I remember Sally...that was so sad about her mother," Rico answered. He was *really* curious now.

"Tell me, Mr. Rodriguez, if you can remember..." suddenly Jake's heart started pounding, "...your third-grade teacher...Miss Annabelle?"

A deafening silence followed. Did he, Jake wondered, forget? How could he forget? Jake's heart kept pounding as sadness started to overcome him with each passing unanswered moment. How could Rico forget?

"I loved that woman." Rico's deep voice broke the silence. The depth of emotion in Rico's voice made Jake's eyes flood with tears. He could not talk for the moment.

"Son, do you know what happened to Miss Annabelle?" Just to hear Rico say her name again sounded beautiful to Jake. She lived in her students' thoughts!

"Yes, I do," Jake's voice cracked at realizing the impact Miss Annabelle still had on her students. With his voice shaking and cracking, Jake continued, "I've spent the past month making the most amazing discovery of my life. It's about Miss Annabelle and her students during your year together in the third grade."

"Jake, where are you calling from?"

"I'm at Boston University."

"I want to fly you down here to Philadelphia. I loved that woman, and I still do. I owe her my *life*. I want to know everything you know. I want to talk to you here, in person. Will you come?"

"Yes, of course."

"Okay, Jake, I'm going to put you through to my secretary. She'll make all the arrangements. I can't wait to talk to you, son."

"Thank you, sir."

That confident, successful voice was replaced by the soothing sound of a competent executive secretary. She asked Jake if he could come to Philadelphia that weekend. When he said he could, she asked him if he would be accompanied by someone. He smiled and surprised himself as he said he most likely would have someone with him. She told him she would call him back within the half hour with the travel arrangements, thanked him, and said good-bye.

Jake sat at his desk in stunned silence, moved by Rico's reaction. Miss Annabelle's students still loved her as they did on the day she left! Jake felt a rewarding sense of justice as he knew something big was starting to happen. He also felt very proud that he was the one making it happen. He wanted to share his excitement with Angie and Jessie, but the report staring at him on the desk before him pulled him back to it, reigniting his unbearable curiosity. Talking to Rico had flooded his veins with adrenaline, and he was ready to spend hours with this sacred report that fast forwarded Miss Annabelle's students ahead twenty-seven years. What surprise awaited on the next page?

Unbelievable. Nattie was *the* Natasha Kemp, producer and host of a nationally syndicated radio talk show. Jasmine, in particular, often listened to the Natasha Kemp Show while driving in her car. Jake started to recall the times he listened to Natasha while in the car with Jasmine, recalling how the radio personality so stunningly fixed relationships right over the radio airwaves through a powerful blend of applying deep, consistent principles to surface, ever changing pragmatisms. Recalling her shocking effectiveness, Jake looked down at the report, eager to read more.

But, he stopped himself; before Jake could read more, he closed the PI's report.

"I'm getting value overload," he muttered to himself. He was burning with curiosity, but he knew he was still hearing in his head his call with Rico while, at the same time, trying to read about Natasha. ...Each student now had such profound accomplishments that he realized he could absorb only two or three pages of the PI's report at a time.

Tomorrow, Friday, classes would start for the spring semester. He had an early class. Tomorrow afternoon he'd fly to Philadelphia. He'd be up too late if he continued the report. He put it in his suitcase to bring with him on his flight south.

*

A soft smooth hand slipped its way into his hand as the forward thrust of the plane pulled Jake back in his seat. Jake looked over at Jasmine and smiled reassuringly while squeezing her hand. She had always been a little afraid of flying, but when Jake asked her to go with him to Philadelphia, she was too excited to decline. Besides, she knew she had to overcome her mild phobia if she was to become a journalist.

After reading some of Jasmine's work, Jake had asked her to co-author the article about Miss Annabelle and her students. Jasmine was a skilled writer. She was a real pro who trained hours each day researching and writing on very involved subjects.

Moreover, unlike anyone else, she understood at all levels what was being discovered here about Miss Annabelle, her husband, her students, and man's next mentality.

Jake pulled the PI's report out of his carry-on luggage and put the report on his lap. He also had a copy of the report in his hand and gave it to Jasmine.

"Here's what her students are doing now," he said. "You'll be amazed." Jasmine started reading the first page, which told the story of her media hero, Al Patterson.

Jake opened his report to the fifth page, back to Natasha Stokov Kemp. She produced and hosted the unique, nationally syndicated three-hour morning radio show on happiness and love. She also developed her techniques into a workshop and personally trained qualified representatives to deliver those workshops across the country. The techniques in her workshop and advice on the air were uniquely focused on generating happiness *first* to open the door for lasting romantic love. She specialized in existing marriages, emphasizing that the initial attraction and chemistry pulled the couple together, but the lack of happiness eventually smothered the flame. Once she put them on the path to happiness, the flame returned.

Natasha demonstrated through real-life situations, live on her radio show, over and over again, that lasting happiness fulfills people who are motivated and have a passion inside for their life's work. Because of a woman's biological nature, Natasha identified, a woman can get that motivation and passion inside from her life's work and/or from her husband's work by contributing to his life's work, which might include making his life more efficient through a well-run home and dedicated child rearing. People who were motivated and passionate about their life's work, Natasha demonstrated to her twenty million listeners, advanced beyond their routine ruts into exciting, creative careers. Those people discovered lasting happiness. And lasting happiness opened the floodgates to lasting romantic love.

On her radio show, she would take calls mostly from married couples with husband and wife both on the telephone. She would spend up to fifteen minutes per couple, helping them identify their deepest motivational roots, placing them on the path they were meant to travel in life, even as a hobby initially. Soon, she would tell them, they would become the persons they were meant to be and become filled with a lasting happiness. Once they became filled with happiness, she proved over and over, they'll want to celebrate their happiness and will turn to their spouses. The flame will reignite and burn brightly again. This time, it won't flicker out because the permanent happiness inside wants to always celebrate with one's loved one.

Lack of happiness blew out the flame, she told her daily audience. If she could not clearly get the couple on the path to happiness during the phone call, she would give them a free comp to the next Natasha Workshop in their area.

The workshop was a three-day, hands-on experience with spectacular results. It cost couples two-thousand dollars to attend the famous workshops.

Couples were often a bit surprised the first day because the workshop was so unlike any other marriage retreat. Natasha's workshop had none of those emotional feel-good exercises designed to bring out the tears and temporarily whip up emotions into a romantic euphoria. Natasha knew such techniques worked only temporarily, just long enough to justify the pricey retreats.

Her workshop was well known among marriage counselors for its permanent results. And if not for those well-known results, many couples would have sunk into skeptics after the first day. Right from the beginning, it seemed to couples that perhaps they were attending the wrong workshop. The word "love" did not even come up until mid-morning the second day. There were no feel-good exercises to do with love. But Natasha wanted it that way, for she knew the cause-and-effect order to happiness and love. And her method worked.

The entire first day of the Natasha Workshops focussed on each individual making a unique, internal discovery. Each person was put through a series of tests to discover his deepest motivation in life: what if he could do anything he wanted — something active and productive, not passive entertainment such as watching TV, or watching a movie, or watching sports — what would it be? What does that person naturally enjoy so much that he or she would elect to pursue it in place of his or her typical entertainment, night out, or weekend activity?

Like so many self-improvement seminars, Natasha stated that

the obvious key to success was devotion and drive to a particular career or interest. But, unlike those self-improvement seminars, she explained from years of observation that devotion and drive never lasted...unless it truly grew from one's deepest motivation in life. To find that deepest motivation unique to each individual was the breakthrough, she emphasized. For instance, Natasha's deepest motivation was psychology. She would gladly read an interesting book about psychology on Friday night rather than seeing a movie. Or, after going to dinner with her husband, she would much rather get to a book on psychology than watch TV. She could easily spend her evenings and weekends learning about and working on her interest. In fact, that was how her weekend workshops got started in the first place. Although she would take time out to do other things, she had to tear herself away from her deepest motivation in life to do other things. The motivation and energy her life's work generated, naturally pulled her back to her work all the time. How lucky I am, she thought, to be doing what truly motivates me. In her workshop, she got others to discover their deepest motivation inside.

She learned that once a person discovered his or her deepest motivation, the door opened to the life he or she was meant to live...a life that would eventually evolve from the typical routine rut to an exciting, creative career. All the rules of discipline and effort still applied, but without one's deepest motivation working for him, his door to *major* success remained closed; his work remained a chore and a boring trap. Happiness would wane, and the flame that first lit up the marriage would flicker out.

Natasha discovered that most people never knew about their deepest motivation. So they could not naturally summon the physical and mental energy needed to rise into the exciting realms of creative success and lasting romantic love. Discovering one's deepest motivation equipped a person with an endless source of energy, which opened the way to exciting value creation, happiness, and love.

To discover one's deepest motivation in life, her workshop would have each person look for clues, such as a particular subject he or she tended to read about or was always drawn to. No matter how impractical it would seem to pursue one's interest, that was beside the point. For, once one discovered that deepest motivational root, then Natasha would have that person start pursuing it as a hobby to give that root some nourishment and a chance to grow. She told each attendee to always wonder in the back of his or her mind: can I make this hobby a commercial endeavor or the source of my livelihood someday? For, when one's livelihood is his deepest motivational drive, she explained, then he has achieved his ambition in life. That person, she proved over and over again, enjoyed lasting happiness and romantic love. Natasha's workshop consisted of breakthrough Neothink techniques that resulted in a staggering percentage of its attendees discovering, eventually pursuing, and going on to experience spectacular success financially and emotionally. Her unique techniques actually flipped the very reason a person almost never recognized, no less pursued, his or her deepest motivation: *impracticality* because he or she could not make a living from it. Her techniques flipped that around so that recognizing and then pursuing one's deepest motivation became *very practical* as his or her unique path to wealth and success in the top 1%.

In her workshops, Natasha learned that perhaps the most universal common denominator among people was a deep desire for a better life. It was also their least understood feeling, especially once they suppressed their desire through a sense of resignation. She noticed that suppressed desire for a better life usually manifested itself in a strong religious belief for a better life in the hereafter.

Natasha studied many people over several years. She discovered that their suppressed hope was first reawakened and then fulfilled once they found and pursued their deepest motivation.

People suppressed hope for a better life — for the life they were meant to have. Their deepest motivation pointed them to that life they were meant to live. Once they pursued their deepest motivation — their *essence*...the person they were meant to be — they no longer needed suppressed hope.

So her workshops took unhappy people — including those suffering from camouflaged unhappiness — and helped them get on the path of the life they were meant to live. Those who pursued their deepest motivation became happy people who, lo and behold, fell back in love with their spouses! They stopped subconsciously living for the afterlife and instead started living to get the most out of life, each and every precious day.

*

A jolt shut off Jake's conscious realm like a switch and turned on the world of sensory perceptions around him. The plane skipped twice on the runway. He looked at Jasmine who had also been absorbed in the PI's report the entire flight and had the same disoriented look on her face. ...Now, they were about to meet Rico.

"Let the adventure begin," he said as the plane headed for the gate.

CHAPTER
THIRTY

Inside the airport, Jasmine spotted a well-dressed chauffeur holding up a sign that read "Jake Catchings". Jake and Jasmine each carried a medium sized carry-on suitcase; they were staying just the weekend.

They bypassed the luggage area and went straight through the airport and out the front. There, still running at the curb, was the limo. Inside the temperature was toasty. Jake notice the temperature control for the back seat was at seventy-two degrees. He took his coat off and stretched his legs out as if his body was saying, "It doesn't get any better than this!"

Jasmine snuggled up against Jake. They were going to meet someone who would become part of their new world, a world different from anything they had ever known before. They both felt a range of feelings stirring inside — a mixture of excitement, nervousness, strength.

Philadelphia was drab, but after fifteen minutes, they were surrounded by beautiful countryside. Another five minutes and the limo turned off the country road onto what appeared to be a little well-kept road lined with trees. After a thirty-degree turn in the road, Jake and Jasmine both leaned forward and looked ahead in awe. Suddenly appearing before them was a mansion so massive that the large mature trees around it looked like smaller, young trees. The Danish design was made of brick and layered sheet rocks. Several "A" shaped peaks, each the size of a large custom home, rose across the front of the mansion. As the visitors got closer, their senses shifted from the massive size to the rich detail. Beige-tan-and-brown sheet rocks rose from the ground, beautifully staggered with sections of deep red bricks in an almost artistic, interlacing design. Neither Jake nor Jasmine had ever seen anything like it. When coming closer still, their senses refocused from the beautifully built house to the resort-like grounds and gardens that surrounded them and made them feel as though they were visiting royalty in England, forgetting they were just a few minutes outside of Philadelphia.

"You'll stay here, at Mr. Rodriguez's home," the driver said, smiling at the college kids' reaction.

"Wow," Jasmine said in a whisper. She was wondering how many rooms were in that edifice.

The driver pulled under the porte-cochere at the front doors. One of the doors pulled back, and a friendly-looking woman in uniform stood in the doorway to greet them.

The chauffeur got out and opened the car door for Jake and Jasmine. "I'll be here whenever you need me," he said as Jake and Jasmine got out of the car. Then he took Jake and Jasmine's suitcases and walked inside.

"Guest Room Twelve", the friendly woman said; then she turned to Jake and Jasmine. "I'm sorry, would you like two rooms?"

"That won't be necessary," Jasmine said. She was a conservative girl who had only one boyfriend before she met Jake. But she was also a person who knew what she wanted, and she knew she wanted Jake. They had been together once, but her decisive choice to stay together in one room made him feel really good. He was falling in love with her, too.

"Wonderful," the friendly lady said. "Welcome to Mr. Rodriguez's home. My name is Mrs. Green; please ask me for anything you might need. ...Did you have dinner yet?"

"No, we're starving," Jake said while walking up the steps and looking inside. His eyes darted around the huge foyer, not so much admiring the mansion as he was hoping to see its owner.

"Perfect!" Mrs. Green said as if solving a little scheduling mystery. "Mr. Rodriguez will be home in about twenty minutes, and you'll have dinner with him."

Jake and Jasmine followed Mrs. Green through a plush hallway lined with watercolors to Guest Room Twelve. I bet those are expensive paintings, Jake thought, feeling a little ashamed that he would not recognize famous art. Inside, Jake and Jasmine felt as if they had checked into a luxury suite.

What a change from that dump Rico grew up in, Jake thought, remembering what Angie had told him about Miss Annabelle's visit to Rico's childhood home. Jake realized Rico's home was manifestation of the power of the Neothink mind.

Since stepping inside Rico's mansion, Jake's and Jasmine's senses worked overtime as they observed and absorbed. The ceilings were twice as high as any home they had seen before; the rooms were at least twice as big. Jake particularly noticed the art...beautiful, classical art. Special lighting illuminated the paintings and gave the walls a colorful glow. Expensive millwork, woods, rich golden velvets and leathers spread throughtout the ceilings, walls, draperies, and furnishings.

"It's so beautiful and elegant in here," Jasmine said, "yet it's not afraid to be lived in."

Jasmine loved going through the inside of nice homes. A few minutes after admiring the room they were staying in, Jasmine sought out Mrs. Green. "Would it be all right if Jake and I looked around the house?"

"Yes, of course, dear!" Mrs. Green chuckled even before Jasmine finished asking. ...Every guest must ask her that question, Jake thought.

Jasmine led the way. She left the entryway at a right-angle from the hall that took them to Guest Room Twelve. Jake thought they were walking East, toward the back of the house. They were walking through a long, beautiful room decorated with a lot of gold objects and fabrics. At the far side of the room were French doors. The awestruck college students walked through the glowing room. Jasmine opened the French doors, and they stood looking into another long, beautiful room full of dark green and burgundy fabrics, dark red drapes, and lots of books. "Maybe this is the library," Jasmine said. She walked in. "You know, each one of these beautiful rooms has a purpose."

Just then, the French doors on the far side of the reading room burst open. Three children ran across the dark, redwood floor in a gleeful gallop. The littlest one, a cute dark-blond boy about two years old, kept yelling, "Yay, daddy's home! Yay, daddy's home!" as he struggled to keep up with his older brother and sister. They ran right past Jake and Jasmine without breaking stride. The oldest was a gorgeous little brunette girl with big brown eyes, fair skin, full lips, maybe six or seven years old. She reached the next set of French doors a step ahead of the middle sibling who was midway in height between the little lady and the little golden boy. She threw open the French doors Jake and Jasmine had just closed, and the little stampede vanished into the distance. A moment passed, then Jake and Jasmine heard "Daddy!" "Daddy!" "Daddy!" followed by squeals of laughter as each little member of the charge reached its destination.

Jake heard Rico's deep, loving voice, and Jake shivered in disbelief for a second. This is the same Rico, he thought, *the same Rico* in third grade on the tapes.

Jake and Jasmine followed the path the stampede had just blazed. After what seemed like an unusually long walk to the front door, they saw him. He was kneeling on his right knee. The little one was sitting on his daddy's left thigh; daddy's right arm was wrapped around the lovely little girl; the other arm around his other striking son who looked like a little Rico. Rico gave full attention to his children. They were telling him about the highlights of their day.

Jake and Jasmine stopped before Rico saw them. They instinctively did not want to interrupt this special moment between father and children. The look of complete contentment on the children's faces, especially that little two-year old who could not talk much, but who quietly savored his moment on daddy's lap, struck Jake. He did not know much about children, but he knew that look of complete contentment was something very special.

Rico was a handsome man about six feet tall. His Latino looks, thick 5 o'clock shadow, and a noticeable scar just under his left eye gave a clue to his tough-guy roots. Obviously, the man could be intimidating if and when he needed to. His strong looks made his gentleness with his children something beautiful to watch.

"Living poetry," Jasmine whispered to Jake.

Rico heard the whispering and looked up, straight at Jake and Jasmine.

"Hello Jake," he said, standing up to shake hands, scooping the two-year-old up with his left hand and extending his right.

"It's nice to meet you, Mr. Rodriguez," Jake said, walking over to shake his hand. "This is my girlfriend, Jasmine." Jake and Jasmine both felt a surge of joy by their first use of the term "girlfriend".

"Call me Rico," he said, shaking Jake and then Jasmine's hands. "And these are my most precious treasures Rosa, Rico II, and little Tony," he said raising the little boy with one hand, like toasting a glass of wine. The three children, even the little one nestled in his daddy's arm, said a sweet, yet strong "Hi."

"Two of my most precious treasures are missing. Mrs. Green, where's my Monica and my Olivia?"

"They're upstairs, sir. Monica's on the Internet." Mrs. Green seemed to know everything that's going on, Jake thought. "Dinner's waiting for you, sir."

As they went inside, Jake noticed that Rico's skin was surprisingly light, in contrast to his dark hair and dark brown eyes. He was born with strong features and was very handsome with prominent eyebrows resting over his exceptional eyes that were windows to his strong character within. He was a man of strength, yet tenderness. He looked healthy, strong, refined by success. A tough guy, no mistake. But a refined man who lived by his mind and no longer relied on his tough physical roots.

A few moments after arriving in the dining room, an adorable ten-year-old girl and her beautiful mother entered.

"Ah, my other precious treasures," Rico said jubilantly. "Jake and Jasmine, meet my wife, Olivia, and my oldest, Monica."

The ladies were striking if not stunning. Olivia moved gracefully across the room toward Jake and Jasmine. Her blond hair rested on her small, bare shoulders. She was tall for a woman, with the long limbs of a model.

Monica, her daughter, looked so much like her mother, Jake had to look twice to realize Monica was just a girl. She was a few inches shorter and her hair was a shade darker than her mother, but the mature expression on her pretty face and her poise made her look years older.

"You have beautiful children," Jasmine said to Rico and Olivia.

Through the dinner, Jake felt moved by the joy, the *love*, that filled the room. Jake could not forget the look in those children's faces as they raced to see their father: nothing else in the world mattered. ...What an incredible love they have for each other.

Jake witnessed how rambunctious the two-year-old was throughout the dinner and could not get over how still little Tony sat in Rico's lap earlier.

Rico had everyone at the dinner table laughing over a most endearing story: two weeks after school had begun, he had called Miss Annabelle at her house to ask her out to a movie, for she was his first crush. Rico was a good storyteller, and he elaborated on his embarrassments to his children's and wife's delight.

"Jake, when you walked into my house, you must've brought my memory banks with you. I haven't thought about that crazy story in twenty-five years!" Rico said. That statement seemed to challenge his memory. He began to remember names and ask Jake what they were doing now.

With some help from Jake, Rico remembered all eleven classmates. Jake told him everything he knew and promised Rico to fill him in over the weekend on the handful he had not yet read about.

Something changed in Rico's expression. He became quiet. Jake studied Rico's expressive eyes; they were aflame. Everyone at the table stopped and looked at Rico. His kids and wife had seen this look before. They knew some big idea was coming. Jake and Jasmine wondered, what thought is brewing inside that handsome head?

Finally, Rico released his thought for all to share: "We must have a reunion!" Yes! Jake thought, that's exactly what I want to do.

Rico was a man of action. Once he made up his mind to do something, nothing could stop him. "Jake, I must have that PI report tonight. Give it to Mrs. Green after dinner, and she'll make a copy for me. We will have a reunion. I'll draft a letter tomorrow, and we'll send it out by Federal Express."

Jake nearly leaped out of his skin. It was really going to happen. What could possibly match the thought of meeting and being among these people?

*

Later that night Jake and Jasmine, both in the middle of reading the PI report, decided to take a break and walk through the mansion.

The edifice was big, the rooms were big, yet there seemed to be no end to the number of and purpose to the rooms: they came upon a big and open gymnasium room, a huge play room, an indoor swimming and jacuzzi room, an indoor tennis court "room", an arts and craft room, computer room, office, lots of guest rooms, library room, movie room, gallery room, conference room, study room, workshop room, a place that looked like a "museum" room, and other mysterious rooms they did not know the purpose of, along with big, "normal" rooms of most houses. The design of the house was obviously well thought out for maximum effectiveness for the leader of an empire.

During their journey into the lifestyle of the rich and famous, Jasmine opened the French doors to yet another large room. A slight breeze of warmth wafted by Jasmine and Jake, caused by the six-foot high stone chimney crackling with a fresh fire. A burgundy leather chair off to the side slowly swiveled around. It was Rico. He held the PI report, opened about halfway.

"Excuse me," Jasmine said, genuinely sorry for intruding on someone so powerful and busy, for at that very moment she thought of her father and how busy he once was and how much he needed his privacy. Instinctively and apologetically, she retreated.

"Jasmine, you and Jake come on in here," Rico's tone was warm; he was naturally paternal.

Jasmine and Jake stepped down into the cozy, sunken den and sat on the burgundy leather couch directly across from Rico, perpendicular to the chimney.

"I want to thank you very much for bringing the turning point of my life back to me." Rico paused to collect his thoughts. Jasmine took the opportunity to clarify that Jake had done everything and that she would help him write the story.

"Thank you, Jake," Rico continued. "You know, this report is very moving to me in many ways. Everything...everything is coming together from my starting point twenty-seven years ago in Miss Annabelle's classroom. The love my teacher and my classmates felt in there was...so different, like the love my family feels when we're all together. Not until I met Olivia fifteen years later and we had our children did I know those feelings again."

Rico paused, and he seemed to drift off as would someone rediscovering his past and rethinking his present. He said, "I'll tell you a little story to attempt to describe this love." He paused again to find a starting point.

"I was at the park with Monica the other day," Rico exhaled, his eyes looking inward at the memory, "and she finally said the words I'd been dreading for two years. She said, 'Daddy, let's not come here anymore, it's boring." Rico grimaced and dropped his head involuntarily. Jake sensed something rare in Rico's emotions. How could a man so powerful and strong be so moved over a simple comment of a growing, little girl?

"I'd been taking her there since she was two. I can still see her trying to climb up the stairs to the slide. I remember teaching her what lightning and thunder was and how far away it was as we sat on the monkey bars one night and watched a distant storm. Ever since she was two, she always wanted me to join her on the swings or going down the slide. And then her sister and brother came along. She loved playing with them, and she was so protective of her siblings. I love that about Monica. Sometimes, I'd just take her alone to always keep that special bond we formed when she was a toddler, when she was still our only child. It was Monica who made me discover my endless love for having children. I never knew. I grew up in a family with an angry, drunken father who hated me and a mother who was always stressed out and yelling. Imagine what a beautiful surprise it was for me when I felt my love for my child grow inside me and root into the very deepest places inside my heart. I'll tell you, I had no idea, but I first discovered that love at the park with Monica, and it's been growing ever since.

...But I knew, even before she said she didn't want to go there anymore, that she'd outgrown the park. That precious part of our lives was over. ...I realized that our life together as Daddy and my *little* girl was over, forever. We've been going to that park since she was so little, and we had so many beautiful times there. I can't believe how *fast* the time passed by. At that rate, pretty soon our life together as father and *child* will be over."

Jasmine was overwhelmed, but fought back her emotions. She felt strong parallels to the love between herself and her father, and she became aware that her own father had struggled with these same feelings as she grew up...and moved off to college.

"Watching my children grow has made me acutely aware of the finite nature of life. Sometimes it's so hard to stay at work and not spend the afternoon with my kids. I've cut out everything from my life outside my work in order to spend evenings and a good chunk of my weekends with my kids. I cut out golf; I turn down invitations to social events and clubs. My work and my family are my life. And for a man in my position, I squeeze out an extraordinary amount of time to be with my family. I know how mercilessly fast time rushes by. What's more, it's those phases of life — only a few fast years to an entire phase — and then that precious experience is over forever, such as Monica being my little girl."

Jake was beginning to realize that Rico's love for his family went beyond any parent's love Jake had ever witnessed. Rico's love went to a new level. Jake was in awe as he realized this new level of love was the level of love felt by the God-Man. Caring for children has always been a measurement of evolution — the more evolved, the more love and care for the children. Now, Jake was realizing this unusually strong family love was actually an indicator, a gauge, of the next evolution of man.

"My kids love to be with me. Whenever I leave to go to work, they beg me to stay home...or to take them with me. I started taking Monica to the office with me on weekends when she was six. She'd get so excited. Now, I take Monica and Rosa. They play computer games; Monica does her homework. But if they have somewhere to go and can't come with me, I miss them so much that I'm actually not as productive. I can't wait till Rico is a little older...and, of course, little Tony."

Jake saw that little face again sitting so still and content on Rico's lap just after tearing through the house like a little terror. A high-energy little two-year-old sat still as a statue on his dad's lap. Jake could see that these children so much wanted to be with their dad that they would rather be with him on Saturday mornings at the office than out playing with their friends. Jake was fathoming the power of this new level of family love. Jasmine swallowed; her eyes were glassy. She was hanging on every word of Rico's story.

"Last year I had a small stress-related heart attack that turned out to be a warning but not life threatening. During the heart attack, I could only think about the devastation my children would go through if I died. As I rubbed my chest and my secretary called 911, I discovered then that my fear was not for me, but for my children *not having me* if I died. I love them more than I love myself. I just can't bear the thought that someday I'll die and will leave my kids...and never be with them again."

Olivia walked into the room so quietly that no one noticed her until she slipped her hands over Rico's shoulders from behind and leaned over to kiss him. Her blonde hair flopped around her face. Her timely presence saved Jasmine from breaking into tears. After kissing Rico's cheek, she hugged him and looked up at Jake and Jasmine and said, "Hi." Jake saw the same love on her face for her husband he had seen on Angie's face for Jessie. Rico rested a hand over his wife's hand.

"My wife is my soul mate," he said. "I realize now that it was my experience in third grade that made me know that no woman before Olivia was right for me. And my experience made me know that I was in love with Olivia. With this report, I'm remembering now how special I felt in Miss Annabelle's class, and how close I felt to her and my classmates. I didn't feel so special or close to anyone again until I met Olivia. I guess that's why it's so easy for me to shut out socializing with others. I only feel close to Olivia and my family. ...And now, reading this PI report, I'm remembering special feelings twenty-seven years ago I'd forgotten all about. Those were my only true friends before Olivia and my children."

Superpuzzle

Whereas Rico was rediscovering his special feelings from twenty-seven years ago, Jake had been discovering those feelings for the first time...ever since this adventure began. He was looking forward to sharing those feelings with Rico, a comrade in a special world different from the rest.

"Did you, back then, sort of feel like you were your own little civilization, completely different than civilization around you?"

The faraway thoughts behind Rico's eyes came back to the conversation at hand. "Yes...yes," he said, realizing that Jake had entered this other world. "Yes, that's it. We were a *civilization* of our own. We were meant to be together." He paused to reminisce. After a minute, he said, "We must get my classmates, Miss Annabelle and Mr. Melbourne together again. We're going to have that reunion, Jake...a GREAT reunion! Olivia, we'll be the host of the great reunion!" Rico was looking up at his wife, "Darling, I know you've always wanted to hear about my childhood, but I never talk about it. Tonight, I will talk. I'll tell you everything. Thanks to Jake, I now recall where my life began."

CHAPTER
THIRTY-ONE

Reunion. That word sounded beautiful to Jake. He had met only Rico, Angie and Jessie, but having listened to their stories and every classroom lecture, Jake really felt he was reuniting with these people.

These people! These people were from another world of their own, a world in which Jake knew he belonged. Since they were eight years old, these people lived in this other world. Just what would happen when they came together as adults? It was a mighty thought. Jake could barely stand the anticipation.

After classes Monday, Jake walked to Kinko's and made twenty copies of the PI report. As he was leaving, he ran into one of his fraternity brothers.

"Hey, bro...where you been lately?" the fraternity jock asked.

"Been real busy," was Jake's reply. As his fraternity brother pursued his curious line of questioning, Jake could not stop his inner feeling that nagged him to get away from his frat brother. Jake had little interest in the world of fraternities or their parties any longer. Try as he did, Jake just could not see himself spending another moment at the fraternity house. As he listened to his peer talk about what Jake's been missing, Jake knew that during these past few weeks, he had been pursuing his calling. He could not imagine himself doing anything outside this new world he discovered with the only exception of going to his classes and doing his studies. Of course, Jasmine was part of his new world. With that thought came an enlightenment.

"Thanks, Derrick!" Jake practically shouted. "You just helped me solve a big problem! I've gotta run. See you later, bro."

Jake grabbed his stack of reports, paid the cashier, and he nearly ran out of Kinko's. Derrick shook his head and muttered something about love and another one biting the dust.

Out in the fresh cold air, Jake never felt so good. "All right!" he yelped as he walked through the snow-covered campus back to the dorms. After running into Derrick, Jake knew he was going to quit everything beyond his classes, studies, this reunion project, and time with Jasmine. He knew he would have to quit his night job as a waiter at the local favorite Steaks & Wines restaurant. He had enough money saved, and he made up his mind to focus on the reunion.

At four o'clock he showed up to work and told the manager he had to quit and was giving two week's notice. The manager looked at Jake for a long moment.

"Yer the best hustler in the place. Jake, I count on ya here. Did ya get a better job somewhere else?"

"No, no," Jake reassured him. "I've gotten involved in a major project; I need to put all my spare time into it. ...Before now, I never knew how precious time could be."

Jake liked the manager. He was a hard-working man in his mid-twenties who was raising a family and never had the resources to go to college. He alone made the popular restaurant run like a watch. He had the natural good looks of a competent young man with self-confidence and maturity beyond his years. Jake and his manager had an unspoken bond based on admiration for each other's work ethics.

"I'm sorry to see ya go," the manager said. He thought for a moment, and then, out of his respect for Jake, he opened a series of questions, "How soon do ya start this project?"

"I'm waist deep in it already and going in fast," Jake said while hanging up his coat.

"How ya gonna to pay yer bills?" the manager asked. He was not being nosy. It was his way of showing concern.

"I have a bit saved. And, I have a pretty nice coin collection in my safe deposit box from when I was a kid. I can sell some of my gold coins if I need to."

"Yer really into this project, aren't ya?"

For the first time, Jake noticed a *young* man before him, somber...silently saying good-bye. At that moment, Jake saw the manager differently. His life was tied to this restaurant. Jake was merely using the restaurant on his way to much better things. Without planning to, suddenly filled with compassion, Jake heard himself say:

"I'm sorry," and he instantaneously thought, why did I say *that*? But he knew he was sorry that he could not give the manager wings to fly to the heights Jake himself was preparing for.

"I'll tell ya what," the manager said, covering up his sense of loss. "We're slow this time of year. Put yer coat back on and get to work on yer project, hear me?"

Jake looked at his friend and smiled. It was a gift, the only gift the young family man could afford. Jake knew the manager would be waiting tables himself until he could find a replacement.

"Thank you," Jake said. His tone of voice made it fully clear that he had just received a gift.

The manager put out his hand to shake Jake's hand. "It's the least I can do. I've enjoyed working with ya, Jake. Good luck out there." His expression changed from boss to friend. "And, ya go to the top. I can see the first atom of self-motivation or lack of it in every young man and woman who passes through here, ya know. Yers is the best."

Jake knew that this was the last time their paths would cross; this was good-bye, forever. For a moment, Jake did not want to let go of the manager's hand. Then he heard himself say the oddest thing.

"Someday things will be different. Not just for me, but for everybody. Things'll be better, a lot better."

They nodded and forever parted.

*

The reunion letter was impactful and fun to read. Jake admired Jasmine's writing skills as she helped Jake put together a brief and exciting history of events that led up to the four-page reunion letter. Jake and Jasmine had convinced Rico, while spending the weekend in the beautiful mansion, to let them write the reunion letter.

Jake was never so excited about his future as that Wednesday afternoon when he and Jasmine walked into the campus post office with a stack of fifteen large manila envelopes. Each envelope contained the reunion letter and the PI report. All twelve former students (including Rico at his request) and Miss Annabelle and Mr. Melbourne (addressed to Miss Darlene Belle at her publisher's address) were getting sent the package, and so were Jessie and Angie, of course. That added up to fourteen packages. Jake decided to also send the lawyer who had helped Miss Annabelle, Bruce Salinski, an invitation. He knew that Rico would approve. In tracking him down through the Internet and discovering the boundary-breaking work Salinski was doing as perhaps the first profoundly honest lawyer, Jake could not wait to meet the man. He, too, belonged in this other world of fully integrated honesty.

Including Jasmine and me, Jake thought as he looked at the stack to be mailed, that makes nineteen of us — seventeen people who already live in this other world and two who want to get there, Jasmine and me. What, oh what, Jake wondered, could these people create if they came together, as adults, on a common goal as they did in third grade when they produced the amazing *Breakthrough News*. Working alone, they were changing the world in a big way. The thought of them coming together sent a rush of excitement through Jake.

As Jake and Jasmine dropped the packages through the mail slot, Jake trembled for a second.

"They're all coming, you know," he said.

"How do you know that?" Jasmine asked, knowing that those people were running empires and could not so easily break away.

"I know what they once had twenty-seven years ago. Over the years, they forgot. They'll all react just like Rico. You'll see."

The complete confidence in Jake's tone moved Jasmine. She let sink in what was happening. ...What will it be like being in the same room with people like Al Patterson, Theodore

Winters, Sally Salberg, Ian Scott, and Daniel Ward? For the first time since she knew him, Jasmine heard Jake's voice tremble: He turned to her, eyes big and dancing; he grasped her shoulders, and whispered, "What have I done?"

*

The phone was ringing as Jake opened the door to his dorm room Friday afternoon. He dropped his books on the couch on the way to the phone.

"Hi," Jake said, already knowing it was Jasmine, of course, calling about going to the movies later that evening.

"Jake?" she said, sounding a little odd.

"How are you doing?"

"Jake, I'm doing fine. My name is Dr. Sally Salberg, and I received your letter today."

Jake's heart raced. He was talking to the likely winner of the Nobel Prize...the woman who developed a cure for influenza and whose discoveries were now leading medical science toward a cure for cancer.

*

Before the weekend was over, he had talked to three Nobel Prize nominees — Dr. Sally Salberg, Dr. Ian Scott, and the great Theodore Winters — and over half the others. By Monday, all the former students had called and confirmed as well as a delighted Jessie and Angie and a surprised Bruce Salinski. Jake knew he would not hear from Miss Annabelle and Mr. Melbourne for another week or so since they lived in Australia. But, Jake received a surprise call from her Tuesday evening. Apparently, Angie emailed Miss Annabelle to see if she would make it to the reunion. Miss Annabelle told Jake that she and her husband decided they had to come, even if some risks were involved.

Less than one week after he sent the reunion letter, everyone was confirmed to attend the reunion. Jake had talked to or met every one of the nineteen except for Miss Annabelle's husband. In three weeks, Jake and Jasmine would personally meet them all.

Superpuzzle

*

Jake had no more interest in his old activities or friends. For a couple of days, he wrestled with the thought that maybe he was becoming a snob, now that he had rubbed elbows with Nobel Prize nominees and multimillionaires. He felt guilty for not wanting to spend time with his old friends anymore. When he expressed his feelings to Jasmine, she helped him see that he was rising to another level that demanded more out of him than his old friends and activities, which had nothing to do with becoming a snob.

Jake was grateful for her support, but she could see he was still bothered. Jasmine said, "I've always been a bit of a loner; I never had a lot of friends like you did. So, I know I can't relate to what you're feeling. But, I can *prove* to you that you're neither becoming a snob nor is this going to your head."

"You can?"

"Yes, I can. Just last Tuesday when we were addressing the reunion letters...do you remember what we talked about?"

Jake cocked his head. This was intriguing. "We talked about a lot of things," he said, still in the dark.

"I know we did, honey. But who did you go on about for...oh...at least an hour?"

Jake grinned, "Yeah...OK...I rambled on about Jessie and Angie. God, I love those people."

"Exactly, Jake...you love *them*. They're an honest, salt-of-the-Earth couple. They're not rich or famous. Jessie's a janitor and Angie's a housewife. They're *honest* people, Jake, and I see in your face: *that's why* you love them. ...If you were a snob or if this were going to your head, you wouldn't light up like you do when you talk about Jessie and Angie."

Jake was floored. He grabbed Jasmine and kissed her. "Thank you, darling. Thank you, thank you." The false guilt vanished.

*

Three weeks clipped by in a hurry. Jake kept his anticipation under control by working endlessly in the evenings with Jasmine

384

writing about his experience. Jasmine was right when she told Jake, back when they were spending the weekend with Rico, that this project would not be one article but a series of articles.

They worked frantically over those three weeks. They had planned to have the paper to hand out at the reunion. As they got into the project, it grew well beyond a three-week job. But the reunion was the unmovable deadline. Jake and Jasmine worked until two in the morning, night after night. The night before they were to fly South to Rico's home, two days before the reunion, a bleary-eyed Jake and Jasmine smiled with deep satisfaction as they stood in the 24-hour Kinko's at 3:00 a.m., looking at their 128-page booklet, bound in a rose cover titled *Miss Annabelle* and subtitled *The Beginning • The Reunion • The New Beginning.*

The booklet contained a lot. It was packed full of information the former students and their teacher would very much enjoy reading. Jake revisited several of the most invigorating lectures, reminded them of some of the fun and light moments, summarized important events such as the separation of the teacher and her students, how and why it happened. He also included a current update on the seventeen people coming to the reunion, not including Jasmine or himself, and he wrote a long editorial with his own input and conclusions.

Jake, along with Jasmine's professional writing style, put together a riveting booklet in just three weeks. In a few hours they would travel to Rico's. As they stood there in Kinko's at 3:00 in the morning, exhausted, for the first time they had time to be nervous about the big event.

*

Jake and Jasmine took off classes Friday to be at Rico's by midday to help out. The guests would arrive Saturday afternoon for the reunion, which would start at 4:00 p.m.

Rico opened his home to his former soul mates to stay with him for as long as they could; his house could easily accommodate them all. They all told Jake they would stay over Saturday and Sunday nights, which was a long time for this group of powerful people. About half of them would stay a day longer.

As per Rico's instructions, Jake encouraged them to arrive at any time, a day or two early if they could. But their schedules forced them to arrive Saturday afternoon.

Jake and Jasmine arrived the day before. The house did not cease to overwhelm them. They were staying in a different room this time, with the window facing the back view. Jasmine loved the views from the mansion. Everywhere she looked, her eyes were filled with the beauty of nature. Snow-white grounds bordered by rich green pine trees. The air was fresh and filled with a pine aroma from the pine wood burning in two fireplaces.

After they settled into their five-star room, Jasmine looked out at the coveted view.

"Jake, look!" she cried out.

"What...wow! Let's go check it out."

They ran down the back, grand spiral staircase like a couple of kids and out the back door. There before them was a sprawling one-story glass building that was not there when they were here a month ago. In front of the glass building stood a large arch, sort of like a miniature St. Louis arch made out of block glass and golden neon lights brightly shining: "Thank You, Miss Annabelle!"

Walking inside the glass edifice, Jake took a deep breath and whispered to Jasmine, "Would you look at that!"

They were surrounded by beautiful, lighted fountains and flower gardens.

Jasmine took a deep breath through her nose and whispered back, "All those flowers smell so good!"

Although it was the middle of February, the scented air inside was warm and moist, like a green house. As the couple walked around, they were amazed as the beauty in there went on and on...it seemed to be the size of a football field inside.

"Jake, this reminds me of a book my father read to me when I was a little girl. It was called 'The Secret Garden'."

"Isn't it beautiful in here?" another woman's voice said so gently that it fell just short of startling the young couple. Then from around a large bush trimmed into the shape of a cuddly, sitting bear, came the soft blonde hair and fair skin.

"Hi Olivia," Jake said as Jasmine smiled.

"Welcome, you two."

Conceiving the Superpuzzle

"This place is like a dream..." Jasmine said.

"Like dreams innocent children have," Olivia said smiling. "That was what Rico wanted. That's what I tried to capture."

"Oh, you did...I've already had memories of my father when I was just a child, and we were so close," Jasmine said.

"Thank you, dear," Olivia said, tilting her head in compassion and reaching out, touching Jasmine's shoulder.

Jake, the analytical one, started asking about the structure of the building and how it got here in just three weeks. It turned out to be a temporary structure that gets picked up and reused at expensive gatherings such as this.

"I've fallen in love with this place, though," Olivia said. "And so have the kids. It's *our* secret garden. I don't know if we'll take it up after the reunion or just keep it here permanently."

Jake realized that Olivia had been working just as hard and as long as he and Jasmine had been working over the past three weeks.

"You're doing something very special for your husband," he said.

"So are you, and I want to thank you for that Jake...and you too, Jasmine. Rico had a hard childhood. He had disowned that part of himself and never talked about his past. He lost touch of who he was and where he came from. These past three weeks have been the most beautiful, most rewarding weeks since we first fell in love. He talks almost every night about his childhood, always about that year...that wonderful class...about his teacher, that wonderful woman whom I cannot wait to meet and thank...and about his amazing classmates, soul mates whom Rico had almost forgotten about when he blanked out his traumatic childhood. It's like a part of my husband had always been missing, unreachable. Now, that part of him is alive and warm and lovable. God, I'm so glad you came along, Jake." She walked over and hugged Jake and then Jasmine.

"I thank you on behalf of my husband, myself, and my children. You should see him play with them now, like he's a kid again himself."

Jake and Jasmine felt loved by Olivia, Rico, and their children. Jake felt love for Rico and Olivia and their children,

Superpuzzle

for Jessie and Angie, for Miss Annabelle, for everyone who was coming to the reunion. Is this the way of the other world, he wondered, people creating magnificent values for each other, feeling deep, deep thanks and closeness and *love* for each other?

388

CHAPTER
THIRTY-TWO

The big day was here. All morning Mrs. Green was bringing people through the oversized front doors. Each time she did, Jake's heart jumped as he wondered, with the enthusiasm of a child, who could it be? So far, every arrival was hired help for the big event...waiters and waitresses, musicians, dancers, artists.

This must have cost a couple of hundred thousand dollars, Jake thought, not sure if he was exaggerating to himself or not.

While watching the musicians carry in their equipment, Jake spotted Rico. The handsome man had a lot on his mind. He stood still and silent, slowly looking around. When he saw Jake, he walked over to him and asked him about Miss Annabelle.

"Hi Jake. Miss Annabelle and Mr. Melbourne are flying here from Australia; that's a long flight, and they'll be tired. When do they arrive?"

"Don't worry, sir—" Jake started to answer, but Rico put his hand up and told Jake to relax and call him Rico as always.

"Okay," Jake continued, taking a deep breath. "Miss Annabelle and Mr. Melbourne arrived yesterday in Philadelphia. They decided to stay there in a hotel to sleep off the jet lag. She told me that if she stayed here the first night, she'd stay up all night talking to you. And she wanted me to warn you

389

that tonight she's staying here and that you'll be up all night visiting with her."

Rico laughed. He could not wait to see her again. He turned to walk away, then swung back around and said, "Last night I read the whole booklet *Miss Annabelle: The Beginning • The Reunion • The New Beginning*. I want you to know, I savored every line. I laughed; I cried, and I longed to be with these people again. You and Jasmine gave us a priceless gift. Every one of us involved with Miss Annabelle will feel the way I did last night reading your booklet. It's a treasure. Thank you."

Jake smiled. It was a powerful high to create a meaningful value for people of this caliber.

*

At three o'clock Jake saw a dozen or so handsome men in black tuxedos line up on one side of the entryway and an equal number of beautiful women in black evening gowns line up on the other side of the entryway. They would escort the arrivals to the glass Reunion House.

Just past the entryway on the left, in the receiving room, gathered an ensemble of musicians with string instruments. They began playing Vivaldi's *Four Seasons*.

Jasmine squeezed Jake's arm. The college students never experienced anything like this before.

Then, all at once, it all began. In a space of fifteen minutes, nearly everyone arrived. The anticipation, then the sudden flurry of arrivals, reminded Jake of standing at the finish line of the Boston Marathon. The front door would open, and Mrs. Green would whisper a name to the gentleman in the tuxedo who, in turn, would turn around and loudly announce the arrival. He and one of the beautiful ladies would walk the arrivals to the back and outside again for a moment along a red carpet, under the magnificent arch and into the dreamland where Rico awaited them.

The first to arrive were Theodore and Cathy Winters. Jake was in awe of what filled his eyes. Here was the great Theodore Winters in person. He looked untouchable, radiating a power bigger than life. And on his arm was the most beautiful woman

Jake had ever seen. Cathy, the little fat girl, had grown up to be an international supermodel. His power and her beauty mystified the room. Jake wondered, "Will I really talk to *them* tonight?"

As each arrival was announced, Jake mentally attached him or her to the child in Miss Annabelle's class. As he did this, he could see the innocence of the child still in the face of every one of these powerful people. Suddenly, there *she* was: Miss Annabelle. Jake could feel Jasmine shaking his arm gently, acknowledging the guest of honor. But he could not hear anything. He was wondering, "Does she look even more adorable in person now in her early 60s than she did in the photos he saw of her at Angie and Jessie's house taken twenty-seven years ago?" When her coat was removed, her bare shoulders and arms were small and defined. Her skin was supple and smooth above her breasts. She wore a white evening dress that women forty years younger would wear, but this petite body and beautiful face looked like a living Barbie doll. With one glance in her eyes as she walked by, Jake could feel mysteries and secrets that lay within, mysteries and secrets that she gave to her twelve little God-Men twenty-seven years ago. He wanted to see her longer so he followed Miss Annabelle and her handsome husband — known to the students as Mr. Melbourne — to the Reunion House.

The young man in the tuxedo and the young woman in the black dress walked them to the back while carrying their coats. Just before stepping outside to go to the Reunion House, the escorts placed Miss Annabelle's and Mr. Melbourne's coats back over their shoulders, and they stepped outside. Miss Annabelle gasped and looked up at the glowing message woven through the glass arch: *Thank You, Miss Annabelle!*

Inside, the six or seven former students who had already arrived were gathered together, with Rico standing in the middle. The young man in the tuxedo loudly announced, "Ladies and gentlemen, it is my pleasure to introduce to you: Mr. and Mrs. Melbourne!"

Everyone stopped and turned. Jake was glad he was witnessing this moment. Faces turned red and eyes turned glassy. No one moved for a moment, as though allowing their pasts to collide with their present. Rico finally walked from the center of the crowd toward his childhood inspiration, his eyes fixed on her.

"I'm Rico," he said quietly, "and I've missed you."

Miss Annabelle looked at Rico as a mother would look at her long-lost son. Time reversed. She could still see, in his eyes, the nine-year-old boy the very last time she saw him, that sad day before leaving for prison over twenty-six years ago...her little Rico bursting into tears, running over and hugging her, crying in her arms for one precious moment before turning and running to his bike and riding away, looking back, looking back at her for one last glance before losing her for years to come. *I can never forget that moment,* she realized; I thought it was the last time I'd ever see him. Now that she saw Rico as a man before her, reality hit her hard: *I never got to watch my precious children grow up.*

"Oh, Rico, I've missed you so much," the beautiful lioness said. She walked over and hugged him. When she started talking again, Jake noticed she was crying. "I've missed all of you so very much," she cried, "and I felt *so bad* about leaving you!" Jake felt an eruption of emotion inside when he looked around and saw Rico and the other former students fighting back tears.

Yet, today was proof of what Miss Annabelle had known back then when she left for Australia, the only reason she was able to leave: the new way of thinking, *Neothink,* was in them. She had planted the seed; today she witnessed how that seed had grown in her twelve students.

*

After the initial shock was over and things settled down, dinner was served. After dinner, each former student, Miss Annabelle, Mr. Melbourne, Salinski, Jessie and Angie, and Jake were each planning to stand up and give a five-minute talk about what they were doing in their adult lives. Before the five-minute talks began, they had an hour to mingle.

Jake first met Debra Kirkland. He remembered her — she was the daughter of the parents who owned the two hamburger restaurants called Kirkland Burgers. Since then, she built the family hamburger business into the famous national fast-food chain called Debbie's French Fry City. As Debra said a few nice things to Jake, expressing her appreciation for bringing the class together again, Jake remembered how it all started twenty-seven years ago when she noticed that good french fries were addicting and were the number-one reason for repeat customers. She talked her parents into putting emphasis on the french fries. Her parents purchased two big, stainless steel state-of-the-art french fry deep fryers and, upon Debbie's insistence, put them right out in the open behind the counter. Those state-of-the-art deep fryers were always working because they guaranteed french fries hot, fresh out of the fryer. They cooked smaller quantities to keep that policy of serving only hot french fries fresh out of the fryer. In the small town of her parent's original restaurants, Debbie was able to easily monitor the frequency of repeat customers. She suggested to her parents the bold move of *giving away* the delicious french fries for free with every order of a hamburger and a drink. That strategy introduced the "addictive" fries to everyone who walked in, and the *free* fries gave those who liked the fries a subconscious tug to come back whenever they were deciding where to go for fast food. Her parents tried her idea, and they started the free french fries to coincide with the name change to Debbie's French Fry City. The profits soared. The two original restaurants became so profitable, her parents opened two more in Buffalo. ...To this day, over twenty-five years later, french fries were still free with any hamburger and drink at Debbie's French Fry City all across America.

Next, Jake met Jeremiah Jones, an attractive man with a baritone voice. He was articulate with an impressive vocabulary. Each statement he made seemed to have profound thought behind it.

Jeremiah orchestrated the fastest-growing church in the country called the Church of God-Man. But of course, Jake thought, I remember Jeremiah's piece in *Breakthrough News* written over twenty-six years ago. The underlying message of his church was based on Ian's scientific work about abundant conscious civilizations existing throughout the Universe, nearly all of which obsoleted conscious death. Jeremiah's Church rested on a scientifically based idea system *for living* versus a mystically based idea system *for dying*. He explained that the Church of God-Man, also referred to as the Church of Life, was the first and only church that viewed human death as an anomaly among the Civilization of the Universe. "People should not die," he told Jake, "but since we still do on Earth, we must lift ourselves to the next level of thinking that Mr. Melbourne calls Neothink. When enough people do, then the technology to achieve immortality will come quickly, and that is my motivation behind my Church."

His Church called for self-improvement, particularly for what it called "fully integrated honesty". Fully integrated honesty meant that within one's scope of knowledge, he or she act only with honesty. Jake remembered, from something he had heard while listening to the tapes of Miss Annabelle's lectures, that fully integrated honesty led to integrated thinking and puzzle-building Neothink.

The idea of pure honesty sounded easy enough, but Jeremiah explained that our minds constantly go through rationalizations and tricks in order to not be consistently honest with what is best for the individual. "The matrix of illusions we grow up in helps deflect our minds away from pure honesty," Jeremiah told Jake and Jasmine. "As we learn to detect and end those subtle dishonesties, we begin to see *what is* and can start building mental puzzles of Neothink to evolve toward the God-Man."

Recognizing the discipline such a church would put on the average person, Jake asked, "How did your church become the fastest growing church in the country?"

"The glue that holds this together," Jeremiah explained, "and causes new people to stay with us, is the extraordinary emphasis we put on business and social advantages. In fact, those *life advantages* are the secret why all religions are successful. The majority of people subconsciously attend church because of the personal and business advantages they get by networking with others. We honed in on and explicitly emphasized business and social advantages to outcompete other religions at their own game. In fact, we take those life advantages to the next level, which I'll explain in my little speech later."

Jake could not wait for those five-minute speeches. Everywhere he turned here, he realized that something spectacular opened before him. In the middle of that thought, he turned around and listened to Robert Chapman talking to Natasha Stokov Kemp. "Oh yes," Jake quietly muttered, "this is Bobby and Nattie."

Bobby owned the international phenom called: Thank God It's Friday (TGIF) Employment Placement. Jake listened in fascination as Robert Chapman told how one person in thousands lives the life he or she was meant to live. Natasha agreed, saying she learned from her workshops that, of the thousands of different jobs that exist, one deepest motivational root exists in each person, making the odds thousands to one against a person living the life he or she was meant to live. As they talked, Robert and Natasha realized their businesses had great affinity. They could cross reference customers. She could refer her workshop attendees to Robert to land their dream jobs, and he could refer his clients to Natasha to find true love and complete the person they were meant to be.

Robert's specially trained counselors would get each person who comes to his company to uncover, through a series of techniques, what that person had always been drawn to, perhaps unkowingly. Natasha's workshop did something very similar. Jake listened in fascination as they compared their techniques on how to get down to a person's deep, motivational root.

Robert's company helped his clients make the self-discovery of something he called their "Friday-Night Essence", which is something productive that person would enjoy doing on a Friday night. Robert pointed out that if one's job were his Friday-Night Essence, he would naturally come back to and focus on or do research on his "Friday-Night Essence", even in the evenings and some on the weekends. That kind of "downstream focus" for one's livelihood, instead of the usual "upstream battle", was necessary to get into the top 1% in any field. ...Jake felt a strong chemistry between Natasha's workshops and Robert's employment agency.

Once Robert's company discovered a client's Friday-Night Essence, releasing his or her "downstream focus", his company would place his client in a related job. His company searched the entire world if necessary. Companies loved his placements because the employees who discovered their calling were motivated and happy. He tracked the success rate of the employees his agency placed. A whopping 96% rose to the upper echelons of management.

With that success rate, his company did a couple of things that were unprecedented: 1) it contacted companies that were NOT hiring to alert them of a match, and 2) his employment placement company contacted companies with a match, even if that person did not meet the required level of experience or education. Robert explained that the deep-rooted motivation rekindled by one's Friday-Night Essence releasing his or her "downstream focus" outperformed experience and education every time. Because of his company's phenomenal reputation, businesses usually hired his recommendations, oftentimes even if those businesses were not looking to hire.

Jake stood to the side listening to this and began wondering, "What's *my* Friday-Night Essence? Who was *I* meant to be?" He felt, ever since January and his trip to Duncan Elementary School, that he was somehow opening the door to the life he was meant to live. He also felt he would make that self-discovery before the weekend was over.

"What if you can't find a match?" Natasha asked.

"Those whom we can't find a match to place, we help them introduce the life they were meant to live into their day-to-day life. We set them up on the deceivingly simple technique brought to light by Theodore — the mini-day system. For a person to make his or her Friday-Night Essence his or her livelihood is that person's life ambition, whether he consciously realizes it or not. Using the mini-day concept, we visualize that person's Friday-Night Essence at a commercial level. Then, we break into physical movements what it would take to get to that commercial level. Those physical movements are each given a block of time and placed in the evenings after work and on weekend mornings. That person's evenings and weekends suddenly look similar to the evenings and weekends of the world's most successful winners. And because those mini-days are that person's fun and exciting Friday-Night Essence — who that person was meant to be — he or she *stays on that schedule* of focussing, learning, and producing in the evenings and weekends. Over three-fourths of our clients who are set up this way eventually build a successful business doing what they love to do. Many thousands have gone on to become multimillionaires."

"We really need to get together and talk," Natasha said.

Jake sat down in his chair, overwhelmed by the value these former students were providing to the world. He could barely wait for the five-minute speeches. As if his thoughts were being answered, Rico got up and announced the start of the speeches.

"Who'd like to go first?" he asked.

Ah yes, the beautiful eyeful, Cathy Winters volunteered. She was the girl who used to never talk, Jake remembered. She was now proportionately perfect. Her closely tailored evening gown suggested a body with sleek, feline features. But what struck Jake, when the spotlight found her, was her eyes. No animal in the wild could conquer her, he thought, for she is the superior mental animal. Having been fat as a child and having been seeded with Neothink in third grade, this anomaly of superior intelligence with physical beauty was created.

She began by telling what that special lunch in third grade meant to her when Miss Annabelle sat next to her. Jake watched Miss Annabelle as Cathy told the story, and as he saw the teacher's face quietly fill with love, he knew: she still loves them like her own children.

"Since that day in the lunchroom, I wanted to become beautiful, sweet, and smart like my teacher. I idolized her, and I grew to love her more than my own family. She became my heroine and my role model. Determined to show her I could do it, I started to diet. But I started to get so nervous because I didn't know if I could stay in control. That was my biggest fear — could I keep control and stay on my diet. Then I realized the temptations *at home* were just too great. There were too many snacks around the house. My whole family was obese and there were cookies and cake everywhere. By accident, I made a discovery. This part of my story I didn't tell you in third grade because I was too embarrassed: to get some control at home, I'd close my eyes when I'd go into the kitchen to blind myself to the cookies, ice cream, candy. I went straight to the same place in the kitchen to fix myself the exact same thing each day for breakfast. And when not in school, I did the same for lunch, fixing myself the same lunch every day. My mom would yell at me, but I fixed my own dinner, too — the exact same dinner, every day. I also fixed the exact same snack every night. At first, I would close my eyes when I walked through the kitchen and put my hands out to feel my way to the counter. I'd clear off a space to fix my meal and not look around me, so as not to see all those goodies. But a strange thing happened: do you remember? I wrote about it in that fabulous *Breakthrough News* we published."

Jake looked around. A few of the students were smiling and nodding. All the students had that "oh yeah, remember that?" look, and Jake knew that look was for *Breakthrough News.*

"After about three weeks, I noticed the cookies and things didn't bother me. I started walking right by them, with my eyes *opened*, and I didn't feel tempted. I only craved my set meal — the same thing I'd been eating for three weeks. Wow, what a revelation: I now had *control*! I discovered that we can condition our cravings to certain foods, and we can condition our hunger to certain quantities. That was the beginning of my famous diet. On other diets, those million-year-old forces of hunger and cravings work against you and control you, but on my diet, you condition those powerful forces to *work for you,* and you control them."

Again, Jake was moved by the value these students have brought the world. He reflected on how millions of obese people had gotten slim and sexy using the Cathy Winters Diet — the lose-fat-and-*gain-a-life* diet — bringing them happiness and quality of life while averting disasters such as heart attacks, diabetes, high blood pressure, and strokes.

Cathy looked at her third-grade teacher and said, "I wish you could be me for one minute to feel my emotions from the inside and know what a wonderful life I have. Thank you, *thank you* Miss Annabelle for noticing me when you sat next to me. I'll never forget that first hug you gave me—" Cathy's voice got emotional, and she paused for a moment, "I'll never forget that you noticed me. That made me so determined, and I have never lost that determination ever since. Thank you..."

Cathy knew her life would have gone down the drain if not

for this woman. "I don't know if you remember, but one day in class you asked us to imagine something that seemed bigger than life. I never told anyone, but I was imagining being a supermodel. Because of you, my dream came true." She walked over to hug Miss Annabelle.

"I've been waiting twenty-six years to do this," she cried as she and Miss Annabelle, too moved to talk, hugged. Jake looked around at the other former students. Emotions were building, held back by the dam of composure. The dam sprang a leak when Miss Annabelle talked.

"Oh, I'm so sorry I had to leave!" Miss Annabelle said. For twenty-three years, she held that tormenting sentence inside. Mr. Melbourne, who looked dashing and debonair, gently rubbed her back as she talked to her students. "I'm so grateful for this day to be with you again. You know, my heart never mended, not after all these years." She had to stop talking to catch her breath before continuing. "But seeing you again, hearing about your happy lives, is finally healing my heart. You're all thanking me, now let me *thank you* for the love and happiness and beautiful memories you all brought me back then...*and now. Thank you so very, very much...my dearests.*"

Jake could feel the depth of her gratitude, and so could her former students. No one could talk right then, so Rico asked Jake if he could stand up now instead of at the end as scheduled. Jake was nervous about standing in front of these great people, but was caught by surprise so he had no time to think about his nervousness.

"Ladies and gentlemen, I'm awestruck by all of you. My name is Jake Catchings and—" suddenly his audience burst into applause. Jake was stunned...*what's this?* Rico walked over and whispered into Jake's ear that they were grateful to him for starting what led to them all getting together again. Until now, Jake had not felt worthy of being there. The applause gave him a sense of belonging and much-needed boost of confidence. He relaxed and continued with a smile, "Thank you. I'm the college student who figured out that you, with all your outstanding successes, had one common denominator — Miss Annabelle. Thanks to her and the beginnings twenty-seven years ago, every one of you here today is so profound! I feel that in your presence, I'm discovering the power of human life. When Miss Annabelle planted the seeds of Neothink in you as children, you were amazing. Now that the harvest has arrived as adults, you're awesome. I come to you as an outsider and stand at a distance and observe. Through you, I see a different world than the one I've always lived in. Your world is driven by passion and fueled with compassion. Each of you is changing the world for the better in some important way." Jake paused, as if hesitating to say it: "But what if all that individual puzzle-building power combined together into one huge superpuzzle? As I sit here and observe...somehow I feel something huge is to come out of all this. I guess that's because two months ago I listened to all the tapes of your year in third grade and saw what power radiated from you as a group when you worked together as children. I look around this room today and can't help wondering what would happen if you put your great minds together now, as adults. What would such a supermind create?"

Jake had just delivered quite a stirring thought. Now, he changed gears and went on to tell several stories from those third-grade tapes, bringing back vivid memories for the former students and their teacher. Some of the stories were funny, bringing laughter and joy to the crowd. Other stories reminded them just how much power they did generate as a group. ...They loved this college boy, and everyone knew he was a soul mate. At the end of his talk, he told Miss Annabelle how deep his feelings had grown for her, even though she did not know him. And he told her how much Jessie and Angie had helped him and how much they loved her and missed her. Then he called Jasmine up on the speaker's platform with him.

"This is my girlfriend, Jasmine. She's studying to become a writer and journalist. She helped me make this gift for you. Thanks to her, it's enjoyable and easy to read. Here is a booklet for posterity that documents your year together." As Jake and Jasmine handed out the booklet they had worked so hard to finish, they felt gratitude radiating from these people from a different world.

Jake sat down, feeling very proud, knowing he had injected a meaningful value into this new world.

Rico next asked Bruce Salinski to speak, the honest lawyer

who had defended Miss Annabelle and Mr. Melbourne during the criminal lawsuit. The former students had never met him. Rico introduced him as the first lawyer who cut through the hopelessly decaying legal profession to a career of pure honesty.

"It was so difficult because pure honesty in my profession starts with exposing the judges," Salinski began. "It's not *pure* honesty if you don't expose the judges' ego-justice, and the judges control a lawyer's career. My decision of pure honesty almost caused me to starve. After defending Miss Annabelle and Mr. Melbourne, the judges punished me in trial after trial because I had exposed ego-justice. They were out to squash me like a bug. Judges are like a special fraternity, and word got around. I couldn't win a case in court for two years. The prosecuting attorneys would not settle because they knew they'd win in court. They had all the leverage. Clients rightfully abandoned me because I was a losing cause. Potential clients stayed away. I had no income for nearly a year.

"One day, I read in the paper about a small entrepreneur whose business was destroyed by the IRS. Moreover, he faced criminal charges. No trial lawyers would defend him — they were all afraid of the IRS, especially the Criminal Investigation Division. Besides, the IRS froze all his accounts; he had no money to pay a lawyer. So, I called him. I was right: he had no money, but I said I would defend him anyway. I explained my situation and that my defense would be a totally different approach based on widescope accounting and pure honesty. He had nothing to lose since he was going to prison anyway. So, he agreed to my radically different approach. We were both at our lowest points; we were both ready to thrive on exposing the evil that put us there. ...Well, that was my famous Golden Helmet trial and the turning point of my career."

Jake listened in fascination as Salinski told the story about the start-up entrepreneur who could not squeeze the cash out of his small company to pay his corporate taxes. He could not get the cash out because it was tied up in inventory and other assets. Although his company had made nearly $200,000 in profits, he had no cash. By the time this small businessman could clear the cash to pay the IRS, it was nearly time to do the next year's taxes. Of course, the same thing would happen again and again, each year. What do I do? he worried. He had sleepless nights fretting over his dilemma with the IRS. The compounding fear and uncertainty of how to handle the situation caused the start-up entrepreneur to never get into the system. He just did not know how to handle the dilemma, and the IRS caused too much intimidation for him to sit down with them and figure it out. He just never knew how to get in the system with his cash flow problem.

Salinski did not defend the fact that the original entrepreneur had not gotten into the system. Instead, he turned to widescope accounting: to the contribution struggling start-up entrepreneurs make to society and the net gain not only to society, but to the *IRS itself*. This start-up entrepreneur, with every penny of profit needed for inventory and assets to keep the business functioning, employed fourteen full-time employees. All fourteen were paying personal income taxes. In the early stages of this and any fragile infant company, cash flow was its nutrition, and every penny was needed for its demanding growth. To suck out cash each year for profits that show up on the books only, profits completely reinvested to keep up with a baby company's growth, would starve the baby and kill it. The fourteen jobs and potential hundreds of jobs would die forever. And this baby was the most precious entity of any economy — this baby job creator who should be able to grow up and create not 14 jobs, but hundreds of jobs (all paying income taxes). Job creation, Salinski emphasized, is the greatest value one can contribute to society...and it is the greatest gift to the IRS itself.

Through his passionate delivery, during the Golden Helmet trial, Salinski was able to move the jury. Jake could see why: In just a few minutes today, Salinski demonstrated that the carnivorous Criminal Investigation Division that raided, ravaged, and destroyed the small publishing company was really preying on a baby business for the benefit of the beast's own ever-growing appetite to support its agents of force. The Golden Helmet was a metaphor: the precious start-up entrepreneurs would wear the Golden Helmet to protect them from the beast. The start-up entrepreneurs must be left alone by the beast during the ever so fragile early years of feeding their baby companies with precious assets so the baby can grow. The seedling companies pay the greatest value to society and to the IRS by creating jobs.

This particular entrepreneur Salinski was defending was completely willing and wanting to work out his debt to the IRS, but the CID did not care about that. That Criminal Investigation Division used the opportunity to pounce and prey upon the defenseless baby company, raiding it with sixteen armed agents and breaking constitutional rights without any accountability or recourse. The IRS ripped the baby apart and ate it alive.

"In my closing argument," Salinski was saying, "I asked the jurors to ask themselves if they ever entertained the thought of starting their own business. I said if there was even a remote chance that they just might consider someday starting their own business, then they must protect themselves and their families *right now* — this was their chance right there and then to protect themselves by placing the Golden Helmet on the defendant and setting him free. I said, 'He's not a criminal; he's a hero! He's what makes society exist! Every business, every job you, your children have ever had started because of this kind of hero: the rare person who goes through the labor of giving birth to a business. That person works long days and late nights to bring prosperity and jobs to society. We must preserve and protect those rare benefactors to society and must never, *never* let the beast destroy them!'"

Jake instinctively shouted "Yeah!" and stood up, clapping his hands hard. Everyone in the room was cheering. Man, Jake thought, this Salinski can move a crowd. But it was no act. He was so dynamic because he dissected justice and injustice at the heart. No sound-good politics, no look-good illusions affected Salinski. He was a true doctor of justice who went right to the heart of the matter. His ability to cut through hundreds of years of illusions built through politicization of society was breathtaking. For Salinski, justice overpowered anything else in the courtroom including the judge, which made Salinski unrelenting at battling injustice at all costs. Jake knew that any jury listening to Salinski would feed on his fearlessness and strength that stood up to tradition and the Establishment. The famous Golden Helmet trial rocked the nation as the jury ignored the ego-instructions of the federal judge and ignored the political laws and came back with a not-guilty verdict on all counts.

With that historical verdict, Salinski became the small businessman's hero. Judges feared him because he could overpower their ego-justice influence over a jury. Moreover, he could often overturn a trial in the higher courts, putting a ceiling on a district federal judge's career. Young idealistic lawyers from around the county wanted to come and work for Salinski. He hired a number of those young lawyers and developed a whole new approach to law called Widescope Accounting Law. Widescope Accounting Law, for the first time, went toe to toe against what had previously seemed to be an unstoppable, decaying legal system that ignored honesty, replaced by talented battles among skilled lawyers. Before long, when traditional lawyers went after value producers and ran into the new Widescope Accounting Lawyers — WAL nicknamed *the wall* — for the first time the value destruction stopped in its tracks...like running into a brick wall. For the first time, the legal process was shifting: toward supporting and upholding the value producer instead of envying and destroying him.

WAL was so effective because it would expose the envious, inadequate souls of those pressing the regulations or lawsuits against benevolent value producers. WAL cut through the illusions of politicians, regulators, tort lawyers and their "compassionate" souls. WAL cut through the matrix of illusions to show what nasty people those charming-in-appearance people really were. Before long, politicians, regulators, agents of force, prosecuting attorneys and judges secretly feared going against WAL because their own souls went on trial. The prosecutors became the prosecuted.

Salinski's Widescope Accounting Lawyers became so effective at exposing the agendas of those who attacked value producers that government agents and other value destroyers steered clear of businesses represented by WAL. As a competitive result, small businesses all over the country were hiring protection from WAL at a rapid rate. Salinski's WAL became the fastest-growing legal practice in the country's history.

WAL was the first and only legal practice that refused the manipulative truth oath that led to a dishonest chess game of "truths" taken out of context by talented lawyers. Instead, WAL created the *honesty oath* that allowed its lawyers to adhere to honesty, which gave them the freedom to put every out-of-context "truth" into full and complete context. The honesty oath replaced the words "I swear to tell the truth..." with "I swear to speak with fully integrated honesty...". The Ninth Circuit Court of Appeals ruled in favor of the Honesty Oath, which became the only oath WAL recognized.

I'm sitting among geniuses, Jake thought. No...it's something different. These people...what is it? *What is it?*

Mr. Melbourne was asked to talk next. What a good-looking man, Jake thought. In his sixties, he maintained his hard-body outdoors look. He was slim with broad shoulders and old-fashioned, dashing movie-star looks.

"Well, I look around the room at you, twenty-six years after I last saw you, and I am so moved by what I see. Do any of you remember that picnic you had with my wife near the end of our school year together, when I joined you in the afternoon?"

Jake looked around. The former students were smiling and nodding.

"I told you then that you were different. Your minds were working in a different way than your schoolmates in the other classes. I was still writing my book about that new mentality, which I then called the mind of the future and, later, *Neothink* for new think. In the third grade, you were already showing signs of the new mentality. Today, you are showing the world the next level of values achieved through living the new mentality. With Neothink, you have surpassed intelligence and its two-dimensional, linear arrangement of thoughts. You have formed a new mind space created through building four-dimensional, mental puzzles that take you to the next level unreachable through intelligence alone. Now, you might wonder, why did I jump from two-dimensional to four-dimensional? While building your mental puzzles, a point came for you when you saw what the puzzle-pictures looked like when complete. That never-before-seen puzzle-picture, that you were building, was the future. You conquered the future — the fourth dimension of time. Indeed, once you saw that puzzle-picture in your mind, you knew exactly what the missing pieces to the puzzle-picture looked like, thus you knew with omnipotence exactly what to do to complete the puzzle and create your future. Again, you conquered the future. And by conquering the fourth dimension, with the future puzzle-picture now your guide in life, you no longer needed external authorities to tell you how to live.

"When the people all around us evolve into Neothink and guide themselves through this new mind space that creates their futures and paves their roads in the present, then the institutions of external authorities will collapse because people will use the authority of their own minds in charge of their own futures. That means governments and religions, both built on external authorities, will collapse as we know them. They will be replaced by structures that serve objective law and spiritual harmony that have no basis in external authority. In fact, two examples of those new political and religious structures already exist, both built through Neothink puzzles by two people in this room: the Twelve Visions Party by Daniel Ward and the Church of God-Man by Jeremiah Jones. Only their version of politics and religion will survive mankind's final evolution into Neothink."

Mr. Melbourne went on to explain that Neothink was man's second great leap of power as significant as his first leap of power from the automatically reacting "animal" mentality of the bicameral man into human consciousness three-thousand years ago. "When the masses leap into Neothink," he said, "the world will advance into financial and emotional prosperity beyond anything we can try to imagine now. What would the world be like if hundreds of millions of people created values at the level of you twelve?"

Jake's mind started wandering as he wondered, "What will that world be like?" He fancied the thought of the whole world filled with hundreds of millions of geniuses like those in this glass house. Moreover, they would be free of debilitating politicization as governments and theocracies came crashing down. Just what would the changes be? The thought was so titillating, Jake missed a portion of Mr. Melbourne's talk. When he caught himself daydreaming, Jake scolded himself, for he knew he should not miss one word from the mouths of geniuses like these.

"Underlying this Neothink mentality is total and complete

honesty with oneself to see and act on reality," Mr. Melbourne was saying. "If you cannot see through illusions created by external authorities or created by your own internal feelings, investments, or desires, then you cannot snap together reality, because illusions fall apart into nonrealities — into nothing. You cannot make the leap into the new mind space of building Neothink puzzles, for a person must snap together reality to steadily build a mental puzzle called Neothink. He cannot snap together illusions because they disintegrate into nothing, and no puzzle takes shape. So the ordinary person today never enters the new mind space of Neothink...he can never build a puzzle to reveal a breakthrough puzzle-picture. He has no power in life. If he could pierce through appearances to the essences, he would discover what you have discovered...the opposite of his boring life: the world of exhilarating stimulation. His growing puzzle-picture would take him to the next level – never reached before in his endeavor — by knowing what the missing puzzle pieces looked like to the prosperous future he's created in his mental puzzle. Through hard honesty used to cut through appearances to the essence of things — to reality — one can begin snapping together knowledge and building real mind puzzles. I was so very impressed the first time I watched you twenty-seven years ago...you were eight-year-old kids building mental puzzles! Then I learned your teacher's secret: she persistently cut through appearances to the essence of things — to reality — in her general lectures. We all know what trouble that got her into with the school board. Her relentless integrity to reality created some shocking lectures, such as the one with Ian questioning the existence of God...or the early lecture about love. It was her integrity to honesty that led to our twenty-six-year separation from you, whom we loved more than anything in this world.

"Well, what happened to your teacher and to Bruce Salinski are examples of how difficult this consistent and complete honesty is in our world, in our anticivilization. People become ostracized and punished. But that'll change. As also exemplified by you, your teacher and Bruce, the competitive advantages will take over. You and your successes are microcosms of what's to come worldwide.

Superpuzzle

"It's one of the greatest moments in my life to stand here and listen to the amazing breakthroughs you twelve former students have accomplished. And I must include Bruce Salinski, too. Of course, he's not one of my wife's students. But he made the decision to make the leap into adhering to this consistent, hard honesty. He cut through illusions to the essence — to reality — in the decadent legal field. He began snapping together reality and building a powerful Neothink puzzle that broke him through to the next level never reached before in law. He, like all of you, is a testimony to the power of honesty.

"Anna and I...we love you so much. She told me, when we learned of this great reunion, that she had to attend. Her life would forever be incomplete, she told me, if she didn't see you again. Thank you, all of you, for making her life complete. And thank you for being the greatest living examples to the books I've written."

As the students clapped for this paternal man whom they loved, again Jake could feel how this other world was filled with *love*. He remembered Mr. Melbourne explaining before how these leaps of power — from the bicameral mentality into human consciousness three-thousand years ago and from consciousness into Neothink today — bring man a whole new emotional existence. This rich love, Jake thought, would fill civilization as it filled this room once the masses evolve into Neothink. Some of the wonderful changes of the other world, he realized, would not only be great wealth and health and other unbelievable values...but a world of powerful love based on these super value exchanges.

Theodore Winters stood up to talk. Although a slight physique, he projected power and strength. As he spoke, his words reverberated with wisdom.

"The collapse of government as a politicizing machine will free millions upon millions of start-up entrepreneurs to pursue their dreams. Businesses will have to shift to an entirely different paradigm to remain competitive. And that shift is exciting news for the ordinary person.

"I began sensing this shift twenty-seven years ago when I was building my door-to-door business at eight years old. Today, I have built my success upon that shift into the next paradigm

408

of business. The world will follow when the external authorities collapse. The external authority problem today keeps people trapped in the division of labor, in nonthinking jobs of labor, which are physical, *not* mental. My new paradigm frees people by putting them in the division of essence, in jobs of the mind, which are mental, *not* physical.

"The essence of business is always the same, from its inception to its death: create a value, improve it, and market it. That essence is how a business makes profits. Today, only a handful of people in any business work on the essence of the business. The majority shut off their minds as they perform the labor. Tomorrow, most people in most businesses will work on the essences of their businesses. Yes, they'll create, improve, and market the values. They'll open their minds and make profits as they leap from jobs of labor to jobs of the mind. They'll become entrepreneurs of their *mini-companies* within the company. The division of essence will divide companies into jobs of essence instead of jobs of labor...into 'mini-companies' or jobs of the mind. That division of essence springs free the greatest asset within every business: the employee's integrating mind.

"Today, most people are stuck in set routines and are miserably stagnant. They just do their routines and don't think. But their minds are begging to and designed to integrate knowledge, build Neothink puzzles, and get exhilarated over their competitive creations. Mini-companies can be formed in every existing business today. It's a matter of first identifying the money-making purposes behind the company's basic responsibilities and, second, putting together those responsibilities with the same money-making purposes into the mini-companies. Instead of dividing a business by its labor — which cuts off the essence, the money-making purpose — any CEO can divide his business by its essence, by attaching the responsibilities to their money-making purposes to create mini-companies and to keep every job tied to the money-making essence of the business. Then, all employees become internal entrepreneurs. That new paradigm of business releases the employees' human potential. Moreover, they become happy, super stimulated people building their creations. I see it all the time in my business."[1]

Theodore went on to talk about how to grow a division-of-essence company through spreading the "genetic code" of the original entrepreneur through a technique he called replicating. Replicating passed along the entrepreneurial spirit and thought patterns, which would obsolete the inferior technique of delegating. Delegating passed down routine ruts.

He talked about essence tracking reports and monthly essence meetings that enable him to snap together his many companies into a single Neothink puzzle to easily lead his empire forward.

He talked about his personal mini-day schedule that broke his day into physical movements that, like the assembly line that broke production into physical movements, enabled him to tenfold his work capacity. And he talked about his potent power-thinking technique that he did every morning in the shower. He would look into the future at each active project to its completed form. Then he would look backwards and figure out the steps needed to achieve that completed image, and he would insert those steps into his high-action mini-days that moved him through enormous amounts of work. That mini-day/power-thinking team was his secret behind his legendary reputation of moving through complex projects in a day or two that took competitors months. ...Theodore made every person in that glass house wish he had a pen and pad to write down his revelations of business.[2]

Theodore concluded his talk with gratitude to Miss Annabelle. "Her lectures," he said, "were my roots that grew into who I am today."

Next Natasha spoke. "Theodore said people will go from boring jobs of labor to exciting jobs of the mind," she said. "Robert said to me earlier that people will discover their Friday-Night Essences and love to go to work. I say, following this job revolution will come a love revolution. People will live their

---

[1]Author's Note: To see the details of Theodore's Neothink breakthrough into the new business paradigm called the division of essence, and to see how to divide any business today into the division of essence, see *SOS Secrets*, nonfiction, 315 pages, first month.

[2]Again, all those revelations are found in *SOS Secrets*, nonfiction, 315 pages, first month.

entire lives with the spectacular feelings they had during the first few months while first falling in love!"

She went on to explain how love comes from happiness, and how most people down deep are not happy with their livelihoods. Her workshops worked on the problem today, she explained, "but the new world tomorrow with no more external authorities and with those exhilarating jobs of the mind linking up with people's Friday-Night Essences will bring about a world not only filled with wealth, but also filled with motivation, exhilaration, happiness *and love*."

Love. There's that word again, Jake thought. A world filled with *love*...

Daniel Ward got up to talk next. He looked at Mr. Melbourne and said, "You're absolutely right, sir. The whole idea behind the Twelve Visions Party is *not* politics, but the removal of external authorities. As humanity advances into a mentality that no longer needs external guidance, the Twelve Visions Party will be the only survivor. The Twelve Visions Party serves one premise: protection of the individual from physical aggression. The government would exist for protection only and would consist of courts, police, prisons, and a national army. I think you're all familiar with the sub-trillion-dollar Protection Only Budget that would change our current government of offense to a government of defense. And I think you're all aware of the Great Replacement/Great Displacement Program: entrepreneurs will replace career politicians, and we'll displace, to the private sector, government programs that have nothing to do with protection of the individual and his property. The result of the Twelve Visions Party will be a government that runs like a business *accountable to results* on how well it protects its citizens. ...Of course, changing our current government of offense that politicizes more and more aspects of our lives...to a government of defense that protects the individual and nothing more, will cause a major political revolution. The thousands upon thousands of laws, regulations, and litigation that exist because today's government aggressively politicizes our lives...will vanish. Enterprise, technology, and medicine will finally be free of politics. The progress and prosperity can only be touched upon in my Twelve Neothink Visions. I believe you've all heard of my abbreviated Six-Visions Campaign."

Daniel expanded on the fact that the peaceful political revolution would set off a great Technological Revolution. He compared it to the computer revolution of the 1980s and 1990s, but said the coming Technological Revolution will occur in *every* industry. The result, as with computers, will drive up everyone's buying power a thousand to ten thousand times. "People will be rich," he said.

Jake now knew the answer to his question earlier: these people were not mere geniuses, they were something much more. "What is it?" he had asked. Now he knew: they were the first wave of the next level of humanity. They had a different mentality altogether as Mr. Melbourne had said. But now Jake understood: they were the *next evolution of man.* These twelve former students, their teacher and her husband, and the lawyer will, Jake thought, change the world. They're the answer to humanity's eternal prayer for a better world...a world brimming with love.

Sally Salberg walked to the front to talk. She was petite, beautiful, and she was the most powerful woman Jake had ever witnessed. She started where Daniel ended, "Following the political revolution and the collapse of external authorities and the many regulatory bureaucracies such as the FTC and FDA," she said, "there'll undoubtedly be, as Daniel said, a great Technological Revolution throughout all industries — the medical industry included. The political revolution will be the first domino to go. Once it falls and takes down the regulatory bureaucracies, then comes the great Technological Revolution, a medical revolution, a job revolution, a love revolution and, I'm sure, a legal revolution as Mr. Salinski was implying, a religious revolution as Jeremiah implied, and, as Miss Annabelle demonstrated through us, an educational revolution. From what Mr. Melbourne says, all those revolutions will be the result of man's next evolution into God-Man when people use Neothink to guide themselves completely without any further need for external authorities. As the metaphor *God-Man* implies, man will be his own God, his own authority and guide. Mr. Melbourne was right: the world will change in the most incredibly wonderful ways."

She just summed up the power being uncovered during this reunion. Imagine, Jake thought, a revolution occurring in every existing structure of civilization, from wealth to love! He realized that the dawn of a new civilization was arriving.

"It is in that mental oasis — dreaming ahead to the coming changes of good that surpass even our imaginations — that I want to talk to you today. You may be the only people who can enter this space with me. ...I'll start by asking you a simple question..."

She is the epitome of beauty, competence, and power, Jake was thinking...what a pleasure to watch and listen to her.

"What is the only thing really, *really* wrong in life?" she was saying. "Failed relationships...divorce? I'd venture to say no, for failed relationships are part of life from which we can learn, grow, and go on to even better love. Failed business ventures...bankruptcy? For the same reasons, I'd venture to say no, for failed business ventures are part of life from which we can learn, grow, and eventually go on to greater success. The only thing really, *really* wrong with life is...*death*. Death is *not* part of life; there is no learning, growth, or anything better to come from death. Nothing can be gained; everything is lost."

Jake looked around the room. Everyone was hanging on her every word: She had, in one statement, reached deep into her former classmates' souls and plucked their deepest nerves. Does she know a secret to averting this eternal tragedy of death? These people who loved life so much wanted to know.

"When you experience devastating losses in your life such as divorce or bankruptcy," she continued, "your mind, subconsciously at first and consciously later on, immediately goes to work on fixing the problem. In time, most honest, productive persons will overcome and rise again. When you experience the devastating loss of a loved one, your mind tries to do the same thing. Subconsciously at first and consciously later on, it tries to fix the problem. The honest, productive person enters a torturous emotional war that will end in total, unforgiving defeat. His mind will attack the problem of having lost a loved one over and over again, and his emotions will get battered and defeated mercilessly battle after battle. In the end, years later after a long and weary fight, his psyche will surrender to the fact that this is the one and only problem the honest, productive mind cannot conquer. Again, I submit death is the only thing really, *really* wrong with life. Human death is *the problem*. To cure *the problem* has been my underlying, driving motivation behind all I have done in the medical world. My ultimate goal is to cure aging and end death."

Jake's heart started beating hard and his eyes started blinking fast when he realized what Sally was saying. Still, in disbelief, he asked himself, what is this Nobel Prize nominee saying? Is she talking about staying young and living forever? Jake had come across hokey life-extension theories, but here the famous Sally Salberg, the epitome of competence, said her whole drive in life was to eliminate death! The real possibility of immortality landed with a hard impact in Jake's guts. He'd never thought much about dying until now. But suddenly, with the real possibility of *not someday dying*, the idea of dying seemed repulsively irrational.

"My discovery of the flu vaccine came about during my work on cancer. My approach toward cancer, specifically controlling the production of cancer cells, ties directly into my work on aging. I'm working toward controlling cellular growth: to shut it off in the case of cancer tumors...and to turn it on to cure the ultimate disease of cellular degeneration or aging. As an outgrowth of this work, I'm involved with doctors who, by combining their techniques, may offer temporary solutions to averting death, which would buy people time to make it to the definitive cure of aging itself.

"I feel you are the only people in the world to whom I can express the unfathomable loss I feel when a loved one dies. How can this civilization *accept* the loss of loved ones? How, particularly, *can you*?

"I feel completely alone among the medical world in feeling the panic, day and night, to cure aging before another loved one dies. I witness other doctors caught up in this fight to save life when operating on a dying individual. But every healthy person alive is going to die to cellular degeneration. Aging is merely a disease — the most horrific disease that ever existed — *the* disease that wipes out *every single person!* The disease is so big that no one sees it for what it is. It's humanity's most universal illusion. When you clear the illusion, man's greatest moral duty on this earth is to cure this disease that kills everyone — *everyone*! It'll kill you, your spouse, your brothers and sisters, your parents and your precious children! I live day and night as a research doctor — the only doctor — driven to bring an end to this horror. Can *you* see through the illusion?"

Sally mesmerized the people in the room.

"We stand over our loved ones as they helplessly die one by one. And we accept that their irreplaceable spirit — the greatest value in all the Universe — is gone because the *replaceable* tool, the body, gave out! When the day comes when you look at a loved one's lifeless body lying in a casket, the face expressionless, with no more glow radiating from the eyes, cheeks, and lips...glance up atop the coffin at a picture of your loved one. See the face beaming with life and expression, then look back at the expressionless face in the casket. At that moment, you'll realize the face and body in the casket are *NOT* your loved one. Your loved one is the glow, the expression, the thinking, radiating spirit...and that spirit — that everything — is *gone*. The expressionless face and motionless body in the casket no longer have anything to do with your loved one. The body was merely the tool that housed the spirit — housed your loved one. Your loved one is gone *not* because the spirit needed to die. Your loved one is gone because the tool — the goddamn shell — gave out!"

She's right! A shot of adrenaline shot into Jake's veins; his heart was pounding. She's right! He couldn't take his eyes off her. He wanted to look at the others, but he couldn't take his eyes off Sally.

"I cannot accept the irreplaceable spirit dying because the replaceable body gives out, and my intolerance grows every day. Most people don't understand me. I'm different. Media personnel interview me and think I must be the most satisfied 36-year-old woman alive. I've already become a legend, they tell me. They say I'll win the Nobel Prize. But I'm *not* satisfied. I'm tortured by the thought that every person I see, I touch, I hug, I love is doomed to die. The more I love and feel, the more I can't stop thinking about the cruelty and irrationality of it all. Is life and love some kind of cruel joke?

415

Yes it is, and I've devoted my life to fix that. I can't imagine doing anything else until this atrocity is removed from civilization."

Sally paused. No one moved. The tinkling of the fountains, as if suddenly amplified, filled the hush. The people in that glass house were frozen, as if they'd been wandering around in the dark and someone, Sally, suddenly shined a bright light directly into their eyes.

"I'll never forget Miss Annabelle's talks about *the value* of our lives. And I'll never forget her compassion and her love for me. I remember looking into her eyes and seeing so much concern for me and my mother, who was dying from ovarian cancer. I could see, and can still see in my mind's eye, the pain behind Miss Annabelle's loving eyes, pain because she couldn't help me from losing my mom." Sally looked at her third-grade teacher, and her voice changed from strong to soft and vulnerable. "I still have that very special letter you sent me after you left the country. I could feel your pain, in every line, for having to leave...when my mom was dying." Sally was wrestling with her voice to be able to say what she wanted to say. "But I want you to know that the happiness my mother and I found in each other caused a remarkable physical reaction in my mother. The doctors said they never saw anything like it and believed that her happiness caused her cancer to go into remission. She lived another six years, and we lived every day with so much closeness, love, and happiness because we knew how *precious* our time together was. During that time, we spent more time together and shared more love than others do in their entire lifetimes. At the end, we both knew how lucky we were. Near the end, my mom told me it was you who pointed her, in a time of confusion, to me and to the preciousness of our remaining time together. She told me, if I ever saw you again, to thank you for her. I have waited a long time to tell you this." Sally's voice broke apart as the memory and image of her mother thanking her teacher came back. "From my mother to you, *thank you* Miss Annabelle for showing her the preciousness of our love. And from myself, *thank you* for your love and insights that helped make my life with my mom a cherished treasure and my life after my mom a gallant adventure."

416

Jake now saw the sensitive little Sally he had heard on the tapes. She was emotional, but she had one more thing she wanted to say, "I love you, Miss Annabelle. ...Could I get one of your hugs?" It was a preciously vulnerable moment in this strong woman, brought on by the beauty of everlasting love for her teacher and trust among her former classmates.

Miss Annabelle cried out, "Oh, Sally," as she rushed up to hug her. Jake, again, felt the compassion and love of this other world as he watched two broken hearts mend. He knew that leaving Sally caused Miss Annabelle her deepest pain when she was forced to move to Australia and go incommunicado twenty-three years ago. Jake watched Sally and her teacher hug...and heal. He could imagine Sally as the little girl in third grade, eyes wide with fear after learning about her mother's illness, and her teacher, eyes full of pain and compassion, hugging the little girl. Knowing how deeply Miss Annabelle loved her students, Jake could imagine how it must have broken her heart to leave the little Sally, believing her mom could die at any time.

Jake had to rethink, for a moment, why Miss Annabelle had to leave and be incommunicado in the first place. The reason was so irrational, so absolutely meaningless, that his mind did not naturally retain it. He had to really think for a moment to remember the irrationality that his mind naturally disposed of. ...Oh yes, it was the INS and IRS. For Christ sake! Those two *nothings* caused this pain and destruction! In the presence of the benevolence in this room, Jake knew those destructive *nothings* were going to someday vanish from the face of the earth as people saw through the illusions to the malevolence of those self-serving institutions that blocked everything good and stimulating in life. As Jake watched Sally and her teacher, the word that rang in his head was *innocence*. Then, when he thought of the nothings that separated them, the only word that came to mind was *evil*.

It was during this emotional moment when Sally and Miss Annabelle hugged and her former classmates wiped their eyes that Jake emotionally broke through to what was happening within Sally and within the others in the glass house: it was a war of two worlds. The innocent and pure value creators versus the evil value destroyers...the external authorities who wanted to rule over civilization versus the God-Man who ruled over his own life and future.

Several moments passed, and Jake looked around the room again. Something peculiar was happening that was sobering. As the former classmates regained their composure, the normal rumble of quiet talking amongst them between speeches did not return. Only the tinkling of the garden's water fountains could be heard. Jake looked at Rico, then at Theodore, Ian, Natasha, and Jeremiah. They sat in paralyzed silence. Their eyes were big, and their minds were working. It seemed as if these powerful people who had seen it all, suddenly laid eyes on a new life form. Jake knew exactly what stunned these people who were normally too powerful to be stunned, for Jake felt it too. It was Sally's passion about the most important responsibility for oneself, one's loved ones, and humanity. How could she put her skill and ambition toward anything else? With that single question, she had grabbed her former classmates' deepest thoughts and stretched them to the point from which they could never retract and be the same. They would never be able to see the world the same way again. The scale of importance in their lives was, in one impassioned speech from Sally, thrown completely on its end by the immense weight of imminent death pushing everything down. That big weight had to be removed to get their lives back in balance again.

Miss Annabelle dabbed her eyes and turned to her former students. Jake could not help noticing how beautiful she still looked in her 60s.

"I've been overwhelmed here tonight by your accomplishments and your love. You're all creating such important values for the world. In turn, I've never seen such happiness in adults before as I do in your eyes. When I look at you, it's almost as if I'm looking into your eyes when I taught you so long ago. Your expressions of youth have not left you. Seeing you like this fills a large void within me with happiness. The hardest thing I ever did in my life was to leave you so many years ago. If I had stayed, I would have been sent back to prison because I would not have been able to stay away from you. I would have violated the restraining order, which would have violated the conditions of my probation. When I left, the emptiness inside from being torn from my beloved students after three years in prison, caused me months of depression. My loving husband, my soul mate, helped me through it. I could not return, however, to my greatest love in life: I never returned to the classroom. I couldn't bear to be torn from my students again. Politically ambitious adults in today's anticivilization, which includes every school board, can't tolerate pure honesty with its laser-like rays that cut through illusions to the essence of things — past illusions to reality. So, I knew the outcome would be the same wherever I taught. Therefore, I never taught in the classroom again.

"Yet, I knew I couldn't stray from my teaching method of honesty and reality. I did pursue my teaching method — my secret formula I'll call it since school boards reject it. Since I couldn't be in the classroom, I distilled the core of my classroom teachings — *the secret* — into a technique parents could use. From that, I wrote my best-seller *How To Raise A Genius Through Five-Minute Bedtime Stories*. My husband, by the way, published and sold the book. No major New York publishers would touch it. In that book, I teach parents to tell a five-minute bedtime story that breaks the boundaries of the child's normal thinking pattern, always adhering to reality. After all, breaking mental boundaries through integrating reality is the process of Neothink. This technique exercises, stretches, and strengthens the child's mind, preparing that young mind to take off on its own into the realm of Neothink. In my book I encourage, as one very effective boundary-breaking event, to cut through any particular illusion such as Santa Claus, the Tooth Fairy, the Easter Bunny, and God. Cut through to reality, I say. That teaches the young mind how to cut through illusions in this world to reality, which equips that young mind with power far beyond peers. I also encourage parents to tell their children how things are made or why things are as they are. For instance, tell the child how the combustion engine of the car they drive to school in works. Explain how the gas ignites a spark on the spark plug, causing a bolt of energy that pumps the pistons that turn the axle, which turns the wheel. These five-minute bedtime stories get their young minds seeing deeper into the world around them, deeper into reality and what *makes* the world around them. Later

419

on, seeing deeper to reality will help them look deeper at everything, including the spoon-feeding of the media and politicians, to see past their sugar-filled illusions to what constitutes those complex situations. These bedtime stories break the normal boundaries of thoughts of children. The parents, in time, will begin to notice their child carries a power other children don't have. The child will seem emotionally mature beyond his or her years and unusually able to solve problems. Those are the early signs of a future great value producer.

"After John published my book, I started my Internet class. I realized that the great thinkers and achievers during the Golden Age of the Greeks and during the Renaissance often had great thinkers as tutors who broke thinking boundaries in their pupils' minds. I realized I could become the tutor for thousands of children over the Internet. Every day I put up a boundary-breaking 'lecture'. I've built the world's largest educational following in the eight years I've done this. As I listen to the fascinating values the twelve of you have brought to the world, I fantasize over what my half-million web students will have done for the world twenty-seven years from now. The twelve of you have each built magnificent Neothink puzzles that have brought never-before-seen values to the world. You have lived with the advantage of being able to see through illusions to the essence of things. You have been able to see through the way things have always been done to better ways of doing them. You have created the future in the framework of your endeavors. ...Now, I ask you to create the future of the world. I ask you great lovers of life, great competent people who know how to succeed, great achievers with powerful resources...I ask you to pull together and build the mother of all Neothink puzzles for yourselves and for all humanity for all eternity. I felt it...and I saw it in your eyes after Sally's talk. Were we not asking ourselves the same question: how can I do anything but defeat death? I saw a clue twenty-seven years ago of the synergy when the twelve of you got together to accomplish something: your spectacular *Breakthrough News*. *Do it again, now.* Death is your nemesis. Together you can create the Neothink superpuzzle that can forever end death for you and for humanity."

Jake looked around and saw Miss Annabelle's former students

nodding as she talked. What a shocking idea, Jake thought. These people have changed the world by building powerful Neothink puzzles that reveal puzzle-pictures that break through to the next level, to new paradigms of politics, business, love, law, education, and medicine. Just what would happen if these people, the world's first wave of Neothinkers, came together and poured their Neothink capacity into one synergistic Neothink superpuzzle to accomplish humanity's greatest feat of all time — to end the worst natural disaster, *death,* and to cure the 100% fatal disease, *aging*? Just what would happen? Jake tried to ponder that question, but he couldn't grasp the mechanics of it. As the thought fizzled from his mind, he looked at the beautiful Miss Annabelle, serious yet smiling proudly at her former students. Still, after twenty-seven years, she was pushing them forward to the next level.

CHAPTER
THIRTY-THREE

Jake was too excited to sleep in, although he was up until 3:00 a.m. the night before. Three and a half hours later, at 6:30 a.m., he got up and took a quick shower. He was careful not to wake Jasmine. He quietly left the room and went downstairs to the morning room. He was surprised to find the bright morning room as filled with people as it was with the morning sun. The former students and their teacher were buzzing over some idea. Jake stopped, before anyone saw him, and listened.

"The media perpetuates politics, and politics retards progress," Al Patterson was saying. "My media can turn a lot of people on to Danny, which'll force my competitors to cover him. We must put full effort on getting Danny into the White House. It's the only way to slash regulations and free the medical industry to advance like the computer industry."

"I was up most of the night, too, thinking about Sally's mission," Jeremiah said, jumping right in. "The promise of immortality has given the false religions a powerful drawing card since the beginning of man. But the church leaders are the only salesmen who can promise the product *after you're dead and gone.* My Church will now use biological immortality — *before* not after you die — as a central goal that we'll strive toward. My Church of God-Man will now become a major supporter of the Association for Curing Aging and Death. And to achieve the goal of biological immortality, we need to elect Daniel Ward for President, for he'll set free medicine, science, and business from politicization to accomplish this great feat, Project Life — the most important event of mankind. The Church of God-Man alone would generate eight to ten million votes for Danny."

"That's beautiful," Al responded. "My media approach will be less direct. The idea of living forever is too strange for most people. So, I'll concentrate on what matters most — their wealth and health. I'll continually emphasize how their buying power will multiply a thousand times when industries are not regulated by the government, just as the relatively nonregulated computer industry. That'll mean ordinary people will get rich and live like millionaires without changing a thing they're doing now. They'll also live increasingly without disease as the medical industry races forward like the computer industry once it's no longer politicized. I'll drop in, occasionally, the thought of eliminating the ultimate disease — aging."

"I can accelerate public acceptance," Theodore Winters injected. "Once I put up a lot of my own money, everyone will take the Association seriously. But it's got to be a business investment, something I'm seriously planning to make profits from. I see the PR going something like this: Mr. Winters believes that Project Life has the greatest profit potential of anything in the history of his company. He believes biological immortality will be the biggest consumer product of all time. ...If the PR goes something like that, then everyone will want in. The Association will be flooded with investors. Sally, you must put together a sliding-scale projection of how long it would take with X amount of funds. I'll start by putting 50% of my profits into the Association, and I'll raise that in increments up to 80% or 90% under two conditions: 1) as long as there's a chance to cure aging in *my* lifetime, and 2) as long as I have the controlling ownership of the product."

"Do you realize the amount of money you're talking about?" Sally stammered.

"Of course I do, it's my company!" Theodore laughed. "But what better way to spend my money? You said it yourself: 'The only thing really, *really* wrong with life is death.' I've spent

Superpuzzle

my life solving every problem I've ever encountered. My inevitable death is my most devastating personal problem multiplied by eternity. So, I'm determined to do everything I can to solve it. And believe me, as much as the money is Sally, that's not my greatest contribution. My greatest contribution is taking the controlling, commercial responsibility. By doing that, I'll lift your breakthroughs and solve all the commercial problems and limitations...not unlike lifting Fleming's penicillin from a mold to a mass commercial product. You give me the breakthrough, and I'll market it to the world!"

No one doubted Theodore Winters. They knew that once they gave him a product, he would figure out how to profitably, affordably bring it to society. Sally, Al, Jeremiah, and the rest radiated with confidence knowing Theodore's heart and soul was into the Project Life.

"The timing...oh, the timing is good," Ian said. He folded his arms across his chest as he stood up, but he never looked up. He started pacing while staring at the floor. Jake was not sure if Ian even realized he was voicing his thoughts. "My first paper since the stadium experiment will be released later this year. In it I'm revealing the first predictive-chart breakthrough since Mendeleyev's Periodic Table in 1871. My Overlay Charts will be the tools to eventually demonstrate the theory that very advanced God-Man created the Universe and controls the mass/energy dynamics of the cosmos. Think about it — wow. My Overlay Charts will eventually prove that, although the concepts of God and heaven are antiquated and downright silly, a Civilization of the Universe does exist, and it was created and is controlled by immortal God-Man. I'll add a postscript about the new Association for Curing Aging and Death that demonstrates rational man's inevitable journey to preserve his consciousness, moving us closer to joining our immortal brethren throughout the Universe. Oh my, the academe will have a harder time with this than they did with Darwin's Natural Selection." Ian burst into laughter. Jake sat down on a chair in the corner. No, Jake thought, these people have no external authorities whatsoever. They...they're beyond any and all authorities. These people *are* the authorities. Their minds are limitless.

"Yes, Ian. Yes. Yes. Yes!" Al acknowledged. "I see what

you're saying, and I'll give it beautiful coverage. Preserving our own consciousness is the natural course of God-Man...beautiful!"

"I've always focussed on the fundamental of first achieving happiness to open up one's capacity to love," Natasha said. "I've always talked on the air about achieving happiness through making values for society. The biggest problem, though, is that opportunity is so limited out there. But with Danny in the Oval Office, opportunity would skyrocket in his free, Twelve-Visions society." Jasmine silently slipped in and sat on Jake's lap, leaning against his chest, feeling cozy and content. Natasha continued talking, not seeing Jake and Jasmine in the back. "People today are so stagnant. Twenty-three million people listen to me each week. Within a few months, I'll convince the majority of them to vote for Daniel, because his Twelve Visions Party will free society. Opportunities for people to achieve the happiness and love they so desire will flood society."

Jake started adding numbers in his head: eight million in Jeremiah's church, twenty-three million who listen to Natasha, that's thirty-one million people. Whoa, that almost would be enough to win a three-way election. Jake got excited. This just might work!

"I have never done this before, but I can see the time is right." Jake looked around the room, not sure who was talking. Then Jake saw him, between Rico and Debbie, seated directly across the room. It was Robert speaking. "I show people the person they were meant to be. I've always turned each client inward to discover his or her Friday-Night Essence. With no escape from the crippling effects of politics, I've never discussed politics with my clients. Now, with an escape from the crippling effects of politics, an option for us through Danny and his Twelve Visions Party, I'll stress to my clients the importance of ending politicization of business so they can soar. My clients deeply believe in me and my reps because we change their lives for the better. They'll listen to what my reps have to say to them. And my clients will spread the good news across their landscapes of peers and friends."

"Word of mouth is powerful, Robert, and your clients go on to become top management; they hold lots of power," Salinski said, winking at Robert and carrying this most fascinating

425

conversation along. "Similarly, my law firm deals with the pulse and power of civilization — the market businessmen. The destructive legal and political world knows me and fears me. The productive business world, where all legitimate power and values come from, loves me. My Widescope Accounting Lawyers will now show the market businessmen their definitive savior: Daniel Ward and his Twelve Visions Party. His party's Prime Law is protection in its purest form. I've memorized it:

The Prime Law
(The Fundamental of Protection)

Preamble
*The *purpose* of human life is to prosper and live happily.

*The function of government is to **provide the conditions** that let individuals fulfill that *purpose*.

*The Prime Law **guarantees those conditions** by forbidding the use of initiatory force, fraud, or coercion by any person or group against any individual, property, or contract.

Article 1
No person, group of persons, or government shall initiate force, threat of force, or fraud against any individual's self, property, or contract.

Article 2
Force is morally-and-legally justified only for protection from those who violate Article 1.

Article 3
No exceptions shall exist for Articles 1 and 2.

Bruce Salinski looked at Daniel and said, "That's brilliant, Daniel. That would end all abuse, forever. And without abuse, especially without governments saddling and riding the business world, the values businesses bring to the world would multiply faster than what the computer industry has enjoyed."

Daniel stood up and thanked Salinski and the others. Then he said, "Now, the question remains: *why* am I running for President? What motives lurk deep within me? No matter how good my political ideas might be, my politics would all cycle back to something bad if I had any other subconscious motives besides what we've been planning today. For example, if I wanted to become known as the man who cleaned up our government, or if I wanted the glory of saving our businesses...then I'd have deeper motives of glory and, ultimately, power. If my political agenda were an end in itself, then everything would eventually cycle back to bad. But my political agenda is not an end in itself. It's just part of the ride to a more distant destination that brings us together today.

"Here today, I hear and feel my deepest motive in life within each of you. Ever since third grade, I could never accept the idea of people dying. It all started through Miss Annabelle's lectures: my sudden awakening to values, especially the greatest value in the Universe — human life. I was so profoundly affected by seeing Sally struggle with the inevitable loss of her mom." Daniel glanced over at Sally. She smiled at him like a loving sister. Jake suddenly saw them as children again; they looked so innocent. "I used to feel so sorry for Sally and her mom. I'd lie awake at night thinking there must be some way to fix that tragedy in our otherwise beautiful world. The idea that her wonderful mother would die soon had a lasting effect on me. As a teenager, I found myself thinking the unthinkable: how do we cure fatal diseases...*including aging?* Slowly, persistently, I put together the mental puzzle to ultimately curing death by creating the sociopolitical conditions to spring free geniuses such as Sally, Ian, and Theodore. I became convinced the geniuses in medicine, science, and business could cure aging and death if not held back by the power manipulators in government. That brought me to politics. I tried for years to communicate my idea to people. They'd either scoff at me or glaze over in boredom. To them, I was somewhere between an overly optimistic dreamer and a fanatical weirdo. I gradually figured out the formula that created a buzz, eventually standing ovations, wherever I'd go. I abandoned political ideas and created the Six-Visions Campaign. People were too busy to listen about politics, no matter how good my ideas were. I left politics of good ideas to the hapless Libertarians. Then I created my Twelve Neothink Visions of the future and selected the six most stimulating Neothink visions for my campaign. Let me tell you, people were not too busy to hear about how they would become millionaires and romantic lovers! They didn't care about politics, but they *loved* hearing about their *own* prosperity-explosion. Suddenly, I had large crowds around me every place I spoke. But underneath it all, my personal motive is what we all here realize we want — to save our lives and our loved ones. As Sally so poignantly expressed: I never again want to look into a casket at another loved one. What we're doing here today, bringing together our strengths in business, medicine, science, politics, and media, is the way to accomplish Project Life. Because Project Life is my ultimate goal in life, my deepest motive is right for this; I am the right person for the presidential run. I have no motives for fame, glory, or power. I just cannot accept letting human consciousness — the greatest value in the Universe — perish because the physical organs give out. We need to replace the failing organs or the whole body to rescue the infinitely valuable consciousness. Eventually, we must cure aging."

Jake looked into Jasmine's eyes as if he were startled. "What is it?" she whispered. But Jake's mind was on fire. He stood up and lifted her with the strength of three men and placed her gently back on the chair. "I see it!" he yelled. Everyone looked over in surprise, not having noticed him there before now. "Mr. Melbourne," he shouted in his exuberance, "don't you see it? It's what you told us last night!"

Mr. Melbourne smiled knowingly and nodded at Jake.

"You're creating a Neothink puzzle here," Jake continued. "No, let's call it a Neothink *superpuzzle*. What Daniel's saying is that his political agenda is a piece to a larger puzzle — *a superpuzzle* you're planning today to go out there and build. You're snapping together the puzzle pieces that'll bring you that never-before-seen puzzle-picture of biological immortality. You're creating the future, and you're snapping together the pieces to bring about that future — that never-before-seen puzzle-

428

picture. You fifteen or so people — you're going to control…no, I mean, you're going to *create* the future of the world!"

Jake was panting from excitement. This revelation astounded him. He had read before about the Illuminati whose secret members supposedly controlled the world, and he always dismissed it as coming from paranoid conspiracy theorists. But as he stood there panting, he wondered if it were true. Perhaps there was a group of people using Neothink to control the world as he had just witnessed. But *this* group, he pondered, *these people* — aren't they the newly emerging Illuminati? In fact, they're going to catapult civilization out of the anticivilization, into the immortal Civilization of the Universe!

Al Patterson, who was still standing, walked over to Jake and put his hand on Jake's shoulder. "Make that seventeen people," he said. "Son, I read your booklet last night. I was moved by your conceptual grasp of what's going on here, and I was impressed by the quality of the writing. It was piercing, entertaining, and you captured the big picture. I want you and Jasmine to work as a team, working for me on this mission."

Jake's body went numb. He looked at Jasmine whose mouth had dropped open in shock. At that moment, a release of adrenaline rushed through his body, thawing out his numbness, sending life back down into his legs and feet. That new life felt different than ever before. Suddenly, he knew his deep motivational root had come to life. At that instant, he knew the person he was meant to be.

"I'd be honored to be part of this great mission," he said strongly and without stutter.

"Oh yes, me too," Jasmine echoed.

The missing pieces were clear. The future was waiting for these omnipotent people to snap together. The energy in that room radiated with such force that Jake fantasized, for a moment, the walls of the morning room blowing apart and waves of energy flowing out of this room, across the world, washing away the illusions, stimulating the people. For, Jake had just witnessed the big bang of the Civilization of the Universe.

In his moment of finding himself, Jake met eyes with Miss Annabelle. She looked on the proceedings like a proud mother. Her children were together again. And this time, they would

Superpuzzle

do something so magnificent as to save all human life.

Putting Together
The Pieces

Book Two Of
Superpuzzle

2 of 3

The Secret Society Reunites

A Word From The Author

Superpuzzle is a journey into a new world. The new world, however, is not fantasy. The new world already exists in the Society of Secrets. That new world is civilization's destiny; it is your future rapidly coming your way.

Keep in mind, this journey is preparing you to come into tomorrow's new world early, before others, to join Earth's first immortals deep inside the inner circle of the Society of Secrets.

Your journey into the new world has three very different parts, broken into these three historic books of the Society of Secrets (books of faction[1]). The nature of the journey changes from one book to the next. The nature of Book One, for instance, is: filling the reader with the emotions of the new world, which help you discover a deeper love for life. Consider that everyone born in our world expects to die. That is all one ever knows, all one ever sees. But, there is another world that will become available to us — a world where people no longer expect to die. The life-is-everything, death-is-unfathomable emotions from that world have never been communicated in our world because every person born on Earth expects to die and accepts it.

As a young boy, I was told by a renowned Du Pont scientist and leading Society member — my own father — that human aging and death should be eradicated before I got old. The source was so credible that, from a very young age, I believed I would not die. Moreover, I was witness to the secret society's deepest inner core and its secret mission. Deep in my own heart, I never expected to die. With one foot in that other world, I was able to feel its life-is-everything, death-is-unfathomable emotions. I was able to feel a deeper love for life. I communicate those extraordinary emotions through the characters, particularly the children, in Book One. They never accept death. Emotionally, they are immortals trapped in a mortal world. Now, as adults in Book Two, they must break free from that mortal

---

[1]Faction (new definition): A literary work that builds an unbroken line of logic based on facts. Although the story line crosses over into fiction, the line of logic remains steadfast nonfiction.

433

world. To do so, they must take extraordinary actions.

As emotionally moving as Book One is — as you discover within yourself your own deeper love for life — the nature of the journey changes in Book Two, from filling you with the extraordinary emotions of the children to showing you their extraordinary actions as adults...as God-Men. Watch them as they execute the powerful actions needed to save themselves and their loved ones from death — from death everyone around them expects and accepts.

As you witness their actions, you might realize that *Superpuzzle* is more than a journey...it is a map. It is a map for mankind...a map out of this world, into the new world where man becomes the person he was meant to be, living the exhilarating eternal life he was meant to live. Keep in mind this tantalizing thought: there are people here in the Society of Secrets executing this map — people you will meet, including Earth's first immortals. Remember, this book is faction, *not* fiction.

Let us now pick up where Book One left off. Book One concludes with the reunion. Miss Annabelle's former third-grade students, together for the first time as adults, conceive the superpuzzle for eradicating death. They determine the three pieces to the superpuzzle to be: 1) get Daniel Ward elected as President of the United States, 2) depoliticize America, 3) set out to develop, in the new freedom paradigm, the cure to aging and death. Miss Annabelle looks on, the proudest "mother" alive as her "children" come together as superachievers and set out *together again*...this time, to save all human life. Now, in Book Two, watch as they put together the pieces to the superpuzzle.

It is here, in Book Two, where you will experience an epiphany, for it is here where you will discover within yourself, if only for a few moments, your own deepest desire for immortality.

CONTENTS

Book Two
Putting Together
The Pieces

I.

Oval Office

CHAPTER
THIRTY-FOUR

My god, I work for Al Patterson! I'm part of their superpuzzle! I can't believe those superachievers invited me into their circle...to work with them!

Jake lay on his back, staring at the ceiling in his dorm room, reflecting on the fairy-tale weekend in Rico's mansion with the world's most powerful people. *They're now part of my life*, Jake pondered. *Oh man, my whole life has changed...who will I become?*

He rolled off the couch and sat at his computer. He began pursuing search engines and web sites about the twelve superachievers.

"Look at these," he whispered when he came upon hundreds of testimonials on Robert Chapman's website.

"Oh, and look at this," Jake said moments later, "Chapman's TGIF employment agency helps each client discover his Friday-Night essence. What a value. He gets placed in a job he'll always love doing, even if he had to work on everyone's typical shut-down night — Friday night."

Jake searched the other superachievers, too. He sat there glued to the testimonials and stories on the businesses and values created by the twelve former students of Miss Annabelle. *I feel like I'm going to burst from excitement*, he realized. Shivers ran down his spine. He heard his own voice in his head say, *I guess I've discovered my Friday-Night essence.*

*

Miss Annabelle was deeply disturbed since returning to Australia from the reunion in America. John Melbourne knew his wife's heart was torn in two when she came to Australia many years before. He always felt profoundly sad about that situation. Now, after the reunion, their first trip back since leaving America when her students were just children, he could see her despair.

"You buried half your heart and its feelings twenty-six years ago, my love," he said a few days after returning from the reunion.

"The reunion brought up all those feelings again," she said. She drew in a deep breath and said, "Darling, I want to go back. I need to help my students get Danny elected."

John could see in his wife's eyes the love of a mother who would risk everything for her children. He knew if he and she went back and were caught, they would return to prison to serve out their original sentence, three more long years. He weighed the consequences.

"Anna, we're going back," he said, "we're going home." He nodded and added, "Of course, we'll have to hide our identities."

"Oh, honey," she said, then she burst into tears of both sorrow and joy. Seeing this made John's heart ache. He knew the tears of joy falling from her lavender eyes were because she would be whole again. The tears of sorrow were for the years stolen from her life, for not being with her beloved students while they were growing up...their innocent youth forever gone, forever missed.

*

"Shhh...they're coming!" said Sally. The foyer in Rico's mansion, filled with Miss Annabelle's former third-grade students, was suddenly quiet. The doorbell chimed; Mrs. Green walked over to the door, she flashed a smile at the former students, then pulled open one of the two large doors.

"Surprise!" yelled the twelve superachievers. Miss Annabelle gasped and raised her hands to her mouth. Then she walked over the marble threshold with her arms out, as though she were pulled toward her students by a magnet. She began embracing them.

Mr. Melbourne watched as the superachievers surrounded her like children to give their former teacher a hug. Even now as accomplished adults, he thought, they longed to have her back in their lives again. All of them were robbed of her love and precious value since they were nine-year-old children.

Rico's house came to life with the same love and energy that had filled the reunion. *This is so right*, Mr. Melbourne thought. He watched his wife with her students. *She's so happy.* He watched her float around the room like an angel, in heaven again...in heaven as she was twenty-seven years before, a long, long twenty-seven years before.

*

All afternoon the students and their teacher visited in Rico's den. Mr. Melbourne listened as the conversations shifted back and forth between the past and the future. *They love her*, he thought. *They need her.*

After a couple of hours, Mrs. Green called them into the dining room for dinner. The long Victorian-style table sat them all.

"I've noticed something exciting is happening with my on-line class," Miss Annabelle said after they were all seated. "I call it *upward pressures*. Young children are pulling their parents, to some degree, into the world of *what is* and into the power and excitement that grows in that world. ...It reminds me of how you all brought your parents into a world full of childlike hope..." her voice trailed off, "before that night of horror, which changed everything." She paused for a moment. She slowly shook her head and put that demon to rest. Then, she continued, "Do you remember that School Board meeting in the gymnasium when your parents supported me?"

Mr. Melbourne looked around the long dinner table; all twelve students were nodding. Ah, there they were, sitting before him.

Superpuzzle

After twenty-six years of separation, he could barely believe they were together again. He could still see them as they were during the miracle year. He could still see the way Ian would sit up so straight with his eyes so wide during a lesson, especially when learning about the cosmos. He could still see the tender little brown-eyed Sally, dealing every day with the inevitable loss of her terminally ill mother. He could still see the tough-guy Rico, so macho and yet so sensitive and caring for his teacher and classmates...and now, for his own family. Mr. Melbourne could still see the rotund and withdrawn Cathy whom no one talked to or even noticed...until her metamorphosis into a beautiful, outgoing girl during the miracle year. He could still see the dirt-poor little black fellow, Reggie, being raised by his hard-working single mother. Mr. Melbourne could still see the tall and skinny Jeremiah who was smothered by his mother's religious obsession. Mr. Melbourne could still feel little Debbie's determination to help her parents' fast-food business. He could still feel little Nattie's touching desire to save her parents' marriage. Mr. Melbourne could still see Robert Chapman as little Bobby who wanted exciting jobs for his parents, so that they could be happy again. He could still see the enterprising Teddy who pulled his family up from the brink of poverty and brought them wealth and even moved them into a custom home. Mr. Melbourne could still see little Danny who was never afraid to take on a bully and who fought a much bigger boy to defend his teacher's honor. Mr. Melbourne could still recall Alan orchestrating the most exciting event in the history of Duncan Elementary — *Breakthrough News.*

What an amazing group of children they were, Mr. Melbourne could not stop thinking. Remembering the Miracle Year, lost in distant thoughts, he quietly whispered, *"They sure were something."* Mr. Melbourne shook is head and slowly repeated, "They sure were something."

He looked around the long dinner table again, at the former students. Just look at them now, he thought. He pondered the achievements of each former student: Ian is nominated for the Nobel prize in physics for his demonstration of an unsuspected ether during the Superbowl halftime laser-light show; Sally is nominated for the Nobel prize in medicine for her miracle

442

molecules that render the influenza virus harmless to humans; Theodore is nominated for the Nobel prize in economics for his company-without-a-country phenomenon that caused a rapid proliferation of jobs worldwide; Cathy is a beautiful supermodel and a renowned public-relations leader; Reggie owns the cable music station Grassroots Music that's become the entertainment story of the century; Debra's built the most successful fast-food business since McDonald's; Natasha is a national talk-radio host who has become a living legend for reigniting the flame in fading romantic relationships; Robert brings people to the jobs they love most in order to discover happiness in life; Rico owns the largest meat-distribution business on the East Coast; Alan runs the most rapidly growing media empire in the country; Jeremiah orchestrates the fastest growing church in the world; and Daniel, a renowned developer, is now running for President of the United States!

Mr. Melbourne could not stop thinking: They've all grown up to be living proof of what I write about in my book — they've all broken through to the next mentality. They've become unstoppable God-Men.

Suddenly, Al burst with an idea. "I want to do a series of specials for children on my cable station," he said. Al looked at Miss Annabelle and said, "I'm sensing the potential of those upward pressures you talk about. Imagine this: you, the famous Darlene Belle, author of *How To Raise A Genius Through Five-Minute Bedtime Stories*, will talk directly to America's children about the value of electing Daniel Ward for president. The upward pressures will generate a lot of interest and votes!"

"I'd love to do that show!" she said. Mr. Melbourne saw happiness radiate from his wife's eyes, for she was now helping her students put together their superpuzzle.

Ideas on getting Daniel elected flowed at the dinner table. *Indeed*, Mr. Melbourne thought, *here comes another miracle year.*

CHAPTER
THIRTY-FIVE

Miss Annabelle and Mr. Melbourne were staying in Rico's mansion until they could get their own place. She worked day and night preparing the TV special. She loved working in Olivia's peaceful glass house where the reunion was held. After two weeks, she and John took the train to New York and headed to the Patterson Building to record the first show.

"I'm leaving the content totally up to you," Al told her. "I have to tell you, I can't wait to see you teaching again!"

When the recording began, Al sat in a chair and watched. Twenty-seven years earlier, he loved sitting in his chair in third grade listening to this woman. Listening to her now, those twenty-seven years seemed to vanish. He concentrated on her every word, as he did in the third grade. Her knowledge was a gift.

At first, he was taken aback when Miss Annabelle addressed her child audience. Working in the adult world for so long, he had forgotten how deeply and directly she could talk to young children. After awhile, however, he shook his head and smiled, reminiscing the old days of her enchanting lectures twenty-seven years ago...

"I'm talking today *not* to the parents of the house, but to the children," she said. "I'm talking to you little ones because only

444

you can feel how wonderful it would be to live *forever*. People die because we haven't yet figured out how to stop aging. With enough knowledge and technology, aging can be stopped. You, your parents, your grandparents don't need to get old and die!"

Al was filled with bemusement as he listened to her lecturing the big picture that he himself could not yet write about. Furthermore, she was telling that big picture to *little children!*

"Geez..." he uttered, "they're just kids!"

"Exactly," he whispered a moment later, talking to himself, "she's addressing *kids*, and I'm addressing *adults*. I have to wait until much later into the superpuzzle to introduce our ultimate goal of immortality, but she can go straight to the big picture with little children."

He remembered that he and his classmates were only eight-years-old at the start of the miracle year.

"Let me warn you," Miss Annabelle continued, as if reading Al's thoughts, "your parents will not feel so excited as you do about living forever. That's because their lives fall far below the exhilarating lives they were meant to live.

"But I know a man who can do two very wonderful things: 1) he can get your parents that exhilarating life they were meant to live and would never want to let go of, therefore never want to die, and 2) he can bring about the end of aging so we never get old and die.

"Wouldn't that be wonderful! That man is Daniel Ward, and he's running for President of the United States."

She went on to explain about biological immortality, how unrestricted business would deliver it, how "bad people" today restrict progress, and how Daniel Ward would stop the bad people. She even went on to explain who those bad people were and why they were bad and why they did their bad acts of suppression.

Al was sitting up straight; he was smiling. He looked like a happy third-grader who loved listening to his teacher.

*

The Darlene Belle special for children was shown all over the country the next day on the Patterson Channel. Millions of children and parents watched.

Two weeks later, Miss Annabelle came to New York to tape the second show. John had an appointment in the city and would join her at the studio later. When she walked into the Patterson Building, two neatly dressed men in the lobby approached her.

"Annabelle?" one asked politely with a smile.

"Yes?" she answered, a little confused.

"Criminal Investigation Division, IRS!" the other said sharply. "You're under arrest for tax evasion." He handcuffed her and, like a pre-planned escape for bank robbers, the two men abruptly led her out of the building, to curbside where a car was waiting. They physically hastened Miss Annabelle into the backseat with them, and the car drove her away before Al could run to the front.

"Of course!" yelled Al when he reached the lobby, "anything that'll help Daniel's campaign will have the full might of the government looking into it!"

Al felt a great impact upon his heart. His precious Miss Annabelle was swept away by IRS agents!

"The powers that be," muttered the young cameraman standing next to Al, "damn, they trample all over our rights."

*

Bruce Salinski received Miss Annabelle's call from the holding cell. He immediately left his office and drove to the private landing strip for his private plane. His hired pilot would fly him from Buffalo to New York City. In the air, he spoke into his micro-cassette recorder: "Annabelle Melbourne could be put in prison for a long time — at her age it would be a life sentence — because of the amount of taxes involved. She hasn't lived in the United States for twenty-three years. All that time, she paid Australian income taxes, but the IRS considers her a U.S. citizen who owes taxes on the money made from the royalties of her best-seller. Of course, she couldn't pay U.S. taxes because she couldn't reveal who she was as she quietly lived her life in exile in Australia..."

"She's devastated," he said lastly into the recorder.

Putting Together the Pieces

*

Salinski ran into the jailhouse and saw John Melbourne and Al in the lobby. John was very loud and upset.

"You can't stop me from seeing my wife!" he yelled at a defiant bureaucrat.

"The IRS will feel the full wrath of my media empire if you don't let her go immediately!" threatened Al.

"Guys, guys...let's get calm," Salinski pleaded. "Let me handle this." He got himself cleared; he found Miss Annabelle very shaken up.

"I can't be away from John again, Bruce. I just can't go through prison and separation again...not now, not at my age!" She was trembling and cold...and panicking.

"I won't let that happen," he promised as he wrapped his jacket around her. After he felt Miss Annabelle was stable, he left her and met John and Al in the lobby.

"She's okay for now," he told John. "They're not going to let her out on bail. They'll say she's a flight risk. We've got to work fast. Al, will you give me the front page of all your dailies tomorrow? I'm gonna try to get her out of here quickly."

"They're yours." said Al.

"When's the latest you can receive my missive?"

"To get in all markets, I'll need it in six hours."

"Six hours, it'll be in your email." Then Salinski turned, and with both hands, he grabbed John's face to get his undivided attention, and whispered, "YOU keep a low profile. Stay out of sight! I won't lose this time. I promise you!"

Salinski's mind at that instant jumped to another place as he turned around and rushed out of the building.

CHAPTER
THIRTY-SIX

"Bruce Salinski here."

"Hi Bruce," John Melbourne said over the phone. It was an hour since they had left the Metropolitan Correctional Center. "I've never been so goddamned scared in my life, but I didn't call to whine. I called to tell you I think there's someone who could benefit you right now."

"Who?" Salinski asked.

"This morning when the IRS was apprehending my wife, I was having a reunion of my own with a young man. He was the little boy I brought across the country with me, from Mexico to Florida, twenty-three years ago. He was just four-years-old then. Remember...the border police caught his parents and sent them back to Mexico?"

"Oh yes...I remember you telling me about the boy. What's his name?"

"Oscar. Oscar Sanchez. I tracked him down when Annabelle and I moved back here. He flew up to New York this morning to see me. Oscar's become an immigration lawyer. He's young, and he's really bright; he's honest, and he's driven with a passion. I called and told him what happened. He wants to help."

"I'll call him, John. I could actually use him. Where's he

staying?"

"The Sheraton Manhattan Hotel on Broadway. I told him you might be calling. He's followed your work and the success of your Widescope Accounting Lawyers for nearly ten years, which he says has been a great inspiration. He's excited to meet you, and he's very upset that my wife and I are in this situation. He's highly motivated to help us in every way he can."

*

Miss Annabelle was denied bail. After the arraignment the next morning, she went back into the holding cell. She began wondering what might happen to her, and she began to tremble at the thought. Before she got too far into her ominous thoughts, however, the jail guard called her over and slipped her the morning Patterson Paper.

"This might warm you up," she said with a wink.

Miss Annabelle looked at the paper. Across the top was a blaring headline: **Sue Government!**

The article was written by Bruce Salinski. As Miss Annabelle read, she felt the same deep feelings of pride for Salinski as she did twenty-three years before when he stood up to the dishonest judge. What she read really did warm her soul.

She walked over to a bench against the wall while reading the article. As she read, she felt a calm come over her. She was the only person in the holding cell with a smile. Curious cellmates peeked over her shoulder. She did not mind. She just kept smiling as she saw how Salinski jumped past appearances to *what is* by using his special trademark: widescope accounting. His power of fully integrated honesty was in fine form as he explained in detail how it was our abusive government that kept Miss Annabelle from coming home and paying her income taxes. He explained what happened from the very beginning — the original ego-justice trial, the three years in prison, the devastating restraining order separating her from her beloved students, the spiteful deportation of her fiancé, the cruel and vindictive denial of travel/visitation rights. He articulated the impossible situation she was put in by the government, which drove her out of her country, although she desperately wanted to stay with her students and friends. Of course, back then, no one knew what heroes her students would become from her special educating techniques.

Miss Annabelle started laughing when she got to the part where Salinski did something most wonderful: he turned the tables and put the government on trial. He calculated income taxes paid by twelve average adults in one year and the income taxes paid by Miss Annabelle's twelve students in one year. Then he multiplied the difference by seventy-eight. That number was derived by figuring if she had taught the following year, twenty-six years ago, those students would have turned into twenty-two-year-old college graduates earning income twelve years ago, assuming some would go to college longer cancelled out by some who would go to college less. The class after that would have been earning now for eleven years, the class after that for ten years, etc., adding up all those earning years to the total figure of seventy-eight earning years lost because she was forced out of the country by our government. Of course, their earning power as twenty-two-year-olds would be less than at thirty-six years old. So, he reasonably divided the total by three. Based on that, the grand amount of actual income taxes lost because she was forced out of the country was eleven billion dollars, and that was before interest was calculated. Moreover, there would be twenty-seven times the number of God-Man Group geniuses in our country earning long into the future, he wrote. Salinski convincingly argued that the eleven billion dollars in lost tax revenues were public funds, which belonged to the people. He named both the State of New York and the federal government as responsible parties. His article included a cutout form that the reader would fill out and send in to be named on the class-action lawsuit. The amount of the lawsuit, the cutout said, when calculating past interest and future losses, could add up to a figure of somewhere between forty to fifty billion dollars.

Salinski knew that, legally speaking, he was on thin ice. But more important, he knew the impact his message would create.

That afternoon, Al and Mr. Melbourne got the call from Bruce Salinski. Mr. Melbourne had stayed the night in New York City at Al's penthouse and was at the Patterson Building all day awaiting his wife's fate.

Putting Together the Pieces

"The Justice Department's releasing her," Salinski said. "Better yet, the IRS zeroed out its jeopardy assessment against her. I just had to agree not to pursue any more class-action lawsuits. Oh, and I got the government to drop its charge against her for illegally fleeing the country twenty-three years ago. As I'll explain to her, there's no statute of limitations if one flees while on probation. But the charge is gone. Probation has been dropped. She's now a free woman! And that's not all. Thanks to Oscar's ingenious work — he leveraged the media attention surrounding my artical in the Patterson Papers — as of this afternoon, *you're* now welcome in this country and will be able to get your work visa."

John Melbourne could barely believe his ears.

"Oscar was fabulous," Salinski continued. "He has a brilliant mind and a dogged determination. We worked shoulder to shoulder all night. You're right, this young man is driven with passion. In fact, I'm so impressed, I'm going to expand WAL (Widescope Accounting Lawyers) to take on immigration and the racist INS with Oscar in charge. He had to catch a plane back to Florida, but tomorrow he'll be back here to discuss our new venture."

Mr. Melbourne was reeling from all the wonderful news.

"C'mon," said Al. He and Mr. Melbourne stepped outside Al's glass office. "I HAVE AN ANNOUNCEMENT," Al yelled across the floor. The news staff, journalists and reporters, secretaries, administrators, layout and computer personnel stopped their business and looked up. "Annabelle and John Melbourne," Al shouted while wrapping his arm around Mr. Melbourne, "are now free of all charges and free to stay in America!"

Cheers erupted across the floor. Celebrations filled the Patterson Building. Al's employees loved him, and thanks to Jake and Jasmine's recent article, they knew about Miss Annabelle and Mr. Melbourne's special place in Al's past.

*

"There's Salinski," said Al as they parked. He pointed toward the entrance of the Metropolitan Correctional Center. "Let's catch up with him."

451

Al and Mr. Melbourne ran to the building. Inside, they all walked together toward the receiving area.

"The power you wielded," Mr. Melbourne said to Bruce Salinski, "to force my wife's release in twenty-four hours, must be understood. I'm deeply grateful...and deeply curious about this Civilization-of-the-Universe power you demonstrated. You utterly defeated the most feared bureaucracy in America."

"Anna's sudden release was a combination of the article in the Patterson Papers and the government's fear of going up against my WAL — my Widescope Accounting Lawyers," Salinski said. "After two decades of image-destroying defeats against WAL, the government knows that my article and class-action lawsuit is *not* a matter of me putting all my guns up front, such as the intimidation tactics of so many lawyers. To the contrary, the government knows from experience that my show of strength up front is but tossing out a rock. Relatively and figuratively speaking, bullets and then bombs would follow." They reached the receiving area and stopped walking. They both glanced around for Miss Annabelle. When they saw she was not there yet, Salinski turned and faced Mr. Melbourne.

"Even if I do occasionally throw out a bluff," Salinski continued, "the nature of fully integrated honesty and widescope accounting grows stronger and stronger into an unbreakable matrix that wraps itself around the dishonesties of a value destroyer as I gather more and more knowledge. And that's how I got my reputation of eventually crushing the value destroyers who go up against me."

"John!" Miss Annabelle screamed in sheer delight the instant she saw him.

Mr. Melbourne ran to her. Salinski smiled as he watched them embrace like two teenagers in love.

That's one government bureaucracy out of the way, Salinski thought, breathing relief. *But there'll be others.*

After their loving embrace, Miss Annabelle walked over and gave Bruce Salinski a grateful hug.

"*Thank you,*" she said. "I wouldn't have lasted in there, not this time." She got teary-eyed as she and her husband expressed their deep gratitude and love for Bruce Salinski.

He nodded. "Now, let's get Daniel in the White House,"

Salinski said. But inside, he had never felt so moved as he did at that moment, knowing he had saved, this time, two people he loved but could not save twenty-six years before.

They turned and started walking toward the exit. "We owe Oscar a lot of credit, too," Salinski said. He winked at Mr. Melbourne.

"Who's Oscar?" Miss Annabelle asked her husband.

"You remember my adventure coming up from Mexico twenty-three years ago?"

Miss Annabelle thought for a moment as the three of them walked through the building, then her face lit up in recognition. Before she could say anything, a loud cry suddenly filled the building. "There they are!"

Miss Annabelle gasped. Her twelve former students, even Reggie who lived in Los Angeles, were all waiting for her. Sally ran over and hugged Miss Annabelle.

"We couldn't stand to lose you again," Sally said. She was trembling. Miss Annabelle could feel how much her return to America meant to these twelve superachievers, even now as adults.

"Oh, Sally," Miss Annabelle whispered. "I love all of you, so much...so very much." She looked at the people she loved so dearly. Even twenty-six years apart could not diminish their love.

The Group went straight from the Metropolitan Correctional Center to the Patterson Building. Miss Annabelle said she was ready to tape the next show, and her former students wanted to watch.

At the studio, Al had chairs brought into the recording room instead of the viewing room. Miss Annabelle would have a live audience.

The taping of the show began. Miss Annabelle paused and looked, one by one, into the eyes of her former students: Sally, Rico, Robert, Daniel, Cathy, Theodore, Ian, Debra, Jeremiah, Reggie, Natasha, and Al. Although they were no longer children, she still felt enormous motherly pride and love for them. They could see she was living one of her happiest moments, for she was with her beloved children again. Suddenly, a beautiful smile burst across her face. Her sigh of disbelief gave away her thoughts: *Does this mean John and I can stay in America now, here with our loved ones?*

CHAPTER
THIRTY-SEVEN

Back in Boston, Jake and Jasmine worked day and night on their articles for the Patterson Papers, working around their classes. Getting Daniel in the White House...that thought motivated them beyond anything they had felt before. Several times since the reunion, Jake considered leaving school for a year to focus all his efforts on the mission. School seemed so irrational now. Most of his professors came across as slow, socialistic idiots who had no clue on how the real world of value-exchange worked.

One Monday after classes, Jake and Jasmine went to the new Debbie's French Fry City that had just opened in town, and they ordered double cheeseburgers, a medium drink and, of course, the free fries.

The cashier blurted, "If you take a look at the Six Visions of Wealth and Happiness, we'll be glad to upsize that at our expense!" She gestured to a printed sheet of paper on the tray. Jake and Jasmine looked down and saw a picture of Daniel and his six campaign visions (selected from his Twelve Visions) listed in big, easy-to-read text. They burst into laughter.

"Well, Debbie found her way to contribute to the mission," Jake said. "What a bold idea!"

"Yes, we'd love to look at the Six Visions," Jasmine told

454

the cashier.

"Upsize it!" she gleefully blared into the microphone.

Jake and Jasmine got their order and sat down to eat. The food was fresh, crisp, and tasty. The french fries, though, were exceptional.

"Yeah," said Jake, "the fries are downright addicting. I'll be back here by Thursday."

Jasmine agreed. Then she noticed, for the first time, that the stack of papers Jake had been carrying under his arm were not Patterson Papers. "What's all that?" she asked.

"See for yourself," he said. He put the stack of papers on the table and pushed it toward her.

She looked at him quizzically then at the papers. "No way! The AP?" She looked closer; then she squealed in delight. There on the front page of the top paper *The Orange County Journal* was their article titled *How You Can Become a Millionaire...Without Lifting a Finger* subtitled *Your Twelve-Visions World.* She raced through the stack and saw their article in twenty-one major daily papers.

"We broke through!" she screamed.

"And they all printed our by-line!"

"Oh my god, Jake!"

When they got back to Jake's room, a message from Al Patterson himself was on Jake's message machine. It was short and to the point:

"Can you kids take time off from school and move to New York City to work at Headquarters? I need you here to help get Danny in the White House. Oh, by the way, congratulations! You're fresh and you're hot. Your articles will go over the wire service from now till elections in November. I hope you can get here. If you can, I'm tripling your pay."

Jake and Jasmine packed that night.

*

Jake and Jasmine arranged a conference call with Daniel the next morning before leaving Boston to move to New York. As Daniel's strength grew, he attracted more and more attention, both good and bad. The negative attention particularly concerned Jake. He saw trends in the media before Daniel could, and Jake did not like what he saw. The young journalist wanted to warn Daniel about the negative trend.

Sam, a young man in his thirties who had an unusual full head of grey hair, was Daniel's top numbers man in his development company in San Diego and had been helping in the campaign. Daniel called Sam into his office during the conference call.

"Sam, I've got Jake Catchings and Jasmine Kahil on the speaker phone," Daniel said as Sam entered his boss's office. "They're the new Patterson reporters I told you about. Sam, tell us how we're doing."

"Momentum's building," Sam said. He closed the door to the busy office building behind him. "You've suddenly leapfrogged beyond just an interesting sideshow to a potential contender. Your poll numbers are still low, but they've suddenly surged past that one to two percent realm, approaching double digits. There's excitement, there's a buzz."

"I have some heavyweights behind me now," Daniel replied, defining his surge in the polls, "such as the Church of God-Man with eight million members, Miss Annabelle's web site of nearly two million subscribers, Debbie's French Fry City with millions of patrons; I have substantial funds behind me now with financial backing from Theodore Winters and the others in The Group; and I have major media exposure through the Patterson Papers and Natasha's radio talk show." Daniel stopped for a breath, then finished by saying, "Sam, spread the word: we're ready to make this a fight!"

After a pause, Jake said, "Something's really been worrying me, Daniel; some prominent journalists throughout the established media have begun referring to you as *the atheist* because of your belief in Ian's work on the origins of the Universe." Jake shook his head. "That worries me because it brings you a lot of negative attention from religious groups, including fanatical religious sects that would not accept a man like you as President."

"Jake's concerns are certainly warranted," said Sam. He

nodded at Daniel and added, "You've begun receiving hate mail."

"And I think it's going to get even worse," said Jasmine.

"Why?" asked Daniel.

"Because, the Democrats and Republicans have caught on. They've started calling you the 'godless, heartless choice'."

"In fact, and this is what bothers me," added Jake, "the media and the mainstream political parties have launched such a barrage of attacks on you these past few days that it almost seems as though they're doing more than trying to win votes away from you."

"What do you mean?" Daniel asked, a little alarmed.

"It seems almost as if they're intentionally inflaming the kooks — the religious fanatics." Jake pulled a daily newspaper from his folder and read from a front-page, character-assassination article on Daniel. Jake slowly and clearly stressed an eerie line:

"Heroes have died for God."

"What!" said Daniel. "That's almost suggestive. ...But why all the attention? Why, at this point, wouldn't I be flying below the radar? I mean, it's not like I'm threatening either party, not yet."

"Obviously they're afraid of you," said Sam, "and they're trying to knock you off while you're still small, before you get too much momentum."

"Look," Daniel said, "I have money growing in my war chest. I have influential supporters. My campaign is reaching society from several different angles, from executives and entrepreneurs by way of Robert Chapman and Bruce Salinski to teenage music lovers by way of Reggie Tucker. The bottom line is: we're all going to die if we don't do this. I'm not backing down."

CHAPTER
THIRTY-EIGHT

Jake and Jasmine's first assignment when they arrived at Headquarters later that day was to cover Reggie's new music sensation. Reggie recently broke through to a new music sensation that was sending shock waves through the music world of young adults. One of his Top 40 productions was *Twelve Visions Party*. It was a song about Daniel and his potential world. The morning after arriving at the executive offices of Patterson Press in New York City, Jake and Jasmine were on a plane to Los Angeles.

Standing outside the Grassroots Charts building in Los Angeles, Jake thought: what a forty-eight hours! He and Jasmine left Boston College and landed in New York at the national headquarters of a major newspaper chain one day, and now they stood before the national headquarters of a major entertainment cable station the next day, three-thousand miles away.

Going inside, Jake noticed many similarities between the two operations. Most noticeably was the exciting intensity in the air. Both operations ran on unmovable deadlines. The people were charged up; they moved with purpose. Jake loved the atmosphere inside places like these. With those deadlines, a lot got accomplished.

Back in New York City, Patterson Headquarters produced *The*

New York News and oversaw the production of all markets. The first impression Jake got at Patterson was: big rooms filled with lots of people. Although there only one day, Jake could see those people were focussed.

The rooms were not as big and the people were not as many at Grassroots Charts, but Jake noticed the people were just as focussed. The rooms contained mazes of audio/video equipment and the walls appeared to be made out of TV monitors, rows and rows of TV monitors.

At both Patterson Press in New York and Grassroots Charts in Los Angeles, Jake noticed how people looked attractive when they were focussed on their work; they really looked *with it*, he thought. After all, their intensity reflected the essence of man: *creating values*. It felt good to be in this high-paced environment.

An attractive middle-aged woman in a tight red skirt and tight white blazer received Jake and Jasmine in the waiting room. The waiting room overlooked the action on the floor at Grassroots. She led them down a few steps and onto the busy floor. Jake loved being in the middle of the action and thought how fun it would be to work here. The attractive receptionist opened the glass door into Reggie's office.

"Hey guys!" Reggie shouted across his expansive office. His presence with his dark, chiseled features, focussed eyes, rich voice immediately filled the room with a sense of competence. That's the look of a man creating breakthrough values for the world, Jake thought. Reggie stood up from his desk, opened his arms, and said, "Welcome to my second home."

His spacious office was lined with three levels of viewing monitors on three walls. The room had a large retreat with clothes closets, dresser drawers, an executive bathroom with a shower, and a pull-down bed in the wall.

"I spend a couple nights a week here. This place never shuts down. I even have a bedroom and a playroom for my kids, right through that door. They love it here, and I love having them around. You know, my eight-year-old picked the last eight out of ten nighttime rotations that made it to prime time. And now he loves my new sound that's receiving raves. Come on!"

Reggie led them out of his office and down a long corridor.

Superpuzzle

As they followed, Jake noticed that Reggie's broad shoulders seemed to nearly fill the width of the narrow hallway. He led them to a small wooden door; he ducked his head and went inside. Jake and Jasmine followed. The other side of the small door opened to a large recording studio. There they stood, in the engineer's room. Reggie picked up a phone on the wall and called for Dennis. A moment later, the pleasant engineer with a gentle English accent walked in and greeted the three of them.

"Take *Twelve Visions Party* from the top, my man," Reggie told the friendly engineer. Then Reggie disappeared through another small wooden door. A few seconds later he reappeared through the large glass window in a huge room directly in front of them as Dennis brought up the lights. Wow, Jake thought, this is the first time I've been in a recording studio.

Suddenly, a loud yet pleasant female voice-over shouted, "Twelve Visions Party...it's time to party!"

At that instant, Reggie leaned into a mic and rapped with the chorus:

(Chorus)
> Now we're here to party...Now we're here to party!
> Come on join the party...Come on everybody!
> Now we're here to party...No one else can see this through!
> Come on join the party...Come on now, we want you to!

Then Reggie stopped rapping and the unique female voice rapped out:

(Verse)
> You wanna live like a millionaire (uh hu!)...vacation first class (class act)
> You wanna drive a fancy car (Oh Yeah!)...and never look back (heard that)
> You wanna live in a mansion (that's right)...pay everything cash (big stash)
> You wanna party with the winners, no doubt, yeah, and always lead the pack, yo Jack say!

460

Putting Together the Pieces

(Chorus)

Twelve Visions Party, it's time to party!
Now we're here to party...(Now we're here to party!)
Come on join the party...(Come on everybody!)
Now we're here to party...No one else can see this through!
Come on join the party...Come on now, we want you to!

(Verse)

Hey, you, in the old shoes
Dump...them...no-money blues
Neo-Tech can make you all rich
Come on now and hear this pitch:

Buy a car, dollars in the jar
Think computers if I've gone too far
Where today your money can buy
A thousand times over years gone by

Impossible to do? Wait, I'm not through
Regulations stir poverty brew
Up 'til now we waited like fools
For Uncle Sam to make it all cool

Some have to whore so they can afford
Basic needs in life they can't ignore
But once technology is free to soar
You'll buy everything in the whole damn store

Stomp bureaucrats and politicians
New technology is really kickin'
A brand new party that'll soon be stickin'
Dollars in our pockets...come and get 'em!

(Chorus)

Twelve Visions Party, it's time to party!
Now we're here to party...(Now we're here to party!)
Come on join the party...(Come on everybody!)
Now we're here to party...No one else can see this through!
Come on join the party...Come on now, we want you to!

461

Superpuzzle

(Verse)

Your money's worth a thousand times more!
Technology's free to soar!
Regulations out the door
So you can live on the wealthy shore

Think computers if I go too fast
Where your cash really lasts what a blast
Regulations pass as trash
With America's newest smash

You say you wanna be rich?
Technology is the trick
When a buck's worth a thousand dollars
Even the poor folks stand up and hollar!

(Chorus)

Twelve Visions Party, it's time to party!
Now we're here to party…(Now we're here to party!)
Come on join the party…(Come on everybody!)
Now we're here to party…No one else can see this through!
Come on join the party…Come on now, we want you to!

(Bridge)

All right, okay. Yo! What's the Twelve Visions Party?
…What! Who said that? Check this out:

Visionaries see New Technology!
No longer regulated like pornography!
Life ain't what it oughta' be? (Noooo!)
Who's through with apologies?

Twelve Visions Party — that's our name
New Technology — that's our game
Ask us again and we'll tell you the same —
Twelve Visions Party — that's our name

462

Putting Together the Pieces

The Twelve Visions Party has begun
Soon be wealth for everyone
Live in luxury and fun
Find you place out in the sun

Wealth and health — it's all so plain
Freeing technology is our aim
Seeing you rich is now our game
Twelve Visions Party, we're glad you came! SAY!

(Chorus)
Twelve Visions Party, it's time to party!
Now we're here to party...(Now we're here to party!)
Come on join the party...(Come on everybody!)
Now we're here to party...No one else can see this through!
Come on join the party...Come on now, we want you to!

(Fade Out)
Who's gonna put his power away...a whoo! There he is!
Who don't care about it anyway...a whoo! There he is!
Daniel Ward, he's our man...a whoo! There he is!
If he can't do it, nobody can...a whoo! There he is!

Who's gonna put his power away...a whoo! There he is!
Who don't care about it anyway...a whoo! There he is!
Daniel Ward, he's our man...a whoo! There he is!
If he can't do it, nobody can...a whoo! There he is!

(Rap)   Ou! Ou! Ou! Ou! Ou!
Vote Daniel Ward for President
To Get Rich! Peace!

The music stopped, and Reggie ran across the recording room and burst into the engineering room like Alice falling back through the looking glass.

"What do you think?" he asked.

"That was so cool!" Jake answered. "I mean, really cool! It moves and the lyrics work."

"I believe the sense of life in the lyrics, carried by a street

463

sound that really moves," said Reggie, "is making this music rise on the charts. And as for the other artists who are copying us and rising up too, listen to their lyrics. They've caught on! The youth and young adults of the world are *asking* for this new way of life, and we're giving it to them."

"What do you predict for *Twelve Visions Party*?" Jasmine asked.

"It goes to prime time rotation next week. My son picked it to go number one on Grassroots Charts and top ten on the Billboard charts. He's pretty good at picking winners now. I hope he's right. Then, Daniel can use it as a well-recognized campaign song."

"What plans do you have with this new sensation? Will you put together an album based on the Twelve-Visions ideas?" Jasmine asked. She jotted down notes for an article.

"I've started a subsidiary label company called Vision Records. The debut album *Twelve-Visions World* will be released next month. You'll be hearing more and more of this music on the radio in the months to come. It's drawing the kids and young adults to the Twelve-Visions World. It'll be a good push for Daniel."

"*Twelve Visions Party...*" Jake said. He knitted his brow while trying to capture a fleeting thought. "Did it...uh...one day just start getting air time on the radio?"

Reggie smiled and said, "They wouldn't have played it in a hundred years! The Establishment is threatened by the coming Twelve-Visions World. But that's the power behind Grassroots Charts; the power of the open marketplace breaks through the power of the closed Establishment. The people ultimately want what's best for them."

Jake did not relax his brow. "Why, then, did the established media start publishing our articles about the Twelve-Visions World?"

"For the same reason. Whereas I have Grassroots Charts rounding up the open marketplace behind my music, you have Patterson Press rounding up the open marketplace behind your articles. Your articles reflect the unique values of the future Twelve-Visions World that people now want to see."

"But, most other media are largely dishonest and politically and philosophically the opposite of our articles," Jake said. He sensed that Reggie could help him make sense of this mystery. "It honestly surprises me every time I see our articles printed in papers outside the Patterson Papers. It's like, the enemy is giving us a platform to destroy him."

"You're absolutely right," Reggie said, "the enemy is giving you a platform to destroy him. But the Patterson Papers gave the enemy no choice just as Grassroots Charts gave mainstream radio no choice. Every market the Patterson Papers go into, what happens?"

"Patterson outcompetes and drives the local daily out of business."

"Right. Likewise, Grassroots has taken so much market share away from mainstream radio, they have no choice but to give their listeners what we're playing...or they're going to lose their listeners to us altogether. Al and I have leveraged the power of the marketplace against the power brokers. The radio stations must play our music; the daily papers must publish your articles. To survive, they've got no choice."

Jake relaxed his brow, for now he understood. Given *a choice*, the Establishment would ignore anything to do with the coming Twelve-Visions World. But the children of the Civilization of the Universe took away the Establishment's choice. Their ideas were entering mainstream America.

*

On the plane flight back to New York, Jake began working on the article about the new sound of Vision Records. The catchy beat of *Twelve Visions Party* kept going through his head as he began his article:

"I am reminded of the philosopher Ayn Rand who left Russia after the Bolshevik Revolution. She believed, when she witnessed the artists adopt the communistic ideals, the battle was lost. As I leave Grassroots Charts I believe, having witnessed the artist adopt the Twelve-Visions ideals, the battle is won. We will have our Twelve-Visions World. And Daniel Ward is our fast-track ticket there."

CHAPTER
THIRTY-NINE

Back in New York at their new jobs, Jake and Jasmine could not put out articles fast enough. Daily papers around the country routinely published their articles. People enjoyed reading them. Jake and Jasmine were *hot*. Their articles were fresh and focussed on the Twelve-Visions World. As with Reggie's *Twelve Visions Party*, they figured the *subject* was hot. It was. Other journalists around the country began shifting to the Twelve-Visions ideas and making the AP regularly.

Yet, Jake and Jasmine's popularity kept rising above the others and began surpassing well-known journalists. *Why?* Jake wondered.

The answer came during the next gathering of The Group at Rico's mansion. The question came up, and Bruce Salinski said without pause, "I can tell you exactly why you two are the hottest journalists in the country; I know because of my own experience. We share the same common denominator: we stand alone using fully integrated honesty in two fields dominated by dishonesty. Generally speaking, journalists and lawyers today are one and the same: they have no regard for honesty; they only care about winning the game. They selectively use true facts out of context; they pursue manipulated truths. They do very well financially that way. I went through a dark period when I made the lone choice to do what I knew was honest. I changed the nature of the trial by bringing all the facts together into context; I pursued non-manipulative honesty. The resistance of the proactive political judges nearly killed my practice. But now, I'm the most sought-after lawyer in the country. Good people, good businesses need my protection. You two, working off the long roots of Patterson Press, are quickly becoming the country's most read journalists. Your readers implicitly sense you don't yield to dishonesty or pursue manipulated truths. You aren't interested in rising up by tearing down. The world's changing. The momentum's on our side now."

*

The next article by Jake and Jasmine seemed to cause a tipping point in Daniel's campaign. Jake had noticed a few correlations to Daniel's rise in popularity:

"The first correlation is the new money flowing into medical research," their article stated. "America hasn't seen anything yet, however. Just you wait until Daniel Ward is elected. The medical research money will be so abundant that both major and obscure diseases will be eradicated one after the other like falling dominoes. Very simply, Daniel Ward represents eliminating cost-prohibitive regulations, making it viable for businesses to invest in medical research.

"Another correlation with Daniel's rise in popularity is the widespread shift in businesses to investing more money in research and development. We see the trend everywhere we look, across the industrial landscape. This phenomenon is occurring because both the present and future risks of business-growth get dramatically lowered by the possibility of a president who would eliminate bureaucratic regulations and harmful litigation. Research and development, by the way, are the seeds to job creation and value creation. Is it any surprise the economy is showing new, robust strength, and the stock market is soaring? The experts have a hard time trying to explain the soaring economy. But it is very simple when you understand the correlation of the economy to Daniel Ward's rising popularity. Moreover, with funds flowing into research and development and into higher-risk, technological ventures, some of the payoffs are already reaching the economy. Advancing technologies are already beginning to drive prices down and buying power up. The country is on the outer edge of a great Technological Revolution that Daniel Ward talks about in his Six-Visions campaign speeches. As he explains, the Technological Revolution is going to dwarf the computer revolution, during which buying power will multiply thousands of times. I link these exciting economic happenings that the economic experts cannot explain...to the cause: Daniel Ward."

Jake and Jasmine's revealing article was titled *Daniel = Health & Wealth*. It ran all over the country in over five-hundred daily papers. *The Wall Street Investor*, the nation's largest business daily, also published a front-page column analyzing Jake and Jasmine's article, confirming their correlations as accurate.

"It is a historical fact that presidential elections during peacetime are controlled by the economy," *The Wall Street Investor* printed. "The article by Patterson journalists Jake Catchings and Jasmine Kahil accurately tied a rising economy to Daniel Ward, not the incumbent."

After reading the article, Daniel told Jake and Jasmine, "Even more important than the money now pouring into medical research and into research and development will be the *freedom* in which medicine and business will function. For one thing, the rise of the individual entrepreneur in that coming Freedom Paradigm will be something to see. I can see it now, before others. The value creation and the affordability of those values will be unprecedented, so it'll take until the Freedom Paradigm actually happens before others will see the medical and personal bonanza, too."

In the weeks that followed, Daniel's campaign really took off. Some political analysts pointed to Jake and Jasmine's article as the launching pad.

*

"Not again," Jake said angrily under his breath.

Daniel walked to the podium to talk to another standing-room-only crowd, this time at Long Beach State University. But Jake was looking past the impressive crowd, focussing his eyes toward the back of the auditorium. There, Jake read the threatening signs held up by adults significantly older than the college-student crowd.

"What is it with those people?" he muttered. At each campaign talk, Jake noticed and worried about small but very vocal packs of religious fanatics who seemed to be following Daniel from speech to speech, holding up signs such as: *No God? No Daniel!* and *Heed Our Warning: Go Back to Hell!* Jake even saw one sign that read *Satan Must Die.* But the small groups of kooks did not seem to bother Daniel. He never backed down from threats — not as a child, not now.

Jake relaxed when Daniel began his eloquent speech.

"For true political change, a candidate's political ideas, no matter how good, are meaningless in campaigns and absolutely powerless for becoming elected," Daniel said to open his speech. "I dismiss my own political ideas — ideas people are starting to call brilliant — as not really having anything to do with my surging popularity. In fact, I dismiss my exciting political ideas as not really political ideas per se. I'm merely outlining the *political structure* that'll remain when humanity leaps beyond the old mentality dependent on external authorities...into the next mentality in which man's own mind easily integrates knowledge and, with certainty, becomes its own authority."

Daniel confounded crowds. He did so to break them out of their conditioned patterns of thinking. As Jake watched the unusual campaign speech, he was reminded how Jesus confounded the crowds he talked to. In preparation for a major article about the rapidly expanding Church of God-Man, Jake was in the middle of researching both the Bible and interpretations of the Bible. He learned from Mr. Melbourne that non-Biblical Jesus confounded his crowds because he talked to the bicameral peasants from an entirely different mentality — from the new human consciousness. He confounded yet stimulated them.

This is so interesting, Jake thought as he listened. Daniel talks to his crowds from the new Neothink mentality. Just look at these people, this really gets their interest up. Daniel talks to them from a much bigger picture, far beyond himself. He's the forerunner doing the legwork — the messenger — for the

469

political structure that'll survive humanity's change into the new mentality that accepts no more external authorities.

As the crowd looked confounded, Daniel went on to chart history from the bicameral man to the conscious man to the coming Neothink man or God-Man. Jake smiled at how the crowd earnestly listened.

"The bicameral mind had no internal mind space, and it automatically reacted to external stimuli and external authorities," Daniel said. "Then, as language developed, the metaphor — using something to describe something else — gave man the internal mind space to separate from the external world immediately before him. That separation from the external world eventually let him step back into his internal world within him to analyze the external world around him, subjectively think about it, make decisions, and control his life...the mind of today."

Jake saw many of the faces in the crowd light up as Daniel introduced them to the next level — to Neothink. "Through Neothink-puzzle-building, the mind of tomorrow," he said, "you'll snap together mental puzzle-pieces and see, as with any puzzle, what the completed puzzle-picture will look like well before it's finished. So, with Neothink," he explained as the crowd seemed to lean forward for this information, "man can both see and create his future, freeing him from any need for external authorities guiding or directing his life whatsoever. With the rapidly approaching leap into the Neothink mentality, external authorities such as political leaders can pack their bags and go home. Soon, there'll be no more politicians in politics." ...Like charismatic Jesus, Jake thought, Daniel confounds yet fascinates his crowds.

As Daniel's confounding talk continued, Jake realized a common denominator had already begun emerging everywhere: the collapse of external authorities had already begun. That explains the burst of popularity of the Church of God-Man and the Twelve Visions Party, he thought; although people don't yet know how to articulate it, the time's come for them to jump past external authorities. The people's eyes are still covered, but not their hearts. They long to be free from external authorities.

*

"May I speak to Robert Chapman please?"

"May I ask who's calling?"

"Jake Catchings."

"Just a moment, Mr. Catchings. I'll get him for you."

Jake had called TGIF Headquarters in Chicago to catch up on a powerful puzzle piece he heard Robert Chapman was creating to snap into the puzzle of getting Daniel elected.

"Jake?" It was Robert's voice.

"Yes, hi!"

"Hey, congratulations to you and Jasmine on your outstanding articles. I look forward to reading them every morning."

"Thank you, sir..." Jake said, still too in awe of these superachievers to completely relax around them.

"Call me Robert, okay my friend?"

"Okay," said Jake, a little nervously. "Robert, I want to catch up with what you've been doing at TGIF."

"I've got something new and powerful working, around the country. You've probably heard."

"Can you tell me about it?"

"Sure can. Natasha and I've spent a lot of time together since the reunion sharing information and techniques on bringing out people's deepest motivational roots, helping them discover the persons they were meant to be and the lives they were meant to live. Through Natasha's encouragement, I've started workshops across the country that guide people into making the self-discovery of the persons they were meant to be. Before starting these TGIF Workshops, only those who came to TGIF to find an inspiring job went through the program. Now, I've started these workshops all over the country for anyone interested in simply discovering who they were meant to be, not necessarily looking for another job. The TGIF workshops have become a national phenomenon, which I've snapped into Daniel's run for the White House. As a matter of fact, are you in New York?"

"Yes, at Patterson Headquarters."

"If you'd like, there's a TGIF Workshop tomorrow afternoon right there in Manhattan. Would you like to attend? It lasts about three hours."

"That's perfect," Jake said. He looked at his schedule. "That's perfect for my article."

471

Superpuzzle

"I'll have my secretary call over and let them know you and Jasmine'll be there. I'll give you to Helen now. She's got all the details."

The next day while sitting in the three-hour afternoon workshop, Jake leaned over and whispered to Jasmine, "This workshop, making this self-discovery, is the ultimate feel-good experience, but a real, permanent feel-good experience that directs people into their most exhilarating lives!"

As the exciting three-hour workshop came to an end, everyone in the room was on a high. They all had in their hands their self-discoveries of the persons they were meant to be, which had eluded them all their lives.

"Look around," Jake said to Jasmine. "Look at the expressions on their faces."

Looking around, Jasmine noticed childlike glee. "The chains have broken," she heard Jake saying, "these people have just been released from their stagnation-traps. They would've died in those traps if not for Robert. That's why they look like this — like someone saved their lives today."

While the attendees took in deep breaths, their lungs titillating in euphoria, the workshop leader left them with a moving thought. He said, "You're now on your way to an exhilarating life. Now that you know your path and how to travel that path of exciting downstream focus to an exhilarating life, think for a moment about those who you care about, who are lost as you once were. They go on with no promise or hope, suppressed in stagnation day in and day out. You know what that's like.

"I'll leave you with this thought: *everyone*, all your loved ones and friends, can have exciting lives. They can live the exhilarating lives they were meant to live — they can have that permanent happiness and lasting romantic love. A time will come to where every business works with its employees in the same way I worked with you today to discover your Friday-Night essences. That will come when businesses shift to tomorrow's division-of-essence structure from today's division-of-labor structure. People will discover their own paths they were meant to travel in life...their unique paths to deep and permanent happiness. They'll become the persons they were meant to be.

472

They'll feel exhilarated, which'll generate energy that constantly flows into their romantic-love and family lives. This shift will happen when Daniel Ward is elected President of the United States and depoliticizes America. The wide-open freedom of the business world will drive forth the shift into the much more creative division of essence and then into the division of Friday-Night essences. Remember what I'm saying here the next time you see a loved one. Why shouldn't life be wonderful for everyone? Why shouldn't he or she be the person he or she was meant to be, living the good life he or she was meant to live? With Daniel Ward as President, the whole country becomes a TGIF Workshop."

The joy felt in the attendees in contrast to the absence of that joy in their loved ones moved everyone there. Jake looked around and saw tears in some of their eyes. He saw tears on Jasmine's cheeks. She saw Jake noticing her tears and said, "Wow, I didn't expect that; he made me think about my father just then. I feel so much love and so sorry for my dad. I want him to be happy — really happy — again." Jake nodded somberly. Every single one of these people, he thought, will vote for Daniel.

*

On the drive back to their office, Jake and Jasmine were quiet, feeling the profundity of the workshop. After a few minutes, Jake shook his head and took a deep breath. "Each member of The Group is throwing a powerful blow directly into the gut of the anticivilization," he said, his adrenaline was flowing, "and together, they're throwing some mighty combinations. I'll tell you, Jassy, they're going to bring the matrix of illusions to its knees."

*

In New York, Jake and Jasmine never worked so hard in their lives. They witnessed one after the other, the life-lifting values of Miss Annabelle's former students who now corralled those immense values and converted them into votes for Daniel. Jake

473

and Jasmine put out a major front-page article about Daniel's march toward the White House every other day. Jake orchestrated the "big idea" and the strategy from article to article, leading up to the election. Jasmine was his researcher and editor who made each article well researched and exciting to read.

"The momentum just keeps building. Could it be," Jake wrote in one daring editorial, "that Daniel is really *unbeatable?* He is still far behind the other two candidates, I know. But could the puzzle-picture already be formed by the world's most competent minds who are now snapping the pieces into place?"

He kept wondering, could The Group's body blows to the anticivilization be just too powerful? Maybe, just maybe, the anticivilization doesn't stand a chance.

The Group worked day and night to put the pieces into place in order to get Daniel elected. But Jake knew that getting Daniel elected was *not* the completed puzzle picture. Getting Daniel elected was a piece — a major piece — of the superpuzzle. The superpuzzle, that Jake would not write about yet, was curing aging and death. Politics, business, science, medicine, happiness, and love were the pieces to the superpuzzle of immortality. The Group knew they needed to snap down politics first.

Jake often wrote notes, touching upon the bigger puzzle if Daniel were elected. But Jake knew he would not yet write an article about the bigger picture for some time to come, although he *really wanted* to write about that big picture. Just three weeks after arriving at the Patterson Building, Jake submitted to his boss the briefest of brief notes on a major headline about the big picture that he was just dying to write:

"Al, what follows is the simple concept of a four-part series I want to write. Please read over my notes and let me know if I can proceed. Thank you. Jake."

"If Daniel is elected, the sea change in politics would end external authorities such as all those debilitating regulatory bureaucracies that stifle business, particularly hurting the entrepreneurs by making research costs too prohibitive and too risky. Ending those regulatory bureaucracies would cause a business boom of 'garage' entrepreneurs much like the largely unregulated computer revolution. To remain competitive,

especially with the bombardment of 'garage' entrepreneurs, businesses would go through a major change to unleash 'in-house' entrepreneurs of their own, which would bring out the businesses' greatest asset: their employees' minds. Jobs would go from labor intensive to mind intensive. As employees learned how to live through the essence of man — their minds — they would love going to work, especially as businesses helped them discover and fulfill their Friday-Night Essences, much like Apple Computer's employees during its exciting early years. Employees would discover the persons they were meant to be and leap from their stagnant, boring routines into exhilarated, happy dynamos. They would regain their deep motivational drives. Those exhilarating motivational drives would inevitably lead them to creative success and wealth. Becoming deeply happy people, excited about work and their competitive creations, they would rise into a new, emotional existence capable of sustaining romantic love — intense romantic love as experienced during the first few weeks of falling in love...but for their entire lifetimes. Wealthy, deeply happy, and intensely in love, the subtle burden of stagnation would vanish and people would be able to, for the first time, honestly desire immortality. With universal desire, an unprecedented energy and funding would be put behind a project greater than the Manhattan Project or the moon project...the project for curing aging and death — Project Life. And without the burden of regulatory bureaucrats — without politicization of our industries — businesses would be able to, for the first time, supply the human race with biological immortality.

Jake knew all this was going to happen after Daniel was elected, perhaps within a decade. But Jake would not write an article about that bigger picture, not yet. Al knew best when the time would be right.

"Not yet, Jake," Al told him after seeing his notes, "not yet, young man."

CHAPTER
FORTY

By mid-summer, the polls showed Daniel's numbers had nearly doubled in three months. But he was still pulling half of what the Republican and Democrat candidates were pulling in their dead-even race. With three months to go, the established media said Daniel had come on too late.

Jake and Jasmine, Miss Annabelle and Mr. Melbourne, her twelve former students, and Salinski worked around the clock toward getting Daniel elected. Thousands of members of Jeremiah's Church of God-Man went door to door, campaigning for Daniel. Jeremiah had been flying around the country giving the bigger picture in speeches to his many churches, the bigger picture about Project Life. Jake knew the country as a whole was not yet ready to read about immortality. But the eight million members of the Church of God-Man were ready for that bigger picture, for the goal of the Church was to achieve immortality *before* one dies. Daniel winning the White House was the first step, and they knew it, bringing millions of votes to Daniel. Moreover, Jeremiah had discovered a catalyst that was pulling in new members at an accelerated rate and would pull in millions more.

Jeremiah knew that by supporting a political candidate, his church would lose its tax-exempt status, but that was okay. After all, once Daniel became President, the IRS was going to vanish.

Jake and Jasmine took an early flight to Wilmington, Delaware to rendezvous with Jeremiah on his grueling East Coast tour. He had been on the road nearly nonstop since the reunion and had spoken at hundreds of his largest churches. He was on his last and most demanding leg — the densely populated East Coast. He would arrive in a city such as Wilmington and give his talk to seven or eight churches in one day. He would talk at one church, field a few questions, then walk out the back to his car and be driven to another church and another and another, averaging one per hour. The church heads notified their members of the day and time of Daniel's scheduled talks. The churches where he talked were packed, no matter what time of the day he talked. Members would take off from work to hear him talk.

On this day, he would talk at nine of the churches in the Wilmington area and eight the next day, unable to stay longer to reach the other churches in the city and suburbs. Members of those other churches crowded into the churches where he was giving a speech.

Jake and Jasmine joined Jeremiah at 7:30 in the morning, at the Holiday Inn for breakfast. They were surprised to see how much weight he had lost since the last God-Man Group meeting.

"Hi Jeremiah," Jake said to the tall, well tailored man who was staring at a stack of papers on the table.

Jeremiah looked up from a massive itinerary. "Hi, you two," he said. "Here, sit down."

"You look tired," Jasmine said. She and Jake noticed immediately Jeremiah's loss of weight, and they were concerned. His healthy body and face with its usually healthy bronze complexion looked drawn with dark splotches under the eyes. He was a tall man with an athletic build, but today his suit seemed a size too big for him.

"Do you feel alright?" Jake added.

"I'm fine," Jeremiah answered in a deep burst of laughter. "The East Coast leg has me eating breakfast and a late dinner, no lunch, so I've dropped a few pounds, and I've lost a couple of hours sleep from my normal routine. I've had to skip my runs and workouts. But..." he smiled, and there was that glow of the eight-year-old child in his face, "it's crunch time!"

Suddenly Jeremiah looked away. "Excuse me, ma'am," he said to the waitress, "can we order now?"

They ordered breakfast, and Jeremiah told the waitress they were in a hurry.

"Are we late?" Jake asked.

"No," Jeremiah said, "it's just a habit I've adopted. I need everything in my life to be in a hurry now."

Jake and Jasmine understood perfectly.

Jeremiah looked back at his itinerary and said, "I have basketball arenas locked up for the final weeks of the East Coast tour. I'll talk to thousands at once instead of hundreds."

Jeremiah then looked up. He smiled again at Jake and Jasmine and said, "Starting in four days, I'll speak at sports arenas in each city, so instead of speaking eight or nine times a day in one city, I'll give one speech in two or three different cities a day. I'll cover a lot of ground these last twelve weeks."

"Do you think all eight million members will vote for Daniel?" Jake asked.

"I do think nearly all my members will vote for Daniel. But, the number isn't eight million — it's four million members domestically, eight million worldwide. However, I've asked that each American member convinces, completely, at least one other person that Daniel Ward is his choice. That would put the number up to your eight million votes."

After they ate, Jake and Jasmine rode with Jeremiah to the first church on the speaking itinerary. Their car maneuvered around the side streets to the back, and they walked in through a back door. Jake and Jasmine looked up over the stairs to the speaker's floor and beyond to the crowd; their mouths dropped at what they saw: Over six hundred seats, all full, but more breathtaking was the overflow of people standing in every corner and in every opening and in the aisles. It seemed that more people were standing than were sitting.

"Were any of the other churches packed like this?" Jake asked.

"All of them," Jeremiah said. "We've had to pay dozens of fines to fire departments along the way because the churches let so many people in."

Putting Together the Pieces

Jake and Jasmine unfolded two folding chairs and sat down off to the side in the back where they could study the crowd. They could feel the energy in the room.

"What a force," Jake whispered.

Jeremiah turned to the crowd and approached the podium quickly as though he were in a hurry. He had no tentative motions as one might before addressing such an overwhelming crowd. He looked up, smiled, spoke into the mic. His deep voice filled every corner of the church. Jake did not know that Jeremiah's voice was also heard outside through speakers where hundreds more people stood on the front lawn and in the street to listen. Jeremiah's benevolence rang out over the crowd.

"Today I'll tell you about *the catalyst*," he began. "The Church is evolving. Listen closely as I recite the Church of God-Man's Pact for Eternal Life:

"We are members of the Church of God-Man because we live in an anticivilization that accepts the insanity of human life dying. Our anticivilization retards the natural business dynamics and the resulting technological and medical progress that would quickly cure aging and death. We join together to shift the competitive odds enough to drive out the support structure of the anticivilization, which means all its business subjects.

"We know we cannot, ourselves, cure aging and death...our individual focus needs to be where we have maximum leverage in life. We realize that pure business dynamics, with the resulting rapid technological and medical progress, would bring us immortality. Pure business dynamics cannot happen in today's politicized anticivilization. Pure business dynamics can happen only in tomorrow's nonpoliticized Civilization of the Universe.

"We shall form a Business Alliance to drive out all businesses that create the support structure of the political anticivilization. We shall drive every last one of them out of business or, if they want to survive, drive them into the nonpolitical Civilization of the Universe. At that point, with no more business support, the destructive political forces of the anticivilization that retard progress will, once and for all, collapse.

"Our Business Alliance will effectively start the nonpolitical Civilization of the Universe — let's call it the C of U — among ourselves. Here's how it works: In a sentence...we'll make every attempt to give our business to other members. Of course, they must earn it. But, in our pact for external life, we'll seek out and give every consideration to members for doing business. Whether we're buying goods, hiring employees, or using suppliers, we'll give first consideration to members of the Church of God-Man. In time, this extra consideration will give members of this Business Alliance a spectacular advantage over competitors, over those subjects supporting the destructive structure of the political anticivilization.

"To keep the business dynamics pure and uninhibited, we will not unconditionally do business with fellow members, for that would lead right back into an anticivilization based on politics, dishonesties, laziness, and irrationalities. Instead, we will make the extra effort to seek out and give every consideration to members, who still can be outcompeted by subjects in the anticivilization. But, what we're doing is significantly shifting *the odds* that a Church-of-God-Man member will get the business or job in order to give the alliance a growing competitive advantage, which over time will drive out competition in the anticivilization. Let's reiterate: those business subjects who support the destructive structure of the anticivilization will be driven out of business...or they will, out of survival pressures, be driven into the C of U.

"Members of the Church of God-Man's Business Alliance may openly do business with subjects in the anticivilization. Members may do what gives them the best competitive edge. But, members will be motivated to do business with their fellow members in the C-of-U Business Alliance because members will be treated better and will get better results. The same concept applies to using professionals such as lawyers and doctors, for fellow members will be treated with that extra care...as would a family member.

"Now, we must go back to the reason we're forming this alliance: to drive out the destructive political anticivilization that both prevents the rapid technological and medical progress that would enable us to cure aging and death...and creates the possibility of nuclear or biological holocaust. As this alliance grows and gains momentum, businesses and individuals will be tempted to join for the competitive advantages they would gain.

But we want our members to be sincere about driving out the anticivilization for the ultimate goal of curing aging and death.

"Therefore, to pressure people to grasp the C of U and to accelerate the nuts and bolts of our goal, members of the Business Alliance will pay for this value, as follows: businesses and professionals will annually pay 4% of before-taxes profits to the Association for Curing Aging and Death. Individuals without a business or a profession will pay 2 1/2% of take-home pay. Again, the financial obligation: 1) accelerates the nuts and bolts of our ultimate goal, and 2) pressures the pretenders to see the big picture. Upon signing this Pact for Eternal Life, one becomes a member of the Church of God-Man's Business Alliance."

Jeremiah looked up from the paper he was reading and said, "I believe our Business Alliance will knock down the anticivilization in less than five years."

He paused as the crowd applauded, whistled, and cheered so loudly that Jake's right ear started ringing. The intensity of the crowd's reaction surprised Jake. These people, he thought, must be deeply knowledgeable about the C of U and its benefits in order to cheer like that.

Jeremiah went on to talk about why electing Daniel would dramatically accelerate the race to biological immortality. Jeremiah's predictions usually proved accurate. The collapse of the anticivilization, he explained, meant immortality two or three years after that.

Jake was transfixed by Jeremiah's passion and charisma. Everyone listening, Jake thought, can feel Jeremiah is in a hurry — in a hurry to end human dying.

After a fifteen-minute question and answer period, Jeremiah waved to the crowd, turned and told Jake and Jasmine to come along. They walked straight out back and got into the car and drove away for the next church.

"Just eight more to go," Jeremiah said to Jake and Jasmine with a smile and a wink.

"Jeremiah," Jasmine said, pencil and pad in her hands, "that was so exciting! I can see how the Pact will ultimately drive out the support structure of the anticivilization. Your speech gave me chills. ...But, I must ask you, isn't delivering the same talk

481

several times a day too routine for you?"

"Yes, and its driving me crazy," Jeremiah said. "But I decided to do it because my speeches at my churches, delivered by *me,* are adding so dramatically to getting Daniel elected. Television would be a bust because, outside of my Church, people don't want immortality, not yet. On TV, I'd actually lose votes for Daniel. We've got to get Daniel in the White House. Everything we need to do to achieve biological immortality will get catapulted by having a Twelve-Visions President."

CHAPTER
FORTY-ONE

The scene at the next church was the same: crowded beyond the fire code. Daniel delivered his talk, fielded questions, and rushed with Jake and Jasmine back to his car to be driven to the next church.

Once they sat down in the car, Jake said, "When the teenage gal asked you how long until we achieved biological immortality, you talked about breaking the three anchors to the anticivilization. I've never heard about that before."

"I've inherently known it all along, but I explicitly identified civilization's three anchors to the anticivilization after the last gathering at Rico's."

"What are they?" Jasmine asked. She pulled out her paper and pencil. During the question and answer period earlier in the church, Jeremiah mentioned them but did not elaborate.

He glanced at his wristwatch. "We've got about a ten-minute drive," he said while they drove along U.S. 202, "just enough time to tell you what I've finally been able to articulate. ...There are three anchors keeping our civilization in an anticivilization. They are:

Anchor #1) Politicization of society,

Anchor #2) Stagnation of our lives, and

Anchor #3) Expectation of our deaths.

Superpuzzle

"Anchor #1 cuts off the progressive means to achieving biological immortality, and Anchor #2 and #3 cut off the emotional desire and drive," Jeremiah continued. "But, when one anchor breaks, the other two will also break soon thereafter, and civilization will sail into the Civilization of the Universe, or perhaps more accurately, civilization will be free to make the leap into the C of U. Daniel's election means Anchor #1 breaks.

"Let's consider what breaking an anchor means. To break Anchor #1 means to depoliticize America, which'll happen through Daniel's program. To break Anchor #2 means to catapult people from their routine ruts to their Friday-Night Essences in Theodore's new division-of-essence business paradigm. Then, people'll discover the persons they were meant to be, the lives they were meant to live; they'll discover eternal exhilaration, and they'll desire eternal life. Robert's TGIF Employment Agency is helping thousands of people discover their Friday-Night Essences, but we must move faster, much faster. And that's why I'm driving hard to get Daniel elected, for once Anchor #1 breaks, his six campaign visions will come true and Anchors #2 and #3 will soon snap, too."

Jake recalled the speech Daniel delivered at Boston University eight months earlier when Jake first heard Daniel's Six Visions of a depoliticized country: 1) millions of unrestrained Neothink geniuses will rise and take care of all our needs, and they will cause 2) a great Technological Revolution, driving priceless values down to a fraction of current costs, making everyone very wealthy as well as 3) very healthy as medical and health technologies soar and eradicate diseases while costs collapse, 4) the new business paradigm rises up in the free and prosperous supersociety; boring, routine jobs of labor get replaced with exciting, creative jobs of the mind, resulting in 5) deep individual happiness from creative — not stagnant — lives, which will rekindle permanent feelings of romantic love and exciting family love, and finally, 6) the new Neothink, puzzle-building mentality will naturally spread through everyone, creating futures full of extraordinary values, happiness, and love. ...Yes, Jake thought, the Six Visions were what attracted him to the Twelve Visions Party, even before he knew about Miss Annabelle and her students.

"After the reunion," Jeremiah continued, "I thought a lot about The Group putting together the Neothink puzzle of getting Daniel elected. At the time, I kept thinking we needed people, a lot more people to pull it off. I thought that maybe three fourths of my members would vote for Daniel, which would be about three million of the four million American members. I kept thinking about each person's role in The Group, and I estimated what I thought would be the number of votes each person could generate for Daniel. I have to tell you, the numbers kept coming up short. Then, one evening, when I had reached the deepest level of thinking I'd ever reached, I had an epiphany. That's the moment I knew how to get enough people to vote Daniel into the White House. Now, in three months, I estimate that twelve million Church of God-Man members and near-members will vote for Daniel."

"Twelve million!" Jake exclaimed. "I thought there were only four million members in America."

"Yes, but I have convincing data that shows eight million more will join soon, and they're voting for Daniel."

"That's incredible!" Jake said. "That's by far the biggest group of people voting for Daniel. How did the number of votes, those near-members, jump three fold?"

"By understanding the nature of Anchor #3," Jeremiah said with a wide grin. "Before the reunion, I built the Church of God-Man by doing my best to communicate the *real* tragedy of conscious death. I spent fifteen long years building the number of American members to four million members. Now I estimate that membership will triple over the next few months. To understand what happened, you must understand how my deepest emotional soul and those of my classmates from Miss Annabelle's third-grade class are very different from others. Because Miss Annabelle taught us the supreme value of conscious life, we learned and absorbed in our deepest emotional souls, as young children, that human death was *unnatural*. Almost all other children grow up in our anticivilization learning and absorbing in their deepest emotional souls that human death is *natural*. They grow up expecting to die. Every emotion growing up is woven around that expectation of someday dying. Now, Sally went even a step further than the rest of Miss Annabelle's students. That year in third grade, Sally went to medical libraries and studied cancer with her mother. She started believing she could someday cure cancer. She told me a couple of years later, as a young girl around ten years old, she believed she could someday cure aging, too, so people would never die. As a child, she grew up believing in her soul that she and others she loved, besides her mom, would not die. When she enlightened the rest of us, we quickly believed that too. Almost all other children grow up believing in their souls that they and their loved ones will absolutely die. The emotional perspective of human death in Sally and her classmates was a world apart from almost all others. Every emotion growing up was woven around not ever dying. And that different emotional perspective can't be communicated to others. They simply don't have any way to emotionally relate.

"The students of Miss Annabelle emotionally know the *real* tragedy of human death. Almost no one else does. If they did, we would have immortality by now. We, the students of Miss Annabelle, know the *real* tragedy of human death because we feel it from the Civilization-of-the-Universe — the C-of-U — perspective. Everyone else feels human death from the anticivilization perspective. Emotionally speaking, we're immortals trapped in the mortal anticivilization. The anticivilization will kill us if we don't stop it.

"When you feel death from the C-of-U perspective, you then know the most profound tragedy — the tragedy of an eternally happy C-of-U person trapped in the anticivilization and destined to die. The certain death of loved ones and of oneself is a tragedy more powerful than anyone in the anticivilization could ever know. But, that unfathomable tragedy of eternally-happy life lost for eternity — that infinite loss — can never be communicated from a C-of-U person to an anticivilization person. The anticivilization man just can't begin to feel what the C-of-U man is feeling or expressing.

"For fifteen years, I tried to communicate that emotional expression through the Church of God-Man: the infinite loss, the need to remove the unfathomable tragedy and cure death. But I always felt, when I talked to my church members one on one, they did not *really* understand or feel the tragedy of human death...not as I did. During those fifteen years, my U.S. membership steadily grew to four million.

"A few weeks ago, I had my epiphany: I finally realized that in trying to break Anchor #3 and fill people with the C-of-U perspective of human death, I was trying to do something impossible. I realized people wouldn't feel that C-of-U perspective until civilization was in the C of U. And that's when I had my marketing breakthrough that essentially was: do not try to break Anchor #3, just weaken it enough to break Anchor #1. Then Anchor #2 would break next, and Anchor #3 would break soon thereafter.

"This truly was an epiphany. To weaken Anchor #3 would be a far easier task that would pull in many, many times more people to bring together a massive, motivated force that would target and break Anchor #1 by voting Daniel into the White House.

"So, several weeks ago, I stopped trying to communicate the incommunicable C-of-U perception of death. I widened the appeal dramatically by not trying to implant a feeling people couldn't feel. Instead, I now merely *shift* their current anticivilization perspective slightly toward the C of U. That shift may last just a few years. But by backing off from my C-of-U perception that would frighten the anticivilization man, the Church is going to sign up millions and millions of new, excited members. They get in for *the cosmetics* of curing aging and regaining their youth, and they know voting for Daniel will bring about their sought after fountain of youth..." Jeremiah stopped abruptly and looked out the window.

"There's church number three on today's agenda," he said, pointing to a large church with hundreds of people standing outside who were unable to squeeze inside.

The car parked in the back, and the three of them walked toward the back entrance. Just before they got to the back door, Jake said, "What's the difference between before versus now...now that you're just shifting their perspective?"

"Before, I tried to explain the whole picture of the C of U and emotionally communicate the supreme value of our lives versus the anticivilization and the insane destruction of the supreme value. Now, I just focus on the cosmetics of curing aging, something that appeals to most people. I keep away from the profound meaning of curing death; that'll come in time. I focus on the specific that'll achieve their personal desire of curing aging, which is: depoliticize our country."

That's brilliant, Jake thought, just *shifting* people's perspective to pull together a much larger force, large enough to vote into office a Twelve-Visions President and cause Anchor #1 to break. That's ingenious, Jake suddenly realized, how Daniel's Twelve Visions are doing the same thing: just *shifting* people's perspectives, especially involving Anchor #2. Daniel's not trying to convince people of a C-of-U perspective of living an eternally happy life as a value creator, nourished by his deepest motivational root.

No, Daniel isn't trying to communicate that C-of-U perspective that opens up a life of value creation, great happiness and wealth, just as he and his former classmates live. Instead, he's just shifting the stagnant person's perspective slightly to something that person, trapped in the anticivilization, can relate to: becoming wealthy as prices tumble from the Technological Revolution that'll rise in the wake of depoliticizing America.

Jake now clearly saw the strategy of how to generate large numbers of people to create a force great enough to break Anchor #1. Jeremiah no longer tried to break Anchor #3; he just weakened it by slightly shifting people's perspective away from passive acceptance of their deaths as unavoidable, unnegotiable, and natural. And Daniel did not try to break Anchor #2; he just weakened it by slightly shifting people's perspective away from passive acceptance of their stagnant, financially challenged lives as their fate in life. By slightly shifting perspectives, easily graspable within the anticivilization, the two former third-grade classmates captured a force of tens of millions of people focussed on one common cause: depoliticize America. That huge force was pointed directly at Anchor #1. Break Anchor #1, then Anchor #2 would soon break as society would no longer be held down, and soon thereafter, Anchor #3 would break as people's lives would become exciting again, as life was in the distant, forgotten past as the toddler.

As Jeremiah delivered his talk to the hundreds of people who lined the aisles and filled the seats and corners of the church,

Jake looked at him with a new sense of awe. Jake saw someone different before him, someone he had not seen before. Jeremiah and his classmates twenty-seven years ago absorbed a different emotional perspective as children, which became the embedded perspective in their adult souls. And those twelve immortals were bringing that C of U, carried within themselves, to the world for everyone. As he listened to Jeremiah, Jake was filled with a powerful feeling; in fact, as Jake watched, he was filled with *only* that one feeling: *Jeremiah and his former classmates are our saviors.*

Jake knew that he, himself, and Jasmine could not yet feel the C-of-U perspective. Their own perspectives were obviously different than most of those around them, but were still part of the *shifting* perspectives in the anticivilization. Jake realized that Jeremiah, Sally, Daniel, Rico, Ian, Theodore, Reggie, Robert, Cathy, Debbie, Alan, and Natasha felt things Jake could not feel. Their souls were different. They never emotionally entered the anticivilization. Yes, Jake thought, they're our saviors.

CHAPTER
FORTY-TWO

Jeremiah finished answering questions at his third church, smiled, waved good-bye to the crowd, and hurried out the back to the car to be driven to the fourth church. In the car, Jake continued the conversation they were having earlier.

"Today you've been talking about the Pact for Eternal Life and its Business Alliance. Is that part of shifting people's perspectives?"

"The Pact for Eternal Life," Jeremiah said with an unrestrained smile, "don't you just love it? I'm approaching this mission at two levels: bring people in through the idea of curing aging, and move them to the next level through the Business Alliance. In this politically driven world, the Pact and its Business Alliance is sort of the gateway into the business-driven Civilization of the Universe. Think about it: my Church is bringing in millions of people at an enormously rapid rate, especially now that I'm just shifting people's anticivilization perspectives. My churches can't be built fast enough. With all those people with shifting perspectives about their lives and deaths, I searched my mind over and over for a way to take them to the next level. I knew I couldn't communicate the C-of-U perspective or its emotions that I have inside me. But with these millions of people, I thought, there must be a way to get them

490

to the next level.

"At our churches, we create an environment powerfully conducive for your average value producers to leap to extraordinary value creators by discovering their Friday-Night Essences. Hundreds of thousands of our church members have gone to Robert's TGIF employment agency. And our members are very big on Theodore's division-of-essence business paradigm. Business has always been huge with our members, and their networking is spectacular...like the lifeblood flowing through our congregations. Our members are by far the most successful group of any religion including Jews and Mormons. ...Have you been to a Church of God-Man recently?"

"Not since summer, but I'll be sure to go next Sunday," Jake said. He felt a little embarrassed.

"When you go, you'll feel the surging electricity in the air. The excitement's really building now. It's as close to the Civilization of the Universe as anything on Earth next to the monthly gatherings of The Group. It was during the Sunday congregations that I developed the idea for the Business Alliance and the Pact for Eternal Life. The Business Alliance was already happening on its own in my churches. Consider that people's shifting perspectives are a matter of desire or want, say, to live longer or to become wealthy. The Business Alliance takes them to the next level, for it brings the competitive drive and competitive advantages into their lives. The Business Alliance brings them past shifting perspectives, closer to the business-driven Civilization of the Universe."

Ingenious, Jake thought. "But why has it become, as you call it, *the catalyst*?" he asked.

Jeremiah nodded and sighed. "First of all," he said, "by starting the Pact for Eternal Life, I formalized and universalized the Business Alliance into a synergistic, worldwide force. The Internet gave us the tool to effectively do this. Now, to give you a clue as to how powerful this catalyst can become, do you recall the fable about the King of India rewarding one of his ministers with one grain of wheat for the first square on a chessboard, and doubling the number of grains for each new square?"

"All the wheat in the land couldn't pay the man," Jake said, recognizing the tale.

"The Pact could have a similar, geometrical growth pattern throughout the business world," Jeremiah continued. "With millions of members in the Church with whom to start this alliance, we have a sizeable source to get this off the ground and working effectively. Now, the thing I really like about the Pact is that it delivers competitive advantages to those who join. Like the chessboard, each business owner who joins will leave behind several business associates who will increasingly lose business and will be, through competitive pressures, eventually tugged into the Business Alliance. You'll see. It's going to be a spectacular catalyst. This is a way to pull in millions of others and to drive the anticivilization literally out of business."

"Oh, yeah, I can see how each business owner who joins would cause others to be pulled in after his business," Jake said.

"Once the Pact for Eternal Life and its Business Alliance gets going, it'll not try to persuade anyone of anything. It won't even interest itself in *shifting* anyone's perspectives. The growth of the Business Alliance will be driven by competitive advantages. We'll witness, as I said, the emergence of a different, business-driven world. That business-driven world will be the birth of the Civilization of the Universe on Earth."

"Damn, that's exciting," Jake said. He grasped the power of the Pact and its Business Alliance. Jasmine was writing notes. Then she stopped and looked up.

"How will the upcoming election affect the Pact?" she asked.

"If Daniel doesn't win, the Business Alliance could drive the anticivilization out of business and bring the Civilization of the Universe to our world in seven or eight years and immortality in nine or ten. But with Daniel elected, the two pincers working together would bring us immortality in about half that time, which I'm counting on."

Knowing Jeremiah's reputation for accurate predictions and timetables, Jasmine jotted down the tentative headline for the upcoming Sunday edition of the Patterson Papers: *Biological Immortality In Five to Ten Years!*

That evening, she faxed her notes to Al Patterson at his home. He read the notes and loved them, but he stopped Jasmine and

Jake from writing the article. Al called Jasmine and Jake an hour after he got her notes. "It's too soon," he told them. "We must hold off on your exciting article for now. It explains too much and could, ironically, hurt Daniel's chances. There's a great fear of immortality among most mortals. I'm sorry, guys, but we're in an anticivilization."

*

The next morning, Jake had just come out of the shower at about 5:45 a.m. when someone started banging on his hotel room's door. Jake reached over and opened the door, wearing just a towel around his athletic waist. Jeremiah stood wide-eyed and disheveled. He talked very fast.

"Jake, the first church I'm scheduled to talk at is on fire! I'm going there now."

"I'm coming!" Jake said, putting on his pants and grabbing a shirt and his shoes and chasing down the hall after Jeremiah, barefooted and bare chested.

"Jasmine, I'll call you!" he yelled back at the room. She was still asleep when Jeremiah had banged on the door, and she didn't have a chance to get her clothes on.

Jeremiah raced to his church driving the rent-a-car. Jake was glad to be wearing his seat belt. On the way, Jake called 911.

When he and Jeremiah arrived, a dozen or so people had gathered outside. The tall flame seemed to be spreading around the back and sides of the church.

"Is anyone in there?" Jeremiah asked an observer.

"I don't know."

Then Jeremiah yelled so loud that his voice snapped every observer out of the hypnotic spell caused by the flames. "IS ANYONE INSIDE?"

"I think one of my cleaning women is still in there!" a frightened middle-aged Cuban woman cried. She had just arrived at the same time as Jeremiah and Jake.

Jeremiah ran over to her, placed his hands on her shoulders, and asked, "How do you know that?"

"Because I don't see her anywhere!" the woman screamed while looking around and beginning to panic. Then her hands fumbled around in her purse and she pulled out a cell phone. Her hands were trembling when she turned it on for the first time that day and started dialing. "Oh my God," she said, her voice shaking in fear, "I'm calling the cell phone I have her carry." A second later the woman screamed "Maria! Where are you! Oh! Oh God, Maria!"

Jeremiah grabbed the phone.

"Maria where are you?" Jake could only hear half the conversation. "Can you run downstairs? Maria, just look straight down at your feet, don't look at anything else. Maria...Maria! You MUST."

Suddenly he thrust the phone back at the Cuban woman, turned around and ran for the church.

"Wait!" Jake screamed, and he sprinted to catch Jeremiah by his arm. "You're NOT going in there!"

Jeremiah spun back around, grabbing Jake's arms. "Jake, she's frozen with fear. She can't move. I have to get her out."

"But look!" Jake said. He pointed at the inferno; Jeremiah looked. The long yellow flames seemed almost lifelike. They reached up along the sides, groping, indulging, dancing with sinister delight. The early-morning, semi-dark twilight accented the bright flames.

Jeremiah looked back at Jake and yelled, "Everything we're fighting for will be over for Maria totally, completely, *gone*. I can't let that happen in my building!"

Jeremiah turned around and ran straight for the inferno, straight through the front door. Jake could not believe the heat on his own face and arms from the blaze, and he was a good fifty feet away.

A few seconds after Jeremiah ran into the church, Jake could hear him yelling, "Maria! Maria! MARIA!!!"

Then, he stopped. He's got her and is on his way out, Jake hoped. Suddenly, there was a loud explosion, and the flame rushed across the front of the church, filling in the front doorway. The back and sides of the church had been burning for some time. Now, the front was engulfed in flames.

"He's trapped!" Jake heard himself shout. "Oh, god, where's the fire department! What can I do!"

Jake felt himself begin to panic, but he stopped himself.

494

What can I do? What can I do?

After a moment, the most painful feeling he ever felt overcame him as he realized he could do *nothing*.

The church crackled and popped like a big bonfire. The flames flowed like fluid from the windows, but curled up toward the morning sky. Two minutes passed. Jake knew that was too long. The fire was too powerful. Three minutes...

Suddenly, Jake was aware he was running toward the church.

He had no idea what he was going to do. He got twenty feet away and threw his arms across the front of his face. The heat was unbearable. That's when the realization hit him: no one could be alive inside that blazing inferno.

"Jere!" he screamed. "Jeremiah! JEREMIAH!!!"

The heat pushed Jake back now as he screamed for this one of the twelve saviors of civilization to come out.

Backing up until he could bear the heat, Jake just stopped and stared. His eyes were squinting from the heat. Overcome by his helplessness to help Jeremiah, Jake began to cry. He just watched, shook his head, and cried. Too much time had passed. Too much time.

Just as the last drop of hope had drained from Jake, he thought he saw motion deep within the thick flames in the doorway. Was it real or an illusion? Then the motion turned dark...it was a head! Then a torso, then a full figure black as coal, running hard and fast through the flames — carrying a woman! Jeremiah and Maria! Jeremiah had done it! Run man, *run!* Suddenly, the burnt-black figures fell onto the burning floor. They did not move.

The sight had frozen Jake, for an immeasurable instant. But that instant ended the moment it began, and Jake broke from his stance and ran as fast as he could for the doorway. He did not let the heat stop him or even register. He ran up the burning stairs and grabbed the two unrecognizable figures, blackened by fire and smoke. Jake grabbed them by their collars and pulled. Suddenly, the heat penetrated Jake's skin and made his escape very fast, like a reflex, like yanking the hand from a hot stove. Jake, though, would not drop Jeremiah or Maria. Jake cried out in pain as the heat pierced the skin on his face, neck, and chest. He walked backwards, down the stairs. He pulled Jeremiah's and Maria's unconscious bodies, bouncing along with him. It bothered him that neither Jeremiah nor Maria felt the pain. Their bodies were smoking, and Jeremiah's smoldering pants seemed to be melting right into the flesh on his legs. Jake could not hear them moaning or coughing, and he feared why not. They certainly could not be peacefully breathing.

A loud burst went off on both sides of Jake, and behind him. His feet suddenly felt cool, almost cold. Then, he saw firemen spraying Jeremiah and Maria with powder from fire extinguishers. Someone was spraying Jake, too.

They're finally here, he thought.

Before he knew what was going on, he was in an ambulance with Jeremiah. Maria was in another ambulance.

Jake was sitting alone as he watched two men and a woman working frantically over Jeremiah.

Jake tried to see between or around the paramedics to look at Jeremiah. As they moved about, Jake got a glimpse that revealed the shocking sight of a man who looked beyond death. His skin was charred and crisp in some places, raw and oozing in other places. Below his knees, his pants were melted into his legs.

Finally, one of the paramedics moved, and Jake could see Jeremiah's face. Jake could not recognize him, however, through the distorted, blackened features. Jake focussed on the oxygen mask covering Jeremiah's mouth. *Was he breathing? Is he alive* was all Jake could think. *Is he alive?*

CHAPTER
FORTY-THREE

While Jeremiah was being tended to in the ambulance, Al Patterson was in the air being flown by his company pilot to Wilmington.

When Al got a call from Jasmine from the hotel, he left for the airport. Ten minutes in the air, in the company's Learjet, Craig from the Patterson Building contacted them on the radio. "Mr. Patterson, they took him to Christiana Hospital. Sir..." Craig hesitated.

"What!" Al shouted.

"Sir, I'm sorry to tell you this...they think he's DOA — dead on arrival."

Not able to accept it, Al yelled back, "Who said they think he's dead?"

"Jasmine called here again. She got to the scene just after Jake and Jeremiah left for the hospital. People at the scene said they thought he was dead."

For the first time, an employee of the Patterson Media Group, the pilot, saw his boss's vulnerable side. Al's eyes dropped down, his head hung forward, and he didn't move for the rest of the flight. The pilot looked at Al's profile. The pilot had never seen someone so profoundly crushed.

The pilot, as many of the Patterson employees, knew a lot

about his boss and his past. He knew, from recent articles by Jake and Jasmine, that his boss was one of Miss Annabelle's famous, twelve former classmates. But he did not know that Miss Annabelle's twelve former classmates never felt death was natural; they never accepted death. He never knew that, together, they were going to cure death. And now, Al was told, his soul-brother had just died.

The pilot turned toward Al and put his hand on Al's shoulder. He knew Al did not, not yet, accept Jeremiah's death — not until he heard it from the doctor. The pilot sadly sensed...oh, what a blow Al was walking into.

At the hospital, Al moved swiftly to find Jeremiah — yet every move to find Jeremiah filled Al with fear of the unthinkable. One of the nurses led him toward the back of the ER. She pulled back a curtain. The sight of Jeremiah was shocking. But the jolt in Al's heart was a jolt for joy.

"*You're alive!*" Al said as he bolted over and grabbed Jeremiah's hand, as would a brother. "Some people at the fire told Jasmine you didn't make it." Al did not have to say the words, for the emotion in his voice and the desperation in his grip said it for him: I couldn't bear to see you go. *I love you, brother.*

Jeremiah's eyes were open, but he could not move. His mouth was covered with an oxygen mask that was full of condensation. He turned his eyes, which looked so big and white within the blackened skin, to look at Al. Jeremiah blinked slowly, gratefully as a critically wounded man would who suddenly saw his beloved brother by his side. The two men looked into each other's eyes, held onto each other's hand, and absorbed strength and joy from each other.

After a minute, the technician who was working around Al and running tests on Jeremiah said, "Sir, I need you to step back for a few minutes."

When Miss Annabelle arrived, her whole expression collapsed upon seeing her Jeremiah. She gently hugged him. She held him and cried for several minutes as he kept whispering into his oxygen mask, barely moving his lips, "I'll be okay...I'll be fine." Hearing him, she would calm down and nod, pull her head back and look at him, and then start crying all over again at the devastating sight.

Two hours later, still in the ER, the burn specialist and pulmonologist concurred on good news. "We're raising his condition from critical to serious," said the pulmonologist. "He's a strong man, a very strong man."

Al, Miss Annabelle, Rico, and Sally inhaled and exhaled deep breaths as waves of relief washed through them. Sally walked out with the pulmonologist to review the x-rays and test results. Rico went to the waiting room to inform the others from The Group and to give another a turn to see Jeremiah since only four visitors were allowed to be with Jeremiah at a time.

The doctors checked Jeremiah into the hospital and moved him to an intensive care room. He was in a lot of pain, so the doctors continued to sedate him.

While he slept, skin specialists worked on his body. They removed melted garments, treated the burn wounds, and cleaned him up. Throughout the day, more members of The Group arrived.

Jeremiah was a bachelor, so he had no immediate family. He had not seen his mother and father for years, ever since he started a church that contradicted the Biblical Jesus. So, he had no family to speak of.

The Group was his family. During the third grade, Jeremiah discovered a new world of reason and logic. At home, he was immersed in a world of mysticism and hardcore religion. During the miracle year, the home closest to his heart became Miss Annabelle's classroom, and his lovely teacher knew it after visiting his residence during the Christmas holiday break. His classmates and his teacher became his closest family back then. And, ever since the reunion, they had once again become Jeremiah's closest family.

When the doctor returned to treat Jeremiah in the intensive care unit, he asked who in the room were family members. Miss Annabelle explained they all were, in essence, his family members.

*

Two doctors who had been working on Jeremiah in the intensive care unit finally talked to The Group.

"Internally, he's in good shape. I had numerous tests run earlier in the ER. He inhaled a lot of smoke, but his blood oxygen level is improving quickly. He's out of the woods with that. Barring his external injuries, he could be up and walking around in a couple of days. We'll be able to release him in two weeks."

When Jake watched the expressions on Jeremiah's former classmates' faces, he knew they reflected very different feelings than even himself. He could see in them the very thing Jeremiah had told him about just the day before. These people did not, could not accept death. The loss of Jeremiah would have ended their world.

"After I cleaned him up," the skin doctor was saying, "he was in better shape than I'd expected. The worst damage is on his legs. He has third-degree burns from his knees to his ankles. But I would say he could still walk out of here in two weeks."

"What about the lady he saved, Maria?" Jake asked.

"She's in surprisingly good shape, too, about the same as Jeremiah internally, and maybe in a little better shape in terms of burns," the skin doctor said. "Her family's here, and we've talked to them."

*

Late the next day, Jeremiah got up and stiffly walked to Maria's room. Her mother and father greeted Jeremiah. The doctors had told them about Jeremiah saving their daughter's life. Her mother started crying and thanking him.

"We're very grateful," her father added. He looked up at Jeremiah and placed his hands gently on Jeremiah's arms. "Because of you, our daughter is alive."

The Puerto Rican parents lived in a small circle of acquaintances in America and had no idea Jeremiah was a powerful man of influence.

They invited Jeremiah to their house for a celebration once he and Maria were better. Then, they stepped aside so Jeremiah could approach Maria's bed.

Putting Together the Pieces

She was awake and smiling. The day before, while inside the fire and smoke, she could not see Jeremiah's features, but she knew those eyes. They were strong and intense and driven by a mission; at the same time, they were gentle and overflowing with love.

"Your eyes," Maria said with a sexy Puerto Rican accent, "I'll never forget them as long as I live."

Jeremiah sat on the bed next to her. He was aware of feeling blissful joy looking at this beautiful life that still existed because of him. He absorbed the moment and just looked at Maria with sheer pleasure. Then, in a sensual yet paternal move that he could not stop, beyond normal boundaries that no longer existed for the saint who saved her life at immense risk to his own, Jeremiah rubbed the palm of his hand gently along the side of her face, down along the side of her neck, down over her slight shoulder, down along her soft arm, over her small hand and out along the curve of her hip. The sight of her breathing sent pleasure through him. His eyes were ablaze. "I'm so glad you're alive, Maria," he whispered from the deepest reaches of his soul. Without another thought about his impossibly packed schedule in the weeks ahead, Jeremiah said, "I'll be at the celebration when you go home. I want to celebrate your life."

When Jeremiah turned to leave, Maria grabbed his arm. "Wait," she said in a rush. Jeremiah smiled and turned back to her. "Why did you come inside to save me? There was no way out, but you came and got me...a complete stranger. *Why?*"

"Love," Jeremiah whispered.

"What? You've never even seen me before."

"Someday...you'll understand." Then Jeremiah gently kissed her forehead and left.

Three days later, Jeremiah walked out of Christiana Hospital to the protests of his doctors.

"We've got less than twelve weeks to election day," he told Jake and Sally, who were there at the time. "I haven't even had a chance to talk yet at sports arenas. I'm walking out of here, and no one's going to stop me."

Jake looked at Sally for her professional opinion. She watched Jeremiah shuffling around the room, getting his things together.

"He'll be okay," she said. She smiled and shook her head. "He'll have it no other way."

That first night out, he spoke at the First Union Center where the Philadelphia 76ers played. Jake and Jasmine attended. Jeremiah filled the place…21,000 seats. Jake and Jasmine sat in the press box. Jeremiah was wheeled to the center podium on a wheelchair. The crowd noise fell to a hush. Most of them knew of his heroics and critical injuries.

Jake was aware of thinking what a dramatic sight it was: Jeremiah covered with bandages, in the center of the large sports arena, slowly standing up from the wheelchair, refusing help, then slowly shuffling to the podium to speak.

His voice was so weak that the volume on his microphone had to be raised. Yet, Jake thought, Jeremiah's fragile appearance and weak voice made him look and sound like a man of steel. Indeed, he could overcome anything.

As Jake listened to the frail, weak voice from that figure that looked so small standing alone in the middle of the arena, Jake got goose bumps. The smallness and frailty of that wounded man in his weakened voice filled the air with an unbeatable strength — the strength of a God-Man.

The next day, Jeremiah spoke at two sports arenas, talking to tens of thousands of members and near members. Moreover, people just interested in the Church-of-God-Man phenomenon were attending by the thousands at each sports arena. The sports arenas were packed. Jake was in awe of the force behind Jeremiah's exploding religion. Shifting perspectives was his secret.

Jake called Jeremiah the next day to see how he was doing.

"We're going strong again, stronger than ever," Jeremiah reported.

Twelve million votes from Jeremiah alone, Jake thought; nothing can stop this man. Then Jake started thinking how Jeremiah's unbeatable nature was the nature of the twelve former classmates, the eternal soul mates: they were unstoppable, unbeatable, unconquerable. They were the twelve original God-Men.

"Nothing can stop 'em," Jake mumbled while hanging up the phone, "nothing at all."

CHAPTER
FORTY-FOUR

"I'm in."

Those two words, spoken by Theodore Winters to Jeremiah Jones, would have a major impact on the world.

That week, Theodore Winters and the other powerful members of The Group joined the Church of God-Man's Pact for Eternal Life, which sent shock waves through the business world. The week following Theodore's inauguration into the church's Business Alliance, he met with his seven empire heads. An "empire head" was a master neothinker who created and coordinated several companies within Theodore's sprawling empire.

"Send your senior teams of accountants on a mission," Theodore said to open the meeting with his empire heads. Jake, who was present, watched in awe the power this physically small man possessed, confidently coordinating perhaps the world's most valuable empire. "Get bids from potential new suppliers — all up and down and along your vertical and horizontal business empires. Those potential new suppliers, from trucking companies to software programmers, must be members of the Church of God-Man's Business Alliance."

Within a week, Winters Inc. started switching to several new suppliers — to those members who were competitive. Many of

503

the old suppliers lost their biggest account when they lost Winters Inc.

One of Theodore's longtime suppliers — supplier of envelopes for Winters Inc.'s direct-mail program that advertised his Company-Without-a-Company/Without-a-Country software — telephoned Theodore, his good friend, after losing his business.

"Ted, why'd you drop us after all these years?" asked Tom, the owner of Atlantic & Pacific Envelope and longtime friend of Theodore. Tom felt confused and hurt.

"Listen, Tom," Theodore answered, "we've been friends for a long time. But I value my life more than our friendship."

"Okay, but what does that have to do with business?"

"Everything, Tom. It's misguided business that gives the power to the anticivilization that's going to kill me and my wife and eventually our children."

"What are you talking about?"

"I've explained it to you three times before, and today you're still in the dark. There'll be no more explaining or persuading, Tom. Money and actions speak louder than words. It's up to you now to learn for yourself about the anticivilization versus the Civilization of the Universe. Your survival depends on it."

"But, Ted..."

"I say this for your own good, Tom: *to hell with our friendship.* As long as I have a competitive alternative, I'm finished with you and others who go on giving power to the anticivilization. I love ya, Tom. But I can't go back to your world. You must come into mine. ...Good-bye, Tom."

Theodore hung up the phone. He sat at his desk staring at the wall. He sighed deeply and sadly, then he spun his chair around to his computer to see what other business friends he was parting ways with. He felt sad, yet strong.

*

The owners of the old suppliers quickly learned why Theodore was switching: to do business with their competition whose owners were serious about curing aging and death. Soon, every owner of the old suppliers Theodore left, most of whom depended on his business, were seriously looking into the

Church of God-Man and the Association for Curing Aging and Death. Less than a month later, over half of them joined the Business Alliance, including Tom.

How rapidly and effectively survival pressures work, Jake thought as he researched this phenomenon for an article. At his desk in the Patterson Building, Jake stopped writing his article for a moment to grasp the big picture. He slipped deep into thought: Jeremiah's approach is a critical ingredient to achieving the goal, for his approach attacks the massive support structure of the political anticivilization. Jeremiah's approach is working from the inside, taking apart the structure, whereas Daniel's approach is working, in a sense, outside the structure. Daniel's approach is offering a new "political" structure that civilization will go into as the old structure collapses.

Both approaches, Jake knew, were crucial to succeed rapidly.

*

"I've expanded the length of my talks at the sports arenas since I only deliver two a day," Jeremiah told Jake just before going out before a completely filled Madison Square Garden two weeks after he left the hospital. "I expanded my speech to articulate the growing happiness people will experience in the Twelve-Visions World. I make them feel it now."

"Feel what?" asked Jasmine.

"That longer life will be a cherished gift."

"Today, you're all going to discover the meaning of limitless happiness," Jeremiah said to open his new speech.

During the speech, waves of emotion rushed through Jake. When it ended, Jake could feel the hair on the back of his neck standing on end. A thunderous standing ovation rocked the Garden.

"Yeah!" Jake hollered. He stood up and smacked his hands together too. He couldn't stop, for Jeremiah's speech stirred Jake. He leaned against Jasmine and yelled through the noise, "Everyone felt it, right in the heart, what life now really is: *immense happiness*. What a speech!"

Jake and Jasmine wanted to catch up with Jeremiah. They

stopped cheering and quickly made their way to backstage. But when Jeremiah came backstage following the thunderous ovation, he rushed past Jake and Jasmine.

"I'm really sorry, guys," he said sincerely, "but I must get back to my plane."

"Where to?" Jasmine asked, "Off to another city to talk?"

"Not today," he said. He stopped and turned around. "I'm heading back to Wilmington. Today Maria's going home from the hospital and her folks are having a homecoming celebration. I'm the guest of honor, and I don't want to be late."

Jasmine smiled at Jake and raised an eyebrow.

The next day, Jake and Jasmine called Jeremiah.

"How's everything?" Jasmine asked, trying not to sound nosey. She really wanted to ask, "How was your date with Maria?" Jasmine knew Jeremiah had to have an attraction for Maria to disrupt his mission.

"Oh, the alliance has catapulted the Church of God-Man; I can see it working already," Jeremiah said. "New memberships are already soaring past the previous rate."

"Oh," Jasmine said, flatly. She had to refocus from where her thoughts were coming from. She heard Jake saying, "Man, that's exciting!"

"A surprise to everyone is the rapid number of *individuals* who don't own a business joining the Church, specifically to be part of the Business Alliance," Jeremiah continued. "It's early, but I can detect many unforeseen advantages surfacing for the individual in the Business Alliance. First, individuals can use the alliance to find work with companies in the alliance because many of those companies have already advanced into the new business paradigm — you know, the division of essence, Teddy's business breakthrough. Those businesses seek employees who want to release the power of their minds. So, imagine individuals excited to leave behind their dead-end, routine ruts still stuck in the division of labor. In the Business Alliance, they can find open-ended jobs of the mind. And the businesses in the alliance find those ambitious individuals a clear cut above others and have begun hiring them." Jeremiah stopped talking. He thought for a moment, then said, "You know, the Church of God-Man will

506

become, in essence, a *business religion.* Isn't that the way our cousins in the Civilization of the Universe exist? Isn't a business religion the religion of the Universe, for business means creating and putting expanding values into society?"

After another pause, Jeremiah continued, "The alliance is also becoming a source for single men and women to meet each other with strong, common interests. It's becoming a powerful social network for friendships of all kinds at all levels. Lifelong friends, soul mates, baby-sitters, wholesome friends for children are being generated through the Business Alliance."

"Single men and women?" said Jasmine. "Like you and Maria?"

Jeremiah laughed.

What a wonderful thing business is, Jake found himself thinking. It brings us every value we have...even romantic love.

*

Al called Jake and Jasmine into his glass office overlooking the floor of the Patterson Building.

"I've got Bruce Salinski on the speaker phone," Al said as they walked into his office.

"Hi Bruce," they both said.

"Hi. You guys doing okay?"

"Wonderful," Jasmine answered. She reached over and placed her hand on Jake's arm.

"Well, I'm back down here in Wilmington. I've been asking questions and following the investigation. It's not good news."

"Oh?" Al uttered.

"A woman walking her dog saw and heard two men just hanging out around the side of the church that morning."

"You said she saw *and heard* them," Al said. "Do you know what she heard?"

"Yes, I do. And this is what concerns me. They seemed to be chanting some kind of prayer. She heard them say several times they were going to set free the people of the Church of God-Man from their blasphemous sins."

"Do you think this is an isolated incident?" Al asked

nervously.

"The experts say this could be the start of a malignant action," Bruce said. "But the upside is, they believe the two men were acting alone — extremists — neither in coordination with nor with the support of their religious sect."

"What makes them so sure of that?" Jake asked. He was worried about the threatening signs by religious groups he had seen along the campaign trail.

"Investigators have told me, Jake, that if a sect sanctioned this act, they would have claimed responsibility, which no one has. These were two religious kooks, acting alone".

"Thank goodness for that," Jasmine whispered.

*

That Sunday, Jake and Jasmine attended a congregation in one of the many New York Churches of God-Man. As newcomers, a gentleman at the door handed them a book titled *TVP: The Cure to Aging*. Jake looked at Jasmine. They nodded, knowingly, and smiled. That's so true, Jake thought, Daniel's Twelve Visions Party will depoliticize America, which'll lead to the cure to aging...and death.

They did not know anyone there, but they were amazed at what they stepped into. The Church was spacious with a large balcony, and it was packed with hundreds of people. Jake and Jasmine walked inside. A man they had never seen before was delivering a sermon. He was talking about Dr. Ian Scott's breakthrough that life on planets, which statistically speaking often evolved into *conscious* life, was part of the natural phenomena throughout our Universe and, as such, conscious life was the third fundamental component of existence, which Einstein overlooked, focussing only on mass and energy. The speaker recapped Ian's breakthrough, explaining that consciousness becomes the *controlling* component of existence and takes over the overarching dynamics of the cosmos. Jake and Jasmine took a seat and listened:

"Immeasurably enormous amounts of, if not infinite, existence exists within black holes and gravity units," the speaker said. "God-Man has taken over the cosmos to the point of creating

508

new realms of existence by unfolding black holes and gravity units. He is a value creator, and he creates the greatest value in the Universe: new realms of existence that'll eventually evolve conscious life, the third fundamental component of existence.

"When the very advanced God-Man becomes a creator of new realms of existence, which evolve consciousness, we call him Zon. For, he becomes the Creator of conscious life. The ultimate role of consciousness is to become *the creator*.

"What about *our* Zon — the very advanced God-Man who created the realm of existence that we are part of? *Our* Creator. How do we repay Him, thank Him...honor Him?

"Consider that the success of His creation — that is, our galaxy and our Universe — increases with the more values it contains. Now, you can live in Zon's Creation and be a value producer who earns a living but adds no new values into Zon's house, so to speak; or you can leap to a value *creator* who creates and adds new values into Zon's house — *adds* values to the Universe. ...Your way to repay our Zon, thank Him, honor Him and yourself, is to make the leap from value producer to value *creator*."

Jake reeled backward in his chair. What an insight! He did not expect such advanced understandings to come from ordinary people outside The Group. He looked at Jasmine, a little stunned over it all. These people, whom Jake never saw before, seemed nearly as advanced as The Group. And there are thousands of these Churches around the world, Jake thought, with people delivering sermons like these every week to millions of people! What a force, Jake pondered, what a force...

After the sermon, the hundreds of people walked into an adjoining room that seemed to be a large ballroom. Over the next hour, Jake and Jasmine experienced something beyond anything they had ever known before. They walked into a large crowd in which they estimated half were value *creators*, and the other half were value producers who would soon, in this magnificent environment, leap to value creators.

Jake had felt so stimulated in only one other environment — in the monthly meetings of The Group.

"Darling," Jasmine said, gently shaking his arm, "do you feel it?"

Superpuzzle

Jake did not have to ask her what she meant. He knew, and he did feel *it*.

"We're in the Civilization of the Universe," Jasmine continued while letting go of his arm and slowly turning around, with her palms up, in a 360° circle. Her eyes moved back and forth and her face was full of wonder, like a child enjoying a new sensation. Then she whispered, "We're in the house of pure love."

As Jasmine slowly turned in the house of love, Jake saw again, in his mind, the house of love in Wilmington being devoured by flames of hate. *Man*, he thought, *I hope we don't see anything like that again.*

CHAPTER
FORTY-FIVE

"The world's changing," Al said to Jake and Jasmine. They sat in Al's glass office. "The Church's Business Alliance has assaulted the business support-structure of the anticivilization. The enormous wealth generated from the Business Alliance goes into Sally's Association for Curing Aging and Death. Salinski's powerful counterattacks against the anticivilization are changing litigation. Daniel's moving campaign speeches are changing the way people view society, Robert is thrusting ordinary people into entirely new lives as powerful shakers and doers, Debbie's reaching millions of man-in-the-street patrons with Daniel's six campaign visions, Theodore sends out heavyweight influences throughout the business world, Sally's causing new perspectives and mounting breakthroughs in the medical world, Cathy's organizing highly visible PR projects that bring about Twelve-Visions-Party awareness, Reggie's music seems to be shifting our youth to the Twelve-Visions-Party agenda, and Miss Annabelle's web site for children and TV specials and their upward pressures are changing parents' view of life and society. Of course, we're giving massive media coverage to Daniel and his campaign; Natasha is, too, on her radio talk show, and Rico so graciously keeps us together with our monthly meetings so we can create and coordinate our efforts. These are the pieces to our first

Neothink puzzle snapping together. That puzzle, of course, is getting Daniel elected."

And that Neothink puzzle is a piece to the superpuzzle, Jake thought; nothing seems to be able to stop these God-Men.

However, the challenges were going to a new level.

*

Sally arrived at Rico's mansion late for the monthly meeting. She entered the meeting room and spoke to no one. She sat in a chair in the back and buried her face in her hands. Jake was not sure, but he thought she had been crying. Miss Annabelle walked over and put her hand on Sally's shoulder.

"I know why you're upset," Miss Annabelle said softly.

"You do?" Sally asked, looking up from her hands. She felt a little better someone else knew.

"Yes, I saw the report on the Internet this morning."

The others in the meeting looked at Sally and felt compassion. Jake could see that, indeed, she was on the verge of crying. He knew that something must have shattered her to bring this powerful woman to tears; he felt so close to Sally and these awesome people...these people who could let their guard down around each other and expose their vulnerable sides. At that moment, Jake felt a lot of love and trust in the room. Like so many years ago, Sally's sensitive side was pulling The Group closer together than ever before.

"The government just stopped my progress on human cloning. What am I going to do?"

"I'm so sorry, darling," Miss Annabelle said. She reached out and rubbed Sally's shoulder.

Jake admired the way Sally carried the full weight of medically curing aging and death on her own feminine shoulders.

"It's just too much," Sally cried, "everywhere I turn I run into political stoppage. Every time I or anyone moves a step forward toward curing aging, the ethicists start loudly complaining, the media gives them an audience, the politicians jump on the cause and get their photo ops, and their three-ring circus brings on the bureaucratic regulations that destroy our progress...every step of the way! We'll never, *never* cure aging

512

and death, not this way!"

"No, not this way," Daniel concurred. "Those bureaucrats are getting as many regulations passed as they can before the election to give themselves a bigger cushion — more justification for their bogus livelihoods." Daniel shook his head. "They really think that by piling up more and more regulations, it'll be harder or take me longer to get rid of them!"

"They're also doing it to stop your momentum," Bruce Salinski said. "Just as the IRS and Justice Department tried to knock Annabelle out of the picture, the FDA has been trying to knock Sally out. She's too valuable to your campaign and your chances of winning. Too many millions of people in Jeremiah's Church of God-Man want Sally to succeed, driving those millions of voters to you. That's the connection. The FDA's trying to break the momentum."

"You know," said Daniel, "the Church of God-Man has become my single largest base of voters. You're absolutely right about the connection: if they stop Sally, they figure they stop votes for me."

Jake, too, had observed the rapid, almost desperate escalation of regulatory control of the medical field since his article a few months earlier titled *Daniel = Health & Wealth*. Whereas businesses were pouring money into medical research with the possibilities of Daniel's success, the politicians and bureaucrats were, in a desperate effort, pouring regulations onto the medical field...especially aimed at derailing Sally's breakthrough work.

Jake moved closer to Sally. Her face was a picture of beauty and determination, shattered by devastation and frustration.

"You know, three weeks ago I was asked for at the hospital by a father who was losing his daughter to a blood infection that had gotten out of control. I don't see patients now, but because of my research on blood infections, they requested me when her doctors were losing her." Sally's expression became motionless. Her eyes got big and were staring. She was watching the moment again, in her mind.

"When I got to the hospital, it was so unbelievably sad. This beautiful little five-year-old girl was lying on the bed, her eyes swollen shut by a 108° fever, lying there with nothing but her panties on, her little tummy convulsing, her little ribs sticking out. Her father was sitting right beside her on the bed, holding her tiny hand in his, stroking her forehead with his fingers. He...he didn't see me at first; he was shaking; he was so scared he was going to lose her. When he noticed me, he looked up, and his face filled with hope. I was his only chance.

"Then I heard her...and it broke my heart. She was delirious from the fever. But you know what she kept saying?"

Sally looked up at Miss Annabelle and couldn't say it. Tears rolled down her cheeks one after the other. Miss Annabelle leaned over and hugged Sally as a mother would hug a child. Sally buried her head in Miss Annabelle's shoulder and began crying, but Sally still wanted to tell them.

"She kept repeating," Sally finally said, "over and over again, in the weakest voice, lying there with her eyes swollen shut, mumbling, 'Don't worry, Daddy'll save me. Don't worry, Daddy'll save me...'"

Sally broke down and wailed long and hard into Miss Annabelle's shoulder. Everyone in the room looked down upon hearing that; they all knew by Sally's pain that the little girl had died. Sally allowed her buried pain to come up, and she cried for five full minutes. When she calmed down some, she finished her story. "Just before she died, she regained consciousness for a fleeting moment. She only half opened her eyes and saw her dad. Although she was dying and in a lot of agony, none of that could stop the natural reaction upon seeing her dad. A weak smile sprang across her face, showing him the happiness he caused to fill her heart. I saw her little white teeth. A whisper full of instant joy, deep love, and tragic longing flowed from her lungs, *'Daddy...'* It was all she could say, but it said everything to him. She exhaled, and died."

Sally leaned into Miss Annabelle and cried. Miss Annabelle cried; everyone in the room quietly cried.

"The little girl's name was Kelsie," Sally managed to say a minute later. "Her father...oh, he's devastated. His little girl died with him on her lips...he was her hero. She thought he could do anything. But he could do *nothing* to save her."

No one in the room could talk. They just shook their heads, sighed, and tried to clear their eyes. It was as if they knew and loved Kelsie, as if she were one of them. They knew the supreme value of that child...gone now, forever.

During the silence, Jake thought of how much pain Sally goes through — the one person in The Group on the front lines of battling death.

After a few minutes, Sally regrouped and continued, "I'm sorry for dragging you all down, but I'm at the end of my rope. I just have to let some of these feelings out. Losing Kelsie was so hard. God, I just can't take it, seeing an innocent child die. And then, seeing the devastation, *the pain*, in her daddy's eyes. Oh..." Sally gasped.

Jake knew Sally was seeing Kelsie's dad in her mind's eye. As Sally was reliving the memory, her lips suddenly started quivering as she drew in a breath.

"His eyes," she said, her voice shaking, "were screaming out for Kelsie. His eyes were screaming, 'Come back to me, Kelsie. Please come back. I *need* you, Kelsie!' He won't let go of the pain for many, many years...if he survives this."

Sally took two deep breaths, then continued.

"Kelsie died because politicians and their bureaucrats have so slowed down my progress and my peers. To justify their livelihoods, those politicians and bureaucrats long ago politicized the medical industry. Little Kelsie was among their victims. Her life was stolen from her by bureaucrats. That's the price we pay for politicized medicine. Sometimes, I just can't cope with the losses." Sally looked down and shook her head.

"It must be *so hard*," Miss Annabelle whispered.

After a long pause, Sally said, "I'll see Kelsie and her dad in my memories for a long, long time. I'll never forget them."

CHAPTER
FORTY-SIX

Miss Annabelle knew Sally needed to talk some more about this torment she alone carried on her shoulders and in her heart. She needed to share some of the agony. A few moments of silence passed as Sally remembered Kelsie and her dad. Miss Annabelle pulled a chair over and sat next to Sally.

"Is there anyone else you'd like to tell us about?" Miss Annabelle asked her.

"I'm going to lose another precious life soon," Sally said, willing...almost eager...to talk. "His name is Eric. A few months ago, Eric was such a tough young man at twenty-three years old. But now, he's so frail—" Sally caught herself before her composure stumbled again.

After a moment, she continued, "I've been doing experimental work on his aggressively spreading cancer. But soon, I'm going to lose him. I just...I just can't move forward fast enough because of all the regulations blocking my research and preventing the development of crucial drugs." Sally shook her head. "And now...my cloning research." She became angry and blurted, "It's as though a mother is running to save her toddler in the street from getting hit by an oncoming truck, and the FDA is standing there holding that mother back as she watches the truck strike and kill her child. Every time I lose someone, it's like watching that truck strike him and violently kill him. While the FDA holds me and stops me from saving him. No mother would ever get over it...never. Neither will I."

*

The run for the presidency was moving forward with growing momentum. But the quest to cure aging and death could never move fast enough. And, as The Group had identified, the political burden on the medical field, particularly aimed at Sally's work, had been growing at a record pace as Daniel's popularity grew.

Sally suffered deeply. Every lost life was a devastating failure to her. ...Just four days after the meeting of The Group, after having told them about Eric, he died.

Sally had spent a good bit of her career around cancer patients during her experimental work on curing cancer. She had seen a number of patients die; several of those had been part of her experimental programs; some of them she had gotten very close to. But none affected her quite in the way losing Eric had.

Now she worked only on cancer patients who directly tied into her research on curing aging and death. Eric was one of those patients whom she had grown very close to. He was a young 23-year-old man with a rare form of aggressively spreading tumors that were devouring his young life. When Sally first met Eric, he had a strong body and a strong character. He lived alone in Manhattan and came to the Salberg Cancer Clinic after his cancer was discovered. Eric worked as a trader on the floor of the New York Stock Exchange, and he first went to a doctor when his energy faded to the point that it interfered with his work. The doctor ran some tests that revealed Eric's cancer. What made Eric's case so rare was his young age. This sort of malignant tumor usually attacked older bodies.

Sally's heart broke, piece by piece, as she watched this strong young man sink in a few months into an altogether different person in appearance and confidence.

Eric's parents lived in Toronto. He did not tell them about his cancer. He believed in Sally's work and thought he and Sally would prevail. But when Sally could see the tumors were not going to stop growing and spreading, she sadly told him. Then, he told his parents.

His mother moved in with Eric, and his father flew down every weekend. Eric did not last long, however. Three weeks after he told his parents, he died in the middle of the night in the hospital.

That last night, as Eric's condition rapidly worsened, the nurses called Sally and Eric's mother to the hospital at about 1:30 in the morning.

When Sally arrived, Eric was very white and cold. He had lots of blankets on him. His mother was at his side, still in her nightgown.

When Sally arrived, she wrapped her arm around Eric's mother and gave her a hug. Then Sally leaned over and kissed Eric on the forehead. When her lips touched his skin, he was ice cold.

"Thank you, Dr. Salberg," Eric said, "for trying so hard to save me."

He knew this was the end. Sally knew it too. She always had a very, very hard time with the end of a person's life. Tears started rolling down her nose and dripping on Eric. She had almost always stayed strong in Eric's presence; this was only the second time he saw her emotionally give in. The first time was when she told him he would not make it.

"I'm so sorry I couldn't save you, Eric," she said, as she tried to wipe her tears that kept falling onto his cheeks.

"Please don't feel that you failed me," Eric said, seeing the look on her face. "You've done so much...so much."

Sally, at that moment, wanted to scream that Eric was *not* to die. She couldn't bear it, for she knew if her progress had not been so slowed down by the FDA, she would have been able to cure Eric and all people dying of cancer.

Suddenly Eric groaned. He was in pain. Sally ordered a pain killer, but Eric stopped her.

"I want to have all my wits at the end," he said, so innocently. "The pain tonight will be worth it."

Eric's simple statement and acceptance of his death gripped Sally by the heart. She leaned over and hugged him one last time, and she cried as she kissed his cheek. He lay there like a helpless baby, unable to hug her back. She looked into his eyes one last time.

"You're a hero, Eric," she said, and she rubbed the side of his face with her hand and her thumb, and she saw the innocent child there. Eric looked into her eyes and smiled a beautiful, proud smile...as a boy would smile if he were told he was a hero.

Then Sally stepped aside, leaving the end for Eric and his mother. He and his mother talked about many things over the next hour, recalling beautiful memories. It broke Sally's heart as she heard him tell his mother his ambitious plans that now would never happen. He knew they would never happen, but he wanted her to know what he had planned to do with his life. He wanted his mother to know she would have been very proud of him.

During their beautiful, yet heartbreaking talk, Eric would break into loud moans as the pain gripped and twisted his body.

As he and his mother talked, the attacks and his moans grew longer...and longer.

Everyone in the room would stop and be silent, feeling unbearable compassion for Eric, and fear that Eric would not pull out of each gripping attack. When the violent pain would release its grip, the gentle conversation between Eric and his mother would continue as if nothing had happened.

Sally had never seen anything like this. The strength of Eric was showing itself to her at the very end. He's so strong, and so *brave*, she thought as she quietly wept in the corner. And then, the violent pain gripped Eric and did not let go. Eric was fighting with all his energy to win this battle, to survive this moment to spend a little longer time with his mother. The grip of death would not let go, and Eric was not breathing...but then like a miracle, after nearly two minutes, Eric exhaled and said, simply...

"Where were we, Mom?"

Sally could not bear to hear the physical torture Eric endured any longer. She rushed over to Eric's side.

"Would you like just a little something for the pain, dear?'

Eric smiled and shook his head. That was the last time they

519

would look at each other, but it was a very special moment for Eric. For, he could see that Sally had never before seen someone with the physical and mental strength that he possessed. That meant a lot to him.

Sally wrestled with her lips to give him a smile that saluted his courage. Her admiration for Eric unmistakably filled him with pride during his last, fighting moments.

The next ten minutes were filled more and more with Eric fighting the attacks of pain. He tried to continue his last conversation with his mother, but he couldn't get enough time between attacks to communicate now.

His poor mom was losing him, *her son*, and she knew it now. Sally could not take it, but she forced herself not to run over and anesthetize Eric. As he groaned and twisted and groaned and twisted, Sally knew this attack had lasted too long.

"Mom!" Eric suddenly yelled, then groaned, then yelled again, "Mom!" Sally looked over. His eyes were staring straight up, and Sally knew his vision was dark and he couldn't see his mother anymore.

"Mom!" he yelled again, with panic in his voice. "Ma!"

His mom was leaning over him, crying and yelling back, "I'm right here, darling! I'm right here!"

But Sally knew he could no longer hear her, either. Then what happened next, Sally would never forget.

"Mama!" he yelled as tears started streaking back from the outside corners of his eyes, "Mama!" sounding almost like a baby crying for his mother. His voice was filled with fear. He did not want to die. He was too young; he was scared beyond anything he had ever known, and in his fear he wanted his mother, just as he did when he was a baby.

His devastated mother wrapped her arms around him and hugged him with all her might. She was crying, "Oh my baby...my baby!" But he could not hear her or feel her. He was all alone now. Sally's heart was being torn apart as she listened to Eric and his mom, in his final moments, as fear conquered his strength...and dignity.

Then he cried out again, "Mama!" His cry was slower, but filled with even more fear. Sally gasped and helplessly shook her head.

Then he cried for his mama, over and over, slower and slower, like a record slowing to a stop, scared and crying out for the person he loved most, "Mama! Ma Ma! Ma Maa! Maa Maaa... Maaa Maaaa... Maaaaa..."

And his life was gone.

Sally looked over at Eric in his mother's arms. He was born from her womb, and he died in her arms.

CHAPTER
FORTY-SEVEN

Sally told The Group the sad news: she had lost Eric during the past month.

Over the past two months, Sally had lost Kelsie and Eric. She took the loses extremely hard; Jake was wondering how much more she could take.

"How are *you* doing?" Miss Annabelle asked.

"When someone young dies..." Sally said, "there's something about it that takes a big part of me with them."

Miss Annabelle nodded.

"When you watch someone die," Sally said, looking down, "you only *see* it — you don't know what's going on inside his or her mind...but when you *hear* someone die, as I heard Eric, you hear everything...you hear his sad, dying feelings...you hear his fear, anxiety, and loss as the life leaves him. That person's very closest friend and soul mate all his life was himself. And when that person is dying, he's losing himself...his best friend, companion, and soul mate." Sally's voice became softer and higher as the pain from her heart flowed over her vocal chords. "And he's losing himself forever. After a whole lifetime together, losing himself frightens him beyond anything he's ever experienced. When Eric was dying, I could hear that god-awful fear in his voice."

After hearing about Eric, Jake sadly understood what Sally meant. Jake looked at the passionately driven, attractive woman named Sally Salberg before him and found himself thinking that someday, once she cures aging and death, and probably not before then, this sensitive woman overflowing with love and compassion will be a spectacularly loving wife and mother.

"The only thing that keeps me going is my progress to end this total and complete loss and the pain that's left behind. *My progress*...that's it," Sally emphasized. "And then, my progress gets halted by politicians and bureaucrats. Kelsie and Eric both died because my progress has been so slowed down. I'll never cure aging and death, not this way."

"You're absolutely right, Sally," Daniel said, gently. "You'll never, *never* cure aging and death in this politicized anticivilization. Your progress will always be sabotaged. But once I'm elected, all that'll change. There'll be no more FDA, no more politicization of the medical industry. There'll be no one to stop your progress. ...Sally, I wish I could promise you I'll be elected in November. It'll be close, but I can't say for sure."

"Maybe I can," Ian said.

Sally looked at Ian, hope filling her eyes, those big brown eyes pleading with him to continue.

"I have, all ready to snap into place, the final puzzle piece — the scientific proof — to Daniel's Twelve-Visions World...his Twelve-Visions World actually at work out there," he said. "And that *proof* out there will guarantee his election here!"

"Out where?" Sally asked.

"Out there!" Ian said, waving his arm in an arch before her. "Throughout the cosmos!"

"Tell us!" said Mr. Melbourne, always fascinated by Ian's discoveries, ever since he was in the third grade. ...Sally dabbed her eyes with a tissue and nodded for Ian to continue.

"The final piece comes with my first wave of Overlay Charts," Ian began. "Those Charts provide overwhelming proof not only that conscious civilizations exist out there, but that they exist in a world free from governments and wars. In other words, the advanced civilizations all function through Daniel's political structure...and this is no longer theory. My Overlay

Charts *prove it*.

"I'll be releasing all my findings in a few days — just in time for the entire country to read about it and see it on TV for a few weeks before the voters go to the booths. Now, let me tell you—"

Suddenly, a frightening scream, followed immediately by a child's screams, filled Rico's mansion. Rico ran out of the meeting room. The other men followed. A moment later, the women walked from the meeting room to encounter a heart-jolting sight.

In the large entryway, they watched two men walking down the long stairway, each pushing a gun against the back of the heads of Olivia and Monica, Rico's wife and eleven-year-old daughter. Monica was crying.

"Daddy...help us!" she cried when she saw her father.

Hearing his daughter's plea, hearing the fear in her innocent voice, being helpless to end this violence instantly, seeing his precious treasures with guns pressed to their heads, sent Rico through the most crushing fear and pain his heart had ever endured.

"Let them go! I'll pay you whatever you want!" Rico demanded, walking straight toward them.

"Stop!" The gunman behind Olivia screamed. For a brief second, both gunmen pointed their guns at Rico, then back at his wife and daughter.

The gunmen looked unstable. Although their guns were fixed tight on their targets, their heads kept jerking around nervously, toward every sound. They made it down the stairs with their woman and child prisoners, onto the marble entryway floor.

The taller, thick-haired gunman with frightened eyes, standing behind Olivia, suddenly yelled, "We've come in the flesh for Jesus Christ our Lord to save you from your sins. Your work here on immortality is Satan's work. We're here to free you!"

The shorter man holding Monica shouted, "Then we'll free the people of all your churches, just as we did in Wilmington!"

Jeremiah's eyes expanded, and he had to remind himself of the guns pointed at Monica and Olivia to refrain from charging these fanatics who burned down his church and nearly killed Maria and himself.

"What's more, your atheistic mission to take over the presidential office and deliver us to a godless state will end today!"

Mr. Melbourne instantly recognized their mindset and whispered, "Fundamentalists... hallucinating religious fanatics. If we don't stop them, they'll kill us all in a few minutes once they're done preaching to us and praying for us."

Jake's worst fears, seeing those fanatics along the campaign trail, had come true. Daniel's polling numbers were coming on strong, and he still had over a month to go, causing these religious fanatics to panic and lose their sanity.

Jake's mind jumped to the secret service recently assigned Daniel since he was now considered a serious presidential contender. Unfortunately, Jake thought, Daniel had asked the two agents to wait outside, and since Daniel was not the president, they obliged. Rico's mansion was so well built and insulated, the two secret service agents obviously never heard Monica's screams. *What do we do now?*

Jake was staring at the gunmen and desperately trying to think of what to do, when he saw Rico moving toward the men. Even during the stress, Jake was taken aback by the strength radiating from Rico's face. He was rising to the occasion. The battle had begun between a Civilization-of-the-Universe father in the next dimension of love for his family...versus the anticivilization man oblivious to love.

"God forbid it!" Rico hollered, and then he raised his arms toward the heavens and walked swiftly toward them.

"Lucifer!" the man holding Olivia screamed. At that moment, both predators panicked and pointed their guns at Rico. That's exactly what Rico's objective was as he instinctively struck like lightning. The two guns discharged, a muffled pop pop. Silencers. Blood splattered across the light marble tiles. Jake instantly registered that the blood on the tile was *dark*, not bright, meaning lots of it...a *deep* and serious wound. But Rico had the man closest to him, the one who had Monica, in his grip. Rico first snapped the gunman's wrist backward, and his gun fell to the floor a few feet away. Although wounded and bleeding, Rico quickly lifted the man then slammed him to the marble floor. But Rico crouched behind his new captive so his partner could not get off another shot. The religious fanatic in Rico's grip went limp, and Rico lifted him like a Raggedy Ann doll and formed a human shield between himself and the other gunman. Monica kneeled behind her dad.

Jake could not recognize Rico's face. It was from another life...another place. Like a domesticated wild animal suddenly faced with a life-threatening moment, Rico had reverted back to the wild. He looked savage, primitive.

Then, in a beautiful moment, the pure love filled his face again as he turned his head around to look at Monica. With love flowing toward her from deep inside, he said, "Get out of here, darling. Go now! Run back there, and get out!"

The contrast in Rico's face was beautiful to see...and breathtaking.

Then that flash of beauty disappeared after Monica ran behind Miss Annabelle; he reverted back to the wild, primitive beast. Forming a sacrificial human shield, Rico planted the gunman's knees on the floor and wrapped his right arm around the man's neck and knelt right behind him, pushing the man downward upon his knees — down hard — until the gunman's belly curved out like a bow. Rico, kneeling behind this man who had just pointed a gun against the head of Rico's beloved daughter, pulled back his massive left arm and pointed his big fist at the fundamentalist's lower back. He was nine feet from Olivia and looked directly into her captor's eyes.

"Let her go or I'll snap his back like a twig!" Rico commanded.

"No! We'll die for God!" the man holding Olivia cried, and then he started chanting a prayer. Suddenly, Rico's captive closed his eyes and chanted along with his partner.

"It's me you want. I'm the godless presidential candidate!" Daniel yelled. "Take me and let these god-fearing people go. Let 'em go!"

But the fanatics did not stop chanting. They did not even pause. They were in some kind of trance. The political ads that seemed to encourage religious fanatics to "die for God" flashed through Jake's mind.

Rico's breathing quickened. He implicitly knew that when the prayer ended, so would Olivia's life. Through a great internal discipline, he switched from his powerful physical attempt to save his wife's life to his mind and dug deep, deep, deeper to find a way out of this. The fusion of intensity in this C-of-U man seeking biological immortality for his family and faced with their deaths — was incredible to watch. The determination not to let priceless value be wiped out was an image Jake would never forget.

Rico glanced at the gun on the floor a few feet away, but he knew that option would get Olivia shot. He had to go straight to the problem — the gunman on Olivia.

Suddenly, Rico looked up. Everything seemed to move in slow motion. He let go with his right arm that was wrapped around his captive's neck and slid the arm off. When Rico let go of his captive, the religious fanatic sat straight up after being released from his bowed position.

Rico's freed prisoner suddenly stopped chanting. He started screaming senseless, frightening guttural sounds that seemed to gush involuntarily from him. No one in the room knew that Rico's left hand had reached under the gunman's ribs and squeezed his heart until it ruptured. Visibility of his hand had been blocked by his victim's angle and by Rico's body. The gunman released a horrifying noise no one in the room had ever witnessed before. The sounds got so violent that his partner stopped too and looked at him.

"He's possessed!" Rico shouted. "Satan has taken him! Your presence here in the Lord's name is blasphemy! You've been tricked by the Evil One!"

The noises barked and hissed violently from the man before Rico. His eyelids fluttered like insect wings. His face twitched and twisted. His tongue suddenly stuck straight out, causing his partner to gasp and his face to fill with fear.

"Satan will seize you, too, unless you stop your blasphemous work here!" cried Rico.

Mr. Melbourne did not know what caused the gunman's horrific condition, but Mr. Melbourne did know exactly what Rico was doing with it. He was creating intense stress upon the fanatically religious, armed man to send him into a bicameral, controllable state like the primitive man who would obey the commands of "the gods".

Superpuzzle

The man on his knees would not stop emitting grotesque gurgling noises. Rico repeated over and over in a powerful, commanding voice, "You've succumbed to Satan! Pray for mercy! You've succumbed to Satan! Pray for mercy!"

Then the gunman on the floor started vibrating beyond what was humanly possible as the horrifying gurgling noises gushed from his mouth with more and more force. His cheeks twisted and flapped against his jowls. His head started shaking harder and harder, faster and faster. A white foamy froth bubbled and splattered from his mouth. Rico stood up as the gunman before him timbered sideways to the floor. His whole body shook and his legs crisscrossed and curled up as he gurgled as though he were being electrocuted. It was beyond a seizure; it looked supernatural.

Rico raised his arms above his head. Miss Annabelle gasped upon seeing Rico's white shirt soaked in blood under his left arm and down his side. Rico looked up and bellowed, "Lord, he knew not what he did. My Lord, have mercy on his soul!"

The gunman's eyes rotated back in their sockets, showing all white. His body stopped shaking and a long, wind-like breath left his lungs.

"The evil spirit has left him," Rico whispered into the stone silence. Rico dropped his arms. "Can you feel it?" he asked, softly. "It's still here." Rico fixed his gaze in the lone remaining gunman. "It's coming for you, you know," Rico said calmly, as a matter of fact.

An eerie silence followed. The gunman did not know what to do. Watching his partner die a stunningly horrifying death with no explanation or apparent physical cause, the armed man's eyes were huge, and he started hyperventilating.

At that precise moment, Mr. Melbourne released a cry that sounded like the voice of God:

"I command you: drop your tool of the Devil, NOW!"

The armed man shrieked. He did not drop the gun, but he looked away from Olivia in the general direction of Mr. Melbourne, though his frightened eyes looked up...toward the large windows behind Mr. Melbourne that exposed the cloudy sky. The gun angled slightly off Olivia's face. Like a leopard, Rico ran two quick steps then leapt toward the gunman. The armed zealot turned toward Rico and twisted the gun back toward Olivia's face. His finger squeezed the trigger, and the gun went off.

All three fell to the ground. Daniel was already running toward them. Rico had his hand on the back of the zealot's head and like a sped-up movie, rose to one knee, and smashed the gunman's skull against the marble floor three times — bam! bam! bam! — and let go. In an instant, it was over; the gunman's body rolled over onto its back. Jake knew, the moment he saw the gunman's head, he was dead.

Daniel wrapped one arm around Rico like a brother as they both rolled Olivia over. Rico and Daniel leaned close to her face...and saw no blood.

Her eyes were closed. Rico had seen two people shot in the head at close range when he was a boy, and he knew they did not always bleed. He put his large hand under Olivia's chin and turned her head to one side, then the other. He saw no hole or discoloration.

"Rico...Daniel...let me...let me!" Sally said as she forced her way between the two men. She leaned directly over Olivia's face that seemed too peaceful, too serene. Sally quickly ran her fingers around her head and down the back of her head to her neck, and then searched for a pulse.

Miss Annabelle was behind Rico, lifting his shirt, desperately trying to find where he was shot. She feared he was very seriously injured, even though he fought off the symptoms while protecting his family.

Reggie jumped over the crowd and made sure the other gunman was not capable of rising again. He, too, never would.

Sally was still checking Olivia when Miss Annabelle screamed, "Oh no! He's hurt really bad, Sally...oh...he's *really* bleeding!" Miss Annabelle had found the bullet wound and began to panic as would a mother upon seeing the blood rushing from a hole. She had his shirt up and pointed to the blood streaming out of a wound somewhere under his left arm, around his armpit. She started shaking. Sally moved in to take over.

Monica, who had been holding her mother's head on her lap, turned all white.

"Dad, oh Dad! DADDY!" the eleven-year-old screamed as

529

she crawled over to him and saw the bleeding.

Sally, somehow remaining calm under the crisis, winced when she saw the blood coming from just below the armpit. She knew if the bullet tore open part of his heart, it would be fatal. She was scared, but tried not to show it.

"Put your hand right here, Jake. And press! Someone get him to the car." Jeremiah picked up Rico like he was a baby and started running to the door, Jake right beside them, pressing his hand over the wound. Daniel scooped up Olivia and ran after them. The adults were silent with the fear that they could lose their Rico and Olivia. Monica was crying hysterically as she ran after her mom and dad.

Mrs. Green had the stretch limo and the chauffeur at the front door, waiting. Rico, Jeremiah, Jake, Daniel, Olivia, Sally and Monica squeezed into the back like a paramedic team. Rico and Olivia lay on the seats and the others were kneeling on the floor of the stretch limo's cabin. Theodore got in the front. He called the hospital's emergency room to get everything ready.

"What blood type is he?" Theodore yelled back to Sally.

A moment later she called back to him, "O positive! Tell them we'll need four units!"

Rico sat up so Monica could sit next to him, and he put his good arm around her. She was scared and crying, and her father's embrace calmed her down a little. They sat across from Olivia, watching her closed eyes for a sign of life. Rico was shaken to the core, afraid that she'd been shot in the head. Sally told Jeremiah it was okay for Rico to sit up, but she wanted Jake to support Rico because he was dizzy.

While studying Olivia's vital signs, Sally gave Jake and Jeremiah instructions to clean up Rico while keeping pressure on the wound so she could examine it.

"You can lean on me, Daddy," Monica wept, and then kissed his side.

While Jake and Jeremiah were tearing open his shirt and wiping his side clean, Sally further inspected Olivia.

"Larry, stop!" Rico shouted to the driver. On the field, playing, were Rico's other three treasures. "Let them in, Larry."

Before the limo came to a full stop, Daniel jumped out. "I'll ride with them to make room for the children," he said, pointing at the secret service agents who were frantically following them. As the limo stopped, Daniel leaned his head back into the car and put his hand on Rico's arm and said, "You hang in there, brother." Rico nodded and then looked back at his children.

The chauffeur got out, ran around the car, and opened both back doors as wide as they could go. Rico's heart throbbed painfully as he saw each of his little darling's faces burst into smiles upon seeing him. They instantaneously started running to the car, Rosa in the lead, Rico Jr. next, followed by 3-year-old Little Tony, all three of them yelling, "Daddy! Daddy! Daddy!"

God, I hope their mommy is okay, Rico thought. Then, seeing their faces collapse when they saw him bleeding, he thought: God, I hope *I'm okay*. Seeing their faces, suddenly he felt a jolt inside, like a powerful body blow to his soul. For the first time in his life, Rico grasped what a tragedy it would be for his little treasures if he or Olivia died and were not there for them growing up.

"Monica, Daddy needs Band-Aids!" little three-year-old Tony exclaimed, overwhelmed but trying with all his heart to deal with the situation.

Monica nodded. She was scared, cold, and shivering. She had just been through great trauma; she did not know if her mom and dad were dying, and she felt her daddy's weight growing on her shoulders as he started to lose strength because of his loss of blood.

"Rico," Sally said as the children crawled into the car, "Olivia's vital signs are good. She's not seriously hurt. She's in shock, but she'll be okay."

Rico suddenly felt a storm of emotion wanting to release itself, the sudden relief that Olivia and Monica were *now safe*. His little treasures crawled to him and curled up against him. The intense look on his babies' faces, even on little Tony's face, so filled with love, slammed into Rico's heart and, for a moment, he couldn't say what he needed to say. He swallowed and forced himself to talk, for if he didn't, he could tell the release of emotions from having almost lost his wife and daughter would erupt.

"Guys," he said to his children, "there's been an accident.

Mommy hit her head, but she's going to be okay. I've been shot. That's why I'm bleeding."

"By bad guys?" Little Tony asked, trying to comprehend the situation.

"Yes, darling...by bad guys."

Monica started hugging her dad and crying.

"Dad, I'm scared," she cried.

"I'm going to tell you guys a secret, okay?" Rico whispered.

All four children nodded. Rico turned his head away from Sally and said softly to his children, "When I was a boy, I learned where the organs in the body were because there were bad guys who had knives where I grew up. I had to know what to protect. Now, I can tell you, I don't think anything serious got hit in me. The wound's on my outside ribs. I might have a broken rib, I'm bleeding a lot, but I'm okay."

Monica smiled a little and said, "Really?"

"Let's see if the good doctor agrees," Rico said, and then he winked at Monica.

"I love you," Monica said, and she hugged him tighter.

"Me too. Me too." Rosa and Rico Jr. said. "Me too!" Little Tony shouted.

"Sweethearts," Sally said, turning her full attention now to Rico, "I'm just going to take a closer look at your daddy's wound. Rico, let's lift your arm up, and place your hand behind your head," Sally said while helping him move his arm. When it was up, she could examine the wound. She told Jake to remove his hand. When he did, blood pulsated from the wound. Monica and Rosa started crying. Rico Jr. and Little Tony's eyes widened with fear. Little Tony started breathing very fast. Although he was trying not to, he was on the verge of crying, too. Sally moved her right hand around the wound, then suddenly pinched hard into Rico's ribs. Miraculously, the bleeding nearly stopped. Monica and Rosa's crying softened, and Little Tony's breathing relaxed some.

"Can you lean forward a little," Sally said while helping him; then she stretched her neck to look at his back. After a moment, she sat him up and looked at the front again.

"Very interesting," she said in a tone that brought a sense of relief to everyone.

Rico winked at his four treasures.

"What is it?" Monica asked hopefully.

"I found where the bullet entered — right here," Sally said, pointing to the hole with her left hand, and I found where the bullet exited — right back here," she said, pointing around his shoulder to his back. "Between the entry point and the exit point, there are no vital organs. The bullet missed his heart. He'll need blood and some stitching, but he'll be okay. ...Your mom and dad are going to be fine, children."

"Oh, Daddy, you were right!" Monica said, hugging him and putting her head against him. "You were right!" Although her siblings were smiling, she couldn't stop crying.

Rico smiled and pulled her close with his good arm and said, "I can't tell you how I would be if I had lost you or your mother. To be without you..." Rico stopped. He couldn't say it. Monica cried and nodded...and she hugged her dad all the way to the hospital, looking up at his face the whole way.

"Is Mom okay?" Rico Jr. asked. "How come she's not moving?"

"She's unconscious," said Sally, "but she's not really hurt. She just fainted. She and your dad will both be okay."

Theodore called Miss Annabelle, who was with her husband and Jasmine in the car directly behind them, and told her the good news.

"Thank you, thank you," Miss Annabelle cried. "Oh, I'm so relieved! I'll call the others. Tell Rico and Olivia we love them!" She dialed the others in their cars, who were all following their precious Rico to the hospital.

Sally found exactly where to apply pressure to drastically slow the bleeding. As she sat with her thumb and fingers clasping Rico's side just below the armpit, observing and talking to Rico, suddenly she broke into a gentle moan of pity.

"Ahhh...look at their faces," Sally said. She gestured with her head toward Rico's four children. All four had their heads tilted back like little birds, staring at their father's face. They were intensely watching his every expression, watching out for any decline.

Rico had also noticed their four little faces studying him, including little Tony who normally would not sit still for five seconds.

The realization of having almost lost his precious wife and daughter, combined with his children's vulnerability and total love for him, overwhelmed him. He had been struggling to keep his composure, but suddenly tears rushed down Rico's cheeks. His children had never seen him cry.

"It hurts, Daddy?" Little Tony asked when he saw his daddy cry, putting his tiny hand on his father's leg.

"Not too much," Rico answered gently. "Sometimes a father thinks of what might have gone wrong, and how much he loves his children and wife, and that can make him cry."

Little Tony, looking intensely at his father as he talked, nodded and gently said, "yeah," as though he completely understood. Rico Jr. quietly put his hand on his dad's leg, too. Rico's girls both hugged him tighter.

"The thought of anyone of us no longer in our family is too sad," Rico continued. He looked at Olivia who was still unconscious but breathing smoothly. "That came too close to happening. ...But everyone's going to be okay now," Rico reassured his children as he stretched out his good arm, scooped them together, and hugged them all.

"Everyone's going to be okay, Daddy?" Little Tony echoed, looking at his daddy then at his mommy. The little fellow just wanted to hear it again.

Rico looked at Little Tony...such a little guy in such an intense crisis. Rico swallowed as he observed this little rock handling himself like a man.

"Everyone's going to be okay, sweetie."

CHAPTER
FORTY-EIGHT

In the emergency room, while receiving blood, Rico was put under anesthesia to clean and close the wound. The procedure went smoothly and took less than an hour.

He awakened an hour later. Monica and Olivia were holding his hands, smiling at him. Rosa, Rico Jr., and Little Tony stood right next to his side. Little Tony's head barely cleared the bed.

"Daddy, the doctor said you'll be okay!" Little Tony announced. "I like that doctor," he added. Rico laughed. Oh, he thought, it feels *so good* to laugh with my family!

Then he looked at Olivia, and all the memories of their lives together flashed through his thoughts. Her eyes were red from crying. As they looked into each other's eyes, suddenly Olivia burst into a smile and she cried and she leaned over and hugged her husband.

"Oh, Rico...I was *so scared*. You were bleeding so badly. Oh my love...you're okay. I'd be lost without you!" and she kissed him and cried in his arms. "Thank you, oh *thank you* for saving our precious Monica!" She buried her eyes into his large shoulder and cried. In a high voice, her eyes still buried, she barely said, "And thank you for saving me! ...You stepped in front of bullets to save us."

Rico leaned his head against hers and kissed her hair.

"Olivia," he said, "no bullet will ever stop me until you and our treasures are out of harm's way."

Olivia was swept away by Rico's love. She pulled her head back and stared into his eyes. She was able to smile, and she shook her head in disbelief of this man who loved her and their children so deeply. He filled the secret gardens in her soul with bright, beautiful flowers.

Their four children watched and smiled proudly at their parents. They loved to see their parents so much in love.

*

Thirty minutes later, Rico was up and able to sit in a wheel chair and leave post op. He already had both his arms around his five treasures. The doctors wanted him to stay overnight to watch him, but Rico said only if they had a room large enough for his whole family.

After he got settled in his large room with Olivia and his children, the doctor let the members of The Group in to see Rico.

"Oh! I didn't know you were here!" Rico stammered gleefully upon seeing the crowd coming in. They had already given their reports to the police.

The police felt this was an isolated incident. But just in case, they put two officers outside Rico's room for the night and suggested he get good, private security at home...especially during meetings of The Group.

"That commandment was timed perfectly," Rico said to Mr. Melbourne.

"Your approach to take over his bicameral mind was brilliant," Mr. Melbourne replied.

"It was straight out of your book," said Rico.

A man and a woman, who Rico did not recognize, entered the room with The Group.

"Mr. Rodriguez, we know you've been through a lot, so we'll try not to be here long," the woman said politely. "I'm Detective Shannon Brice and this is my partner, Detective Dave Phillips. Your friends answered most of our questions, but there's still a mystery we need answered."

536

"Rico," Daniel said, "how'd you get that guy to make all those noises to look like he was possessed by an evil spirit?" He had asked the question no one could answer.

Rico knew it would be best for Olivia and the kids not to hear about the gruesome details of the attack. They needed to eat anyway, so he asked Olivia to take them to the cafeteria to get something to eat. Rico made sure one of the officers outside the room escorted them.

After they left, Rico turned to Detective Brice and said, "Before I let go of my grip around his neck with my right arm, I pushed my left hand under his ribs and wrapped my fingers around his heart. I had him sideways just enough so the gunman on Olivia couldn't see my left hand. It looked to him that when I let my headlock go, his partner sat up on his own, a freed man. But it was my squeezing his heart that made him stiffen straight up like that. Those noises were because I squeezed his heart until it ruptured. When you hold a man's heart like that, he can't get up or fight. He's paralyzed."

The detective's face grimaced. She tried to look unaffected, but she could not hold a poker face, for she had never confronted a man who had just killed another with one bare hand.

"Where'd you learn that?" Daniel said when the detective did not speak.

"I heard my uncle describing it while my dad and I visited him in prison when I was a boy. He said he could get anyone 'to talk' that way."

After a pause, Mr. Melbourne said, "Well, it saved everyone's life back there." Then he sighed deeply and added, "You caused enough stress to slow down the man on Olivia just long enough to make your move."

"I couldn't have done it without you," Rico said. "We were a good team, today."

"They're both dead," Detective Phillips said.

"I know," Rico said. "I wouldn't have stopped until they were. Anyone who threatens to kill my family like that will not live to see their day in court. You can quote me on that."

"Amen," Reggie responded.

Detective Brice nodded. After a pause, she glanced around the room, then back at Rico. Jake noticed her eyes were unmistakably admiring Rico as she gazed upon him. "We've got all the information we need. Thank you, Mr. Rodriguez," she said, looking at him, appreciating him a little longer. "Thank you all," she added, glancing at the other people in the room.

"Thank you," Miss Annabelle said, who was standing right by Rico's side.

*

When Olivia and her four shaken but happy children returned from the cafeteria, Rico was explaining how the motivation behind violence and crime, even fanatical religious violence, would vanish once Daniel's Twelve Visions of the future world kicked in. Wealth and prosperity would come too easily, risk free, in too large amounts. Moreover, external authorities would be too uncompetitive and vanish, including religions, as people became self-authorities, easily, definitively.

Suddenly, the pitch of Rico's voice changed. "Come here, my darlings!" Rico called out to his family, seeing them outside the door. "Come and sit here with me." The kids ran in and climbed onto his bed.

Jake noticed the same look of bliss on the children's faces and on Rico's face that Jasmine called "living poetry" the day they met.

"So, Ian, you were about to tell us the final piece to our puzzle picture of the Twelve-Visions World," Rico said, anxious to get off the bleak happenings of the day and onto something exciting and positive. He gestured for Ian to continue.

"You sure this is the best time to talk about that?" Ian asked, concerned about Rico's stamina.

"Yes, to hear the final piece to the puzzle is the best medicine for me and my family right now. I'm very serious," Rico said, knowing he and his family needed to hear *good news* about the antithesis of the violent anticivilization.

"I'd love to dispense that medicine," Ian said. He nodded. He understood. "Well, I do have that final puzzle piece, and I'm ready to release it to the world," Ian continued, leaning forward in his chair, his eyes big with excitement, like a story teller about to tell a great story. "That piece of the puzzle came from my first Overlay Charts..."

As Ian started his amazing story, Rico's eyes shifted to Monica. He looked at her light brown hair so neatly manicured, her beautiful big brown eyes so soft and warm, her full pink lips so gently curving against her innocent face. She looked more and more like a little lady these days, but Rico could still see in her face that two-year-old sitting next to him on the monkey bars at the park, counting how far off the lightning was. He remembered looking at her on those monkey bars and seeing a glow of wonder on her tiny face as he explained to her what thunder and lightning were. He studied her now, concerned how she was handling the day's trauma. She was the very essence of sweetness and innocence...mercilessly thrust into the anticivilization's world of violence and force.

Religions and governments were the cause of violent wars since the beginning of the anticivilization. Today my innocent child, Rico thought while studying his Monica, encountered one of those two pillars that built the anticivilization upon a world of violence and force. Rico studied his precious Monica to see if something had changed, if some of her innocence had been killed on this day. Inside his head, he kept asking, are you okay, sweetie? But Monica did not see her dad studying her, for she was absorbed in Ian's fascinating story about the light he studied in some far-off corner of the Universe. I'll be darned, Rico thought as he watched Monica. As she listened to Ian, Rico saw that same glow of wonder radiating from her innocent face as he did years ago on the monkey bars when he told her about the lightning in some far-off corner of the sky. She'll be okay, Rico said to himself as he silently lamented how the years flew by...thank you, Ian my friend, for pulling my little girl back into the Civilization of the Universe.

CHAPTER
FORTY-NINE

Jake could not stop thinking about how Ian brought Monica back into the Civilization of the Universe. That's a beautiful common denominator among these God-Men, Jake thought. They bring the child of the past, buried deep within people, back into the Civilization of the Universe, which happens over and over again around these superachievers.

As if on cue, that night Jake was reading remarks by a Saul Tannenbaum posted on a TGIF Internet discussion board that stated, "Robert Chapman rescued my child of the past." Then, Jake's eyes widened. Would you look at that, he thought, Saul says here he's convincing hundreds of people to vote for Daniel Ward for President! Jake snatched the phone to call Saul's phone number that appeared on his testimonial.

"Shoot," Jake said while glancing at the clock's late hour. He put the phone back down and sighed. "I'll have to wait till morning." He turned back to his computer. "I'll call Saul Tannenbaum first thing. I've got to talk to him right away."

*

"Hi!" Saul called out. "You like my signs?" Jake and Jasmine had just arrived at Saul's modest home in New Jersey.

540

Saul's front yard had eight or nine signs encouraging people to vote Daniel Ward for President. "I campaign for Daniel Ward. I figure I've gotten him about two hundred votes."

Jake looked curiously at Saul. His face and arms were permanently darkened and dried out from too much sun exposure. The creases on his forehead were deep. When he smiled, many more wrinkles showed on his weather-beaten face. Jake realized he was beginning to stare, so he pointed to the signs and asked, "Do you work for his campaign?"

"No, no, no. I do what I can in my spare time."

Jake squinted at Saul who was standing in his doorway. Jake nodded and thought, *what a force*. He wondered if others who attended TGIF also generated dozens or hundreds of votes. He had lots of questions, but only asked, "Why?"

"Because I want to live forever," Saul answered matter-of-factly, then he gestured for Jake and Jasmine to come inside. "It's still a little messy since I've moved here from Chicago," he said. They sat down in the living room.

Jake could not stop noticing Saul's face. Despite the sun damage, it was pleasant to look at.

"You two drink iced tea?" Saul asked them. Jake and Jasmine nodded.

Saul went into the kitchen to get iced tea; Jake leaned over toward Jasmine's ear and said, "He must be a Church of God-Man member."

Jasmine nodded.

Jake leaned closer and whispered, "Hey, I know Saul's face looks old, but notice his expression...it's just like a kid. Look at him when he comes back in."

"Here we go," Saul said as he walked into the room with the drinks. Jake noticed Jasmine chuckling at Saul.

"I'm sorry," she said, still laughing, "your expressions...has anyone ever said you look very youthful?" Her tone of voice was more emphatic than a mere compliment. She seemed really tickled that this man, whose face looked as though it had been through a lifetime of hard labor, came across so fresh and childlike. The contrast seemed almost beautiful.

"You would've thought I looked like a miserable old man if you saw me a few months ago," Saul said. "Robert Chapman changed all that. To appreciate what that man did for me, I'm going to tell you something I'm very ashamed of, okay?"

Jake and Jasmine nodded. Saul sat down and drew in a deep breath. He exhaled slowly and said, "I tried to commit suicide. ...I was that bad off."

He hesitated. Jasmine immediately said, "Tell us about that, Saul." She knew to point a general, sweeping statement toward specific details. She knew that would help get Saul talking.

Saul took another deep breath and looked down, as though he were too ashamed.

"It's okay," Jasmine urged. "Just take your time."

Saul sighed and nodded. A moment later, he started telling his story:

"I...I remember the pain in my sleep caused more than a nightmare. You know, in nightmares you see bad things but don't feel anything. Well, this time I actually *felt* the pain in my sleep. I *felt* two spikes being twisted into my eye sockets.

"I cried 'help...help me' in my sleep, which actually woke me up. Those words barely came out as a dry whisper even though I was yelling as loud as I could.

"I tried to get up from the bed. My head...oh Christ, my head. I fell back onto the bed with my hands desperately squeezing my head.

"I wondered, What's happening to me! The sound of big machines churning filled my head and wouldn't stop. The noise was so loud I didn't know if it came from outside my house or inside my head. But the loud sound didn't matter because of the pain, the god-awful pain.

"I got up into a kneeling position. The more upright I became, the more my head pounded. But I knew I had to get up and out of there or I would die. I looked over at the end table next to my bed; that became my target to rest my hands on to give my body the support it would need to get up from the bed. And there I saw the reason for my wicked head problem — the empty prescription bottle." Saul stopped talking. He had said too much.

Jake realized Saul had never told anyone the story of his suicide attempt. Reliving the details in his mind was traumatic.

Yet, Jake also recognized Saul's need to continue — to get it out. So, Jake gently said, "Geez Saul, that sounds pretty awful. How'd you get out of there, anyway?"

"I never thought I would. The deafening buzz in my head got even worse when I stood up. I tried to walk but became disoriented and fell hard. I got on all fours and crawled, but then I started to vomit. Once I started heaving, I couldn't stop. There I was, violently heaving over and over, but nothing came up. I had never in my fifty-eight years experienced anything like it.

"I felt a desperate thirst throughout my chest and throat. The dry heaves were merciless, the pounding head unbearable. I physically could not take it. I wanted to die." Saul took a deep breath. Jake nodded.

"After a long time, my heaves subsided from sheer exhaustion. I collapsed on the floor; my head was pounding so hard I wondered if my brain had hemorrhaged.

"I crawled to the head of the stairs, turned around and slid down feet-first on my stomach. When I got to the bottom step, I could see out the panel of windows onto my front yard where two daily newspapers lay in my driveway. That's when I knew I'd been unconscious for two days. Now, I knew the cause of my pain was dehydration. Yeah, I nearly killed myself."

Saul shook his head in disbelief and disgust. "Four days later, I sat in my room, telling myself, 'I survived, but for what?' That question ran through my mind over and over again.

"I nearly died, I sat there thinking. Goddamn it, I nearly killed myself.

"The only semblance of a feeling inside me now was a logical sense of gladness that I survived. Although I prayed for something to end my life, I didn't want to commit suicide for the sake of my children and grandchildren."

He paused. Jake saw the unmistakable love a father holds for his children and knew Saul was reflecting on his children and grandchildren. Jake saw sadness on Saul's face, perhaps sorrow for the way things turned out.

"Two years ago, when I started getting suicidal thoughts, I got rid of my gun. Sometimes I'd wake up with a start in the middle of the night, disoriented, my heart racing, flush with an impulse to take myself out. 'Do it, do it, do it!' the impulse commanded. It seemed to be an invisible force pushing me up from my bed and toward my gun. The force was so strong, I was sure I'd blow my brains out if I'd kept my gun.

"I suffered every day from depression. I saw no way out. I survived my suicide attempt, but for what? Suffering awaited me each day. It was a sad end game. Sitting in my room four days later, I stared out the window. I was lost.

"I finally got up from my chair and went outside to check my mail. 'Ah yes,' I said in a breath of relief. '*Scientific American.*'

"The only relief I got in those days was reading about the natural sciences, particularly astronomy and physics. Caught in a depressed closed world shutting down on me, I felt relief from searching the possibilities of the Universe.

"I read the articles in *Scientific American* for the rest of the day, then went to bed. When I was lying in bed, I reached over to briefly look through the daily paper. And there I saw the headline to an ad: *Discover the Person You Were Meant To Be, and Live The Life You Were Meant to Live.*

"The ad was placed by Robert Chapman's TGIF Employment company. The idea of a change of employment didn't attract me. But the child of the past within me sat up and took notice. That child of the past was drawn to the headline, and nothing could keep me away now; the child within me wanted to discover the person I was meant to be, the life I was meant to live...but never had."

There it is, Jake thought, the trademark of these superachievers. They really do bring back the child of the past.

Saul stopped talking and filled his lungs with air. He looked away. Jake noticed a faraway look come over Saul's eyes, as if he were distancing himself from the present, going back into the past.

"Jake," Saul said. He turned his eyes back toward Jake.

"Yes?"

"I'm going to tell you now about my encounter with Robert Chapman. I want to tell you everything that happened, exactly what he said to me. I want to tell you everything, because he saved my life, you know..."

"I want to hear *everything*," Jake reassured Saul, barely able to contain his excitement to learn everything he could about Bobby — the former student of Miss Annabelle — now all grown up as Robert Chapman the superachiever. Jake could not wait to learn about Robert's power to do great things in this world.

Saul nodded. He closed his eyes for a moment as if saying a little prayer. Then, he launched his story...

*

"I sometimes still get involved in the seemingly most irreversible cases," he said to me as he entered my waiting room. I was stunned to see Robert Chapman himself. He looked directly at me and added, "I can already see you suffer from suicidal depression."

"I don't know why I'm so depressed," I said. I felt ashamed; I could still barely believe the man talking to me was the famous Robert Chapman.

"I do," Robert said. The certainty in his voice surprised me.

"You know why I'm so depressed?"

"Yes. Imagine having lived your whole life never knowing the person you were really meant to be. Let me ask you something: did you, many years ago, wake up feeling sad every morning?"

"Yes! And I never knew why!" ...I was sitting there wondering, *How'd he know that?*

"And now, you wake up indifferent on a good day and depressed on a normal day."

"Yes."

"That depression is because you never discovered the person you were meant to be, and you never found the path you were meant to travel in life. And as you get older, your subconscious is telling you that soon you will have lived and died, never knowing who you really were and never knowing the life *the real you* was meant to live. Your depression is a warning, Saul, a signal that won't stop."

I just sat there, staring at Robert. I was confused, and I wanted to hear more, but I was reluctant to say a word so as not to disrupt anything Robert was going to say next. I let him continue.

"The child of the past within you knows I'm right."

"How d-d-d-do you know?" I stuttered.

"Fifty-eight," Robert said. Then he looked up from the chart. "You're fifty-eight. Many of the good experiences of life are over. There's less and less left to mask the burden of life. The depression is telling you loud and clear: you lived your whole life as the wrong person."

"I just want to end the depression, one way or the other."

"What would you give to discover, right here, today, the person you were meant to be all your life?"

Although Robert's question was only rhetorical, before he could say another word, I said, "Ten thousand dollars, seriously, I'll give it to you, Mr. Chapman." I meant it, and I knew my eyes were intense. I think he wanted to know I was determined. But then, I drifted away from the moment. I started daydreaming about who I really was meant to be.

"Saul, look at me. I want you to be brutally honest with me today, okay?" Robert said. He was looking hard at me and nodding to emphasize his point. "Otherwise, we're wasting time."

"Okay."

"Then, let's get started."

"Why me?"

"What do you mean, *why me?*"

"I mean, you're one of the most powerful men in the world. Why are you personally spending so much time helping me?"

"Because I'm going to save your life."

That night, I had my best night's sleep in over a year.

CHAPTER
FIFTY

"I'm not here to get another job, you know," I told Robert the next day at TGIF.

He just laughed.

"I'm here to discover who I was really meant to be. That's all."

Robert looked me over as if he were sizing me up. "Do you know what every person's ambition in life is?" He finally asked.

I was puzzled. "Isn't it different for everybody?"

"It's the same for everyone," Robert said quickly. "Every person's ambition in life is to make one's living doing what he or she loves most, that which impassions him. Very few people actually do their day's work feeling any passion whatsoever."

"But I'm going to retire soon."

"Yes, you'll retire from the stagnant life of producing values — the same values over and over again. But, once you *create* values that never existed before, you'll never give it up. Nothing is so stimulating as creating. It's exhilarating, it's addicting. It's what man is born to do. In fact, the older you get, the more you'll push to create your next new value, because it might not ever exist if you die first."

"But...but what about..."

"What? Time to smell the roses? You tell me, Saul, how

good is smelling the roses? What do you do in your evenings and on your weekends?" Robert looked at the weekly schedule I previously filled out during my initial visit. "I don't see much here."

I felt my forehead tighten. My eyebrows rose in painful wonderment. Indeed, I certainly had run out of things that interested me, and I mostly suffered from depression in the evenings and on my days off.

Robert lectured me: "Man was not meant to sit around and smell the roses. That's a flat out myth, pal. We're the only living creatures who can *create*. Man was meant to *create values*. Along that path of creating values upon which we were meant to travel, we do like to take time to stop and smell the pretty roses along the way. We do that through spending valuable time with our precious loved ones. But we don't just stop and stay there smelling the roses. We soon resume our journey along that exhilarating path of creating values. Now, that is how man was supposed to live."

For the first time since I was a young man, I felt something I had long since forgotten about: genuine *excitement*. I said nothing, just letting myself feel that long-lost feeling that felt so good. The new sensation surprised, even shocked me, sort of like a teenager's first, unexpected orgasm. I knew this new feeling was a mystery to explore.

"You mean...you think I'll be working somewhere else?" I finally said. After over thirty years in the Post Office, I couldn't even imagine working somewhere else. I was aware of my cheeks tingling and my lips...they wanted to smile, which confused me. I hated going to work all my life, and I couldn't understand why this question made me feel...*euphoric*. The next moment, however, a shot of fear tore through my body. With no forethought, in a gust of panic, I involuntarily whispered, "Why do I feel this way?" I desperately searched Robert's eyes for an answer.

He said, "You're excited for who you'll meet — the child of the past. At the same time, you're scared about the child seeing you now as a man wasting away. Saul, you're afraid of facing the fact that you wasted a huge chunk of your life." Robert remained brutally honest, cutting no corners.

"Yes...yes," I said, still whispering, "I'm excited; I am *really excited*...and I'm scared; I'm *really scared*."

"It's okay," Robert said. He put his hand on my frail under-exercised shoulder. "Your mind suffers from atrophy; your soul suffers from contradiction. But when we get your mind and soul functioning the way they were meant to, you'll get strong, Saul, very strong. You'll see."

I took a deep breath and nodded; my body shivered with excitement and fear.

"We'll continue this tomorrow, Saul, you and I. We're going to be completely honest with each other, right?"

I nodded.

"We're going to find that child of the past in you Saul."

I nodded again.

"I want you to leave here today with one thought. Let me ask you, how long did you work at your career in the Post Office?"

"Thirty-eight years. I'll retire in four years."

"Once you live in harmony with the way your consciousness is supposed to function by *creating* values, you'll create for another forty years, easily. And that's not factoring in the rapidly advancing biomedical field. It's very likely you'll soon be able to live your life over again — the right way — but we won't get into that. I just want you to know you have a lot to look forward to."

I suddenly remembered I had tried to kill myself less than two weeks before. My face started twitching. I heard myself say inside my head, *I would've killed the innocent child of the past had I killed myself.* Tears filled my eyes. I asked Robert, "Is there really a child of the past still within me?"

He nodded. "The child is buried inside you," he said, "inside everyone except for those who purposely took another life. Those humanoids killed the child within themselves. But not you, Saul. The child of the past who wants to live forever is in you."

His words gripped my heart. My lips started trembling. I took a deep breath and nodded. For the first time as an adult, I started to cry, just for an instant.

*

"I...I feel good," I whispered in disbelief when I awoke the next morning. I noticed another surprise as I got dressed — I was *whistling*. I stopped and smiled. "When was the last time I whistled a tune?" I asked my reflection in the mirror. "I can't remember when."

I was still opening the door to Robert's office when Robert said, "Ready?" I nodded.

We sat in large, soft leather chairs in Robert's office. Robert gave me a writing pad of paper, a pen, and a printed sheet that looked like a weekly planner, not yet filled in.

"Okay, Saul. Write down on this piece of paper what you did during your evenings and weekends over the past week. I want you to go in more specific detail than the sheet you filled out initially."

When I completed filling in my actions done in the evenings and weekends, Robert looked it over.

"Hmmm," was all he said. "Now, Saul, take a few minutes and think back over the past two months. I want you to write down as many activities that had nothing to do with work that you engaged in, as many as you can remember. If you watched television, write down the shows you watched. If you read any books or magazines or articles in newspapers, write down what they were about. If you have a hobby, write about it. ...Okay, Saul, get to work. I'll come back in twenty minutes."

When Robert returned, I had written quite a bit of information down. Robert read through it all.

"Good job. Do you shoot pool?"

"Huh? Oh, umm, sure."

"I'll rack 'em, you break 'em," Robert said. He motioned for me to follow him.

Robert pulled back two cherry-wood French doors. When I walked into the large retreat, I suddenly relaxed. I looked around at the bar, the leather couches, the books, the artificial putting green, and the plush cherry-wood pool table.

"What would you like to drink?" Robert asked me.

"I don't know...I guess iced tea. Or, is a beer okay?"

"Sure, help yourself to the fridge."

I got a Heinekin while Robert racked the balls. We pulled

out our pool sticks.

"You mind if I smoke?" I asked. "I always smoke when I shoot pool."

"Ashtray's on the bar."

A half hour passed; we were into our third game of eight-ball. I opened my second beer.

"What kind of things did you like doing as a child?" Robert asked casually.

"Oh, let me see if I can remember. Umm, I liked sports. I was on little league baseball teams and the high school team."

"Did you like school?"

"Umm, I think I was about normal. I liked it, but I really looked forward to the holidays."

"Were there any subjects you really liked over the others?"

"No."

"Any subjects in which you did exceptionally well?"

"Wait a minute...I actually did enter the science fair projects every year. And in our school that wasn't mandatory. Come to think of it, science was always my best subject in school. I always read and did my science assignments."

"How about extracurricular reading? Did you ever read anything beyond your school assignments?"

I thought for a moment. Robert watched my expression. My face must've suddenly filled up with recognition. I gasped; Robert raised his eyebrows.

"I did! I was reading something...I think it was a magazine. I remember because I entered a contest through it."

"Tell me about this contest you entered."

"I'd forgotten all about it. We had to make a toy airplane that could fly. The plane that flew the farthest won the prize. Most of the kids built some sort of paper plane or Styrofoam plane."

"What was yours like?"

"Oh, I remember now: I was so afraid I was cheating! I thought long and hard how to build a plane that could outfly other homemade planes. After about two weeks of constantly thinking about it, I lay in bed one night when it suddenly hit me: the key to the longest flight was *not* in the plane, but in *the launch*. These were not real planes with engines. These were toy planes with no engines, which made them *gliders*. The glider launched at a higher altitude would glide longer. So, I went to work putting together a ten-foot pole with a claw-like grip on one end to hold my plane and a trigger release on the other end to release my plane. I made my glider out of Styrofoam and my wings out of very thin particle board. I used a small spring to close the pincers tight enough to hold my plane on the end of my ten-foot pole. I ran a wire down along the pole and made a loop for my finger. One tug and the pincers pulled apart, releasing my glider. The contest was in the middle of a big field. You should have seen the look on my competitors' faces when I heaved my pole into the air, yelled like a shot-putter, and released my glider when my arms and pole went straight up over my head. Ah, I remember now, my glider soared beautifully, way past all the other markers. I remember feeling really proud and nervous at the same time, for one kid kept yelling, 'He can't do that — that's cheating!' The judges questioned my dad if he bought my 'plane set' from a store. But when the judges examined my plane and pole, they could see it was homemade."

"Did you win?"

"Nope. I got second place. The winner was a genius — or his dad was. They built a tiny propeller engine and put it on a homemade plastic frame. Their plane flew three times as far as mine before crashing into a tree. Forty-something years ago, something like that was unheard of."

"How did you do in your science fair projects?"

"I did really well," I said. My childhood was all coming back. "I placed in the top ten in state three out of four years, which is quite an accomplishment in Illinois."

"In your evenings-and-weekends chart, the only extracurricular reading I see now is *Scientific American*."

"I love that magazine."

"Saul, did you ever, in high school or afterwards, want to be a scientist?"

I know Robert noticed my face light up. I couldn't conceal my smile.

"I guess I never even considered it because I knew I couldn't go to college. You have to go to college to be a scientist. No

552

company would hire a high-school graduate."

"Saul, forget about all that for now. Forget about your education. Forget about your age. Forget about how it would be impossible and impractical for you to be a scientist. Forget all about that. I want you to wonder what it would be like to be a scientist."

"What kind? ...I really love astronomy and physics."

"Okay then. We're done here today. Go home and wonder what it'd be like to be a scientist who studies the far reaches of the Universe."

"Like the great Ian Scott?" I said. I could feel my face beaming like a boy with a big dream.

Robert smiled. "Like the great Ian Scott."

CHAPTER
FIFTY-ONE

I cracked open the door to Robert's office and said, "It's four o'clock."

Robert had a knowing smile. "I see a completely different look on your face," he said. "What's new?"

"My life," I said. I walked in and shut the door behind me. "I don't know if I'll ever be a scientist, but I couldn't log off the Internet last night. I read everything Dr. Scott has published. I'm...I'm so into it."

"How did you feel when you woke up this morning? During my years of teaching, I've found that a person's waking moments in the morning offer a good emotional sense of his happiness."

"But I never woke up this morning; I didn't get off the Internet until I had to go to work!"

Robert smiled. "Bingo," he said, "you're discovering something I call *downstream focus*. Saul, my friend, I think we're on to something. Let me ask you, have you ever heard of the Church of God-Man?"

"I've heard about it, but I'm not the religious type."

"It's not religious. It's a church based on Dr. Scott's theories and proofs of the Universe. I want you to attend one. You'll hear a lot of talk about living forever."

"Living forever...I read a lot about that last night. I've never even thought about it before."

"That's because you've never discovered the life you were meant to live."

I stood still, and I realized I hadn't felt depression for three days, not since coming to TGIF.

"At the Church of God-Man, you'll meet many, many people pursuing their Friday-Night essences. You'll possibly even discover an opportunity, especially through the Church's business networking. Normally at this point, I'd find a job for you that matches up with your Friday-Night essence. But in your case, I'll hold off on that and suggest you go to the Church."

I sat down and leaned back in the big, leather chair, but my moment of rest would be short lived. "I've never been a socializer, never," I said. "But you know what? I can't wait to go."

"I'll see you back here in three weeks."

*

As Jake listened to Saul's story, the college student was overcome with the power of Robert Chapman to single-handedly take a life that had plummeted into a living hell and in three days turn that life right-side up and send it soaring. "Saul, excuse me," Jake said. What he had just heard made him interrupt the story being told. Jake realized that Robert had sent Saul to Jeremiah's Church of God-Man and that Ian Scott motivated Saul and that Saul was convincing people to vote for Daniel! Jake could see the synergy occurring from these former classmates working together.

After a rewarding moment knowing he had brought the former classmates together again, Jake said, "I'm sorry, Saul, please continue. Your story is fascinating to me."

Saul continued telling his story about his time together with Robert Chapman. "Let me fast-forward three weeks to my next visit with Robert..."

*

"I'm exhausted in a good way," I reported in the doorway,

even before I was asked. "This must be how it feels to win a marathon."

"Oh?"

I walked in and sat down on the leather chair. I took a deep breath and said, "I'm leaving the Post Office after thirty-eight years. You were right. I met someone at the Church who offered me a research position in Cosminergy Co."

"I know about Cosminergy," Robert said. "That's the company devoted to capturing energy sources from the cosmos — cosmic energy. They're the leader at converting commercial products to solar energy."

"Yes, but I learned the company puts a large percentage of its profits into research to uncover new sources of energy in the cosmos. I'll work in that research division. They said someone with my energy-level will be a good asset. I'll be taking a pay cut, but I've never been so excited in my life."

"Your energy-level, Saul. That's what this company noticed in you. Where did it come from? When you came here a month ago, you were one of the most lifeless persons I've ever met."

I smiled and said, "You know where my energy comes from, don't you boss?" I felt triumphant. "It's my passion. Science, especially understanding the cosmos, that's my passion."

"We're done here, my friend," Robert said. He looked triumphant, too. "I see a man streaming along with downstream focus. In other words, to focus on your livelihood is no longer an upstream struggle. Instead, it's your passion. You're now living your life's ambition, Saul. Oh, and do you remember telling me you couldn't be a scientist without going to college?"

"Oh, yeah. That's okay; I love research. It's the closest thing to being a bona fide scientist."

"Well, with downstream focus, you'll become a scientist all right," Robert said. "Did you know the highest paid author who ever lived, after adjusting for inflation, never completed high school?"

"No kidding?"

"When he was a young man, he was an illiterate dockhand on the docks of Oakland."

"You're kidding!"

"Back in the late 1800s, an illiterate dockhand had *no shot* of getting a piece of literature published — none. But once this dockhand discovered his passion — writing — he educated himself at a blistering pace and became the most famous writer of his era. His name was Jack London."

I was stunned. Furious thoughts and dreams rushed through my awakened mind.

*

"You've discovered the person you were meant to be," Robert said. It was our final follow-up meeting seven weeks later at TGIF. "You've discovered your passion, your deepest motivational root, your Friday-Night essence. You've reunited with the child of the past. You're living your life's ambition, travelling the path you were meant to travel, living the life you were meant to live. You're making your living pursuing your passion. Even though you got a pay cut, I predict you'll make many, many times what you could ever make at the Post Office."

"Why?" I asked. I sensed why, but I could not articulate why.

"Because before, you were a value *producer*. Now, with your passion and energy, rushing along with downstream focus, you'll eventually become a value *creator*. Your value creation will continue to bring more and more unprecedented values to the world, and people will want those unique values. You'll eventually become rich. Every value *creator* making a living on his vector of creation eventually becomes rich."

"I haven't felt depression once in ten weeks," I suddenly said. I'd been storing up courage to tell him something, and now I blurted it out before I could back out, "I...I never told you, Robert, but I was more than suicidal, I actually nearly killed myself a few days before coming to see you." I wanted to say a lot more, but I couldn't speak. I opened my mouth, but nothing came out.

"You never needed to tell me. In fact, I was pretty sure you had."

A wave of relief rushed through me. I looked down and said, "For the first time in my life, I'm..." my voice cracked, and I cleared my throat. "I'm *happy*." I paused. Robert must have

557

known I was not finished and stayed quiet. After a moment, I looked up and continued, "When I thought I was happy at times over my life, I really wasn't."

"How do you know?"

"Because I never before wanted to live forever. I'd feel times of great joy before, but not the deep underlying happiness I do now."

"You're cured, Saul. You're cured of the debilitations of the anticivilization."

"You saved my life, Robert Chapman." Suddenly I looked away. "Someday, I'll be able to do something magnificent for you. I promise you."

"Someday, create and place a valuable puzzle piece into a superpuzzle that'll benefit the human race, including me. That's what I ask of you."

I nodded and sadly shook Robert's hand. I knew this was the last time I'd have the privilege to speak to this incredibly busy superachiever. I held onto Robert's hand just a little longer to say, "You did so much more than just save my life. You changed my life into something *so wonderful*...so *exciting*. You not only lifted me from my nightmare, but you placed me in this wonderful dream come true." I let go of his hand and shook my head. I was already missing Robert. "All I can say now is...I love you for what you've done for me and for others. *Thank you*." I suddenly reached out and hugged my teacher. I had never hugged a man before in my adult life. When I let go, I couldn't say anything more. I just nodded at my teacher and turned to go.

"Saul," Robert said. I turned back around. "We'll run into each other again someday...I know we will."

I was able to smile this time, and I nodded.

After I left Robert's office, outside the door, I had to wipe away the water in my eyes with my fingers. Robert's secretary just smiled. She'd seen this happen many times before.

*

I arrived home and climbed the stairs to my bedroom. My head hung low from my shoulders. I just hope, I thought, Robert

558

knows what a difference he's made within me. He's making this magnificent difference in thousands of people like me. I stopped climbing the stairs and shook my head. Damn, what a hero.

I reached the top of the stairs and entered my bedroom. I saw my bed upon which I had tried to kill myself, and I realized that every time I looked at that bed, I was filled with disgust.

I had discovered downstream focus, had begun *creating*, and was now living my life's ambition and feeling the exhilaration of life every day. I attended the Church of God-Man weekly and now felt the drive for biological immortality. I was filled every day with euphoria. Yet, every night and morning the sight of my bed where I nearly ended my life, oblivious to the preciousness of life, filled me with disgust. On an impulse, I leaned over and tore the bedspread and sheets off the bed.

"I never want to feel this disgust again!" I said.

An overpowering rage rising within my soul like a great spirit, took control of my body and made me suddenly wrestle the queen mattress up off the bed. With my arms spread wide apart, I hoisted the mattress off the bed and lifted it over my head, yelling like a weight lifter. Anger fed me strength; I walked across the room with the mattress above my head. I growled with every step. When I reached the french doors that open onto my patio, I kicked them open. I tried to walk out onto the patio, but the queen mattress hit the sides and top of the doorway and stopped me. I lowered the mattress onto my head, leaned my shoulders forward, knitted my brow, and grunted loudly as I twisted and forced my way through the doors. I tore through the opening, then stood on the patio. I planted my feet and lifted the mattress again, straight up above my head, until both arms were straight up.

"I'll never look at this reminder again!" I shouted, oblivious to the neighbor's children who, I realized later, had stopped playing in their backyard to watch me. I think they were petrified by my sight. With a ferocious yell, I heaved the mattress into the air, over the patio. The power behind my demon-releasing toss kept the mattress gliding through the air longer than what seemed natural. It seemed to soar in slow motion through the air. Finally, the mattress landed halfway to the back wall in my backyard, onto the cement patio, sending a cloud of dust into the air. I clinched my fists and raised my arms straight up over my head; I tilted my head back, squinting into the sun above. Oblivious to the world around me, with a force greater than anything the neighbor's kids had probably ever heard, I let out a majestic command: "I want to LIVE! I want to LIVE FOREVER!"

Then, I noticed the children. They smiled at me. Although they were a bit startled, their fear seemed to melt away, for I was now one of them.

*

"Wow," Jake said.

Saul returned from his past and perceived Jake and Jasmine sitting across from him.

Jake looked at Jasmine and shook his head. The life-lifting power, he thought, of Robert Chapman just takes my breath away; he turned a depressed man who tried to kill himself into a man so exhilarated by life that younger men would envy him!

"That's an amazing story, Saul," Jake said. "We're going to publish it in the Patterson Papers, if that's okay with you?"

"Yes, it's okay. I want everyone to know what Robert and TGIF can do for them."

"Is there anything you want to add to your story?" Jasmine asked.

Saul thought for a moment and then said, "Let them know that if they don't have the exhilaration for life already inside them, they must go to TGIF. Everyone who does will discover his Friday-Night essence just as I have. Then, they'll discover permanent excitement. They'll actually want to live forever. They'll thank themselves for the rest of their lives that they went to TGIF. ...Oh, and tell your readers that if Daniel Ward is elected, the workplace will open up and *everyone* will discover his Friday-Night essence. They'll thank themselves that they voted Daniel Ward for President!"

Jake nodded as Jasmine jotted down those final notes. Then, Jake excused himself to use the rest room. When he returned, as he and Jasmine were about to leave, Saul asked them, "Are

560

you going to see Robert Chapman?"

"Yes, within the month," Jasmine answered. She and Jake would not dare miss a monthly meeting of The Group.

"When you do...could you give him a message?"

"Sure."

"Tell him, I'll make him proud of me someday."

*

On the drive home, Jake could not stop thinking of the life-changing power of this one former student of Miss Annabelle. The twelve of them together, Jake pondered, could change the lives of everyone the way Robert changed the life of Saul.

"Man, that was moving," Jake said after a long stretch of silence during the drive back to the city. He remembered that Robert Chapman, as an eight-year-old, wanted to find jobs for his parents in which they could be happy. He certainly provides that beautiful value to people now, Jake thought.

"I have to tell you something very touching," Jasmine said. Jake, who was driving, glanced at her curiously as she said, "Honey, when you excused yourself to the rest room, I asked Saul where his wife was. ...You know what he told me?"

"What?"

"He told me that when depression overtook him, he loved his wife too much for her to live the rest of her life with an unhappy husband. He knew his unhappiness would be hard on her and drag her down. He loved her and wanted her to be happy. So, he asked her to socialize without him and meet another man. He told her that once he felt she'd be taken care of and was in good hands, he'd give her a divorce to let her go to her new man, her new life. ...Oh honey, isn't that the saddest thing you ever heard?"

Jake glanced at Jasmine. Her eyes were teary. "Ahhh...that's really sad," Jake said, thinking of Saul back there in his house, all alone. "What happened?"

"Saul pushed her away...because he loved her too much to pull her down with him. She's remarried now to one of Saul's former co-workers."

Jake felt a knot forming in his throat. "Did you ask him if

561

he wants her back now?"

"Yes," Jasmine said. She sighed heavily. "He said, 'I want her back more than anything in the world.' Then he got very sad and said, 'But I have to let her go, I can't play with her life like she's a yo yo. ...It's just that I had no idea this life-lifting miracle would happen to me.' He dropped his head, and I thought he was going to cry."

"What did you say?"

"I told him to let *her* decide."

Jake nodded at Jasmine's wisdom.

CHAPTER
FIFTY-TWO

While thinking over his interview with Saul, Jake realized all Saul's problems had been solved at TGIF except one: the tragedy of losing his wife. Of course, Jake knew that the expert with that kind of problem was Natasha Stokov Kemp.

"Let's do research on Natasha and her work," Jake suggested in a staff meeting at Patterson Press.

"You know," said Al, "I can remember her in the third grade telling us how she saved her mom and dad's marriage. She sure can save marriages today, from what I've heard."

"Besides," said Jasmine, "we need to report on the work Natasha's doing for the campaign. God, I can't believe the election's less than a month away! We need to snap her puzzle piece into the puzzle."

Al quickly agreed and sent his two young reporters to Natasha Workshops Headquarters in Detroit.

When Jake and Jasmine arrived at Natasha Workshops Headquarters, they were pleasantly surprised to find Robert Chapman there, too, meeting with Natasha in her office. They were sitting on the couch.

"Hi!" Jasmine and Jake said together when they saw Natasha and Robert.

Superpuzzle

Natasha shook her head while a beautiful smile grew across her face. "You two look so wonderful together! You're the epitome of...happiness, productivity, energy, looks, and love all rolled together."

"Thank you," Jasmine said. She was a little embarrassed.

As Jasmine thanked Natasha for her compliment, Jake noticed how Natasha and Robert looked wonderful together. Jake had never seen them together outside of the reunion and the meetings of The Group at Rico's mansion.

"Please, sit down," Natasha said, gesturing to the chairs facing the couch.

"How'd that meeting with Saul go?" Robert asked Jake after he and Jasmine were seated.

"Saul's incredible," Jake said. He noticed that Robert, in his mid-thirties, had that same childlike expression on his face as his student had.

"He wanted us to tell you that he's going to someday make you proud of him," Jasmine said.

"He already has," Robert replied, remembering his energized Saul. After a moment revisiting the past, Robert's expression changed, and he stood up and walked around Natasha to the side of the couch, then sat on its arm, right next to Natasha. He looked at Jake and said, "TGIF and Natasha's Workshops are joining forces."

"That's right," Natasha added, looking enthusiastically at Jake and Jasmine. "Robert and I realized there's such an affinity between the two. We're really teaching our customers the same thing — how to find their deepest motivational root in life. That's the cause. The effect they're looking for when they come to me is romantic success. The effect they're looking for when they come to Robert is career success. But the cause underneath both our businesses is the same."

"So, we can bring in more people, and offer them more comprehensive results by combining our businesses."

Jasmine was jotting down notes. Jake was smiling and nodding. What a great idea, he thought, now people can cover business and love all in one place. Geez, this is exactly what Saul needs! Jake's thoughts were broken by Natasha's attractive signature voice.

"How about we seal it with a kiss?" she said. She giggled playfully and looked up at Robert. He leaned over and the two beautiful soul mates innocently, romantically kissed. Although the kiss was quick and playful, Jake was stunned. Jasmine looked up and gasped as would a child. The history...the power, the magnificence of these people, Jake thought, and they're falling in love. How wonderful, how natural...why not until now? And then Jake was hit with a jolt of pride knowing that *he* had brought them together, again.

*

"Hi Stacey," Jake said over the phone to Al Patterson's secretary, "is Al in?"

"Hi, Mr. Catchings; he's here, just a moment, please."

A few seconds later, Al answered, "Jake, how are you and Jasmine doing there? Do you have a good story about Natasha for us yet?"

"We have a *great* story," Jake said. He noticed he always felt *so good* whenever he talked to Al.

"Al?" It was Jasmine on the other phone.

"Oh hi, dear," Al said in a paternal tone. During the eight months since the reunion, Al had learned about the injustices the media inflicted on her father when she was a girl, not only destroying her father's lifetime investment in building a shopping center, but forever destroying his self-esteem. Al had learned that he, himself, had become Jasmine's hero and his media group was the one place she had wanted to work for. She wanted to support value creators and nullify other media and their journalists who wanted to destroy value creators. He felt like a second father to Jasmine.

"Robert's in Detroit, too." Jasmine said.

"I've heard that TGIF and Natasha Workshops are close to merging, which I think is a perfect match."

Jasmine giggled, "That's not all that's merging."

"What do you mean?"

Jasmine felt a little nervous to tell Al, although the budding romance between his former classmates was not supposed to be a secret. She said, "When you think of Robert and Natasha,

565

what other perfect match do you see?"

Silence followed. Then Jake and Jasmine could hear Al's lips smack and knew that sound was him suddenly smiling.

"Robert and Natasha...you mean? They're *personally* together?"

"Yes!" Jasmine squealed.

"That's just so unbelievably wonderful!" Al boomed over the phone. "Oh, that's...that's so wonderful...Robert and Nat. After all these years, Robert and Nat! ...How do you like that! Tell me, how do they seem together?"

"We only saw them briefly," Jake answered, "but they looked like they always belonged together. And...they really look *happy*. I mean, like they were teenagers together. ...Was Natasha married before?" Jake asked, not recalling if the PI report a few months before addressed her marital status.

"She was," Al answered. "She told me at Rico's place that the lessons she learned from her first marriage and its failure gave her the deep wisdom and experience to launch her talk shows and workshops. I think she just never found anyone at her level before. I think the same is true for Robert. Those two are on the same wavelength; they'll be passionately happy together. Robert and Nat!"

"Natasha is going to spend the weekend at one of her retreats," said Jasmine, "and she's going to deliver parts of the seminar herself. She said she likes to drop in on her retreats from time to time, and she asked us if we wanted to go."

"By all means," Al said. "Natasha's national radio show is the only media out there besides us that's pushing for Daniel. And her retreats are a lot like TGIF, pushing people into the Civilization of the Universe. Go ahead, you two, and get us a *great* article, okay?"

"We'll get you nothing less!" Jake answered. When he hung up the phone, he wondered, somewhat sadly, about his boss who had a reputation as a quiet playboy, privately going from beautiful girlfriend to beautiful girlfriend. Jake was surprised he felt a little sad for Al and did not know why, exactly.

CHAPTER
FIFTY-THREE

The retreat in the plush woods in Southern Michigan during summer was beautiful to all five senses. Upon arriving and checking into one of the cabins, Jake and Jasmine ventured onto one of the trails through the woods mapped out on a pamphlet. Two hours later, as they walked along the trail back to camp, a lone hiker, a middle-aged man, caught up to them.

"Hello," he panted, catching his breath.

"Hi," Jake and Jasmine said. "Are you here for the Natasha Workshop weekend?" Jasmine asked him.

"Yes, you too?"

Jake and Jasmine nodded.

"I'd never take you two for having problems. I've watched you for about ten minutes before I could catch up to you. You two are in love!" He was laughing and very puzzled.

Jake and Jasmine laughed. "I'm Jake Catchings and this is my girlfriend and reporting partner Jasmine Kahil. We're reporters from Patterson Press. We're doing a story on Natasha Stokov Kemp and her Natasha Workshops."

"I can't believe it! I've read many of your wonderful articles. I get so much from them; I look for them. I'm very honored to meet you," the man said, offering his hand to Jake. "My name's Mike, by the way." Jake and then Jasmine reached out and shook Mike's hand.

"You put so much value into your articles. I really learn from them. They're actually addicting. I read your paper and look for your articles every day."

"Well, thank you, Mike," Jake said. I bet, Jake thought, Mike just touched on why Jasmine and I get printed through the wire in so many papers beyond Patterson: our articles are addicting! What a great feeling to know that!

"We have another half mile to walk," Jasmine said. "Would you mind telling us your own personal story, Mike? We like to get personal accounts when we can. They always add to the article."

Jasmine had just asked Mike to tell her his personal tragedy. But the sincerity in her voice made Mike's inhibitions seem to vanish. Still, he was a little self-conscious.

"Are you sure?" Mike said shyly. "It's just about my separation with my wife after nineteen years of marriage."

"Just?" Jasmine said gently. "Yes, we're sure, as long as *you're* comfortable."

"Well, I guess I'll begin with why I'm here and she's not. A couple of weeks ago, I went to a park she and I used to jog through. I sat on one of the picnic tables and wrote her a letter. As I sat there, I was thinking that the only thing that had changed since our wonderful times there was that the leaves on the treetops all looked blurry to my older eyes. It was two weeks after our separation when I sent her the letter.

"We decided to get divorced although neither one of us really *wanted to*. But we knew our excitement for each other, around each other, was long gone. And we decided to take this step now while we were both still young enough to experience another exciting long-term romantic-love relationship once again. My best friend told me that the separation will be very hard for awhile. He'd gone through it himself. But then it'll get better, he told me. When it does, then I'll start looking forward to meeting someone with whom I'll feel alive again. That's what he told me. He also said that I'll hope the same for my ex-wife, too.

"Last week, I got a letter back from my wife. She wrote, 'I go to that park, too. I was happy to realize that those special

568

years we had are still special to you. Even though we decided to give each other a fresh start, a part of me will always belong to you.'

"I really hurt inside when I read her letter. I hurt because we once had true, exciting love. And it was hopeless to try to get it back. We tried everything. In the end, we made the tactical decision to split.

"I've always been a man who could not just throw values away. So, I decided to attend one of the famous Natasha Workshops. On the registration form under the question 'Why are you here?' I wrote, 'I came alone since my wife and I have already separated. I just hope to get some answers as to what happened to a love that was once so strong, perhaps so my next relationship, if I find love again, will not fade and flicker out.'

"I got here this afternoon, signed in and was directed to my cabin in the woods. I felt a little strange being here alone. But, I don't care anymore. I just want to figure out how something so good could just fade away.

"I walked through the woods until I saw you two. You know, I was behind you on this trail for about ten minutes. You remind me of my wife and me fifteen years ago. As I watched you and remembered my wife and me of yesteryear, I thought of how we would have once loved walking through these woods together.

"The odd thing is," he mumbled, "why don't I feel for her *now*? She's still an attractive woman. Yeah, she's still even sexy. So, what's wrong with me?"

The three of them walked up the stairs into the dinner hall. They looked around at all the couples inside this rustic lodge that reminded Jake of a ski lodge. Their lives, Jake thought, are going to change this weekend.

After dinner, the answer to Mike's question started to unfold when Natasha surprised everyone as the leadoff speaker. Jake and Jasmine noticed a special glow about her as she stood at the podium. She was radiant, a woman in love.

"Look around you," the attractive brown-eyed blonde announced to the applauding couples. "Who do we have here?"

Jake was surprised to see most of the couples were middle-aged folks, such as Mike.

"The couples who come here are not young couples not getting along, looking for a boost. The couples who come here usually are those such as yourselves, who once long ago fell dearly, deeply in love. The years stole away the feelings of love, and now you're left feeling empty with each other. When you're around your spouse, you sometimes say to yourself, 'She or he doesn't make me happy anymore.' You have all thought that, right?"

Jake looked around and saw people sadly nodding.

"I want each and every one of you to know: your inability to feel happiness with your spouse *is not his or her doing*. But, that inability to feel happiness with your spouse *is* why you can't feel romantic love for your spouse. Now, let's dig into happiness and love and how to get them and sustain them. Let's start with the nature of human consciousness:

"The nature of human consciousness is to create. How do I know that? Over the years, I've seen that every person who *creates* new values lives with deep and permanent happiness. People who *produce* values, the majority of people produce values, grow weary and, eventually, do not feel that deep, permanent happiness. The reason for that is: producing values leads to stagnation — doing the same routine over and over again as most people do. Our minds are the only minds on Earth that can create values that never existed before. That's what our minds are made for. That's what we were born for.

"Now, I'll say something I don't talk about on the air during my radio talk show. Whereas the nature of all human beings is the same — value creation — the avenues to value creation for a woman and a man are somewhat different. To understand this difference, we must start with the biological differences between a man and a woman inside the private world of an intimate relationship.

"During lovemaking, the man is physically larger and stronger; he physically dominates the woman; he takes her and penetrates her. She is physically smaller and weaker; she physically and psychologically surrenders to her man; she gives herself to him and allows him to penetrate her. That is the biological nature of man and woman involved in an intimate relationship.

"The fact that a woman gives herself to her man makes it important that he is worthy of her, someone she can look up to and admire. Of all the men who would have her, she has chosen this particular man to surrender to. He is a reflection, to her, of her own value, for he is the man she allows to take her. For a woman to be happy in a relationship, she must be able to admire and look up to her man. She must be proud of him.

"A man in an intimate relationship, on the other hand, is not physically taken and dominated by his woman. He does not physically give himself to her. He does not physically and psychologically surrender to her. Therefore, she is not a direct reflection, to him, of his value...his work is that reflection, to him, of his value. Whereas he does not need to look up to her to be happy, a man must be able to look up to his career and be proud of his work to be happy.

"Now, looking at what I just said another way, we can say that a woman, no matter how creative in her career, will not be happy if she is with a man she does not respect, admire, look up to, and is proud of. Whereas a woman can go as far in any career as any man, her romantic partner should be more accomplished than herself. And a man, no matter how wonderful his wife may be, will not be happy if he does not respect, look up to, and feel proud of his work.

"Now, by understanding all this, which comes from our biological natures, and by understanding that the psychological nature of *all* human beings is creating values, we can approach creating values differently whether one is a woman or a man. Since a woman gains happiness when she can look up to and admire and be proud of her man, then supporting or contributing emotionally and tangibly to *his* value creation is a genuine source of happiness for her. His smooth-flowing value creation because of her support becomes her value creation, too. Therefore, a woman has two avenues to value creation: pursuing her own career and/or contributing to or supporting her husband's career, which could validly include being an effective housewife and interactive mother who makes homelife smooth and rewarding for her husband. Both are sources of value creation, thus happiness for her.

"The man, on the other hand, has one avenue to value creation: his career. Biologically speaking, he does not *gain* his happiness by looking up to his woman, per se. He gains his happiness through his drive to create values for the world, whereas he *experiences* his happiness through his woman and children. With his one focussed drive in contrast to her dual drives, he is more free to drive and become more accomplished in his work, which brings her happiness, too.

"The point I'm making is that everyone gains happiness by creating values. A woman goes about that in two possible ways, sometimes working both ways at once: through her own value creation and/or through a supportive role to her husband, freeing him to drive and, perhaps, even contributing to his drive. A man goes about creating values in one way: through his single drive on his work.

"Now, those are the only routes to happiness for women and men. There are no other routes to happiness. Anything else that may seem like a route to happiness, say something like love, is *not* a *source* of happiness; it is not a *cause*; it is an *effect*. First, you must have the deep, permanent happiness through the avenues to value creation, then one can feel love with one's spouse and with one's family.

"That deep, permanent happiness constantly emits a feel-good sensation throughout one's body and soul. That feel-good sensation stimulates lots of energy. And that abundance of energy overflows into our love lives and family lives.

"On the other hand, without that deep, permanent happiness, we have no feel-good sensation inside. We have little emotional energy...not enough for romantic love and joyous family love.

"That brings me full circle as to why you're here today — because you have no romantic love...you have nothing left. And that brings us to how you'll fix that — by achieving abundant happiness through value creation.

"Now, I have wonderful news for you. To empower the solution of achieving abundant happiness, I'm officially announcing to you — the first to know — that Natasha's Workshops are merging with TGIF Workshops. Robert Chapman's company is the expert at sending you onto your avenue of happiness, which is needed to bring back the special falling-in-love years to your life.

"Tomorrow morning, you'll begin the TGIF process to discover your Friday-Night essences, your deepest motivational roots, which you read about in the pamphlet handed to you when you checked in. By tomorrow night, each of you will have a handle on your Friday-Night essence.

"Sunday will be spent on aggressive exercises to battle off the programmed responses within us regarding love, particularly the subliminal scolding we've received most of our adult lives in the anticivilization for being happy and in love. When you leave here, you'll be walking along your path to happiness, which will reignite the flame of romantic love that burned out long ago."

As the couples clapped, Jake looked around and saw *hope* on their faces — hope for a better life.

*

The next day the crowd was surprised when Robert Chapman himself headed up the first-ever workshop exercises for the premier weekend of the merger. Jake sat in awe of the power in this man. As with Saul Tannenbaum, the people in that room were turned around from sinking into a living hell to soaring high into Heaven on Earth as Robert uncovered their Friday-Night essences. Yes, Jake thought as he surveyed the crowd, these people will discover the child of the past lost within their souls, and then, they'll want to live forever.

When Robert finished his mesmerizing workshops, he convinced the people in that room to elect Daniel Ward. If they elected Daniel Ward, Robert explained, businesses would begin shifting from the division of labor to the division of essence in the new Freedom Paradigm. Their loved ones and friends would then be free of their lifelong stagnation traps.

The following day, Natasha taught the techniques to begin letting the warm flame of love back into their souls once they discovered their paths to happiness.

Her central message was close to her heart. She said, "We all die too soon. Before we know it, our experiences of life, *our everything*, is over. That inherent sadness of life gives us

573

every right to extraordinary happiness for every moment we have." She sighed. Then she added, "And I promise you, once you permanently experience that extraordinary happiness and forever feel madly-in-love with your spouse...well then, you're never going to want to grow old and die. Once you get to that place, go to your neighborhood Church of God-Man."

That Sunday night, they gathered for the farewell party in the dinner hall. This time, Jake noticed, the look of hope on the couples' faces had been replaced with determination, for now they each knew their own specific path to happiness and exactly *how* to travel that path. Furthermore, they knew their love would eventually blossom again and this time never fade.

"Did you find the answers you came here for?" Jake asked Mike.

"Beyond all expectations," he answered. "And I'll tell you what, I'm voting for Daniel Ward come November."

*

"The weekend was a spectacular success," Natasha said after everyone had left. She leaned over the back of Robert's chair and kissed his cheek.

The inaugural weekend of combining TGIF and Natasha Workshops left Robert and Natasha exhausted...and happy.

"It certainly was," he said, reaching around and pulling Natasha onto his lap and moving in for a long, romantic kiss.

"Mmmm...that was nice," Natasha said softly. Her eyes lured Robert back for more. The nighttime air in their cabin was fresh and cool enough to make their body heat feel cozy.

Robert brushed Natasha's hair back to see every curve of her eyes. From deep in his soul, he confessed, "Ever since our first kiss, you've been like an unbelievable reward to me — my reward for everything I've done right in my life."

"I love you," Natasha whispered as she lifted her head to kiss his lips. Between kisses, she added, "I have some secrets to tell you, you know."

"Oh?" Robert said, drawing back and playfully looking at her with a suspicious expression.

"I've saved this secret for many years." She looked up, into his eyes. "Bobby," she said, a little nervously, "I've loved you ever since third grade. Did you ever notice I always sat next to you?"

Robert drew back his head further. "You've *loved* me ever since *third grade?*"

Natasha nodded. "The way you wanted to make your parents' life better, the way you wanted to make everyone's life better, would melt my heart."

"Really?"

Natasha nodded. "You know what?"

"What?"

"Watching you get so concerned over searching for a way to improve your parents' lives inspired me. You made me determined to figure out why my mom and dad fought all the time. With that determination, *I was* able to figure out why, and I saved their marriage."

Robert thought for a moment. "Yes...yes I remember now. You got your mom interested in your dad's accomplishments."

Natasha looked up at Robert and nodded slowly. Then, she turned her eyes down and said, "And then, in the seventh grade, your family moved to Illinois, and I thought I'd never see you again. It broke my heart." She turned her eyes back to Robert and whispered, "I'm going to tell you another secret...okay?"

"Okay."

"I was in love with you all over again the moment I saw you at the reunion."

Robert kissed her on her lips. Then he asked, "Why did you wait so long to at least give me a clue?"

"Well, going back, we were just kids when you left. But...the day I got married, I couldn't stop thinking about you." Natasha was whispering. Robert had never felt so touched. "And when I saw you at the reunion—" she stopped. She searched his eyes. "Relationships are sometimes so difficult to get started," she lamented.

Robert held her tight. "My god," he said. "And just think how unlikely that reunion was in the first place."

Robert and Natasha shuddered from the thought and held each other tightly, reassuringly, as the blissful sensation of love rushed through their bodies.

Superpuzzle

*

Back in New York, Jake and Jasmine met with Al in his glass office overlooking the expansive floor of Patterson Press. Jake had called for the meeting and started talking first: "You know, these people going through the TGIF and Natasha Workshops have much more leverage toward the mission of getting Daniel in the White House than we had any idea about. The fellow in New Jersey, Saul Tannenbaum, went through TGIF, and he alone has gotten as many as two hundred votes. Even if we discount for potential over-optimism and cut that figure in a fourth, that's still fifty to one leverage! I don't know if they're all like Saul, but there's some powerful leverage for getting Daniel in the White House coming out of those TGIF and Natasha Workshops. And they're being held all over the country now.

"I get the sense that once people go from those workshops to the Church of God-Man, as Robert and Natasha always encourage, people catch 'immortality fever' as Saul did, and they start campaigning for Daniel."

"Ah yes," Al said, "I loved your article about Saul, the guy who was suicidal, who now lives for immortality."

Jake nodded.

Al smiled and sighed. He sat there nodding and looking proudly at his two young reporters. Finally, after a long moment of silence, he said, "Robert and Natasha's Workshops, Jeremiah's Church of God-Man, Reggie's music, Jake and Jasmine's articles in Al's paper...don't you see? The pieces are coming together."

CHAPTER
FIFTY-FOUR

"It's the final piece to the puzzle!" shouted Ian. He sat up straight on his stool and proclaimed, "This'll assure Danny's victory!"

Ian then leaned over his stack of notes. What an initiation of my Overlay Charts, he thought; I've potentially discovered a whole new Universe! These Overlay Charts just might bring me the greatest discovery about the cosmos ever made. What a way to demonstrate their power!

He twisted from his stack of equations to his computer and called up his six complex "kitchen sink" information charts he had developed over the past several months. He leaned closer toward his computer screen to study each of six different anomalies that appeared older than the Universe. "The final piece'll come tonight," he said. "This'll reveal a beautiful picture. At the very least, this'll prove that conscious civilizations exist throughout the Universe. And I know its gonna show they control the cosmos to the best living conditions for conscious beings. The charts'll show those civilizations survived their nuclear-decision thresholds, which means adopting Daniel's TVP political structure of no external authorities. Violence and force'll not exist out there. How else could those anomalies exist?"

Superpuzzle

Ian sat at the edge of his stool, hunched over a desk full of papers covered with numbers and equations. It was 2:30 in the morning. Hovering over stacks of numbers and equations at two in the morning was becoming a common occurrence for Ian, not unlike the industrialist John D. Rockefeller who used to sit over stacks of numbers on his desk at two in the morning, but loved it because, as he had said, he "discovered in those numbers a whole new world." The past few months, Ian possibly discovered in his numbers *a whole new Universe.*

His excitement created so much energy that he was sleeping less and less, yet continued to gain energy as his discovery seemed more and more probable.

It all started when Ian took a strong interest in the anomalies throughout the cosmos that seemed to be much older than the Universe itself. They were such mysteries to him that needed to be understood. He searched the data for common denominators. He gathered the information to build his charts from the reams of data collected on the anomalies, available to any scientist. Tonight, he knew he would find something... something big. For, tonight he would put theory into practice and conduct his first wave of Overlay Charts.

He pulled up six more complex information charts with the same information as the other six, but based on Ian's mathematical equations of normal mass/energy dynamics as they should pertain to the specific anomalies. He put everything he could think of into the "kitchen sink" charts, except for the known factor of age discrepancy. He was looking for something, but he didn't know what. "Finally, tonight, after months of meticulously building my two sets of charts," he said, "I'll electronically superimpose them." The anticipation was driving him crazy — it had been for months.

That afternoon he had added two more hard drives to his computer to handle the size of his files tonight when he would overlay the two sets of charts.

"Finally, I'll put my overlay program to work," he said, setting an alarm on his computer to go off when the program was finished. Then he lay down on the couch next to his computer and fell asleep. The program would take about three hours to run.

Putting Together the Pieces

At 5:38 in the morning, the alarm woke Ian. He did a fast, effortless sit-up. Instantly wide awake, he stared at his computer screen, which lit up his face in the dark room. His eyes were bulging with excitement. After pushing some buttons and studying the screen for 60 seconds, he found what he was searching for.

"Oh baby," he cried, "Oh baby!" Then he clicked the cursor again, paused, and pushed it four more times.

"Oh god, it's the same within each anomaly," he said. "That's no coincidence — that's consciousness doing that. Jesus...that's God-Man at his best, that's Zon!"

Ian buzzed his wife through their home-and-observatory intercom system. It was still dark outside. Ian's wife, an attractive, energetic country girl who had become fascinated by Ian's work, was used to being buzzed in the middle of the night and early in the morning. In fact, she looked forward to it. These were the most precious moments: coming into Ian's office, seeing him so exhilarated, at his happiest moments when he made his powerful breakthroughs that advanced the world.

Sometimes during these happy moments, she would watch him, just the two of them in the middle of the night, and think to herself how much she hoped he and the God-Man Group succeeded in their superpuzzle of ending human death. During these moments, she knew she could not bear to ever lose him. And if she did, she knew these would be the happiest moments that would forever stand out in her memory...powerful memories of so much value and happiness that the loss of him would be too overwhelming.

Sometimes she wondered why she suffered such thoughts of someday losing him. Tonight she realized why: because his value to her and to the world was so very great, and his love for life and their love for each other was so very powerful that the inescapable loss of him in the anticivilization was inconceivable to her. Yet, it was unavoidable. Her thoughts would fight with the unbeatable foe...in the anticivilization.

In the darkness, she came into his workplace with a sweet smile, her floppy black hair bouncing on her slight shoulders. When Ian looked at her, her soft fair skin seemed to glow. Even while making the most important breakthrough in his life, the sight of her made him stop for a moment and just look at her.

"Diana," he said, pausing a moment longer to enjoy looking at her, "Diana, my first Overlay Charts, and look at what they've given me."

Diana had become quite learned in physics because of her fascination with Ian and his work. She walked over and stared at the Overlay Chart on the computer. Then, Ian pressed the cursor to the next chart, then the next. She understood the concept of the Overlay Charts, but she was too excited to figure out the specific revelation.

"I can see the squiggles, and they're consistent on each one. What does it mean?" she asked, too excited now to study them further.

"Look here," Ian said, pushing some buttons on the keyboard. "Let's strip away the Overlay Chart and about 90% of the other charted information that ended up showing no variances. Now, here is the first chart of one of the six anomalies that appears to be older than our Universe. What you see there is, given its age and mass, what cataclysmic activities such as supernovas or big bangs *should have* occurred, mathematically speaking based on its mass and energy. ...Now, here is what actually occurred."

He superimposed it with another chart.

"Ian...look at that! Look at that variance," Diana said.

"Now, look at this," Ian said, bringing up the second set of Overlay Charts for the second of six anomalies.

"The variance is the same!" Diana said again.

"The odds for one of those to be a fluke of nature is beyond calculation. But for two of those to look like that means those anomalies are being controlled by consciousness."

"Oh Ian, I'm so proud of you!" she said from deep within her soul.

"Now, look at this, my love." Ian brought up the third anomaly.

"My darling, it's the same variance!"

Then he brought up the fourth, fifth, and sixth anomalies, which each showed the same variances.

Diana gasped as she watched the Overlay Charts come up.

"We're seeing our cousins at work out there, the gods of the Universe," Ian said as they stared at the charts.

"Explain to me what they're all so precisely doing," she said, looking away from the charts to Ian's face that glowed from the computer's light. When she looked at his dynamic eyes, she thought he was so sexy...this explorer and conqueror of knowledge. She was so proud of him she wanted to kiss him deeply right there, but she refrained.

"Here's what I believe we're observing, and will be able to calculate and confirm over the next few weeks," he said. He looked at her. "We're looking at drastically reduced cataclysmic activity. Big bangs, supernovas, unaltered mass/energy dynamics that *should be there*, are not there. That's proof of God-Man controlling the cosmos to the best conditions for conscious beings. It seems that random cataclysmic events must be too invasive; they must screw things up. It further suggests that creation becomes the exclusive domain of consciousness, forbidden to the reckless, unthinking, unaware, uncalculating mass/energy forces of nature and kept as an exclusive dynamic of calculating, planning consciousness. This would explain the older age of those anomalies, why they're older than our Universe. No big bang would be allowed to affect those areas controlled by Zons, including the big bang of *our* Universe. That would strongly suggest two fascinating thoughts: 1) our big-bang Universe was created by a Zon, and 2) those older anomalies represent another Universe that existed before our Zon-created Universe! And with the Overlay Charts as my tools, I'll be able to actually *prove* everything that's being suggested here."

"Ian, this is breathtaking. It advances the understanding of our Universe by decades."

Ian nodded. "Yes, it does," he said. "But even more important will be the immediate effect this has on the man in the streets. By knowing that the natural order out there is to live forever and to take control of nature to preserve our consciousness will accelerate our work right here on Earth, right now. The perspective of the average person will change, from seeing life from a close-ended anticivilization perspective to an open-ended Civilization of the Universe perspective in which precious life is immortal. And that's what we need in order to throw society behind the drive for biological immortality."

"God, I love you Ian," Diana said. She reached for him, and

581

they embraced in a tight kiss. Moments like this came often as their love for each other drove them together...into each other's arms. When admiration and love filled them and ran over the edges of capacity, Ian and Diana were driven together to express and relieve the love inside that was bursting at the seams. As so often happened, they became powerfully aroused. In one swoop, Ian lifted her one-piece nightshirt to expose Diana's naked body underneath, illuminated in the dark room by the bluish computer light. This cute little country girl transformed into a sophisticated woman...her lower back and hips curving with the smoothness of buffed pinewood, her breasts protruding, aroused, ready and waiting to be manhandled.

Her womanhood in that blue light, her protrusions and curves casting shadows about her body, drew forth the raw sexual animal in Ian. He yanked off her nightshirt and stared briefly. The moment quickly became too long, a tease, and he wrapped one arm tightly around her back and pulled her against him. He rubbed his hands all over her, one up and down her back, the other up and down her front, grasping for pleasure, his hands hungry for her flesh. He knocked his keyboard to the floor and lifted her up onto his computer desk and draped her back across it.

"Yes, yes, yes!" she encouraged Ian as he took off his shirt. He dropped his hands back onto her body; he could not wait to have more of her. He leaned over her; he slid his lips up and down her flat belly and over her breasts. His arms twined around her legs; his hands massaged the inside of her small vanilla thighs.

"Oh...God..." she gasped.

Ian buried himself into the writhing little female beneath him. His head was spinning. He felt exciting power as his every thrust brought ecstasy to her body. *She's mine!* he shouted in his head. *All mine!* And he thrust himself into her over and over. After several minutes of rhythmic, heavy breathing and moaning, she suddenly cried out and arched her back. His hands tightened around her arching, twisting body. He planted his thumbs firmly across her belly; his long fingers wrapped around and dug into her back. With his hands tightly around her waist, holding her steady, he thrust into her faster and harder. They moved in fluid motion. She moaned louder. Her small body suddenly stiffened, stopping her motion like a freeze-frame, breaking their rhythm as she pressed her pelvis hard against him. At that moment Ian overpowered her and moved her back and forth, lifting and crashing her petite body into his, over and over again.

"Oh, baby! Oh, my love! Oh!" Diana called out. She returned to his rhythm with a desperate thrust of her hips. Their bodies crashed into each other again and again as waves of tension rushed through them both.

And then, after one last frantic meeting of bodies, the storm ceased. Ian let her go and collapsed onto her. The room became very peaceful. Their souls became very peaceful…their love expressed, relieved. A moment of nothingness passed, and then Diana rubbed her fingers lightly down Ian's back.

"You're my hero," she whispered. "I want you, *forever.*"

CHAPTER
FIFTY-FIVE

Jake and Jasmine co-anchored the breaking news on the Patterson Channel, revealing Ian's stunning discovery to mankind:

"Dr. Ian Scott's breakthrough science, known as Overlay Charts, show us where very advanced conscious beings named Zons altered the course of mass/energy nature," Jake reported. "The first set of Overlay Charts reveal a stunning discovery: an entirely different Universe than our own Universe. We will go through the discovery in detail, but first you must know how the Overlay Charts work..."

The camera-shot jumped to Jasmine, who explained the charts in simple terms: "Dr. Scott first charts the way natural phenomena should occur based on the predictable course of mass and energy. Then he charts how natural phenomena *did* occur. He then electronically superimposes the two charts. The squiggle or variance proves conscious interference altering the course of nonconscious mass/energy nature. Thus, his Overlay Charts not only prove that consciousness is a component of existence, but proves that it is the *controlling* component and perhaps even the *creating* component. Einstein identified only mass and energy as the fundamental components of existence."

"Now that Dr. Scott knows how to create Overlay Charts,"

Jake continued, "he says he'll create many others. Dr. Scott's Overlay Charts may have started the next major wave of predictive charts since Mendeleyev started the wave of predictive conscious-controlled chemistry and physics from his spectacular Periodic Chart of Elements in the late 1800s. Dr. Scott's Overlay Charts, however, could eventually predict even much-advanced events in physics, biology, chemistry — even literature, art, and most other fields of knowledge."

"He says future Overlay Charts will prove that consciousness controls the course of mass and energy through *creation* — *creating* new realms of existence as well as other creations that are unique to consciousness," Jasmine added. "Dr. Scott predicts that *creation* is a phenomenon that belongs *only* to consciousness. If that theory is proven, he says, then the creation of our Universe had to come from advanced consciousness — a Zon."

"In any case," Jake said after Jasmine lit the fuse to an explosive concept, "now let us get into the details of the first set of Dr. Scott's Overlay Charts that actually reveal an entirely new Universe much older than our own."

Jake and Jasmine explained the stunning discovery. Those first six Overlay Charts caused a major sensation around the world as people saw the proof that man — God-Man — controlled the Universe...actually controlled *two* universes!

In the days that followed, the growing number of Overlay Charts strongly suggested that the seemingly far-out issues in Daniel's campaign, such as eliminating well over a trillion dollars from the budget by ending all aspects of government that acted as external authorities — everything except for national defense and local protection — was the natural order of advanced civilizations that protected and preserved conscious life.

"Not one of my thousands of spectrographic analyses show man-created nuclear explosions at the level of bombs," he told Jake in a follow-up interview. "The growing number of Overlay Charts strongly suggest that peaceful, borderless business — not warring governments, religions, nations — is the natural order out there. The Civilization of the Universe is driven by value creation, by value creators or God-Man, and is filled with compassion, peace, and love."

Exactly as Jasmine and I felt at the Church of God-Man and

in the monthly gatherings of The Group, Jake found himself thinking as Ian was talking.

That night, Jake wrote an article titled: *The Indisputable Message.* He summarized the indisputable message at the end of his article: *Not only is Daniel Ward's Twelve-Visions political structure the natural order, but we'll destroy ourselves through nuclear war or terrorism with our escalating power to wipe out all life on Earth...if we do not get on Ward's structure that eliminates external authorities, violence, and war.*

*

In three weeks, the members of The Group would see if their amazing puzzle all came together to bring the nation a Twelve-Visions President. As they came into Rico's mansion, one by one, Jake saw in his mind each of their pieces of the puzzle snap into place. When all were present, Al Patterson presided:

"Ian snapped the final piece — the scientific proof — into the puzzle that revealed the Twelve-Visions World to the people. Talk of Ian's discovery is on everyone's lips around the world during these final three weeks before the election. That proof of the Twelve-Visions World opened the door for a Twelve-Visions President. Way to go, Ian...way to go."

CHAPTER
FIFTY-SIX

The news came as no surprise in mid-October. It seemed more like a worldwide salute to the three great accomplishers as the Nobel Prizes were announced: Dr. Sally Salberg — Medicine; Dr. Ian Scott — Physics; Theodore Winters — Economics. Jake and Jasmine concluded their coverage by writing that if Daniel got elected, he would win the Nobel Peace Prize. By eliminating every act of government that had nothing to do with protection from physical aggression, their article explained, then the mechanism for building political power would vanish, eliminating the impetus of war. And wherever war was needed for self-defense as in defense from terrorism or from threat of attack, the objective would be to swiftly remove the evil ones to bring back peace. In the end, peaceful, economic value exchange would prevail, obsoleting violent political power struggles.

*

Jake sat in his brownstone in New York City, with Jasmine, working late on their final article before the election. Jake stopped writing. He quietly started reflecting over the past ten months, starting with his New Year's Eve discovery of the big three accomplishers' common denominator in Cheektowaga, his stay with Jessie and Angie, the reunion, and the campaign. As Jake reflected over the past year, a disturbing fact entered his mind: most polls on this day showed Daniel statistically even with the Democratic candidate, Senator Cater Olson, and the Republican candidate, Governor Richard Fairbanks, in a three-way deadlock. The Patterson polls, however, showed Daniel had pulled even with the other two candidates in its last national poll three days earlier. Daniel has all the momentum, Jake pondered. To have caught the two neck-and-neck front runners with a few days to go, Daniel should have surged past them into the lead like a racehorse who catches and surges past the lead horses down homestretch, for all the momentum belongs to him. Do the other pollsters know something the Patterson Group is missing?

The road to the White House, Jake reminisced, was surprisingly unchallenged despite the bruises and bandages, those close calls, those hospital visits and jail visits. Daniel getting elected will essentially eliminate the Establishment, Jake pondered, actually end the powers that be. Yet, the members of The Group — these God-Men — built and snapped together the puzzle pieces to Daniel's campaign with relatively little problem.

Sure, that was a close call when the religious fanatics stormed The Group's meeting and shot Rico, Jake thought. Of course, those were the same fanatics who burned Jeremiah's church and nearly killed Jeremiah and Maria. But those two fanatics were a fluke, an odds thing...like getting hit by lightning. And, yes, the FDA turned up its destructive ways out of desperation, but that was only a temporary hiccup. Jake's face grimaced as he remembered how the IRS snatched Miss Annabelle from the Patterson Building, but the way Salinski erased the feared bureaucracy's power in twenty-four hours exemplified why no one and no authority could stop the run for presidency. The ease with which Salinski single-handedly deflated the most feared bureaucracy in the free world epitomized the lone God-Man going up against the might of the entire, multimillennial anticivilization.

The twelve former students of Miss Annabelle, Jake thought, are the first God-Men on Earth. Their souls and psyches never entered the anticivilization, *just as Jeremiah explained to me down in Wilmington*. They were never part of the anticivilization's illusions and never part of its emotions. The twelve former students had no ties, no investments in the anticivilization. Therefore, they were able to freely move ahead with forming the puzzle pieces to Project Life. They moved ahead powerfully, guiltlessly, with no internal conflicts, no external confusions. They saw through to the essence of things and clearly knew *what is*. The anticivilization's powers-that-be depended on illusions and emotional investments and could not push around the God-Men. The reality-grounded God-Men's feet were solidly planted on Aristotelian ground. No, the powers-that-be simply could not go toe to toe with Miss Annabelle's neothinking God-Men without getting outflanked, just as Salinski swiftly, easily outflanked the IRS and Justice Department.

The IRS, the fluke kook attacks, and a frantic last-ditch regulation frenzy by the FDA caused some strains during Daniel's run for the presidency. It was a battle, Jake thought, but a battle the God-Men were sure to win.

Out of the blue, Jake remembered the manager at Steaks & Wines. The memory filled Jake with a good feeling. I told you, Jake thought, seeing his former boss's face in his mind's eye, things would get better someday. Now they will.

"This'll be one of the three major pieces to the puzzle of biological immortality," Jasmine said, startling Jake.

Suddenly, Jake felt it right down to his bones: for the first time, he *knew*, he *really knew*, that biological immortality was going to happen — he was *not* going to die! *Yeah!* he thought, *yeah!* Seeing how the God-Man Group formed the puzzle-picture of Daniel's presidency at the reunion, and then went out and matter-of-factly snapped together the pieces, he knew the puzzle-picture of biological immortality would be the same. In fact, as Jasmine had said, as of Tuesday they would have already accomplished one of the three pieces: Daniel's election. That puzzle piece would clear the way for the other two pieces — depoliticizing America and then achieving the technology. Those two puzzle pieces, he thought, were just a matter of time now for these amazing God-Men.

Jake leaned back in his chair and did something he did not

do often: he pulled the lever that lifted the foot rest. He put his head back and spent some time recalling the efforts of each member of The Group to get Daniel into the White House: Ian came through with the final piece, Jake reflected, the scientific proof of the Twelve-Visions World, the proper and prevailing world of conscious life. With his Overlay Charts, science would not, *could not*, be denied.

Rico's trusting nature, his well-known reputation of hiring downtrodden former prisoners, captured the hearts of the blue-collar working man, despite the cries from the leaders of labor unions not to vote for Daniel. Cathy's PR projects shown around the world on the Patterson Channel brought glamour and beauty to the campaign. Theodore's powerful business impacted the business world when Winters, Inc. joined the Church of God-Man's Business Alliance and shifted its business to members of the alliance. Robert's TGIF Employment Agency and his seminar circuit with Natasha and her romantic-love retreats convinced tens of thousands of people to vote for Daniel. Many of those shakers and doers carried wealth and influence. Many of them, such as Saul, recruited others to vote for Daniel.

Natasha, Al, Jake and Jasmine took the fatal blow out of the major weapon of the anticivilization — the media. The four of them took the traditional death knell of a candidate of value — *the media* — and turned it into his biggest asset. Reggie used art to point the youth toward their most prosperous futures — Daniel's Twelve-Visions World. Debra was the "populist", showing her millions of patrons — the man in the streets — their great prosperity-explosion by voting for Daniel.

Jeremiah developed and corralled an *entire religion* behind Daniel. Jake paused for a moment to think about what Jeremiah was accomplishing: Just as powerful a puzzle piece as his Church, Jake thought, was his Business Alliance. In just three months, businesses are defecting from the anticivilization at an alarming rate to join the Church of God-Man's Business Alliance. A vacuum gets left behind as those businesses switch their business to members of the Church's Business Alliance. That vacuum, in turn, pulls even more businesses in. Yes, Jake thought, more and more businesses join the Business Alliance for the competitive edge needed to survive, and ever since

Theodore joined, the growth and power of the Business Alliance has expanded exponentially. The votes, influence, and money going to Daniel's campaign from the Business Alliance already rival the Church of God-Man itself, Jake thought, and the Business Alliance is just getting started!

Miss Annabelle developed and corralled an international school — her internet school — behind Daniel, with its highly effective "upward pressures" on millions of parents. Mr. Melbourne released his first novel entitled *The First Immortals* that told the story of Miss Annabelle and her students in the third grade, their separation, the reunion twenty-seven years later, and the run for presidency. Then he projected forward what would happen if the Twelve Visions Party choice for president were elected so the reader could get an idea of what the Twelve-Visions World would be like. He had worked on the thousand-page epic novel for seven years. Specifically for the campaign effort, he released his novel for free over the Internet by mid-summer prior to the elections. Over the next four months, it was estimated from the tens of millions of hits that close to nine million Americans read the free, on-line edition.

Sally brought to the world a medical drive to end aging, which millions upon millions of people passionately, even desperately wanted. Her message was clear: when Daniel is elected, I will succeed. Salinski dominated the legal world with a new power that nullified the anticivilization and its attackers of values. And, of course, Daniel presented the only sound political plan in the history of the human race, described in his Six-Visions Campaign, which Debra printed for every tray at Debbie's French Fry City.

All of this, Jake thought somewhat in disbelief, was done in *nine months*. "The God-Man Group," he said, dropping his head backward onto the chair, euphoric and in awe, "has brought the people a far more *stimulating* choice in Daniel and his Twelve-Visions World than the other candidates. In short, we outcompeted the anticivilization." Jake turned his eyes toward Jasmine and smiled at her.

Yeah, Jake thought with a relaxed smile across his face, each member of The Group worked as hard as he or she could, each in his or her own way, to bring together the puzzle. All in all, he thought, we faced little resistance. There was very little the powers-that-be could do in the presence of the God-Man.

Jake knew now The Group was the new Illuminati. These few people are using Neothink and are driven by love to create the future of the world, he thought. Although he could not yet write about the big picture, not a day passed during which he did not stop to say in his thoughts, "Thank you, Miss Annabelle."

CHAPTER
FIFTY-SEVEN

"We've got big trouble!" Jake said over the phone when Daniel answered. Jake and Jasmine were in the Patterson Building preparing the news teams for election day. Daniel was at his campaign headquarters in Atlanta. "The election's tomorrow, and they've set a booby trap for you!"

"Hello Daniel, it's Al. I'm here in my office with Jake and Jasmine."

"Hi guys...what's this booby trap?"

"This morning Carter Olson issued a challenge to you and Richard Fairbanks to so-called 'give the American people a chance to break the stalemate tomorrow at the booths'."

"Just ten minutes later," Jasmine said, "Richard Fairbanks announced on national TV that he accepted the challenge. He added that now the American people would see if Daniel Ward had the courage that it takes to be President by accepting the challenge. All of a sudden, the Networks are announcing they'll carry the impromptu debates tonight as a public service to the American people."

"Of course," Jake said, "it's a conspiracy that's been planned for weeks. They've surely got facts after facts lined up to overwhelm you. That's their weapon — using *true facts*, but using those inarguable, *true* facts out of context to create

593

illusions. That's how politicians and the media have controlled this anticivilization since the beginning. You can't argue with the facts, 'cause they're *true*. They're thrown at you like spears from a thousand different angles. Before you have time to pull one out, you're hit with three or four more. Before long, you're unable to stand. You succumb. You fall. These two candidates are supersmart people, they're shrewd, and they'll cut you to ribbons with facts...especially when you don't have time to prepare!"

"No doubt, you'd be walking into an ambush," Al said calmly.

"Don't do it, Daniel," Jake said. "It's a sucker trap."

""You don't need it," Jasmine said.

"Yesterday's Patterson polls showed you winning 38% of the registered voters," Jake concurred. "If you refuse the debate, Olson and Fairbanks and the network news'll play it up to make you look nonpresidential, even cowardly. That might cost you a couple of percentage points, but you'll still win. If you accept the challenge, you risk losing the whole thing. For our goal, the bigger picture, it's not worth the risk."

Finally, Daniel spoke, "They've avoided me like the plague throughout my entire campaign. They're clearly afraid of me. Why this sudden challenge and show of confidence?"

"They're desperate," Jake said. "They know the other too-close-to-call polls are tainted. They know you caught 'em and passed 'em and that they're going to lose. This is their only chance."

A long pause followed.

"Daniel?" Jasmine finally said.

"I'm still here, dear," he answered.

"I think the best way is to flat out reject the challenge," Jake offered, "and to point out why they're making the challenge now, in the first place. Let's bust 'em."

"No," Daniel said, "I'm going to accept the challenge."

Al smiled. He knew Daniel would not back down.

"But, Daniel—" Jake pleaded, but Daniel cut him off.

"Listen to me, Jake, politicians and members of the media have manipulated truths — as you say, true facts — far too long. You're absolutely right. Reality disintegrates as they manipulate truths to create their illusions—"

"Then…why would you do this?" Jake interrupted. "I just don't understand."

"Because manipulators of truth have never confronted an integrator of honesty. I'll take on their fast-flying truths with fully integrated honesty, even if I'm unprepared, because I can go *beneath* their true facts and pull them into context and hold that picture up for the whole world to see. I'll put their agendas to *my test* — wide-scope accounting. In the end, who benefits society? Nothing'll escape me. I'm the integrator. Face to face with me, those disintegrators are through. I'm gonna make 'em pay for their dishonest souls. You'll see."

*

Jake swallowed. "I can't believe he's doing this," he whispered to Jasmine. The camera crews from the Networks, the cable news stations, and international TV set up equipment in the large Madison Square Garden. "I don't like it. We had this thing wrapped up."

Al heard Jake whisper to Jasmine and said, "Don't worry Jake, he'll be fine."

"But, these two career politicians are the cream that rose to the top, they're slicker than the slickest courtroom lawyer, they have years of training at convincing crowds of people, and they're smart — they're brilliant, Al. Before Daniel's run for the White House, he barely ever gave a public talk."

"Jake's right," Jasmine said. "And to amplify the problem — they've planned and coordinated their attack for weeks if not months whereas Daniel has no preparation."

"Now that's where I think you're wrong, dear," Al said with a smile and a paternal nod. "Daniel's weapon is, as he said, fully integrated honesty, which enables him to tie down every floating truth, every illusion to wide-scope accounting. Their illusions will disintegrate as he integrates truths into contextual reality. If you ask me, they're the ones walking into a trap."

"If he doesn't get rattled," Jake said. "Remember, Al, it's three against one up there. I just hope he can hold up."

"*Three* to one?"

Superpuzzle

"Carter Olson, Richard Fairbanks, and Harry Schwartz, the mediator."

"Three to one, ten to one...I think Daniel will do fine," Al said.

"I sure hope so," Jake muttered. "I just hope this isn't because Daniel can't walk away from a fight."

*

Daniel Ward met face to face with Carter Olson and Richard Fairbanks for the first time at 8:00 p.m. EST, sixty minutes before the debate would broadcast live around the world. They sat in a conference room at the studio with the mediator, cable news anchor Harry Schwartz, who was explaining the rules of the debate.

After one quick explanation of the complicated technical rules, Harry Schwartz asked, "Are the rules clear?"

Carter Olson and Richard Fairbanks nodded and got up and left. Daniel stayed behind.

"Well, I have some questions," he said, "but would you first mind repeating the rules again? There's a lot of technicalities in there." Daniel required another half hour with Schwartz to get a good grasp of the rules.

"Thank you Harry; you've been very patient," Daniel said while getting up to leave the conference room. As Daniel was walking toward the door, he stopped and turned around. "By the way, Harry, do you know how to detect collusion?"

"What?"

"You know — subtle, invisible cheating?"

"Umm, it'd be hard to detect something that's invisible, right?"

"No, not really," Daniel said. "You can detect invisible cheating when actions are out of whack with logic."

"Oh?"

"Do you suppose Carter and Richard mastered all those technical details of the debate in less than ten minutes...especially when their entire political careers are riding on how they do tonight? That seems a little out of whack with logic, don't you think?"

596

Harry Schwartz shrugged his shoulders awkwardly, and with a stiff smile, in a weak voice, he said, "I don't understand what you mean."

Daniel stood there looking at the seasoned network news journalist. "Oh, I think you understand."

*

"Welcome to our first ever presidential debate on the eve of the election," Harry Schwartz said to the country at 9:00 p.m. EST. "Tonight you'll see your presidential candidates under unprecedented pressure. In past presidential debates, a candidate hurt in a debate had time to recover and regain ground before election day. Not so tonight on the eve of election day. This is do or die. Ladies and gentlemen, I present your presidential candidates: Senator Carter Olson your Democratic candidate, Governor Richard Fairbanks your Republican candidate, and Daniel Ward your Twelve-Visions candidate."

Daniel knew that his opponents were going for a knockout — they needed it to win. And they'd both be swinging at him.

"We start the debate tonight with opening statements limited to two minutes. We'll start on my left with Governor Richard Fairbanks."

"Thank you, Harry. First and foremost on my agenda, as your next president I would reduce the size of government. I believe, as do my opponents, that government is far too large. I believe we must cut nondefense spending programs to the bone, but continue putting money into national defense. The major budget cuts in government would quickly reduce the Federal government's suppressive regulations that hold back business and hurt our economy. We've already seen indications of the prosperity explosion that'll come from the paradigm shift I propose. I've always felt that all three candidates feel this way about reducing the size of government. I've always seen eye to eye with Daniel Ward, for instance, on our common goal to reduce government and promote business."

Okay, Daniel thought, I see what's going on here. He's trying to obscure the difference between himself and me in order to siphon off votes. He's using meaningless words to create the illusion that he's for a protection-only government as described in my Twelve Visions.

"It's just that," Richard Fairbanks continued, I've spent my life in politics and know how things work in D.C. Daniel Ward has no political experience. Jumping straight to the White House would overwhelm him, and I'm afraid that his campaign promises will not be effective, whereas mine will."

So smooth, Daniel thought, so clever. He then attacks me as not being able to carry out the Twelve-Visions agenda to depoliticize the country on account of my lack of political experience! Then he tells the people they'll have to vote for a career politician to depoliticize America!

"On that, we'll have to end your opening statement Governor," mediator Harry Schwartz said. "Now, it's Senator Carter Olson's turn. You have two minutes to make your opening statement, Senator."

"Thank you, Harry. Thank you America for tuning in to this historically important debate. I go along with everything the Governor said. Look, we all want the same thing; we all want what's best for America. And right now, reducing government to boost the economy is best for America. Any of us will do that for you. But I do see inherent problems with Daniel Ward. I agree with the Governor that Mr. Ward is naive in politics and would not be as effective as the Governor or myself in meeting his goal...our goal. I also take issue with the fact that Daniel Ward is an atheist. Our country was founded on Christian principles; good Americans have a deep love and respect for God. And finally, I suggest caution on some of his blanket statements involving segments of the population that will essentially lose their identities and hard-earned rights while being swept into the whole. I want to be sure we protect those segments of the population during the major changes to come. No one should be left high and dry."

"Okay," said Schwartz, "and with that we'll have to go to Daniel Ward."

"I understand how to make all the people wealthy, healthy, and safe, including the poor," Daniel began, wasting no time. "You see, I understand what depoliticizing America really means. Depoliticizing America means ending political careers — *every* political career including the office of the President as we know it. Now, I find it amusing watching two, lifelong career politicians trying to sell to the American people that they're ready to depoliticize America and end their own livelihoods! I have a job to go back to. They don't! We'll see here today just how much we really do have a so-called common goal. And I'll conclude my opening statement by saying that the smallest, most unprotected minority is *the individual*. The Prime Law, upon which my political party stands, gives rights and protection not to vote-gathering *segments* of the population, but to the smallest minority in most need of protection — to the individual. I won't read the Prime Law, but you can read it on the Twelve Visions Party web site." Daniel turned his eyes toward Schwartz, indicating he was done, but then he added as an afterthought, "Oh, and Senator, your Daniel-is-an-atheist attack mode seems awkward since the release of the breathtaking Overlay Charts three days ago."

"The what?" Carter Olson said, looking at Fairbanks who looked away.

"Uh…Governor Fairbanks," Schwartz said quickly, "you have the first session to express yourself on any subject. The other two candidates will respond. You have one minute."

Al looked at Jake. "Feel a little better now?"

Jake's face relaxed. The tension left. "Yeah," he said, smiling at his boss, "I should've known."

"Well, there are differences between Mr. Ward and me," Fairbanks began, trying to save face before Daniel spoke again, "but my differences are, in my opinion, much better suited for the people. For instance, my budget cuts will not cut off money to many of our seniors or children in need. My approach is more rational and compassionate and based on many years of political experience. For example, I plan to phase in my budget cuts over seven years to prevent a socio-economic shock. I have a sunset clause after four years to abandon the program as a safety precaution if the cuts are hurting and not helping. Mr. Ward plans to push everything through at once, which any economic expert'll tell you would send the social well-being of this country into cardiac arrest. Finally, I'll be able to push my budget through because of my political experience, whereas

Daniel Ward may not get very far with his budget."

"Thank you, Governor," Schwartz said, signifying the end of Fairbanks' one-minute expression as per the rules of the debate. "Now, Senator, you may respond on the subject at hand — the budget."

"Thank you. Governor Fairbanks and I come within close proximity of each other in regards to the budget, and I think that's a good indication that our government-reducing approach is the solid approach. Daniel Ward's approach is too radical at best, heartless at worst, and very naive. Congress will never go for what he's proposing. If the American people want effective change, they should stick with us. Reform is good, but radical change can hurt a lot of people. I say that not to criticize Daniel. I think he's been very valuable to American politics. From my heart, though, I'd just hate to see people get hurt."

"Thank you, Senator...well said," Schwartz, the supposedly unbiased mediator, said. "Now you have sixty seconds to express your point of view on the budget, Mr. Ward."

"The Governor and Senator agree my budget lands somewhere between radical and heartless. It's true: my budget is both radical and heartless. The problems with today's budgets are that they're full of politicians' big hearts used as a ploy to get voted into power. Remember, I'm going to *depoliticize America*, which means taking the politicians' big hearts out of *everything we do in D.C.* And America, just getting a whiff of that radical and heartless budget, has already begun to respond. I refer you to the Patterson Press article *Daniel = Health and Wealth* by Jake Catchings and Jasmine Kahil. You can read that well-researched article on the Twelve Visions Party web site."

"Okay, that's enough," Schwartz said with a little edge to his voice. The room of media personnel was quiet. It was plain to see: this was going to be a long night for those who supported the Senator and Governor.

"Do you see now, Jake?" Al whispered, "In whatever direction they float to craft their illusions, in whichever way the wind blows, Daniel can ground them with honesty."

*

Putting Together the Pieces

Election Day. The Group gathered at Daniel's campaign headquarters in Atlanta. Everyone seemed nervous, except Daniel. This was the most leveraged day in humankind's history, for Daniel's election would open the path to Project Life.

As Daniel cheerfully greeted the members of The Group, Jasmine asked him, "Aren't you at least a *little* nervous?"

"I guess I'm just too battle-worn," he said. "Before the run for the White House, I lived in my peaceful community near San Diego. I'd delivered only a handful of public speeches in my life. The past year, I've delivered that many per day and travelled nonstop around the country. I'm just relieved election day's finally here. I think it's overriding my nervousness."

Outside and inside the building, teams of camera crews were set up to cover the elections.

The election results started off very close.

"It seems the many polls that had predicted a close race were accurate," the Networks repeated over and over. "What do you think," anchormen kept asking their studio experts. "Will this one go down to the wire?"

The last Patterson Press poll had shown Daniel pull ahead slightly, beyond the margin of error, which now appeared to be wrong. The establishment media appeared to be right afterall in having dismissed Patterson Press as being partial.

"Something's gone wrong," Sally said. She and The Group monitored the election results with Daniel from a private room in his campaign headquarters. She looked around at Daniel. Jake could see that she was alarmed.

"I wonder if every last registered voter on government assistance has gone to the polls," Reggie said. "Afterall, their backs are against the wall. They're desperate."

"You might be right about that," Rico said. "They're scared to death of changing to a productive, happy life. ...Look at that — Olson just won New York!"

"That puts him in the lead for electoral votes," Jeremiah said.

Jake looked around the room. He saw anxiety on the faces of Miss Annabelle and her former students — except for Daniel and Al.

"Maybe our calculations were wrong," Debra said. "I don't

think we fully calculated the desperation factor."

"They're announcing Fairbanks won Pennsylvania," Robert called out.

"Oh no!" cried Miss Annabelle. She saw The Group's dream slipping away. *Can this be happening?*

"Nothing's wrong," Daniel reassured everyone. "What we're seeing—"

"Look at them working their illusions!" Sam blurted, his head glued to the television. "They know darn well the results will shift in Daniel's favor as the election results go West. But they're getting Olson's voting base to the voting booths by withholding what they know to be true."

"Ah, let 'em have their last moments of dishonest journalism," Daniel said. "It won't be long before the Patterson Group leaves those clowns in the dust."

"As the day goes on," the Patterson Channel announced soon thereafter, "the Networks' hopes for a nail-biter will fade. Daniel will steadily pull away. As the votes go West, Daniel's numbers will continue to climb."

In the end, Daniel pulled 41% of the popular vote and easily won the election. The Republican candidate received 29% and the Democratic candidate received 27% of the popular vote. Minor parties pulled 3% of the popular vote.

"A landslide," Mr. Melbourne said. He relished those words. He and his wife looked at each other with the proudest of expressions. They both looked around the room at their twelve "children". Like overwhelmed parents, they just stood there and absorbed the happiness on their children's faces. "They did it darling," he softly said, "they really did it." Miss Annabelle just nodded and wiped the tears from her eyes.

On this wonderful day, the little civilization originally from Cheektowaga enjoyed a well-deserved celebration party. Jake could not believe his eyes as he watched Sally get up and dance with Jeremiah in the victory celebration. She was smiling, which Jake knew was rare these days. Next thing he knew, Natasha and Robert were dancing, too. Daniel and his wife Marcy got up to dance. Soon, everyone was dancing, including Jake and Jasmine. The Twelve-Visions World — the Civilization of the

Universe on Earth — was coming!

*

The next day, the stock market enjoyed a party of its own. Theodore had predicted that American stocks would climb more the day after Daniel Ward's election than any other day in their history. True to Theodore's prediction, the Dow Jones Industrials surged a record 1653 points. The Nasdaq soared to a new record day, too. No one person was quite sure what would happen, but the collective market knew, as it always does — knew that the Twelve Visions Party was a good thing.

II.

Street Fight In D.C.

CHAPTER
FIFTY-EIGHT

Daniel was going to Washington, D.C. The anticivilization and the Civilization of the Universe were about to collide.

"The two worlds are going to war," Jake wrote as the subtitle to the paper's headline *Look Out, D.C.!* His opening sentence read, "This will be the first war in history that will be wonderful to watch."

Daniel was fearless. He never hesitated to take on a bully. He did not waste a moment to take on the government. Indeed, the war of two worlds started the day Daniel entered the White House, during a budget meeting.

"I want the word to get out that everyone in Washington, D.C. with a political job should start looking for a real job," he announced in all sincerity, "because I'm gonna depoliticize America."

He repeated that warning during his State of the Union Address, looking straight into the eyes of the career politicians who nervously chuckled, as though Daniel were just kidding them.

They're pathetic, he thought. But one lifelong career politician was not chuckling. He was the Senator from Massachusetts. *He's the heavyweight here*, Daniel noted in his mind.

*

Superpuzzle

As he promised, a few days after his State of the Union Address, Daniel submitted his famous Protection-Only Budget, nicknamed his Solar-Eclipse Budget because, as he put it, "I'm going to eclipse every last one of those solar-high spending programs. The politician's spending-world is going to get awfully dark."

Congress was stunned by his budget that cut out well over one trillion dollars over the following year alone. Not knowing how to approach the President's budget, the House members asked Daniel to come and talk to them to explain his budget; they said he could schedule his presentation after he had time to prepare. But Daniel said there was no preparation needed. The next day he stood before the House of Representatives.

"You want an explanation? It's all very simple. I eliminated anything that doesn't have to do with physical protection and paying off the debt. I stuck to my campaign issue that the federal government exists for one purpose: to *protect* its citizens from initiatory force and coercion and for no other purpose. I insist that the other so-called purpose of the federal government, to improve peoples' well-being through programs for the so-called social good, is a vote-gathering scheme used to buy votes from specific segments of the population, and I vow to end those tax-the-producer, give-to-the-nonproducer vote-buying schemes. There's a lot of glory and power that comes from spending money, and Congress has gotten very comfortable spending money. But you're spending other people's money that you didn't earn. It's not the government's job to spend money for the so-called social good. Your job is *not* multipurposed. Your job has *one* purpose and is very simple. In fact, your job and mine have the same purpose. That purpose is to protect our citizens from initiatory force, which requires a system of laws and justice. Any other purpose our government pursues is done to build politicians' — *your own* or *my own* — glory and power...and is bogus.

"Let me say it again to make this very, very clear: Today, our government wrongly exists for two purposes:

"The first purpose, to physically protect the people and their property with police, courts, prisons, and national defense, is *the* legitimate purpose of government. Government must defend against and punish initiatory force. Coercion and fraud are forms of initiatory force.

"The second purpose, to promote social 'prosperity' and provide social 'well-being' through social and regulatory programs 'for the social good', is *not* a legitimate purpose of government.

"Yet, most of you, our career politicians, focus your energy on that second illegitimate purpose of government. Spending other people's money on social programs brings you unearned personal glory and political power for your re-elections. You are, however, incapable of the second purpose. You are incapable of putting out the enormous effort required to truly help others. Sure, you spend our money on programs ostensibly designed to help the people. Indeed, you receive a lot of popularity and votes by spending our money on such social programs. But those programs are doomed without the in-the-trenches effort and business experience needed to make on-going spending honestly productive and fiscally sound.

"Looking back at an analogy in the last century, Hillary Clinton tried to spend our money to so-call enhance our medical well-being when her husband was President. She wanted to win popularity through her proposed immense spending program for national healthcare — spending other people's money. Yet, Hillary never got down in the trenches to truly enhance our medical well-being such as someone like Florence Nightingale who got right down into the blood-stained hospitals during the Crimean War. She learned, worked, and improved the nitty-gritty details to forever enhance the well-being of health care. Hospitals used to be a place *to go to die*, but Florence Nightingale's breakthroughs in cleanliness and sanitation made hospitals the place *to go to live*.

"Florence Nightingale, by the way, reminds me of the heroic market businessmen and women who get down into the nitty-gritty details to enhance our well-being in all areas of life. Hillary Clinton, on the other hand, reminds me of all of you who never get down into the trenches of real work, who do not spend the real effort to enhance the well-being of anyone. Like Hillary, you spend *for you* — you spend other people's money to become more politically popular and powerful.

"Enhancing the well-being of the people...that whole purpose of government is an immoral hoax, an illusion you all use to acquire and spend our money for your own political popularity, power, and re-elections. But you never fooled me. Soon, you'll no longer fool the voting public. During your long run in power, you've really made a mess of things. You've greatly hurt, not helped, the American people. Now, it's all going to catch up to you.

"Only those whom I call market businessmen — people who are very different than many of our big-business leaders today — can truly enhance the well-being of the people. Only true market businessmen and women put out the required effort and have the required know-how and experience needed to help others. Functions of government that fall into that second purpose of helping the people must eventually break from our government and go to market businessmen and women who will do a competent job fulfilling those services.

"The homeless, the poor, the old, education, social services, health care, medical research, foreign aid, the environment, the economy...that all falls under the bogus second purpose of government — to enhance the well-being of the people. With you career politicians erroneously handling that second purpose, those programs designed to help the people are falling apart. You go on hurting our society in order to soak up the glory, popularity, and sumptuous livelihoods that go with spending other people's earned incomes on illusionary social programs. Those costly programs and growing government debt got America into serious economic problems before I came along. By taking those social programs away from government — from you politicians — and giving them to competent market businessmen and women who'll make the programs work, our government will remove its debt, and taxes will fall in half.

"Then our government will be focussed on its one proper purpose — to protect the people from initiatory force and coercion, which includes protection from our leaders, *from you*. Focussed on its one proper purpose, the government and you politicians would no longer be able to suppress society's progress. You career politicians and my regulatory bureaucrats would no longer choke our economy with self-aggrandizing laws and regulations. You'd finally be out of the way! Many lawyers and lawsuits would vanish as American businesses surged forward, bringing everyone along with them.

"The Twelve Visions Party Constitution — the Prime Law — guarantees a government of defense, of serving purpose-one only. As you know, a joint resolution has been introduced in Congress to propose the Prime Law as an amendment to the United States Constitution. It's being called the Prime-Law Amendment, and it allows our government to protect its citizens from initiatory force and coercion — and nothing more. The process to pass constitutional amendments, however, usually takes a couple of years and could take longer. I need to depoliticize America as fast as I can. So, my other plan to eliminate the bogus second purpose of government is through the budget.

"I presented you with my budget — my Protection-Only Budget. My budget sufficiently funds the one and *only one* proper purpose of government: *physically protect the people, which includes justice.* My budget funds a *government that defends the people from initiatory force.* My budget eliminates funds to the second and bogus purpose of government: *creating illusions of enhancing the social well-being of the people.* In essence, my budget eliminates the funds that allow government to control the people through initiatory force.

"If you pass my budget as is, market businessmen in the private sector will quickly move in to handle 'the void' created by eliminating the second and erroneous purpose of government. Then those social programs will actually become successful and will honestly help the people who need help. I have many, many examples I can show anyone here who is interested in talking to me further.

"Now, even more important, without the many laws and regulations holding down progress, *all our citizens* will undergo a great prosperity explosion as their buying power multiplies manyfold, similar to what we witnessed during the mostly unregulated computer revolution throughout the late twentieth century.

"I suspect by the look on your faces, however, you will not pass my Protection-Only Budget. If you don't, the great prosperity explosion will still occur during my presidency. You see, I've planned for a two-phase transition to take our country into an inevitable new government structure that will lift our citizens — ordinary people — into a new world of wealth and happiness. Phase One — the first transition — is called **The Great Replacement Program**. The current government structure stays the same. The budget stays the same, but the people will see the financial bonanza of voting into office, during the mid-term elections, a change from career politicians to market businessmen. Market businessmen and women will replace career politicians in Congress and in state politics. Market businesspersons are super-competent people who know how to make an institution fiscally sound. They'll have no re-election fever or political agendas. In essence, they'll have every motivation and competent know-how to free the economy and then get back to their businesses. They'll halt the escalation of self-aggrandizing laws, litigation, and regulations that are holding down the progress of American business and technology and holding down our standard of living.

"With those market businessmen right in the current government structure, well, they'll clean up the mess — especially the programs ostensibly designed to help the people. Those faltering programs that supposedly enhance the well-being of the people keep deteriorating under the control of you self-serving, incompetent career politicians. You politicians are playing an elitist game for yourselves, to remain on as a ruling class. All your programs so-called for the people will eventually collapse as the Soviet Union did under seventy years of career politicians playing the elitist game only for themselves. Remember, that government, too, was ostensibly for the people.

"The Great Replacement Program will put market businessmen and women — real value creators — in our government. They'll truly sacrifice a few years from their in-the-trenches business careers to help their country. They'll be the true public servants unlike you elitists who selfishly rule over us and use the public for your own glory and power. Market businessmen and women will free the economy. They'll make government spending accountable; they'll rescue the programs designed to help the people before those programs collapse, social programs such as social security, veterans benefits, medicare, medicaid, social services, the homeless programs, our educational system, disease research, and so on.

"As the market businessmen and women evolve those programs into radically different, totally effective self-sufficient programs, those programs designed to promote genuine social well-being will begin breaking off from government where they do *not* belong. Those social and regulatory programs will fall into the hands of private market businessmen and women where they do belong. This'll begin Phase Two of the transition called **The Great Displacement Program**. Taxes will fall more than in half as the taxpayer is relieved of those programs. Government spending will fall more than in half. The budget deficit and growing debt will be corrected. And, finally, the truly needy will be helped along a path to independence, especially as freed industries drive down the cost of living to fractions of where it is now.

"The Great Displacement Program simply means displacing the programs that fall under the second purpose — the erroneous purpose — of our government: *to so-called promote social well-being*. The new government structure with one and *only one* purpose will do two things immediately: First, it will make us safer than any other possible scenario, for every dollar and every energy will be focussed on protecting the individual. Second, the new government structure will lift the ordinary person at once out of his or her stagnation-trap, for the new government will immediately put a halt to the laws, litigation, and regulations — the heavy burden on society — being generated throughout the three branches of government for their own power *at our lifelong cost*. The economy and opportunity will soar.

"By my third year, with many market businessmen and women in Congress and with enormous pressure on the rest of you, my Protection-Only Budget will pass. There'll be no more money to fund the debilitating regulatory bureaucracies that put the presidency upon a huge hierarchy of power. Private regulation is proven to be far more effective and far less corrupt. Again, I have many, many examples I can show anyone here who is interested in talking to me further.

"True to my campaign promise, I submit to you my Protection-Only Budget, nicknamed my Solar-Eclipse Budget because it eclipses every last one of government's solar-high spending programs. By my third year, those of you still looking to spend tax dollars on anything beyond physical protection and paying off the debt — spending tax dollars where they don't belong — will have entered a cold, dark place."

Daniel stopped his address and looked across the sea of politicians before him. After a moment, he shook his head and added, "I still see nothing but blank faces. ...All right then, picture this: the producers and creators — they're the Sun, the warmth, the light. From that warmth and light grow many beautiful values. However, in any beautiful garden, eventually weeds will grow. Indeed, in our beautiful country, more and more nonproducers and parasites hurt society, especially hurt our future generations. Those nonproducers and parasites now spread like weeds. I'm the weedkiller. I'm coming in and cutting off the nonproducers' and parasites' light. My budget is their permanent solar eclipse...is your permanent solar eclipse. Society doesn't need to grow you, not anymore. The *existing* parasites will have to change from parasites to producers and become part of the light...become value creators. You can do that by focussing on your one proper purpose of protecting citizens and their properties from initiatory force, coercion, and fraud. The elite ruling class that politicizes all aspects of our citizens' lives is soon to be a closed chapter of history. A new government that protects its citizens from initiatory force and does nothing more will open a new chapter to our future. I don't think it gets any clearer than that."

The House was silent.

*

The next day, the Senator from Massachusetts called for a meeting with Daniel. They met privately in the Oval Office.

"You've had a good ride," the Senator said, "but here's where you must stop crafting your sell to the gullible American people. The campaign stops now. You can accomplish some of what you promised, but in small, spoon-fed portions. That way, you keep your constituents happy, and they'll keep you in office. You've got to settle down now and learn how to work the system here to get what you want. Work with us, and we'll give you what you need."

"But I never was crafting a sell to the American people, never," Daniel said.

"C'mon Dan. Listen, the reason you're here is 'cause of us, you know."

"You'll have to explain that one to me."

"Why do you think the voters traditionally keep Congress and the White House split parties? It's the inherent voter's voice telling him to keep power divided. Well, Congress is filled with the most power-hungry bunch of congressmen and senators, like me, in its history. So, the voters wanted you because you're so damned against political power."

Daniel was amused. He studied this lifelong career politician before him and realized the source of his political staying power was his honesty at playing the dishonest game of politics. Seeing *what is* in the political arena gave him an edge over the other politicians held back by rationalizations and vested emotions. This senator was able to move in any direction that benefited him. By remaining honest within the closed boundaries of the dishonest game itself, he always knew reality, which is always the source of power in any situation, even in a dishonest situation such as politics. During the silence, the Senator spoke again.

"You can't win, Mr. President. But you don't know that yet, do you? Don't you know that down deep the people want us? They're enjoying the economic benefits your insurgency has brought to the economy. But they need us. They want to be baby-sat. They want a father. It's hardwired into their brains, and that's why you can't get rid of us. In the end, you lose."

The Senator's right, Daniel thought, the people *did* want to be led by politicians. The current mentality is plagued with the bicameral-like, primitive need for external authorities. But that's my mission, I'm the catalyst for sending the people to a new mentality — a leap into the Neothink mentality in which people will naturally integrate knowledge to lead themselves. They'll no longer need external authorities baby-sitting or fathering them. They'll no longer need a ruling class suppressing them.

"I think you're wrong," Daniel finally said, "and I think you know it. You're scared, Senator, that's why you're here. Soon, there'll be no more of your kind."

615

Superpuzzle

The heavyset senator turned to leave. "Fuck with me?" he said without emotion as he left the Oval Office, "Big mistake."

*

The Solar-Eclipse Budget was too much for Washington. The House of Representatives, both Republicans and Democrats, started impeachment considerations on the charge that the President was mentally unfit for high office. They held small, secret meetings to spread their intentions.

When Daniel heard about this conspiracy to impeach him, he recruited Sam and Ziggy, the top two numbers men in his development company back home.

"Men, I've got a situation here," Daniel said after Sam and Ziggy arrived at the White House. He was aware that he was happy to be working with his top two men again. "A congressman confidentially told me they're going to try to impeach me. I called you here to help me read the public. My gut sense tells me Congress will have a hard time getting public support. You're my best numbers men, and I can trust you."

"You want us to read what the public is thinking?" Sam asked.

"Yes. You know, the way you do when you're reading the surrounding residents to a major new project...no one is more accurate at getting into the thoughts and feelings of people than you two."

"We won't let you down," said Ziggy.

One of the first things Daniel's men did, with his permission, was leak to the press the story of congressmen secretly meeting about removing Daniel. Al, Jake, Jasmine, and Daniel decided to let the story break in the liberal media first, before the career politicians had planned. His men followed public reactions where the articles appeared and found that the American people were livid at those congressmen.

Daniel's men called a meeting with their boss after two weeks. "The most shocking data involves welfare recipients," Sam explained. "They're evenly split. About half want to give you a chance! During the short time you've been in office, buying power has been rising rapidly, and the economy is booming. The welfare recipients already live better than before you took office because their entitlements go nearly twice as far, and good-paying employment is opening up for those who want to rise up. The whole country is living better at every economic level."

"The reason that's so significant," said Ziggy, "is that welfare recipients are the lowest denominator. As we told you a few days ago, everyone else is just plain pissed off at the idea of removing you."

"Another standout statistic is the rise of millions of entrepreneurs," Sam said. "The possibility of removing bureaucratic regulations caused just the opposite results of the illusion the people were once led to believe."

"That's right, with widescope accounting, those regulations never protected consumers or small businesses or opened up competition," Daniel said. "Regulations did just the opposite: they prevented the risk-acceptable rapid progress that would've saved consumers' lives. Regulations also protected corrupt elements of big businesses, specifically the political businessmen who are tacit partners with politicians. Regulations protected those lazy big-business political businessmen from the hard-driving market entrepreneur."

"And what's happening now proves you out," Sam said. "With those cost-prohibitive regulations on the way out, a new breed of market entrepreneur is quickly ferreting out new value creation to build astonishing values and profits. Those entrepreneurs are creating new ways of approaching medicine and business never seen before. Those entrepreneurs are rising everywhere and are bringing exciting ground-floor career opportunities at a ten-to-one ratio to those around them."

"Millions of these newly freed entrepreneurs are rising across America, even throughout inner-city America," Ziggy said. "They're pulling up people all around them."

"The country's changing, Daniel," Sam said. "It's changing quickly. The attitude of even third-generation welfare recipients is changing. You have to realize, the Church of God-Man's Business Alliance has come out of nowhere like a supernova and has really weakened the grip of the career politicians on civilization. The business world, including the ordinary employee, more and more wants the freedom you're offering."

"What's happening," said Ziggy, "is this: the businesses that join the Business Alliance not only are doing very well, but it seems most have switched over to Theodore's division-of-essence structure. The employees are discovering what it means to become motivated in-house entrepreneurs on their Friday-Night essences. They can sense — they can almost *smell* — the success and exhilaration that's coming their way from your Freedom Paradigm. Every day, thousands more want what you offer."

Sam nodded. "Our conclusion is," he said, "Congress won't dare suggest that the President is a madman."

Daniel's men, as usual, were absolutely right.

Congress returned a normal budget. Daniel's reaction sent waves of fear through the lifelong career politicians. A few days after receiving Congress's spending budget that maintained the status quo, Daniel appeared on national television:

"Instead of closing down the government," he said, beginning his somber announcement, "I've researched every congressman's role in ignoring my Protection-Only Budget. Let me announce to you the congressmen who completely ignored my budget. My numbers-men tell me those congressmen will be replaced in the mid-term elections. I've named the approaching event *The Great Replacement Program*. Because the American people have seen with their own eyes their buying power beginning to soar and the medical industry making huge gains against debilitating diseases, the American people will replace those Republicans and Democrats with market businessmen who run for office under the Twelve Visions Party. The market businessmen of the Twelve Visions Party are nonpoliticians sworn to the Prime Law (see pages 682-683). Those nonpoliticians will pass my Protection-Only Budget in its entirety."

Daniel then went on to name each congressman who ignored his budget. As he did, his viewing audience, the American people, dreamed of what would soon happen to their buying power. Even the welfare recipients were changing. Instead of living in the ghetto, one by one they realized they would actually live as millionaires live, for buying power would multiply a thousand times.

CHAPTER
FIFTY-NINE

The phone woke Jake with a start.

"Hello?"

"Hi Jake; I'm calling from the White House."

"Oh, hello Daniel."

"Jake, I'll get straight to the point. I'm asking if you and Jasmine can live in Washington, D.C. for the next three-and-a-half years. I need you in the White House Press Corps. You two along with Al and Natasha are my only media allies."

"Daniel, we'll be there. You can count on us."

Despite widespread speculation, Jake and Jasmine were the only two people Daniel recruited from The Group. He did not appoint the powerful members of the God-Man Group to his Cabinet, although they would have served if asked. Twelve-Visions oriented people were excited about the potential dream team. Here were some of their hopeful appointees: Miss Annabelle as Secretary of Education, Theodore as Secretary of Commerce, Debbie as Secretary of Agriculture, Bruce Salinski as Attorney General, Robert as Secretary of Labor, Rico as Secretary of Health and Human Services, Ian as Secretary of Energy. They also hoped Sally would become the Surgeon General.

But the dream team never materialized. Daniel explained in a sobering announcement that he was not interested in political power or political reform.

"Unlike other presidents who built their teams of political allies to either expand political power or to bring about reform, I'm *only interested* in depoliticizating America," he announced on national television. "I don't need to build a team for that purpose. I simply don't need power. I don't need department heads to depoliticize America. I only need to slash the budget. In fact, my goal is to eliminate all but four Cabinet positions, just retaining the Departments of State, Treasury, Justice, and Defense. I need only the budget and a three-year battle with Congress to accomplish my initial goal. After the midterm Great Replacement Program, Congress will back the Protection-Only Budget. Then the Executive Departments will no longer have money to exist except for the Departments of State, Treasury, Justice, and Defense."

*

Jake and Jasmine quickly learned the art of mingling at the frequent political social affairs and parties. They got inside information that was available no other way. They now understood why politicians put on an average of fifteen pounds their freshman year in Washington, D.C., for life there seemed to be little more than parties and socializing.

They had been there less than five weeks, and they were reluctantly driving to what must have been their thirtieth social event. They disliked these ego-boosting political parties but attended to stay in the information loop.

This afternoon's gathering brought them to a restaurant where politicians frequently lunched. Jake and Jasmine headed to the banquet room in the back. They split apart, as usual, to cover more ground and gather more information. Jasmine went to the food display around which several conversations were in high gear. Jake headed to the bar.

Jasmine leaned over to scoop punch from the bowl labeled "nonspiked." A slurred Massachusetts accent spoke to her from behind.

"I don't blame you for not touching the mixed drink. You've gotta hold out for the good stuff."

Jasmine turned around to see the wide Senator from Massachusetts talking to her. He obviously did not know who she was. He knew only that she was young and sexy. He figured she was a young, wide-eyed intern or staffer or young research editor for the mainstream press. He never bothered to get her name. He just called her sweetheart.

"A few of the power brokers here will have a little get together later on. Will you join me, sweetheart?"

"May I come with my fiancé?" Jasmine asked.

"Is your fiancé rich and powerful?"

"Well..."

"Sweetheart, listen to me. With a package like yours, you can do better...much better. Do you know what I'm saying to you?"

"Yes," Jasmine said. She decided to take a risk and do some whitehat cheating with this destroyer of values. "Yes, I understand."

"Welcome aboard. Here's the address of our host," he said. He pulled out a card from his suit pocket. "See you there in two hours." The Senator then drifted away, smiling, shaking hands, laughing and coughing.

*

"The address is in Alexandria," Jake said. He held the Senator's card. "I'll hire a limousine service to take us. Security will be watching, and I'd run into problems waiting outside in our car. In a limousine, I'll just wait inconspicuously in the back seat. ...You know, I don't like this idea of you alone at a private party with him, not at all."

"I don't like this either," Jasmine said, "but it's a way to get the enemy's plans. I'll carry my cell phone and call you if I have a problem."

The address took them to a large white mansion in an upscale neighborhood. Several expensive cars lined the curb and driveway.

"Play it safe, darling," Jake said. He hugged her. "Leave the minute you don't feel safe. Remember who you're dealing with in there."

621

"I'll be careful, my love," she assured him.

Jake watched his beautiful wife walk toward the mansion. He wondered, just what underneath is motivating her to do this? Regardless of the information she might acquire, this is a bad idea. But she's determined. Something's driving her.

Before she reached the doorway, she stopped and reached in her purse and pulled out her phone. Jake's phone rang.

"What is it, darling?" he asked.

"I just want you to know that this senator and his allies in Congress were and still are the biggest supporters of the bureaucrats who destroyed my father. That's why I'm going in there."

"You're a precious person," Jake said, "I love you. Remember, I'm right out here."

A doorman in a tuxedo greeted her and took her coat. About a dozen wealthy, powerful men and as many young, beautiful women mingled in the large party room. Before Jasmine could observe much more, an arm slid around her waist, startling her.

"Glad you made it, sweetheart," the Senator from Massachusetts said. "Come with me."

He took her over to the bar.

"Mikey, pour the lady and me a glass of the good stuff," the Senator said. A moment later, he was sniffing the wine, then took a drink. "Ah, yes. Here you go, sweetheart. Fifteen hundred bucks a bottle. Our host tonight is very rich. He contributes a lot of money to me and my political action committee and to the Democratic Party. I do him a lot of good politically; I've managed to keep the regulations tough enough and expensive enough to hold down those dog-eat-dog entrepreneurs from rising up and eating him alive. I guess you can say, I make his business a lot easier for him; and he keeps my PAC well funded and me in Washington."

What amazed Jasmine was that this powerful senator actually sounded proud of this relationship that was void of integrity and ethics. Instead of being ashamed, he was boasting.

After about thirty minutes, the men gathered in a smaller room with comfortable leather chairs. A fire was blazing in the fireplace. The Senator took Jasmine along, although she noticed only two other women went inside with the men.

"Gentlemen," the Senator said, "let's begin."

"People don't like change," an older man said, "and his changes are so drastic that I think he's vulnerable."

"I agree, Murray, but we must move fast," a younger man added.

"Why?" the Senator from Massachusetts asked, although he already knew why.

"Because once people's standards of living start rapidly climbing, which they will as he reduces political control over the economy, nothing we say or do will be able to stop the people from wanting more reduction of our power."

"So, what do we do?" the Senator asked, although he already knew what to do.

"We need to scare the people — make them fear his radical changes. He must look like a nonfeeling monster. The media will oblige. As Murray said, right now he's still vulnerable. We must move fast and hard."

"But some House members tried this already, and it hurt them," one young man protested.

"They're amateurs," the Senator said. He looked at Jasmine and winked. Then he turned to the men in the room and said, "Okay. You all know what to do and who to talk to. Spread the word."

As though they were speaking in code, the subject changed and the party continued. The beautiful young ladies were back. The Senator looked at Jasmine sitting next to him. His eyes roamed over her entire body.

"I...I need to leave," said Jasmine. She stood up.

"No you don't," the Senator protested, "the party's just begun." He stood up and put his hands on her.

"I'm sorry, but I have to go."

"Sweetheart, I can't wait to get to know you...much, much better." He slid his hand across her back.

Jasmine crossed her arms across her stomach and leaned forward. "Cramps," she whispered. "It's my time of the month."

"*Ah...Christ*," the Senator whined. He reluctantly let her go. "It sure as hell isn't the wine," he barked as she feigned her cramps. Then, he raised another glass of the good stuff and poured it down his throat in one breath.

CHAPTER
SIXTY

Daniel wanted to see Jake and Jasmine. While sitting in the waiting room, Jake walked up to a plaque on the wall. "There they are," he mumbled, "the Twelve Visions." He leaned forward to read the Twelve Visions, their 410 pages reduced here to twelve theme sentences:

The Twelve Visions

  I. People tap their long-lost, deepest motivational roots.

 II. They unearth the exhilarated, creative persons they were meant to be.

III. They embrace the creation-driven life they were meant to live.

IV. They demand science and business to advance rapidly and rescue mankind from serious diseases and, eventually, from the disease of aging.

V. They evolve a new business paradigm that nurtures and rewards their growing creativity.

VI. They establish Neothink businesses to accommodate limitless value-creation.

VII. They discover happiness-driven romantic love.

VIII. Busy creating values for the world, they barely have time for or interest in snacking, and they slim down to the healthy bodies they once envied.

IX. Through puzzle-building Neothink, they see beyond today's scholars and experts.

X. They become the geniuses of society, breaking boundaries and bringing us priceless values.

XI. They evolve a new political paradigm based on the Prime Law of Protection *only,* securing peace while setting free the existing and potential geniuses of society...freeing them to bring us priceless values for less and less costs, causing our buying power to soar to unprecedented heights.

XII. Those freed geniuses of society quickly answer the number-one demand from the happy and wealthy people everywhere: *cure mankind from disease including cellular degeneration because we want to live longer, disease-free lives!*

Jasmine walked up beside Jake and said, "The Twelve Visions are beautiful."

He nodded. "Especially when you know their full context."

"Jake and Jasmine," a secretary said, "the President will see you now."

*

"If something had happened to you...I don't even want to think about it," Daniel said.

Jasmine and Jake sat before Daniel in the Oval Office.

"What were you two thinking? Jasmine, I want you to stay away from that senator."

She nodded.

Daniel took a deep breath. "Look, I'm touched by what you've done," he said, softening his tone, "and the information you got is a powerful asset for us. I appreciate that. But all that means nothing to me if you get hurt. You must know when to back off in this game. There are certain boundaries you don't cross."

The young couple nodded. They agreed with Daniel. Then Jasmine cleared her throat and said, "I had a personal motivation to go in there, too." She went on to tell Daniel the story of her father. "This senator most vocally encouraged the EPA's campaign to 'stop the rise of a rash of environmentally intrusive shopping malls across the country.' His demagoguery ultimately caused my dad's business and self-esteem to go bankrupt ten years ago," she began.

Daniel listened to her story. He stopped lecturing about her judgment. He just nodded in acknowledgment and said, "I understand. But let's agree right here, right now...no more undercover-type episodes. Do we agree?"

Again, Jake and Jasmine nodded.

"I can see our role here in Washington, D.C. will be quite different than our course to get me here," Daniel said to his two and only media allies in the U.S. Capitol. "We won't be building a puzzle. Instead, this'll be a street fight. My sole objective is to depoliticize America as quickly as possible. Their sole objective is to get me out of office as quickly as possible."

*

The Senator's skillful web of illusions started spinning in the media two days later.

Jake and Jasmine brought some of the major papers with them and went to see Daniel.

"It's begun," Jake said. He put copies of three different

626

dailies on Daniel's desk. Daniel leaned over and read the headline *Can A Developer for the Rich Really Care About the Poor?*

When Daniel shook his head in disgust, Jake quickly said, "We're ready."

"Tomorrow," Jasmine immediately added, "the Patterson Papers will release our article titled *The Magicians are Coming! The Magicians are Coming!*" Jasmine smiled. "We've outlined, step-by-step, word-for-word the private party I attended. But we withheld everyone's name. I now know every person who spoke in that meeting by going through a who's who photo file. We refer to them, for now, as *the magicians* who, with their assistants in the media, will create the illusion that our President is, in their own words, 'an unfeeling monster who will destroy the little people through radical changes designed to benefit the rich'."

"That'll backfire because the people love this president," said Jake. "We'll let the people's anger grow. Then, we'll direct their anger to the head Magician in charge."

"We just want to make sure you're okay with us exposing the private meeting," said Jasmine. "We know how upset you got when I went to that party."

"I don't want you two to put yourselves in those undercover-type circumstances, particularly you all alone, Jasmine, not with those people. An article, though, doesn't concern me in the same way."

The media war was on; the anticivilization fired first, but Jake and Jasmine's article was the shot that caused America to turn her head and watch. Their article went into such detail — and the Patterson Papers were known for never taking situations out of context — its readers were fascinated by the inner-circle account.

Jake and Jasmine's next article, four days later, was the front-page headline of the Patterson Papers. The headline read *Will the Master Magician Please Stand Up?* Again, Jake and Jasmine did not state any names. They kept the country guessing...and the Senator from Massachusetts squirming.

The media attack on Daniel seemed to be weakening since Jake and Jasmine's articles already presented in detail the illusion the media would attempt to create.

Superpuzzle

Jake and Jasmine did not let up. This was a fight to the finish.

"Jasmine and I are beating their whole army of journalists!" Jake announced to Daniel.

"Wait until they see our next article," Jasmine added.

"Oh, it's powerful," Jake said. "We go back in time to Miss Annabelle's Miracle Year with her third-grade class. We build background and explain how power-hungry politician Hammerschmidt destroyed her teaching career and cost society dearly. Then, the parallels to the Head Magician are drawn and pulled together. He's using the same illusion-building approach, using the media to build his illusions. His goal is to destroy the President, which would cost society dearly. By revealing the essence of that type of person who gains power by tearing down someone valuable to society, the reader can't help feeling disgust for The Magician. Without stating his name, without seeing his smiling face, the feeling of disgust for the Magician is able to grow in the readers who are following the articles."

Jasmine nodded.

"People around the country," said Sam, his voice coming from the speaker phone placed in the middle of Daniel's desk, "have started asking one another, 'Who do you think that evil magician is?' ...You're right — you're letting the feeling grow by holding back his identity."

"Beautiful strategy," Daniel said. He admired the talent of the two young journalists.

The next week, their fourth article was published: *Allegiance Broken!* The subtitle read, *"Deep Throat Is Back, and He's Ratting On You, Mr. Magician."*

"This is psychological warfare," Jake explained to Daniel. "We're in an anticivilization, and we'll use the same tactics used against value producers for thousands of years."

"This is strategic politics," Jasmine added. "Those found plotting against Daniel will lose their support of the people."

"We've talked to four people who attended that meeting in the Senator's mansion. Al went with us. We had them confirm, on the record, the Senator was there and in control of the meeting. In exchange, we won't report the degree of their active roles in the conspiracy."

"With those witnesses in place, we'll name the date The Magician will be revealed — in two weeks," Jasmine concluded.

"Good work," said Daniel.

"The anticipation around the country has grown from a buzz to an alarm," Sam wrote in an email to Daniel. "Everyone wants to know. Now, even the mainstream media is asking, 'Who is The Magician?' The story has become huge. Even schoolchildren are asking the question. ...And only the Patterson Group knows the answer."

*

The day the country was looking forward to had finally arrived. The Patterson Papers would reveal The Magician. People set their alarm clocks a few minutes earlier to have time to read the headline story. The Patterson Papers printed seventy-five percent more papers to handle the newsstand rush. Still, all regions sold out.

People around the country were surprised when they read the morning papers and saw that the iconic Senator from Massachusetts was The Magician.

He appeared on national television later that morning, and he passionately denied everything. "I'm a victim of the right-wing conspiracy," he cried. "I've met with my attorney; we will sue the Patterson Group for an undetermined sum of not less than twenty million dollars."

Al and Jake, who were watching the Senator's announcement together, laughed spontaneously. "He can't take this to court!" said Jake.

"Of course not," said Al. "He knows that. He's just softening the blow."

Staring at the Senator on national television, Jasmine whispered, "Who's the amateur now?"

Al Patterson announced to the country, thirty minutes later with a broad smile across his face, "Bruce Salinski and his widescope accounting lawyers will handle this case." ...The Senator never filed the lawsuit.

CHAPTER
SIXTY-ONE

"Daniel's program is clearly working," his spokesperson said at a press conference, early during Daniel's second year in office. The comment was the understatement of the young millennium, for the standard of living was rising faster than any time in the country's history. "He submitted his second budget two days ago, essentially a replica of the first that was ignored — deleting about a trillion dollars from the previous budget while beefing up national defense. This time around, members of Congress had best fear losing their constituents if they ignore the President's budget."

Congress heeded the warning. They agreed to seriously deep cuts, about halfway between the President's budget and a "normal" budget.

To their dismay, buying power shot up at an unprecedented rate as millions more entrepreneurs came into the market, and businesses poured their profits back into research, development, and expansion. Unemployment fell to an all-time low. The Dow soared past 20,000. With that demonstration, the country was sold on the President's agenda.

*

Putting Together the Pieces

"God, Marcy, I miss The Group," Daniel said to his wife. "You know, it's been almost three months since I've seen any of them besides Jake and Jasmine. I'm so looking forward to seeing them tomorrow, and I'm really excited about this scientists' summit they're putting on tomorrow." Daniel scooped another fork-full of scrambled eggs, but he did not lift the fork from his plate. "You know, that's going to be quite a crowd, isn't it? An exclusive national gathering of the scientists who belong to the Church of God-Man!"

"Can I go?" said Daniel's six-year-old son, Danny. The boy looked up from his bowl of cereal. His blue eyes were begging his dad.

"Ah, Danny, I'd love to take you—"

"Yes!" yelped Danny. He pumped his fist in the air.

"Oh...no, Danny, I didn't finish. I'd love to take you, but I can't, buddy."

"Ahhh...why not, Dad?"

"It's for grown-ups. There's going to be long, long talks when you have to sit very still and make no noise."

"Can you breathe?"

Danny and Daniel laughed. "You're funny," dad said, "but I'll tell you what...I'll bring you next week with me to Mr. Rodriguez's mansion. How 'bout that?"

"Oh yeah, oh yeah!" Danny said. He did a little wiggle in his chair.

Marcy laughed at her son's reaction. She looked at Daniel and said, "He really loves playing with Rico's kids."

"Yeah, he sure does."

"And I can't wait to play with *you* tonight, Dad," said Danny. He pointed his finger straight at his dad. Daniel quickly reached out and snatched Danny's little finger in his hand.

"Gotcha!"

"Ahhh!" his son screamed in delight. The two of them laughed. Every morning, Daniel ate breakfast with his wife and son. Every night, he played with Danny for about a half hour before Danny went to bed.

"And I can't wait to play with *you*, Danny boy," Daniel said. "But right now, I'm gonna get you!" He leaned over and tickled his boy's ribs. Danny laughed instantaneously. "Oh no, oh no!"

631

said Daniel, "I'm gonna tickle your legs. No, NO! Not the legs!" Daniel dove his hands just above Danny's knees and began squeezing them gently. Danny's laughter burst out of control, and he happily screamed for mercy. A special feeling filled Daniel's soul. ...Hearing my boy laugh, Daniel thought, seeing him happy...just being with him are the most precious, the most meaningful moments in my life.

*

"Ian!"

"Hi, Daniel!"

They shook hands and patted each other on the shoulders.

"Come with me," Ian said. He pointed toward the front of the lecture hall. "The others are already here and can't wait to see you." Ian led the way. As they walked toward the front, Ian looked back and glanced around. "Marcy's not with you?"

"No, she's got bronchitis and needs to rest."

"Dan! Daniel!" Daniel looked up ahead toward the voices calling out his name and saw The Group.

"Hello!" Daniel said. He shook hands with and hugged his former classmates; he hugged his beloved Miss Annabelle and the others. Secret Service agents stood all around him; they concentrated on every gesture.

"Here are the seats we reserved for you and Secret Service," said Jeremiah. He was hosting the event. "You're right here with us."

"Wonderful. It's so good to see all of you! It's been...what? Almost three months?"

"Let's see, you missed the past two monthly meetings," said Rico, "so...you're right, it's coming up on three months."

"You know," said Daniel, "I really feel a loss inside when I miss one of our monthly meetings. Missing two meetings in a row and not seeing all of you for nearly three months...a part of me feels left behind — it really does. I've really missed all of you."

"Oh Danny, we've missed you, too," said Miss Annabelle.

Jeremiah slipped away. A moment later his voice filled the room over the PA system. "Good afternoon and welcome to our first annual gathering of scientists from the Church of God-Man. The Church of God-Man, as you know, represents the *only* group of people to which the God-Man Group — sitting together right up front here — reveals its ultimate goal of achieving biological immortality. And the scientists of the Church of God-Man, here tonight, represent the only group of persons to which the God-Man Group reveals its specific scientific breakthroughs toward achieving its goal of biological immortality. The words spoken here tonight must not leave this room. I'm sure you've noticed: we have very tight security at this highly-guarded, invitation-only event. We've allowed no press on the premises beyond radio talk-show host Natasha Kemp and media-king Alan Patterson and his two top reporters Jake Catchings and Jasmine Kahil. They're, of course, members of the God-Man Group. They won't reveal to the public the very private information you hear tonight. They won't reveal our progress on the immortality superpuzzle until the time is right.

"The first person from the God-Man Group who'll speak to you tonight about our progress on our ultimate superpuzzle is Mr. John Melbourne."

The scientists applauded as Jeremiah turned the mic over to Mr. Melbourne.

"Thank you," Mr. Melbourne said. "It's so enjoyable spending a day with all of you. I know that both Dr. Sally Salberg and Dr. Ian Scott have some mind-blowing technical progress to tell you about today." The scientists applauded again. "Before they do that, however, I'll give you an interesting insight about our next evolutionary leap into God-Man and then Zon.

"Evolutionary leaps by Natural Selection have always yielded physical changes followed by psychological acclimation.

"But today, mankind is about to make an evolutionary leap through our Superpuzzle that's stunningly different by nature. Mankind has been rapidly shedding its limited, follow-the-leader mentality. Society's wide-open Freedom Paradigm, thanks to our President, offers just too many advantages to the limitless, self-leader mentality. Soon mankind will undergo a fundamental emotional change, away from accepting death as the final escape from miserable stagnation at the end...to desiring life as an endless adventure with happy exhilaration forever. That emotional shift for happy, exhilarating eternal life will go hand-in-hand with a psychological leap into immortal God-Man, *followed by* physical acclimation — namely, biological immortality. This is a *psychological* leap followed by a physiological leap.

"The reverse order of this evolutionary leap — the mind first followed by the physical — signifies the power of our minds as we leave nature behind. I need to take a few minutes to explain:

"The ruling class will vanish as Daniel depoliticizes America. Businesses and scientists will soar in the resulting Freedom Paradigm. As we've begun to see, millions upon millions of 'garage' entrepreneurs at home and in-house entrepreneurs in big business will flourish. They've begun rapidly adopting Theodore Winter's division of essence that leaves behind stagnation by bringing the creative mind to their jobs. They've begun exhilarating journeys into value creation, which motivates them and brings them happiness. After all, creation is the literal opposite of stagnation. The way their creative minds work now is the opposite of the stagnant following mode, just doing their routine ruts at work. That stagnation, that lack of creativity, atrophies the mind and eventually destroys the conscious life. That's no exaggeration; the human mind will literally die from stagnation. In fact, when you dissect *why* we still die today with all the modern technology available to us, the reason reduces to the acceptance of death because of stagnation. The human psyche can't live with stagnation beyond eight or nine decades. So, there's never been a drive to achieve immortality.

"But now, the ordinary person's mind is changing from the following mode into an integrating mode that leads itself on an endless journey of creating values. Value creation causes happiness and forever fuels conscious life. These creative people are discovering that their truly deepest desire is for...immortality."

Mr. Melbourne paused to study the scientists. Then, he continued, "The following-mode tendencies come from our obsolete *nature-controlled* minds. I believe most if not all of you have read my bestseller *The Neothink Mind* that reveals our next evolutionary leap from our nature-controlled, externally guided bicameral-like minds to man-controlled, internally guided

Neothink minds. All nature-controlled animals are designed to die. Therefore, our lives are designed in a death cycle with built-in, debilitating stagnation. The old division of labor, those routine-rut jobs of labor brought us unbearable stagnation, which was why people used to say they were working themselves to death. I repeat: growing stagnation eventually kills conscious life, or makes it okay to die.

"I explain in my book that human consciousness was a man-made invention three-thousand years ago; human consciousness was a *leap* beyond nature. Our human minds simply aren't supposed to be nature-controlled, limited, doomed. Human consciousness is supposed to be man-controlled, unlimited, immortal. Conscious man, once free of his deep-rooted, following-mode bicameral tendencies, is not designed to stagnate and die. He is designed to create and live. Creating is an exhilarating man-made activity unique to the man-made conscious mind. Creating is how adults play and have fun. It is the opposite of stagnating. Whereas the *nature-controlled* bicameral mind was designed to stagnate and eventually die, the *man-made* conscious mind is designed to create and eternally live, eternally have fun. Indeed, creating brings back the enthusiastic child of the past within all of us. The man-made conscious mind thrives on creativity. Whereas stagnation is close-ended, limited, terminal...creation is open-ended, limitless, eternal. The human psyche can flourish *forever* with value creation. It can play and have fun forever. Therefore, our minds should live eternally with built-in, expanding creativity and happiness. The new division of essence, the new job of the body *and mind,* brings creativity and happiness to our lives. Never forget, that's how we play. Growing creativity and happiness forever fuel conscious life and make it emotionally unacceptable to die. With the proliferation of the division of essence, soon there's going to be a drive to achieve immortality. We're going to want to play and have fun forever.

"The Neothink mind is our *next* evolutionary leap. It is the conscious mind free of residual following-mode or bicameral tendencies or, as I've explained in my book, the mysticism-free mind. We'll reach the jumping-off point to make the next leap into Neothink through the division of essence as we switch from bicameral-like followers to integrated self-leaders. The old division of labor that emphasized our bodies in stagnant set routines is for robots. The new division of essence that emphasizes our bodies *and* minds in exhilarating value creation is for conscious man. Soon, as I said earlier, we'll fundamentally *want to* live forever.

"Indeed, our fading bicameral-like society with a ruling class telling us how to exist...and our bicameral-like jobs with set responsibilities restricting us to automatons — that all prevented us from becoming purely conscious, prevented our leap into the Neothink mind. Neothink is bicameral-free or mysticism-free consciousness — pure consciousness. Our bicameral-like society and jobs suppressed us in our mortal traps, for we were *not purely conscious*, thus designed to die. Conscious man transcends mortal nature. Conscious man, by nature, is immortal.

"And this gets back to our next astounding evolutionary leap that is soon to occur. Conscious man *by nature* is immortal. The conscious mind can go on creating values and generating happiness *forever*. For the first time, the *psychological* leap must occur first — the leap into Neothink. Then, the man-made physical changes will follow — the immortal body.

"President Daniel Ward is depoliticizing America, which means he's ending the parasitical ruling class. Theodore Winters is introducing America to the division of essence, which means replacing boring stagnation *or terminal mental illness* with exhilarating creation *or eternal mental health*. Their work will create the conditions for the average American's leap into Neothink. Dr. Sally Salberg is working on breakthrough medical procedures that'll bring us the immortal body soon thereafter.

"The entire God-Man Group, in fact, several of whom will talk to you today, are doing some amazing things to put together The Group's superpuzzle of immortality. But only you will see the full picture of that superpuzzle. Only you will hear about our progress today.

"With that introduction, I turn the day over to the twelve original God-Men, which includes four women, who were once classmates in my wife's third-grade class at Duncan Elementary."

Wow, this is fascinating, Daniel thought as he listened to

Sally's delivery. When Sally paused for a drink of water, Daniel leaned over and whispered to Ian, "My god, her breakthroughs are amazing. It's like, since I've missed two meetings, I'm left far, far behind...in your dust! I can just imagine how all these scientists must feel, witnessing this *for the first time!* It's mind-blowing stuff, absolutely incredible."

Robert Chapman, who sat behind Ian, overheard Daniel whispering to Ian. Robert leaned forward and quietly said, "Just wait 'till you hear Ian's breakthroughs over the past two months."

Daniel looked back at Robert and whispered, "Really?"

Robert nodded and said, "Just you wait."

Ian just smiled.

*

"The day was stunning," Daniel said to Reggie, Cathy, and Debra. They stood together, surrounded by Secret Service, enjoying conversation as the scientists left the building. "I'm still staggering from Ian's demonstration that the Universe so precisely breaks down into the optimal division-of-essence for conscious life. And his breakthroughs on conscious-controlled creation as the controlling component of the Universe — man-made *conscious creation* controlling everything including the creation of our universe, our galaxy, essentially our existence. Wow, it's breathtaking and brings the full impact to the meaning of *God-Man*. It all makes so much sense! The division of essence spawns creation — man-made creation used to optimally control the cosmos. His division-of-essence breakdown chart of the Universe shows that God-Man, not mass and energy, controls the cosmos. What was it now, umm...through quantum mechanics and vacuum fluxes, our conscious cousins create and control the cosmos! God-Man is God — *proven* by his Overlay Charts!"

Ian overheard that last comment. He walked over and added, "Proven through highly-predictive Overlay Charts linking the dynamics of evolving business and science with the evolving dynamics of the cosmos, ranging from astro physics to quantum mechanics as they mold into a unified conscious-controlled universe."

Superpuzzle

"You've unraveled perhaps the biggest mysteries of the Universe," Daniel continued. "Creative God-Man and his ultimate division of essence captures the Universe's creation and structure."

Daniel took his thumb and flipped through Ian's *Universe-Capture Discovery,* which demonstrated a division-of-essence breakdown of the Universe. "We're doing some unbelievable things, aren't we?" Daniel said. He looked up at his eternal soul mates. They nodded. Daniel nodded too, overwhelmed by Ian's revelations.

"You know," Daniel added, "the nearly three-month separation from you, when I'm used to no more than one month apart, makes me appreciate even more what The Group is doing. For the first time, I can see our progress as would an outsider. It's almost ungraspable, you know."

"And that's exactly how we felt while listening to your progress on depoliticizing America and creating the Freedom Paradigm," said Mr. Melbourne. "That Freedom Paradigm is critical to achieving the physical cure to aging and death."

"We all know," said Al, "depoliticizing America is the second big piece to our superpuzzle. Of course, getting you elected was the first piece. Sally and the rest of us are gearing up to deliver the third piece — the physical cure — once you snap down the second piece to clear the way."

Miss Annabelle looked on. Her heart pounded with pride. The Group, basking in profound mutual respect, turned toward the door to head back to their homes, rejuvenated, recharged, and ready to bulldoze ahead, creating unprecedented values for the world.

"It's already dark," said Rico, a little surprised. Some people were waiting outside, mostly scientists still lingering with fresh questions on their minds. Some members of the White House Press Corps, kept back at a distance by police and Secret Service, took pictures as The Group walked out.

"Mr. President! Mr. President!" one reporter shouted between pictures, "What was today's meeting about? What were you meeting about in there with all those scientists?"

"Can't tell you," said the President. He smiled. "It's top

secret, and we're all sworn to secrecy."

"Are you designing some new weapons technology for your protection-only government?" asked another reporter.

"I can't discuss what we met about; neither can they," Daniel said waving toward the scientists. He knew the seasoned reporters would try to get information from the scientists. "This matter is closed, gentlemen."

The White House Press Corps stood in force, snapping pictures and still asking questions to no avail as The Group walked by. Suddenly, there was movement within the pack of reporters; there was shuffling — one reporter shoved another out of his way and stepped to the front of the pack and yelled something unrecognizable. The Secret Service agent flanking Daniel's left side instantly leaned into Daniel with right arm extended; the agent pushed his right shoulder hard into Daniel's side at the same moment a distinct *pop pop pop* snapped through the air.

"Ohhh...ouuu," gushed from Daniel's mouth. "Ouuu..." leaked from his mouth again, and he went down to the ground in a crumpled heap. He felt something unbearably hot in his stomach. He felt someone fall on top of him.

I'm shot, his mind registered. The burning heat in his stomach turned into a cold spasm. Feet and hands were all Daniel could see. Secret Service agents dragged him to the car. The edges of his vision darkened to black. The agents pulled Daniel into the car, shut the door and drove away. He sensed Secret Service agents were trying to help him, but he could barely comprehend what was going on around him. *I can't feel.* He lay in someone's arms. Daniel's world went silent and dark, but he was still conscious. *No, this can't be. Am I dying? No, no I can't die...not now!* Then, just before he lost consciousness, he heard a voice inside his head: "I can't wait to play with you tonight, Dad!" *Oh no...Danny boy!* Sadness filled his soul the moment he ceased to know.

CHAPTER
SIXTY-TWO

A blinding light flooded his brain. After a few moments his eyes adjusted, and the bright lights silhouetted a fuzzy figure hovering over him. Confusion overwhelmed him; he just looked...and blinked his eyes, trying to focus.

"Mr. President, I'm Dr. Rosenbloom," said the fuzzy figure leaning over him. "You've undergone surgery to remove a bullet from your abdomen and stop internal bleeding. You're in stable condition now, sir."

I'm alive. ...Daniel tried to talk, but instead he could barely whisper, "What happened?"

Another man stepped to the side of the bed and said, "Mr. President, I'll answer that."

Daniel realized he could see more clearly now and looked up to see Chris, one of his Chiefs of Staff.

"You were shot, sir. You took a bullet in your stomach. Dr. Rosenbloom assured us you'll be okay now."

Daniel nodded.

"We were fortunate, sir, to have secret service agent Ralley Sanders by your side. He pushed you out of the way and took two bullets himself in his shoulder and collarbone. He's okay, though."

"Is he here, in this hospital?"

"Yes. He's being treated and will probably be released in the morning."

Daniel nodded, then softly said, "Who shot us?"

"Abdur Rahmaan. He was a fully credentialed, highly respected Arabic journalist from the Jordanian Press Corps. At one time, he served on the staff of the King of Jordan. He was accredited to the White House Press Corps about a year ago."

"Abdur shot me?" Daniel asked.

"Yes sir. He just snapped; he yelled out in Arabic 'God is great!' and pulled out a gun. Of course, he had to know Secret Service would shoot him dead."

"Did they?"

"Yes sir."

Daniel sighed and shook his head.

"Of course, we have a major investigation going," the President's Chief of Staff continued. "So far, we have nothing that ties him to any terrorist group or government."

Daniel nodded and said, "Keep me informed of everything you find out."

"Yes sir, I will."

"Now, can you get Ralley Sanders in here?"

A few minutes later, a nurse pushed Ralley on a wheelchair into Daniel's highly guarded room. Daniel immediately recognized him.

"Hello Ralley," said Daniel. "How badly are you hurt?"

"Not too bad, Mr. President. Fortunately, both shots hit my upper shoulder area. I'll walk out of here tomorrow. Sir, the doctors told me you're going to be fine, too."

"He'll be fine, but he needs to rest now," Dr. Rosenbloom interrupted. He noticed Daniel's blood pressure had dropped slightly.

"Mr. President," Ralley said, "may we speak in private?" He then looked at Dr. Rosenbloom. "It'll just take about three minutes."

Daniel studied Ralley. His Secret Service agent was calm and businesslike. He looked more like a Wall Street executive than a secret service agent. *This man saved my life*, Daniel thought.

"The President needs to rest now," Dr. Rosenbloom repeated.

He looked at Ralley then back at Daniel.

Daniel slowly, painfully turned his head toward the doctor until their eyes met. "Please, let us speak in private," Daniel said. He had regained some strength.

Dr. Rosenbloom sighed and reluctantly said, "I'll let you talk for five minutes."

The doctor, the nurses, the Chief of Staff, secretary, and the other Secret Service agents left the room. When only Daniel and Ralley remained, Ralley said, "When I got you into the car and had my men drive you away out of danger, I went back. The shooter was lying on the ground. Our agents had shot him, but he was still alive. I whispered in his ear that I'd take out his entire family unless he told me who helped him."

"Helped him?"

"My instincts told me someone helped get him into the White House Press Corps, and I was right."

Daniel's eyes widened. "What'd he say?"

"A very well-connected politician pulled some strings. That politician helped Abdur realize his dreams."

"Did he say who that politician was?"

"Yes."

"Who?"

"Bullfrog."

"Who's that?"

"That's our code name for the senior Senator from Massachusetts."

The heavyweight! Daniel slowly shook his head and said, "How can you be sure he's telling the truth? Wouldn't the Senator have someone else set this up?"

Ralley shook his head. "Bullfrog has used strong-arm tactics before," said Ralley, "never to this extent. But he's very hands-on."

Daniel remembered Jasmine's account of the private party when the Senator discussed bringing down the President, early in his presidency. Yes, Daniel remembered, the Senator — *the Head Magician* — was the hands-on leader giving out the directives.

"Have you notified the FBI?

"Sir, the FBI is crawling all over this. But I must not tell them what I know...not the FBI, not the Justice Department, nobody."

"Why not?"

"We need to do things differently."

"What do you mean?"

"We need to ask ourselves: is this over with, or will there be more?"

"What do you think?"

"There'll be more," Ralley said without hesitation. "The money-source and motivation is too deep. They're going to get you."

"What are you saying?"

"This won't stop till you're dead."

Daniel looked alarmed. "So, don't we want to tell the FBI who's behind this? We need to get them on it."

"They're already 'on it'. And there's a big-time investigation coming. But you and I have a secret they must *never* know."

Daniel listened.

"To keep you alive, we're going to have to break protocol. This isn't a contest with rules. There are no rules. Sir, I've heard you say it yourself: *this is a street fight*. We're in the middle of a street fight, and we can't wait around for the cops to show up, so to speak. To keep you alive, we need to fight back. Bullfrog and his money have people lined up, paid off, planning to take you out even if he were in court...or jail. We need to strike and strike hard. We need to stop the source. And *no one* besides the two of us can know who the source is."

Daniel did not respond for a moment to let Ralley's words sink in. Finally, he took a deep breath and nodded. "You're right," he said. "What do you suggest we do?"

"We tell no one — *no one*. We let no one know that we know who's behind this. If anyone knows we know, that stops our retaliation, because what we need to do will be breaking laws, Mr. President—"

"But not natural law," Daniel said. "You're right, it's the only way. A civilization must be governed by law, but when at war or when in a street fight, those laws, including due process, get superseded by sheer self-defense. I won't survive if I don't swing back."

"And swing back *now*, sir. While you've been recovering, I've been working on a plan. Sir, I need a secret team of my own men, about three men, who are NOT Secret Service. We can't involve anyone officially. We must discreetly dig out the roots to the cancer."

"We're going to dig out the roots with this team?"

"Yes sir. And my team will never know their target until the night of our strike. There's too many investigators, journalists, internet journalists all over this. I'll prepare my small team in secret at an undisclosed location. We'll train for a quick and hard retaliation that'll end any future attempts on your life from this source."

"How are you going to put together a team like that—" Daniel stopped and his face lost its color.

"Sir, I'll get the doc—"

"No...wait. I think I'm all right," Daniel said. He took a breath and his color returned. He spoke more easily. "Tell me, how will you get such a team — *and quickly?*"

"I've talked to your former classmate, Mr. Rico Rodriguez. I know he's had a similar close call. In fact, if you remember, we had a couple of Secret Service agents outside his home, covering you as a presidential candidate back when it happened."

Daniel nodded.

"Mr. Rodriguez told me that after the attack in his home," Ralley continued, "well, you know, he brought in a top security team to protect your meetings. His head of security was the first-line bodyguard of the Governor of Louisiana. I know Manny well. When corruption charges hit that administration, he was let go. Mr. Rodriguez since then hired Manny. As I said, I personally know him. He's well trained, and he's damn good. And I can trust him. Mr. Rodriguez told me we can have Manny and anyone from his team. Sir, this'll speed things up, and we're in a race against time to save your life."

Daniel nodded slightly. "Does Rico know the source?"

"No."

"Ralley," Daniel said weakly, "*thank you* for saving my life. You took two bullets to save my life. I thank you for me, for my wife, and especially for my son."

Ralley could feel the depth of Daniel's gratitude. The secret service agent took a deep breath and nodded. He had followed the political rise of Daniel from the beginning and believed in him.

"Saving you, sir, was like saving the future for my boys. But we're not out of the woods yet."

Daniel paused. He did not know Ralley was a father and family man. Although Daniel's body really needed to rest now, he nodded and quietly asked, "How old are your boys?"

"Five and two."

Daniel had to reflect on that for a moment. Here was a father of two young children — a father who risked his life — who *really* risked it all for Daniel.

Seeing the President pause over this, Ralley said, "Mr. President, it's always been my job to protect persons in high office. But, for the first time, I feel that protecting you really means something. I feel you'll make this a great country for my boys to live in."

Daniel tried to speak, but he had run out of energy. So, he nodded; he was moved. Someone he barely knew before today counted on the President to make the future a wonderful place for the children. *Many, many people are counting on me. This is so very real*, he thought. He closed his eyes. *We've got to succeed.*

CHAPTER
SIXTY-THREE

Manny Franks, Rico's head of security, met secretly with Ralley and Rico in Rico's mansion in Philadelphia.

"We need to put together a four-man team for one top-secret mission," Ralley said. "We have to trust each other with our lives. No Secret Service. Not a whisper to anyone. As you know, the FBI, journalists, Internet journalists are all over this investigation. No one beyond us and the two men we add to the team must so much as have a hint of our mission." Ralley looked at Manny. "Even then, you won't get the details until the night of our strike. We all must be able to take this secret to our graves. And, we need our four-man team quickly."

"My top two men here meet your criteria," said Manny, "and they're good. You, me, and my two men. By the way, they both love our President."

Ralley nodded and looked at Rico.

"As I told you before," said Rico, "use any of my men — whatever will help Daniel. But I do have a question: What if the source, after you retaliate, goes to the press and to the police and files charges?"

"Well, that would expose his own attempted murder of the President, so that won't happen. But if it did, the President said he would admit to the crime, pardon all of us, and let Congress try to impeach him."

Rico nodded.

"I want to thank you, Mr. Rodriguez," Ralley said. "You know, sir, the quick availability of your top three men could save the President's life."

Rico sighed and nodded; Ralley could feel Rico's love for the President.

Ralley turned toward Manny and said, "Can any of you disarm complicated alarm systems?"

"Yes, one of the two men is an electronics expert; the other's an explosive specialist."

"Perfect."

*

That same weekend, still recovering in the hospital, Daniel called Rico on the President's secure line. "Hey, I'm really grateful for the team of men you pulled together for me. You know, we must do this quickly or our whole superpuzzle is in jeopardy."

"...and *you* are in jeopardy, which is unacceptable to me."

"You know, Rico, I can't get some thoughts out of my head."

"What thoughts?"

"If I pull this off and depoliticize America, then the second piece to our superpuzzle snaps into place. The door opens to the third puzzle piece... to finally developing the technology for biological immortality. I mean, we'll be *right there!* Sally will be home free!"

*

Daniel left the hospital earlier than expected, restricted to light activity. When he returned to the White House, Daniel called for Ralley to join him in the Oval Office.

"It's so good to see you up and healthy, sir," Ralley said.

"Thank you, Ralley. And you look great. Your arm's out of its sling."

"They were only surface wounds. I'm at ninety-five percent."

Ralley turned around and closed the door to the Oval Office.

They were the only two people in the room.

"How's progress with Operation Bullfrog?" the President asked.

"We're ready."

"Ralley, I know I can't go with you. So, I want you to look into Bullfrog's eyes at his weakest moment and represent me, my resolve, and make sure he forever fears me."

"Sir, I'll be the messenger. He and his muscle will never touch you again."

Daniel took a deep breath. He could feel the weight of the superpuzzle upon his shoulders. He looked into Ralley's eyes and saw unyielding determination. *He can do it*, Daniel thought.

"Yes," he said, "yes, I believe you can communicate my resolve. You see, I believe in you, too, Ralley. I believe in you, too."

*

That evening, Daniel sat down on his son's bed to play a game of checkers with him. *Ah, it feels so good to play with my boy again.*

Marcy came into the bedroom and sat down with Daniel and Danny. Daniel smiled; he looked at his surroundings. His precious boy was on the bed laughing and playing checkers with him; his loving wife was on the bed laughing and joking with them. *I came so close to never seeing Danny and Marcy again*, Daniel thought. He soaked in this moment he nearly never had. *God, I love them. And I feel so much love from them for me.* He could barely fathom the contrast between his close call with anticivilization-death in comparison to this Civilization-of-the-Universe eternal love. He shook his head in a moment of disbelief; then he thought, *this world of love and compassion all around me must become the world out there outside this room for everyone.* He looked again at his loving wife and his precious boy. *We can and must succeed. This violent attempt on my life must not scare me or stop me...lest the greatest human killer since the beginning of time really will kill us all — me, Marcy, even little Danny, everybody: that damn killer disease, aging.*

Putting Together the Pieces

*

"It's time to put the brakes on another assassination attempt upon the President's life," Ralley said to his three partners in this mission. They sat around Ralley's kitchen table. "I want to thank you men for going to battle for the President. It's a treacherous journey to depoliticize this great country. Our President *must* succeed. With our help, he *will* succeed. Tonight we strike. Manny, I'll turn this over to you, now."

"Here's the playground," Manny said, standing up and flipping open a large detailed layout of the Senator's second home — his mansion in Alexandria.

As Manny described the plan of attack in minute detail, Ralley studied the three men. Their faces were determined and focused. He looked in their eyes and saw competence and devotion. He saw serious, top-ranking executives in their line of work and soul mates in the goal to depoliticize America. *They would not seem out of place at a boardroom table*, he thought. *No, for they're hardworking businessmen providing a priceless value to the world. They're the unseen, unsung heroes.*

CHAPTER
SIXTY-FOUR

A little after 3:00 a.m., Ralley and his men climbed out of a BMW sedan about twenty yards north of the Senator's mansion; The four men quickly disappeared into the hedges. The sedan casually drove away.

The four men hid in the tall hedges along the perimeter of the Senator's large custom home. Ralley pointed toward his electronics expert, then pointed toward the house. The electronics expert raced noiselessly across the yard, disappearing into the shadows. In just two minutes, he gave the signal.

Ralley, Manny, and their other trusted partner, all of them in tight black bodysuits and charcoal-black faces, ran to the house along a path least visible to windows and balconies.

From a quick survey, two bodyguards were on duty in the Senator's home. They were downstairs watching a tape-delayed basketball game.

Ralley and his men pulled stockings over their faces. They unlocked and slipped through glass french doors facing the pool. Ralley went through the house to the stairs; he raced directly to the Senator's room, making sure there was no escape. The other three quietly positioned themselves just behind the doorway facing the backs of the Senator's two bodyguards. Ralley's men planned to take the Senator's bodyguards by surprise and disable them with the new "Spiderman" technology for arresting potentially dangerous people without harming them; Ralley's men would then tape the bodyguards' mouths.

Waiting outside the Senator's bedroom, Ralley heard his three partners quietly running through the house and up the stairs. He knew the Senator's bodyguards were no longer a threat.

Ralley crouched next to the large door and waited. A moment later, his other three men crouched down behind him. Ralley pointed at the electronics expert and then at the door. He moved to the door and crouched on one knee. He slid a small metal tool into the lock. In about five seconds, he unlocked it and nodded to Ralley then backed away. Ralley signaled him to stay on the other side of the door. Manny and the explosives specialist crouched tightly behind Ralley. Then, Ralley grabbed the door handle and sprang inside the room, followed like a shadow by Manny, then by his two other men.

"He's not here!" Manny whispered. He shined his light on the empty bed.

Ralley did not answer. His mind did not relinquish its ready-to-fight alertness. His eyes were sharp and intense as he looked around the room. His men did not need to be told anything. They went straight to work inspecting the room like trained sniff dogs.

"Here it is," whispered the man who unlocked the door.

"Can you get it?" Ralley asked.

"No. It's a vault," he whispered back.

Showing no emotion, the explosives specialist reached inside his pants and pulled out two tubes. The other three men spun around and moved away, facing the far corner. Fifteen seconds later a powerful pop rang out, like a powerful explosion inside a metal box. They turned around to see their explosives expert throwing a man to the ground inside the vault.

"Come on!" Ralley growled.

They raced into the vault. Manny and the lock expert pinned the man in the vault to the ground. Ralley shined the light on the struggling face. He had to look for a moment to realize this was the Senator. The other member of the team stepped back out of the vault to keep watch.

Now, this is the job the President sent me here to do, Ralley

651

thought. "Close the vault and turn on the light," he ordered.

Ralley then focussed on the Senator.

"Look here, murderer!" Ralley commanded. He pulled the stocking off his head and stared into the Senator's eyes. "Looks like it's your turn to die!"

The Senator gasped in terror.

"Right here, right now!" Ralley hissed.

"No! Please, no!" the Senator pleaded. He started crying like a schoolgirl. Everyone in the room saw the puddle growing on the floor, flowing from his crotch.

"Take him out, man!" Ralley said, pointing to Manny, then to the Senator.

"Oh, god...no! Tell the President...I'll do anything he wants me to!"

"No, no you won't. You'll try to kill him again, so I'm going to kill you first. In fact, I'm just gonna do it myself!"

Ralley pulled out his nine-inch switchblade and snapped it open.

"Hold him good, while I carve him up!"

Then Ralley sprang on top of the Senator and cut open his tee shirt to expose his belly, which was flopping around like lemon jello. The Senator screamed and frantically shook his head. Ralley buried the tip of the blade into the Senator's stomach, about one inch deep into his fatty flesh. Then Ralley slid the buried blade around, in a large circle, about the circumference of the Senator's large stomach. Blood followed the blade around, flowing out of the wound a second or so after the blade neatly sliced the skin.

The Senator screamed wildly. Feeling the burning cut, he thought the blade was fatally deep into his guts. Just as Daniel believed only a few weeks before, the Senator now believed he was dying.

Ralley calmly lifted the blade and buried the bloody tip back into the skin, about one inch deep, at the top of the circle. With the Senator screaming, Ralley sliced a straight line from the top of the bleeding circle to the bottom. Then, like some sort of ritual killing, he sliced two diagonal lines in opposite directions, starting about two thirds of the way down the line at 45° angles out to the bottom, outside cut of the circle.

"That'll do it," he grunted.

The Senator was hysterical. When Ralley got up, the Senator looked down at his belly and saw blood everywhere.

Ralley leaned over and grabbed the Senator's hair and yanked his head up. He stared into the Senator's eyes and held back his desire to kill the politician. "I have a message for you from your victim," he said. Then he leaned over and put his mouth next to the Senator's ear.

"Fuck with me?" Ralley said calmly into the Senator's ear. "Big mistake."

Then, like a wave slipping back into the ocean, Ralley and his men were gone.

*

Not a word was spoken about the violent night in the Senator's mansion. Somehow, the Senator managed to keep the media unaware of it. A message spread to Bullfrog's entire network inside and outside the government, however: *no one physically violates the President or his loved ones.*

CHAPTER
SIXTY-FIVE

Six weeks after the night in the mansion, Daniel called for the Senator from Massachusetts to meet him in the Oval Office.

When the Senator entered, he saw Ralley and gasped. The Senator was very nervous. Yet, he passionately hated Daniel.

Daniel was deep in thought over a stack of papers when the Senator entered. Daniel glanced up.

"Open your shirt," he said, uninterested in the parasite before him, but handling this nitty-gritty detail although his mind was somewhere else. The President's voice was so disconnected to this unimportant detail that the Senator did not act, not sure if the President meant it.

Daniel glanced up a minute or so later. "I said, open your shirt!"

The Senator opened his shirt. Daniel waited until it was unbuttoned. "Now, lift up your undershirt."

The Senator frowned. He bounced his eyes off Ralley and Manny, then slowly lifted his undershirt.

"Well, look at that," Daniel said. He was looking at a big, purplish, healing peace sign carved right into the Senator's stomach.

"So Senator, you're a man of peace now, are you?"

The Senator nodded.

"*Good*. I mean that from the bottom of my heart. I didn't like my insides being ruptured — I didn't like nearly dying!"

The Senator could not look at Daniel.

"If ever you entertain the thought again, look down at your stomach and let that scar remind you you're a man of peace now. If you ever forget that, if anything happens to me or to people I love, you'll die a slow, prolonged death. I can describe in detail how your death will take place because I've instructed the Fearsome Four, who visited your home, how to perform those details. You know by now I'm a man who takes care of details. Believe me, these details are already communicated. The Fearsome Four...they don't like you, you know, not one bit. Would you like for me to describe those details I gave to them, exactly how you'll die?"

The Senator shook his head while looking at the floor.

"Okay then, for your sake and mine, I hope you never find out. It might behoove you to have your people do everything in their power to keep me and my family and friends safe. I repeat, if anything happens to me or anyone I love, that'll be the deepest, most ironic peace sign the coroner will ever see."

The Senator wanted to have Daniel killed more than anything in the world, but he would never consider it again.

"Anyone — even you — can go against me in every dishonest way one can think of. But, the moment you use force or threat of force, the same Fearsome Four who visited you in your vault will be on you like a pack of wild dogs. Hands off! Is that clear?"

The Senator sheepishly nodded.

"Speak up!" commanded the President.

"Yes sir!" the Senator said in military fashion. "It's clear, sir!"

Daniel stared at the humanoid before him for a moment and realized his diseased mind would kill millions of people if it meant boosting his own ego. Daniel felt sick looking at him.

"Get out," Daniel said, then he turned back to his stack of papers where real values for the world were being created.

*

During the rest of Daniel's second year in office, the Senator did fight hard and dirty. But he never crossed the line of using or threatening force. He was an automatic liar with no integrity. He would launch any lie to bring himself power or ego.

"The Senator is too late," Sam told Daniel in response to the Senator's mounting lies and attacks. "He's been a formidable foe. But now, too much time has passed. The economy is proving that the Twelve-Visions agenda is a fantastic thing."

"With your direct fight against the political ruling class," Ziggy added, "and with Jeremiah Jones' Business Alliance breaking down the business structure supporting the ruling class, it won't be long now."

"No, it won't," said Daniel. "After the mid-term elections, we'll fully depoliticize this country."

*

Daniel was enjoying breakfast with Marcy and Danny. "America's Capitol," Daniel said to his wife and son, "is the epitome of the anticivilization. It's the last bastion of dishonesty and crime. But here the momentum of the battle has changed. The Civilization of the Universe is coming."

Whoa. Right then he realized he had opened the gateway to the Civilization of the Universe on Earth. *What a feeling!* Daniel felt incredulous pride and happiness.

"We're going to pull it off!" he said to Marcy and Danny. "We're going to end this ruling-class politicization...and then end death."

He would never forget the smile that erupted on his son's face as the boy said, "That means you'll never die, dad!"

*

In the mid-term elections, the Great Replacement Program was unanimous: every member of the House and every Senate seat up for election, one-third of the Senate, was replaced with a market businessman or woman from the Twelve Visions Party.

Therefore, early in the third year of office, Daniel's Protection-Only Budget passed in its entirety for the following fiscal year. Although only a third of the Senate seats were filled with market businessmen and women, the other senators shouldered enormous pressure to go along with the President's Protection-Only Budget, and most did not challenge it. The following year, there would be no more money for any of the Cabinet Departments except for the Departments of State, Treasury, Justice, and Defense. Daniel gave a nationally televised speech to explain what would happen next:

"Since I'm a productive businessman and not a career politician, I'm delighted about ending the unneeded Cabinet Departments and their regulatory bureaucracies. I don't need or want political power." He did not yet reveal he was secretly driven by the deeper goal of creating the Freedom Paradigm that would unleash medical progress toward eliminating the ultimate disease — aging and death.

"Now that the Protection-Only Budget has passed," Daniel continued, "I'll quickly move on my plan for history's biggest multi-trillion-dollar sale of government assets that have nothing to do with protection. I call my plan the *Great Displacement Program*. Programs for the 'social good' and regulatory programs will be sold to the private sector. Now, those private spin-offs will have to provide genuine values people will willingly pay for, or those spin-offs will not and should not last.

"I'll use the trillions of dollars generated by this sale to pay back in full, plus interest, everyone who paid into Social Security. Most of the thirty-five-million seniors sixty-five and older, for example, will receive over a hundred thousand dollars each from the government. That money, remember, will be generated from the great sale. Many seniors will choose to keep their money in dividend-paying, stock ownership in the profitable, private spin-offs. With our seniors nicely set with their small fortunes and with costs of living rapidly falling, I'll forever end the Social Security Ponzi scheme."

CHAPTER
SIXTY-SIX

"We've got a potential problem," Sam said. He and Ziggy called this meeting with Daniel, Jake and Jasmine. "The senior Senator from Massachusetts has been crafting a weird illusion. I don't want it to blindside us."

Bullfrog, Daniel thought.

Sam continued, "And that bizarre illusion is getting traction."

Daniel thought: it's insane how in the anticivilization someone who's been exposed as evil — the evil magician — can still come back and gain followers through clever illusions.

"The standard of living is climbing so fast, everyone's essentially living as only the millionaires lived just a few years ago," Sam continued. "So, of course, people all over the world are flocking to America. And since the immigration laws were relaxed when you took office, foreigners are getting into our country in large numbers."

"Here's what's visually happening," said Ziggy. "As home owners of tract homes build custom homes for themselves and sell their tract homes, the neighborhoods of tract homes are quickly filling up with foreigners."

"I know," Daniel said. "That's a good thing."

"Not if you think those foreigners are here to grab more and more of Americans' newfound wealth and that—"

"I've been hearing that antilogic lately," Daniel said.

"Unfortunately, the Senator from Massachusetts has people believing it."

Daniel grew very serious; he inhaled a deep breath and shook his head. "How can anyone still fall for that tired illusion?" he asked. "All this new wealth is not some big pie that magically appeared and can be eaten up. Don't people know that this new wealth exists because people are *creating* it? And *the more* people creating wealth, the better off we all become. We should be elated to see those ambitious foreigners coming here."

"Of course, the numbers'll prove you out," said Sam, "but the problem is time. He's using this as a case to keep the ruling class going, claiming that we need the Executive Branch with its array of regulatory bureaucracies to circumvent problems and to stand up for our country. He says that foreigners will overrun America and take all this wealth and prosperity away from us."

"I know," said Daniel. "Until now, I figured that rhetoric would just fade away. I had no idea it would pick up momentum as it has."

Ziggy nodded and said, "He says, now get this: in order to protect this awesome course Daniel Ward put us on, we still need American regulatory government to protect Americans' interests."

"Unbelievable," Daniel said. "That reminds me of that debate the night before the elections. Those prostitutes for power will say *anything*. It's so insane I can't even get mad; I'm just amazed by it."

Sam and Ziggy looked concerned.

"Don't worry about it," Daniel said. "If this illusion becomes a problem, I'll expose it for what it is. He's powerless now."

But Sam and Ziggy still looked worried.

"What is it?" Daniel asked.

"The Senator's illusion seems to have emboldened the tort lawyers," Sam said.

"Yes, I know," said Daniel. "I guess it's time. We haven't heard a peep from them."

"They're going to make their move now, I can feel it. They're putting on their brass knuckles, and they're planning to give you a wallop."

"It's actually an ingenious approach," said Ziggy. "With the Senator stirring up sentiments about how America needs the American government to protect American interests in America, the lawyers found what they believe is an Achilles' heel to strike. You've seen the reports on the Internet. The lawyers' next move is to go to mainstream media with suggestions that your stated goal to depoliticize America and dismantle the government and Social Security may be a planned conspiracy to weaken the American government so businesses can have their way, form monopolies, and harm the American citizen."

"You can already see how they're tying their argument to the Senator's so-called immigration problem for an emotional punch," said Sam. "They're starting to say that, by bringing down the government, Americans will be hurt. We're losing our country to foreigners and business monopolies."

"I know. I've seen their approach percolating on the Internet," said Daniel. "They're accusing the Ward Administration of a vast conspiracy with businesses to join together and bring down the government so businessmen can freely rip off the public. They point to the Great Replacement Program and the Church of God-Man's Business Alliance as possible evidence of a conspiracy to financially damage American citizens."

The room was silent. Daniel was weighing the information. Finally, Sam said, "The senators whose terms were not up during the mid-term elections escaped the Great Replacement Program. Now, they're huddling. They know their days are numbered."

"They're holding secret meetings," Ziggy said. "You've seen some of the rumors."

"The thing is," said Sam, "while they're trying to figure out a way to destroy Daniel to survive in politics, a handful of them are actually honest and believe in what Daniel's doing."

Daniel lifted his gaze from the tabletop. He looked around the table at Sam, Ziggy, Jasmine, and then Jake. "This could get serious," said the President.

CHAPTER
SIXTY-SEVEN

"I just don't think Americans' best interest is first on his mind right now," the Senator from Massachusetts said, looking straight into the camera on the nationally broadcast network news. "He's on an ideological mission. Perhaps his ideology is getting in the way of practicality. Don't get me wrong. The President's a genius; he's gotten America to where it is now. But we're going to lose it all if we keep letting everyone from all over the world come and take it from us."

"But Senator," the news anchorman said, "you've never had a problem with immigration before."

"You're right, I didn't. But now, it's threatening our way of life. Every political position I've ever taken is because I want to do what's best for the American people."

"Sir, I didn't mean to question your integrity. We all know you have our best interest at heart—"

"Thank you, Peter. To be honest," the Senator said, looking again into the camera, "I give full credit to the President for the superb job he's done with our economy and standard of living, but I believe we now need to protect Americans from this foreign invasion."

"The President's stated he's going to shut down the office of President as we know it," the anchorman said.

Superpuzzle

"Big mistake," the Senator said. "With all due respect for our President, he's a businessman. And his strong reform was what our country needed to jumpstart the economy. But now, we must protect what's been started. We need to stem immigration."

"We need to regulate?"

"We need what I call *smart* regulations to protect what we've got. We need a lean Executive Branch, yes. But we need three assertive branches of limited government now to protect what we've got, just as our great country calls for in its Constitution. We can't do away with our Constitution. Everyone knows that."

*

"Do you see how I'm setting this up?" the Senator said to his visitor. The two of them sat at a card table in his vault. "I'm going to profess love for President Ward and what he did for our country. In the same breath, I'm going to say how we must protect what we have through smart legislation, regulation, and litigation. We must protect our new way of life."

"Very clever," the famous white-haired lawyer said. "A couple of years from now, Americans'll laugh at your antics. But over the next year, aliens will fill neighborhoods so rapidly that Americans will actually listen to you. If you blow your whistle loud enough, you just might actually alarm them into electing you for President!"

"But not on my own," the shrewd Senator said. He looked directly into the eyes of the dashing lawyer. "I need you. You need me. If I don't become President, we're all through, even you guys. My noisemaking will be just that — noise. But if you lawyers team up with the media and start questioning the conspiratorial nature of Ward's agenda, then I'll get momentum. Notice how, in every public appearance, after expressing my grave concerns about immigration, I'll come back to how we need a limited government with smart regulations and legislation as called for in our Constitution, upon which our country was founded. I'll put that idea out there while admiring Ward's unprecedented work as President. In the meantime, the lawyers and the media will be questioning whether Ward's agenda to depoliticize America is a conspiracy with business leaders to financially harm American citizens. You must frighten the people into believing that their soaring standards of living will be destroyed when the business monopolies take over. Get the people worrying that they have welcomed a Trojan Horse into America. You must convince America that Ward's agenda is an attempt to essentially throw out our government and replace it with greedy American and foreign business interests — a planned overthrow. The lawyers and media must steadily raise the stakes from suggesting *to accusing* Ward's budget and agenda as a time bomb that'll destroy our standard of living when the monopolies and foreigners take over. Suggest a treasonous conspiracy among Ward, a business owner, with other business owners, the Business Alliance, the Great Replacement Program and especially foreign businesses. With those outrageous ideas out there, I'll see if I can provoke Senate hearings to imply guilt. We still outnumber the Twelve Visions Party in the Senate, two to one. The lawyers and media must become the antagonists, the enemies of Ward. I must remain neutral, even praising Ward. It's the only way we can win. And we must persuade the gullible, nonthinking American next year or we lose forever, for next year the new budget kicks in and most political power ceases to be. It's our last chance."

The distinguished lawyer stared with an expression of both disgust and admiration. He knew well the Senator's desire to destroy because the lawyer himself built his wealth by destroying or burdening businesses. The lawyer saw the Senator's lies and illusions for the ugly deceptions they were. Yet, he could not help admiring the Senator's cold political calculations. "You're a ruthless one," the white-haired lawyer said. "God help us all when you're president."

*

"Suddenly, Senator, you're everywhere — on television, in the papers, at public events," the late-night talk-show host said.

"I think Americans are a little concerned right now. They see people filling up their country who are not Americans, and that's a little scary. Soon, we're going to be outnumbered.

663

Superpuzzle

People feel they need some government protection, and they know I'll give it to them. That's why you see me everywhere — the people are calling for me."

"You don't like our president very much, do you?"

"Quite to the contrary, I love our president. He's done wonderful things for our country. I honestly believe he's one of the greatest presidents our country's ever had."

"But you'd love to whip him in the next presidential election."

"Only if the people want my protection. It's all up to the people, which is what our country and its Constitution are all about — the people. ...Let me say something here to help remove this widespread misnomer that I don't like our president: As everyone knows, early in his administration, I was labeled The Magician because I led a secret meeting to discredit him. I did lead that meeting, but it was not out of hatred. I really believed, at the time, I was doing the best thing for the American people. I thought Daniel Ward was acting for himself to benefit the rich. Obviously, and I'll be the first in line to admit it, I misread Daniel Ward's character. He's a great man. He's a great businessman. He's a great American. I hold no grudge at all. I mean it when I say I love our President for what he's done because I love my country. However, now the transition must occur. Daniel Ward must turn the reigns over to those who can properly protect Americans from non Americans. His admirable ideology must now give way to practicality."

"What's wrong with allowing foreigners to come here?"

"Nothing, if the American people want that. If they want foreign children to fill their schools, foreign families to fill their parks, their libraries, their restaurants, and to absorb their property and prosperity...if Americans don't mind sharing their land and wealth with more and more foreigners and watering down the prosperity, then that's okay. But if they want some protection and privilege, and human nature tells me they do, then I'll bring it to them. I'm giving the people that choice. Isn't that what a free country's all about anyway — free choice? And remember, limited government with smart regulations, legislation and litigation is written into the Constitution of the United States. There's nothing wrong with smart limited government; in fact, there are vital benefits of such limited government as our Founders realized and preserved in the Constitution."

*

"It's happening," Daniel said softly. He put down the morning paper. His wife, Marcy, looked at the headline: *Is the President's Agenda Part of a Secret Conspiracy To Overthrow the Government?* She read the subheading *Legal Experts Look Into President Ward's Death Grip on U.S. Government.*

"They mean: death grip on the parasitical ruling class," Marcy said. She picked up the paper and began to read. When she opened the paper to page three, she said, "Did you see the other article?"

"What other article?"

Marcy paused as she skimmed the other article. "I guess it all started with that Senator from Massachusetts," she said. "Now a U.S. Attorney in New York is saying the Administration's agenda could be part of a damaging conspiracy. In the meantime, tort lawyers are organizing for a class-action lawsuit against the Church of God-Man's Business Alliance. Looks like many of the businesses still in those anticivilization dynamics are joining together in this lawsuit. They're saying that the Business Alliance is a powerful, unfair monopoly that violates antitrust laws. ...This reminds me of when both the government and competing companies went after Microsoft."

"This thing's really picking up momentum," Daniel said.

CHAPTER
SIXTY-EIGHT

The Group met at Rico's mansion.

"A class-action lawsuit is forming against the Business Alliance and is gaining traction," Jeremiah said. "Of course, we're going to use Bruce Salinski's WAL — his Widescope Accounting Lawyers — to defend us." Jeremiah looked at Bruce and added, "I've heard the class-action lawsuit will sue us in the trillions. They sense the judges will support them, so the tort lawyers are salivating over their potential payday."

"This'll be the king of all tort," Bruce said. "But the predators will never get past my WAL."

"What we're seeing," Mr. Melbourne said, "is the last desperate frenzy from the anticivilization. It's a pain to deal with, but once it's over, the anticivilization is over, forever."

"There's yet another compounding headache on the horizon," said Bruce Salinski. He looked at Daniel. "There are rumors on the Internet that the Justice Department is looking into both the Business Alliance and high-ranking members of your Administration as part of a larger conspiracy that could financially harm the American people. Some of those bureaucrats in the Justice Department fear what you're doing and know they really have only a year to derail you."

Daniel sighed. All eyes looked at him. He nodded and said,

"The momentum behind them is generated from the mastermind of illusions — the Senator from Massachusetts. He continues to make the point that a government with so-called *smart* regulations, legislation, and litigation — in other words, a smart ruling class — is proper, is good, and is called for in the Constitution. Of course, he's cleverly leaving out historical context and its bigger picture in order to hypnotize the people into a smaller and smaller vision...until he controls their minds and actions. He's skillfully closing off the *context* of the Constitution as written over two centuries ago. When our country was founded, we were separating from extremely oppressive government. In historical context, our limited government of divided power was a brilliant alternative to the oppressive all-powerful monarch. The bigger picture of the Constitution was, in two words: *depoliticize civilization*, which is exactly what I'm doing today, over two centuries later. In proper context, there's nothing more consistent with the Constitution of the United States than what I'm doing to depoliticize America and free our civilization. But the Senator uses the same trick that destroyed all the good idea systems that ever existed. The trick is to latch hold of a brilliant idea system, such as the Constitution, and block out context. They do this by taking a highly *integrated* idea system and *disintegrating* it by selecting and dogmatizing certain words. That's the trick: by blocking out context and turning the idea system into dogma, then the so-called experts of those authoritative tenets come in and establish themselves as a ruling class. By isolating and magnifying the words themselves in the Constitution, the Senator attempts to close off the context and the bigger picture in order to bring back a ruling class while situating himself right on top."

"You're absolutely right," said Mr. Melbourne. "And that trick's been used for thousands of years. The Pharisees and scribes did that to the Torah, against whom Jesus rebelled. Later, clever Constantine the Great did that to the teachings of Jesus. The Scholastics did that to the works of Aristotle. By blocking out context and turning those good idea systems into dogma, the Pharisees, scribes, Church fathers, scholastics set themselves up as the experts, the external authorities of those idea systems, which meant they became the political rulers of the land. That's the same trick the Senator's using."

"I have an idea," Jake said. "The Senator is using the highly visible immigration issue as his soapbox upon which he preaches the need for an aggressive regulatory government, while he really means an aggressive ruling class with himself right on top. His master illusion encouraged the media and then the tort lawyers to speak out against Daniel's agenda, which encouraged the Justice Department to challenge the agenda, the Administration, and the Business Alliance. It's like a crack in the dam. All this momentum against the President's agenda gives tort lawyers the stacked deck from which to sue the Business Alliance. The whole thing's gaining steam, but I think it all really started with the highly visible immigration issue; it's a trick, and I have an idea that just might knock it clear on it's side."

"What's your idea?" asked Daniel.

"Three years ago, Jessie and Angie told me the amazing story of Miss Annabelle and her twelve students. But, as we all know, that wonderful story had a tragic ending: the INS maliciously deported Mr. Melbourne, which forced Miss Annabelle to make the heartbreaking decision to leave the country." Jake looked around the room. Miss Annabelle and her twelve former students were nodding. "We all learned, after Mr. Melbourne and Miss Annabelle moved back here, that twenty-six years ago Mr. Melbourne made a heroic effort to come back into America to keep Miss Annabelle and you, her precious students, close to each other." The former students nodded. Some smiled. "Jessie and Angie told me they'd someday tell me the story of Mr. Melbourne's trek into our country with Mexican illegals. Jessie and Angie are captivating storytellers. I know they're not here today, but we all know we can count on them. Al, can I get a half-hour slot on the Patterson Channel during peak viewing times this week?"

Al smiled. "Just say when."

*

"Good evening and welcome to a Patterson special presentation. My name is Jake Catchings, and I'm a front-page reporter and occasional television co-anchor for The Patterson

Press. Sitting here with me are two very close friends of mine, Jessie Attison and his lovely wife, Angie. Three years ago, during the New Year's break, I drove from Boston University to Cheektowaga, New York to learn the story about Miss Annabelle and her students, which had been hushed up for twenty-seven years prior to my arrival. Many people today know that her students grew up to become superachievers. One of those superachievers is our President of the United States, President Daniel Ward. Jessie Attison was the custodian at Duncan Elementary School when Miss Annabelle taught her twelve third-grade students thirty years ago, during the miracle year. Many people now know the story of the miracle year and its cruel conclusion when Miss Annabelle and Mr. Melbourne, her fiancé then, were sent to prison for three years on false charges. But most people I've talked to don't know or are hazy about the details that separated Miss Annabelle from her twelve former students for a full twenty-six years. In short, a Federal Judge, the IRS, and the INS separated them. It all started when Miss Annabelle and her fiancè, Mr. Melbourne, were released after three years of unjust imprisonment. The INS maliciously deported Mr. Melbourne, an Australian citizen. He fought with all his will to get back into America so Miss Annabelle could stay here and remain close to her beloved students. After three years in prison, they just wanted their little honest civilization again. As before, they planned to continue their weekly teaching and discussion sessions with their twelve former students. Of course, the vicious restraining order and the vicious deportation killed all hopes. ...Over the past couple of days, Jessie and Angie told me the story of Mr. Melbourne's struggle to get back into America. Their story reveals the underlying nature of stopping honest, hard-working people from coming to America."

Jake turned to his guests and said, "Hello Jessie, hi Angie. You know I wanted to hear that story for a long time. Now, I've condensed your story into a cover story that everyone can read in tomorrow's Patterson Papers. Thank you for rescuing an important piece of history."

"Actually, I thank you, Jake. And you know me," Jessie said, "I'll only tell a story if it's told the way it really happened. That's what Angie and I are all about — *what is*."

"Yes, I know that about you," said Jake. "In fact, let's start with a short synopsis of what happened, and then we'll open the show to call-in viewers."

"Well," Jessie started, "as you said, Mr. Melbourne had been deported and was in Australia. Miss Annabelle was heartbroken and in America. She'd been denied travelling and visiting rights. She couldn't go see him. She couldn't see her students either, for she'd been issued a heartbreaking restraining order, forbidden to come anywhere near her former students."

"That restraining order was pure evil," Angie injected. "It devastated her."

"Yeah, it did," said Jessie. "With all that, after three years in prison, she was in bad shape, emotionally speaking. If she left America to be with her fiancè, she'd violate her probation. If she ever returned, she'd go back to prison for her remaining probation period of three years and probably longer. In short, once she left, she wouldn't see her students again. So, with all options exhausted, Mr. Melbourne decided to illegally sneak back into the country to be with the love of his life. Remember, they'd already been separated for three long, hard years in prison. They couldn't be apart any longer. But, it was a risky plan because if caught, he'd be imprisoned and then deported with no chance to ever return."

"Can you imagine if he'd succeeded?" Angie said. "Can you imagine, after the restraining order expired, if Miss Annabelle and her beloved students-turned-superachievers had been together in America all those years of separation?"

"Well," Jessie said, looking at Jake, then into the camera, "that never happened. After his failed attempt, well, you know the rest of the story."

"That's when Miss Annabelle had to move to Australia, and the three-year separation from her students turned into a twenty-six year separation," Angie said. "When she left, she thought she'd never see her students again. She was heartbroken."

Jessie nodded and added, "Until Jake came along and got us all back together again."

"It's the best thing I've ever done in my life," said Jake, "and I'm so excited at how it all turned out." Jake felt a surge of pride inside. Then, he got back on subject and said, "During

670

Mr. Melbourne's attempt to get back to Cheektowaga, New York, you told me he befriended a Mexican family."

"Yes," said Jessie, "Oscar and Polita, and their four-year-old boy, Oscar Junior. And that story of Mr. Melbourne's journey into our country with that Mexican family captures the heart of what's good versus what's bad in this immigration argument."

Jake looked into the camera and said, "America, the foreigners coming to our neighborhoods consist of families like little Oscar's family. You must read their story in tomorrow's Patterson Papers. Oscar's family came here to improve life and build wealth, not take it away. After reading Oscar's story, you make your decision if you will allow that to happen. Now, I'll open this up for our viewers to call in. ...Hold on, I'm getting word from my producer that one of Miss Annabelle's original students is on the line. Okay, let's go first to one of the original students from Miss Annabelle's miracle year. On the line with us now is Rico Rodriguez. Hello, Rico."

"Hi Jake. And hello Jessie and Angie! What a gift you three are bringing America tonight," said Rico. "I just read the story of Mr. Melbourne, Oscar, and his family; it's already posted on Patterson's online edition. I must tell you, Jake, I never had any idea of what Mr. Melbourne went through in his incredible attempt to get back to Cheektowaga! That really moved me, and what a touching story about little Oscar and his family. Today, as you and I know, Oscar has grown up to become one of America's best immigration lawyers, a partner in Bruce Salinski's famous Widescope Accounting Lawyers, better know as The WAL. Oscar helped get Mr. Melbourne and Miss Annabelle back into America for good and without punishment nearly three years ago, back when the INS would've arrested them!"

"That's the point," said Jake, "with no more welfare, immigrants come here to contribute to America's wealth."

"Yes they do," said Rico, "and I want to contrast them to their opposites — my father and his group of criminal-minded friends. They were all Mexicans, legally here but guilty and malevolent. They drained and endangered society through usurping government assistance, through committing armed robbery, through blackmailing and intimidating good people, even murdering an innocent person. People coming here for real opportunity don't have that criminal mind. They're here to work. Like Oscar's family, they have one goal: to produce or create values — to elevate life. And that's all that counts, not their race or nationality. I'm Mexican. I've made many white folk who work for me or invested in me...*millionaires*. Whether I was born here or in Mexico is irrelevant. I've been a boost to society, as has Oscar's family.

"Nowadays, the immigrants play a vital role in taking over jobs of value *production* as Americans evolve into jobs of value *creation* in the new division-of-essence business paradigm. In time, robotics will take over jobs of value *production* as the immigrants also evolve into jobs of value *creation*. Value creation — bringing values to the world that would otherwise never exist — elevates life for everybody."

"Rico," said Jake, "your grasp on the issue is invaluable. Can you stay with us for the duration of the show to help answer America's questions on immigration?"

"I'd love to."

*

During the days following the prime-time special on immigration, Patterson Press was bombarded with correspondence. The people called; the phone lines jammed. The people mailed and emailed their thoughts — thousands of responses. The survey team studied the first few hundred responses and tried to break them down into a few common categories. But after seeing those first few hundred responses, the survey team realized there was essentially one category: *Thank you for waking us up to the Senator's illusion that those ambitious immigrants are endangering our quality of life.* Most of those responses went on to identify that it was the Senator's proposal itself for a return to a ruling class that was endangering Americans' quality of life.

*

"The Senator's done for," Ziggy said.

"Yes, he's through," said Sam, "but the tort lawyers and the Justice Department are moving ahead with their cases."

"It doesn't matter now," said Daniel.

He always seems overconfident, Jake thought, *but he's always right.*

"In three weeks, on Thursday evening, I'm going to address the nation," Daniel told the White House Press Corps. "It's going to be one of the most important announcements of my presidency."

*

"Good evening, America." Daniel spoke directly into the cameras, from the Oval Office. "Our program of depoliticizing America became threatened by a skillfully crafted illusion. The senior Senator from Massachusetts — the infamous Magician — crafted the illusion. The Patterson prime-time special on immigration, coupled with Jake Catchings' cover story about Mr. Melbourne crossing the border on foot with little Oscar and family, published in all the Patterson Papers, let us see through the illusion to the true nature of the INS and of a ruling class in general. The TV special and the newspaper cover story vanished the illusion and prevented American citizens from making a serious mistake.

"From that experience, we learned a valuable lesson. We witnessed just how vulnerable we are to the bicameral mentality of the past that looks for leaders. We're infants in the new Neothink mentality in which we integrate knowledge to develop our own value-creating, society-lifting paths in life without external authorities ruling over us. We've just seen how easily we can fall back and file in.

"Despite all the evidence right before our eyes telling us our prosperity and happiness go up geometrically as we depoliticize America, still we were quick to be pulled into the illusion that we needed a so-called smart regulatory government, which meant political external authorities ruling over us — a ruling class.

"Because we're vulnerable to regrowing a ruling class, I find it important for Congress to pass and for the States to ratify the Prime-Law Amendment to the United States Constitution this year, which I'll explain tonight."

Superpuzzle

"But first, to pass an amendment to the Constitution is an involved process. The Prime-Law Amendment was proposed as a joint resolution over two years ago, since about the time I took office. It could not pass the two-third votes needed in Congress. However, that was before the Great Replacement Program that we enjoyed during the mid-term elections. The Prime-Law Amendment is based on the most fundamental biological act of protecting the individual and his property from initiatory force, which is the *prime* law for a free and prosperous society.

"Once again, the Preamble of the Prime Law states: *The purpose of human life is to prosper and live happily. The function of society is to provide the conditions that let individuals fulfill that purpose. The Prime Law guarantees those conditions by forbidding the use of initiatory force, fraud, or coercion by any person or group against any individual or his property.*

"Article One of the Prime Law states: *No person, group of persons, or government shall initiate force, threat of force, or fraud against any individual's self, property, or contract.*

"Article Two of the Prime Law states: *Force is morally-and-legally justified only for protection from those who violate Article 1.*

"Article Three of the Prime Law states: *No exceptions shall exist for Articles 1 and 2.*

"Because the Prime Law goes down to the fundamental act of stopping initiatory force, it can't be broken apart, taken out of context, and manipulated. The Prime Law is indivisible and unbreakable. No one — not even the senior Senator from Massachusetts through his cleverest illusions — *no one* can gain political ruling-class power over others once the Prime Law is in place.

"We must bring the Prime Law to America as an Amendment to the U.S. Constitution. Once that happens, every government action, regulation, and law must then pass through the initiatory-force filter. The Prime Law becomes the supreme law of the land. It becomes the overarching, Supreme Constitution, so to speak, against which no federal or state law can violate. Its initiatory-force filter will catch every bad law. That initiatory-force filter reduces every law and regulation down to the indivisible, fundamental biological act of man. In short, every measure of law must pass through and survive the initiatory-force litmus test. Existing laws and regulations that violate the Prime Law will be found unconstitutional. Proposed laws and regulations in violation will be caught and discarded. Think about it: each and every law and regulation will be put to the test. The only law or regulation that can pass through this filter must be free of initiatory force — must be pure. In other words, we would soon live in pure freedom with pure protection.

"The Prime Law is the Constitution of the Universe, for all civilizations in the purely rational Civilization of the Universe would function under this one supreme law — the law of no initiatory force or fraud, which is a form of initiatory force. The Prime Law is The Universal Law.

"Of course, with *the law* of no initiatory force, we could never again have old-world regressions such as the latest illusion for a so-called smart ruling-class government. The Senator's cries for smart regulations, for example, would fail the initiatory-force test. Furthermore, we could never be threatened by an organized force of evil such as, ironically, the dinosaurs in my Justice Department and their attempt to stop us from depoliticizing America by challenging my agenda as a conspiracy to harm Americans. With the Prime Law in place, the courts couldn't rule against my agenda in any way without violating the initiatory-force test. Indeed, to go back to the old budget dynamics, for example, demands a force-backed IRS.

"The initiatory-force test is the litmus test for freedom. We have now entered the era of self-leadership. We have finally leapt beyond vestiges of the bicameral mentality and its need for political leaders and a ruling class. The Prime Law — the Constitution of the Universe — fully brings us into the Civilization of the Universe. It is The Law of the self-leader; it is The Law of the God-Man. It is the Supreme Law of freedom.

"Now is the time for Congress to pass and for the States to ratify the Prime-Law Amendment and bring us the pure freedom and protection of the Prime Law. I say this not because I'm concerned about the Justice Department's move to stop me; I say this not because I'm concerned about the tort lawyers' move to bankrupt the Church of God-Man's Business Alliance. It's true that in court the U.S. Attorneys' and the tort lawyers' cases would not hold up against the initiatory-force test. But I'm no longer concerned about either case, not since America listened to Jake Catchings' TV special and read his newspaper cover story, which woke America from the Senator's hypnotic spell. Since America's awakening, the power-hungry bureaucrats, the money-mad tort lawyers, even the ego-driven proactive judges all lost their dishonest power because the people will no longer grant them the power to rule over and burden others. The whole country is against them now.

"The reason I stress that the time is *now* — this year — to pass the Prime-Law Amendment to the U.S. Constitution has to do with a window of opportunity. You see, next year my Protection-Only Budget kicks in. With no more political regulations retarding progress, America is going to prosper beyond anything you can imagine, even now. We will be so busy and so exhilarated by the great prosperity-explosion and by our own personal renaissances, we'll no longer bother with philosophical or political thoughts. After next year, philosophy and politics will become essentially obsolete. Believe me, this is our last opportunity to set in place the purely rational Constitution.

"Moreover, my Protection-Only Budget sets in motion pragmatically what the Prime-Law Amendment locks down permanently as *the law*. Both my budget and my amendment allow only for the one proper purpose of government: to protect its citizens from initiatory force or coercion. Both my budget and my amendment eliminate the second erroneous purpose of government: to so-called promote social well-being. In doing so, both my budget and my amendment eliminate the ruling class. A vanishing ruling class is why America and its people are prospering more than anything ever seen before on Earth. But without *the law* of no initiatory force, with just the Protection-Only Budget, the government could ultimately regrow a ruling class. The Protection-Only Budget quickly cuts down the ruling class, but does not shut down initiatory force. The Prime-Law Amendment, on the other hand, pulls out the roots of the ruling class — initiatory force, which includes forced taxes.

"Let's use the recent close call — the illusion conjured up

by the senior Senator from Massachusetts — as our impetus to get it right and establish The Law of the Civilization of the Universe. Let's lock down my Prime-Law Amendment as *the law*."

CHAPTER
SIXTY-NINE

"I'm seriously considering exercising my prerogative of firing several of my U.S. Attorneys," Daniel said, "especially those building their bogus case against me. Why let them have their dishonest distraction? Why let them slow us down? The country is completely behind me now; the House of Representatives is completely with us now. There wouldn't be any impeachment considerations."

"You're right," said Ziggy. "We did some new polling. As you said, the whole country's behind you now. Nearly ninety percent of the people now believe the conspiratorial case to be exactly what you said it is — a desperate attempt to stop you from depoliticizing America."

"I think you need to ask yourself," said Sam, "which approach will consume less time — firing those U.S. Attorneys or ignoring them. Either way, they can't stop you. It comes down to which approach distracts least from your progress."

"Keep in mind," said Ziggy, "very soon three-fourths of the states will have ratified the Prime-Law Amendment. Once that's done, the conspiratorial case is over. It can't go on once initiatory force is illegal. You might be better off staying focussed on what you're doing and letting the case die on its own."

Putting Together the Pieces

*

"Jake and I have a personal question for you, Daniel." Jake and Jasmine had arranged this personal interview with Daniel in the White House. "Tell us what you're going to do after you leave Washington, D.C.?"

Daniel smiled and said, "I'm going to undertake an exciting building challenge. I've been asked to nearly double the height of the Twin Towers in New York City. It'll be an engineering first to double the height of an existing skyscraper, but with the most recent technologies, I believe it's possible."

"Double the height of the Twin Towers," Jasmine said, "I'm trying to picture it...it'll be the most beautiful thing ever built."

"Remember early in your presidency when the FBI broke up that Al-Qaeda plan to fly our own commercial planes into the Twin Towers, the Pentagon, and the White House?" Jake said.

"That was a close call," said Daniel. He shook his head. "We were only able to intercept that plan by immediately shifting the depleted FBI, CIA, and special forces into a high-gear, anti-terrorism mode when I arrived at the White House. That aggressive protection-only approach alarmed some people, but it thwarted a devastating attack on U.S. soil." He paused and then nodded. "Now, Islam extremism is waning in the Middle East. Our new world offers just too much prosperity to the people. Freedom and great personal prosperity are more acceptable to the people of any civilization than suppressive religion. Nuclear weapons and terrorism are fading toward nonfactors as civilizations around the world follow our lead. And soon, I'm going to double the height of those beautiful Twin Towers!" He smiled broadly. "I'm excited about launching my Office-in-the-Clouds development challenge. Eventually, our famous city skylines will double in height, and I'll be leading that skyscraper revolution."

*

"Good evening, America," Daniel announced to the nation. "I want to take a moment with you tonight to celebrate the rapid passing of the Protection-Only Amendment and to shed light on what this watershed event means to you.

"Over half a century ago, philosopher Albert Jay Nock identified that the state is an antisocial system designed to perpetuate and expand a parasitical ruling class. As we've seen, he was right. It's true that our government perpetuated an expanding parasitical ruling class that lived off the people.

"Our congressmen and senators, for example, were obsessed with themselves despite their doublespeak about doing what was best for the people. Career politicians, interested in themselves, were incompetent at providing genuine values that the people would willingly pay for. They needed the power of force to exist – pay your taxes or go to prison.

"Also, about half of those lawmakers were lawyers. Lawyers by profession study the law, which can make them better lawmakers. However, those lawyers-turned-lawmakers of the anticivilization created destructive laws that generated litigation and expanded the legal industry. Many lawyers existed by draining, not providing values. Lawyers-turned-lawmakers guaranteed themselves lucrative futures as lawyers draining values once no longer re-elected. Generally, they avoided competitive futures as value-producing lawyers or businessmen.

"Those career politicians certainly were not interested in the competitive world of producing values for society. Instead, they ruled over society while draining its values, which included destroying or suppressing jobs. Yes, Nock was correct in his assessment of an elite, parasitical ruling class.

"We now know we never needed the parasitical ruling class. We never needed our congressmen and senators to be what they became. Let's stop to consider, for a moment, what did our congressmen and senators do? They made laws — they were our lawmakers. Their livelihoods consisted of making laws. But did we need all those laws? No. As it turns out, we needed an overarching law, the Prime Law, which has been brought into being as the Prime-Law Amendment. All other laws must never violate the Prime Law, which immediately halts all the unhealthy lawmaking.

"Our elite, parasitical ruling class will soon be eliminated by the Protection-Only Budget and will never return because of the

Prime Law. Your standard of living, which has never risen so quickly, will soar to yet new heights.

"Let's take a closer look at what the Prime-Law Amendment has actually accomplished. First, as you know, over the past century, our government existed for two purposes:

1) To protect the people
2) To promote so-called social well-being.

"To promote the general welfare of the people has been misinterpreted to mean: increase their standard of living or their wealth. Well, we've learned that career politicians *can't* do that; the government cannot and should not exist to enhance social well-being, not beyond physical protection, which includes justice and proper lawmaking, both criminal and civil. Indeed, our politicians spent our money to ostensibly 'promote' our well-being, but they really wanted the glory and power and 'importance' that goes with spending money. They didn't want anything to do with the effort, though, that goes with soundly spending money. Their misinterpretation of the U.S. Constitution led to blatant violations of the Constitution, which could never occur with the Prime Law in place.

"So, they made a mess of things. To enhance our well-being, as we've witnessed, is most effectively handled by unhampered market businessmen and women. That erroneous second purpose of government — to so-called promote the well-being of the people — sprang up over the years through career politicians finding ways to spend money and become more and more likable for re-election. They got their spending money through tax collection backed by force. The Prime-Law Amendment gets rid of all that, forever.

"The one *valid* purpose for our government, as you know, is *to protect the people from initiatory force,* which includes providing justice. The only way to guarantee the protection of *all* people — *equal, unbiased* and *unconditional* protection of all people of all races and all social classes and all career positions in society — is to protect *the individual.* Regardless of race or social status, the Prime Law guarantees everyone his or her unprejudiced rights as an individual, as a minority of one — the smallest of all minorities. Every individual is equally and fully protected.

"Now, to provide comprehensive protection of the individual requires going down to and establishing the biologically irreducible fundamental of protection. As an analogy, to capture the comprehensive nature of the cosmos requires going down to and understanding the irreducible, fundamental sub-atomic particles comprising the cosmos. The irreducible, thus indivisible, incorruptible fundamental of protection is: elimination of initiatory force, which is the function of the Prime-Law Amendment.

"Indeed, comprehensive protection of the individual demands *one prime law* — one overarching, irreducible law: the elimination of all initiatory force against the individual and his property. With that *one prime law*, everyone becomes protected from intentional harm caused by man, including harm from government.

"Therefore, with the passing of the Prime-Law Amendment, the ruling class can never return. Prosperity will continue to soar forever. What great news! Indeed, *one prime law* was always needed; *one prime law* eternally guarantees protection and freedom. That one universal law, the Prime Law, is easy for everyone to remember. I'll read it here:

The Prime Law
(The Fundamental of Protection)

Preamble
*The *purpose* of human life is to prosper and live happily.

*The function of government is to **provide the conditions** that let individuals fulfill that *purpose*.

*The Prime Law **guarantees those conditions** by forbidding the use of initiatory force, fraud, or coercion by any person or group against any individual, property, or contract.

Article 1
No person, group of persons, or government shall initiate force, threat of force, or fraud against any individual's self, property, or contract.

Article 2

Force is morally-and-legally justified only for protection from those who violate Article 1.

Article 3

No exceptions shall exist for Articles 1 and 2.

"With that one Prime Law now in place, it essentially becomes our Supreme Law to which every law must answer. For, the Supreme Law will filter out every law and regulation in violation, namely those that serve the bogus purpose of so-called promoting social well-being, which requires initiatory force. The *prime* law is the biological fundamental, the point of origin, the beginning of all law. Therefore, no further unhealthy law or misinterpretation of the U.S. Constitution can occur. No more violations can happen. Now, government can't tell us how to spend our money or *force* us to pay taxes. As long as we don't commit initiatory force, we're completely free. We don't need ego-and-power-driven lawmakers stirring up legislation with lawyers and bureaucrats using those laws to drain us. We no longer need that parasitical ruling class that not long ago destroyed our prosperity. Their deceptions can no longer pass through the Prime-Law Amendment — including their forced taxes.

"Our government has nearly ceased to be a parasitical ruling class as we switch over to my Protection-Only Budget that ends the funds for the bogus second purpose of government — to so-called promote social well-being. The Protection-Only Budget supplies funds to the one proper purpose of government — to protect the country and its citizens from initiatory force, which includes the proper protection-based lawmaking and system of justice.

"Now, let me ask you, America, what guarantees our government can never again grow a ruling class? Government can grow a ruling class only through force — pay your taxes or go to prison. With the passing of the Prime-Law Amendment, not even the government can use initiatory force and, therefore, will *forever* cease to be a ruling class. Instead, with the passing of the Prime-Law Amendment, the government must function as a protection service you voluntarily pay for. Now, that changes everything.

"Gone are the days of bogus and destructive government, so-called promoting social well-being. Market businessmen have successfully taken over that job. Now, our new government will forever provide the one specific value of protection, which its citizens — its customers — voluntarily pay for. Realize, my Protection-Only Budget wouldn't have been enough because that protection could regress back into a corrupt ruling class eventually if government could use initiatory force against its citizens with a force-backed IRS. In short, that ugly rise of the ruling class is what happened to our original, beautiful U.S. Government idea meant to exist for protection only. The Prime-Law Amendment *forever* stops the ruling class from happening again.

"Without forced tax collection, government power is not a *ruling* power. Instead, it's an *earned* power, earned from ever-looming, potential competition. Our government is now nonthreatening to its citizens — to its customers — and is incorruptible.

"With initiatory force permanently out of the equation of government due to the Prime-Law Amendment, the government holds no ruling power and can never hold ruling power over you whatsoever. For the first time, you're truly free.

"The government will now increasingly set itself up essentially as a reputable business providing the immense value of protection — peace and safety — the priceless value *you gladly choose to pay for.* If you're ever unhappy with the protection service, you can withdraw and not pay...and not be a criminal. If enough people did that, a competitive service would rise to guarantee protection — better protection. Those free-market dynamics guarantee the government will increasingly provide an honest and satisfactory value to you. Those free-market dynamics guarantee your best protection, including national defense.

"With the Prime Law now in place, the prosperity-explosion we're now experiencing will never end. I want you to think about that. Think about our amazing progress, our wealth, our happiness and love...our health. Think about where this life we were meant to live...where it is taking us."

Daniel paused. He smiled and said, "Good-night, near-immortals."

CHAPTER
SEVENTY

"During this final year of your term, Americans are prospering beyond anyone's wildest fantasies," said Sam. He and his staff of numbers-men reported the good news in a meeting with Daniel two months into his fourth and final year as President.

"The entire population now lives in luxury," Sam continued. "People everywhere, with their multiplying buying power, are moving out of apartments and into beautiful new homes. Many industries are booming faster than the computer industry did back in the 1980s and '90s. In this Freedom Paradigm, the great Technological Revolution has arrived. Super entrepreneurs are springing into the Neothink mentality everywhere. They advance new technologies to the next level and the next in every industry."

"The freed medical industry is soaring, too," Ziggy said. "In fact, the medical revolution advances at a faster clip than the electronics revolution. Major disease after disease are being wiped off the face of the Earth. Civilization exudes a warm new confidence; disease and poverty are no longer threats."

Sam nodded and said, "A beautiful irony is happening: while the breakthrough values are becoming more and more priceless, prices are tumbling to fractions."

A moment of silence passed. A strong sense of relief and

victory filled the room. Now that Daniel had accomplished what he had set out to do in the Oval Office, his mind shifted to what needed to be done next. His thoughts drifted ahead: now people are so exhilarated by their creations, prosperity, happiness and love, they *want* to live longer — much longer. Life is no longer a burden, not anymore.

Staring at his numbers-men, Daniel said, "Sam, the timing is right to make Sally and her Association for Curing Aging and Death a national phenomenon."

*

The Group gathered for its monthly meeting at Rico's mansion. The President of the United States still flew in each month for these meetings. Today, Al Patterson was pacing back and forth. Jake watched his boss and kept thinking how the handsome man with dark hair and hazel eyes looked younger than he did when Jake met him four years ago at the reunion.

"A good number of businesses know about the Association for Curing Aging and Death," Al finally said. "Millions of people in the Church of God-Man and its Business Alliance passionately follow our progress. But, the general population knows surprisingly little about Project Life and often perceives it as a belief system of a popular new-age religion." He stopped pacing and lifted his eyes from the floor. He said, "The time is *now* to make the Association for Curing Aging and Death a household word and to place biological immortality in the minds of everyone."

Daniel had reached the same conclusion prior to the meeting. "It's time for the third and final piece to our superpuzzle," he said. He felt deep satisfaction that he succeeded at depoliticizing America, thus putting in the second piece. And, of course, The Group together got him elected to the Oval Office which was the first piece to the superpuzzle. He turned and looked at Sally, knowing the third piece largely fell on her shoulders, and he said, "It's your time to shine."

Jasmine was taking notes and asked Al and Daniel, "Why *now,* precisely?" She knew that, since the FDA no longer existed, Sally had been racing ahead on her medical research projects. And so were many other medical entrepreneurs.

Al answered, "Because the *great fear* of immortality is subsiding." Daniel nodded in agreement. That was a profound statement Al always, always wanted to say. Now that he was finally able to say it, The Group was on its way.

Al drew in a deep sigh of relief. He looked admirably at Daniel. "The political war is won," Al said. "Let me just say, I'm deeply proud of Daniel for his fearless courage and unyielding strength that enabled him to succeed in Washington." Al nodded at Daniel; the President smiled back at Al. Then, Al looked at the others in The Group and continued, "The Freedom Paradigm is upon us. The economy is no longer politicized. Jeremiah's Church and its Business Alliance have accelerated the shift. As we predicted, in the new freedom, 'garage' entrepreneurs acting alone and in-house entrepreneurs acting on behalf of their businesses have risen by the millions. They race forward at such competitive speeds, they had to discover Ted's business breakthrough that captures the greatest asset in business — the employees' creative *minds*. We've witnessed a historic shift from the division of labor to the division of essence. The essence of business — to make money by creating or improving values and marketing those values — is downright exciting! During the shift, we witnessed a job revolution away from stagnant jobs of labor to exhilarating jobs of the mind. Man is a mental animal. His life was boring in a job of labor that emphasized a physical skill. His life is now exciting in a job of the mind that stimulates his mind…especially as the division of essence moves its way toward the *division of Friday-Night essences*. Thanks to Robert's influential workshops and to Jeremiah's Business Alliance, businesses everywhere are discovering their employees' Friday-Night essences. People everywhere are becoming the persons they were meant to be, living the exhilarating lives they were meant to live. Now, the values they go to create and market at work are *their own creations* for the world — a thrilling feeling! Businesses everywhere are setting up this way: their employees enjoying open-ended, entrepreneurial jobs of the mind, pursuing their Friday-Night essences, doing work they love doing more than anything else, making and marketing their own creations for the world. The result of this shift into the new, highly self-motivated business paradigm? Yesterday people were unhappy in their livelihoods and looked to escape their miserable stagnation through sports, hobbies, entertainment, vacations. Today people are happy and excited and look forward to their competitive creations every morning. They're *creators*. They're not looking to escape stagnation; they're looking forward to working on their creations. They're not looking toward the ultimate escape — death. Instead, their happiness grows month after month, year after year as their contributions to society build. Before, their boredom grew year after year as they sank into stagnation. The human mind was not designed to handle stagnation; the human mind was designed for creation. By the time they were in their seventies or eighties, they were ready to let go and die. They *feared* any serious mention of immortality, for they feared prolonged stagnation. ...Not so any longer. Now, people will become even more dynamic and exhilarated at eighty than they were at twenty!" Al looked at Jake and Jasmine. "The great fear of immortality is subsiding," he repeated. "*Now's* the time to place the idea of biological immortality in the minds of everyone."

Natasha locked her big brown eyes on Patterson's eyes. "I can confirm everything you're saying," she said. "The love-lives of people have really heated up in America. Divorce rates have dropped to fractions. Experts say it's because of the wealth explosion, but I say it's more than that; it's because people have reached a new level of happiness. This new level of happiness makes romantic love sizzle. This new level of happiness can only come from *creating* values. For years in my workshops, my secret to successful marriages was to help the man and the woman, in their own ways, to get in touch with their deepest motivational roots. Now, most people are doing that, which leads to value *creation* as you say. Their happiness overflows into their love-lives. Imagine, fifty years of true romantic love and happiness will create enormous desire not to lose the wonderful love and values...to death! After fifty years, a happy couple will have so much more love to live for than the twenty-five-year-old newlyweds."

"What specific changes have you noticed about couples' love-lives?" Jasmine asked Natasha.

"The most notable change I've witnessed, something I never conceptualized in all my years until recently, has been the escalating *reciprocation* I see now as a result of people's deep happiness. It's made me realize, first, the power of reciprocation in love and, second, how reciprocation in love is a direct effect of happiness. For example, historically, the two most powerful love relationships are 1) parent and small child, and 2) man and woman while falling in love. A mother and her baby...Romeo and Juliet. What makes the love so powerful? Well, let's imagine a mother and her baby. The mother is that baby or toddler's whole world. She's everything. The baby is gleefully in love with mom's every gesture of love. The mother feels her baby's full and total *reciprocation* of her love. Now, imagine Romeo and Juliet and the full and total *reciprocation* of their love. Yet, in both situations in the anticivilization, the mother and child and Romeo and Juliet, the full and total reciprocation faded with time...to the lows of parent/teenager disaffection and husband/wife estrangement. As the years passed in the anticivilization, the two most powerful love relationships in existence vanished into indifference or worse...with little or no reciprocation.

"Now I've noticed since the job revolution, since people achieve their human potential, the *increasing* intensity of love in marriages and in parent/child relationships. The reciprocation actually *increases* with time! I'm referring to couples who've been married for years and to parents with older children, including *teenagers!* The intensity and reciprocation of love between more and more parents and their children, even with their teenagers, for the first time since the beginning of time, is surpassing that of mother and infant! Imagine the powerful love we've seen in members of The Group and their children; consider Rico for example: from what he's told us, his love amplifies as his children grow older, for the older they get, the less time Rico has with them before they're gone from his home. Similar to Rico, for the first time more and more parents now love their teenagers with more intensity than when those teens were babies! And the intensity and reciprocation of love between more and more married couples is surpassing the first few intimate weeks of bliss! It's just fascinating to see. I always knew happiness was a prerequisite to love, but I honestly never expected the intensity that I'm seeing now. In the Civilization of the Universe, the previous working models no longer apply.

"This intensity of love has opened a new area of study for me: this whole new dimension to our emotions. Human beings seem to be evolving into a new breed emotionally. I'm fascinated by this new intensity of family and romantic love that I'm observing across the country. Before the job revolution, reciprocation died out because the anticivilization extinguished a person's human potential and deadened his deep happiness, which ended his motivation for love. Instead, the parent, the teenager, and the spouse all turned to distractions in this anticivilization, exactly as Al was saying. They turned away from themselves, their creations, their love for themselves and their love for each other."

The room was quiet. *What a powerful identification*, Jake thought. He looked around. The people in the room were lost in their thoughts about their own children and love relationships. Jasmine reached over and held her father's hand who was attending his first meeting of The Group.

"I...I know exactly what you're saying, Natasha," Rico finally said. "I could never successfully express to anyone just how powerful my feelings are for my children. And the older they get, the more powerful those feelings grow and the more I want to be with them. I feel deeply inside the preciousness of every moment with them. I think down deep I know our time together is limited, and I feel the preciousness more and more as they grow older and our time together grows less. My love for them sometimes consumes me."

Jasmine's dad tightened his lips and slowly nodded. He looked down at the floor, into past days with his Jassy.

"And for Olivia," Rico continued, "I feel our love increasing each year. I guess I'm so aware of the preciousness of what we have in light of the shortness of life to experience everything we will ever have. Sometimes the thought of losing their love to death drives me mad, and I have to shut off the thought of that horrific loss at the end. On the other hand, the shortness of our time together drives me into exciting celebrations of life and love every time I'm with Olivia and my children. The celebrations grow more and more precious with the passing of time."

As Rico expressed his love for his family, Jake realized that Rico had grown up just like his teacher...overflowing with love for his children just as she felt for her twelve "children".

"I know about the other way, you know," Rico continued. "My father. He hated himself for what he did to himself and to society. He was miserable and felt no love for his children, and eventually I didn't feel anything back for him...except hatred."

It dawned on Jake what he was observing and what Natasha was trying to understand: He was observing the next level of emotional existence of the God-Man. The God-Man, the value creator, felt family love and romantic love beyond anything previously known. He also felt genuine love and compassion for his fellowman because of the wonderful values he received from his fellowman, just as the members of the God-Man Group felt pure love for each other. God-Man was the next mentality of man. The emotional jump from ancient bicameral man to conscious man was similar to this emotional jump from present-day conscious man to the new God-Man.

Jake knew now what Al was getting at and why the timing was right to introduce the Association for Curing Aging and Death to the public. For, as more and more people rose into this whole new emotional existence at the next level of happiness and love — at Rico's level — the thought of dying would be appalling, just as it was for Rico. In their old emotional existence of stagnation and emotional estrangement, death was an integral part of rescuing people from boredom and misery at the end. It was the final escape. But, Jake pondered, all that reverses in the new emotional existence of the God-Man — the value *creator* — at the next level of happiness and inseparable love.

Jake never before so clearly understood what the God-Man Group had been doing the past four years: By curing humanity of the bicameral-mind disease of needing external authorities, thereby eliminating the ruling class, the Group had created a world in which everyone's natural emotional desire was for life

— happy, growing, unending life. The world was ready.

"The three anchors to the anticivilization have broken," Jake heard Daniel saying. He was looking at Jeremiah.

"The Six Visions of your original presidential campaign have all come true," Jeremiah answered. "The full Twelve Visions are coming."

Daniel and his former classmates smiled. Miss Annabelle and her husband glowed like the world's proudest parents. Jake planned his next article that would finally be titled: *We Do Not Have To Die.* He looked around the room at the former classmates, and knew his subtitle would be: *Thank You, Miss Annabelle.*

*

Daniel started packing his files six months early. He had finished what he had come to do. He won the street fight and the war. There would be no more political external authorities. Mission accomplished. The government was on the fast track to soon run like a business, with voluntary payments for protection made by the American people.

Danny walked into his dad's office. He was nine years old now and had just finished the third grade. "When I grow up, I'm going to be like you," the boy announced, "and if any bad men come for me, I'll fight 'em, Dad, just like you did."

Daniel looked at his boy for a moment and enjoyed who he saw before him — a fearless, determined boy driven to stop evil, ready to step up against any bully. He reminds me of myself when I was his age, Daniel thought, remembering this time in his own life many years ago, when Miss Annabelle and Mr. Melbourne were being pulled away to prison, remembering his own determination to fight evil...and now seeing that same determination in his boy. Overfilled with joy and pride, looking at his son, Daniel spilled over with laughter.

"I mean it, Dad," his son stressed, not sure why his father was laughing.

"I know you do, Danny, I know you do," Daniel said. He turned serious to respect his son's serious moment. Then, from deep within his heart, Daniel said, "You're the best son I could have ever hoped for. ...I really mean it."

His son stood an inch taller with that unexpected comment, and his eyes gleamed with pride. As Daniel saw the love and innocence in his boy's eyes, the President felt great relief that he was *the last* of the ruling-class Presidents. He silently said in his thoughts, thank God there'll be no more bad guys, son.

III.

The Race for Life

CHAPTER
SEVENTY-ONE

The thirty-six faces staring at Sally did not look human to Jake. They had no expression, nothing that fills the face of an intelligent, emotional psyche. They don't even look curious such as a pet dog might, Jake thought.

He was with Jasmine, Miss Annabelle, and Sally, looking into the faces of paraplegics who were bound to this nursing home because of life-threatening physical complications that required 24-hour medical attention. Most ended up here from a life-altering accident. The average life expectancy once they arrived here was about two years.

They don't know why we're here, Jake realized after one quick look across the sea of lifeless faces. He was glad he had the opportunity to witness their shell of an existence *before* Sally announced her offer.

"Good morning. My name is Dr. Sally Salberg." Jake noticed a number of faces suddenly become more humanlike. Those faces knew about her, but not about the offer she was about to make. "You may have heard of me because of my Nobel Prize for my discovery of the flu vaccine or possibly for my work on cancer. For the past five years, I've led an unprecedented medical research effort known as Project Life. I doubt any of you have heard much about it because we haven't publicized it. We've successfully accomplished what I'm about to tell you...with an ape. Now, we're ready to try it on a human being."

With that proclamation, all thirty-six faces lit up and became human. A wave of pity rumbled across Jake's heart as he saw them hoping so hard for what he and others take for granted.

"The risks of failure are high," Sally said to immediately keep their hopes in check. But to Jake's amazement, not one face winced, not one soul backed off. He then understood that this moment was the first time since these people had their crippling accidents or body failures that they felt like human beings again.

"The operation will take several hours, and the whole procedure will last 14 months from start to finish," Sally said, moving straight into the details. "Simplified: it's a four-step procedure. First, we take a few cells from your body and put them through our breakthrough, rapid cloning procedure to grow a young adult replica of yourself."

Their eyes widened. They were already resigned to the fact they would die here. Now, here was this famous doctor offering them a chance to live.

"Then, procedures two and three would be done over a 20-hour period. In procedure two, I would remove your head and upper spinal region and attach it to our breakthrough robotic body. Essentially, body-robot acts as your heart, lungs, and circulatory system, putting oxygen into your blood and removing carbon dioxide and circulating your blood up through your head to keep your brain alive. You'll be under anesthesia, of course, the entire time. We need to keep your head attached to body-robot for several hours during procedure three. During procedure three, a specialized surgical team will attach the vital nerves from the back of your neck to the spinal cord of your cloned body. Once that's finished, then I'll continue the attachment of your head to the spinal cord and to two artificial support bones, and I'll complete the attachment of veins and arteries. We'll keep you heavily sedated for a few days and will bring you up gradually. Let me be honest: the odds favor the worst-case scenario — you die on the operating table." She paused and nodded. After a moment, she continued, "Then there's a chance you make it, but complications arise and you die in the days that follow. I'd say there's a 65% chance you won't make it through the operation. If you do make it, you might discover you'll be bedridden for the rest of your life, which could be a few days, a few weeks, or a few months. Being our first attempt, I'd say that if you do make it through the operation, there's a 70% chance of complications. Last and by far the least odds is the chance for a complete success. The odds from start to finish are just 10% of complete success—"

One of the patients shouted, "Does complete success mean we can walk again?" All thirty-six faces tilted forward and strained to hear her answer.

"Oh yes," Sally said, "and you get a bonus for making it: your head will be on your cloned body, grown to the equivalent age of eighteen years old. You'll not only walk, but you'll be young again! You'll be given your life back to live over — including the years your accident robbed from you!"

The crowd cheered and laughed. Jake knew they hadn't laughed much since they arrived here. He felt both sad and happy for them. Whereas the first volunteer had only a 10% chance of making it, Sally had previously explained to Jake that, by learning from the first operation, the second had twice the chance. The third, twice the chance of the second. The fourth, twice the third. After the fifth operation, Project Life would be able to go commercial on a limited basis. Forty operations would be enough to launch a widespread commercial campaign. But Jake knew that many of these people would not be around for the second try. To be the first try was their one shot at life, and they knew it.

Jake looked at Jasmine. She was both observing and taking notes. The upcoming week, he thought, will be the biggest week in our careers: the unveiling of Project Life to the public! They planned to release an in-depth seven-part series on the front page of all the Patterson Papers, which had grown to 46 daily papers, including the major markets of Los Angeles, New York, Chicago and Houston. The articles would cover the Neothink puzzle that led to this great event, including the campaign and election and the political revolution of Daniel Ward, the medical, job, and love revolutions that followed the shift into the new freedom paradigm, and the surging Church of God-Man with its Business Alliance of millions of people who were already aware of and driven by Project Life. Collectively speaking, the Church had become the biggest financial contributor to Project Life, surpassing Winters, Inc. upon Jeremiah's implementation of the Church's Pact for Eternal Life with its financial obligation. The seven-part series reached back over thirty years to Duncan Elementary, Miss Annabelle, and her students. The series finale, to appear in the big Sunday edition, would shock the country by accepting applications to be among the first to undergo the future, commercial procedure. It was a risk to accept applications, but The Group had decided that nothing got accomplished faster than a product with a market in place and waiting.

"What is the Fourth Procedure?" a beaming paraplegic asked. His extraordinary voice shattered Jake's thoughts of the upcoming week. When he looked back to the sea of faces, he was taken aback. They all looked nearly a foot taller, almost up to Jake's eye level...almost as though they had all stood up! They were no longer slumping blobs of near death. They were now sitting high, pulsating; their faces were full of color; they were now one with the living. They were now one with Jake.

"The Fourth Procedure," Sally answered, "is a series of breakthrough, skin-rejuvenation treatments to remove years of aging from your neck and face."

The thirty-six patients listened and nodded. God, they look so excited and innocent at this moment, like *children*, Jake thought. The numbers raced through his head at that moment and left him very sad: the odds were one in thirty-six that they would be the chosen one; then the odds were one in ten the procedure would be a success. That meant the odds were 360 to 1 against this dream happening for them, yet there they sat tall and euphoric. At that moment, Jake understood, as he never understood before, the meaning of HOPE.

These people had understandably suppressed or given up hope; they had resigned themselves to the unhappy lives they lived. Isn't that a microcosm of society, Jake thought, before the job revolution? Now, hope was in their lives, and look at them: aren't they now a lot like the rest of society, *after* the job and love revolutions?

"Because of procedure one, cloning your body to physical perfection, no one in here is a better candidate than the next. You all equally qualify for the experiment. And, it *is* an experiment. I want to be clear on that. Nothing we will be doing has been tested on a human being. Everything is experimental."

Jake knew Sally was trying to pare down the field. She wanted no one who harbored second thoughts or fear. That could cause disaster and unnecessary failure. She wanted only the most determined and mentally strong individual. That would create the best odds at success. ...Still, no one backed down, not even secretly. Jake could see determination and fearlessness in every face.

"I've brought a 200-page book for each of you to study; it explains in detail exactly what is involved," Sally said. She knew full well that the thirty-six patients were ready to pick straws. "I'll be back next weekend to talk to you further. We'll proceed with the Operation sometime within the next four months or so."

CHAPTER
SEVENTY-TWO

The banner of every Patterson daily paper across the country read "ARE YOU READY?" The first of seven articles that Monday morning sent the entire country into an electric buzz. In that first article, Jake and Jasmine revealed the names of those behind Project Life.

By Monday evening, the network and cable news were headlining Project Life and the individuals behind it. The former students and their teacher and her husband as well as Salinski, Jessie and Angie were ready. For the next week, they would dominate the television talk shows, news, and radio. Even Daniel, still buried in the details of forever ending a ruling-class government as the last such President of the United States, devoted one solid week to press appearances.

They got the message out.

Project Life was the biggest story of the young millennium. It was *the* story that defined the 21st century. The big, bold question that appeared all week across the banner of Patterson Group papers "ARE YOU READY?" was resoundingly answered by record-breaking television ratings and by dozens of nearly unanimous polls: YES, the public *was* ready!

The God-Man Group was doing what it set out to do: the members were creating the future they wanted — the rational future for themselves and for mankind. The future of *life*.

*

Jake and Jasmine's concluding Sunday article on Project Life appeared, via the AP wire, in nearly all domestic Sunday papers and many foreign papers. Al Patterson had decided to send the exclusive article through the wire without copyright restrictions at the cost of probably a million lost newsstand sales. The benefit to get millions of additional people behind Project Life by letting other papers print the article outweighed the financial profits from another million newsstand sales and premium advertising revenues. Nevertheless, the Patterson Group had become the epicenter of the media world almost overnight.

The Tuesday morning following the concluding Sunday article about Project Life, an in-house entrepreneur from the mailroom in the basement of the Patterson Building ran into the office of Al Patterson's secretary. Her office was a half-level lower than Al's large glass office. Her office and waiting area were surrounded with white walls. A corridor with stairs led up to Al's glass office. All appointments and visitors entered Al's office this way and not through the other entrance that opened straight to the balcony overlooking the floor.

"I must see him," the young man from the mailroom said to Patterson's secretary. He stood there, panting.

"Why didn't you just call up here?" she asked, a little alarmed.

"Because I have to *show him* these," the in-house entrepreneur said. He held up a handful of letters.

"Let me buzz him."

A moment later, Al walked out from the corridor and intercepted the in-house entrepreneur on the way to an early meeting.

"Sir, I...I must talk to you," said the young man.

"Walk with me," Al Patterson said. "What's the problem?"

"You've got to come down and see for yourself, sir. I just don't know what to do!"

"I'm on my way out. Tell me, *what's the problem?*"

"Oh...if you're on your way out, you'll see!"

A few moments later, Al reached the front. He stopped.

"Oh my goodness," he said. He stared at the large semitrailers from the privatized U.S. Post Office lined up alongside the Patterson Building. "What are they doing?"

"Delivering these, Mr. Patterson," the young man answered, handing Al the handful of letters. "*Millions* of them."

Al opened a few of the envelopes and looked inside. They all contained the cut-out application that appeared in the Sunday article about Project Life. Several were photocopies, most likely family members, Al figured.

"Millions of people," he said under his breath, "are ready for this." He jammed his hand into his pocket, pulled out his cell phone, and called Jake.

"It's beyond all expectations," Al told Jake. "Millions of applications for Project Life have arrived. *Millions!*"

*

The meeting room in Rico's mansion was alive with energy. Al had just told The Group about the U.S. Postal semitrailers lined up along the Patterson building delivering millions of applications for Project Life.

"That means that people on a mass scale *emotionally* don't want to die!" Mr. Melbourne said. "The public has shifted to the mind of the future — the Neothink mind. As happy value *creators* on their Friday-Night essences, people grasp the stakes involved: this is a race for their lives and their loved ones' lives. With the possibility of averting death here, people can't bear the loss of another loved one."

"Money is pouring into The Association at a frenzied pace," Theodore said. "Businesses worldwide want to contribute in any way they can to the effort. Project Life is going to surpass the effort put into the Manhattan Project and the Moon Project of the last century. We knew going public would raise enormous funds and assets, but the response is surpassing our expectations."

"I've been thinking quite a bit about making a major change in our plans," Sally announced to the Group at Rico's mansion. Her eyes looked wild with enthusiasm. "With the enormous funds available to us, we can accelerate our program. We could have affordable commercial biological immortality for the average person not in five to eight years as originally estimated, but in *two to three years.*" She nodded, as if to signify that they heard her right: *two to three years!* She explained, "The greatest consumption of time on the age-reversing, four-procedure process is the first procedure of cloning the human body. The Operation itself will occur over a twenty-hour period. Although skin rejuvenation of the face and neck will take several months of treatment, that's a cosmetic step only. With the enormous funds, let's alter our approach. Let's make the decision to clone all thirty-six paraplegic patients." Sally looked at Theodore. "We'll proceed with the first operation, which has only a 10% chance of success. I'll absorb and analyze the data, improve the procedure and then proceed with the second operation in a few months or less. I'll absorb and analyze the data, improve the procedure and then proceed with the third operation maybe a month later or less, and so on, each time dramatically improving and perfecting the procedure. We'll have the bodies, and we'll proceed through the experiments in the order of who would die next without our intervention. In other words, the patient least likely to last in the nursing home goes next. Over three years of repeated procedures, the procedure will be perfected and inexpensive enough to go to the masses."

"Our 'laboratory' of thirty-six experiments," Theodore injected, thinking it through as he talked, "would quickly perfect the procedure. Maybe the first step of the commercial venture can begin: commercially cloning bodies. I'll hire the best bioengineers in the country to study your cloning station prototype and to then design the next generation of relatively low-cost commercial cloning stations for mass production."

Theodore seemed to be thinking out loud as he continued, "Although the market is massive, the cloning stations could be obsolete in a few years. The medical industry is now the phenomenon the computer industry once was. In fact, I feel certain that the medical 'garage' entrepreneurs and their many approaches in bioengineering, genetics, and nanotechnology will obsolete the cloning stations in a few years or less. The cloning stations could end up with a market of only paraplegics, and perhaps only temporarily at that."

Sally agreed. "Either my colleagues will find a way to turn on cellular reproduction like a spigot or a medical entrepreneur will find a way to slow or stop or reverse cellular degeneration to end aging altogether, obsoleting the traumatic head-transfer procedure."

"That's okay with me," Theodore said. "Listen, I love progress, even if it sometimes passes right past me. Saving precious human life is most important to me and underscores that the greatest beneficiary of progress is each and every individual. One value creator's honest gain contributes to the whole and becomes everyone's gain." He paused; his eyes were staring at nothing, the way a person's eyes do when he is looking for an example.

"The computers," he finally said, "gave humanity the first look at that fact: the more individuals who got rich by taking the whole computer industry to the next level, the more costs dropped and the more buying power and values came to the consumers — to everyone."

*

Members of the Church of God-Man increased from thirty million to eighty million members worldwide almost overnight after The Group went public with Project Life. The eager public joined the Church of God-Man in large numbers to get closer to humanity's greatest undertaking of all time. With tens of millions of those members joining the Business Alliance and contributing 2 1/2% of their take-home pay (or more if running a business) toward Project Life, suddenly Sally had many billions of dollars to work with.

The costs of goods had dropped to fractions since Daniel took office. Better and better values for less and less money had sent everyone's standard of living soaring. Now, with the job revolution making nearly all employees their own prosperous entrepreneurs getting a piece of the action, people had a *lot* of money to spend.

Project Life became their outlet. People began pouring thousands of dollars and more into Project Life. Theodore told The Group that once Project Life went commercial, the costs and resulting price would steadily plunge from the early experimental costs. Therefore, those who invested large sums of money were given complimentary certificates that would entitle them and, in many cases, their loved ones to undergo without charge the commercial procedure later on. The most popular bumper sticker in the country was: "I donated three months pay to Project Life."

*

"I'm only limited now by the speed at which I can Neothink and by the speed at which technology can advance," Sally told Jake and Jasmine when they visited Sally's laboratory in Manhattan's East Side. She explained, "Even with all the funds and facilities available to me, still my best asset at this point is the super rapid progress by the many new medical entrepreneurs — the thousands of 'garage' entrepreneurs — who sprang up after Daniel eliminated the FDA. Their breakthroughs are coming at a fast and furious pace, and some of those breakthroughs fit into my current puzzle, some fit into the next level of my puzzle for a more definitive nonaging cure, and some don't fit into my plans but are promising, competitive approaches. The medical world is free again — the new, wild, wild west — and the results just amaze me.

"One approach that doesn't fit in my Neothink puzzle now, but could merge with my work later on, has to do with advancing computers, particularly our recent leap into the quantum computers. The quantum computers have the capacity to store a person's entire brain activity. But would that person's 'I-ness' be lost? When the stored brain activity gets downloaded into a clone, would the 'I-ness' or sense of one's self be the same as the person who physically died? Immortality does *not* exist without continuing the life of the person within, the 'I', despite otherwise identical memories and knowledge."

"It seems to me," said Jake, "that a value of the computer approach to you was the opportunity to define the nature of what curing death is all about: to keep the *I-ness* alive. And perhaps a longer term value of the computer approach to you is a potentially superior method to transfer one's brain from a dying body to the cloned body."

"Well spoken," Sally said.

"What about the work you've done on cancer?" Jasmine asked her. Sally glanced around the lab at the sophisticated equipment and continued, "I've researched your previous projects in preparation for a full-length article about your work on Project Life. You walked away from a promising cure for cancer."

"I'm too buried in Project Life, but you're right, my work on cancer mustn't stop. I turned over my cancer research project to two close colleagues. That research on ways to shut off cellular growth to stop cancer tumors also offers us a head start on how to *turn on* cellular growth to stop aging. It's actually turning into one of the most promising approaches to curing aging.

"But there are several approaches. For example, whereas our approach involves turning on cellular reproduction, I've heard of a promising approach out there that involves shutting off cellular degeneration. The many thousands of new medical entrepreneurs bring an exciting competitive spirit into medicine, comparable to what we've seen previously in the computer industry. The new medical revolution is now the place for the rising, young Neothink geniuses to be."

"How do you feel about that?" Jasmine asked. "How do you feel about the competition?"

"I feel as though it should have been this way a lot sooner...it should have always been this way."

*

Theodore addressed The Group during their monthly meeting: "Over the past few weeks, Winters Inc. did extensive research into the progress of the medical industry, especially biotech projects involving genetic engineering. Based on that research, I've decided to limit our upstart commercial cloning venture to a number that coincides with paraplegics and other physically damaged, accident victims. I feel that, by the time we'll be ready to go commercial, the cloning stations will likely be obsolete to the masses. I did, however, develop another set of plans around the possibility that the path of the immortality business could turn straight into cloning for some time to come if the quantum computers become a cheap, effective method to transfer the contents of one's brain. That jackpot will hit upon demonstrating the 'I-ness' could be transferred along with the brain activity of memory and knowledge."

The competitive stakes in immortality were heating up, just as The Group had planned.

CHAPTER
SEVENTY-THREE

After establishing the new government structure and moving back home to San Diego, Daniel tackled the exciting engineering challenges of raising the height of the World Trade Center. After a few weeks, however, he sensed the country still needed a connection with him. Afterall, he could see the country's completed puzzle picture, and the public longed for his insights. Sam, his devoted numbers man, also brought to Daniel's attention how the people needed his insights still — they needed his well-articulated overviews of what was happening to society. Sam called for a meeting to discuss the matter with Daniel.

"Without a ruling class suppressing civilization, progress is soaring as never before in every imaginable and beyond-imaginable way," Sam reported in their meeting, "and the public needs to hear *why*. Those amazing 'garage' entrepreneurs are springing up everywhere, especially in the medical industry. To keep up with progress, the workforces of big businesses are rapidly evolving from the old routine jobs of labor to the new exhilarating jobs of the mind. Businesses big and small are unleashing their own in-house entrepreneurs to compete with the barrage of super-competitive 'garage' entrepreneurs. Many businesses are even creating new jobs just to get their employees on their Friday-Night essences at work! The values being created are mind-boggling. Every day we hear of new consumer products and breakthrough lifesaving medical technologies reaching the marketplace for less and less costs to consumers. You know, Daniel, people would love some kind of overview of where all this progress is coming from and where it's all heading."

Six days later, Daniel delivered the following speech on national television one Thursday evening, introducing the country to where all the rapid progress was headed — biological immortality:

"Good evening, America. Dr. Ian Scott's Overlay Charts show that humanlike consciousness is the controlling component of existence. That means man was meant to rise up and control nature. Well, now it's time to do that, fully and completely.

"Human beings have been, until now, trapped within the destructive *forces of nature*. The ultimate destructive force of nature, which still controls us, is our deaths. Another destructive force of nature that, until recently, controlled us included the desire in some to rule and control others, as well as the desire in others to be ruled over and controlled. A few other destructive forces of nature included our preoccupation with financial prosperity instead of focussing on our real passions in life, our predatory drive to prey on others' weaknesses in business and sex, and even our physical urges for indiscriminate sex and our endless efforts to be popular came from forces of nature.

"Those are some examples of the forces of nature that work well in nature but wreak havoc on humanity. For instance, leaders of animal clans are absolutely necessary for survival, but political leaders nearly destroyed civilization through economic collapses and violent wars. The drive to mate with the physically superior member of the opposite sex is crucial in nature for the propagation of the species. But for humans who build relationships around both physical *and* psychological reasons of love and admiration, the temptations to be pulled away by the physically gorgeous mistress, for instance, destroys love and families. To live a life seeking prosperity is absolutely necessary in nature for survival, but humans never realized how that pursuit for riches blinded them from their Friday-Night Essences — their deepest passions — and ironically prevented their greatest successes and happiness. The competitive struggle for survival in nature forces animals, even in the same clan, to seek out and capitalize on the weaknesses of others, but in the human race, that deep-rooted urge unnecessarily generates hate, spite, and envy toward our fellowman. Even being popular is a competitive drive in nature to receive better positions, food, and females in the clan, but the drive to be popular per se in humans is destructive to our studies in school, distracting to our careers as adults, and threatening to our romantic and family relationships. And, of course, death itself is very important in nature for evolutionary progress, but humans advance faster than evolution, obsoleting the need for death.

"The forces of nature wreak havoc on humanity because human beings surpassed nature long ago. We should have, long ago, left behind the forces of nature. But to escape the forces of nature, until now, was impossible.

"For the first time, the human race at least in *this* country has been pulled free from most of the destructive forces of nature, which is responsible for the wonderful explosion of prosperity in America. Now the time has come for the human race to be pulled free from death, which will be our greatest triumph over nature. Leading up to our greatest triumph, other triumphs over the forces of nature have been crucial: Unlike gorilla clans, humans in this country no longer have ruling-class leaders who rule over and control society, and people in this country no longer look to be ruled over by external authorities. Society's standard of living has made everyone wealthy, so people in this country now pursue their deepest passions in life and are deeply happy and creative. And now that society's standard of living has made everyone wealthy, we no longer feel the competitive pressures to prey on our peers' weaknesses. Instead, we admire our peers' strengths, and we love our fellowman. And our most basic animal urges to mate with beautiful members of the opposite sex are quickly waning as bioengineering perfects our bodies and our spouses' bodies.

"Until now, the forces of nature had a powerful stranglehold on conscious man. It was the invention of *Neothink* that enabled us as a civilization to break free from the forces of nature. And here's how: through puzzle-building Neothink, an unforeseen phenomenon started happening to society called *the superpuzzles*. As more and more people began building Neothink puzzles, the puzzles themselves started snapping together into superpuzzles. Superpuzzles started growing throughout society. Society has metamorphosed into a *supersociety* of superpuzzles. The supersociety is made of millions of Neothink geniuses snapping together Neothink puzzles, which go on to become Neothink *puzzle pieces* to the superpuzzles. Those superpuzzles, such as the coming medical leaps to end conscious death, for example, are the *forces of the supersociety* that overpower and pull us free from the forces of nature.

"The forces of our new supersociety — the superpuzzles — will pull us free from death within the next few years. The forces of the supersociety have already pulled us free from political leaders, from hatred and envy, from monetary slavery, even from infidelity. The supersociety is a civilization of pure love and admiration of our fellowman, for our fellowman brings spectacular values to us and society by contributing crucial Neothink puzzle pieces to the superpuzzles. We have all felt a lot of that love and admiration lately toward those wonderful research doctors, scientists, and businessmen who keep developing the cures to virulent diseases that once claimed the lives of our parents and children.

"The forces of the supersociety will now zero in on the most destructive force of nature to the human race: *death*. A medical superpuzzle known as Project Life is underway, headed by Dr. Sally Salberg.

"Dr. Sally Salberg once said to the members of the God-Man Group that the only thing *really* wrong with life is death. In a few years or less, there'll be nothing — *nothing* really wrong with life.

"We are leaving behind a mortal anticivilization held down by the forces of nature, and we are heading into the immortal Civilization of the Universe liberated by the superpuzzles."

Jake and Jasmine were busy writing articles and, now, co-anchoring television updates. The day following Daniel's Thursday-Night televised announcement, Jake and Jasmine reported, live, on the Patterson Channel's evening news:

"In a nationwide poll following Daniel Ward's speech last night," Jasmine said, "over eighty percent of Americans reported they thought about *not dying* for the first time."

"The human psyche has started to shift from expecting to die to expecting *not* to die," Jake added. "The *real* tragedy of death has begun to sink in. Now, each human death becomes an excruciatingly devastating occurrence almost beyond conception."

Jake and Jasmine's newscast was right on. A sense of panic had, in less than a day, set in throughout civilization, for people could no longer conceive of losing a loved one when eternity was now an option...an option to those exhilarated people on their Friday-Night essences.

Mr. Melbourne called Jake and Jasmine after watching their newscast on the Patterson Channel.

"The perception of immortality," Mr. Melbourne explained, "has crossed over into another dimension in people's minds — from a desirous idea in the future to a must-have reality of the present. That shift in perception will certainly cause some jolting changes to society, the most heart-wrenching will involve our dying loved ones. People sense that biological immortality is a very real possibility now. People on the verge of dying will increasingly do everything in their power to keep themselves and their loved ones alive and safe until then."

Indeed, Daniel's speech had, in twenty-four hours, amplified the preciousness of life around the world.

*

"Someday, I'll have what you have now," Sally said to Jasmine, helping her with her gown in Guest Room 12 in Rico's mansion. "I'm so happy for you."

Jake and Jasmine had grown too precious to each other to delay their celebration of vows any longer, despite being busier than ever before. The celebration of vows had replaced the traditional marriage concept and its marriage license granted by external authorities. The celebration of vows was a formal wedding of two people expressing their commitment to each other and to themselves.

On this beautiful Saturday afternoon in September, The Group gathered outside in Olivia's favorite garden to share in the celebration of vows between Jake and Jasmine. Their celebration of vows reflected something that had not been reflected in weddings or vows before. Their vows were the first ever to express love and life together from an immortal perspective.

Gazing into Jasmine's eyes under a beautiful, old oak tree at the head of Olivia's picturesque garden, Jake said, "Jasmine, I've jumped to the new world where life is not a subtle burden of dead-end responsibilities. My life is afire, burning with enthusiasm for what I'm creating. And from that fire arises my burning love for you. When you walk into the room, my life lights up; my heart jumps. When the workday is done, being with you is a major event of happiness for me...a celebration! Each and every day I feel the celebration...what a way to live my life! *Thank you*, Jasmine, for bringing the celebration into my daily life. You've become so precious to me, my darling, there are no challenges to my love for you. And soon, the only possible threat that could steal us from each other will end. That horror called death will be conquered, and then we'll have each other forever. I used to think the shortness of our lives underscored the rightness of our extraordinary happiness together. Now I think the expanse of immortality will show us yet a whole new dimension of happiness. And it is with you, my Jasmine, I want to experience and explore that happiness, for all eternity."

Jake's vows went on to open the door to Jasmine's soul. Today was the happiest day of her life. When she turned around, she saw her father, his eyes swimming in the memories of when she was his little girl...those special years between a father and his daughter that, one unforgiving day, are suddenly gone forever. Immediately, Jasmine's eyes were swimming in the same memories of when she was young, and her busy father would come home from work and always spend at least three hours every day with his little girl. Jasmine dearly missed those three blissful hours a day with her dad, and so did he. And yet, as much as they both missed that daily time together, they would never have that again. ...She walked over and hugged her father.

"Oh, I love you so much, daddy. You were always *so nice* to me...I still cherish all those times we spent together. Since I've moved out, I really miss you."

715

"I miss you so much darling," her father said. His thick eyebrows were tightly knitted in nostalgia. "You were my world, just you and me. But I want you to know, when I see you are happy, my whole life lights up."

"Oh, daddy," Jasmine said. She put her head sideways against his chest and hugged him for several moments.

Jasmine's mother had left Jasmine and her dad for a slick American lawyer when Jasmine was just three years old. Jasmine's father, Mozar, lost his wife to a good-looking lawyer who made a lot of money filing deep-pocket lawsuits against honest businesses and settling for hefty sums before going to court. Heartbroken and devastated by the loss of his wife after they had started a family, he formed a special bond with his daughter. He felt a special preciousness growing every day, a preciousness he could put his valuable time into, even when she was just a toddler, for the preciousness was *permanent*; it would always be there. His little princess would always be his little princess, for the rest of his life. He cherished every day with his only child while she was growing up.

"I've been thinking, Jassy, I can work anywhere," he said. He pulled his head back to look in his daughter's eyes. "What if I moved to one of those big homes on the Jersey shore, just outside the City? You and Jake could come and see me or stay with me anytime you'd like. You could stay at my shore house on weekends whenever you'd like."

"Oh dad, yes! I'd love that! Can you, please! Will you?" Jasmine's face lit up as it did when she was a little girl, a sight her father so deeply missed.

He smiled nostalgically, happy to see that smile so full of glee on her face again, a special smile he had not seen for years and feared was gone forever.

"Yes, princess, I'll be there in a few weeks," he said. Jasmine shrieked with joy at his decision that would let them be close again.

She kissed him and turned back around and saw Jake's face glowing for their future...for their beautiful memories still to be created together. She looked back again at her father...his eyes still swimming in the beautiful memories of their past together.

CHAPTER
SEVENTY-FOUR

"It's so large…," Jasmine said, questioning if it was too big for her dad, "over 7000 square feet." Returning from a romantic honeymoon with Jake in Hawaii, Jasmine met her dad at this large remodeled house on the Jersey shore.

"Well, I was going to change a few things so a portion of the house would permanently be for you and Jake…to come and go as often as you please. And," he added, smiling sheepishly, "I wanted it big enough to have bedrooms for any grandchildren…"

"I love you, dad" Jasmine said. She reached out and hugged him tightly. He hugged her back. He felt all the love in his universe wrapped up in that hug.

He told her, when it was time to go, how much he always loved her and how he really looked forward to seeing her often, again.

"I'll change some things with the house, have the work done, and then I'll be here. It won't be long now, princess." As Jasmine walked to her car, she turned back around and looked at her dad for an instant longer than was needed. He looked so young and innocent standing there. Her eyes were drawn to his thick black hair and large dark eyes, lit up by the sun. She thought she saw something she had not seen since she was a little girl. She thought she saw that sparkle in his eyes again. He had been steadily building a publishing business with exciting success, and he felt really good about his newly chosen field. When he's here, she thought, we'll spend a lot more time together. And I'll bring him to the monthly meetings of The Group. He'll grow to love those people and their sense of life. And they'll love him. He belongs with them.

*

"I just finished *We've Come A Long, Long Way,*" Jasmine said, handing the article to Jake. Jake read it over from beginning to end one last time before going to print.

"Surprisingly," he said upon reading the article for the final time, "the world's changes no longer shock me in the least. In fact, they actually seem natural. The descriptions of the old civilization, though, now shock me and seem like ancient history, like the Dark Ages with all the violent wars and crime. It all seems so *long ago.*"

Jake and Jasmine's article qualified "long ago" as two years. They pointed out that knowledge advanced so rapidly now that expressions of time had to be recalibrated. Two years qualified as long ago or long, long ago and the anticivilization now qualified as ancient history. Moreover, today would be ancient history within two years.

"Where do you think the supersociety will be ten years from now?" Jake pondered out loud while still looking over the article. "I guess that question can't be answered, Jassy, because technology advances too rapidly to extrapolate more than a month or two ahead. That'd be like asking, in the previous anticivilization, where we would be in 200 years or 500 years. There could be no answer."

"There's only one way to try to attempt that," Jasmine said, "and it's kind of fun to do. Try to imagine anything and everything that's good for mankind and falls within the laws of science, and there's your answer. It's fun to try because you come up with some really good ideas about the future."

"How about the incredible feeling inside everyone today? That couldn't be foreseen by anyone a few years ago," Jake said.

He knew why people in the anticivilization could not foresee this incredible feeling: life was, beneath all the good experiences, a subtle *burden*. Therefore, the incredible feeling could not be anticipated.

Jasmine thought about what he said. The feeling inside everyone now was so different from the feeling inside everyone a few years ago. She said, "The feeling we now have inside started the frantic drive to end death. That feeling was the turning point from the anticivilization to the Civilization of the Universe."

The turning point. Jake thought about that expression Jasmine used to describe the feeling people now carried inside them each day. Suddenly he stood up and ran to his computer.

"I hope I kept that bit I worked up from my notes but deleted from our last article about burden and boredom!" he said. He ran across the room and started racing through his computer index. "Oh, thank goodness, here it is!"

He printed the short bit about the burden of life and read it out loud to Jasmine:

"The act of living requires responsibilities," he had written. "The problem before was, in the anticivilization, those responsibilities of living were *dead-end* responsibilities. The daily effort put into one's responsibilities of living a self-sufficient life did not go anywhere really significant. There was no Friday-Night essence, no creation. People steadily sank into stagnation.

"So, since the daily effort put into one's responsibilities of self-sufficient living only served a boring routine but did not create anything exciting and new, then the effort for living was really a burden.

"There were, in the anticivilization, many valuable experiences that made life worthwhile, such as pursuing a promising career, falling in love and getting married, having children and raising a family, maybe even traveling and seeing the world during retirement. But those wonderful experiences eventually ran out, and when they did, the burden rose to the surface like static on an old record player. Underneath the songs, the static played, eventually to be the last thing one heard when the songs were all over. No one wanted to listen to the static for long. No one wanted to live for long with only the burden. So, people were ready to die in their 70s. That's the culmination of the anticivilization — one's death.

"The thought of living forever did not appeal to people in the anticivilization; living forever with the burden would have become torture. We could not foresee what we now *feel* inside. If we could, we would have fought for biological immortality long ago. Not until we began to get a clue of this incredible feeling inside did the interest in not dying begin."

Jake put down the paper. How odd, he thought, that *a feeling* changed humanity from the death-destined anticivilization toward the life-eternal Civilization of the Universe. *A feeling!* How people *felt* inside brought about the superpuzzles that now lifted society so rapidly.

"What causes this incredible feeling we all walk around with every day?" Jake asked out loud. "What prompted the turning point?"

For the rest of the day and the next, that question of what caused this incredible feeling weighed heavily on his mind. Of course, he knew the answer involved man's evolution into God-Man and the several revolutions that followed in politics, business, love, and medicine. But, he wondered, what made us feel such powerful harmony within ourselves and with everything around us...with the Universe?

*

Late the next night, Jake lay quietly awake in bed, thinking about Ian's Overlay Charts that proved that the very advanced God-Man, whom Ian and Miss Annabelle named *Zon*, created the Universe we lived in. A Zon created the galaxy that we lived in, too, he thought. And now the Overlay Charts reveal Zons unfolding black holes and gravity units to create new realms of existence in order to release energy into the Universe and, in the larger galactic occurrences, to start the evolutionary life cycle that creates new life...eventually evolving into new *conscious life*, the supreme value in the Universe...making Zons the supreme *value creators*.

At that moment, a great thunderclap shook Jake to his roots.
I can feel the connection between Zons and the incredible

feeling everyone now walks around with every day, Jake thought, and that connection between Zons out there and us down here explains the powerful harmony everyone now feels every morning and throughout every day with himself, with the world...with the Universe!

Jake jumped out of bed and called out: *"Nature's Quintessential Secret!"* Then he said, "I now know how to answer my question: what causes this incredible feeling we all walk around with every day? It all started when man's mind effected Nature's Quintessential Secret and became what man was meant to be — *the creator.* Through Neothink, people one by one began *creating* values, not just routinely producing values, but uniquely *creating* values that never existed before. Then came the division of essence and its job revolution where people who discovered their deepest motivational roots could really exert the new, puzzle-building Neothink in their entrepreneurial jobs of the mind. They created new values in all fields of knowledge, all jobs of life. ...Once this started happening, then their responsibilities for living were no longer dead-end responsibilities. The effort for self-reliant living was no longer a burden that went nowhere. Instead, the responsibilities for living were exhilarating that went to exciting new heights and were open-ended. Each new created value opened up multiple new directions to pursue. The effort for living not only went somewhere, but went to a dimension where man and only man was made to enter: *to creation.* The role of consciousness in our Universe is *creation,* not stagnation!"

"What? Jake...what's going on?" Jasmine asked, slowly sitting up in bed, still half asleep.

"Every morning, when we wake up, what do we feel?" Jake asked her, but in his enthusiasm, he answered his own question, *"Exhilaration.* Why? Because we're finally living in harmony with ourselves, the world around us, and the Universe, for we're finally fulfilling the universal role of consciousness. It's what that sermon at the Church of God-Man was all about four years ago, remember...about *adding values* to Zon's Creation? Let's see: the Universe consists of three fundamental components: mass, energy, and, as Ian demonstrated, consciousness. Human consciousness is the component of the Universe that is *the creator*. The role of consciousness in the Universe is *creation* by unfolding black holes and gravity units...releasing mass and energy, creating conditions for new consciousness. Through *creation*, consciousness brings more consciousness to the Universe, adding growing, open-ended value to its home. When the question is asked: what is man's purpose or why are we here or what is the meaning of life...the answer is: *to create* — to ultimately *add values* to Zon's Creation!

"When Neothink enabled the ordinary person to start *creating*, he discovered something so much more than mere exhilaration — he discovered eternal harmony within himself and with the Universe. The burden lurking beneath the good experiences of life disappeared. The contradiction of stagnation vanished. The anticivilization vanished. Every religious wish vanished, for man's harmony with the Universe was found."

"Jake...you're so right," Jasmine said, now wide awake. "Mankind went from routine ruts to open-ended creation."

"Each person now delivers profound, unique values to the world," Jake continued, nodding in agreement with what Jasmine just said. "His creations click into the large superpuzzles throughout our supersociety. His contributions to the supersociety are loved by his fellowman. He is loved and admired by society. And, he is rich. But he lives for *his creations*. Or, rephrased, he lives *to create*. Man no longer lives for good experiences that mask the burden underneath. In the days of the anticivilization, seeking out good experiences to escape the burden of life actually had drug-addict-like control over people and was the reason for so many self-destructive activities such as overeating, overdrinking, too much partying, promiscuous sex, and distractions...from entertainment to vacations — in the lifelong, desperate quest to escape the burden of life."

He's really something, Jasmine thought as she watched Jake pull together the big picture. She said nothing more, for he was on a roll.

"Nature's Quintessential Secret is the denouement: the forces of nature — mass and energy — do not control the cosmos and the consciousness throughout it, rather consciousness controls the cosmos and the mass and energy throughout it. Consciousness controls the cosmos through being *the creator*...through what ignorance once called God. Consciousness grows the values in the Universe by creating new realms of existence to be filled with new consciousness. Until now, the forces of nature on Earth have controlled mankind. But man has finally turned that around. He has finally pulled free from the forces of nature through becoming, at work, *the creator*...through what we now call the God-Man. Finally, man on Earth has discovered Nature's Quintessential Secret and lives in harmony with the Universe and with Zon, the creator of his Universe."

Jake stopped to catch his breath. After a pause, he concluded, "The turning point came when man leapt from a value producer trapped in his routine rut to a *value creator*. How simple. For then, the burden left, the contradiction vanished, and man discovered harmony with the Universe. Conscious life was not meant to stagnate, which slowly kills it. Man was meant to create, which allows him to grow, forever. The great search for 'something more' in our lives was finally found, for there *was* something more than stagnation — there was *creation*. Nature's Quintessential Secret: man is *the creator*. He's the creator of heavens and earths. He's the creator of eternal life. He's the eternal creator of values. He's the creator...he is God. Eventually, he becomes Zon."

Jake and Jasmine worked the next day for sixteen hours straight on this article about humanity's leap from value producers to value creators. This article, they knew, captured the reason the mortal civilization would now leap into an immortal civilization.

CHAPTER
SEVENTY-FIVE

Jasmine was so busy during a three-city trip that she had not been able to call her dad for nearly a week. On the flight back to New York after the weekend, Jasmine anxiously called her dad in North Carolina. She could not wait to tell him The Group now planned to clone all thirty-six paraplegics, which would accelerate Project Life. Jasmine called her father two or three times a week now. They were getting close again and could not wait for his big move to New Jersey.

Jake stopped writing to watch Jasmine as she called. He loved being around when she talked to her father — she was always so happy and giggling like a little girl. Jake saw the excitement on her face as she picked up her satellite phone and said "Dad!" into the voice-command. As Jake watched his wife, he understood the beautiful nature of family love: even when one's life was bombarded with deadlines as was Jasmine's life leading up to the Operation, love still shined through, unyieldingly, delightfully. Today, she was especially excited to talk to him. She loved hearing his voice. Although he did not call her "sugar pie" since she was a child, the sweetness in his voice was always silently saying, "I love you, *sugar pie*." No other voice in the world could ever be that way to her.

He was not home. Before she went to bed, she sent him an

email.

*

Some noises woke Jasmine the next morning. When she came out of the bedroom, she saw Jake sitting in the nook editing some papers.

"What's that?" she said.

"It's an editorial. I'm really getting down to the difference between a mortal civilization and an immortal civilization." He handed her the papers. "It's still rough, but can you read it over?"

"Of course, honey."

Jasmine sat down at the nook and began reading Jake's editorial:

From Man to God-Man
(Editorial by Jake Catchings)

Until recently, I would see a recurrent theme in the movies and in the story books. Characters depicted as immortals were considered trapped here on Earth usually through some sort of **curse** from which they could not escape, could not reverse.

But, if the curse were somehow broken and the person were allowed to die, relief filled his eyes, peace filled his smile, and a glow of anticipation filled his face as he died and his soul ascended to heaven.

How could our emotions have been so backwards?

That scene, once played again and again in the movies and written in the novels, illustrated the psychological problem of why there was no worldwide, driving effort to cure aging and to achieve immortality on Earth. The writers and producers represented the human race with their fear of immortality — justifiable fear in a civilization in which immortality meant eternal stagnation. In the anticivilization, people were frightened by the idea of immortality and its inherent responsibility yet helplessness to sustain happiness for eternity — a responsibility they just could not fulfill in Earth's old anticivilization. Remember, before the recent switch to value creation, our lives played out some nice melodies, so to speak, but the awful static — the burden of stagnant value production — was underneath the music and would ultimately be all that was left for us. Of course, living forever with the burden of stagnation — with only static — *would* be a curse!

People born in the anticivilization inherently knew their experiences of happiness would eventually be used up and the burden of life would take over. They sensed their stagnation-traps were bigger than themselves and they were helpless at sustaining happiness...**the** crucial emotion necessary for sustaining conscious life. People sensed that the eventual loss of happiness went beyond their ability to do anything about it. They were trapped in a gradual decline, and they knew it. That's just the way it was and had always been. They sensed the only way out was beyond their control. It would take some higher power to pull them free from their stagnation-traps, from the burden. They sensed their all-encompassing powerlessness, the powerlessness of man. Only something more powerful than man — God, they concluded — could pull them from the anticivilization and return them to happiness, that crucial emotion needed for immortality. Knowing they themselves could not fulfill their responsibility of sustaining happiness, they turned that responsibility over to God. For, God was all-knowing, all-powerful and could pull their helpless souls from the burdensome anticivilization, into heaven — a civilization of eternally happy souls.

I can't sustain happiness on Earth, their souls cried, **so come take me, Lord, to a place where I'll be happy for eternity!**

In short, people implicitly knew they were helpless against the anticivilization in the long run and needed something more powerful than themselves to escape it. The gradual yet inescapable decline of happiness heading toward certain depletion as they grew old, and their helplessness to stop it made them turn to the supernatural — to something more powerful than themselves — to save their souls.

A New World

Now, for the first time, the gradual decline of happiness does not occur. Imagine the happiness of a child — that same happiness is within you right now as you read this...right now, always, forever. The burden of life has been replaced with the exhilaration for life. Exhilarating value creation instead of burdensome value production brings us unending happiness. Happiness now comes naturally, from all around us and within us. In fact, the Civilization of the Universe on Earth is sort of what people once imagined heaven to be, only better. We never worry about depleting happiness, not anymore.

We have naturally flowed into our Friday-Night Essences and will eventually create great values that will make us invaluable heroes to the world. That happens naturally to us in this new world. In a sense, like the God-and-Heaven belief, the responsibility for our happiness vanished, too, for happiness comes naturally, as once imagined in Heaven. And, yes, it did take something beyond the ordinary person to free him from the anticivilization and its depletion of happiness. It took the entire shift into the Civilization of the Universe on Earth.

*

Jasmine put down Jake's editorial.

"You're so right," she said. "People couldn't beat the anticivilization; they were powerless against it. So, they turned to the idea of an all-powerful God to pull them free and to take over the responsibility of happiness." Jasmine paused, her eyes twinkled.

"Honey," she said, "I love your editorial, and I want Dad to read it. I think he's finally rediscovered his happiness."

*

"Mrs. Catchings," said Jasmine's secretary at work that afternoon, "it's a bank calling from North Carolina."

Jasmine picked up her phone. "Hello, this is Jasmine."

"Hello Jasmine. I'm calling from your father's credit union in Raleigh. He put your name and work number down here on his commercial loan application."

"Oh, what's he building?"

"He's purchasing several lands upon which he plans to build large, discount bookstores, or *book malls* as he calls them."

Jasmine smiled. She remembered how her father would always keep his building projects secret when she was a girl until he could show her the erected frames. Then, he couldn't stop talking. She laughed inside. *He's back*, she said to herself; *he's back to creating again.*

"Well, I just called to see if you knew how to get ahold of your father. He missed his appointment yesterday for closing the building loan."

"Oh," Jasmine said. "I have his phone number right here, but I'm sure you've tried it. I'm going to try to get ahold of him, and I'll have him call you."

"Thank you, Jasmine."

Worried, Jasmine hung up the phone and went to her computer. "Look at this," she mumbled. "He still hasn't answered my email from last night. He always answers his emails first thing in the morning." She sat at her computer, thinking. Something must have come up with his new publishing business, she thought. She went back to her desk and called his home. His voice mail picked up.

"Daddy, where are you?" she said, pleadingly, after the beep. She called his office. His secretary had not seen him all day, or the day before, but said he had been extremely busy with his business and the move.

Jasmine felt a sinking feeling in her stomach. She called every hospital around her father's home and felt some relief when it became obvious he had not been admitted.

She then called the private Aid & Assist force (A&A) and said her father had been missing for two days. She told them he lived alone, and she wanted them to check inside his house. The officer told her not to worry, that this kind of thing happened all the time, but they would check it out and call her back within the hour.

Forty minutes later, Jasmine's secretary put the call through.

"It's the Raleigh A&A," her secretary said.

Jasmine stood up and nervously picked up the phone.

"Ma'am, are you Mozar Khalil's daughter?" she heard a voice say.

"Yes."

"We searched your father's house, and we found him. Ma'am...your father was unconscious. We rushed him to the hospital..."

Jasmine could not feel her legs beneath her. She knew she was swaying. All she could hear was the sound of her own blood swooshing through her head. But she made herself listen and get the details of how to get by her dad's side.

*

To the nurses, Jasmine looked as though she were lost in oblivion, staring at her father. But inside her mind were thunderous emotions and memories.

She gently slipped her small hands into his.

"Oh Dad," she said so sadly, seeing her precious father like this...frail and unconscious. "The house is waiting for you. Jake and I will be there with you every weekend."

But she feared he would never live in that house, and the special closeness between them that she so missed and so looked forward to having again would never happen now. He had suffered a burst, aortic aneurysm. That burst aneurysm also set off a stroke. Even with the mind-boggling progress medicine had made, operating on the aorta was still a risky procedure. In his unstable state, an operation would kill him. He would have to stabilize first; it was his only chance, yet he continued to deteriorate. The damage would soon kill him. The doctors told her that they could not do much for him now besides make him comfortable.

His eyes were closed. She looked at his thick head of hair and his calm expression. His face was smooth. He looks so innocent and sweet, she thought. She looked more closely at his face. He still looks so young! He can't be...*dying.* On the eve of immortality? No, not *now!*

Jasmine kept her hands in his and leaned over him, looking at her father with all her love. She sensed she would not have him much longer.

Suddenly, as though his senses perceived his princess was there, with a Herculean effort, he opened his eyes and focussed on Jasmine.

"Daddy!" she cried. Her heart jumped with joy just as it did every time he came home from work to be with her when she was a little girl.

Jake sadly watched the profound tragedy happening before him. Although Jasmine's father was perhaps minutes away from death, the intense celebration they felt whenever they were together could not be stopped, not even at the end. The celebration filled them both, perhaps greater than ever before. Her father had lost all motor capability from the shoulders down, but Jake could have sworn he saw her father's hands squeeze hers.

In his weakened state, he was performing superhuman feats...for his daughter. As Jake silently, sadly observed, he realized just how much they loved each other and that her father did everything for her growing up...just the two of them.

"Daddy, *thank you* for the most beautiful childhood and all that time you spent with me. That was *so special*. I can remember everything as though it happened last month. I can never forget those times we spent together," Jasmine said in the saddest voice Jake had ever heard. She could see her father was fading, and this was good-bye. She clutched his hands and leaned very close to him, looking deep into his eyes. Jasmine and her dad suddenly knew this was the last of their special moments together.

Jake noticed as her father faded, his eyes wrestled their way back open, looking at his little princess. He was clinging onto every last moment...every last moment with his beloved daughter.

"Daddy, I *love you*. Oh...don't go. Daddy, don't go!" Jasmine pleaded, trying to keep the life in him with her love.

Then, with a heroic effort, her dad focussed his eyes on her one last time...and he spoke to her. His words were soft and barely audible.

"What, Daddy?" Jasmine asked, putting her ear directly before his mouth. But, she could never retrieve his precious last thought. ...When Jasmine had turned her ear toward her father, he was still there; when she looked back, he was gone. His glow was gone...forever.

"Daddy? Oh no...Daddy? Daddy! No! Nooooo!" she

screamed and wrapped her arms around him, putting her head sideways upon his chest, hugging him as only a daughter hugs her daddy. For the first time in her life, he didn't hug her back. His incredible love for her was now gone from her life...forever.

She lay down on the bed and curled up next to him just as she used to so many times when she was little. When Jake saw this, tears just fell from his eyes in clumps every time he blinked.

"Did I remember to tell you, Daddy, how much I looked forward to walking along the beach with you when you moved to the shore house?" Jasmine asked in complete helplessness. For the first time in her life, her beloved dad could not hear his darling daughter. A few seconds passed in silence. She looked so devastated when her father's wonderful voice did not answer. His gentle voice that was always silently saying "I love you, *sugar pie*" would never answer again. She looked up at her father's face and cried, "You can't hear me anymore. Oh, daddy...you can't hear me anymore. Oh..." Then, her eyes shut tight, her face grimaced and then contracted into tight wrinkles, and she cried with all her might while hugging her dad.

It was the saddest thing Jake had ever seen.

CHAPTER SEVENTY-SIX

Jasmine was drowning in sorrow. She had always had Dad to help her get through the losses...when her childhood pets died, when her mom left. His powerful love and wisdom soothed her pain and reassured her that everything would be okay again, someday. But not now, when she needed him most. She was all alone. Not even Jake could help. How could someone she loved so much be gone for eternity when humanity was weeks away from immortality?

Jasmine could not work, even though the days leading up to the Operation were the most exciting days in human history. She was caught in a crushing paradox that was nearly killing her. The immeasurably valuable event of achieving immortality juxtaposed to the loss of her dad *just weeks prior* plunged the dagger of irrationality to an intolerable level.

Jasmine sank and sank deep into depression. She became despondent. The pain at times turned to numb nothingness; it worsened each day as the Operation approached. She reappeared from her separation from the world long enough to tell Jake that being on the edge of immortality makes her loss too overwhelming.

"I hope things'll change today," Jake mumbled to himself as

732

he rode the subway from the Patterson Building to his brownstone in Manhattan. Jake was deeply troubled. Jasmine had not gone to work since her father died; she barely ate, and she still seemed not to have stabilized from her slide into her own, withdrawn and depressed world. Today was her birthday, and Jake came into the office for a couple hours and now headed home with a mission to try to rescue the love of his life from her fall from life.

"Sweetheart?" he called out when he walked in. But he did not expect her to answer. She had not talked for over a week. "I couldn't wait to be with you, honey," Jake said while opening the door to their bedroom, but Jasmine was not there. She had not left their home since returning from her father's funeral and retrieving some of his belongings that were precious to her.

"Jasmine? Jasmine?"

Jake ran about their home, but she was gone.

Where'd she go? Jake sat down on the couch. He was both worried and relieved that she had finally stepped out. It's a step out of her decline, he thought, but she's in no condition to be out alone. Where do I look for her?

He noticed on the lunch bar an envelope with some pictures spilling out. He sprang back to his feet, scooped up the envelope and started thumbing through the pictures.

"Oh, my little Jasmine," he whispered and sighed. "The pictures are of you and your dad, camping when you were maybe nine or ten years old." Jake saw the sheer joy in her face and in her father's, too. His smile looked more like a laugh than a smile when he was with his precious Jassy. Jake felt a lump growing in his throat. "All that love, just gone now," he said with a deep, sad voice. After a moment, his eyes widened. "Oh...oh yes...her birthday camping trips!" He shuffled through the pictures. "Here we go," he said as he found a picture in front of the campground's sign. He sat at his computer. "Where is it, where is it?" he said. He looked through a national campground web site.

He found Jasmine's campground and printed a map of the area from the web site. He turned and ran out of the door, stuffing the picture and map into the envelope. He ran to his car parked two blocks away.

Superpuzzle

"Jasmine's car's gone," he mumbled as he ran past her parking spot. He got in his car and headed out of the city.

It was late afternoon when Jake arrived. "God, it still looks exactly the same here as it does in the photo," he said, knowing the picture was taken maybe fifteen years before.

"I'll pay for one night," Jake told the campground keeper. Inside the campground, Jake pulled over and pulled out the envelope full of pictures. He studied the pictures of Jasmine and her dad, especially the one that showed their tan and brown tent. Then, he started slowly driving around the grounds, looking for Jasmine or the tent. The shadows from the tall trees covered the entire campground with an early dusk.

"That's her!" he whispered, looking down a hill past a vacant campsite. Through trees and bushes, he saw her sitting at a picnic table. He immediately pulled his car into the vacant campsite. She could not see him on the top of the hill behind her campsite.

Jake parked his car behind a clump of bushes where Jasmine would not see it. Then, he got out and walked towards Jasmine's campsite. She suddenly stood up. Jake ducked in the brush. He saw she had already pitched her tent — the same tan and brown tent — and now she walked to her car and pulled out two sleeping bags. One was red, one was blue. She put the red one back down and hugged the blue one. Then she pressed her face against it and inhaled a deep breath through her nose.

"Daddy," she exhaled. It was the first time Jake heard her speak in over a week. It broke his heart to see her standing there, all alone, hugging her father's sleeping bag. But Jake knew his Jasmine needed to be alone tonight, alone with her happy memories as painful as they might be, precious memories of her birthday camping trips with her father.

So, Jake remained hidden. He would stay the night, however, to be sure his Jasmine was all right.

He went back to his car, rolled down the windows so he could hear Jasmine if she needed help, and continued working on his series of articles on the step-by-step march toward the Operation. He put on his thick ski jacket as the temperature dropped with the sun.

When he looked down the hill, he could see Jasmine between

the colorful Autumn trees and bushes. When dusk turned to dark, he went back down the hill and stayed out of sight, behind the bushes again, to check on Jasmine.

She was sitting in front of a fire. Jake watched the orange glow flickering brightly and then dimly across his wife's face. Seeing her all alone, he tried to imagine what it must have been like, sitting by the fire with her father.

Her sad expression worried Jake. How much pain is she feeling? he wondered. He knew she was deep in her past — deep in memories of her dad.

Jake went back to his car, turned on his inside reading light and continued writing. After some time passed, he realized it had gotten late; Jake no longer heard the sounds of campers. He stepped out of his car; it was black outside and cold.

He walked very slowly and carefully down the hill to check on Jasmine. She was inside her tent. The dome tent was filled with light inside. Jake noticed something strange moving around on the nylon cover of the tent. He looked closer. It's a shadow, he recognized. Suddenly, he remembered his first conversation with Jasmine at the cafe when she told him about her father.

"Animal shadows," he whispered, *"of course."* He remembered the day he met her at Amad's dorm party. Ah yes, Jake reminisced, we went to that cafe hangout, and she told me about her birthday camping trips with her dad, the two of them making animal shadows until she couldn't keep her eyes open.

Jake watched the shadows of different animal shapes form on the tent: little birds, rabbits, cats and elephants. He could imagine that little nine-year-old girl in the picture lying there with her father in pure contentment, on her birthday, absorbed in his wonderful smile that looked more like a laugh, not wanting the day to end. Her father, just laughing and being with her — those were life's most precious and unforgettable times...so precious, Jake thought. He knew Jasmine longed to get close to the preciousness again by going back to the same surroundings, today, on her first birthday without her dad.

As Jake watched the little animal shadows jumping, running, wrestling on the nylon tent, his mind went into an imagination of Jasmine and her dad when she was a little girl, right here on this very campsite in that very tent not so many years ago.

Superpuzzle

Jake imagined the squeals of delight and bursts of laughter emitting from that tent. He could almost see the joy in her face. Inside that tent, life was beautiful for Jasmine and her daddy, not so long ago. ...Life passes so quickly.

The love between father and daughter should be *forever*, Jake thought. He could still hear the laughter.

However, his imagined sounds of the little girl's laughter turned odd. He realized he no longer imagined whatever he was hearing; he was actually hearing Jasmine gently sobbing. He bowed his head. She sounds so sad, so helpless. *Why*, his mind demanded, *why* did a few short years turn all that love and happiness to sorrow and sadness? *Why?*

*

The next day Jasmine went back to their brownstone in Manhattan and back to her bedroom. She looked more devastated than ever.

Jake called Ian. "Do you remember," asked Jake, "the talk Miss Annabelle had with Sally in third grade when it was imminent she would lose her mom?"

"Yes, I do. I remember how Miss Annabelle put peace into Sally's soul."

"It was speculation, I know, but the logic seemed solid."

"The basic idea was that Zon — *the* value creator — wouldn't let his greatest value creation, human consciousness, the greatest value in the Universe, die if Zon had the technology to save our consciousness...our spirit. Of course, Zon *The Creator* would have such advanced technology."

Jake listened and nodded. Then, he carefully explained Jasmine's condition.

"Jake," said Ian, "you know that my Overlay Proofs, demonstrating God-Man controlling the mass/energy dynamics of the Universe, give a lot of weight to the theory that those technologically advanced conscious beings could possibly save our consciousness — our spirit — when we physically died."

"In other words, your theory means that Jasmine's father, his spirit, could still be alive and happy."

"Yes, precisely. Now, this is speculation, but the ether, the

736

existence field that I discovered during the Super Bowl, may act like a super-quantum computer with the circuitry that enables advanced conscious beings to download their knowledge to a Universal Computer of eternal knowledge. Perhaps the ether could also be the tool used by Zons to transceive our consciousness into the eternal Civilization of the Universe at the time of our deaths. ...Of course, that's something we won't know until we fully achieve the Civilization of the Universe on Earth."

"Can you talk to Jasmine?"

"Yes, right away. I'm in New York; I'm leaving for your place now."

"Thank you, Ian."

Ian came over and talked to Jasmine. He spent over an hour going through the scientific background to the theory. Jasmine was separated from the world, but Ian talked. After about a half hour into Ian's description, Jake noticed her eyes were looking at Ian's Overlay Charts as he described them. Jake felt enormous relief. Jasmine was quietly listening. Her sensory perceptions were, for the first time since her father's death, opening up and letting some of the outside world in.

About an hour after Ian had left, Jasmine looked at Jake. She had not spoken in five days. She was a skeleton frame and face, having dropped fourteen pounds in twelve days from eating what little amounts Jake could coax her to eat since she lost her father. Her doctor and two eating specialists were not able to help her.

"Let's go out for a quiet dinner," she said in a weak voice. A mammoth wave of relief rushed through Jake and pushed tears into his eyes.

"Certainly, my love," he said gently.

*

At dinner, Jasmine ate a little, and for the first time since her father died, she entered into some conversation. What she said floored Jake:

"Ian's theory is interesting, but we have no evidence," she said. Jake looked at her in amazement. That was the last thing Jake expected her to say. "I see his theory," she continued, "as

737

a metaphor for the love and compassion that would fill a Zon. But, we must do it ourselves. We must drive forth our civilization to bring it into the Civilization of the Universe. Thinking that Zons do that for us after we die will only hurt our progress. *We* must not let what happened to my father happen to anyone else!"

All Jake could do was look at her in awe and admire her. What strength, he thought, what heroic honesty! If there were anyone who could easily latch onto some wishful thinking, it was Jasmine.

"We just don't know what the dynamics would be for Zons out here. We just don't know," she said, her voice starting to shake. "It would be a mistake to let up on our drive, even now in our final stages. There can be no more life-after-death beliefs — not even saved-by-Zon beliefs — or we won't make it, Jake. It's up to *us*."

Caught up in the determination in Jasmine's voice, he felt like cheering. What *guts* it took to admit this, he thought.

"You're an incredible person, Jasmine," Jake said, overcome with admiration for her courage. He reached out and took her hands in his. "I love you, Darling."

For the first time since losing her father, Jake saw life in her eyes again. He leaned over the table and hugged her. She hugged back. Mountains of respect and love filled them in their silence.

Jake sat back down and looked at Jasmine's face, radiating beauty and strength once again. He realized she was absolutely right. The dynamics of Zons went beyond what he or even Ian could possibly imagine. To do what we need to do, Jake thought, we have to forget about Ian's theory.

Jake's thoughts shifted back to Jasmine who had just lost the most incredible father and precious love Jake had ever seen. Goddamn, Jake thought, of all people...what heroic honesty she has. ...At that moment, he knew the time was right to tell her something he knew.

"Your father was absolutely right, you know," he said.

"About what?"

"Darling, when he was dying, I could see it in his eyes. You filled his last moments with the greatest happiness he ever knew

— *you*. As he clung to his last moments of life, he was immensely enjoying those last moments. He was viewing his greatest creation, his greatest piece of art — *you*."

"Oh, Jake..." Jasmine said, very sadly. The emotional impact caused her beautiful sad eyes to blink several times. She tried to speak, but couldn't. She helplessly looked at Jake and tried to smile.

"Darling, you don't need to say a word," Jake said gently. "I heard what he said at the very end; I'm now going to tell you, OK?"

All Jasmine could do was nod.

"I barely heard him, but there was no mistake: he wanted you to know what filled his soul at that last moment. Darling...he said, *'Being with you is beautiful.'*"

CHAPTER SEVENTY-SEVEN

"I'm here to take cell samples," Sally told the thirty-six paraplegics, *from all of you*." She could barely hold back her smile.

"All of us?" repeated a patient. Her face beamed with hope.

"We're going to clone you all, starting immediately," Sally announced. The smile she had been holding back burst across her face. "You're all going to get perfect new bodies!"

The paraplegics whooped and hollered and tossed about in their wheelchairs. Jake loved this moment. These people who looked so lifeless a few weeks before were now so full of life, like children.

The next day, the Patterson Papers printed Jake and Jasmine's article about the coming thirty-six operations to give the paraplegics new life. The thirty-six operations, the article explained, would perfect the complicated operation in order to bring it to the marketplace. The thirty-six operations, therefore, would ultimately bring new life to *everyone* when the time came.

The thirty-six paraplegics were instantly international celebrities. That week, they appeared day and night on television. On one network, they were called: the last battalion in the last battle of the last war. The metaphor stuck because it was accurate.

Putting Together the Pieces

*

Not until Daniel left Washington D.C. did the people begin to fully understand the magnitude of the feat he accomplished there. Single-handedly, he ended the ruling class in America. After he moved back to San Diego, the people began to realize how indebted they were to this great man. He never wavered, not even during the most difficult life-threatening obstacles. As he always promised, the people now enjoyed breathtaking prosperity.

Daniel's ability to snap together large puzzle pictures and to know what the missing pieces — the future — looked like well before others earned him the title: the Great Neothinker. The people loved him for what he had done for them. They cherished his puzzle-building, future-seeing ability, and they wanted his continuing insights. So, he began to appear weekly on Patterson national television. He chose Thursday evenings to make his announcements. Several months after closing down the ruling class, he made the following Thursday-Night Announcement:

"Most countries are following America's lead. The supersociety-stimulations blossoming in America are just so rich and wonderful. People in America are wealthy and healthy beyond anything the world has ever known.

"As the ruling classes collapse around the world, people everywhere are jumping into the new Neothink mentality. Neothink sprouts out of illusion-free honesty. That free and fertile environment is growing the cure for aging and death.

"The nonpolitical world of heroic businesses and 'garage' entrepreneurs has indeed catapulted society's buying power and health. Imagine, there's no such thing as politicians in America anymore! Over the next year, most countries across the globe will follow America's lead. I have successfully metamorphosed a force-backed, ruling-class government here into a value-creating, accountable protection service. People willingly pay for their local and national protection and justice now. People gladly pay a fee to live in peace and harmony. All other aspects of the government are now private spin-offs serving the consumer, serving not the political agendas. In short, a ruling class politicizing our lives and our businesses no longer exists in America. Politics is quickly fading worldwide as some kind of archaic practice. Borders of countries also seem increasingly archaic. Taxes backed by force are vanishing fast throughout the rest of the world, and without force-backed taxes, you have no ruling classes, and borders seem irrelevant and silly, don't they? The INS has been abolished for over a year and is nearly forgotten. A person has to actually stop to think *why* did we put boundaries between countries — what was the rationale? It's becoming hard to remember the irrationalities of the anticivilization.

"Big bureaucracies such as the INS, FTC, SEC, FDA, EPA no longer exist, and it now seems weird that large buildings were once filled with regulatory bureaucrats who made their livings by stopping the flow of foreigners, for example. Now, integration of value creations dictates the flow of people, not nationalities. Irrational religions have disintegrated in the face of the Church of God-Man. Terrorist activities have vanished.

"Private regulatory services no longer need to discourage dishonesty and unfairness in business. Dishonesty and unfairness have vanished in America. In our creative division-of-essence business environment, dishonesty and unfairness are just too uncompetitive. The value now of the private regulatory service is: it provides businesses with a medium to show off their goodwill and extra efforts. The statistics publicized by private regulating services motivate businesses to do better than their competition, which has turned out to be great news for consumers. The private regulating services have already stimulated some legendary 'value wars' among companies. The 'value wars' bring many exceptional values to consumers including rapidly increasing safety and a cleaner, more beautiful environment among other things. ...You know, businesses in our freedom paradigm start 'value wars' that bring exceptional values to people, whereas governments in the old ruling-class paradigm started violent wars that wiped out the greatest values on earth — human lives.

"During these months following my early closure of the force-backed, ruling-class U.S. Government, with political power fading around the world as archaic irrational illusions of false

742

power...war and terrorism are vanishing too. Honesty, rationality, and prosperity light the world. Without politics, dishonesty, irrationality, there will be no more man-made wars of violence. Only one fatal war remains: the war against the greatest killer of all time — human aging. That war kills everyone.

"By the time all thirty-six operations are completed, Dr. Sally Salberg predicts the success rate will be over 95% and will quickly approach 100% in the commercial arena. So, befittingly, her thirty-six paraplegics are, indeed, the last troops in the last war."

*

Jake looked around the room, filled with the members of The Group. What an exciting life I live, he thought, right in the middle of man's greatest endeavor in history. The cost of goods had dropped to fractions during the great Technological Revolution. Even the uneducated, inner-city individuals woke up to a world in which they were wealthy. Crime simply became too much effort, for being rich happened automatically.

Jake's eyes rested on Daniel. Without war and crime, Jake thought, the need for the one legitimate purpose of government — to protect the individual from initiatory force — had faded away too. Costs for protection continued to drop, just as Daniel had predicted. Moreover, Daniel started North-American-Disputes Arbitrators (NADA) to settle legitimate conflicts throughout society. He hired Bruce Salinski as NADA's president.

Jake smiled as he thought how the concept of no ruling-class U.S. President would have seemed impossible just three years before. Yet, now it seemed natural. He wondered, how did things move *so fast*?

Surely Mr. Melbourne, the philosopher, could explain it, Jake thought as the wise man opened the final meeting of the God-Man Group before Sally would proceed with the Operation:

"Here we are," said Mr. Melbourne, "finally at the final pieces to our first superpuzzle."

First superpuzzle? Jake wondered what the *second* superpuzzle could be.

"We've watched, in awe, the breathtaking changes the past

few years, particularly this past year, and especially the past few months, weeks, and days. As complex as those changes seem, they all reduce to something elegantly simple: a simple but profound shift from a following-mode mentality dependent on external authorities to an integrating-mode mentality that neither needs nor wants external authorities telling it how to live. From that simple but profound shift in our mentality, that you former students of my wife experienced over thirty years ago and the rest of civilization is experiencing now, comes these complex changes in our civilization. External authorities, until recently, thrived throughout the human race. Politicians thrived; theocratic leaders thrived around the world. People sought or at least accepted external authorities telling them how to live, a carryover from the theocracies of primitive bicameral man. Now, people no longer need external authorities telling them how to live. External authorities suddenly get in the way. People have become just too effective and excited to have their progress and their creations retarded by external authorities. Suddenly, there is no place in this prosperous world for external authorities, which explains why governments and religions have nearly faded from the face of humanity. Soon, they will fade from our memory."

Yes, I've experienced that, Jake thought; I've had a difficult time remembering what half of the government consisted of and for what reasons, from just a couple years ago! ...He now understood why the collapse of government and religion happened *so rapidly*: because those were institutions built on external authorities. The overnight rise of God-Man, where people became their own authorities, explained the overnight collapse of those institutions of external authorities.

"Man could have and would have evolved directly from bicameral man into the God-Man over 2000 years ago," said Mr. Melbourne, "if not for Greek philosopher Plato and, later, the Church Fathers, namely St. Augustine, who led humanity into the Dark Ages. Plato and later St. Augustine tragically stopped the burgeoning integrating-mode mentality by infecting it with a following-mode virus, so to speak, a debilitating mental disease that passed from generation to generation. Instead of explaining what happened back then, I'm giving you my latest book called,

From Anticivilization to Supercivilization: Humanity's 2300-Year Detour."[1]

Something Mr. Melbourne said stirred Jasmine. She looked up from her notes. She sighed and collected her thoughts. Then she said, "I've talked to hundreds of people about Project Life. Many of them, maybe as many as one out of five, still make a comment about God...like they harbor a fear of interfering where they don't belong—"

Jeremiah cut in, "Fear had been drilled into their minds for so many years; they still feel ingrained feelings of fear and betrayal and might for awhile. We see the same thing in our Church. People's intellectual side knows they're leaving behind a primitive mythology when they leave behind their old religions. But their emotional side sometimes involuntarily feels things like fear or betrayal or even nostalgia. In time, those deep emotional concerns fade and go away."

"Interesting choice of words: primitive mythology," Mr. Melbourne said. "The voices of the gods, 'heard' by the primitive bicameral man, were the seeds from which all modern religions grew. The 'voices' were actually audio hallucinations experienced by primitive man while under stress. The mythologies of gods or a God and their hallucinated voices would have dissipated after primitive man leapt forward into human consciousness when man gained the mind space to think and make decisions. But the educated elite had too much to lose. You see, the educated elite leapt forward into human consciousness first. They held enormous power over the bicameral peasants who could not think or make decisions. The educated elite, therefore, manipulated the masses for easy money and power. The educated elite, not wanting to lose their power when the bicameral man began to make the leap into human consciousness, successfully created mutations of bicameral man's primitive mythologies. Those mutations were the major religions. The underlying coup of those mutations — those religions — was: *conscious* man was now subservient to a higher cause, an external authority. That subservience was secured by

---

[1]The 2300 year Plato-Augustine mutation of the bicameral mentality is demonstrated in *SOS Powers*, by Mark Hamilton, 444 pages.

overwhelming the subjects with fear and guilt. Of course, the educated elite — the leaders of the Church who were also the leaders of the land — enjoyed easy wealth and power, for they were the representatives of the external authority. In other words, they ruled in the name of God. In short, through religions, the educated elite were able to maintain their power over the masses.

"By the way, a very interesting perspective about Jesus and the Bible that very few people know but is explained in detail in the book I just handed you, is that Jesus was a conscious peasant trying to free the bicameral peasants from the manipulative conscious elite. To do that, he told the bicameral peasants that he was one with God. When you understand the context back then, Jesus was pointing the peasants toward the far more powerful conscious mentality in which the bicameral man could become his own authority, his own voice, his own God. Moreover, the main stories of the Old Testament of Abraham, Moses, David, the Prophets, are stories of specially gifted bicameral men who showed early signs of human consciousness. When you understand the Bible in the context of when those things happened or were written, a whole new perspective unfolds. It becomes *the* document that captures man's leap from the bicameral mentality of the primitive mind to human consciousness of yesterday's mind. Of course, my book captures man's leap from yesterday's conscious mind into today's Neothink mind. But back to the Bible, the educated-elite leaders of the Church changed the context of Jesus and the Bible to fit their brilliantly crafted mutation of the bicameral mind — their religion. I explain how that was so, in detail, in my book.

"Without those brilliant mutations of ancient mythologies, man back then would have discovered Jesus' secret message, just as man is discovering today, that he is the Highest Being in the Universe — the God-Man. He would have served no one and forever left behind his following mode. He would have leapt into the integrating mode and into Neothink. Instead, starting with the early bicameral mutations of religions and carried on by later bicameral mutations of governments, the power of man's mind was retarded by external authorities for 2300 years. All along, religions and governments needed to use guilt, fear, and force to succeed. I think people's comments on fear about God or interfering with God's work are harmless residual feelings that will wash away in time. Has that been your experience, Jeremiah?"

"Yes it has," Jeremiah answered. "They're verbalizing some deeply ingrained emotions. But those pass in time. And through Ian's work, those feelings of fear and guilt will soon be emotionally dismissed as silly as a fear of falling off the edge of the Earth. As we now know, Ian's Overlay Charts prove that the very advanced God-Man or *Zon* controls the cosmos and created our Universe. ...You know, ever since the earliest civilizations, whenever natural phenomena went beyond man's intellectual or scientific reach, he always turned to 'God' as the explanation. As science progressed and explained the previously unexplainable, such as in the tumultuous time of Darwin, the role of God in our psyches retreated. Today, people who still worry about God haven't yet seen Ian's Overlay Charts that give us the emotional, intellectual, and scientific grasp of the workings of the Universe. When they do see the Overlay Charts, the role of God in their psyches will vanish completely. Then, they'll know it becomes *our responsibility* to save our own consciousness in order to join the others in the immortal Civilization of the Universe."

"During the Age of Reason," Ian added, "the predominant belief was: the more we can understand the Universe, the more we'll understand God. The Overlay Charts have brought us our own Age of Reason with a definitive understanding of the Universe. That understanding will wash away those residual feelings of a mystical, wrathful God scarred into so many psyches. For, the Overlay Charts show us God alright — as God-Man...as you and me!"

"Has there been any resistance to Project Life?" Cathy asked.

"No, none whatsoever," Jasmine answered. "Everyone's devoted to it...just those occasional, lingering doubts about God."

That statement, "Everyone's devoted to it..." rang in Jake's ears. The thought that *everyone* is devoted to curing death seemed almost surreal. So much has happened since the reunion — so much dishonesty and irrationality has come crashing down — to be at this point where *everyone* is for immortality! My God, Jake thought, look at what we've done!

Superpuzzle

"Are you ready for the Operation?" Jeremiah asked Sally. Those two were now the heavyweights in this mission. Sally was the product developer; Jeremiah was the marketer. Next, Theodore would step in as the mass marketer, the manufacturer, and the distributor.

"Yes, I'm 100% ready."

*

That night, Jake and Jasmine put the finishing touches on their article titled *The Other Side of Immortality: Why Overpopulation Will Not Happen:*

"First of all, man inhabits just a small percentage of the land on Earth," began the article. "If no one were to die again, it would take another generation to merely double the small percentage of inhabited land. Overpopulation on Earth will not be an issue for well over a hundred years. By then, with man's accelerating rise in knowledge as more and more people break through into Neothink, one can just imagine the level of space exploration and colonization. A hundred years of technological advancement in the supersociety, driven by Neothink, will be like thousands of years of technological advancement in the anticivilization retarded by external authorities. By the time overpopulation becomes an issue on Earth, over a hundred years in the future, mankind will be inhabiting Mars. Earthlings will be mining asteroids for natural resources, which a business in Texas is already researching."

Jake finished reading the final draft and told Jasmine, "You know, originally I included the concept of boredom and how it didn't exist on the other side of immortality. But boredom is so quickly being forgotten and replaced by energy and enthusiasm as people pursue their Friday-Night essences that I decided to eliminate the question of boredom from the article. ...You know, after the reunion five years ago, I tried talking to others about biological immortality, only to find that most adults said they wouldn't want to live forever. I thought the reason for their lack of enthusiasm was boredom. But I refined that thought later on. I realized the act of living brings on many responsibilities, but for most people before in the anticivilization, those were

748

dead-end responsibilities, which amounted to a burden. Their lives were productive, but they were cogs in a wheel, not experiencing *their own* exhilarating competitive creations for the world. Only when a person discovered his Friday-Night essence and built his own competitive creations for the world could the burden of dead-end responsibilities vanish. At that point, his emotional existence turned inside out, so to speak, like a big bang, releasing exhilaration and euphoria each and every day. ...Before, in the anticivilization, even good productive people felt, down deep, that living was a burden. They would enjoy the good experiences within life to mask the burden, but they would be ready to let go of the burden in their 70s.

"I remember once telling Jeremiah, while on the campaign trail generating votes for Daniel, that heaven represented a place where one was released from his relentless day-in-and-day-out dead-end responsibilities...a place where one was released from the underlying burden of living. Heaven and Nirvana, they both freed one from the burden. That's why the silly idea of heaven still gripped intelligent people. I actually think that most people in the anticivilization, down deep, implicitly sensed that the idea of heaven was unrealistic, but they didn't want anyone to tell them that. They *wanted to* believe.

"And you know what Jeremiah said?" Jake asked Jasmine. "He said that people in the anticivilization *wanted to* believe, regardless, because their lives were dull. Jeremiah knew that to believe in heaven was quite invigorating in the anticivilization. Once people discovered their Friday-Night essences, however, their lives changed; their lives were no longer dull. As they became the persons they were meant to be, life became a constant thrill. The thought of living forever here on Earth with all their earthly values sounded a lot more stimulating than living forever in heaven, not to mention a lot more *real*. That's one reason the Church of God-Man that sought immortality *before* you die, not promised to you *after* you die, grew so fast."

"Jeremiah knew that people didn't want to live forever," Jasmine said, "not until the feeling underlying their responsibilities for living could change from a subtle burden to a steady excitement. I think of Michelangelo painting the Sistine Chapel, working around the clock, just taking cat naps. That great artist felt the exhilaration for what *he was creating*. His life wasn't a burden, but a joy. The feeling underlying Michelangelo's responsibilities for living was a steady excitement, not a steady burden."

"Exactly", Jake said. "Only after people discovered their Friday-Night essences and could exchange the underlying burden of life with an underlying excitement like Michelangelo, could they truly want biological immortality. Otherwise, they would still want Heaven or Nirvana."

As Jake and Jasmine wrapped up their article to be printed on the eve of the Operation, Jake looked one more time at the entire portion about boredom and burden. But he left it out of the article.

"Those points are now moot," he told Jasmine, "for the people have discovered their Friday-Night essences. They *really do not* want to die."

The article celebrated the profound victory humanity had *already won* by the concerted drive toward preserving human consciousness. The people now knew they were the highest entity in the Universe *and felt* they must not perish. As a consequence, they had withdrawn their support of authorities such as the FDA and the other government authorities retarding progress, and they exchanged misplaced hope of God and Heaven offering them a burden-free life after death for hope of immortality on Earth and an excitement-filled life forevermore. Project Life would be the crowning moment of humanity's greatest victory.

CHAPTER
SEVENTY-EIGHT

Nearly every TV around the world tuned in. Sally, the God-Man Group, and Martin the patient had decided to let the world watch. Project Life had become a venture with humanity itself. Business stopped; employers and employees stayed home to watch Sally and her team. Families huddled together around their TVs. Ultimately, every person's own life was dependent on the success of the Operation.

Martin Castlebury lay on the operating table, his body shriveled and lifeless. A few yards away in the refrigerated glass cloning station was his cloned body — full and perfect. Although covered with linen, the head of the cloned body obviously had already been removed.

Martin's internal organs had begun noticeably deteriorating three days before. He was only thirty-one years old, but he would be the next to die in the nursing home. So he was the first chosen for the Operation. Sally asked Martin if he would like to say something before the doctor anesthetized him. He nodded.

"I want to thank you, Dr. Sally Salberg." His atrophic body was so void of life, yet his voice and expression were so full of life and love. Families huddled closer to their televisions to not miss a single word Martin said. "I want to thank every member of The Group. I want to thank every person who contributed to Project Life. And I want to thank humanity for its unanimous emotional support. I will not let you down. I'll fight with every breath to be strong and to make this a success. I will not surrender to death."

The emotional impact of this final fight between life and death silenced the world as Martin looked into the camera and continued, "If I'm overcome by events beyond my own will to live, if I don't make it, I want you to know that the Operation is and will always be a momentous victory. The knowledge gained will hurl humanity toward ending the most insanely irrational, and now perhaps the *only* irrational occurrence left: the loss of your life — the loss of everything. ...Now, I'll let you in on what I'm looking forward to most: it is *love*. I'll cherish falling in love and having children to love as the most precious gifts in life. That's what I want so dearly. And with that, I'll say, good night. I hope — *oh, how I hope* — tomorrow, I'll wake up and say, hello."

Parents hugged their children. Martin looked at Sally and nodded. Sally nodded to a doctor standing at the head of the operating table above Martin's head, who released the anesthesia.

Sally, aided by the three top neurosurgeons in the world who specialized in the spinal cord nervous system, began to slowly and deliberately cut into the base of the neck where it met the chest. She carefully cut a thin layer at a time. Her cut was at a slight downward angle away from the head, into the upper region of the torso. The four doctors were very careful not to cut the arteries and large veins.

Jake experienced powerful yet undefinable feelings while watching this medical procedure. He did not feel any sense of repulsion. The Operation was too important, he realized. He had nothing to compare these feelings to. The feelings shot adrenaline into Jake's blood, which energized him. Yet, he was paralyzed. He was breathing hard as though he were prepared to fight. Perhaps he was subconsciously breathing — and fighting — for Martin.

As the aggressive Operation carried on, Jake noticed he less and less felt its importance for humanity and more and more felt its importance *for Martin*. As he watched the doctors cutting into Martin's body, Jake realized that Martin's life was *everything to Martin.* If Martin dies, the world, the Universe dies for Martin.

After slightly less than two hours, the head looked nearly severed. The arteries and large veins and the spinal cord were still intact. At this point, an amazing thing happened: After a partial blood transfusion from Martin's body to the robotic body, Sally cut the major arteries and large veins and quickly slipped them into corresponding tubes waiting on the robotic body. Within three swift minutes, the robotic body was circulating blood to the head.

Body-Robot kept blood circulating to the brain while the spinal cord specialists spent the next four hours slowly detaching the spinal cord, carefully charting their course on the computer screens directly in front of their eyes.

As the operation continued into the afternoon, nearly every household, adults and children, watched as doctors narrated and described the different nerves, arteries, veins, muscles, and elaborated about the robotic body. This was a televised medical marathon. Families settled down into their family rooms together. As the hours moved on, family members may have done homework, ate picnic style, or read, but they stayed right by the TV. The doctors explained that Sally's team had switched life support to body-robot before working on the major nerves because severing the nerves would affect normal breathing and circulatory functions. Similarly, they would keep Martin attached to body-robot while attaching major nerves onto his cloned body before attaching Martin's head to the clone's own breathing and circulatory system. The robotic body, however, could safely serve as a life support for no more than fifteen hours before risking brain damage because its ability to feed the blood with oxygen and remove the carbon dioxide was not as efficient as the human lungs.

After nearly five hours, Martin's head was ready to be moved to his healthy, young cloned body. Humanity held its breath as the world went silent.

Instead of moving the head as Jake believed they would, the head never moved. In a dramatic moment, after five hours of stillness, the withered body, on its own table, separated from the head and was rolled away.

Jake stared at Martin's head and neck, breathing, *alive*, alone and separated from the body. The head lay there, alive and asleep, attached to a man-made machine a little bigger than a TV. Jake stared at the surreal scene. Martin's head looked so small there all by itself. The next moment, though, it looked so large. Nothing there seemed natural. But as Jake watched the doctors moving confidently about, he was aware that the surreal scene did not feel eerie. After a moment, he realized he was feeling proud and strong. A minute passed, and he got used to looking at Martin's head alive and breathing on body-robot. Suddenly, like a drink of warm cider on a chilly morning, a warm feeling filled and saturated Jake and took away the chill. And everything seemed natural — completely natural. He looked at Martin's head alive and breathing, detached from his wretched body, *free* from that prison, and Jake knew at that moment that mankind had transcended man. "We are now *God-Man*," he whispered through the glass to Martin. "We will free you, my friend. We will now be who we were always supposed to be: the real Gods who will free man from all suffering."

The voice of the narrating doctor on television broke the long silence across the world and pulled Jake and the rest of humanity back from their awestruck feelings to the event at hand:

"Free this man today from his sentence in living hell," the TV doctor was saying. "Free humanity tomorrow from its sentence to death."

It was breathtaking: The cloned body was wheeled into place. Sally glanced at the temperature gauge on the glass cloning station. The narrating doctors explained that during the Operation, the cloned body had been gradually warming from a very cold temperature. Moreover, they explained, the cloned head had been previously removed. The doctors began their meticulous work again, in reverse of what had occurred over the previous six hours.

A new team of neurosurgeons replaced the other three exhausted doctors, all but Sally. Now, they began to attach what was severed during the previous six hours. They went to work reattaching nerves surrounding the upper region of the spinal cord.

754

Putting Together the Pieces

The body was still kept very cold, in hypothermia, to preserve it in the absence of blood flow. The doctors wanted to keep the circulatory system off as long as possible. They had also drained over half the blood and would perform a partial blood transfusion from the robotic body into the cloned body just before they switched life support over to the body.

Connecting took substantially longer than severing. After four hours of connecting nerves and suturing several layers of muscle, a third team of neurosurgeons replaced the second team. As planned, Sally would oversee all three teams to the end.

After another four-and-a-half hours, the lower portion of the neck bone was secured to two clamps attached to the backbone. The narrating doctors told us the "deep" work was done. Soon, Sally would connect the main arteries and veins to the cloned body and start it breathing and its heart pumping. Everything had gone picture perfect.

Into the sixteenth hour, the moment everyone was waiting for was close. The narrating doctors on television were telling us that Sally wanted to be using the new body's circulatory system by the sixteenth hour, because after that, the exchange of gases would quickly fall below optimum. The blood would break down as carbon dioxide would build up beyond critical levels and not enough oxygen would travel to the brain.

Jake watched as Sally, without missing a beat, instructed her team to start the blood transfusion from body-robot to the cloned body. Billions of people's hearts around the world started beating faster. They could feel the anticipation building toward the miracle. As nearly every heart in the world beat fast with nervousness, Sally never wavered. Jake admired her as she performed confidently, flawlessly. Billions of people were experiencing waves of chills, but Sally stayed calm. Her rock-like steadiness kept her team focussed and relaxed. No mistakes would be made with her in charge.

During the transfusion, she called for the final team of doctors — the heart doctors. The neurosurgeons left and the heart doctors lined up next to Martin.

"Are you ready?" Sally asked, looking into each doctor's eyes. They all nodded. Suddenly, Sally commanded "Shut him down," and body-robot was done. In quick single movements, Sally removed the arteries and large veins and connected them inside the clone. Jake, who was shivering with nervousness, asked himself, "How does she stay in such control?" The thought went through him that only having gone through the experience of losing her mother as a child gave Sally the discipline, determination, and emotional strength to handle this operation, with the fate of all humanity in her hands.

In a matter of two minutes, her job was finished.

"Let's give him life!" she exalted. She could feel victory. A doctor pushed a tube down his throat and began squeezing air into his new lungs. A moment later, another doctor pulled down the blanket to expose the perfect torso as Sally cried, "Stand clear!" A trauma specialist placed the defibrillator on Martin's beautiful new chest.

Jake, Jasmine, and the rest of the media huddled against the windows.

The body jerked slightly from the electrical shock, and the world waited. No response. Sally snapped more commands and the specialist placed the paddles on Martin's chest again. "Stand clear!"

This time the body jerked more noticeably. The team waited. No response. Sally reached over, adjusted the settings herself, grabbed the paddles, and laid them down on Martin's chest herself.

"Stand clear!"

Something was not right, Jake could hear it in Sally's voice.

The team of doctors looked at the monitors. Their eyes and ears were wide open, begging for a pulse. But nothing happened.

"I'm going in!" Sally announced. She ran a knife right down the middle of that perfect torso as the other doctors leaned over, placing a clamp-like device that opened the chest cavity, exposing the heart.

God, what's going on? In the media, Martin was always a metaphor for humanity, but seasoned journalists in the media room were pleading, "Martin, Martin...don't die, Martin!" Suddenly, Martin was no longer a metaphor or model. He was *Martin*, and during these frightful moments that would yield either eternal death or eternal life, every thought in every witness around the world shifted to *Martin*.

Jake looked at Sally rushing her hands around Martin's heart as her assistants thrust something in his mouth. She looked like an archangel fighting for Martin's life. Sally was the only person of the billions watching who spoke at that moment. She shot out a barrage of commands. She was perhaps the only person in the world, under the enormous magnitude of this moment, collected enough to speak, to lead. Her strength and conviction kept her team focussed, moving flawlessly. Everyone else around the world, Jake included, was paralyzed with fear...for *Martin*.

The body was not responding, not even with a shot of adrenaline directly into the heart. Sally pulled her hands away and turned away from the table. The whole world gasped. Her face was directly in front of the media's long viewing window, and Jake could see into her eyes. There was no panic there. Instead, her eyes were crystal clear...they were to Jake the essence of competence and beauty as he watched the most intense discipline of thought thundering through that great mind. She was searching her mind for an answer. Under this enormous pressure, her mind was at its peak. Jake watched those powerful eyes, in an instant, shift toward the robotic body. Watching those eyes, the talented news journalist in Jake could almost recreate her thoughts: No, she dismissed that thought, for body-robot had expired its conversion of gases and would destroy Martin's brain. Almost instantly, her eyes darted away, toward the corridor where the other thirty-five cloned bodies lay. As quickly as the thought entered, it exited; the other bodies still had the heads attached; there was no time. As quickly as Sally had turned away, she turned back again. Her only chance was to get that heart going. She shouted one final command and with it came the anticipated needle with a second and otherwise fatal dose of adrenaline that Sally injected directly into the heart. It was her last, desperate chance. Immediately she had both hands massaging the heart again.

A hush settled over the world as people held their collective breath. It was as if, for that moment, humanity was one with Martin, and all would breathe with Martin...when Martin breathed.

But his breath never came.

In an ice-cold voice, Sally said, "It's over."

She calmly asked everyone to leave. She did not move as

the devastated doctors one by one left the room. Alone now, she removed the clamp from Martin's chest, removed her gloves, and pulled the sheet up to cover his chest and the open portion of his neck. She did this with such gentle love and care, as if she were tucking her son into bed at night. Martin's exposed face looked young and innocent as Sally rubbed her hand across his forehead as a mother does who is saying good night to her son. She leaned over and kissed his forehead. She pulled her stool over and sat next to Martin, as would a mother about to tell her son a good-night story.

The cloned body's electrical system did not start. Jake could see Sally was trying to weigh what went wrong but was being overcome with emotion. She couldn't stop the emotional tidal wave that was about to hit her.

"I...I'm so sorry, Martin," she whispered. "I'm *so* sorry." She leaned over and cradled his head and rocked it gently, like a baby. She buried her face against Martin, then a great wail rushed from her lungs, heard in nearly every household around the world. She cried the saddest, hopeless cry that rushed up from the deepest depths of irrationality. Death defeated her; it stole Martin away from her.

"I'm *so sorry, Martin!*" she involuntarily cried over and over in pain. She gently rocked his head like a baby, looking at him, stroking his soft hair back, revealing his baby face that looked so sweet, like a boy. Sally leaned over and with all her love, kissed his forehead again. The world wept with her.

Jake stood watching; he could not move. His soul was empty. The priceless spirit, *Martin*, was gone forever...because *the body*, a mere biological tool to carry the spirit, gave out.

*

The world had to recover from watching Martin die. Most businesses stayed closed the next day. People needed to collect their bearings. Rarely had such gloom gripped civilization.

In The Group's gathering two days later, Mr. Melbourne helped the members cope with the loss. He explained that the enormous pain felt across the world for the loss of one man's life finally approached the value of human life. People had risen

758

to the next realm of emotional existence now. They loved their lives, their competitive creations, their spouses and children. They could no longer accept human death, not even for one stranger.

Jake and Jasmine were finishing a healing article dedicated to Martin. Since Martin died, his last words about *love* kept ringing in Jake's ears: "I'll let you in on what I'm looking forward to most: *love*. I'll cherish falling in love and having children to love as the most precious gifts in life." Jake and Jasmine, who had grown deeply in love, decided to have children. What is that great love of children Martin wanted and Rico had?

During The Group's somber gathering, Sally reported how very close the Operation had come to success. In fact, the loss came from the electrical system failing to start, the odds of which were but a fraction of the other possible things that could have, but did not, go wrong.

"What solutions are we looking at? And what amount of time?" Theodore asked.

"The irony of it all," Sally said, noticeably, permanently pained by losing Martin, "is that the Operation told us how incredibly close we are to success and how rapidly we can move into the next operation. I no longer consider the odds of failure to fall in half. I consider the odds of failure to drop by eighty percent. Going into Martin's operation, everything was experimental. We learned just how doable this is. For the next Operation, we have experience and confidence. The electrical system will start up ninety-seven out of a hundred times. But to assure that, the solution is to have the clone's electrical system already going. We must build the counterpart to our robotic body. We must build a robotic head."

"That'll take...what? A good year or longer?" Ian injected. "What about building another body-robot and having two clones in case this happens again? You'll have a backup."

"I've weighed those options, too," Sally assured him. "Building head-robot will be the quickest route. You see, body-robot is a complex computer that removes carbon dioxide from the blood and puts oxygen into it. Building the body-robot required simulating the job of the lungs. ...But head-robot does not need to exchange gases, for the lungs of the clone will be

759

doing that. The robotic head simply will direct the blood in the clone from the arteries into the veins."

"How long before you can go with Operation II?" Jasmine asked while taking notes.

"We can go with Operation II in sixteen weeks."

Only four months! The members were surprised, but no one doubted Sally.

*

Getting past the loss of Martin was hard for everyone, especially for the members of the God-Man Group. Yet watching the loss, the sadness of death amplified the preciousness of life and love. Spouses and families never felt such love and closeness as they did in the days after watching Martin die. Amplifying the preciousness of love and life around the world was Martin's parting gift to the world.

CHAPTER
SEVENTY-NINE

"I've called an emergency gathering of The Group here in New York instead of Philadelphia so Sally can keep working. Everyone will be here tomorrow," Al said. Three weeks had passed since The Operation. "You know, we've had reports from around the world that people are demanding life support for their loved ones who are dying. The cry keeps getting louder and louder—"

"I know," said Jake.

"After the near success of the Operation," Al continued, "a psychological phenomenon is sweeping over the world, a phenomenon we had not quite foreseen or prepared for. The millions of registrations for the Operation sent to us after your article *Are You Ready?* was the cloud before the storm. We knew a storm was coming. But, the storm is beyond what we had foreseen. ...I've sent field reporters to hospitals around the world."

"We know," said Jasmine. "We're moving on this too. Sally's taking us tomorrow afternoon to visit her most frequented hospital in New York."

"You know what," Al said, "I'll go with you. ...In fact, the whole Group'll be here. We'll all go with you."

Superpuzzle

*

"Martin's parting gift to the world — amplifying the preciousness of life all around the world — brought on *supreme* love. Humanity can never go back to expecting or accepting conscious death," Mr. Melbourne explained on the way to the hospital.

How many people die each month?" Jasmine asked Sally.

"Just over a million people die around the world each month," Sally said, "down from six million a month when we had our reunion six years ago." She was proud of those figures, for she had a lot to do with that rapid decline of death, especially her combinatorial molecular approach she started with her miracle molecules that eradicated the flu. Other research doctors used her approach to close off the receptor sites of other viral illnesses around the world via inexpensive injections, making those viruses harmless to the human body. Moreover, combinatorial chemistry and rational drug design were also being used on infectious bacteria to plug up the enzyme-releasing site that increasingly fought off antibiotics, which dramatically reversed the fading effects of antibiotics.

Jake noticed the pride in Sally's voice, yet he could hear dissatisfaction, too. That dissatisfaction sounded almost desperate, as if to say, "We're still losing *a million* conscious beings *a month! A million!*" This woman, Jake thought while looking at Sally, has felt the supreme value of conscious life ever since she was a little girl.

When they arrived at the hospital, they were not ready for what they saw. People who normally would have died were surrounded by loved ones in intensive care...being kept alive on respirators.

The Group next walked into the Critical Care Unit. What they saw broke their hearts. There were three children — two brothers and their sister; the girl was about thirteen, the boys about fifteen and eighteen years old. They were taking turns doing artificial resuscitation on their mother. Sally called in the nurse who started talking before Sally asked a question, "Their mother went flat line about forty minutes ago and their father is also in critical condition. We got her pulse back, and it's kept going because of her three children."

"Where in the hell is her respirator?" Sally snapped.

"Doctor, there are no more respirators!" the nurse said frantically.

"Call another hospital and get one here at once!"

"We've tried that, Doctor Salberg. There are no respirators available in the whole state! We're calling out of state right now."

"Oh God," Sally said, looking back at the exhausted three teenagers and their mother they refused to let die, their eyes pleading with Sally, all of them with sore bright red lips from the extensive mouth to mouth.

"Get one of our paramedic's mouth-to-mask resuscitators up here and teach them how to administer it," Sally cried. "And don't stop calling until you get a respirator here!"

Sally wanted more than anything to jump in and take over. But the bigger picture filled her mind: this pathetic scene was growing by the day all over the world. Her eyes filled with tears as she turned to leave the little family to fend for itself.

"I'll be in my lab," she cried. Then, she rushed out of the hospital. She knew precious families like this were desperately waiting for her operation. She could not delay her work for another moment.

The others in The Group let her go. They knew where she needed to be.

Jake watched her run out. Wow, he thought, her supreme love for conscious life was just given a beating from Hell. We're in a losing struggle to keep conscious life from dying, and she knows it. She knows this struggle to keep people alive is going to escalate into the millions.

Sally's footsteps, as she ran out of the hospital, were suddenly overcome by the most steady, competent voice Jake had ever heard.

"I want my empire heads — all of them — on video conference in two minutes," Theodore said into his mobile video phone.

"Yes, Mr. Winters," a woman responded.

The Group gathered around Theodore in the hallway. They stood quietly, curiously. Miss Annabelle watched her Theodore with enormous pride. In precisely two minutes, Theodore's video phone beeped. He turned it on.

"They're all on, sir," the woman announced. His seven empire heads could all see and hear Theodore. He could see one at a time, but could press a code to see any one of them at any time. He could hear all of them at once, just as on any conference call.

"Thank you. Good afternoon, everyone. We have an emergency on our hands. I'm going to tell you what we need. I want it done at all costs."

"At *all* costs?" one of his empire heads repeated. He never heard that from his boss before.

"Even if I have to spend every dime I ever earned. After you do what I'm about to tell you, I want each of you to take a walk through your nearest hospital. You'll be with me one-hundred percent."

The empire heads no longer interrupted Theodore. They knew by the tone of his voice to listen and do exactly as he said.

"Send your engineers to medical-equipment manufacturing companies and to my cloning-station manufacturing company. Have your engineers learn the technology for manufacturing respirators and my cloning stations. I want you to convert all our factories to manufacturing both respirators and cloning stations — right down the middle — until I say otherwise. Is that clear?"

Jake heard only two words being relayed back: "Yes sir."

"Everyone will cooperate with us once I explain the situation."

"Let us save time," Al Patterson injected. "We'll set up a worldwide announcement in thirty minutes over the Patterson Channel."

"Did you hear that?" Theodore asked his empire heads. "Call the medical-equipment manufacturing companies you'll be dealing with and ask the president to watch me on The Patterson Channel in thirty minutes. ...Got it?"

"Yes sir!"

"Any questions?"

"I have a question, Mr. Winters."

"Who's speaking?"

"Frederick Burgess, code 239."

Theodore punched the numbers 2—3—9 on his mobile video phone, and Frederick Burgess appeared on the screen.

"Go ahead, Mr. Burgess."

"You mentioned life-support respirators. What about other life-support equipment such as, say, the kidney dialysis machine? Do we send our engineers to study the manufacturing of other critical life-support equipment?"

"No, just respirators," Theodore answered. "Kidney failure has been cured."

"Oh, I didn't know that."

"Precisely. The medical world, medical technology, biotech progress, especially genetic engineering is all advancing so fast that chronic diseases such as kidney failure or liver failure are being obsoleted so quickly we can't keep up with it all. Even very complex problems such as cancer, even brain cancer, distressed lungs, strokes, aneurysms, AIDS...they're mostly obsolete or will be soon by the super rapidly advancing new technologies and drugs. But there is one massive disease — the 100% fatal disease — that we have not cured. As you all know, that disease is *aging*. People are dying from age-related causes. The respirators keep the blood and oxygen flowing to the brain, which is what we need in order to keep the brain alive until we can transfer the head to a cloned Body II. All the other diseases have 'garage' entrepreneurs and in-house entrepreneurs directly attacking and arresting them. At Winters, Inc., our greatest leverage to sustain life until the Operation is available...is to manufacture life-support respirators and cloning stations."

"Thank you, Mr. Winters."

"Okay. Let's all get to work. Be sure to tune into the Patterson Channel at the bottom of the hour."

*

At half-past the hour, Jake, Jasmine, and Al were shouting commands, getting the lighting and camera people in place for the live announcement.

"We're rolling," someone shouted.

The lights blasted on Theodore.

Superpuzzle

"Hello. I'm Theodore Winters, talking to you directly from Manhattan Upper East-Side Hospital. The scene here is tragic. Walk the rooms with me for a moment."

Theodore walked through some of the intensive-care rooms, the cameramen following him, and he finished his walk in the little room of the three siblings keeping their mother's pulse going. The nurse still could not get her hands on a paramedic's mouth-to-mask resuscitator. Those, too, were in short supply.

"This is what's going on here, and in every hospital around the world. Every day, more and more tragic scenes like this one, loved ones caught without life support, fill our hospitals." Millions of people listened to Theodore talk as they watched in horror the tragedy going on behind him as three frightened teenage children desperately blew life into their mother. The intensity of the moment nearly caused Jake to burst into tears.

"One of my two mentors, Mr. John Melbourne, explained to me while I was preparing this announcement, what's going on here: before the Operation, the idea of averting death was, more or less, a powerful scientific experiment for people to watch. We came so close to saving Martin Castlebury that a shift in people's perspective occurred. Averting death is no longer just some scientific experiment. It is now a very real *consumer product* about to enter the marketplace. The result is: people, including *children* as you are witnessing behind me, refuse to let their loved ones die with that product so close, so very close. Our hospitals are starting to look like MASH units. My friends, this IS A WAR! I'm declaring a state of national and worldwide emergency. Thirty minutes ago, I gave my empire heads the order to stop manufacturing my usual products and to replace them with the manufacturing of life-support respirators and cloning stations. We want to do everything in our power to sustain every possible life until we can successfully provide them with the Operation. To gear up for such a feat, we're going to mass produce our rapid-cloning machines. Moreover, I'm stating here, on behalf of my supreme love for each and every conscious life, I'm releasing all patents on my cloning station. Every manufacturer who wants to join the effort to save every possible human life may have full access to and our full cooperation in learning my design. I'll supply you with my own engineers to get you going. In fact, this is a *Call to the War Effort* — the war against aging and death. I implore every businessman with manufacturing capacity to join the effort to sustain life and to not let another human being perish!"

Al Patterson had his cameraman zoom in on the unconscious mother being kept alive by her three children.

"Help in any way you can! We're at war against losing another life! We are at WAR!"

After the announcement, The Group immediately left for Sally's lab to hold the meeting there. They could not wait another day. As they were leaving the hospital, they passed a stream of people coming in. Jake grabbed one of them by the arm.

"What are you here for?" he asked the man who was about Jake's age.

"To help those kids keep their mother alive."

Jake nodded. He never felt so close to his fellowman...to complete strangers. Jake could not smile, but his eyes were grateful.

"Thank you, brother," he whispered. He let go and wrapped his arm around the stranger and patted him on the back. "Thank you."

The unity Jake felt among mankind overwhelmed him and brought him to tears. The stranger patted Jake on his back, too. The young man looked Jake in the eyes and said, "I know you, Mr. Catchings, and I understand how you're feeling. You and me — we're going to save lives, as many as is in our power. Now, you go and do what you do best."

Jake nodded. They wearily smiled at each other, yet their eyes shared the determination of two passing soldiers. They parted and went to their battles.

"Love and compassion," Jake mumbled as he walked out of the hospital, past the incoming warriors of life, "love and compassion."

CHAPTER
EIGHTY

At the lab, Sally was working feverishly at her computer. Her eyes were swollen and red. Miss Annabelle walked over and kissed Sally on her cheek.

Without taking her eyes off the computer, Sally said, "That year I was in your wonderful class, and I learned about my mother's cancer, I'd sometimes wake up crying in the middle of the night from a nightmare that mom died. When I realized it was a nightmare and she was still alive, I'd feel so relieved. And you know what was so strange? Those nightmares made me love my mom so much more. I just loved her so much, and those nightmares made me never take a moment with her for granted."

Everyone was quiet.

"What I saw back there in the hospital was a nightmare," Sally continued, "and I love human life so much *more* after seeing something like that!" She swirled around and looked at The Group. "Now, let's end this insanity called death!"

Chills ran down Jake's spine. If this is a *war*, he thought, she's the commander-in-chief. Just look at her, she's going to get the job done! She's going to lead this war against death to victory!

Mr. Melbourne spoke. "Up until the Operation, as I explained to Theodore, the man in the streets thought of immortality as a beautiful idea, a *concept* that would undergo scientific experimentation. After the Operation, his perspective leapt forward, and he thought of immortality as a consumer product nearly available to him and his loved ones. Now that immortality is more than just an idea, now that it's nearly a reality in the business cycle, people just aren't going to let their loved ones die, not before Sally's Operation saves them. So, as we're seeing, they'll do everything to sustain their loved ones' lives now."

Mr. Melbourne then took a deep breath. He looked as though he were contemplating whether or not to bestow upon them something more — some further deep knowledge and wisdom, another secret no one in the world but he knows about human nature. The students seemed to reach out for this knowledge. Miss Annabelle, too. They all waited in anticipation. Mr. Melbourne nodded and sighed.

"The harvest moon," he said, "low in the horizon, always looks so beautiful and large. But there's nothing in the laws of science that causes it to be visually larger than the full moon high overhead. Scientists believe, the unexplainably enlarged visual perception has been hardwired, so to speak, in our brains by nature. Those perceptions of high-in-the-sky faraway smallness versus low-to-the-ground nearby bigness were crucial for survival...from hunting prey to escaping predators. Therefore, even though the moon is the same distance away whether over our heads above us or before our eyes in front of us, our hunt/escape perceptions force us to erroneously see the horizon harvest moon as low-to-the-ground big. After millions of years of hardwiring survival pressures, nothing we do can change the way we erroneously see the large, low harvest moon.

"Let me jump to the survival of the species — survival of the human race. Nature has hardwired our brains, as it has for all animals, with three unchangeable mental programs: 1) survival functions, such as, for example, reflexive sucking, 2) propagation, such as, for example, finding a mate and creating offspring, and 3) *death* in order to let the less-evolved older generation give way to the more-evolved younger generation, making the species stronger and stronger as generations pass. All animals, humans included, are physically, psychologically, and emotionally hardwired that way. After millions of years of survival-of-the-species pressures, nothing can change the way we think and feel and react regarding those three sets of functions hardwired into our brains — survival, propagation, and death. Indeed, we're mentally and emotionally programmed to die; we're hardwired to die, which really answers at the deepest biological level why mankind took until now to focus with any kind of enthusiasm on achieving immortality.

"Even now we're physically, psychologically, and emotionally hardwired by nature to die. But we've learned to simply step around that hardwired program in our minds *to die*. Let me give you an analogy:

"Let's say we were to do an aeronautical calculation involving the low harvest moon for an aircraft maneuver. Even though we perceive the moon as low-and-big, we simply look past our hardwired perception and calculate our maneuvers based on its actual size.

"Similarly, even though we are physically, mentally, and emotionally programmed to die, we now look past our hardwired perceptions, and we maneuver our resources to cure death. No matter what we see, think, or feel about death, we now step around our hardwired resistance in order to cure death anyway."

Jasmine half raised her hand and said, "Sort of like people stepped around their deeply ingrained fears about God before the first Operation."

"That's another good analogy," said Mr. Melbourne. "And now that people are emotionally stepping around their nature-instilled, emotional embracing of death, the world will see a demand to sustain life as none of us could've imagined. I think it's safe to say, our three-piece superpuzzle to achieve biological immortality has just taken on an unexpected fourth piece — *sustaining life*. This fourth piece to the puzzle is going to become an enormous managerial challenge, the likes of which the world has never seen. However, the twelve of you can meet the challenge," Mr. Melbourne concluded. Confidence radiated from his eyes; he looked at the former students. His stare, full of pride and passion, was something to behold...a stare that soundlessly bellowed: *Go to it, my precious ones, go now and SAVE EVERYONE'S LIFE!*

Theodore took Mr. Melbourne's cue and said, "A

manufacturing explosion of life-support respirators must take place to meet the demand of dying people. We should concentrate in this meeting on two things: First, what we must do to keep every possible person alive until the commercial product kicks in and saves those holding on, and second, what we must alter in our plans to meet the needs of those holding on, which'll grow to millions."

"I see a two-pincer attack on death," Al injected. "One pincer will be keeping those who are dying alive until the commercial product reaches them. The other pincer will be reducing the number of deaths from a million a month to a few thousand by intensifying what has already reduced the number of deaths from six million to a million."

Sally was nodding as Al continued, "That pincer involves a myriad of efforts from the pharmaceutical companies to the automobile-safety companies. They must intensify all efforts on eliminating major causes of death, from disease to accidents."

"I also think there'll be a shutdown period," Cathy said. "The majority of people can work from their homes now over the Internet. Over the next few months, as the safety of transportation is mastered, people can become very domestic. With technology advancing so quickly and freely, the economy can withstand this. Al, I can create PR ads about this."

"That'd be great, Cathy. I'll bombard the Patterson Channel and the Patterson Papers with your PR to educate the people."

"I'll develop different approaches," Cathy continued. She paused for a moment to organize her forming ideas. "One approach'll be to the general population about temporarily reducing almost all risks for a few months until the Operation is commercial. Another approach'll be to enlighten the car companies, the pharmaceutical companies, and the 'garage' entrepreneurs of the all-out race to eliminate death from all causes — accidents and diseases in particular. And a third approach'll be to educate people, especially older people, to become the healthiest they've ever been in order to give themselves their very best chances. I'll create the best exercise and health programs to keep them healthy. ...In short, we want to make it really tough to die."

"During this shutdown period, I'd like to turn your exercise and health programs into free PR gifts to reach the masses, if that's okay with you," Al said.

"I'd be *honored*," Cathy said.

"Natasha," Al said, shifting his attention to the attractive radio talk show host, but before he could ask, she was already talking.

"I know what I need to do. I can finally talk to my listeners at my level about the supreme value of life. They'll understand now. I'll introduce them, emotionally, to the real meaning and value behind *eternity*. That'll help them put the proper emphasis on their activities and health to make it to commercial availability of the Operation."

"People are beginning to feel the *real* tragedy of conscious death," said Jeremiah quietly. Then he raised his volume and said, "Here comes the rush of supreme love, Anchor #3 has broken."

"I know what my focus will be over the next year," said Ian. He looked at Jeremiah, then at Al. "I'm going to take my knowledge of physics and pour myself into radically accelerating the development of quantum computers. I believe I can discover how to interface with the 'quantum-computer' human brain in order to download people's minds onto quantum-computer machines. The great mystery, the great challenge, will be whether I can transfer the person's I-ness. Sally and I've talked about this; can I get the mind on the computer to contain *the soul* of the person from whom it came? If I can accomplish that, well then...just imagine."

"That's fascinating," Al said. He looked at Theodore and added, "What does this mean to your business plan?"

"I redesigned my approach the moment we walked into Upper East-Side Hospital," said Theodore. "I originally limited the number of cloning stations being manufactured because I thought the technology would be quickly obsoleted. But with the human race already shifting to our perspective of the supreme value of conscious life, fighting in every way not to let another person die, then I'll go right ahead and manufacture millions of cloning stations and life-support machines to arrest human death immediately. I'm willing to put out the energy and expense, whatever it takes."

Jasmine was writing furiously to capture the information and the passion in this meeting, but after Theodore's last comment, *whatever it takes*, she stopped to dab her eyes with a tissue.

Jake sat in awe. These twelve former classmates, he thought, look at them...just look at them! They've become "activated". People finally felt inside what these twelve had felt for thirty-three years. People finally felt *supreme love*.

"Fabulous, fabulous!" Al said as this puzzle to sustain life came together. Then he glanced around the room at his former classmates. "Okay. This is the day we've lived for. This is the day the human race finally feels as we do about conscious life. We're no longer alone. The *human race* is with us!"

A knot bunched up in Jake's throat. He looked around the room at the saviors of human life. They were nodding. They were beautiful. ...Miss Annabelle's eyes were glassy with tears of love and pride. Mr. Melbourne's eyes were smiling.

"Sally," said Al. The beautiful savior, working feverishly to end human death, stopped staring at the computer and turned toward Al. "What do you think, now that the human race is finally with us?"

"It makes me want to save every life, a hundred times more," she said. Her answer came straight from her heart. "The adults — they're all like children now. They all love life more than anything. I'm not going to let them die." Then she took a deep breath and added, "We need to let every neurosurgeon in the world have full access to my confidential research." She turned her chair halfway around to face Theodore, the consummate businessman behind Project Life. "Ted, now that the people feel as we do and seek life over death, we must jump past where we were with this project. We must give everyone who can do this the knowledge. We must not let another person die."

Although her quest of not losing another life was not possible, Jake knew Sally meant every word of it. All eyes in the lab turned to Theodore. He had sunk his fortune into Project Life, and now he was faced with releasing the information he owned...to everyone.

Theodore's eyes looked at each of his former classmates. Then he said, "We must not merely release it...we must promote it!"

Jake's heart jumped into his throat.

Superpuzzle

"Yeah!" Al shouted. "We'll promote it all right!"

Although adrenaline rushed through their veins, they all stopped talking for a moment to wonder what had just happened. Something...something profound...something about man's relationship with mankind had changed, and they all felt it.

CHAPTER
EIGHTY-ONE

Daniel broke the long silence in the emergency meeting. "I'm going to shift my efforts into this crisis to save and sustain life," he said. "I'm going to put my project on the Twin Towers on hold for now. Saving and sustaining life — now that the people want to live — is the most important project on Earth. I can see there's a need for large-scale coordination. As you said, Theodore, this is a state of national and worldwide emergency. Everyone knows me. I can create a full-scale emergency plan for cities, towns, and rural-living areas that'll maximize community efforts on sustaining life, especially during the desperate shortage of life-support machines."

"You're right," said Theodore. "It'll be at least a few months before the supply of respirators and cloning stations meet the escalating demand. Until then, we need a vision — a Neothink plan — for the community to keep human life alive. With your sweeping visions and attention to details and your experience as President...you'd be the best among us to do that."

At that moment, the image of the three children keeping their mom alive, all by themselves, flashed through Jake's mind.

"I can foresee some virulent mutations of bacteria evolving during the massive effort to keep dying people alive, including infectious people," Sally said. She spun around from her computer. "I'll direct the pharmaceutical companies and the biochemists so they stay a step ahead of those future drug-resistant bacterial mutations. With future-telling Neothink, they'll be able to cure many if not all those potential pathogens before they get started." Sally nodded then turned back around to her computer.

"That's absolutely critical," said Daniel. "I'll have to coordinate with you and the pharmaceutical companies for rapid distribution of those life-saving drugs as they become available."

Sally nodded again as she continued working on her computer.

Jake sat and stared, awestruck by these saviors.

"You know," said Debbie, "I've been building an entire new line of food for grocery stores and restaurants. I've run secret test programs on those new low-carbohydrate foods. Over time, people *prefer* their tastes. But, they have to acquire that new taste, and that takes an emotional shift to feeling the supreme value of life...to want to make the shift to my healthier low-carbohydrate foods. Now's the time. Rico...I'd like to work with your mail-order-steaks personnel to get my new line of food into a mail-order business initially so people can stay at home and still enjoy my foods during the shutdown period. My new line of food and your steaks would go perfectly together. I think our businesses could compliment each other."

Rico raised his eyebrows and nodded.

"And Cathy," Debra continued, "I'll print your exercise programs for the different age groups and hand them out to my patrons and include them in the mail-order packages along with information of the importance of a low-carbohydrate diet and aerobics. I think with the many millions of customers I'll get over the next year, we'll revolutionize people's diets...and exercise regimens."

"That's important, especially over the next year for those who are older or not in great shape," Al said. "Getting healthy and in shape can save their lives. ...Now, is there anything else, anything that can add to this project of sustaining life...or anything that can help during the coming shutdown period?"

"I'm going to finally release *my* songs," Reggie said. "I've written and produced six CDs over the years, but never released them. They're written from the soul of supreme love. Similar to Debra's new line of food, people before weren't ready for my new line of music. Now they are. No one's heard anything like these songs. I remember in third grade, telling you all about mixing classical music with modern technology." Jake noticed several of Reggie's former classmates nodding. "I've gone beyond that. My music fills you with heroic, supreme love. It's inspiring beyond any music that came from the old anticivilization. My music is the first to come from the Civilization of the Universe; my music is a reflection of whom we've become — the immortal God-Man. When I listen to it, I sometimes think of Sergio." Reggie looked at Natasha and smiled. "I sometimes feel like Sergio."

The Group paused, remembering the story about Sergio by Natasha, written in *Breakthrough News* over three decades earlier. ...*Breakthrough News*, Jake thought, I remember Jessie telling me about these saviors at nine-years-old building that historic publication during the miracle year. As Jake watched the former classmates forming this superpuzzle to sustain life, he could sense what it might have been like in third grade with these people. The meeting today, he thought, was a grown-up version of their meeting in third grade when they envisioned *Breakthrough News*.

As the meeting went on around him, Jake started formulating in his head the lead article he and Jasmine would write that night. It would capture their trip to the hospital earlier that day and this meeting in Sally's lab. The headline would capture the big puzzle picture of how The Group and the human race would work together to save every possible human life until the Operation was a routine, commercial product. The underlying theme of the article would be: *finally, people everywhere are shifting to the supreme value of conscious life.* Yeah, he thought, Anchor #3 has broken, the last of the three anchors to break. People finally feel the *real* tragedy of conscious death. People now feel supreme love and are responding with a vengeance.

In honor of my boss and his classmates and their beginnings thirty-three years ago, Jake thought, I'll name the article *Breakthrough News!*

"It's beautiful seeing this great shift to the supreme love for human life," Robert Chapman said. "It's what Jake and Jasmine wrote about a few months ago that has dominated headlines ever since: People have discovered Nature's Quintessential Secret — they're value creators now and they *love* their lives! Everyone does. How could they let a loved one die now? People now want their lives and their loved ones forever."

"We face a great challenge," Rico said. "It's beautiful, as you say, just really beautiful, to see people finally feeling supreme love for human life. But I'm glad we're here now preparing ourselves for the months ahead. Things'll get a lot worse before they get better."

CHAPTER
EIGHTY-TWO

"We're losing."

That was the opening line of an email sent by Sally to each member of The Group.

"The eight weeks since the emergency meeting in my lab," her email continued, "the situation gets more and more impossible. There are no life-support respirators, and almost 35,000 people are dying a day...dying faster than life support can be manufactured and delivered. Factories around the world are gearing up to manufacture respirators and cloning stations, but they tell us it'll be weeks before they can reconfigure and assemble the parts. Respirators could keep many of those 35,000 people who die each day alive long enough to get a rapidly cloned body and then the Operation or the cure to whatever disease threatens their lives."

Each member of The Group read this email in fear.

"The goal is to keep an unfortunate loved one alive until a respirator becomes available," Sally continued in her email. "The respirator usually gives us enough time to arrest the primary problem, be it an infection or virus. With the many brilliant, preventative and early-detection breakthroughs, most strokes, heart attacks, cancers, AIDS are no longer the killers they once were. But people are dying, a lot of people, who would have lived with life-support respirators. Hospitals steadily fill up with families surrounding dying loved ones. When the respirators run out, the manual air pumps are administered. Families are shown by doctors or nurses how to administer them, then left with a volunteer who often has only a few hours of training with the manual air pumps. Oh, it's tragic beyond words."

Each member of The Group worked frantically on snapping his or her puzzle piece into the Neothink puzzle-picture that would sustain human life — sustain it until life could be saved by the commercial Operation.

*

Jake walked through the halls of Manhattan Upper-East-Side Hospital. I dread my trips here, he thought. Rico was right...it just keeps getting worse. What irony, *supreme love* for human life fills these halls as families surround ailing loved ones; *excruciating agony* also fills these halls as families lose loved ones.

Jake took Jasmine's hand as they walked through Manhattan Upper East-Side Hospital with a few members of the Group. Jake knew from experience the first impression was deceiving, for everything seemed under control. In fact, the hospital as a whole actually seemed quite empty. Ever since Daniel depoliticized America, unhindered business and scientists eradicated most infectious diseases, and safety breakthroughs eliminated most bodily injuries. Moreover, businesses and scientists conquered natural disasters and catastrophic weather conditions. So, hospitals were quite empty.

When they entered intensive care, however, the floor was overrun with people on life-support respirators and manual life-support. Here, the hospital looked like a war zone with nurses, doctors, and volunteers doing all that they could to sustain lives as long as possible.

"They've only lost two lives here so far," Jake said to Al, Ian, Theodore, Cathy, Rico, Debbie, Robert, and Natasha.

"Which is miraculous," Jasmine added.

"What about the mother those poor children were keeping

alive?" Cathy asked.

Jasmine grimaced and said, "She's one of the two who died."

"You know," said Jake, "after she died, Jasmine and I talked to her children—"

"Her body could hold up no more, and she went into a seizure," Jasmine whispered. "Her children were holding her during her seizure as she died in their arms. We got here moments afterwards and—"

Jasmine was stopped short by a woman's loud screams followed by a man hollering in great despair. A nurse ran toward the commotion while hysterically repeating, "Oh no, not number three...not number three!"

Jake and the other members of The Group followed her to a room where an older man had just gone flatline. A team of doctors and nurses surrounded him. One doctor was shouting commands as the team tried to get the heart going again.

But they could not revive him; the devastating grief split open the souls of the surviving loved ones. The grief gushed out in bursts of heavy crying in some; the grief paralyzed all emotions in others. The two doctors and three nurses broke down and began crying, too. Jake had seen this once before. Suddenly, it hit him: for the first time, these doctors and nurses were now just like Sally.

Jake looked around the room and realized he and the other members of The Group who were with him...were quietly crying, too, as if they knew this man who died.

Jake became aware of a stream of people who came into the room to see the older fellow, as if paying respect and saying farewell. They came in, one after the other. They left grief-stricken...as though they knew this man.

What's going on here? Jake asked himself. After watching some others, complete strangers, walk in and leave heart broken, and after looking again at the devastation on the faces of the doctors and nurses...he came to realize he was observing a new property of the Civilization of the Universe on Earth. Love and compassion filled this hospital, filled society, filled the world to the point that love and compassion had taken over as man's guiding force.

The supreme love for conscious life was directing man's

actions now. Consummate businessmen such as Theodore were subordinating their personal fortunes to the mission of sustaining and saving as many human lives as they could. Other businessmen around the world were releasing patents and reconfiguring factories at their own expense in order to save human life. Competitive research doctors such as Sally were opening their confidential records in order to save as many human lives as possible. This certainly was a new property of the Civilization of the Universe on Earth, Jake realized. The forces of nature were now part of the past; people did not feel motivated by the same things anymore. Instead, people were now motivated by bringing values to others, and the supreme value of the Universe was conscious life.

Jake felt a painful emptiness inside, such a helpless emptiness, as the weeping nurses removed the respirator from the man, the precious life.

*

"The Group has become the world's orchestrator and coordinator for the emergency effort to sustain every possible life until the Operation is a routine, commercial product," began Jake and Jasmine's article the next morning. "This massive effort to sustain life is an unexpected fourth puzzle piece to The Group's superpuzzle of biological immortality.

"Therefore, the God-Man Group now orchestrates and coordinates *two* puzzle pieces at once: Project Sustain Life *and* Project Life.

"The grave responsibility of those two puzzle pieces rests largely on the shoulders of Dr. Sally Salberg. While the world waits for her Operation II, the world also depends on her neothinking genius to ward off a slew of potential deadly plagues that could get started from bacterial mutations while keeping sick people alive on life support as long as possible. She explained the risks to me recently at her lab: *'Although most infectious diseases have already been eradicated,'* she said, *'the medical world is entering unknown territory by keeping people alive — very sick people — for weeks or months or longer, inviting bacterial mutations, which could set off a plague with no natural*

*defense and no known man-made defense. That is the great fear
— a plague with no human or man-made defense such as the
super flu of 1918. It could spread fast and kill half the people
it infects.'*

"I asked her, 'Won't your ability to see into the future
through Neothink lead the pharmaceutical companies to cures
now, before the mutations occur?"

"Her answer was haunting. In a hollow voice, she said, *'My
biggest enemy is* **time**. *I'm caught in a paradox between the
two puzzle pieces: The more time I spend on Project Sustain
Life, the more lives I immediately save, but the longer it delays
Project Life, and the more people will ultimately die. Yet, the
less time I put on Project Sustain Life, the more people will die
now, not to mention civilization could potentially get hit with a
devastating plague. Actually, if you want to know the truth, the
conflict is tearing me apart. My greatest fear is that something
happens to me before I can bring the Operation to the world.'"*

*

"I've set up two working areas for the two Projects," Sally
explained in her lab on the East Side of Manhattan. The Group
met now in Sally's lab instead of Rico's mansion. The former
classmates and their teacher knew Sally could not take any time
away from her lab. "I pull myself off Project Life at night to
work on Project Sustain Life." She walked them over to that
section of her lab. "I broke Project Sustain Life into two basic
categories: bacterial infections and viruses. There are many,
many viruses around that have never surfaced in humans. I'm
afraid the combination of the weakened state of millions of
people during Project Sustain Life and their exposure to loved
ones, doctors, nurses, and volunteers, could bring out a new virus
that the human system has no defense for. Such a new-virus
plague happened nearly a hundred years ago. The super flu came
from a pig, which killed twenty million people when the world's
population was less than a third of what it is now. The human
system had no defense against that swine flu.

"My work against viruses concentrates on combinatorial
chemistry — the same approach I used to create the vaccine for

the flu, which is a virus. I'm building on that research to develop a megadose of generic molecules that'll plug up the receptor sites on many if not all types and strains of viruses so they couldn't attach onto human cells, which viruses need to do to multiply and cause illness. Without functioning receptor sites, the viruses would pass harmlessly through the human body."

She walked The Group to another set of computers, then continued, "My work on bacterial infections requires studying the many types of harmful bacteria and scientifically extrapolating or predicting possible mutations, and then developing antibiotics beforehand that would arrest a breakout of such mutations. Also, I'm doing something similar with bacteria that I'm doing to nullify viruses. I'm designing molecules to plug up the enzyme-releasing spots on bacteria. Those enzymes, in effect, manifest a mutation that makes the bacteria resistant to existing antibiotics. By plugging up that enzyme, the drugs we have now will continue being effective, which puts us ahead of the game. My efforts on preventing virulent viruses and bacteria are critical at this time, but both projects demand my full devotion and time. I can't abandon Project Life, for that's the bigger solution to saving life."

Jake had noticed that Daniel, who was masterfully orchestrating the community efforts to sustain life in America and abroad, seemed to be deep in thought the whole time Sally was showing them her new lab arrangement. Suddenly, he released a barrage of thoughts:

"Sally," Daniel finally said. He seemed to be almost breathless, as though his internal battle of weighing logistics had winded him. "I'll arrange to have the best minds in the country on viruses and the best minds in the country on bacteria devote themselves to you completely over the next several months, working here in your lab."

"That'd accelerated everything," Sally said. "I'd replicate my Neothink future-seeing approaches through them. I'd have daily essence meetings during which I'd absorb the day's work of my colleagues, then give them my Neothink perspectives."

Jake smiled and nodded.

Jeremiah lingered in Sally's lab after the meeting until the

784

others had all left. Sally did not even know who was or was not still there. She had been hard at work for twenty minutes now.

"Sally," Jeremiah said. She was so deep in her thoughts, his voice did not register, even after he said her name again. So he put his hand gently on her shoulder. She turned her head and looked at Jeremiah for a moment through her glasses.

"Oh, hi Jer." Her voice was gentle.

"Sally, something's been bothering me for some time, and last week I realized what it is."

Sally suddenly felt very compassionate. She saw before her a man who had done so much for The Group's mission and for her lifetime goal to cure death, and yet she never directly gave him personal one-on-one reflection for his immense value to her.

"You can tell me *anything*," she said, hoping, almost pleading with him to confide in her. She was aware of the irony of her feelings at that moment. With the race for life and its almost unbearable time pressures on her, she instinctively protected her time and pushed people away, but not this time. She *wanted* to hear what bothered Jeremiah.

"It's about my relationship," he said, surprising Sally. "As you know, the wonderful lady I saved from the fire four years ago, Maria, and I have been very happy together. I really love her. She's been so supportive of me and has made my life so much happier."

"You're very fortunate."

"I know..." Jeremiah said, then stopped himself. He looked down, then back at Sally, and added, "but for one thing."

"What is it?" Sally said. She turned on her stool directly toward Jeremiah.

"Yes, just one thing," he said. He looked earnestly at Sally's eyes. She sat waiting. All at once, the silence seemed deafening. Jeremiah smiled nervously. "I love you, Sally."

She gasped, but she was filled with unexpected pleasure. Jeremiah could see the pleasure in her eyes. In their visual exchange, neither had to say it, but they both validated at that moment, they were destined to be together. They were Civilization-of-the-Universe children driven to each other; they knew they must someday have each other.

"Jeremiah," whispered Sally during that surreal moment, "are you sure?"

Jeremiah nodded.

"Well then," she said softly...she paused. She knew she was about to say something she had not thought over, but she could not stop herself. "I love you, too," she whispered. They leaned toward each other into the most loving, tender kiss between two innocent souls, driven all their lives beyond physical and emotional boundaries to fight the horror of death, finally finding a warm soft resting place in the kiss of their soul mate.

"God, I want to pull you off that chair and into my arms," Jeremiah whispered. His eyes involuntarily looked down her neck, down past her feminine shoulders, down along her torso, to her slim thighs, and back up, now more deliberately, back to her eyes. "But for now, I won't touch you, Sally. Not until you've accomplished Project Life. No matter how much I want you, I know we must first complete Project Life without distractions. So, I'm not going to touch you, beautiful woman, but be ready for me when the time comes."

Sally's heart was racing. She wanted to surrender to Jeremiah's grasp more than anything else. But somewhere in the back of both her mind and his, they knew that the very thing driving them crazy for each other — their intertwined passions to cure death — was the very reason they must not distract their mission with a passionate romantic engagement.

"I'll be waiting for you," was all she could manage to whisper.

With great discipline, Jeremiah turned and walked out. With great discipline, Sally let him go.

CHAPTER
EIGHTY-THREE

A week later, Sally's lab was buzzing with geniuses. Jake spent two days in the lab doing research for an article. Here, he would put words to something he had been feeling — something previously unexplainable. As he got to know the renowned scientists and doctors in her lab, working shoulder to shoulder to sustain human life, he came to realize that these people were archrivals in the professional world. Yet, here they were, when it came to saving human life, revealing all their secrets — that took decades in some cases — in order to save every last human being.

Jake remembered how governments in the anticivilization would not give up any power or wealth no matter how many lives they sacrificed. Now, Jake watched these businessmen/ scientists in the Civilization of the Universe give up all their power and wealth to save life.

"It's the most beautiful thing you'll ever see," Jake told Jasmine over the phone, "geniuses working so hard here at Sally's lab, working *so selflessly* to save life. You should come on over and witness this."

An hour after Jasmine had arrived, Jake could not find her in the lab. He looked all over for her until, ten minutes later, he finally found her in the lounge area. She was sitting on the couch. Her knees were pulled up, her head was resting on her arms, crossed over her knees.

"Hi love," said Jake, "are you feeling alright?"

Jasmine sniffled and lifted her head. Her eyes were red, and she was crying.

"Oh, Jake," she said, "it really is beautiful in there. I just got overwhelmed by their *love and compassion*. They really are special people, aren't they? I...I just can't believe it, sometimes, when I see all these heroic efforts to keep life from perishing...I—" she dropped her head down and cried, "I just can't believe *daddy's gone!*"

Jake sat down next to Jasmine and held her as she wept.

*

The next morning, millions of people sat down with their newspapers or laptops to read Jake and Jasmine's front-page article *Love and Compassion*.

"Beautiful manifestations of mankind's supreme love have begun to unfold all around us," the article began, "such as the volunteers in hospitals, the world's greatest businessmen reconfiguring their factories to build respirators and cloning stations, the research doctors and scientists developing new vaccines and antibiotics in anticipation of future infectious outbreaks, the entrepreneurs working on methods to preserve us in case of catastrophic accidents...and, of course, those working toward the age-reversing operation itself. And there are changes going on all around us to dramatically increase our safety such as the beautiful monorails suddenly appearing over our heads here in New York City, and the exciting new inventions going into effect at the bottom of oceans to stop deadly hurricanes from forming. And this week we've learned about a garage entrepreneur who has developed a technology that could be instrumental in reducing the intensity of earthquakes. He'll surround faults with a new technology consisting of massive high-powered amplifiers that would activate during an earthquake and counter the shock waves with intense sound waves directed at the fault. The force and frequency of the man-made sound waves would break apart nature's powerful shock waves into smaller, weaker waves that would remove an earthquake's deadly ability to topple buildings. Other technologies are being invented and implemented now to stop every imaginable destructive weather condition or natural disaster, from long droughts to flash floods.

"The human race now has a single focus: making human life immortal...the way conscious life is throughout the Universe and was meant to be on Earth, as demonstrated by the activity of Zons seen through Dr. Ian Scott's Overlay Charts. Making humans immortal brings about our two missions: sustaining life and then saving life...the ultimate missions of love and compassion."

Sustaining life and *saving life* were on everyone's mind, all the time, so much so that they became a unified concept. The phrase for sustain-and-save-life got abbreviated to "SSLife", which got shortened to SSL. SSLife and SSL became the abbreviations commonly used around the world to express anything to do with the process — Project Sustain Life and Project Life — to join the immortals.

*

"Dr. Salberg, I'm sorry to interrupt you, but I think you need to take this call."

Sally reluctantly pulled away from her computer screen and turned to her assistant. "Right now, Lauren?"

Her assistant nodded and said, "Sorry." She reached out to hand Sally the phone.

Sally sighed and took the phone. She pushed the speaker button and said, "Hello, this is Dr. Salberg."

"Dr. Salberg, this is Dr. Chong of the World Health Company, formerly the World Health Organization. I'm calling from Conde S. Juanuario Hospital in Macau, China. We've lost two patients just today to aggressive Super Flu-like symptoms. We're studying the strain—"

"What do you mean *Super Flu-like symptoms!*"

"Sore throat in morning, acute respiratory distress by evening, death within twenty-four to thirty-six hours."

"What's—" Sally stopped to get her bearings.

"We're isolating the strain as we speak—"

"What's your containment status?" Sally asked.

"We have teams working on finding those exposed—"

"Oh my God," Sally whispered. "You must administer my miracle-molecules antidote to all those who have fallen ill and to all those who have had contact. I need—"

"Hold on a second Dr. Salberg; I'm getting some information — hold on."

Sally could hear someone talking to Dr. Chong on the other end of the phone:

"It's not a virus, Dr. Chong. It's not the Avian Flu. It's a mutated, highly lethal, highly contagious bacterial pneumonia. Yet, antibiotics are proving useless. Our only defense, I think, is the same as you planned — aggressive containment and quarantine."

"Excuse me doctors," a woman's voice interrupted the conversation on the other end of the phone, "we have two more people who just arrived with the symptoms. And one of our nurses has come down with the symptoms."

"Oh, not good, not good," said Dr. Chong. "We need extreme quarantine, total lockdown, including you and me now. All doctors, nurses, and staff who come in contact with patients must wear the airtight suits and the airtight helmet-masks. No one leaves the hospital, starting right now. Call the guards to enforce lockdown. Everyone here, including all workers and all patients signed a consent to be quarantined in the event of an outbreak while in this hospital. This is what we've trained for; now we must implement it. Notify security right now."

"Dr. Chong," Sally said into the phone. When there was no response, she yelled, "Dr. Chong! Dr. Chong! Please pick up the phone!"

"Dr. Salberg...did you hear?"

"Dr. Chong, I need you to email me the bacterium images immediately."

"It's already done. It should be—"

"Here, here it is...I've got it here," Sally said. "Let me look at this. Every research doctor and scientist here, gather round. I'm putting the images on the big screen here. Tell me what bacterium has mutated."

"It looks like pseudomonas aeruginosa," a scientist called out.

"Yes, yes it does," Sally agreed, "bacterial pneumonia. Dr. Chong, I'm going to need a vial of the bacteria flown to me immediately."

"I've got a plane ready to go, waiting for your vial."

"Dr. Chong, containment is critical. I don't need to tell you, this is a powerful killer and could explode out of our control very easily."

She could hear him suddenly shout a command to his staff. "Don't use filtered masks; use the air tanks with the airtight helmets, and wear the airtight suits!"

He spoke back into the phone, "Dr. Salberg, I'd better go." Then he shouted to his staff, "I need World Health Company teams to gather and quarantine all people whose paths crossed the sick. You need the airtight coverings on all health caregivers, doctors, nurses, aids."

"You handle containment, and I'll get our cure," Sally shouted into the phone. "Good luck, my friend."

Sally hung up and turned to her scientists.

She looked at her SSL team, then up at the big-screen computer monitor. "This bacterium has adapted," she said, "and we've predicted this adaptation in a world laced with antibiotics for this particular bacterium."

"It has got to be releasing an enzyme that makes antibiotics ineffective," said an SSL scientist.

"That's exactly what I think," said Sally, "and we've already theoretically created the molecule that'll plug up that enzyme-releasing spot. I want you to get busy producing medical doses of that molecule in both injection and pill form. We need to start testing when the bacteria arrives."

*

"Dr. Salberg, I'm Doctor Pete Mansing from the World Health Company. We've got our best teams trying to contain this thing, but it's...it's getting out. In three days, ninety-six people have died in Macau. Over two hundred people are now infected and being treated in an isolated, makeshift hospital tent under our care. Over half of the infected will die. Yesterday afternoon, two Englishmen who had visited Macau last week showed up with the symptoms in a London hospital. One has since passed. And this morning, an Australian checked into a hospital in Sydney with the symptoms. It's getting out. It's getting traction. You must give us a cure before it sweeps through civilization."

Ian was in Sally's lab. He heard Dr. Mansing's desperate message over Sally's speaker phone. Ian had seen horrid footage of people succumbing to the disease. *If I could electronically transfer people's I-ness onto a quatum computer and then back into a clone,* he thought, *there'd be no problem. I'd just get them out of their diseased bodies and into healthy bodies.*

"I've produced the molecule," Ian heard Sally saying. "I've tested it with the live bacterium, and it works. As we speak, six major pharmaceutical companies — with several others on deck — are getting the specifications for producing the molecules in both pill and injection form. One big injection will plug up the enzyme-releasing area of the bacterium, in essence, returning it back to its original state treatable with antibiotics."

"In a few days this thing can grow out of control...into a super plaque. Millions could die unless we get distribution."

Sally too a deep breath. Her scientists could hear the pain in her belabored breath. "This shouldn't run away on us because we have a fairly rapid treatment for the sick. I've also instructed the production of millions of pills for the nonsick to blanket geographical areas where the bacteria have penetrated. The fast-acting injections should rescue most of the sick if given in time. The preventative pills will canvas surrounding areas to make treatment manageable. This shouldn't run away on us. The injectable doses will arrive at the specified hospitals by tomorrow; some doses will start arriving tonight. The pills will start arriving in two days."

*

"Lauren, can I get the latest report?" Sally called out to her assistant.

A moment later Lauren stood next to Sally. Every scientist in the lab listened as Lauren said, "No new cases in four days."

"That puts us past the incubation period." Sally said. The

scientists in the lab sighed in relief and exhaustion. Sally filled her lungs with relief and hung her head in exhaustion. She had prevented a super plague. She had saved tens of millions of lives. Still, her exhaustion sank her into sadness. She rubbed her eyes with the palms of her hands and said, "Lauren, how many died from the outbreak?"

"Six hundred and eighty seven died, doctor."

Sally quietly nodded and rubbed her eyes again.

CHAPTER
EIGHTY-FOUR

"Perhaps we can compare the sensation of what's happening this week in our hospitals to the first rain falling upon a drought-stricken nation suffering from thirst in the old anticivilization," Daniel said on his weekly Thursday-night announcement three months after the Operation. A relaxed smile filled the former president's face as he said, "This past week, respirators and cloning stations have begun arriving in waves at hospitals around the world." In living rooms around the world, adults closed their eyes in a moment of relief and gratitude. "Another wonderful thing happened this week," Daniel continued, "the next level of vaccines and antibiotics originally developed in Dr. Salberg's lab have begun arriving at hospitals." Parents around the world hugged their children, a little tighter than usual. Their children were safe now. "I'm pleased to also report a dramatic decline in deaths from accidents because of a combination of civilization adhering to the shut-down period and because of the new safety technologies advancing rapidly in automobiles, trains, airplanes, subways, and monorails. For the same reasons, deaths from natural disasters are plunging. And people, especially elderly people, have enhanced their health dramatically. Now, with the arrival of the respirators over the past few days, the number of deaths around the world have plummeted to just a few thousand a day, compared to thirty-five thousand a day three months ago. To die now really *is* rare. However, each death is now far, far more devastating."

That somber last comment ended Daniel's weekly announcement and reloaded the passion in everyone not to rest until *no one* died, ever again.

*

Over the next month as the forces of the supersociety moved in and arrested the forces of nature, the number of deaths around the world dropped to a few hundred a day...and then to a few dozen. Four months after the operation, only a few people would die worldwide each day. Sometimes three or four days would pass now without a single death. When a human being did die, it was tragic world news.

This sudden, drying up of human death worldwide caused Jake to wonder: *could the worldwide focus by big companies and lone entrepreneurs end death altogether, independently of Sally's operation?* One morning at work he started an article he titled *The Cure To Aging*. After an hour of little progress, he noticed he started writing down Jeremiah's three anchors to the anticivilization. Jeremiah defined the three anchors during Daniel's run for the presidency six years before. They were: 1) Politicization of society, 2) Stagnation of our lives, and 3) Expectation of our deaths. Then Jake thought about The Group's three original puzzle pieces to the superpuzzle of biological immortality: 1) get Daniel elected, 2) depoliticize America, and 3) achieve the technology in that freedom paradigm, driven by emotional desire to end conscious death. He wrote down those three puzzle pieces, too, and stuffed the paper in his pocket.

He carried around that list of Jeremiah's three anchors and The Group's three puzzle pieces in his pocket for two days. He would pull it out and look at it perhaps a dozen times a day. When he was home with Jasmine the second night, she finally asked him about that piece of paper he kept pulling from his pocket and looking at for two days now.

"Is that private?" she asked, smiling. She knew he wrote notes and studied them whenever he was on the verge of a big-picture insight.

"Oh, it's...it's the three anchors Jeremiah identified that held us in the anticivilization before and the three pieces to the superpuzzle of biological immortality," Jake said, handing her the paper.

She read it over and smiled.

"I remember these," she said. "Jeremiah was right on about those anchors breaking one after the other, wasn't he? First, Daniel had to depoliticize America, then the resulting free economy caused the job revolution that led people to their Friday-Night essences, eliminating the burden of living. Once they felt the exhilaration of life and the *real* tragedy of death, they no longer placidly accepted or expected death, which brings us to right now...sustain-and-save life, the SSL period."

"Yeah, SSL," Jake said. He was nodding. "The cure to aging," he added, slowly choosing his words, "is so very complex. The cure is so much more than, say, finding an antibiotic or vaccine. It's...it's in some ways analogous to the Mad Cow Disease a few years ago. Typical cures such as antibiotics or vaccines could not stop it. To end Mad Cow Disease, they had to kill the cows themselves.

"To cure aging, we had to first kill the debilitating regulations holding back progress. And then, we had to allow people to make the transition to their Friday-Night essences in order to want life over death. Not until those two changes happened — ending politicization of civilization and ending the burden of life — would the physical cure rise."

"You know," said Jasmine, "even if the cure to aging somehow did rise through, say, hitting the jackpot in some biotech project before we depoliticized America, you'd still have external authorities ultimately leading us toward nuclear wars...and the burden of life leading us to unbearable stagnation. Whereas aging might've been cured, death wouldn't have been cured...not without depoliticizing civilization and replacing the burden of life with exhilaration for life."

"You're right," Jake said. "All systems and structures of society were set up for a mortal civilization. But now, since depoliticizing civilization and replacing the burden with the exhilaration for life, the systems and structures are set up for an immortal civilization. Now the physical cure to aging and death *has to* rise — and rise quickly — just as it is happening. The demand is too overwhelming...and technology is free to soar. Those two events — depoliticizing civilization and replacing the burden with the exhilaration for life — actually are *part of* the cure to aging and death. In fact, I'd even say they're the most important parts of the cure. These past two days, I've come to realize that the cure to aging and death is a three-part, cause-and-effect process. Parts one and two — depoliticizing civilization and replacing the burden with the exhilaration for life — are *the cause* parts of the cause-and-effect process to cure aging and death, and part three — the Operation — is *the effect*. As we've seen, once parts one and two — virulent politicization and unbearable stagnation — were cured, then, part three — death — was quickly cured."

"Are you saying," Jasmine said, *"the cure* to aging and death was actually the first two parts of the three-part cause-and-effect process? Parts one and two were the cause and part three is, merely, the effect?"

"Yes. Once you cure parts one and two, then the actual procedure or technology or drug would surface as the effect...it'd only be a matter of time. If not Sally, then someone else. It's just that Sally had a jump on everyone else. *The cure* itself was parts one and two — *the cause* of the process to cure aging and death. As with Jeremiah's first two anchors: once they broke, then the third *had to* break...it was just a matter of time."

"What are the three parts to the process again?" Jasmine asked.

Jake thought for a moment, and then, adding a twist, he said, "Political, psychological, physical...those are the three parts. We ended the external authorities and depoliticized America, which caused people to leap from followers to integrators. We brought about that evolutionary jump into the integrating Neothink mind, which caused people to leap from stagnant value producers to excited value creators. Those two parts — depoliticizing society and replacing the burden with exhilaration — were *the cause*. They brought on the demand for biological immortality and the wide-open freedom for businesses to develop the supply of biological immortality. Don't you see? Curing aging and death was a done deal some time ago. Once civilization removed the political and psychological anchors, parts one and two, then the physical cure was just a matter of time."

"Are you kind of saying," Jasmine asked, "that the cure to aging is NOT Operation II?"

"That's the culmination of *a process*," Jake said. "But a garage entrepreneur might've found a way to avert death before the Operation. Still, if that had happened, The Group cured aging and death, for The Group effected *the cause* by depoliticizing America and bringing Nature's Quintessential Secret — value creation — into people's lives. The Group created the conditions from which the physical cure *had to* surface. They accomplished the superpuzzle to pull off *the cause* part of the three-part process. The effect, then, *had to* rise. It really was just a matter of time. Put another way, Sally would've cured aging and death *a long time ago* if not for politicization...remember?"

"Oh yes, now I get it," Jasmine said. She nodded enthusiastically and added, "The Group essentially developed *the cure* to aging and death some time ago, didn't they?"

"Starting at the reunion six years ago, to be precise," Jake added. "That's when the superpuzzle was conceived. Then The Group effected the cure by getting Daniel elected and depoliticizing America."

"Do you want to write an article about this process...*the cure* to aging?" Jasmine asked.

"No, I put it away. It's a moot point now. It's just fascinating to me that the cure to aging and death was so much more than developing an operation per se. The cure happened before that when we eliminated politicization from our society and eliminated stagnation from our lives." Jake paused to gather his thoughts. After a moment, he continued with renewed energy. "That explains why Project Sustain Life arose with such ferocity. Once we achieved parts one and two, broke anchors one and two, people were cured, in essence, of the expectation of their deaths, anchor three. They not only did not expect to die, but they *could no longer accept death*. At that point, mankind was cured of aging and death. Unhindered consciousness would almost immediately end death, which we're just about to do. We're caught in this little pocket of time, this SSLife."

Jasmine sighed and said, "Oh God, that so underpins why no one, not even one more person, should ever die again."

As the Operation II deadline approached, Jasmine relapsed into depression over the loss of her father. She lost weight again as she struggled with bizarre anxieties over the possible success of Operation II, knowing how unbearably close her father had come to making it.

*

Sally looked up at the brilliant chemists, biologists, and research doctors around her. They had been her team during Project Sustain Life.

When she looked at them, sometimes she was filled with love...sometimes, fleetingly, with hatred. She never felt such paradoxical feelings as she did while looking at those geniuses — her greatest allies on Project Sustain Life and worst enemies of Project Life.

These wonderful people are my lifeline to people being kept alive until the Operation becomes available to them, she thought. She looked around at her co-workers in the emergency lab meeting. *These wonderful people here, putting forth such heroic efforts, also take me away from completing the Operation.*

Trying to keep her voice steady, Sally said to them, "I must ask you the most desperate request I've ever made." She cleared her throat, then said in a steady tone, "Can you force your neothinking to the next level to allow me to concentrate all my time on Operation II?"

Jake was attending this meeting in her lab, gathering more background for his article *Not One More Loss*. He knew Sally, and he knew she paused because she would have a hard time saying what she needed to say next.

She shook her head, then buried her face in her hands. Her team looked confused, concerned.

"Ahhh! This is so hard!" Sally blurted. Then she lifted her face and looked again at her team. "I'm postponing Operation II for two weeks!" Her eyes filled with tears. The others in the room looked down. They all knew the delay meant more lives lost. "It's the hardest decision I've ever made. But I'm not ready. I balance where I put my time — with you or with Project Life. Starting now, my friends, I must leave you on your own. You must go to the next level, *now*. What we saw in Macau could be just a warning, just a baby of a worldwide monster plague that'd wipe out—"

She put her hands over her face to fight back her anxieties. A merciful image appeared behind her closed eyes and brought her peace: *Jeremiah*.

CHAPTER
EIGHTY-FIVE

Destructive and dangerous activities, such as doing drugs or driving fast in cars, had vanished. Children and teenagers, valued their lives too much now to damage or risk their health. The day children, teenagers, and adults had been waiting for...had arrived. Children and teenagers sat down with their parents to watch Operation II.

Leading up to this day, Natasha continually said on her radio show that humanity had discovered three new frontiers of happiness: the *preciousness* of every living moment; the *celebration* of being with loved ones; and the *bigger-than-life* joy people felt every day as they leapt beyond their limited dead-end ruts and began their limitless open-ended creations.

Natasha always told her listeners that when civilization achieved biological immortality, humanity would discover a *fourth* frontier of happiness similar to the *carefree* happiness seen in children. Indeed, once the ultimate deadline, the absurd irrationality of death, was no longer part of their psychological makeup, a heavy burden they all assumed would be lifted from every man, woman, and child.

Operation II began, as did the first Operation, on national and international TV. Jasmine stood next to Jake in the media room just outside the operating room. She had regained some color and a little weight, but she still looked frail.

The paraplegic's name was Andy Konosovic. Although only in his early forties, he had an estimated four weeks to live and would be the next to die in the nursing home; so he was selected for Operation II.

The whole world stopped to watch Operation II. Sally and her team would have their hands not only inside Andy, but inside the heart and soul of nearly everyone around the world. Sally and her team had the power to pull off the heavy burden of imminent death.

Jake watched Sally and her team preparing through the glass. He felt awe. Before she started, Sally turned in his direction to look over the operating instruments behind her. Jake could see into her eyes. He saw the most powerful determination he had ever seen, flowing from the vast mind space behind those brown eyes. At that telling moment, he knew that, as with Jasmine, Sally had long ago let go of her hope that we were saved by Zons after we die, for her eyes screamed, "*We* must save man from death! We must do it ourselves; *I* must do it!"

As the doctors prepared to begin, Jake put his arm around Jasmine.

"How are you doing, Darling?" he asked her.

"It's hard, Jake. It's still so hard." She leaned her tormented head against his shoulder. He held her lovingly.

Sally had the same three teams of neurosurgeons with her and one new team to simultaneously remove the head from Andy's breathing, cloned body.

Andy's cloned body was rolled out. Although covered with a sheet, the viewing audience gasped, for everyone could see it was already alive and breathing.

"A few hours ago," the television announcer explained, "when the cloned body was warmed to the ideal temperature, the system was started. The doctors got the heart beating, and a respirator was attached at the base of the trachea, regulating the breathing." Upon seeing the breathing cloned body, everyone remembered why Martin had died during Operation I.

A moment later, Andy was brought in. "Hello Andy," Sally said. Although just a simple greeting, Jake could hear the unmistakable love in her voice. She leaned toward Andy and softly said, "Would you like to say something before we begin?"

"Yes," he said. Then he looked at Sally. Dragging his speech a little because of a strong relaxant he was given earlier, he said, "I want to thank this great woman, Dr. Sally Salberg, for her lifelong devotion to saving human life. You're a very, very special person, Dr. Salberg. ...I also want to thank Daniel Ward for creating the Freedom Paradigm that enabled Project Life to proceed. I want to thank Theodore Winters and Jeremiah Jones for their financial and commercial drives behind Project Life. Thank you each member of the God-Man Group for orchestrating Project Life. Thank you. And thank you everyone everywhere for your emotional and financial support. You've all made this possible. Thank you."

Andy, lying on his back, then closed his eyes, and the doctor anesthetized him.

The two teams began at the same time. A rush of pride went through Jake as he watched mankind conquering the most destructive force of nature. As he watched the two teams go to work, they almost seemed to be synchronized, almost as if choreographed. There was something about seeing two teams working at the same time doing the same procedure that changed the appearance of removing the head from chaos and brutality to order and finesse.

"Isn't it beautiful?" Jasmine whispered.

Hours later, the exchange of Andy's paralyzed body for the robotic body and the exchange of the clone's head for the robotic head were performed simultaneously. Jake watched in awe and thought, *it really **is** beautiful.*

A respirator attached to the base of the clone's windpipe breathed for the clone. The cloned body and Andy's head looked nearly together as both robotic body and robotic head were positioned downward, underneath to allow the neurosurgeons to work on connecting nerves.

After fifteen hours, the time had finally arrived for removal of the robotic head and the robotic body, making Andy healthy and young again. The television anchor announced, "The moment has arrived for giving the irreplaceable spirit in Andy's head the replaceable tool, his cloned body." Then, in a burst of enthusiasm, he blurted, "Let's give Andy his youth again!" The other announcer cheered, caught up in the excitement of the moment.

"The switch begins beautifully," the television anchor reported. In a hushed voice, he started giving a step-by-step analysis: "Here, at history's single greatest moment of giving healthy youth back to the priceless spirit, Dr. Salberg and her team look like the angels of life. Their arms are moving swiftly; their hands and fingers are working confidently. Not a motion is wasted; the short commands of Dr. Salberg's voice sound like the voice of God."

Again, Jake felt chills and overwhelming pride and hope rushing through him. He wrapped his arm tightly around Jasmine as the announcer continued calling the procedure, "The world has seen this once before, but there's something breathtaking about attaching Andy's head and spirit to an already breathing, living body — knowing that the priceless spirit will take over the faithful servant. The anticipation, the stakes, makes this moment almost unbearable. What will it be? Eternal life, or eternal death?"

Jake's insides were as tight as a knot. His body locked up as he watched the doctors attach Andy's head to his cloned body. As Jake withstood the tension, he thought of the immortal spirit in Andy's head as God, and the cloned mortal body as Man. Sally was creating the first immortal God-Man.

Jake suddenly realized he had held his breath a long time.

"They're now one," Sally uttered. Jake and those around him exhaled in unison and took a deep breath in unison. Those three words — *they're now one* — signified the most important accomplishment ever achieved on Earth.

The angels of life physically did nothing for the next two minutes. No one spoke. All hands stopped as they simply watched. They were observing, watching the vital signs, the breathing rhythm...but most of all, they were quietly absorbing the grand view of the greatness they had just achieved with their own hands. At that moment, they felt suspended somewhere between human and God.

Jake strained to see into their eyes. "What is it like to be *them* right now?" he whispered.

Putting Together the Pieces

Operation II had ended — nearly 20 hours after it began. Sally ordered the respirator to be lowered from doing most of the work to just giving some help. She watched Andy for five minutes, then ordered the respirator to be shut off completely.

Andy continued breathing on his own. He had no need for the respirator. "Unbelievable!" the television announcer burst. The reporters in the media room cheered. People around the world cheered. Jasmine cried, and she whispered, "Oh Daddy, I wish you'd made it." That same sad thought drifted through millions of others during this moment.

The members of the God-Man Group stood next to Jake and Jasmine in the media room. Until now, all onlookers were quietly lost in their own world of thoughts. But at this moment, they turned to each other to share their joy and tears.

Miss Annabelle, however, stared through the glass a moment longer. She walked over and put her hand on the window. She whispered something so quietly that only Jake, who was directly behind her, could hear:

"You've done it, Sally. You've defeated death. You have proven that God-Man will not let man die."

Sally removed the respirator and put some small device over the hole in Andy's neck. Then, she slowly brought Andy up from his anesthesia. The TV announcers said Andy would remain heavily sedated for two or three days. But Sally wanted to bring him to consciousness, if only for a moment. After about twenty minutes, Sally said in a loud firm voice, as if calling to someone in the distance...

"Andy...Andy! Wake up, Andy! I'm Dr. Salberg. Andy...can you hear me? I'm Dr. Salberg. If you hear me, open your eyes. Andy, open your eyes!"

After a struggle with his eyelids, Andy opened his eyes. Sally grasped his hand and leaned over very close to his face.

"You made it, Andy. You made it!" And, by the burst of joy that ignited in Andy's psyche, a smile slowly spread across his face, a smile that pushed itself wide and hung on as long as it could through the returning levels of sedation.

That smile, captured forever on camera, was instantly and forever the logo for one's "I-ness": new body, yes, but still Andy, forever Andy.

Superpuzzle

Theodore Winters walked over to the window. "Now," he said, speaking for the first time since Operation II began, "right now as we watch, nearly a million people are in immediate need of this operation before it's too late. Right now, they're begging us to bring this great value to them. I will bring this to the masses. I'll do everything in my power to bring this to the masses immediately."

Jake shivered. He knew there was only one way to bring immortality to the masses: through the beauty of business...by making immortality an affordable, commercial product. The members of The Group knew it, too. And they all knew that it was Theodore Winters who must be the one to bring the greatest product ever created to all humanity.

Sally looked through the glass at The Group. She shared the accomplishment with each one as she looked into his or her eyes. When her eyes came to Jeremiah, they both shared the accomplishment...and romantic thoughts. But those other wonderful thoughts would still have to wait.

*

"Welcome back," Sally said to Andy, who was smiling triumphantly. It was just one day after Operation II, and Andy was brought up from sedation to full consciousness for the first time. The Patterson Channel brought this momentous moment live to the world. "Let's try saying something. ...The world is watching."

Andy lay in his bed at a 30-degree incline, but he tried to sit straight up. Sally stopped him...not for a while yet. He smiled at her, then ever-so-slowly lifted his right arm. *Is it really me?* Aside from a slight nod, he could not move his neck yet, so he had to wait until his arm rose to almost his chest level before he saw it. When he saw his rising arm, his body jerked and his eyes darted away, startled and in disbelief, and, his concentration broken, his arm dropped. Then, he raised his arm again, higher this time. He looked at its front side and rotated it to see its back side. He slowly reached up and felt his face with his hand and then bit his finger to know what pain felt like down there below his neck. He yanked his bitten finger out of his mouth, and he began to laugh. Then he lifted his other arm and looked at it in disbelief and laughed.

And then, although his neck and shoulders ached when he lifted his arms, he started moving his two arms around and around in front of his eyes, like a child playing a game, laughing at what he saw before him.

"It's me...it's really me!" he cried out with the help of a special amplifying device on his neck. "Dr. Salberg...may I do something I haven't done since my accident? May I give you a hug?"

"Oh, of course Andy!" Sally, too, was overjoyed. She leaned over, and the beautiful angel of life, and her first saved, gave each other a gentle but tight, earthly hug.

Andy's laughter turned to tears of happiness, then he said, "Thank you, *thank you* Dr. Salberg. Although I realize this body is good for another sixty years, I fully realize the bigger picture: I'm now on the other side — on the shore of immortality. Through you and the God-Man Group, I've avoided certain death. *Thank you.* My hope is that you and Mr. Winters can bring everyone over to the shores of immortality. I've only been conscious for a few minutes. But I can say, it's beautiful here. I feel so much joy and love. I'll need a few days to fathom it...but I know I'll feel this joy and love *forever*."

Sally felt maternal love for Andy, who was getting physically fatigued. "I want you to rest now," she told him. But Andy wanted to add one more thought, and he whispered:

"I'd like to have a moment of silence in memory of my good friend, Martin, who didn't make it..."

Sally nodded and looked down, sadly, as would a mother who had lost one of her two sons. Jasmine hugged Jake. She thought about Martin...and cried about her father. Martin and her father were forever left behind as the rest of humanity soared ahead into eternal life.

CHAPTER
EIGHTY-SIX

"Good evening, near-immortals," Daniel said on his first Thursday-Night Announcement following Operation II. "We all watched that magical moment when Andy Konosovic was brought back to consciousness. He was brought back to us...as an immortal. As we watched that triumphant smile spread across his face and felt our own happiness bursting inside us, we all felt as one...didn't we? We cried with joy. Some of us cried for precious loved ones who didn't make it. Now, man has conquered nature. Man has achieved his greatest mission: to preserve himself. Now, we must not let another person die. Project Sustain Life is going at full intensity. Project Life was victorious with the success of Operation II. Now, the Operation must be brought to everyone who needs it. Now that Project Life is successful, another person must not be allowed to die in Project Sustain Life. Thus, SSL has entered in its most intense phase. Dr. Salberg spends endless hours with neurosurgeons from all over the world, teaching them her Operation at an exhausting pace. The Operation must become a routine procedure *almost immediately*. We can't back off until everyone is safe from death."

Daniel's short Thursday-Night Announcement was a bit of a shock. People were expecting a moment of celebration to cap off a riveting week. The idea of not backing off until *everyone* was safe from death had not had a chance to register yet with the masses. But that idea was well on the minds of the members of The Group.

Three weeks after Operation II, the Group met in Sally's lab. As the members arrived, Sally did not stop working on her computer, although she verbally greeted everyone as though she were looking right at them. Jake perceived she was very frustrated. When everyone was present, she turned around to face The Group. Miss Annabelle gasped, but before she could question Sally about her health, Sally started talking.

"I know I look terrible. I'm only getting an hour or two of sleep. But what's worse, I can't move the Operation to other doctors fast enough. I teach about one-hundred at a time. That takes about five long days. Between those lessons, I need a couple of days to study and research for advancements. I'm going to do this for five more weeks, then I'm going to begin their observation phase. I'll do another Operation on our next patient. I'll have the eight-hundred prepared doctors study me and the close-up image of my hands on a large screen as I perform the Operation. Al is taping every angle of the next Operation, and I'll later edit and narrate the tape and each procedure. We'll send the doctors I've trained a narrated DVD. Moreover, we're putting the whole thing on my web site so all qualified doctors can get a head start before coming to my intensive program. Ted's providing the doctors who've gone through my program with the equipment and supplies and cloning stations to go back to their practices and begin the Operation on those who need it. ...Ahhh, it's all going so slow!" Jake was right; Sally was very frustrated.

"Eight-hundred doctors around the world performing the Operation in a couple of months or less sounds pretty good to me," Reggie encouraged her.

"And things have really calmed down," Daniel added. "Supply has finally caught up to the demand for life support. The pharmaceutical companies have flooded the market with your antibiotics, miracle molecules, and vaccines that quickly stop nearly all infections and viruses in their tracks. Many of the elderly have their bodies now being cloned. Ted's released his patents and has sent his engineers to factories all over the world to accelerate the war effort on getting cloning stations to all the elderly. The death of a human being is really rare now. We're holding on very well with Project Sustain Life." Daniel was reflecting the positive back to Sally, although he knew it wasn't good enough. Losing one life was not good enough.

"Actually, whereas we'll need millions of cloning stations," Theodore said, "once we get the Operation going to the masses, we'll be able to clear out the current cloning stations and make room for other patients, which means we won't have to make a cloning station for every elderly person. In any case, you make a good point that things have really settled down. We're in control now."

"I know we're not losing many people now," Sally said. "But I know a breakdown point is coming when the elderly on life support'll start breaking down, and we'll start losing them. I couldn't bear that." She looked at Miss Annabelle. "The urgency I feel is...is overwhelming. People's *eternal* lives rest on my shoulders. How can I...just how can I take time *to sleep?* I'm becoming an insomniac; that's why I look like this. It's the unacceptable idea that people'll start dying because I couldn't get the Operation to them in time that keeps me awake."

What a hero, Jake thought. What a woman. What love for conscious life.

Everyone in the room must have been thinking the same thing, because everyone was quiet. The *love*...the *supreme love* was driving everyone, everything.

"I have something that may be of value to you," Al finally said. He looked at Sally, then at Daniel. "A 'garage' entrepreneur contacted the Patterson Group and informed us she's developed a computer program that enables robotic hands to perform the severing portion of the Operation in about a sixth of the time as human hands."

"What!" Mr. Melbourne exclaimed.

"Not only that," Al said, nodding at Mr. Melbourne, "just one doctor could oversee the severing portion of *ten* Operations at once. She also said she's working day and night to develop the robotic hands to the point they could, with 'ultra-sound eyes', also attach the head to the clone. I was going to send Jake and Jasmine to interview her before today's meeting, but I had a scheduling conflict."

"Al...that's exactly what we must have!" Sally cried out in desperation. The intensity of her reaction surprised Al. He realized he may have underestimated the immediate potential of the robotic hands. "That could be the solution to this problem. The results of me teaching other doctors how to do this will be only a linear increase. Instead, we need a geometrical increase, which is what this could give us."

"It'd be sort of like going from hand-built cars to the assembly line a century ago," Theodore explained. "Al, let's get this person on a video conference *now!*"

A few minutes later they had the "garage" entrepreneur on the large-screen video conference phone in Sally's lab.

"Charlene Clement," Al said to the young, attractive redheaded woman on the video screen, "I'm Al Patterson, and I'm with the members of The Group. Specifically, to my right is Dr. Sally Salberg and to my left is Theodore Winters."

The young woman turned red, obviously overwhelmed by meeting the members of the legendary God-Man Group. "Hello," she said. "I'm *so* honored."

"If your creation can do what Al told us," Sally said, "believe me, the honor is all ours!"

Sally's comment put Charlene at ease, for she suddenly felt the mutual value exchange occurring and realized what an important piece to the superpuzzle she had to offer.

"Al just told me that through a computer program you developed, robotic hands can sever the head in a sixth of the time as human hands," Sally said.

"That's completely true, no exaggeration," Charlene responded. "And with robotic hands doing the severing, one doctor can oversee ten Operations going at once. If I can complete the next challenge — the robotic hands doing the attaching — then one doctor could perform *many* Operations in a day."

"How does it work?" Theodore asked.

"It works, in concept, like the new, computerized robotic arms that trim fancy bushes and hedges," she replied, still a little nervous. "Have you heard of those?"

"No, I haven't," Theodore said.

"Flexible nylon arms, robotic arms that hold electric trimmers, each have a custom computer program that was programmed to shape the bush into an animal or something. The program tells the arm exactly where to move and trim, with accuracy to a fraction of an inch. My program and robotic hands work the same way in concept, but with an accuracy of ten-millionths of an inch, using laser technology."

"But every anatomy's different," Sally said.

"Not a problem. We do a series of CAT scans and MRIs with dye, then we scan the images into the program."

"Brilliant!" cried Sally.

Jake could see Sally's face lighting up like a fresh fire in a cold, dark room.

"But, how do you know it'll work?" Sally asked. She was almost pleading.

"Because I've done it — on an ape."

"Hee Haw!" Sally screamed, pumping her fists into the air, "I was hoping you'd say that!" Everyone in the lab felt their hearts jump, and then they burst out laughing at Sally's outburst. It was only the second time Jake had seen Sally *laugh* since the reunion five years earlier, the first time being with Andy after the success of Operation II. "Charlene, can you get to my lab today with all your lab notes?"

"I'm on my way."

"Oh, and Charlene..."

"Yes?"

"Drive carefully."

CHAPTER
EIGHTY-SEVEN

"I plan to clone a supply of generic bodies to have ready for people caught in a rapid, unexpected decline in which there is not enough time to clone their own bodies," Theodore emailed members of The Group. "And, as Cathy pointed out, at a future date we could clone their original bodies from stored DNA matter when time, technology, and emotions permitted it."

Ian replied, "I'll release a statement saying that the I-ness contained in one's head is really all that matters."

Sally replied, "I love the idea of generic clones; people who would otherwise die will now have eternal life."

Al replied, "In tonight's news, we'll report on your proposed generic clones. Great idea!"

That evening on Patterson Channel's nightly news, Jake and Jasmine reported on Theodore's plan to clone generic bodies. They finished the Patterson News with a recap of SSLife:

"Winters Inc. manufactures about half of the world's cloning stations," Jake reported. "Four months ago, Theodore Winters sent his engineers to his competitors and to other manufacturing factories around the world to help set them up for manufacturing cloning stations. He released his patents and engineering secrets to set up his competition because he doesn't want to lose one more — *not one more* — conscious life. His supreme love for conscious life overrode every expense, every investment."

"Daniel Ward, our former and last ruling-class President of the United States," Jasmine added, "orchestrates the worldwide effort of coordinating those cloning stations as well as respirators, antibiotics, medicines, vaccines, and many millions of doses of the new miracle molecules. Dr. Sally Salberg's lab has recently created its fast-acting defendant molecules that people are calling the 'antibiotics of viruses'. Upon coming down with a virus, a person can take an injection of the defendant molecules. Those miracle molecules plug up receptor sites to render the virus harmless, unable to attach to our cells."

"And finally, in our *A Look Ahead* segment," said Jake, "Dr. Ian Scott is holed up in his home office developing a quantum computer. The quantum computer will easily store the amount of information in a human brain, Dr. Scott tells us. The theory he pursues is that he can bypass the Operation to download the human brain onto a quantum computer and then download that stored information into the clone's *tabula rasa* or empty, physically identical brain. Such an electronic transfer would surpass the Operation. But more important, storing the information of the brain on the quantum computer would protect immortals from dying from rare, unavoidable catastrophes — such as the bizarre catastrophes responsible for our last seven deaths. With this approach, not one more person would die."

*

"Good evening, near-immortals," Daniel said to open his Thursday-Night announcement. That salutation had become his personal trademark. "Sustaining and saving life consumes just about everyone's thoughts these days. It's been nearly two months since the success of the Operation, and Dr. Salberg is preparing to do the procedure once again with about eight-hundred doctors watching and learning. The value of life, the *supreme love* for conscious life, is so overwhelming that any FDA-type regulations around the world collapsed long ago. Thoughts of political or religious wars just poofed away, dismissed forever. People are now driven to not let another single human life die, and they just can't believe they used to let external authorities retard progress, which condemned every person...*to death!* The memory of governments and religions as higher causes repulses people. Governments and religions were all, in the end, guilty of genocide. Of course, that's behind us now.

"Now, let's look at today and what's before us." Daniel then paused. He looked straight into the camera. His viewing audience could *feel* the intensity in that immortal's eyes. In a voice that never had and never could accept death, he said, "Human death is rapidly declining. Amid the spectacular results of SSLife, an ominous cloud hangs over the human race. A sense of desperation is growing at the Association for Curing Aging and Death. Dr. Sally Salberg informs us that we have a small window to get the Operation to the masses. In a few months, she believes that window will slam closed as a tragic breakdown of many of the elderly on life support will begin. She calls it life-support fatigue failure. Large numbers of people will begin dying again. Unless we discover a breakthrough that allows us to perform the Operation on at least a million elderly within the next six months, we must brace ourselves for a merciless wave of human deaths."

Daniel's Thursday-Night announcements were usually short, just two to five minutes long, directly to the point, which made his announcements the most powerful and most watched communication, minute-for-minute, on the planet. Nearly everyone watched them. Tonight, after his stunning announcement, waves of anxiety rumbled through civilizations around the world. Swells of determination filled those who could possibly somehow do more — doctors, scientists, entrepreneurs, businessmen.

*

"I've noticed that during this intense period of sustaining and saving lives, businesses have changed," Jake said during the weekly idea meeting Al held with his journalists. "Sustaining and saving life comes before *everything* — before competition, before profits. And now, with the smooth success of Sally's third and fourth Operations over the past eight weeks, people just flat out won't accept death. I realize that the degree to which people and their businesses pour money, even their fortunes, into sustaining and saving life is a temporary condition until civilization is safely within an immortal world. But I know that after the SSLife period, things'll never go back to the way they were before. This outpouring of pure love, people caring for and fighting for the survival of everyone, *everyone* for *everyone*...is changing the properties of human existence."

Al raised his eyebrows and said, "I like the direction of your thinking here, Jake. Can you develop an article on this by Wednesday?"

"I'll get on it."

"During this SSL period," Jake summarized in his article two days later, "we're witnessing an amazing show of love and compassion. Sustaining and saving life override everything else. Businesses forsake trade secrets, profits, and patents. Doctors and scientists forsake guarded research. But what about after this war against death? Will things go back to the way they were before? My conclusion is: whereas supreme love might not dominate society in the same way as it does right now during SSL, supreme love will still continue to drive society forward.

"Consider how the ordinary person, with the new Neothink mentality, is becoming more and more creative. Direct head-to-head competition throughout society is getting replaced with something very different...with *creation and coordination* throughout society as businesses and entrepreneurs create and snap in pieces to the growing superpuzzles that drive society. Instead of fighting for the same market shares, businesses and entrepreneurs more and more work in harmony, such as Dr. Sally Salberg and the other doctors, such as Theodore Winters and the other businesses, creating and snapping vital pieces into the larger SSL superpuzzles that drive society, from which they all benefit. After SSL, new superpuzzles will form, and people will increasingly work in harmony, creating and bringing together the pieces."

Through his observations, Jake began to prepare a more widely integrated article projecting what he believed business would be like in the future. The notes for that article continued to grow, into a Neothink puzzle. After a few days, Jake realized he had more than a projection of the course of business. He actually had a projection of the early formations of the Civilization of the Universe on Earth. He brought his projection to the next meeting of The Group, which was again held in Sally's lab.

"Brrr...it's chilly out there!" said Jasmine. She and Jake stepped inside Sally's lab; Jasmine kept her coat on to warm up from the early December cold New York air. She and Jake looked around and noticed Charlene was there, too, working on a computer program.

"How's she coming?" Jake asked Sally.

"She's wonderful. It's going to work!" Sally said. For the first time since Jake had known Sally, her face seemed relaxed. "Charlene's a godsend."

"It's really going to be analogous to the difference before and after the assembly line," Theodore said, walking in after Jake and Jasmine. He, too, looked relaxed. "Charlene came through with our breakthrough."

It's just amazing, Jake thought, how *one* garage entrepreneur comes along and ends a crisis in order to save millions of lives. He heard himself saying in his thoughts, "This underscores my Neothink vision into the Civilization of the Universe. *Competition* increasingly gets replaced with *creation and coordination*, for nearly everyone now is creating and contributing something new. ...If I get a chance, I'll tell them about my vision before this meeting's over."

After everyone arrived, Sally made an announcement: "Well, my friends, this is going to work. Charlene came through with pure gold!"

The members of The Group cheered. They could feel that Sally's tension had broken. And that meant only one thing: soon everyone would safely be in the world of immortals.

Jake looked around the room. *Look at that*, he thought, *their anxiety is gone. These saviors of civilization look so beautiful — all of them.* He savored the moment. *I don't know who looks more proud: the young Charlene or the older Miss Annabelle.*

"Next week, I'll do the fifth Operation, this time with

Charlene's robotic hands," Sally continued. "I've been taking about two months between Operations, but with these robotic hands, well, soon after my fifth Operation I'll be able to do the Operation on three patients at once. Then, soon thereafter, on ten patients at once! The sixteen-hundred doctors who've gone through my course will observe next week. In four weeks, we'll send out six hundred of the robotic hands to those doctors. And Ted promised me another thousand robotic hands will go out over the next seven weeks."

"It'll be like running the marathon in an all-out sprint trying to meet that schedule," Theodore said. Ironically, he was relaxed and smiling. "But I'll meet that schedule all right. I wouldn't settle for anything less."

Sally continued talking. *Ah yes*, Jake thought, *how refreshing to see her talking with a smile on her face! How young and beautiful she is.*

"The doctors will begin the Operation as early as four weeks," Sally was saying. "Many of them will be using the robotic hands. As they get a little experience, they'll rapidly scale up performing the Operation, eventually overseeing several Operations at a time. They're also in charge of replicating their knowledge and skills to hundreds of other doctors in their parts of the world. As I said, Ted is manufacturing the robotic hands to go to those doctors. Bottom line…in six months, aside from an extremely rare, unavoidable catastrophe, the entire human race will be safely, and I mean safely, in the world of immortals!"

For the first time in the six years Jake had known Sally, she started *really* laughing. It was the laugh of an angel, the angel of life. Members of The Group were cheering, laughing, and crying. Jeremiah and Sally silently knew this wonderful night was the night they would let free their desires for each other.

Jake looked around the room again, at the God-Men who saved civilization. Their eyes were fixed on Sally. Jake had a flashback to the reunion nearly six years before in Rico and Olivia's glass edifice when Sally asked them how they could possibly do anything else until they cured aging and death. He remembered how that question mesmerized these people. For, they were the first immortals trapped in a mortal world.

Now, here they were, six years later, mission accomplished.

Finally, after thirty-three years, they could let their supreme love flow freely and openly from their souls; they no longer had to protect and hold back that pure love from the cruel anticivilization that once killed the supreme value all around them daily, including their loved ones.

Look at their faces, Jake thought. Just look at those faces filled with supreme love for conscious life. *They did it!* They accomplished their superpuzzle. They got Daniel elected, depoliticized America, accomplished Project Life and Project Sustain Life, and now they're bringing civilization, with the help of a genius "garage" entrepreneur, into the immortal Civilization of the Universe on Earth. These people, Jake thought, *really are* saving every living person's life for all eternity. Just as their beloved Miss Annabelle had hoped for, one Christmas Day thirty-three years ago, her students have cured conscious death.

Jake sat in awe among civilization's saviors and began to wonder: as more and more superpuzzles come together in this supersociety to create the Civilization of the Universe on Earth...what will it look like? As *superpuzzles* snap together to create the Civilization of the Universe, just what never-before-seen puzzle-picture will unfold?

Beholding The Puzzle-Picture

Book Three Of
Superpuzzle

3 of 3

The Secret Society Triumphs

A Word From The Author

Immortals begin on Earth. In that Twelve-Visions World, loss of human life, loss of the supreme value quickly vanishes. One of the most significant declarations of the anticivilization, September 11, 2001, passed by with no death or destruction, no 9/11 attacks, our irrational political/religious warring world replaced with a rational business/science peaceful world.

That new world of immortals and peace, however, is not fantasy. It already exists right now right here in the parallel society — the Society of Secrets of the fortunate few. Deep inside the SOS reside Earth's first immortals...that is, those who went through a psychological evolution into God-Man — value creators void of the burden of life.

Now, it is time to behold their world — the puzzle-picture of tomorrow's new world after man's psychological evolution into God-Man.

Realize, Books One and Two have already started *your* psychological evolution into God-Man, which qualifies you to come into tomorrow's new world early, before others, inside the inner circle of the Society of Secrets.

Your psychological evolution into God-Man started in Book One, *Conceiving The Superpuzzle,* when you experienced the emotions from the new world, emotions not felt by adults in our world. You experienced the twelve students' deeper new-world love for life as they conceived the superpuzzle: rescue the supreme value in the Universe — human life — from death. Experiencing their emotions awakened the child of the past within you and brought back, if only at moments, your own long-forgotten deeper love for life.

Your psychological evolution into God-Man continued in Book Two, *Putting Together The Pieces,* when you experienced the actions needed to get into the new world, actions that could someday actually clear civilization's path into the new world. You experienced the grown-up students accomplishing their deepest desire for immortality as they successfully snapped together the pieces to the superpuzzle. Together they got Daniel Ward elected President of the United States. Overcoming enormous obstacles, he depoliticized America. Then, in the new Freedom Paradigm, Dr. Sally Salberg discovered how to defeat death through The Operation. Experiencing their extraordinary actions to cure death made the child of the past within you sit up and take notice and remember, if only at moments, your own long-lost desire for immortality.

The first two books have begun your psychological evolution into God-Man. Therefore, you are ready to see your future in the new world. You are ready to behold the puzzle-picture. You are also almost ready to join Earth's first immortals deep within the Society of Secrets, after you absorb Book Three.

Let us now pick up where Book Two left off. Book Two ended with the success of The Operation. The struggle to sustain life — to help the dying hold on for The Operation — became an overwhelming worldwide drive...a desperate drive for life. To let *one* life die, when mankind essentially had achieved immortality, was unfathomable. Yet, the availability of The Operation could not meet even a fraction of the demand. The magnitude of the tragedy of death drove the God-Man Group, particularly Dr. Sally Salberg, into superhuman efforts in Book Two. Now, in Book Three, we continue the story a few months after Sally and The Group acquired a "garage" entrepreneur's creation of the robotic hands — a godsend that could geometrically expand the availability of The Operation.

Turn now to the final leg of this tripartite journey to our future world. Unfortunately, some remnants of the anticivilization still remain. The God-Man Group, counting heavily on Dr. Ian Scott, is challenged at yet another level. As you proceed deeper into this final leg of the journey, the battle resumes with some tragic consequences. Through those painful tribulations, Miss Annabelle's former students gradually pull together the *full* puzzle-picture.

It is here in Book Three, but not until the end, where you will fully see, for the first time, what tomorrow will bring. That is when you will experience your third epiphany, for that is when you will enter the new world and join Earth's first immortals deep within the Society of Secrets.

CONTENTS

Book Three
Beholding The
Puzzle-Picture

I.

The Last One
To Die

CHAPTER
EIGHTY-EIGHT

"I'm getting the most wonderful news from our reporters around the world," Al said to Jake and Jasmine in his glass office overlooking the floor at Patterson Press.

"Me too," said Jake. He knew what Al had heard.

"I want you two to research our major cities and prepare our front-page article on what's been developing."

"North America or worldwide?" Jasmine asked. In the new commercial flights that exited and re-entered the atmosphere, a flight halfway around the world lasted only a few hours.

"You judge after you observe the hospitals firsthand," Al answered. As in-house entrepreneurs, Jake and Jasmine were so integrated with the numbers, from costs to profits, Al gave them one-hundred percent responsibility for most decisions now. "Your research could bring you anywhere; you decide."

"First stop, Los Angeles," Jake said to Jasmine. The limo drove them to LaGuardia Airport. Swarms of garage and in-house entrepreneurs working together day and night creating new technologies, reaching the marketplace quickly without cost-prohibitive bureaucratic regulations holding them back, their new technologies obsoleting existing technologies and steadily turning over new generations of safer and safer products...made flying and driving almost as safe as walking and running.

"Take us to the UCLA Medical Center," Jake told the cab driver at Los Angeles International Airport.

"Let's go straight to the ICU," Jake said as he and Jasmine arrived.

"It's relaxed in here," Jasmine said the moment she and Jake walked into the intensive care unit.

"Look!" said Jake. He pointed down a corridor.

Jasmine looked down the corridor and squinted for a brief moment, but the next moment her eyes sprang wide open as would a child's eyes after spotting Mickey Mouse. "Yes!" she said, "Vacant respirators and cloning stations!"

"Can you believe it?" a woman said. She stood behind Jake and Jasmine. When they turned around, they saw an attractive nurse who was smiling.

"Almost as surprising," said Jasmine, "is to see a nurse in intensive care with enough time to speak to us."

"And with a smile on her face!" Jake added. The three of them laughed.

"The past two weeks, it's been like this," the nurse explained. "It's as though the fever's broken and everything's getting better around here. We've definitely gotten over the hump. We've even let a few of the cloning stations go to consumers who weren't critical. The doctors said they'll have time to begin giving the Operation to some general consumers."

Jasmine looked at Jake. "That's unbelievably good news," she said. "You know, very, very few people are going to die now."

"Let's keep going West, Jassy, to Asia. Let's see if this fantasy's happening there yet."

*

"Hi Al."

"Oh, hey Jake! Where you calling from?"

"We're in Buenos Aires. In a few hours we'll be in Dallas. We'll be back in New York tonight."

"What's your conclusion?"

"In America, we're actually seeing the Save-and-Sustain-Life frenzy — that horrifying SSL panic — subsiding. Death is definitely being arrested. You wouldn't believe how exciting it is to see extra respirators and cloning stations turning up in hospitals!"

"Oh, I can believe how exciting that is—"

"And we're just a few months into the robotic hands!" Noticing he was practically yelling while walking through the airport, Jake tamed his wild tone and added, "Some places abroad still struggle in the all-out panic mode, especially those areas that held onto political leaders longer. But I think in three to four months, even the worst of those areas should begin to experience a glut in cloning stations and respirators, especially as North American manufacturers ship their extras abroad. Between Daniel orchestrating the Save-and-Sustain-Life program and Theodore leading the charge in production, those SSL leaks will get plugged quickly. The whole world is in Daniel and Theodore's hands now."

Al was quiet. Jake suspected Al was feeling proud of his two former classmates and close friends. Al...Daniel...Theodore, pondered Jake. At that moment, the thought crossed his mind of going back and listening again to the tapes from the Miracle Year some thirty-three years ago. What would it be like to hear Alan, Danny, and Teddy again...as eight-year-old third graders?

*

During the flight home on one of the new rocket planes that exited Earth's atmosphere during the flight, Jake keypunched furiously into his laptop. He wanted the good news in the morning Patterson Papers.

Jasmine was quiet, her head resting against Jake's shoulder. After several minutes of silence, Jasmine lifted her head from Jake's shoulder and looked at him. "I can't help feeling, over and over again, every time something amazes me," she said, "how much daddy would've loved it here in this world." She looked down, and slowly added, "I was just remembering my first airplane trip with him. I was five. When the plane went down the runway, and I first felt that thrust and then the liftoff, I couldn't stop laughing." She paused, remembering. "He'd been on many flights before, but he laughed with me. He laughed as though it were his first time, too." She shook her head and took a deep breath. "Oh...I wish I could take Daddy on his first rocket-plane flight. He'd start laughing...I just know it."

*

The monthly get-togethers at Rico's house were also wonderful social gatherings and had expanded into monthly weekends together. Rico and Olivia loved hosting the weekends, although everyone offered to host. But Rico and his wife genuinely loved doing it, and everyone loved Rico's house and gardens in the country.

Every meeting since the reunion when Jasmine and Jake flew down to Rico's from Boston University, Jasmine always thought of her dad and how much he would have loved these meetings. Often when she listened to Rico talk, his loving nature made her remember her father. At first, after her loss, she felt sad listening to Rico, remembering her father and the love they were robbed of. Now, she loved listening to Rico and remembering her father. She loved watching Rico's powerful paternal nature. She loved hearing the unspoken words in his voice whenever he talked to his Monica who was sixteen now. Jasmine could always hear, in the sweetness of his voice, Rico silently saying to his teenager: "I love you, *sugar pie*."

Today, the sky was bright blue, and the temperature was in the mid-70s. Jake and Jasmine walked through Olivia's gardens with Miss Annabelle. The young couple was unusually excited. They were asking Miss Annabelle questions about raising a genius, just like the title of her best-seller, for Jake and Jasmine were going to have a baby. Jasmine was among the last wave of women who would need to endure pregnancy. Several companies were selectively growing parents' babies in man-made "placentas". The mortality rate of those external babies was nearly perfect.

Jake bent down to look at an unusual flower and, hearing but not seeing Miss Annabelle, he noticed her voice did not carry the weary sound of a woman in her late sixties; her voice carried youthful resonance as rich and full as a blooming flower is in color and moisture. Jake leaned over the flowers; the sweet scent filled his lungs. Miss Annabelle's sweet voice filled his head.

"I'd love to teach your child someday," she said. "Is it a boy or a girl?"

Jasmine answered that it was a boy, but Jake's mind ceased to hear the conversation. He could focus only on the thought of Miss Annabelle teaching his son. What a precious gift that would be!

The three of them walked the garden paths back to the mansion. Inside, Jake saw that most members of The Group had arrived; he felt a jolt of joy upon seeing the members along with their spouses and children.

Today, Jasmine would open the meeting. She and Jake would take down notes for a major full-section article, the size of a small book, to commemorate the God-Man Group. The article would eventually appear in a special Anniversary Edition for the success of Operation II. The banner across that Anniversary Edition would read: *Inside The Group that Started It All.*

The adults and teenagers gathered in the large informal meeting room. The children were taken to the play areas with the babysitters. Jake watched as Rosa, Rico Jr., and Tony gave Rico and Olivia hugs and headed off to the play areas. Look at how they've grown, Jake thought. Tony's now the same age Rico was in Miss Annabelle's class! And look at Monica; she's now a young woman who sits through our long meetings. Jake then noticed Daniel's son Danny saying bye to his dad and mom, Marcy. He looks about ten or eleven, Jake guessed. Danny ran after Rico Jr. yelling "Ric...Ricci wait for me!"

It's amazing, Jake pondered while watching Danny Jr. run after Rico Jr., will those two build superpuzzles together someday, just like their dads?

It dawned on Jake that only Rico and Daniel from The Group had children, although Reggie and his wife Naomi were soon expecting their first. Jake specifically wondered why Robert and Natasha never had children despite being together now for six years. Jake also wondered about Ian and Diana, and Jake especially wondered about Theodore and Cathy who had been together ever since becoming childhood sweethearts.

What surprises me, he thought, is how much they love life and especially children. Maybe they don't want to bring children into this mortal world, Jake thought. Or maybe, they can't get distracted from the superpuzzle, not yet.

Comfortable chairs, love seats, and couches wrapped around the informal meeting room where they met this day.

"Today I want to ask each of you to take a few minutes to tell us what you love doing most, now that living forever is a given," Jasmine said to start the meeting.

As Miss Annabelle's former students answered Jasmine's question, it became clear that what they loved doing most in life was *what they were doing.*

But, of course, Jake thought. His eyes widened; he was remembering his very first conversation with Jessie over six years before: Jessie was mopping the floors of Duncan Elementary; Jake was asking the receptionist questions about the Nobel Prize nominees — Sally, Theodore, and Ian. The quiet custodian, Jessie, approached the curious college student, Jake, and started telling him the story of Miss Annabelle and her students. And it was during that first conversation, Jake remembered, when Jessie told him about the first day of school starting the Miracle Year, when the children told Miss Annabelle what they wanted to do when they grew up. And throughout the Miracle Year, the students showed strong interests such as Ian and the cosmos, Teddy and business, Sally and medicine, Bobby and job improvement, Natasha and relationship improvement, Reggie and music, Cathy and weight-loss and beauty, Debra and fast-food marketing. *But of course,* Jake thought, *you could spot their natural, deepest motivational roots — their Friday-Night Essences — when they were just children!* Today, thirty-three years later, most of them were doing what most interested them their whole lives, even as children, ever since the first day of Third Grade.

Growing up seeing below the surface, seeing *what is,* they never lost sight of their deepest motivational roots, and they naturally pursued what they loved most. Success and happiness and powerful family and romantic love came naturally to them. How elegantly simple, Jake thought.

One after the other, the former students elaborated on their current ventures and growing puzzles of creation and their moving love for their families and friends. Jake saw how exciting their lives were and how happy this room was.

When it was Miss Annabelle's turn to talk about what she loved doing most, she talked about her worldwide internet educational phenomenon that was by far the largest daily course of any kind in the world. Over seventy million children and nearly as many adults now logged on daily. Her internet course, she explained, was not a teaching curriculum. It was more of a "wise man" tutor — her general lecture of past, electronically translated into most languages.

But as Miss Annabelle talked about what she loved doing most, Jake noticed her expression seemed distant, as if her thoughts were somewhere else. He heard a weariness he did not hear in the garden. She was describing her creation, but noticeably absent was the passion that filled her former students. Suddenly she stopped talking. She didn't say a word for several seconds.

The silence raised everyone's concern. She then turned toward Jasmine and said, "When did you say Jake Jr. is due?" Miss Annabelle seemed to have forgotten what she had just been talking about.

"July 31st," Jasmine said.

"I'd *really* like to teach that boy," said Miss Annabelle. She looked at Reggie and Naomi and said, "And I'd *really* like to teach your little girl." She looked at Daniel and then Rico and said, "Oh, how I'd love to teach your children." She looked around the room at her former students. "Teaching the twelve of you was the last time I taught in person. Teaching the people I love brought me the happiest times in my life. I want to teach children and become part of their lives again." She paused to allow her thoughts to catch up to her emotions. "Of course, I'd always keep my internet school going. Teaching in the classroom would probably help me expand the value of my internet school. I stopped teaching before because I could not bear the thought of being torn from my students again, which was inevitable in the anticivilization."

Daniel smiled. It had been nearly two years since completing his great sale of government assets to private enterprises. The government no longer functioned beyond its proper purpose of protecting the peace; but a large trust fund had been set up, after the sale, to finance vouchers into a private educational system. America's moms could not, at first, let go of the security of government-guaranteed education. Now that the ruling-class government had collapsed along with all external authorities, the fund still existed because it was a financial fund in a private banking system backed by covenants.

"I never wanted that big educational trust fund," Daniel said. "It works against rapid advancement, but the moms wanted a cushion. But do I see a real opportunity here?"

"What are ya thinkin'?" Theodore asked. He smiled, for he knew what Daniel was thinking.

"Miss Annabelle's Schools of Geniuses!" Daniel blurted. He displayed the same enthusiasm that often filled his voice in third grade, which made Jake smile and remember when third-grader Danny fought a school bully to defend his teacher's honor. "Ted, what an investment," Daniel continued, "with the return of *the* teacher of the children of the God-Man Group, nearly all parents would send their children. *The* Miss Annabelle will teach in the flagship school, and our other schools will be built on her system."

"Yes!" Theodore said, instantly making the idea sound. "In fact, that would be our goal: to teach *every* child. Of course, anyone could compete with us, but our results will keep the business in our schools. ...Ah, I can see it now..." Jake had seen this look in Theodore before and knew the brilliant man was deep in a creative place no one else could so quickly and effortlessly reach. Then Theodore continued, "Here's how we'll get *all* children. We'll let *anyone* come *for free!*"

"How could you possibly bankroll that?" Ian asked, rolling the logistics and numbers through his scientific brain.

"Well, I'll give them an option: parents can pay annually, which most will. But ninety-five percent of the advertisement will be built around this idea: We are so confident that *the* Miss Annabelle system will make your children become geniuses, that *we* will be willing to pay for their private education, and when they become rich, they can repay us then with interest. Since the world is so prosperous now, almost all the parents will pay now. But a small percentage down on their luck will take us up on the offer. So, I can bankroll this all right. The power behind this is our confidence to make that offer — to put our money where our mouth is: if they don't get rich, they don't pay! With Neothink, all our students will go on to become great value creators, like us. The *power* behind our schools will be the return of the famous teacher of the children of the original God-Man Group — the teacher who invented Neothink education."

Amazing, Jake thought. These people take every value put before them, such as Miss Annabelle's desire to return to the classroom, and maximize that value to its awesome potential, such as teaching *every* child with her system. And then, Jake pondered, they follow up and make it happen!

While Jake shook his head in awe over the nature of the first immortals, he realized the room had gotten quiet. Everyone was looking at Miss Annabelle. She was overwhelmed by Theodore's offer. She smiled at him. Her memory brought her back to her classroom thirty-three years earlier when Teddy was the classroom's little nine-year-old executive during their miracle year together. She could feel her heart throbbing. She knew: *the classroom* was where she needed to be. Her eyes were laughing. Finally, after thirty-three years, she would return to the classroom! Teaching children one-on-one was her Friday-Night essence, and she could feel her deepest motivational root growing again inside.

World-renowned Theodore Winters would spread his third-grade teacher's creation across the country and eventually around the world. Jasmine was writing furiously. This was a big story, and she knew it.

"Jas, Jake, you guys getting this?" Al Patterson asked.

Jake glanced around the room. Miss Annabelle's former students were all looking at her. ...Oh, the love Jake saw in their faces. They had that same wide-eyed expression a child has when his or her mom or dad is exceptionally excited about something — that special expression that shares in the parent's moment of joy and silently cries out, "I'm so glad you're happy; *I love you*, Mom!"

Jake focussed on Al. "The new educational paradigm for immortals: Neothink Education," Jake said, answering Al. Then

Superpuzzle

Jake looked at Daniel and added, "This is exciting and emotionally charged news. The media group will be a valuable vehicle to help us jump past the educational trust fund into the much superior, pure privatization by Ted. Look at what we're offering the moms of America: The same teacher who taught the original twelve immortals who grew up to form the original God-Man Group will teach *your* children. I know how they'll emotionally react because *I felt it* when Miss Annabelle said she wanted to teach my son. She's every parent's heroine, every parent's, every child's dream teacher! ...Now, we add to that formula the biggest business hero of all time, Miss Annabelle's very own Theodore Winters. He'll buy the former public schools and turn them into Miss Annabelle's Schools of Geniuses. Miss Annabelle will then replicate her Neothink techniques to all the teachers in her schools. The moms will perceive this as a huge leap forward for their children and agree to jump past the trust fund into this best possible scenario. ...Al," Jake turned to his boss, "I'll outline and chart a media blitz."

Al was nodding. "Always coming through with the big picture," he said. "That's why I love you!"

*

Jake awakened early the next morning. Jasmine was not in bed. "Jassy?" he said. She must be somewhere in this large guest room, he figured; maybe she's in the bathroom. "Jassy?" he said, louder this time. But she did not answer.

Jake got out of bed and looked out the window. Olivia always gave Jake and Jasmine this particular guest room because it overlooked their favorite garden — where they got married. When Jake looked out the window, there under the old oak tree, where he and Jasmine read their vows a year and nine months ago, stood Jasmine, staring at the sunrise.

Jake quickly put on some clothes and pulled on a sweater. He went into the garden and approached Jasmine. She was looking the other way.

Softly, so as not to startle her, Jake said, "Hello."

She turned slowly around. Jake could not help the rush of attraction he felt for her every time he was near her. The sunrise radiating through her long hair, the gentle light wrapping itself around her cheeks as she turned, took Jake's breath away. Then he noticed her eyes. They looked peaceful, but sad.

"How are you, my love?" he asked. He reached out and lightly brushed her face with his fingertips.

"It's so beautiful here," she said. She looked up at him and tilted her head. "I love it here. I see our wedding in my thoughts when I'm here."

"That was such a happy day, wasn't it?" Jake said. Jasmine smiled and nodded, but her eyes were sad. "Jassy, you're seeing your dad here, this morning, aren't you?"

Jasmine nodded, and her smile sank…into a frown. "I keep seeing him when he stood right over there. He was just standing there with tears in his eyes, watching me…" Jasmine started crying.

Jake put his hand on her shoulder.

"I really loved him," she cried. She leaned into Jake and pushed her face into his chest. "You know," she said in a broken voice that helplessly dropped to a whisper, "we were *so close.*"

"I know you were, darling."

"No, I mean we were so close *to making it to immortality.* We were actually in the early SSL period when Daddy died. His death was actually one of those rare, catastrophic events…you know?"

Jake ran his hand down her hair. He knew she was right.

"We really need to…" she looked up over her head, frustrated that she couldn't say it.

"I know," Jake whispered. He hurt inside, seeing her in such pain. "We need to definitively end catastrophic events that kill people."

Jasmine was nodding and crying.

*

Convincing the moms from the Atlantic Ocean to the Pacific Ocean took less than three weeks. The Patterson Papers ran a series of articles by Jake and Jasmine describing the exciting prospect of a full-scale replication across the country by Miss Annabelle herself, personally replicating her methods directly to the very teachers who would teach America's children...in a Theodore Winters school system. The media group took polls every day and witnessed how, with each article, the polls shifted dramatically away from the trust fund to pure privatization.

Daniel made several appearances on the Patterson Channel. He was a giant among heroes — the last ruling-class American President who, along with his Twelve Visions Party, led the world through the peaceful political revolution, which was followed like dominoes by the great Technological Revolution, the medical revolution, the job revolution, the love revolution, humanity's evolution into Neothink, and the final triumph: biological immortality. Because of Daniel, the whole world went through a great prosperity explosion and, ultimately, onto immortality. Daniel never cared for the Educational Trust Fund, although he understood why the moms wanted it, and he knew it was only a temporary transition. "And what better transition could there be than what's being offered here," he would ask his television audience, "offering our children the legendary Miss Annabelle and legendary Theodore Winters?"

With Patterson Papers across the world wrapped by Jake and Jasmine's special section *Miss Annabelle: Teacher of Superachievers*, the polls shifted overwhelmingly in favor of ending the trust-fund covenant eight years early to make way for Miss Annabelle's Schools of Geniuses. By mid-June, the agreement was official: the next school year would resume Miss Annabelle's great journey that began thirty-four years earlier in a third-grade classroom in Cheektowaga, New York, where sat Teddy, Danny, Sally, Ian, Jeremiah, Alan, Nattie, Cathy, Bobby, Debbie, Reggie, and Rico.

*

Miss Annabelle ran into the living room and snuggled up against her husband on their leather couch. "I feel as I did when I met you over thirty years ago," she said. "I'm halfway through my lectures...*my lectures*. Oh, I love saying that again!"

"You don't know how happy it makes me to see you like this, darling," Mr. Melbourne said. He reached his arm around her. "You know, during the miracle year, we were our own shining Civilization of the Universe in the anticivilization. There was *nothing* in the world so precious and rewarding as your class. After we moved to Australia, I knew every year that passed was another year without that extraordinary preciousness. I felt profound sadness knowing what you were missing."

"Oh, John...it was hard. It still hurts when I think of how many years we missed out on being with our students and teaching in a classroom. That's the person I really was meant to be. ...But I had no choice. Wherever I taught in the anticivilization, the result would've been the same. And I just couldn't bear being torn away again."

"I know, darling," Mr. Melbourne said. The back of his throat tightened into a knot. He squeezed her against him and kissed her on her cheek.

A smile broke across her face; her cheek pushed against his lips. "But now, I'm going to start again," she said. "I've never been so excited!"

Mr. Melbourne knew, as he watched her glow with that happiness of old, she was whole again. Now, she was neothinking the pieces to the puzzle of her school year...again.

"I've worked nearly every waking moment since our meeting at Rico's preparing my base of lectures. When I'm not developing my lectures, I'm replicating them to the other teachers over video conferences." She paused, studied her husband, and added, "I'm just worried that you don't see me much now, and you won't see me much over the next three months. You know? I'll be busy day and night. ...Are you going to be okay with that?"

Mr. Melbourne just smiled and hugged her. It was a celebration. "Remember, I fell in love with you when you were on this busy schedule," he said. He finished his thoughts in silence: *Ah, she's back again, Miss Annabelle, the beloved teacher.*

*

Miss Annabelle could choose any school in the country to teach, making it the flagship school. She said her choice was not difficult: she chose Cheektowaga, New York in what was formerly Duncan Elementary.

*

The fall arrived; a fresh breeze blew across the country. Families with school children waited for this day — the first day of school. They could feel the excitement, for a new era was to begin — the era of the Miss Annabelle Schools. Parents and grandparents knew their children and grandchildren would grow up to be geniuses like Miss Annabelle's twelve God-Men.

She elected to teach third grade, just as she did thirty-four years ago to this day. She chose the same room.

Jake was in the room early. He wanted to surprise Miss Annabelle with his presence on her first day teaching. But he hardly expected her to be surprised, for her morning lecture had turned into the biggest media event of the year, and third biggest ever next to the Operation and Operation II. The Patterson Group would send her morning general lecture live around the world on the Patterson Channel.

"Are the interpreters all here?" shouted the engineer.

Al got the idea to televise her general lectures when he remembered that thirty-four years ago, many parents at Duncan Elementary listened to the audio tapes of her general lectures. Adults around the world wanted to tune in; so he would bring them Miss Annabelle's daily general lectures for the entire school year.

Of course, for this first show, Miss Annabelle would expect to see Jake, Jasmine and Al there. But Miss Annabelle would not expect what happened this morning. To Jake's delight, at 7:25 a.m. Sally and Jeremiah walked in, holding hands. They hugged Jake and Jasmine.

"We had to come," Sally said. Then she squealed like a delighted child. Jake noticed Sally was trembling with excitement. Suddenly, he could see the little eight-year-old Sally in her face, the vulnerable little girl who sat in this class thirty-four years ago on this day. As he looked in her eyes, he knew what he did not know before: this event was a pilgrimage, a journey back to the beginning.

"Sally," he said, looking at Sally and Jeremiah, "you're all coming, aren't you, all twelve of you?"

She nodded as a shiver ran through her.

"We *love* her, Jake," Jeremiah said from deep within his heart.

Jake suddenly felt a chill run down his own spine. This is where it all began...right *here*...with Sally and the others who would be here today. The world as we know it now, he thought, and everything we will know in the future, started *right here* in this room with *these people*. This very day, thirty-four years ago, was the beginning of the new world — the Civilization of the Universe on Earth.

Jake went back to work, setting up and running tests. During all this, like witnessing history, Jake watched Miss Annabelle's former students, her first loves, stream in one by one and sit in the back.

The pace to get everything right for a live show was always hectic during the last thirty minutes of sound checks and final lighting adjustments. Jake also was getting nervous that he had not yet seen Miss Annabelle. With five minutes to air time, during the final "panic" to get in position, Jake noticed a striking young woman standing just outside the door. She glanced in the room a couple of times and seemed to be waiting for someone. The children were seated, and the broadcast was about to begin. At 8:00 a.m., the cameras would roll. Patterson had his most experienced anchorman to introduce Miss Annabelle.

At 7:58 a.m., Jake feared something terrible had happened to Miss Annabelle, knowing that averting serious accidents or even death was not yet foolproof on Earth. She was nearly seventy years old, and she had undergone a strenuous four months working seven days a week replicating her techniques to thousands of teachers across the country and perfecting her Neothink education. Theodore, who had also been concerned about her frantic four-month pace, had tried to get her to slow down and finish the replicating during the school year. But Miss Annabelle insisted the replicating had to be completed before the school year started so as not to betray the moms' trust. In fact, for the first three straight months following the epiphanous meeting at Rico's, she pushed herself seven days a week, fifteen-hour days to get the replicating completed one month prior to the start of school. She had told Theodore that she needed a month of undisturbed privacy before school started to complete her cutting-edge preparation, which she would replicate the following year to the other teachers per positive results. Neither Jake nor her former students had seen her during the entire month.

Jake looked toward the door and suddenly realized the young woman was a substitute teacher. God, I hope Miss Annabelle is okay, Jake said to himself. She wouldn't miss this for anything.

"We roll in thirty seconds," the engineer commanded. Jake rushed his way from the back toward the door to bring in the substitute. He knew she would know the material well because of Miss Annabelle's extensive replicating program. Just as he reached the doorway, the stunning substitute looked straight into Jake's eyes. Her eyes were laughing as she stepped past him into the room. He knew her...from somewhere before. At that same instant, as if everything were moving in slow motion, he heard distinctly twelve individual gasps. Jake turned around and shouted, "Roll it!" And the cameraman jumped in on cue just as the beautiful young woman began to sing, "To dream the impossible dream..."

Jake and the former students grinned from ear to ear, and there was not a dry eye among them.

"She did it," he whispered. And it was during this precious moment as he gazed at the beautiful, singing teacher, he realized the Operation removes all injustices and makes everything right. The thirty-three years she had missed experiencing her greatest love in life were not gone forever, for now she could have those years back again.

"This year you'll learn how to pursue your dreams," she started, pausing to glance at her new class of eight-year-olds, "You'll learn how to create beautiful values lots of people will want to pay you for. But instead of an impossible dream, your dreams will become exciting, growing realities." She looked up and glanced around the back of the room at her twelve wonderful proofs. Jake could see it in her eyes — she was remembering them as little eight-year-olds again. On this day thirty-four years ago, they stood up as little children and told her what they wanted to do when they grew up. Jake could see it in her eyes

— she was remembering exactly what they told her back then. Her eyes caught Daniel's eyes, and she remembered him as little Danny bravely standing up first and announcing to her and to the class that he wanted to build tall buildings when he grew up. *He was always my little brave hero.* One by one, she looked into the eyes of each of her twelve original students. Her heart was gripped by love and nostalgia. Jake could see she was overwhelmed. For the moment, she could not talk. She could not continue.

From nearby, Jake heard someone gently whisper, "Come on, girl, you can do it." He looked down to see Angie and Jessie. As Miss Annabelle's eyes gradually met theirs, she got her strength back and was able to continue.

Amazing, Jake thought, they're still a soul-mate team to this day! Angie and Jessie...helping Miss Annabelle through the hard moments. Jake's thoughts were replaced by a rush of joy, knowing that Miss Annabelle and her husband lived back here again, in Cheektowaga, where it all began...united again, with Angie and Jessie.

*

Back home in New York City three days later, Jake looked at Jasmine and said, "God, you're beautiful."

She loved the impulse in his voice. She carried Little Jakey over and placed him in Jake's lap. He rubbed his fingers back and forth through his son's baby hair that stood straight up.

As he admired his boy, he started thinking how people alive during the jump from the anticivilization to the Civilization of the Universe would always know how it once was like in a world of dishonesty and irrationality when people once died. "Those who know," Jake whispered to his son, "will someday be the tiniest percentage of the population as civilization grows and spreads throughout distant planets, asteroids, and galaxies. The tiny percentage who know, those rare originals, will always carry a special knowledge that no others can know: *the contrast* between the two worlds." Little Jakey stared at his dad. "Mom and I will always see an added shine of appreciation for the world we so very, very fortunately made it into."

Superpuzzle

Jake looked at his infant son and knew he would never, *never* have a conception of purposeful *bad*. As Jake held his son in his lap, the new father felt deep within his soul the supreme value of life and could not help wondering about Ian's theory: *were our lost loved ones of the former anticivilization saved by Zons?* We had now jumped across the gulf to the Civilization of the Universe, so it was now okay to ponder Ian's theory.

Jasmine watched Jake cradle their handsome son, Jake Mozar Catchings, and said, "I wish my father could have seen him." She was remembering the last time she looked at her father when he was healthy, outside the big Jersey home. She remembered his gentle face that always held so much love for her. As she watched that memory in her mind's eye, she realized the sparkle in his eye really was there. Oh, had you been living now, she lamented, we would have had *forever* to share...me, my Jake and Little Jake, and you, daddy.

Jake smiled at her and said, "Maybe, my darling, maybe your father will see Jakey. You know, maybe Zons did save us before we learned how to do it ourselves. I say this now because *bad* has vanished from our planet. Maybe, somehow, the good can now be reunited."

The sorrow in Jasmine's face softened. Although both she and Jake knew they were reaching beyond Earthlings' realm of knowledge, she finally let herself feel the hope, and the logic, in Ian's theory. After witnessing the all-encompassing, all-out drive by God-Men to eradicate conscious death on Earth, she wondered: wouldn't that all-out drive be even greater by Zons to eradicate conscious death in the Universe? She silently vowed: if this is so, whoever was responsible for saving my father's spirit, I will someday repay with a worthy value.

She smiled and pulled Big Jake and Little Jake against her bosom, shuddered from the preciousness of the moment, and she whispered, "We're missing you, Daddy. If you're out there, someone here, who is very special, wants to meet you..."

CHAPTER
EIGHTY-NINE

The next morning, Jake woke up enjoying a memory from Miss Annabelle's inaugural class in the new world. He lay in bed, smiling and remembering...

"You guys know what this means, don't you?" Miss Annabelle asked Angie and Jessie in the celebration that followed the broadcast. Miss Annabelle, who now looked about twenty years old, swooped her hand across the front of her body. She looked straight at Angie and said, "We can now have children!"

Angie and Jessie broke into the most wonderful smiles accompanied with an expression Jake had never seen before. Then he realized why those smiles were unlike any other. They were reflecting the rebirth of the most precious part of their souls, which they had to, in the anticivilization, let die: that most precious part of the soul that *creates life*.

"Oh, Jessie," Angie cried, "let's do it. Let's have *lots* of children!" The Operation was now available for purposes other than saving life. Now, people who wanted youth again or wanted children again could have them. Having lots of children was very feasible now because the cost of living was so low, and the fetus was now grown outside the body. And becoming young and fertile again was not the only option. A business in California cloned babies for parents who could not fertilize an egg. Nevertheless, Angie liked the idea of being physically young again with children. Jessie liked that idea, too.

"Yes!" Jessie said, "Let's have a dozen. Let's have six boys and six girls!" Mr. Melbourne had joined them, and the four of them laughed together — that same hearty laughter Miss Annabelle loved to hear thirty-four years ago. ...Ah, what a memory, Jake thought. He loved those four people so much; to see them happy like that, after all they had been through, just really moved him.

*

"Good evening, near-immortals."

Daniel's Thursday-Night announcements brought beautiful news to the world these days. Tonight was no exception. People around the world huddled around their televisions to hear the President who ended the ruling class give his announcement:

"Dr. Salberg's prediction nine months ago that everyone who needed the Operation would have it in six months...was right on. Three months ago the last wave of persons barely hanging on with life support underwent the Operation.

"The month to month acceleration of saving those million people barely hanging on during Project Sustain Life was stunning. Theodore Winter's comparison of the robotic, automated Operation to Henry Ford's assembly line proved to be accurate.

"Now, over the past three months we've seen elective Operations. I have a prediction. I'm integrated with what's going on in hospitals worldwide; I know the numbers. And I believe a few million elderly people will undergo the Operation over the next year. Now, here's the interesting thing: once those few million elderly undergo the Operation, then people wanting the Operation will drastically slow down.

"That's right, after a spectacular surge of the Operation, capping off at a few million, something strange is going to happen: the number of Operations will start steadily declining. The new medical technologies increase health and extend life so dramatically, people won't *need* the Operation until much later in life. For a period of time, the Operation might almost seem unnecessary. Technology advances so rapidly in our supersociety that people keep getting healthier and healthier. Life expectancy now expands faster than time passes.

"But then, after a dry spell, the Operation will surge again as people feel comfortable enough to go through the procedure, not to save their lives, but to return to a youthful body full of energy.

"Yes, the members of The Group, of which I am one, achieved their superpuzzle of biological immortality. We created and snapped together the three pieces — the Twelve-Visions President, the depoliticized America, the Project Life. Moreover, we successfully tackled and snapped down the surprise fourth puzzle piece — Project Sustain Life. We always knew sustaining life would be an issue, but having spent our entire lives surrounded by mortals spellbound by the anticivilization, we were taken by surprise at the sudden, universal intensity of sustaining life.

"The desperate fight to sustain life, to *hang on* for Project Life, amplified the supreme value of conscious life beyond America, all around the world. Looking back, the Saving and Sustaining Life period, otherwise known as the SSL period, terminated any residual, perceived value in 'higher' authorities such as governments and religions. The SSL period terminated the ruling-class everywhere — to the four corners of Earth. Of course, 'higher' authorities could no longer survive in America once we ratified the Prime-Law Amendment and sold off the ruling-class government and replaced it with a super-competent protection service. 'Higher authorities' soon vanished around the world as other countries were quick to follow our lead. And it was Project Sustain Life that cleanly, completely finished the job. Imagine, if you can, an assault on conscious life once we entered the SSL period! Yet, some governments and religions around the world still tried to assume their 'higher' status than conscious life, just as they did in the anticivilization! Can you imagine? Of course, they got their 'higher' power through *conquering* and *plundering* the supreme value. Remember how governments and theocracies conquered and plundered the supreme value through fraud, force, and coercion? Almost as bad, remember how religions conquered and subjugated the supreme value through fraud, fear, and guilt? Well, the heart-wrenching SSL mission, to sustain every single life, so intensified the supreme value of the individual that the people terminated the last pockets of 'higher' authorities around the world, very quickly. In some cases, they literally exterminated those 'higher' authorities.

"And now, Project Sustain Life is behind us. In fact, I've finally returned to my next great challenge of doubling the height of New York City's beautiful Twin Towers. Indeed, The Group's superpuzzle is safely snapped down, and people no longer die...except for rare catastrophes, which are rapidly vanishing around the world as tens of millions of garage entrepreneurs and in-house entrepreneurs quickly eliminate risks in every imaginable endeavor. By the way, have you heard of the two new odds-tracking supercomputers timing the number of days to definitive immortality? One computer weighs millions of possible factors to give us the segment of time until the odds say we'll lose another human life. That predicted segment of time keeps getting longer every day. The second supercomputer projects the length of time before mankind achieves the technology that eradicates *catastrophic* death, our only remaining source of death. Perhaps that'll come from the millions of garage and in-house entrepreneurs — the geniuses of society — through a vast array of technologies that effectively eliminate essentially every possible fatal catastrophe. I'm betting that the definitive cure to catastrophic death will come from my soul mate and former classmate — the great Dr. Ian Scott. He's working on a single technology that could keep us from losing a loved one or self, no matter what catastrophe might strike, through electronically storing our minds and souls. But that's another story for another day. The predicted segment of time to eradicate catastrophic death keeps getting shorter. Now, think about this: the only source of death is catastrophic death. When the predicted length of time until a person dies next, which keeps getting longer every day, reaches the predicted segment of time until we eradicate catastrophic death, which keeps getting shorter every day...then the odds tell us no one else will die.

"That'll be *The Great Moment*. After The Great Moment, I'll drop the 'near' in 'near-immortals' when I greet you. For now, as long as there are fatal accidents, we'll all eventually die.

...Good-night, near-immortals."

*

With risks rapidly declining, longevity soaring, and few people now needing a Body II, sometimes people had to remind themselves in happy disbelief that they were actually *immortals*.

Those most aware of their immortality were the Body IIs, particularly those who had been hanging on by a respirator during Project Sustain Life. So, Jake and Jasmine met with several Body IIs in preparation of an article titled *Laughing In Unknown Territory*. The million Body IIs had gone where no man had gone before. Jake and Jasmine discovered no surprises.

"Body IIs are exhilarated and euphoric," the Patterson reporters wrote. "The world around them and the happiness within them just keeps getting better and better. With the Neothink mentality, they never run out of value creation and happiness. They never run out of love."

The conclusion of *Laughing In Unknown Territory* was: consciousness was designed for and destined for immortality.

Mankind had met his destiny.

*

As human death became a thing of the past, the conditions of the human race became more and more extraordinary. Every day things happened that made life better, from new technologies introduced into the world...to spectacular new forms of entertainment.

One of the new technologies to rise in the Twelve-Visions World was the anatomical adjustments to overcome the force of nature that made some people physically stunning and others repulsive, some beautiful and others ugly.

"Everyone should be physically attractive," Cathy explained when The Group convened at their favorite meeting place, Rico's mansion, on the eight-month anniversary of Operation II. "No, everyone should *be beautiful*."

As Cathy talked, Jake realized how natural this new

851

technology was. Not only did people, even and especially lifelong devoted spouses, rightfully care about looks and sexuality, but having just cured human death — by far the worst of the forces of nature — enormous research had gone into the human anatomy. Therefore, Neothink geniuses had abundant resources to use toward conquering another force of nature: the random chance of beauty, or lack of beauty, of the human body.

"People everywhere are taking their bodies in for their beauty/body adjustments," Natasha said. She nodded at Cathy. "Married couples can't believe how beautiful and sexy their spouses are becoming, which I can tell you is heating up their bedrooms!" Natasha laughed so contagiously that everyone in the room started laughing. Jake noticed Sally laughing.

"The Twelve-Visions World certainly is a physical world," Natasha continued, talking through a smile. "The Twelve-Visions World is also a very emotional world. People live with Nature's Quintessential Secret — as value *creators*. They're just *happy*. They're vibrant, they're *alive* with energy and feelings. As I foretold my listeners, the happy people have fallen madly in love again with their spouses."

Jake pondered the state of things that she described. Certainly the Twelve-Visions World was a prosperous world. Prices of the new technologies continued falling to fractions. In time, anyone could easily afford anything of value to oneself, including the face-and-body adjustments. The Twelve-Visions World was wonderfully physical, emotional, prosperous. And another thing, Jake realized, people had turned into very sensitive, loving individuals driven by love and compassion.

Jake wanted to tell The Group about an article that he and Jasmine were about to release, an epiphany titled *Believe It Or Not: We're Immortals!* describing the Twelve-Visions World. He and Jasmine were exceptionally excited about this article. He felt the moment was right to tell The Group about it. As he was gathering his thoughts, getting himself ready to speak, Jake looked again at the faces of Miss Annabelle's former students. He noticed how at ease they looked. The original twelve immortals, trapped in an anticivilization that would have killed them, took it upon themselves to free themselves from their death sentences...just as their teacher had hoped for. Now, as Sally had predicted at the reunion over six-and-a-half years before, there was *nothing* wrong with life. They were at peace.

"We've written our first article," Jake said to the relaxed group, "from the other side. I mean, from the immortal side. Jassy and I were almost freaking out, in a good way, writing this thing. For the first time, we really *felt* what it means to eternally experience what we named the *better-and-better phenomenon*. Everything just keeps getting *better and better, forever and ever!*

"What an asset life is — what a gift the future becomes! For the first time, we *felt it*...that this better-and-better phenomenon was *now ours — for eternity*. Man, if you think about it for long, it just blows your mind. Try imagining it."

Jake noticed the twelve former students were smiling at him, and he suddenly realized they had felt and anticipated these feelings ever since the reunion, over six-and-a-half years ago, whereas Jake was just getting hit with these feelings — these euphoric realizations of what immortality *really meant* — just now. ...Of course, he thought, these original twelve immortals, these twelve who fulfilled every child's deepest natural desire to live forever, who *made themselves* immortals, were the first to know the feeling of being an immortal. They actually knew it all their lives because they never went into the unnatural world of illusions. They stayed out of that anticivilization and were the first to carry out the primary mission of conscious life: to salvage and preserve the supreme value — conscious life — to never die. Every happy child since the beginning of conscious man wanted to live forever, Jake pondered, but that desire unnaturally disintegrated in adults as they hopelessly drifted into the anticivilization. But the desire never disintegrated in these twelve original immortals who never drifted into the anticivilization. They carried that life-mission into adulthood and rescued the supreme value — rescued themselves — and everyone else, too. At that moment, Jake felt a rush of love for these twelve people unlike anything he had felt before. *They saved me*, he thought. *They saved Jasmine and Jakey.*

These twelve knew the feeling of being immortal first; the *other* members of The Group, Jake realized, including Jasmine and himself, were the next to know what being an immortal in the Twelve-Visions World really felt like.

"The rest of the world has not shifted yet to our perspective," Jake continued. "Humanity will be helped along by our article. As they become capable to perceive...to absorb that this better-and-better phenomenon will be theirs *forever and ever*, they'll be filled with a permanent euphoria — the euphoria of being an immortal."

CHAPTER
NINETY

The Freedom Paradigm created during Daniel's presidency enabled new technologies to race forward at unprecedented, exponential speeds. Out of this Freedom Paradigm arose the next wave of computers — the quantum computers.

Ian had been isolated in his country home in Olean, New York since Operation II experimenting with his quantum computer, leaving only for the monthly meetings with The Group. Fifteen months after Operation II, during an October chilly spell, Ian called his wife into his home office in the middle of the night.

"Diana," he said as she came in wearing a soft, gray wool nightshirt, "storing the human mind onto one of these quantum computers will be relatively easy — that's not the problem. Capturing the I-ness — the person's soul, what makes him *him* — that's the problem."

"What do you mean?"

"Look at your arm. Go ahead, look at it."

Diana stared at her petite, left arm. "Touch your arm with your other hand. Go ahead. Now, squeeze your arm, and keep staring at it. That's it. Now, ask yourself, 'Is this arm *me*...my soul?' Does your arm contain your soul, your feelings, your thoughts, *you*."

Diana paused, then she dropped her arm and slowly looked

at Ian. "Hmmm," she said. "No…it's not *me*, not my thoughts and feelings."

"It's just part of the physical tool that carries *you*," said Ian. "Now, close your eyes and ask yourself, 'Who do *I* love?'"

"I don't have to ask; I love *you*," Diana said.

Ian laughed. "I know you do, precious. But close your eyes and ask yourself, anyway."

Diana closed her eyes and asked herself the question. Then she smiled. "I see what you're trying to tell me. *That's me.* That 'I' in 'Who do *I* love?' is *me*. That's *me*."

"Yes! That 'I' is your *I-ness*, your soul, your feelings, your thoughts, *you*," Ian said. "I can transfer the information in your brain to a cloned body, maybe right now. Everything will look and seem identical to those who know you. It'll have your personality, even your memories. But that clone — to *you* — will be sort of like your arm…it won't contain *you*, your I-ness. It won't be *you*, not to you. To her, yes — it will be her, but not to you. When you die, *you'll* be gone forever."

"Where does that leave your project?" Diana asked.

"I think that tonight, I've solved a piece to the puzzle of transferring the I-ness," Ian said. "I was stuck on how the I-ness could possibly be in two places or three at once — say, in the original person, then in the download onto a quantum computer, then in the download from the quantum computer into a clone. Going on the basis that the I-ness can be only in one place, otherwise it's not the same 'I', made me think this wouldn't be possible. But, now I think it can be explained."

"How?"

"Well, it gets into quantum physics, and it gets pretty technical. But let me just say that a subatomic particle, say an electron, can be at more than one place at any given time. It has to do with an electron being a charge affecting the molecule. That negative charge can exist in different places at once. If I can give the I-ness *a charge*, in theory I can activate it on the download into the clone, bringing back one's I-ness. The memories will be lost from the point of his download to the point of his death, but his I-ness will come to life in the clone. He'll be a few memories short, but it'll be *him*."

Diana was trying to imagine a person's I-ness dying, then

reappearing in the future somewhere else, alive again. The look on her face made Ian smile.

"I know it's not easy to understand. I'm not even sure how it'll work myself. I just sense there's something to this approach. I'll work on this a few more weeks...then maybe I'll be able to better understand and explain it."

"I love you, Ian." She gave him a loving kiss.

Ian went back to work. Diana sat in a chair and watched him for about an hour before she went back to bed. She knew he did not know she was still there, watching him. He was too caught up in his creation. She just loved to watch him sometimes, and secretly admire him.

*

"If there could only be two of me," Jeremiah whispered as he leaned back in his Jacuzzi. "How can I do this?"

A few minutes later, Maria darted from the back door to the Jacuzzi and quickly slipped into the Jacuzzi and cuddled against Jeremiah, giggling like a little girl. "It's so cold outside!" she said in her sexy Puerto Rican accent. "But as long as you have no place to go, let it snow!" She laughed, then kissed his cheek.

This is going to be so hard, Jeremiah thought, *for her and for me*.

Now that the SSL period was ending worldwide, Jeremiah and Sally knew they would come together into a swirling tornado of love. Jeremiah could not get himself to tell Maria. He *really loved* Maria. He did not doubt his decision, though, for Sally was his eternal soul mate. *But Maria...he'd find himself mourning...she's so innocent; sending her away is like sending away a child. I love Maria as a woman and a wife and a wonderfully innocent child. We're so happy together. How can I send her away? How can I do that to her?*

The thought made Jeremiah feel sick inside. *How can I hurt her? I can't hurt Maria. I can't!* A self-hatred for inflicting pain on Maria began pounding in Jeremiah's chest as he held his sweet Maria. Once again, he could not tell her.

Maria curled up against him and said, "Something's been bothering you, I know." She reached around his chest and hugged him in a gesture that showed she was there for him, to offer support.

Supporting me even now, Jeremiah cried inside, *always giving every bit of herself to me.* Jeremiah looked into Maria's totally devoted, completely giving eyes. He nearly cried. She was *his*, one-hundred percent *his*, forever...in some ways, like a beloved daughter. Looking into her eyes and seeing her complete love caused an invisible hand to clutch his throat and squeeze it until he could barely breathe. *Ah*, he thought behind his sad eyes, *I really love her, too.*

*

The next day, Jeremiah went into the city to see Al Patterson, who always felt like a brother to Jeremiah. The wind outside sent a biting chill through him.

One of the most sought-after bachelors in the country, Al had a similar background with women as Jeremiah. Al knew how rare it was in the past for a Civilization-of-the-Universe soul to find a soul mate in the anticivilization.

Jeremiah arrived at Al's plush penthouse a block away from the Patterson Building. Once inside, Al could see Jeremiah was troubled. They sat across from each other in the den.

Jeremiah could not find the words to talk, so Al broke the ice. "You're in love with Sally," he said.

"Yes, more than I can describe," Jeremiah confessed.

"Then why are you troubled?"

After a moment, Jeremiah said, "Because I can't leave Maria. She's too innocent and wonderful to hurt like that." Jeremiah's eyes darted around the room. Al remained quiet. "Before I saved Maria from the fire six years ago, I'd been with several women, many of whom I met through my church. But with each one, as I began to reveal my deepest soul of not accepting death and my desire to eliminate death, I knew she could not go there with me spiritually or emotionally. I increasingly felt empty. My woman would feel a sort of fear knowing she could not emotionally fulfill me. ...You know how it is."

Al nodded as Jeremiah continued, "But who could? I began to wonder, who would I feel eternally happy with? I lived in the Civilization of the Universe, and just about no one else did.

"Then I saved Maria from the fire, and my world changed. Every time I looked at her, I felt a surge of happiness in the knowledge that this beautiful life still existed because of me. Every time I saw her happy eyes, every time I heard her laugh, my whole insides would become full of euphoria. All that beautiful happiness would not exist, I'd reflect over and over, if I hadn't saved her.

"Maria never feared me, even when I revealed my deepest feelings to her. She loved me with every pore of her body and would go anywhere with me, even into the Civilization of the Universe. She made herself feel what I felt in order to share everything with me and to support my passion. And I *was* able to feel and share my passion with her. ...You know how rare that was."

Again, Al nodded, and Jeremiah continued, "Imagine her believing she was going to die a horrible death, and at the last moment being spared death. That experience gave her a special appreciation of life that broke her through to the other side — the natural side all young children feel — to where she did not accept death or ever want to die.

"She was a simple cleaning woman who had a hard life of hard labor. Being the oldest of five children, she left school at ten years of age in Puerto Rico to clean hotel rooms and bring money into the family. She did the same once she and her family arrived here.

"But even with a hard life, she was *always* sparkling and happy. She *really loved* her parents and siblings. And they loved her."

Jeremiah stopped an instant before his voice cracked. He cleared his throat and continued, "I love this happy and loving nature about her. When I rescued her and her family from their hard life, she fully devoted herself to me. To this day, she supports everything I do. She works hard to make my life efficient and smooth. She gets out of bed before me every morning to fix me a healthy breakfast, prepare my clothes, organize my reading materials. Maria's a very organized person, and she speaks quite good English. She works hard every day as my personal secretary. As she learns my work, she takes care of more and more minor things in my schedule to free me up for more important business. My efficiency has improved, I estimate, by thirty to forty percent since Maria moved in with me. No matter how stressed out I get, just looking at her calms me down inside and fills me with peace and love...every day, many times a day, for six years now."

Jeremiah lifted his eyes to look at Al. "How can I *leave her?* How can I do that *to her?* How can I do that *to me?* I...I can't."

Al did not know how to answer. He could see how much Jeremiah loved Maria, although Sally was his eternal soul mate.

*

"Maria?" Jeremiah said that evening when he walked into his New Jersey home, just outside of Manhattan, "Maria, I'm home."

She always ran to the entryway to greet him. For the first time, she did not instantly appear.

"Maria?" Jeremiah called out. Still he heard no sound in the house. Then, he saw an envelope on the banister addressed to him. He picked it up and pulled the handwritten note out of it. He knew the handwriting was Maria's. He read the short message out loud:

"I know about you and Sally. I must go. I'm very, very sad right now. Please, do not look for me. I love you."

"Oh, my precious!" Jeremiah yelled, dropping the note and putting his hands against his head, "I'm so goddamn sorry!" He imagined the pain she was going through and clinched his fists, filling his hands with his hair. He pulled his hair hard and screamed, "Ahhhh...I HATE MYSELF!"

Jeremiah called Maria's cell phone. No answer. He called her parents. No answer. He rushed to the LaGuardia Airport and got on the next flight to Wilmington. He knew Maria's mom would know where her daughter was. He suspected Maria was with her parents. He could not think of anything but finding Maria, and comforting her.

Beholding the Puzzle-Picture

When he got there, Jeremiah ran into the home he had bought for Maria's parents. He was dazed and forgot to knock.

"Maria! Maria!" he called through the house for his devoted love. "Maria, please answer me!"

"Hello, Jeremiah," Maria's mother said gently as she came in from the back of the house. "Jeremiah, honey, Maria's not here."

"Ma...I must find her. Please tell me where she is."

"Oh, Jeremiah," Ma said, reaching for Jeremiah's face and rubbing the hair back from his sad eyes, "you really love my daughter."

"Please Ma, where is she?"

"Don't you understand?" She looked into Jeremiah's eyes. "No, you don't, so I must tell you. Come...sit down."

Jeremiah sat on the couch, and Maria's mother sat next to him.

"She LOVES you, Jeremiah," Ma said, stressing the word *love* in her Puerto Rican accent. Although her accent was thick, she had worked hard to expand her English vocabulary. "Maria loves you too much to stop you from your soul mate — the other child of the Civilization of the Universe. Maria knows you're not able to leave her. So, she left you because this must be. Jeremiah," Maria's mom put her hand on his hand, "*your* happiness is the most important thing in the world to Maria. Don't you see — it's the ultimate love. She figured it all out and knew you could not leave her, so she left you so you could go to Sally — your *eternal* soul mate."

Jeremiah closed his eyes and leaned back in the couch, stunned, sad, lifeless, and he listened.

"Maria told me you would not stop looking for her until you found her. And she knows once you found her, you wouldn't be able to leave her, nor could she leave you. Jeremiah, you *must* let her go." Suddenly, Ma took Jeremiah's hand in hers and her voice got firm. "Maria said if you look for her, she'll leave the country and never come back in order to set you free to love Dr. Salberg. I know my daughter, and she'll do it, Jeremiah. She loves you so much." Tears quietly fell from Jeremiah's closed eyes as he listened, "You must not look for her, son. You must let her go. This is what she wants."

"But—"

"Shhh...she'll not let herself stand in the way of the love she knows you'll be happiest with. This is her ultimate gift to you, Jeremiah. Take it. Take it for her and go...go to Sally."

*

Jeremiah had fallen asleep on his couch. For days, Jeremiah relived in his mind his memories with Maria, starting with the day he saved her life. Often, he would break down during a memory and cry.

"So much turmoil," Sally whispered. She sat in the chair and watched him sleeping. His face, she sadly noticed, did not look peaceful and happy as it should, as he deserved. *Is there a way Maria and I can share Jeremiah?* She shook her head. Two lovers would not be right for him, she thought, for the amount of time needed for *two* romantic relationships would hamper his drive to create world-changing values and *especially hurt his goal and mine to definitively end human death.*

She got out of the chair and slipped onto the couch next to her troubled man. She lightly rubbed her fingers from just above his eyebrows back over his forehead and back through his hair. "Oh, my darling," she whispered upon noticing he had fallen asleep with a frown on his face, "I'm so sorry."

For weeks, every night when he fell asleep he would think of Maria. Often, at the point of dozing off, he would imagine himself as two people, living two lives — one with Maria and one with Sally.

Things got very confusing because Sally felt she just couldn't take him away from Maria, even though Sally loved him too much to stay away from him. He felt these feelings, too. But, they could not separate from each other.

*

"Sally?" Jeremiah said, rushing into her penthouse. "Look at this! Look, it's a letter from Maria addressed to both of us." He tore it open. He looked at the letter for a moment before sitting next to Sally.

Jeremiah cleared his voice and began to read out loud:

"My dearest Jeremiah and Sally,

"I love you very, very much Jeremiah. I love you, too, Sally because you and Jeremiah are soul mates. You have been soul mates for thirty-four years, ever since you were just children. And you will be soul mates *forever*.

"I cannot tell you it doesn't break my heart to let you go, Jeremiah, because it does. It really does. Every morning I wake up early and am heartbroken because you're not next to me sleeping like an angel. You're not there for me to cook your breakfast and get you ready to go out and improve the world. You're not in my life to take care of you. I loved taking care of your every need, my darling. I'm heartbroken when you don't come home to me at the end of the day. I still look for you, every morning, every day, every night. Jeremiah, my love, *I miss you*. My fingers, my arms, my heart screams for you all day and all night. Every part of me cries, *come home to me! Come home to me, my love!*"

"Oh, Maria," Jeremiah said. He wiped the tears from his eyes and continued.

"I know you're very sad right now, my darling, because I know how sensitive you are. Oh, how I want to hold you and soothe you. And I know you are fighting back tears, too, Sally. I could never be angry with you, because *you* are Jeremiah's eternal soul mate. To be angry with you would be to be angry with him, and I could never be angry with him. I want you to know something that was hard for me to understand at first: Dr. Sally Salberg...I love you, too. I love you for being the one person in this world who will make Jeremiah feel the heights of happiness he deserves. I love you because you have the same soul as Jeremiah. With him, you will reach the heights of happiness *you* deserve."

Jeremiah had to stop reading. He could see Maria's innocent face as he read her letter. He could imagine her voice, telling him this. And by imagining her telling him this, he could hear the pain in her voice and see the sadness in her eyes. And what hurt the most was, as he imagined her telling him this, she was not touching him. All their years together, whenever they talked, whenever they worked through a problem, she would always be hugging him or holding his hand.

"Sally," Jeremiah said hoarsely, "could you finish reading this to me?"

Sally was overcome with emotion. "Of course, precious," she barely whispered. She took Maria's letter from Jeremiah's trembling hand; Sally cleared her throat and read the rest of it to him:

"I know it is hard for you and for Sally not to feel sad about me. I can help you here so you can get on with your relationship and the happiness you two so deserve. Jeremiah, my darling, although this will not happen for quite some time, realize that I can someday be happy with someone else. You two, though, MUST have each other. You two *are one* in your mission to stop human life from dying. The human race, including me, has been saved by the two of you with the help of The Group. There's a new kind of love in the world now — *eternal love.* I will not stand between you because no one else is as good for you in this new world of eternal love as each other. But me...as hard as it is for me to believe this right now...I will someday be able to be happy with another man. Although I cannot feel this way now, I know it is true.

"I'll someday see you two again. But that will not happen until I'm genuinely happy with someone, so all of us can be happy and share good feelings.

"Please, *please*...do not look for me. We all know this is the right decision for all of us. Yet if you were standing before me, my beloved Jeremiah, I could never have the strength to let you go. So I beg you, for my sanity, do not look for me Jeremiah, not even in your thoughts. Turn now to Sally. Look into her eyes and promise yourself, for me, that she is now the only one. Today, start your journey together and know that your happiness, Jeremiah and Sally, will make me happy and will help me to rise again.

"The sun is setting on our life together, Jeremiah. That is very sad, I know. Oh, how I looked forward to having children with you! ...But a beautiful sunrise has begun for you and Sally. It is time for you to enjoy that beauty. In time, I will see a beautiful sunrise again, too.

"Good-bye, my darling. From every part of me, thank you. *Thank you* for the most wonderful years beyond anything I ever knew could exist. Thank you, my love, for saving my life. Thank you for making me always feel as though I was the most important thing in your life. It was all so wonderful. And thank you for all you have done for my family. From deep inside my heart, *thank you* my love. ...You and Sally are incredible people, and I'll love you both, forever. Your eternal admirer, Maria."

Sally could hold her emotions in no longer; she bowed her head and cried. She scooted closer to Jeremiah. He was crushed. Sally reached over and rubbed Jeremiah's hair and kissed his head. "What a beautiful person she is," Sally softly said, knowing the dear loss from Jeremiah's life. Jeremiah quietly cried and nodded. Then, they did what Maria asked of them: they turned to each other. Jeremiah reached for Sally, and they held each other. And then they cried in each others' arms; they cried for Maria who had no one to hold.

CHAPTER
NINETY-ONE

"If there ever were a man who, in the old world, seemed to have already reached the highest peaks of value creation," Jake and Jasmine's article began, "that man would be Theodore Winters. But to the contrary, in the new world, he blossomed. He breaks through to the next level so effectively that he usually works without competition. He recognizes and anticipates changes. By the time a major need hits civilization, oftentimes Mr. Winters provides the paradigm shift to the next level.

"And he has done it again: in this politically free world, he saw a unique phenomenon occurring in business. Consider as people become their own garage entrepreneurs or in-house entrepreneurs at their places of work, in their mini-companies, they become more and more independent, running and building their jobs, their mini-companies, on their own through their own integrating minds. At the same time, as people become more and more self-reliant, they are more and more dependent on other mini-companies for the support structure, acting as contractors, service companies, and suppliers. The business world is interlocking, largely through the web, and forming the supersociety. This phenomenon, this seeming contradiction of greater individual independence yet at the same time greater individual interdependence, is actually no contradiction at all.

No, it is one of those new properties of the supersociety that could not exist before in the anticivilization. Through this independence/interdependence phenomenon, Neothink superpuzzles are forming as working men and women turn into entrepreneurs — into creators — and begin integrating their business needs.

"Seeing this phenomenon, Mr. Winters developed phenomenally powerful internet programming that allows one person to run a major company, all by himself, by deeply integrating throughout the entire business world. For example, a major publishing company can be run by one person at his website, interacting with dozens of other websites involving all the responsibilities including printing websites, distribution websites, fulfillment websites, shipping websites, customer service websites, writers' websites, accounting websites, all of which are run by their own entrepreneurs, integrating with others through Mr. Winter's system.

"Mr. Winter's original invention of the division of essence or, perhaps more accurately, the *division of Friday-Night essences* has led to this entrepreneurial world that maximizes mind and motivation. From everyone's deepest motivational root grows the supersociety. Each person becomes the fiercely independent creator, yet his or her business snaps into the superpuzzles of the supersociety through Mr. Winter's latest invention, this brilliant software system."

Shortly after releasing his supersociety software, it captured nearly the entire business world, for every business, every entrepreneur had to have the software to function dramatically better.

"I've decided to rename my supersociety internet program, simply, *Business*," Theodore announced to The Group during a monthly meeting at Rico's, shortly after releasing the software. Until then, it had been packaged as Winter's Supersociety Software.

"*Business?*" questioned Reggie. "Isn't that a bit general? If you're going to rename it, why not something a little more sexy...something like Software of the God-Man or Software of the Superpuzzles?"

"Hey, I like those names, Reggie," said Theodore, "and

you're right, *Business* sounds a bit general and a bit dry. But I've realized, *Business* is not just a name — it's what the software *actually is*.

"Consider that the superpuzzles, such as Project Life among others, are the manifestations of our supreme love for conscious life. Now consider that the garage entrepreneurs and the in-house entrepreneurs, those value creators who make up nearly the entire workforce, create the pieces to the superpuzzles. Now, you need something to connect the value creators to the superpuzzles. You need some dynamic process to snap their pieces into those puzzles. That dynamic process has always been: *business*. And now, in our Twelve-Visions World, it is my supersociety software fulfilling that dynamic process. Through its efficiency, the whole world — all the entrepreneurs — are turning to my supersociety software to snap together their value creations, their puzzle pieces, into Neothink puzzles and superpuzzles...to perform *business*. Not only is there no better way, there's no *other* way to define my software other than *Business*."

Jake sat in stunned silence. Back in the anticivilization, Theodore had created the paradigm shift of business from the division-of-labor to the division-of-essence. Now, in the Civilization of the Universe, Theodore had created *business* itself. Indeed, supreme love and value creation — that is, the superpuzzles and the value creators — drove the Civilization of the Universe. And *Business* made it all work.

*

Jake and Jasmine visited Theodore and Cathy in one of their half-dozen luxurious homes. Jake and Jasmine wanted to get a deeper understanding of the power behind Theodore's division-of-Friday-Night-essence internet program *Business* that enabled everyone to easily become an effective entrepreneur on his or her Friday-Night essence. They also wanted to personally tour Cathy's newest sensation: a *Business* resort.

Theodore and Cathy's beautiful home sat in the Laguna Hills overlooking Laguna Beach, California. Jake had been there before, but Theodore's office looked different, beautifully different.

Facing a curved glass wall that overlooked the town, beach, and ocean, stood one charcoal grey chair on a pole with electronically adjustable footrests. Attached to the chair was a computer keyboard and a large computer.

"I can sit in that chair and face any direction with the push of a button," Theodore said. "Of course, the computer and keyboard move with the swiveling chair."

"Where's the other computers...and all the books?" Jake asked. He remembered the stacks of books and papers the last time he was there. At least ten computers filled the room back then, and the walls were lined with books.

"Got rid of 'em all," Theodore replied. "My new supersociety software obsoleted my need for computers and storage memory. I used to think it was impressive to run my empire through a dozen computers. Now I only need *that*," he said, pointing to the futuristic chair and workstation. "I even cleared out my books; they're all on line and easier for me to read on the new optic-friendly screen. I like the research options I get by reading on-line."

Jake was amazed that the world's most powerful man could run his empire from *a single chair*.

"It's the ultimate in comfort," Theodore said. He chuckled. "I can even tilt it back and sleep on it for a short night's sleep if I'm pushing on a project."

Jake looked at Theodore and remembered someone once saying that striking contrasts made beautiful art. Jake thought about the contrast of this man. Theodore was small, only about five-foot, seven inches tall. He weighed only about 150 pounds. But he created more values for mankind and commanded more respect and power than perhaps anyone who ever lived.

"So, you conduct most of your business right here?" Jasmine asked.

"That's changing some, lately," Cathy answered. Jake saw a proud look on her face. He and Jasmine knew what she had been developing from articles in the local Patterson Paper.

"My wife's started something wonderful that's really changing my working environment," Theodore explained, "and *I like it*. I think it's going to be big. And it works so well with my new supersociety software. ...I'll let you explain it, my love,"

Theodore said, looking at Cathy.

"Instead of explaining it, why don't we show it to them?"

"We'd love to go," Jasmine said. So, the four of them climbed in Cathy's large Mercedes, and she drove them for about ten minutes to the place where she and Theodore spent two or three days a week while in California.

*

"It's beautiful in here," Jasmine said as they turned onto a small country road and drove past rolling green lawns, ponds, waterfalls, and picturesque woods filled with large, colorful trees.

"Our unique underground irrigation system enables us to simulate the woods and plush vegetation seen on the East Coast," Cathy said. "And our warm, Southern California weather causes those beautiful deciduous trees to change in November." The leaves were turning, and freshly fallen multi-color leaves covered the sidewalks.

People were jogging or walking or riding bikes on the trails that wove through and around the woods. Others were playing golf on the lush course that aesthetically blended with the rolling hills and creeks and flowed through the woods. *It all looks like a beautiful, three-dimensional painting,* Jake thought.

Jake noticed that many of the people were in pairs or groups of three or four as they did their activities...and they seemed to be in passionate discussions. Some, however, were alone. They looked happy and focussed on exciting thoughts.

After a five-minute drive along the winding road, they arrived at the buildings in the center...grand, open buildings with walls of flagstone, surrounded by pine trees and ash trees.

The place looks and smells like a country-club resort, Jake thought. He walked inside one of the three large buildings. Upon sweeping his eyes around once, Cathy's conception clicked in Jake's mind.

"Genius!" he shouted.

The big picture hit Jake instantly, and he was in love with the place: looking to his left through a glass wall were two-hundred charcoal grey chairs on poles with workstations, identical to Theodore's chair and workstation at home. About half the chairs were occupied.

To his right, open and exposed to everyone was a large state-of-the-art exercise room. And beyond that exercise room was a glass wall facing a large, elaborate outdoor swimming pool with waterfalls, Jacuzzis, an indoor/outdoor patio café. The pool area looked like a tropical paradise. Although the autumn air was chilly, Jake noticed people in their bathing suits outside. The outdoor pool area circulated warm air by convection. Adults and children swam, played, and visited.

"The swimming pool!" exclaimed Jasmine. "I read about that at Patterson Online. It just opened two days ago. It's exciting to see!" Swimming pools had been closed and filled in and would have stayed that way until curing catastrophic death.

"Wow, the first reopened pool in the country," said Jake. "I read you developed a device to prevent catastrophic death from drowning." ...As Jake spoke about the pool, his mind continued absorbing the big picture of the business resort.

"So you read about *MyLifeSaver*?" said Cathy.

"I saw it in the article," Jake answered, "but tell me how it works." He continued looking around.

"Here, I'll show you," Cathy said. She walked across the entryway to a counter and picked up one of the many rubber-like wristbands. Jake studied it. He saw noticeable lumpy bulges around its middle and metallic polka-dots around its top and bottom.

"One of our own in-house entrepreneurs, Louis Vanderbilt, created it," Cathy explained. "Each person who enters the pool area is fitted with this simple bracelet, his very own MLS or MyLifeSaver. His MLS bracelet is equipped with special sensors and software that register pulse and breathing patterns. If a person gets into a problem, the MLS bracelet discharges an ingeniously designed flotation that inflates so tall it literally pulls the swimmer by his wrist safely above and out of the water, and it emits a loud alarm for our several highly-trained lifeguards. A team of statisticians studied our pool area and determined essentially no chance of a drowning."

"The beauty of in-house and garage entrepreneurs," Jake said.

"Louis Vanderbilt..." said Jasmine, "isn't that the creator of the new jewelry line—"

"Yes," said Cathy, "he's the same in-house entrepreneur who invented the new smart-jewelry everyone's starting to wear now."

"You're kidding," said Jasmine. "I'm wearing one right now, see?" She pulled an attractive, polished stone necklace from under her brown turtleneck.

"Yes, that's a Louis Vanderbilt creation," said Cathy. "It's already saved several people, especially elderly people, from hard, potentially fatal falls. The smart-jewelry is equipped with special computer software that can determine the difference between fast coordinated movements versus a fall. Upon registering a fall, the airbags deploy and, in your case, protects the head."

Jake took a deep breath and looked around. People were everywhere. Those people were entrepreneurs using Theodore's new software, creating their values for the world, exhilarated by their Friday-Night essences. If they were not working, they were visiting one another or spending time with their children. Jake walked around. He found a daycare center filled with fun and educational games. He smiled and nodded. He thought, I love what I see.

"It's Cathy's project," Theodore said. "When I found myself liking it, I knew it was the wave of the future."

Jake nodded and smiled...a *Business* resort.

"Are you hungry?" asked Cathy.

Jake was too absorbed to answer. Jasmine laughed and said, "We're starving."

They walked across the walkway to a large, gourmet restaurant with a breathtaking view of the golf course, gardens, fountains, and countryside.

"Come on," Cathy said. "The fountain show is about to begin." They went upstairs to the second floor with a panoramic view of the entire grounds. Jake realized the restaurant sat on top of a hill. As they sat down for dinner in the packed restaurant, the water fountains suddenly burst fifty feet into the air and danced synchronously to majestic opera music.

"This place is happening," Jake said as they settled in their seats. People were engaged in passionate, exciting discussions. Jake strained his ears to listen in on some of those discussions at the tables around him. He heard people talking about creating new values that never existed before. He looked around, completely absorbed in his surroundings again. Finally, he nodded and smiled. "I feel right at home here," he uttered.

"Pretty soon, you can literally be at home here," Cathy said. She winked at Jake and smiled. Jake realized that this place, such a beautiful place filled with passionate value creation, was a personification of Cathy — such a beautiful woman filled with passionate value creation. Jake realized that, if he stopped and just looked at her, the moment amplified her beauty.

"What brought about this fabulous creation?" he asked Cathy.

"You know about my childhood," Cathy answered. "I was a fat kid and a social outcast. Midway through my year with Miss Annabelle, that started to change. Ever since that year, even though I couldn't express it as a child, it's always been clear to me that man is a social animal. One day, I was watching Ted sitting in his office, all alone, all day long...and I felt something was terribly missing. He seemed so isolated. He didn't seem to mind, though, because he was excited about his creations. But I knew a crucial ingredient was missing. The monthly meetings of The Group at Rico's were so refreshing and so productive. Those productive weekends at Rico's started me realizing how much Teddy gained at those meetings. Those meetings seemed to fill him up with fuel, both creative and emotional fuel. Also, the love he felt at those monthly gatherings was so deserved.

"When Teddy developed the new software, I realized he freed nearly everyone to conduct business anywhere, anytime. That's when the idea of the business resort was born. Instead of isolating oneself at home, he can thrust himself into a place full of stimulating people and energy."

Theodore nodded. "It's a beautiful marriage of the virtual world and the tangible world," he said.

"Yes...yes it is," Jake said, looking around him inside the gourmet restaurant and then looking out through the glass wall, out over the soothing scenery of lakes, trees, creeks, and rolling lawns being tucked in for the night by a puffy, pink sunset. "You spend two or three days a week here?"

"Yes. I've identified three major advantages I get here. First, I meet a lot of value creators on spectacular vectors. I've generated more business in two months than I would have in two years before. Second, I just enjoy, as Cathy was expressing, sharing an environment with other value creators. Even if I'm not socializing, it's stimulating being around them. And the third advantage gets very personal. Remember that time in the hospital room after Rico was shot?"

"I'll never forget it," Jake said.

"Remember the LOVE in that room?"

"I'll *never* forget it."

"In the business club, whether interacting with others or keeping to myself, I feel that same LOVE. I know those value creators are creating vital Neothink puzzle pieces to important superpuzzles that'll greatly benefit me and my loved ones. They're all in there working hard and integrating their lives around their creations. The love I feel in there is so rewarding, Jake. ...I don't get that same supersociety stimulation working alone."

Jake knew exactly what Theodore was talking about, for Jake's job brought him in contact with many value creators. Jake knew about that feeling of love.

"When you feel that love," Theodore continued, "then all of a sudden, life seems so simple."

Jake took a moment to look closely at Theodore, leading perhaps the most complex life of any man alive. He sat peacefully, leaning back in his chair, relaxed, enjoying his company, absorbing the moment.

"Simple?" Jasmine said.

"Simple," Theodore said. He nodded and took a sip of his iced tea.

Jake and Jasmine looked at him, waiting for an explanation.

"Love," he said while putting down his drink, "drives civilization. The superpuzzles are born out of love for conscious life. You two wrote about that in a recent article."

"Are any born out of pursuing profits?" Jake asked, interrupting Theodore, but wanting to clarify that point.

"No," Theodore said. "The superpuzzles themselves go beyond an individual or a business. They're conceived out of love for mankind's well-being. Individuals and businesses contribute to the superpuzzles, which, by the way, are where the profits go — to the individuals for their contributions toward

874

building the superpuzzles. But the superpuzzles themselves are bigger than the individuals and the businesses that build the superpuzzles. The superpuzzles themselves are beyond their builders and beyond their profits. The superpuzzles *are* love."

Jake was nodding. He understood perfectly.

"The individuals and businesses — that is, the 'garage' entrepreneurs and the in-house entrepreneurs, who make up nearly 100% of the workforce now — *build* those superpuzzles of love. The entrepreneurs are the value creators. ...So far," Theodore's eyes were twinkling as he looked at Jake, "how does civilization shape up?"

"Uh..." Jake uttered, a little off guard, "superpuzzles of love...uh...and...entrepreneurs of value creation?"

"Precisely!" Theodore looked pleased at Jake's answer. "Now, do you remember how we bring the two together?"

Assuming the pupil's role, Jake smiled because he knew the answer.

"Business!" he said proudly. "Your *Business*."

Theodore leaned forward as though he were confiding in Jake, Jasmine, and Cathy. The consummate businessman then passionately continued, "Don't you see, the progress of civilization, of *human life*, snaps together into a simple three-piece puzzle: *love* creates the superpuzzles, *value creators* build the pieces, *business* brings the pieces to the superpuzzles. The progress of life is a simple three-piece puzzle. I realized its simplicity while sitting here, watching these value creators building the world's superpuzzles, and doing it all through my supersociety software, *Business*."

*

Cathy named her business resort, simply, *Paradise*. The success of Paradise grew so quickly that she made plans to increase the CEO chairs and workstations from 200 to 1000 within the first few months. She also planned to build a luxury hotel on the premises so people could enjoy extended stays.

At the next meeting of The Group, Daniel, who had recently visited Paradise, told the members of a sweeping vision.

"Cathy's Paradise incorporates *the mind* through the

workstations equipped with Theodore's supersociety software. Cathy's Paradise incorporates *the body* with a state-of-the-art gym, running and riding trails, and other physical recreations. Cathy's Paradise incorporates *the soul* with its open format for socializing and interacting with other value creators and loved ones. After spending a few days in Paradise, I became a believer: *everyone* should live this way. In fact, everyone would want to after experiencing the creative atmosphere, the fluid value exchanges, and the stimulating respect and love for one another. It was just so rewarding. What Cathy has successfully done is to maximize one's emotional integration with one's value creation.

"So, Cathy and Theodore," Daniel continued, directing his attention to them, "I've developed a proposal for you: I want to build a master-planned community — twelve-hundred custom lots and six-hundred luxurious residential tract homes throughout your Paradise."

"That'll be spectacularly successful," Theodore said. He had probably the best judgment in picking winning marketing ideas of anyone alive. "What greater attraction could there be for a place to live?"

"Your new internet software, *Business*, is ultimately what makes everything work; it's the nucleus that pulls it all together," Daniel said. "Residents of these communities will go to work, as you do Theodore, in the business club's Entrepreneur Center, two, three, or four times a week — whenever they want to be around others. The Entrepreneur Center holds together the business club, and the business club will hold together the community. The mind/body/soul business resort is what will make the community so attractive to live in."

Theodore reflected for a moment, then said, "With your experience building luxury communities before you were President, and with your vision, teaming up with Cathy's business resort and my software...this'll be *dynamite*."

Cathy said, "Let's go over your proposal tonight!"

*

Theodore, Cathy, and Daniel had earlier said that any

members of The Group who wanted to attend were welcome to come to the meeting. They all came to hear about the powerful new living concept in the new supersociety. Theodore was taken aback by the scope of Daniel's vision.

"Building a master-planned community in Paradise is just the beginning — Phase One of a three-phase vision," Daniel said to open his intriguing proposal. "In Phase Two, I envision building Paradise communities around the world. Phase Three of my vision goes a step beyond the master-planned communities. I envision self-sustaining '*master* master-planned communities' that include grocery stores, shopping malls, restaurants, cinemas and other entertainment and sports complexes. Cathy's business resorts will be the common denominators that pull people together, around which *self-sufficient* communities can grow...and eventually *cities* can grow."

Cities? Jake asked himself in amazement. *Paradise Cities!*

"Theodore's software is the nucleus that enables people to go to the business clubs day after day. The business clubs enable the community to form, the community enables the stores, malls, restaurants, cafes, entertainment and sports complexes to form, and eventually the cities to form. Someday, everyone would want to live there."

Jake was in awe. He knew Daniel well, and Jake knew Daniel had captured a neothink vision. He sees an entire new living paradigm, Jake thought, for he said *everyone* would want to live there. Jake nodded and pondered how once again these people took every value before them, such as Paradise, and maximized the value to its awesome potential, such as Paradise Cities where most people eventually would live!

"I believe entertainment and sports will continue to flourish in the supersociety," Daniel was saying, "and I'm including them in my designs for *Paradise Cities*."

That comment made Jake remember that in previous articles, he had written that good entertainment would thrive in the supersociety for two very important reasons: First, quality entertainment provided enjoyable avenues to spend time together with loved ones. Second, quality entertainment brought people genuine pleasure as reflection of the heroic nature of the God-Man. People worked hard at their value creations, and

877

entertainment such as a good movie or play or symphony, brought them rewarding value reflections. A good movie or play, for example, metaphorically reflected to God-Man his own challenges that he himself overcame.

Jake reflected on how surprised he was, however, by the survival and revival of sports in the Twelve-Visions World. As civilization made the leap into the Civilization of the Universe, he always felt in the back of his mind, without giving it much thought, that sports would wane and eventually die out. He figured sports was a *physical* activity and people in the Civilization of the Universe were interested in using their *minds*. But as sports flourished, Jake got to the bottom of *why* they did, and he wrote a popular article about it called *Why Sports Will Never Die.*

As he reflected on his famous article, he remembered realizing that sports were metaphors for the competitive drive and challenges people experienced as value creators. Watching athletes compete with every last ounce of will and determination they could muster, sprinkled us with a reflection and an appreciation of ourselves and our own determination to succeed over our challenges.

Jake remembered that, while writing his article *Why Sports Will Never Die,* he realized *why* the survival and revival of sports surprised him so: he had previously viewed *physical* sports as he would a *physical* job in the old division-of-labor job structure. He did not view sports as *metaphorical entertainment*...legitimate, good value reflection for value creators.

The reason for a sports *revival*, ironically, was in the nature of going from a mortal life to an immortal life. Life was open ended. Teenagers and young adults could make a sound decision to spend a decade mastering a sport and competing for the experience. "Becoming immortals," Jake wrote, "is full of surprises."

However, Body IIs showed no interest in performing in competitive sports. They were too into their value creations. They were soaring on their Friday-Night essences. Competing in sports could not satisfy them, no matter how young and healthy their new bodies were.

Suddenly, Jake shook his head.

What am I doing? He realized he was not hearing Daniel. Jake forced himself to stop thinking and start listening.

"I envision the Paradise Cities eventually as, in essence, 'mini-cities'," Daniel was saying, "that'll begin to spring up in clusters around each other to form larger counties that support ever larger mega entertainment complexes including larger shopping malls, multitudes of restaurant rows, luxurious cinemas, and elaborate sports parks, amusement parks, and theme parks of many variations. There'll always be exciting places for loved ones to go and spend time together."

"Bravo!" Theodore yelled while clapping. Everyone in the room applauded. "I've always loved your sweeping visions. I loved your Twelve Visions six years ago of a completely new world — the Twelve-Visions World that has now prevailed. And I love your three-phase vision today of the Paradise Cities. Oh yeah, they'll prevail, for as you said earlier, the Paradise Cities truly maximize the integration of people's personal lives with their exciting value creations. I also love your office-in-the-clouds vision of doubling the height of our city skylines. How's that progressing? And, how does that fit in with the new Paradise City concept?"

"To answer your first question, Ted, the progress is going wonderfully," said Daniel. "We'll actually start construction on the Twin Towers soon. Now, to answer your second question...how will our current cities fit in with the new Paradise Cities? There'll be a major migration of people to the Paradise Cities. However, to remain competitive, I believe the current cities will eventually evolve to bring in the attributes of the Paradise Cities. In fact, I'm not just the General Contractor of the Twin Towers project. I have a major equity position and am the most influential member on the development team. The added top half of the Twin Towers will, in themselves, be Paradise Cities! It's my breakthrough concept in skyscraper development. In both towers, I'll develop an Entrepreneur Center surrounded by its Business Resort, surrounded by luxury condos-in-the-clouds living, surrounded by many choices of entertainment from movie theaters to bowling alleys, ice skating, quality Broadway plays, shopping centers, grocery stores...all in the added top half, high in the sky. A person would never have to leave, if he so chose."

"I really love everything you're doing," said Theodore. Several members of The Group nodded and made enthusiastic remarks on Daniel's neothinking.

Daniel smiled. He almost felt embarrassed by The Group's accolades. He looked at Cathy and Theodore for a few moments, his partners-to-be in the forthcoming Paradise Cities, and completed the extent of his vision.

"The mind/body/soul perfection of our Paradise Cities will make them *the* place to live. I can see a great exodus from both rural and urban communities to our Paradise Cities. Because of Theodore's internet software, the greater portion of the populace will no longer need to live in large cities. And, people will no longer want to live in suburbs with little or no social connection between the residences, not having been designed around the business clubs. More and more people will relocate to our Paradise Cities and function better both financially and emotionally. Our Paradise Cities will redefine the housing and living structure of our country and the world."

I knew it, Jake thought. Jake was, again, in awe of these people. Paradise City was the new living paradigm for the new supersociety.

*

"In the first wave of twenty master-planned projects," Daniel announced to The Group, "the custom lots sold out in the opening week, and the residential luxury tract homes sold out in the first month, before we broke ground!" As partners with Daniel, Theodore used his empire's great financial resources to finance several master-planned communities at once, woven throughout Paradise Business Resorts.

"Selling out so fast is unprecedented." Theodore said. "The master-planned communities are each being built on a portion of land surrounded by much larger acreage of land that Daniel, Cathy and I own. The master-planned communities will eventually grow into future Paradise Cities...and then Paradise Counties."

"Because the new master-planned communities are selling out

almost as fast as they're announced," said Daniel, "I'm able to move almost at once into the next construction phases of grocery stores, shopping malls, restaurants, and cinemas. These Paradise Cities will very soon start to change the landscape of North America."

"Extrapolating that rate of growth," said Theodore, "if we can leverage it, I estimate that within ten years, over 65% of the continent's population will live in Paradise Cities. The magnitude of constructing these mini-cities is mind-boggling. We're talking about moving two-thirds of the continent's population out of residential communities that developed, in some cases, for hundreds of years...moving all that population into the Paradise Cities — in just ten years!"

And then, Jake thought, we'll have a Paradise Country.

*

Cathy was keenly aware of how social gatherings were, by nature, valuable for value creators. The value exchange and value reflection that went on added to their lives. The exquisite five-star dinner parties in the gourmet restaurant were open to all members. Cathy went all out on the monthly parties, bringing in live music acts with a new theme each month. The food and drink were the best quality one could find anywhere. The Paradise dinner parties were an instant attraction.

"They'll become a lasting tradition of Paradise communities everywhere," Cathy told her husband after seeing their unanimous popularity each month. "I'm going to get these going in all our Paradise communities."

During one of those pleasure-filled evenings, Theodore walked outside onto the second-floor patio that wrapped around the gourmet restaurant in their flagship Paradise community near Laguna. He absorbed the beautiful music of the harp as he studied the stars that flickered in the clear night sky.

Cathy broke away from the celebration to find her husband outside. She walked up behind him and wrapped her arms around him and leaned her head against his back.

"That sky so full of stars brings back a memory from long ago," he said to his beautiful wife while placing his hand over hers. "Do you remember that night we camped out in our sleeping bags with Miss Annabelle?"

"Oh yes..." Cathy's face lit up while seeing Miss Annabelle and her eight-year-old classmates in her mind's eye. "I remember that camping trip with the class. That was at Lake Pinewood."

"Yeah, remember that?" Theodore was still looking at the star-filled sky. "You remember her wondering if science would someday explain all that beauty up there?"

"Yes...the parents stayed quiet. I remember."

"She was right, of course. Ian's demonstrated how it all got there through Zons. Lately, I've been thinking I want to join forces with Ian. Soon I'll be releasing my next Neothink creation *EssenceTalk* that'll shift the communication paradigm on Earth. While developing *EssenceTalk* for Earthlings, I couldn't stop wondering how Zons communicate. What's their paradigm? What do they have working out there?" he sighed. Then he turned around, wrapped his arms around his wife, and looked at her with his powerful eyes and said, "I'll find out some day. Then, I'll tap into it."

Theodore sighed again. Thoughts filled his head: My Division-of-Friday-Night-Essence Internet Software *Business* captured the nature of the supersociety, facilitating the superpuzzles. His thoughts drifted beyond Earth: What kind of supersociety do they have out there? What kind of Universal Computer or Universal Web is working out there? What kind of "supersociety software" do they use? What kind of *Business* connects their value creators to their superpuzzles? What scope do their superpuzzles of supreme love cover? Division of Friday-Night Essences...Paradise Cities...what are their counterparts?

CHAPTER
NINETY-TWO

"Ian and I have joined forces, and we're pushing beyond Earth, into the cosmos," Theodore announced to The Group. Miss Annabelle looked on. Jake watched her glow with pride. "Our company will undertake profitable space explorations. Our company, called *Beyond*, will harvest asteroids for minerals and study them for eventual habitation. *Beyond* will soon bring in Cathy and Daniel, for we plan to build in the future the first luxury business resort on the Moon, with eventual plans to build the first two cities on the Moon, one to be called New Disneyland in honor of Walt Disney and his first 'cities' on Earth for celebrating family happiness...and the other to be called New Paradise to celebrate the first 'cities' on Earth for celebrating the mind/body/soul harmony of the God-Man. *Beyond* will also develop technologies to interdict potentially harmful events of the cosmos.

"But perhaps, in the long run, the most aggressive push by *Beyond* will be designing experiments to go deeper in understanding the ether — the existence field that Ian proved during the halftime show of the Super Bowl seven years ago. I imagine that in the ether exists the communication structure for Zons...their *EssenceTalk*."

"And I suspect," Ian added, "the ether contains the Universal

Computer where all the knowledge of the Universe is stored...and maybe more. Maybe, just maybe, the minds of our lost loved ones who died in the anticivilization were 'downloaded' into this super quantum computer at the time of their deaths."

*

In the Spring, Theodore released *EssenceTalk,* a stunning addition to his supersociety internet software. "Love of values," he announced to The Group, "made *EssenceTalk* possible. Now that people everywhere are value creators, they understand intellectual property and the years of effort that go behind scientific and business breakthroughs. Therefore, people innately respect and emotionally could never steal other people's hard work, including intangible information. Of course, we still have copyright laws and patents to settle complex, honest legal disputes, and we will probably need those legal avenues, for a while anyway. But people just aren't interested in lifting other people's ideas, for that brings no happiness. People are too honest and too busy on their own vectors of creating values.

"Therefore, both 'garage' entrepreneurs and large businesses have nearly no more secrets. They expose most of their progress on their web sites. It's safe, and it's better this way, for people's deepest motivational drives are actually put out there to help complete the superpuzzles that bring the giant leaps to society. By having all their information on their web sites, any entrepreneur or business can search and find missing puzzle pieces. This is where *EssenceTalk* brings the world the next communication paradigm. Here's how it works:

"Almost every working person now works as an entrepreneur — either alone as a 'garage' entrepreneur or as part of a bigger structure as a 'mini-company' or in-house entrepreneur — all using my supersociety internet software, *Business,* integrating and coordinating with dozens or hundreds of other entrepreneurs in order to operate their businesses. It's a new world of bringing together puzzle pieces to build the superpuzzles. Therefore, my supersociety internet software *Business* reaches the web sites of nearly every working person worldwide. Those web sites contain everything about their owners' work, their essences, their pieces of the puzzle. Today, almost nothing is held back.

"*EssenceTalk* works more or less like an advanced search engine. A person searching for some missing pieces to a Neothink puzzle, for example, will key in a description of what he or she is looking for. *EssenceTalk* then searches nearly everyone's web site worldwide and pulls up the specific portions of each web site that relates to the missing puzzle piece.

"Because of *Business* and *EssenceTalk,* Neothink puzzles and superpuzzles — even the most technical medical puzzles or physics puzzles — can be completed in a fraction of the time."

Over that summer, *EssenceTalk* quickly took off. Missing pieces to superpuzzles were found and solved. *EssenceTalk* accelerated Robert Chapman's work on placing each value creator in a company that needed his or her Friday-Night essence. *EssenceTalk* sent civilization through a phenomenal shuffle as people discovered exactly with whom and where their value creation was best directed. Then, society went through a giant riffle and then settled in perfect order like a neatly stacked deck of cards. People's efforts were redirected exactly where they needed to be.

During society's giant shuffle-and-riffle that summer, *EssenceTalk* became Theodore's greatest business tool to build and complete Neothink superpuzzles. He met a "garage" scientist through *EssenceTalk* who had been experimenting with the idea of re-celling aged bodies back to eighteen-year-old bodies. Theodore had the scientist meet him at Paradise City near Laguna and went for a long walk through the wooded trails where the flower beds were in full bloom.

"Can you give me an idea of how it works?" Theodore asked his new friend, Rudy. In the anticivilization days, Rudy would have Theodore sign a confidentiality agreement before going into details. But not now.

"It works by in-situ, undifferentiated, immortal stem-like cells replacing the entropy-ravished cells of the aged body," the quirky but brilliant scientist said, somewhat confusing Theodore. Then Rudy went into a long, detailed description that carried them through their walk and through dinner at Paradise's gourmet restaurant.

Superpuzzle

That night, Theodore held a video conference with Ian, Sally, Jake and Jasmine.

"Well, my friends," Theodore began the meeting, "the cloning stations just might follow in the footsteps of the old respirators."

"You've found another way!" Sally said. She had returned a major portion of her time to working on cells, specifically to turning on the growth of cells. Theodore knew she would be a leading factor in bringing Rudy's work to the marketplace.

"I think so, Sally...I think there's another way." He was smiling as would a child about to tell a great story. "And if you, Ian, and I get involved, we just might have the age-reversing serum ready in a year. The 'garage' scientist's name is Rudy..."

"A serum?" Sally repeated. Jake noticed, even through video conferencing, she was glowing with excitement. She could not hide her love for life. Although the Operation was her baby, she was ready to move on to the next level: a simple, age-reversing serum. Jake noticed Ian, too, was beside himself.

At exactly the same moment, Sally and Ian both asked, "What's his web address?" They knew the details would be there.

*

"We must expand the reach of The Association," Theodore said urgently to his soul mates in their monthly meeting in Rico's mansion. The Association for Curing Aging and Death had dropped the last part of its name and was now called, simply, The Association. "We must now meet the overpowering demand to eradicate catastrophic death. Through *EssenceTalk,* I've recruited many 'garage' entrepreneurs with brilliant approaches. But, we must also find a way to preserve the mind in catastrophic accidents. I know the definitive approach is Ian's pursuit of storing one's brain activity onto the quantum computers."

"The big challenge is still not resolved," Ian said. "Can the I-ness be preserved?" Pain twisted and tormented his face. "I feel a powerful calling from humanity...a calling to use my Neothink ability to eliminate catastrophic death. I feel the weight on my shoulders — the weight once carried on Sally's shoulders."

"The whole world knows," Theodore said, looking straight at Ian, "that if anyone can end catastrophic death by electronically transferring their mind and soul, Dr. Ian Scott is that person."

Ian nodded.

Theodore hesitated, as though he were not sure he wanted to say more. But he gave in and added, "Such a feat would also catapult *Beyond's* work on the ether. Determining that the I-ness could be preserved in a quantum computer here on Earth would multiply the odds that our lost loved ones are preserved in a super quantum computer beyond Earth."

Jake noticed you could hear a pin drop. He realized that everyone in The Group was racing with thoughts...thoughts of recovering lost loved ones.

"Where do we stand now on ending catastrophic accidents that kill human beings?" Theodore asked. He turned his question to Jasmine.

Jasmine reported: "The manufacturers of cars, supertrains, and rocket planes, as you can imagine, undergo *enormous* pressures to make their vehicles so safe that people can scarcely die in one of them. Their engineers are in-house entrepreneurs who work around the clock on radically improving the safety of their vehicles. At the same time, arguably the most productive force behind eliminating the risks of travelling, as well as other activities, prove to be the 'garage' entrepreneurs. All those 'garage' and in-house entrepreneurs snap more and more crucial pieces into the superpuzzle of eliminating the risks, and they have darn near fit in every piece. The 'garage' and in-house entrepreneurs also are quickly arresting human deaths from natural disasters, including weather calamities."

Theodore nodded. He knew the time was now for The Group, Ian specifically, to attack the problem of catastrophic death from the standpoint of ending it, definitively.

The original God-Man Group still met at Rico's mansion every month. This was where and when these important business ventures arose such as the Paradise Cities, Beyond, age-reversing serums, and storing one's brain activity on a quantum computer. Moreover, the members of The Group knew that if anything life-threatening developed, they would work together to remove the threat as they did with Project Life. And so would millions of others.

Who would believe, Jake often reflected during these meetings of The Group, that when the God-Man Group started Project Life, the idea of curing death was, however incredibly, not a major concern of the people! For, in those sad days, they were mortals, shouldering the burden of life.

CHAPTER
NINETY-THREE

"As you know, I've been working day and night on electronically recording the mind's information onto a quantum computer," Ian said to the Group. "The problem has always been how to transfer not the information, but the I-ness. Whereas memory, knowledge, even feelings can be captured, once a person dies, the I-ness dies with him. Even if we download his mind's information from a quantum computer into a human clone of himself, his I-ness is gone. The clone will have the same memories, knowledge, and even feelings. But the person who died...is gone. Imagine a flame. Say the flame on the Olympic torch goes out. We can light the torch again, but it's not the original flame.

"So, I knew there had to be a continuum of the I-ness. But how? I finally discovered the answer by going deeper and deeper into understanding, biologically, *what is* the I-ness. The I-ness...what *really* is it? Through numerous experiments, working with volunteers, I'm discovering the I-ness is your deepest, most intimate emotional interrelationship with yourself. And through *you*, through that deepest emotional interrelationship with yourself, you put through, during every waking moment of your life, your feelings about and judgment of yourself, others, and the world around you. It's a seamless flow of interpretations, judgments, and feelings that make you *you*. No one else could have *your* I-ness. And no technology could artificially simulate your I-ness. Your I-ness is completely unique, and once it's gone...it's gone. But, I suspect it can be captured. You see, the I-ness, biologically speaking, is made up of the electrical impulses constantly being fired in your brain all day long from this deepest, emotional interrelationship with yourself that flows effortlessly from moment to moment. As I said, those electrical impulses can be captured...and stored.

"But first, to make this clear, let me go back to my analogy of the flame on the torch and the big problem of the continuum. Once the flame goes out, lighting the torch again would bring about a new flame, not the old. It looks and acts the same, but it's not the original flame. Similarly, downloading the information of your brain from a computer to a clone would be like relighting the torch. The information, knowledge, even the memories would be the same, but it's not the original person, not the same I-ness. The continuum was broken. But, what if we lit a *second* torch directly from the original flame of the first torch? If the flame of the first torch went out, and we lit it again with that second torch...wouldn't the flame be the same flame as the original flame? You see, the continuum exists.

"As you know, I grew clones of my volunteers. The clones, of course, all have tabula rasa minds — blank minds — with no information whatsoever. I realized the electrical impulses of the I-ness physically functioned independently of information and memories in the mind, per se. For instance, whether or not you visually witnessed, say, a particular car accident does not change *who* you are — your I-ness.

"I've developed and finessed the technology to capture the electrical impulses of the I-ness and to later put that into my volunteer's clone — into his blank tabula rasa mind. At first, I remapped those electrical impulses on the quantum computer once a month. But as my technology improved, I increased my mapping of the I-ness to weekly...although the process still takes nearly a full three hours. In time, it'll take a few minutes and, eventually a few seconds...and ultimately even less. The frequency of mapping the I-ness is crucial because the electrical impulses are not primary — the person's' deepest, subjective, emotional interrelationship is primary. And there's nothing predictable there — it's one-hundred percent chaos. So, we strive for greater frequency. The better your technology, the more frequently you would remap the I-ness. I could see, perhaps in the advanced Civilization of the Universe, the capturing of the I-ness might even be constantly occurring at every moment of our existence, not just at certain updates or just at the moment of our deaths.

"So, as my I-ness volunteers live their lives, the electrical impulses, the electrical charges of their unique I-nesses, are recorded on computer to be later transferred to blank brains physically identical to theirs — their *second torch*."

Genius, genius, genius, Jake kept thinking as he listened to Ian.

"But...but when a person dies...what about *that* person?" Jasmine said. "It's like, when the flame dies, even if you have a second torch with a flame taken from the original flame...still what about that original flame — that existence — that ended?"

Ian nodded. "Let me adjust the metaphor," he said. "Say the original flame rose from a torch that was actually two separable torches tied together. Then you untie the two torches with the single flame burning bright above them. As you pull away the second torch, the single flame breaks into two flames. Put the two torches back together, and you have a single flame. Pull them apart again, you have two flames — but the same, original flame. And with our technology increasing so fast, before long we'll reach a point that we're capturing the I-ness all the time at every moment, not through periodic updates. In other words, eventually we could never put out the flame.

"Anyway, let me ask you, have you ever seen a *clear* flame? You know how, if you pour lighter fluid on a flame, it can leap and a large part of that flame goes clear and seems to disappear — but that flame's still there...have you ever seen that?"

Jasmine nodded.

"Well," Ian continued, "the physical state of that flame changed, but the flame was still the same flame. It may not be the best analogy, but that's a way to understand what should happen. One's physical state changes, like that invisible flame that always reappears again in the yellow state, but his flame is the same flame. His I-ness is captured and the mapping of that electrical activity is stored on the quantum computer. The I-ness can leave its original *physical* housing...the original physical tool, so to speak, that carried it — one's brain. And when the I-ness goes to the computer its physical state changes, but returns when it goes back into the clone.

"This technology will obsolete the Operation, even for catastrophes," Ian continued, looking at Sally who was smiling and nodding. "When one's body finally gives out, or by the extremely rare circumstance that an accident kills his body, we will soon download the entire information stored in the quantum computer into his clone and then activate the electrical impulses of his I-ness. The information will go onto the brain first, then I'll give it what I call the Ian-Scott Charge — the electrical impulses of his I-ness. For, the I-ness is the deepest way in which one interprets all the information in his mind. It'll all happen while the clone is asleep. When we bring him to consciousness...he'll be the same person.

"Ian," Sally said, "You're incredible."

"Thank you." Ian took a moment to feel pride from her reflection, a very special feeling from a fellow research scientist/doctor and a deep, deep friend and soul mate. "The Ian-Scott Charge is my greatest achievement." Then Ian looked at Theodore, the master businessman, and said, "Very soon, people should be able to download their minds weekly, then daily into a quantum computer. It'll take just a few moments. They should ultimately be able to download right at home. If anything were to happen, a catastrophic accident, we'd be able to download the contents of one's brain into a clone and then activate the Ian-Scott Charge.

"Even with the eighteen-again serum, people can have accidents. But with this, we can retrieve them. The Ian-Scott Charge should definitely cure catastrophic death." Ian looked at each member of The Group and added, "I'm now ready to test what I just described."

*

"George, there are questions I can't answer yet until we do

892

this," Ian told his volunteer who lay on the bed next to Ian. "But I can guarantee you no harm can come to you." George nodded. Ian gestured toward his right where George's young clone lay on the other bed and said, "I just can't know the nature of the I-ness once I download your knowledge, memories, feelings...and the Ian-Scott Charge into your Body II. You're the first." George nodded again. "You ready, my friend?" George smiled and nodded.

"Okay, let's get started," Ian said, looking up at his anesthesiologist. "I'm going to sedate you, George, just as we discussed." Ian looked back down at George. "Although I don't have any physical need to sedate you, we don't know the emotional reactions to this procedure. We'll eliminate potential complications from that unknown by keeping you and your clone in a light sleep until we complete the download."

"Okay, I'm ready."

Ian smiled at George and then looked up and nodded. A moment later, George was asleep.

Ian and his assistants watched George and his young clone lying side by side on hospital beds. Both George and his clone had what looked like fine white fibers connected to their heads, some running under the skin, both connected to a quantum computer about the size of a cup, sitting on the table between them.

"Let's get started," Ian said, "Phil, check the connections on George; Melisa check the connections on George II."

"Everything's good," Phil said a moment later.

"Here too," Melisa said.

"Okay, let's start the program," Ian said, viewing the large computer screen. The screen displayed several angles of the brain and superimposed myriads of color-coded lines.

"We'll start here with his memory banks," Ian said, zooming in on one of the images. "Then we'll download the left side of his brain, followed by the right side. Lastly we'll map his I-ness."

"Okay," his two assistants said as they studied the screen, showing the brain in a variety of colors indicating brain activity.

After over three hours of loading George's brain activity into the quantum computer, Ian said, "That's it. We got it all. And we got the charge of I-ness." Ian took a deep breath and said, "Melisa, check George II's connections again, we're ready to do this."

Melisa nodded. A moment later, she said, "All good."

"Let the download begin," Ian said. "Follow the same order — memory banks, left brain, right brain...the charge of I-ness last."

The Group was in and out of the viewing room, watching the large monitor. As each section of the brain was downloaded, that section would turn blue on the monitor to indicate that section was done and complete. Jake watched as pieces of the red and orange image of the brain turned a cool blue. As Jake watched Ian in awe, it suddenly hit him: Damn, he thought, these God-Men will never stop...look at that one man, Dr. Ian Scott. He's not going to let another person die, no matter what.

"Whereas the key to unlocking the mysteries of the Universe is understanding its smallest subatomic units," said Ian, "the key to unlocking the eternal Civilization of the Universe is capturing its smallest fundamental units — our I-nesses."

By late afternoon, both George and his clone were still sedated, but the wires were off, and their shaved heads were treated. "Okay, let's bring them up," Ian announced as he walked into the room after gathering The Group outside. The anesthesiologist cut back the light level of sedation as Ian stood back and observed closely. After several minutes, he said, "George...George. It's time to wake up. *George.*"

Very weakly, at precisely the same instance, George and his clone said, "Yes?" Both George and his clone slowly turned their heads to look at one another. "I don't believe it," said the younger George, the clone, "I'm inside my clone." He looked at George a moment longer, then said, "But, who are you?"

"I'm George," the original George said.

"No, I'm George," the clone said. "I'm inside my Body II." Then George II looked at Ian and said, "Dr. Scott, the experiment is a success." Then after a pause he said, "But, who's inside my old body?"

"I'm still here in my same body," George said to Ian. "I

guess the experiment didn't work." Then George looked at his conscious Body II and said, "But who's inside my clone's body?"

"Gentlemen," Ian said, "There's a lot of unanswerable questions right now. I want you to both relax. There's a number of tests I'm going to run on both of you for the next few hours, both a series of verbal tests and electronic tests. Sometime tonight, we'll start to have our answers."

Ian turned around and took a deep breath. *Amazing*, he thought, *just so amazing*.

*

Later that night, after Ian spent the entire afternoon running tests into the evening, Ian and The Group met in the conference room.

"It failed," Ian said.

"Are George and George II okay?" Sally asked.

"Oh yes, they're doing great. I learned some profound things. But, as of now, this procedure will not cure catastrophic death."

"So," Mr. Melbourne said, "the I-ness did not transfer into the Body II."

"Actually, I'm convinced it did," Ian said. "The Ian-Scott Charge is a complete success."

After a stretch of silence, during which Ian was trying to think of a way to explain what had happened, Jasmine said, "I just don't understand."

Ian nodded. "If we walked into that room," he said, gesturing his head toward the room George and George II resided, "and told them one had to die, only one got to live, what would they say about that?" Ian looked around and then said, "They would both say, '*Not me, I'm not dying*.'"

Jake glanced around at the former classmates and their teacher. Some were nodding.

"This'll sound bizarre," Ian said, "but they're both George — they both have the same I-ness. They will over time — no, in fact, they are *right now* acquiring different I-nesses. But at the point of transfer, they were the same person. And yet, because they're physically separated, neither one is expendable, for that loss would be a supreme loss, which means my

895

experiment — although it greatly advances my knowledge — will not stop catastrophic death. If I store one's brain activity and map one's I-ness, I can download all of that into a Body II if the person dies from a catastrophe, and Body II *will be* the same person with the same I-ness, and yet that same person *who died* is gone."

"But...I still don't understand," Jasmine said.

"I need to digress a little," Ian said. "To do this, though, I need to talk to you a little, first, about when my mother died. She died from a congenital condition. She would've died when she did, regardless of her environment, standard of living, stress level, even the fact that she smoked — none of that mattered. She would not have lived a day past the day she died at sixty-six years of age.

"When she died, I thought a lot about my childhood, recalling memories of being with her, remembering our times together, remembering my mom and dad together. One day, I asked my dad to tell me how he and mom met. I knew the story, but once she was gone, I just wanted to know more details about her...and about my dad, too. After he told me the happy story of how he and mom first met, and after asking at least a dozen questions about it, I couldn't get over how the odds were so slim that these two people from different parts of the country happened to be at the same large university at the same spot at the same moment. For one thing, my mom almost went to a local college.

"As I thought about that, I realized how unlikely my own existence was. Then I thought: my mom could have just as easily met and married someone else other than my dad. And right at the sad time of her death, instead of my brother, sister, and me grieving, some other siblings would be grieving over *her* loss. It'd still be *her*, my mom, her same sweet I-ness if she had met and married someone else; but it'd be *other people,* a *whole set* of other people, right then grieving over *my mom's* death!

"I began thinking about how strange that seemed. That started me thinking more deeply about the I-ness and the many different directions *the same I-ness* can go. Remember, it'd be the same person, *my mom* who died, but a whole different set of children grieving over *her!*

"I really started thinking about this I-ness. I thought about my own I-ness. Early in my adult life, I struggled over a decision whether or not to move to Japan. A large company there was courting me and would give me enormous research facilities and freedom. Eventually, I chose to stay here. But had I gone to Japan, today over twenty years later, I'd still be *me*, my I-ness would still be *me*, but I'd be a completely different person with a whole different life — a life of different circumstances and experiences. For one thing, I would've never met Diana."

Ian paused, smiled at Diana, then continued, "But I'd still be *me*. But I'd be a *different me*. But still *me*."

Jake looked around and noticed everyone in The Group was hanging on every word Ian said.

"You see, George II came from George's I-ness; they'll become different people as they experience different circumstances. But George II came from and was George's I-ness. I know it's pretty hard to comprehend right now. They don't see and feel and smell what the other does or anything mystical, of course. But they're both the original *George* who was separated. They're now different people with the same original I-ness. I've created a second person with the same I-ness as the original. Just think of the Japan version of *me* versus the United States version of *me* — two different persons with a whole different life of circumstances, but still *me* with the same *I-ness*. George and George II are obviously *different persons* now. But, at the very start anyway, they had the same I-ness — like separating two torches that were tied together — breaking the same flame into two. They both came from the same flame. But once you separate them physically, they *are* two different flames. Jasmine was right all along — you extinguish one, and you do extinguish a flame...a life."

"It's all so bizarre," Jasmine said, "but I think I understand."

"Fascinating stuff," Mr. Melbourne said, thinking out loud. "But what else, exactly, did you expect to happen in this experiment?"

Ian shook his head. "I went into this not knowing what to expect," he said. "I needed to do this experiment to further understand the I-ness and the nature of transferring the I-ness."

Mr. Melbourne nodded and said, "Do you still believe you'll be able to cure catastrophic death using this quantum computer approach?"

When he asked that question, an even bigger question seemed to transcend it: *Do you still believe our lost loved ones could be saved by some kind of universal computer?* For, everyone in that room knew if the approach was fundamentally flawed, their hopes of someday reuniting with their lost loved ones were over.

Ian exhaled. "Right now, I don't know," he said. "I just don't know."

Tension filled the air. Jake looked around at the strained look on the faces of the former classmates. He could see pain in Ian's tortured eyes, an unwarranted pain that cried out, *I'm personally responsible for every catastrophic death from here on out.*

CHAPTER NINETY-FOUR

"You're the most influential man alive," Jake said to his boss in his glass office overlooking the floor of New York's Patterson Press. "You've kept the Patterson Media Group brilliantly focussed on the greatest values to the man in the streets, including backing Daniel's run for presidency, supporting his depoliticizing America, driving civilization behind Project Life, and reporting always on the extremely valuable new technologies since the beginning of the Patterson Papers, especially since the rise of the Technological Revolution. In the anticivilization, you influenced people through value, not illusion. Now, Alan Patterson, *you* are the media."

Al Patterson did not say anything. He was thinking about what Jake had just said. After a long minute, Al spoke, "You know, Jake, I guess you're right, although I've never thought of it that way. I've always captured values in our media stream — only values. That's all I think about in terms of my influence in the world."

"And that's exactly why you're so influential, because everyone knows that and wants what you offer."

"And why are you telling me this?"

Jake paused. He knew Al and the other members of The Group were not overjoyed with a lot of accolades for their magnificent creations. But Jake and Jasmine were sometimes stubborn about getting some of the value reflection these people so deserved into enduring articles. Finally, with a stubborn tinge to his voice, Jake said, "Jasmine and I want to do an article about you — *The Most Influential Man on Earth*."

Alan shook his head. "Save it," he quickly answered without thinking. "I'd never publish it. Besides, that title belongs to Ted."

"We're going to do an article on Theodore — *The Most Powerful Man on Earth*. But as far as influence, in one day you can direct the entire world into a mission."

"Won't publish it, Jake. My media's about the best values out there; it's not about me, son."

Jake knew Al would react this way, so Jake said the word he had prepared for the occasion. He said it not out of anger, not defiantly. In a calm, thought-out manner, he simply said, "Hypocrite."

"What?" Al was not mad; he was merely amused.

"Okay, Mr. Patterson," Jake challenged, "you built your empire on pure integrity — presenting values, and values only, to the man in the streets. Well, Mister, you and your empire deliver one of the greatest values the man in the streets has ever known next to immortality itself...and you know it!"

Ever since Jake first saw his boss in action, conducting the morning-after meeting in Rico's bright morning room at the reunion, Jake never saw his boss stumped and at a loss for words as he was right now.

Jake smiled victoriously. "The article'll be ready in a week." Then Jake couldn't stop himself. He burst out laughing like a rude teenager. He could barely say it: "Jasmine and I'll be interviewing you till you're sick of us!" Jake got up, but couldn't stop laughing. Unexplainably, the more he tried to stop, the harder he laughed. He started laughing so hard he was doubling over as his boss just sat there before him, dumbfounded. Jake could barely stand it as every time he glanced at his boss, his insides felt as though they were being tickled without relief.

Jake stumbled with laughter toward the door of the office, all red-faced and doubled over, knees bent like a wounded animal. Al could no longer fight the incredulous spectacle and

900

his employee's contagious laughter. Suddenly, just as Jake reached for the door, Al burst into laughter. Jake slowly turned around, and the two men looked at each other and just laughed. Al stood up but dropped one hand to his desk from laughing so hard. People outside the glass office could not hear them, but they could see them doubled over and laughing. The sheer glee in their heroes' faces, and the humor of seeing their ridiculous gestures, spread like a laughing gas first to those closest to Al's glass office, then throughout the floor.

When Jake finally turned to open the door, he and Al were surprised by the laughter that greeted them from the floor. Jake walked out and yelled, "We're going to put our boss on the front page for all the good he's brought humanity!"

The work force spontaneously cheered, for most employees there, such as Jasmine, had come to Patterson Press because Alan Patterson was their hero.

Jake walked through the floor, past his fellow workers who were giving him high-fives and giving Alan the standing ovation they always wanted to give him.

Whoa, Jake thought, *where on Earth did that laughter come from?* Jake looked back over his shoulder and saw his modest boss sheepishly smiling and acknowledging his employees' applause. That image suddenly sent the humorous sensation through Jake's middle again, so he rushed into his office, shut the door, and burst out laughing.

"What's so funny!" Jasmine exclaimed.

"I don't know how to explain it," Jake blurted. "It's...it's some kind of new feeling that just blows me away when I see Al getting some of the recognition that man deserves!"

"So, he said we can do the article?"

"I had to trap him, just as we planned."

"*Just as* we planned?" Jasmine asked. She broke into a broad smile. "You mean, the *hypocrite* plan?"

Jake was laughing and nodding.

"You're kidding?" Jasmine laughed. Jake shook is head.

Jasmine screamed in delight and joined in Jake's laughter.

*

901

Superpuzzle

Jake and Jasmine were doing an article on each member of The Group.

"This is turning out to be the most awesome series we've ever done," Jake muttered while reading over his first draft of their article on Debra Kirkland titled: *The World's Wealthiest Woman*.

"It's amazing how, during the SSL period, she grew an empire several times the size of Debbie's French Fry City," Jasmine said. She was nodding while reading her copy of the article. "Her broad-reaching lines of delicious, low-carbohydrate foods are served now in most restaurants and in all grocery stores."

"But that's just the tip of the iceberg," Jake said. "Look how she took her fortune from her fast-food chain right to the laboratory, hired the best chemists and microbiologists to molecularly construct the Kirklandextrim sugar substitute and the low-carbohydrate modified flour. Now, most bread products and treats come from her mills and refineries."

"Hmm." Jasmine said, still glancing over the first draft that Jake wrote. Usually, a first draft was a skeleton article based on second-hand, literary research only. The following drafts would fill in the article with first-hand, on-site research. Jake looked at Jasmine and knew what her expression meant.

"What's missing?" he asked.

Jasmine finished glancing over the article. "It's such a good start, but you left out everything about her love life."

Jake looked befuddled. "You know, come to think of it, I know nothing about that." He thought for a moment. "Do you?"

Jasmine shook her head and said, "Let's visit her...at her place."

*

Jake and Jasmine arrived at Debra's house on the North Carolina beach. The housekeeper opened the door. When they walked inside, they could see straight through Debra's house, through the living room's two-story windows, out to the Atlantic Ocean. The curve of the back wall let them see her private half-mile stretch of beach glistening with white sand Debra had imported from Costa Rica. The bleach-white sand glowed in the sunshine and sent a wondrous illumination filtering through her two-story glass windows, filling her large home with a brilliant natural light that filled Jake with energy.

"What a view," he said. He and Jasmine stood in the foyer, staring straight through the open, 22,000-square-foot house, through the two-story windows, across the white Costa Rican sand and out to the ocean. The rolling whitecaps were the same brilliant white as the sand.

"It looks just like a painting," Jasmine said.

"Oh, I know," said Debra. She walked down the stairs that hugged the wall to Jasmine's right. "I built this house to pull in that view."

They followed Debra into the large, open great room. Jake looked around at the unique ceiling angles and alcoves for sitting areas and said, "Who was your architect? The home is magnificent."

"Thank you, Jake. Actually, I worked with a structural engineer and designed it myself," Debra answered.

"Yourself?" he said.

"Yes. It wouldn't be right otherwise. I designed it to get the most out of my day as well as for the feeling I get in here. I love the unique light on a beautiful beach on a sunny day. So, I imported the whitest sand I could get and put in all this glass." She flipped a switch, and the glass panels, which Jake thought was a structural glass wall, slid apart right in the middle and continued sliding apart with the panels stacking behind the two small solid walls on both sides of the glass wall. The back wall of glass was suddenly gone — the great room opened directly to the beach! "As you can see," Debra continued, "the beach comes right up to my house in the back. My house captures the light from the beach, and I love that feeling."

"Do you ever sit out on your beautiful beach?" Jake asked, noticing her bare shoulders and arms were very fair without any hint of a tan.

"I love to lie out and read, but I always sit under an umbrella because I don't tan. My mom was Irish."

Jake was noticing that Debra's light brown hair had a reddish hue in the natural lighting.

Jasmine said, "Your mom *was* Irish? You mean *is* Irish."

Debra turned away. Jake saw her shoulders rise and then drop from a deep breath, then she dropped her head. "I didn't say anything when it happened," she said quietly. "I couldn't begin to talk about it after it happened. If you don't mind, I still can't talk about it."

"Okay," Jasmine said gently, her voice shaking slightly, knowing the unforgettable devastation of losing a loved one, especially now. "If you ever feel you want to talk, you can talk to me."

"Maybe I'll call you about it someday. I lost my parents three years ago. It's just so painful to lose someone right when we were so close to immortality."

"I know exactly what that devastation is."

"I know you do." Debra turned back around. "You two want to go for a walk along my beach?"

"We'd love to," Jake said. "You know about the article we're doing about you, right?"

"Jasmine told me about it. Are you sure about the headline — *The Richest Woman*?"

Jake and Jasmine laughed. "She did the research," Jake said. He pointed at Jasmine. "And so far, she's never gotten it wrong."

A moment of contemplative silence passed, then Debra smiled and said, "Well, when you consider one's wealth is a reflection of the values one's created for society, that makes me quite proud of myself. Now, kick off your shoes and let your feet enjoy some of the softest sand in the world!"

The three walked through the beach mansion and out the back.

"Umm, doesn't that feel good!" Debbie said. She tilted her head back, closed her eyes, and filled her lungs with the summer sea air.

Jake and Jasmine let themselves feel the warm sun on their faces and soft sand under their feet; they absorbed the gentle ocean breeze and tasted the salty ocean air. It really does feel and smell good out here, Jake thought.

"I'd love to walk along the water," Jasmine said.

"I'll race you!" Debra shouted, surprising Jasmine and Jake.

The world's richest woman then sprang ahead, kicking up the sand as she raced for the water.

Jasmine laughed and chased after her.

Jake stood there, watching the two women in disbelief for a moment, then he realized he would not stand a chance of beating them if he did not get moving.

All three reached the water side by side, laughing as hard as they could. The race was so close, they ran at full speed right into the water and were not able to stop until their thighs were soaked by the waves.

They were laughing so hard the waves were knocking them off balance. They struggled back to the beach and fell onto the warm white sand.

The moment reminded Jake of the laughter he and Al shared a couple of weeks earlier in the Patterson Building.

"You're so much fun!" Jasmine cried through her laughter. "I can't believe you're not sharing your life with someone!"

"Oh, believe me, I intend to," Debra said. "I *really* intend to!" They all laughed.

"But why not, if you don't mind me asking, until now?" Jasmine asked. "I mean, look at you! You're beautiful. You're fun. You're amazing. You're everything a man dreams of!" Jake could feel in Jasmine's voice that she looked up to Debra.

"Oh, thank you, honey," Debra said. Although Debra was in her early forties, her fair complexion and youthful sense of life made her look as though she were in her mid-twenties. "But I don't feel as though I've missed out. When you first met me at the reunion over seven years ago, I was in my mid-thirties. I'd been too busy building my national fast food chain to devote myself to a relationship. Besides, I never forgot what Miss Annabelle told us in third grade. She told us girls that we must look up to and admire our man. I believe in that, and as of the reunion, I hadn't yet met such a man. Then, at the reunion, my perspective of the world around me and of my life changed. I don't know if it had hit you yet, but it hit me hard at the reunion: we *were* going to live forever. I knew it by the time Sally was done speaking."

Jake and Jasmine listened in amazement. Jake remembered Jeremiah telling him how the twelve students saw everything differently. Jake knew he did not feel the impact that he would live forever until the night before Daniel was elected. Debra, however, felt it the day of the reunion.

"Everything, every measure of my life changed that day. Right then I knew that nothing was too late, not anymore. Since the reunion, I've thought in different terms — in terms of immortality. After the reunion, I didn't want a distraction until we made it, for now my age was truly irrelevant. I decided to wait until we completed the superpuzzle of biological immortality before sharing my life with a man."

That control, that widescope grasp of time and life, fascinated Jake and Jasmine.

"And now that we've achieved that superpuzzle?" Jasmine asked playfully.

Debra laughed and, still sitting on the beach, threw her head back, a spectacle of beauty, and yelled into the ocean breeze, "Bring on the men!"

The three of them laughed like three kids. Jake loved her innocence. He realized he had not seen this side of Debra before. Maybe it was a side of her, he thought, she would not show anyone before The Group's superpuzzle was finished.

CHAPTER
NINETY-FIVE

"A reputation's been building in our Paradise City," Mary Ann, an in-house entrepreneur who oversaw the daily operations of the new luxury hotel in Paradise City near Denver, informed Cathy during their weekly Essence Meeting. In less than a year, the hearts of several paradise cities began beating across the country. "A steady stream of customers are telling us that, during their stays, they got in touch with feelings that had been forgotten about or blocked out."

Cathy was about to ask, "Like what?" But a thought snagged her tongue. After a moment, she nodded, freed her tongue, and said, "You're so right. My own husband has uncovered important feelings inside that, before, he never knew he missed."

When Jake heard about this growing reputation, he researched it and wrote an article about it. "The Paradise Cities are the first societies on Earth built from the perspective of the Civilization of the Universe," his article concluded, "therefore, feelings that once before had to be suppressed out of survival in the anticivilization are free to surface at the Paradise Cities. Releasing suppressed feelings at Paradise Cities is becoming a living legend."

*

"I have an idea," Cathy sent out in an email to members of The Group. "Let's have this month's meeting at Paradise near Laguna in the new hotel. You'll all be my guests...I'll set everything up."

All were quick to agree; they were excited to go.

In fact, with Cathy's insistence, all but Ian agreed to stay for an entire week. Ian would have to leave after two days to get back to his I-ness work on his quantum computer at home. The others decided the visit was the ideal time to test the CEO stations and to, after the two-day meeting, go to work in the CEO Center and experience what so many people were raving about. ...Because "garage" and in-house entrepreneurs loved to work at the Paradise business clubs, and because they were CEOs of their companies and mini-companies, the workstations were increasingly referred to as the CEO stations, and the Entrepreneur Center was often called the CEO Center.

The members of The Group arrived full of anticipation. They knew Paradise Cities were the wave of the future.

Cathy reserved the entire top floor of the luxury hotel for her guests. As the members of The Group arrived, Jake felt a special excitement in the air. They would spend an entire week together. What, he wondered, would come of it?

"I'm approaching the week at Paradise on two levels," he told Jasmine after they checked into their suite overlooking the rolling hills and treetops. "On one level, this'll be our first experience working in the CEO stations three-thousand miles from our office. On another level, this'll be an experiment in which we'll observe these powerful God-Men together in this atmosphere for one full week."

"Let's do a day-by-day analysis of what takes place this week," Jasmine suggested.

Two days of meetings passed. Each day, Jake and Jasmine talked to each member of The Group about how the experience was going. On the third day, when they asked Debra, something interesting happened.

"You both know I'm ready now to meet a man and fall in love," she said. She laughed innocently. "I gave that away loud and clear on the beach. But, you know, I've been feeling something the past few days here that I've never felt before, at least not like this. I suddenly feel a longing for having children. I guess I didn't let myself feel it before, not until we achieved the superpuzzle. But it's all coming up now."

Ah, yes, Jake thought, remembering the burgeoning, living legend of the Paradise Cities...here people get in touch with their deepest feelings. Suppressed feelings just float to the surface like buoys to show themselves in the large lake of one's soul.

Jasmine was smiling. She knew these deep feelings would be surfacing in others this week, too, in Paradise.

*

One of the highlights of spending an entire week with The Group, for Jake and Jasmine, was the personal time they got to spend with their boss. They got to know him on a personal level more during this week than they did over the previous seven-and-a-half years.

"He's so kind and sensitive," Jasmine told Jake on the fourth evening as they dressed to go for a three-mile run through the trails with their boss.

The light tapping of a key on the door filled the room. Al was dressed in his black and yellow running outfit and was ready to run. They left the room together and walked through the spacious halls decorated with paintings and sculptures.

Outside, the evening air was a comfortable 72°F. The sun was setting. In one glimpse across the hills and trees, Jake felt for a moment as though he were in a painting. Although his fourth day there, he could not get over the view of soft green hills surrounded in the distance by the vast Pacific Ocean.

Jake and Jasmine had already published their article about Al titled *The Most Influential Man on Earth*. After several interviews and dozens of hours of research, they thought they knew just about everything one could know about someone else, including his stubborn position on remaining a lifelong bachelor. But as they ran along the wooded trails, Al said something that made Jasmine stop running.

"I've been hit with a sudden desire to have children," the

forty-three-year-old media king said without looking at his two top reporters.

Jasmine stopped running first, followed by Jake. They could not believe what they had just heard. Jake had a flashback to his private interview with Al about his love life. Al told Jake a similar story that Jeremiah had, about living in an altogether different world, a world in which people, trapped in the anticivilization, could not understand or relate to. Therefore, Al could not find a woman who could really relate to him, so he retired his romantic life to simple sexual gratification. That arrangement was efficient, practical, and least intrusive on his value creation. He never married. He had casual girlfriends who quickly perceived the nature of the relationship. His romantic life stayed that way, even during the development of the Civilization of the Universe on Earth. He seemed content, romantically taking care of only his physical needs in order to minimize distractions and to focus on expanding his empire of values.

Al told me, Jake remembered, that he had been with a couple of women whom he believed actually could relate to him, to his soul. Those women had made the leap to the Civilization of the Universe. They had leapt into the God-Man mentality. Al said he could have gone all the way with either one of those women into an eternal, romantic-love relationship. *But, what stopped him?* It's so strange, Al doesn't know. He only knows that something was holding him back. I really questioned him during our interview, Jake recalled. It was almost like...hmmm...like he's waiting for someone else...sort of like his subconscious knows why, but he doesn't.

Now Jake and Jasmine stood on the running trail having just heard their bachelor boss announce he desired to be a father.

Al saw his running partners had stopped running, and he turned around. "What happened?"

"You, the eternal playboy, just said you want to be *a dad,*" Jasmine said.

"Well, to be honest, I overheard Debra talking to you two yesterday in the meeting suite, and ever since then, the thought has been bouncing through my head...and perhaps pounding in my heart."

All at once a mysterious puzzle seemed to snap together. Jasmine looked straight at Al and said, "My goodness, could it be that you've loved Debra all along?"

"Could she be the woman you've been holding off for all this time?" said Jake.

Al looked as though a pail of water had been thrown on his face. His eyes were wide, blinking. And as a man known to quickly reject anything not true, after a long moment passed, he had not rejected Jasmine's suggestion.

Suddenly, without saying a word, Al robotically walked past Jake and Jasmine; then he started running back from where they came.

"Al?" Jake called out. "Are you okay?"

"He's never been happier than right now," Jasmine said as they watched their boss running into the sunset. "He's just discovered true love."

Al ran faster and faster as he stared at the hotel, knowing Debra was in her room, alone, waiting for him. By the time he reached the Paradise Hotel, he was in an all-out sprint.

The elevator door opened and he walked briskly down the corridor to Debra's room. He knocked on the door. A moment later, Debra opened it. She instantly *felt* the look in Al's eyes: *he wanted her.* And in that same instant, Al knew by the look in her eyes that she surrendered to him, completely. He stepped inside. Without saying a word, he wrapped one hand around her waist and shut the door with the other hand. He pulled her against him. His grip was powerful. He buried his lips into hers and pressed her against the wall. She moaned; it was automatic, instinctive. Then, as Al physically overtook her, she moaned again; it was deliberate, pleasurable. Al did not take her to the bed. He loved her — loved her all over — right there against the wall. Al was an experienced lover and Debra had never experienced anything so pleasurable in her life as Al stook claim to every inch of her body. In Al's arms, her body was being filled with pleasure. The pleasure kept filling her and filling her until there was no place left in her body to store all that pleasure. She started moaning more and more loudly as there was nowhere left where all that good feeling could go. Yet,

Al kept filling her with it...pouring pleasure into her faster and faster as it filled her and pushed itself to the edges of her skin. She began tingling all over; her skin was like a balloon being overfilled and rapidly pressed outward.

Dominated by this incredible man, not able to shut off the pleasure, her body started shaking and tingling. With no shut-off valve to the pleasure, she had to burst. She suddenly, involuntarily screamed, "Oh! Oh! Ohhhh!" and she burst into orgasm. She had *never* felt anything like this. The power of her orgasm swept up through her and caused her to lose reality while this man unabashedly loved her like a man who'd just been released from prison — the prison of never experiencing true love. Al loved every inch of her with every inch of his body, loved her up against that wall and on her bed throughout the night as though he were making up for the past seven-and-a-half years of not taking this step.

The next morning, they both lay exhausted in each other's arms. "I wasn't a virgin, physically speaking," she whispered while stroking Al's chest, "but my soul was a virgin." Then she leaned over and kissed him passionately on the lips. After the long kiss, she sighed. "Not anymore."

"You know," Al confessed, "my soul was a virgin too, until last night."

Debra hugged him tightly, lovingly, and quietly said, "I think I was waiting for you ever since the reunion. I think I was a little intimidated by you...and I didn't let myself know I wanted to be yours."

"Why were you intimidated by me?"

"Because you've been with so many beautiful women; I guess that intimidated me."

"As many women as I've slept with, I never, *never* felt anything like I felt last night — or right now — with you. I've kept all my women at a distance because I wanted you all along. If I had only known..."

Those were the most beautiful words Debra had ever heard. "Oh, *I love you!*" she cried, fighting back tears.

Al rolled sideways, flipping Debra onto her back. She nestled her head against his arm. He looked into her eyes and said, "I want to marry you, *here*. This is where I let myself look into my heart to find you. I want you to be my wife for eternity."

"Yes...*oh yes*, my love."

*

That night at Paradise's beautiful dinner party, Al and Debra were dancing closely. Miss Annabelle sat in her chair and watched them. After several minutes, she leaned over to her husband and said in a hushed voice, "The boundary between them has finally broken. The last of my girls is with her true love."

CHAPTER
NINETY-SIX

"Al and Debra aren't the only ones," Jasmine said to Jake. They were getting ready for a morning swim and were already wearing their MyLifeSaver bracelets.

"What?"

"Last night, during that incredible dinner party, I was busy."

"I know you were. I couldn't find you half the night."

Jasmine laughed and said, "I talked to Robert and Natasha for awhile. And later, I talked with Jeremiah and Sally. You know, this place is enchanted. It's like…it casts a romantic spell on lovers."

"I'll say," Jake said, remembering the past few nights with Jasmine.

"I'm serious!" She was blushing. "Natasha told me she and Robert decided to do their celebration of vows soon. They decided it *here*, after seven years together."

"Really?"

"And that's not all. Sally told me she and Jeremiah decided to have their celebration of vows soon, too."

"Really!"

"I have an idea." Jasmine turned quickly to leave, wearing just her bathing suit.

"Where you going?" Jake asked. He looked amused,

wondering what her sudden mission was all about as she ran back in and slipped on shorts and a T-shirt over her bathing suit.

"Can't tell you...it's a surprise!" she called out over her shoulder as she ran out the door.

*

That night at dinner, The Group's sixth and final night together at Paradise, Cathy stood up and said, "I propose a toast."

"Here's the surprise," Jasmine whispered in Jake's ear. She gently nudged him in the ribs with her elbow.

"First, I want to thank all of you for being my guests at my flagship Paradise. I'll often look back and smile upon our week together as one of my fondest memories. Here's a toast to our wonderful week together...and to many more to come!"

"Here! Here!" members of The Group said as everyone took a sip of champagne.

"*Thank you*, Cathy, for this beautiful memory," Miss Annabelle said. "Everything was so well done *and so pleasurable*."

"This week made me believe I'll eventually move to a Paradise City," Al said. "The CEO Center is wonderful in every way that you, Ted, and Daniel described. I love it here. And Ted's *Business* is phenomenal."

"What about your building and presses in New York?" Reggie asked.

"I love my building, the presses, and the energy there every day getting our papers out. But times are changing. You've seen what's happening, right Jake? There's a lot fewer people in the Patterson Building nowadays. More and more of our people work on-line from different locations." Jake and Jasmine were nodding. "I see the Patterson Building eventually as an edifice for the presses with maybe just a handful of people in the building. The Patterson Buildings will eventually run like oil platforms with a handful of people running the presses and, eventually, like oil drills pumping alone perhaps without any persons present. Everyone else will work on-line through Theodore's *Business*. Those people working for Patterson Press will be in-house entrepreneurs working at the CEO Centers in

Paradise Cities around the world, putting together the Patterson Papers through *Business*."

"Very interesting," Reggie said.

"I'm hooked," said Bruce Salinski. "The love and admiration in the air is so stimulating."

"Once you've stayed here, it's hard not to live here," said Mr. Melbourne.

Cathy was glowing from those reflections of her new living paradigm.

Jake leaned over to Jasmine and whispered, "What's the surprise?"

"It's coming."

"The growing Paradise Legend lives on," Cathy continued. Jasmine nudged Jake in the ribs. "Some of you have told me that special feelings surfaced that put you in touch with your deepest selves. In fact, a full *half* of my former classmates have told me they discovered, during this week, that they're soon getting married!"

They all burst into applause. They cheered, someone whistled. They already knew, but they could not hear enough about the good news.

"Now, Jasmine came to me with an idea, which I love: What if we all come here again, very soon, for three beautiful weddings? I'd love to host the weddings. Afterall, from what I've been told, the marriages were conceived right here!"

Sally looked at Jeremiah; Debra looked at Al; Natasha looked at Robert.

"Cathy," Al said, "I can't think of any better place to marry Debra or any better way than with my closest soul mates. I, for one, love the idea. And *thank you* for making that generous offer."

The others gleefully agreed, and as they thanked Cathy for her kindness and efforts, Jasmine whispered in her husband's ear, "Do you like the surprise?"

"I love it!" said Jake. He was amazed that their one week in Paradise led *half* of the original children of the Civilization of the Universe into marriage. Simply incredible, he thought, but oh, how natural.

Beholding the Puzzle-Picture

*

"Where is it?" Jake, back in New York City, said to himself as he searched through the archives in the editing room of the Patterson Channel. "Ah...here it is." He called up Daniel's premier Thursday-Night announcement delivered after he closed the office of the President three years earlier.

Jake had planned to take a few quotes from the speech about the forces of nature and use them in a made-for-TV special on the two original Operations of Martin Castlebury and Andy Konosovic. "I spend too much time looking back at the anticivilization, trying to make sense of the senselessness," he said to himself while loading the archives file into the computer. But before long, he thought, I'll no longer care to make sense of what went on back then.

"Here we go," he said. Daniel's original Thursday-Night announcement began to play. Jake listened. When it ended, he dropped his head between his hands. It was not a gesture of completion or relaxation. Rather, a ferocious bombardment of thoughts pulled Jake's focus inward. Those thoughts tied his mind into a knot: the forces of nature...animalistic lust, preying on weaknesses in others, pursuing immediate financial gratification, political power, being led, seeking attention, turning to external authorities...those forces of nature Daniel talked about were enormously *stimulating*, Jake thought, were they not? Those forces of nature created powerful yet destructive stimulations that attracted us to them. Those stimulations certainly helped mask the burden of life in the anticivilization...with death being the ultimate relief at the end. Were those destructive stimulations not unlike the drug addict who could not get off his spiral-of-death stimulation because he could not go back to the nonstimulating, boring world of being sober?

As Jake sat there with his head down, wondering about those destructive stimulations that once masked the burden of life, wondering about the drug addict, about external authorities, war, school shootings...a bizarre thing happened: *Jake uncovered the mother of all illusions.* His head rose, his face looked bewildered, and he had to say to himself: "Can it be?"

He picked up his automatic pencil and tried to write some

917

notes, but his hand would not cooperate. The thoughts were coming too fast. So, he just sat there and let himself think:

All along, thirty-five years ago, Miss Annabelle thought the adults were simply too taken in by the matrix of illusions to see *what is*. No, Jake just realized, they never were fooled by the matrix. Down deep, they implicitly knew *what is* all along! The matrix of illusions was a tacit agreement among all adults; they all, on an implicit level, let the harm and damage happen.

It's like the smoker, Jake thought. He knew smoking was bad for him, and the more someone got in his face to show him *what is*, all the statistics about clogged arteries, high blood pressure, and lung cancer due to smoking, the more that honest person was pushed away by the smoker. For, the smoker knew *what is* — and didn't want to hear it!

Most adults, in the end, pushed Miss Annabelle away. Implicitly, they knew the illusions existed, and like the smoker, they didn't want to hear *what is*. And now, on the other side of the gulf and safely in the new mentality, Jake knew why: in the end, pulling society free from the anticivilization had nothing to do with seeing *what is*. For, as the smoker, adults already implicitly knew. Pulling free from the anticivilization had everything to do with feeling greater supersociety *stimulations* than the spiral-of-death stimulations of the anticivilization! The human need for stimulation explained why, before the supersociety, the people needed the external "authorities": *for stimulation*. The adults needed the destructive stimulation of external "authorities" to break the burden of life just as a smoker needed a destructive cigarette. Church and its illusions, for example, offered a lot of lifelong stimulation. Government and its constant effects and changes on society offered a lot of lifelong stimulation. Humans need and seek stimulation; people in the anticivilization were no exception, and they sought the stimulation readily available to them from external "authorities". The people knew external "authorities" were false and destructive, but people needed the stimulation just as the smoker needed his cigarettes. The illusions of "social good", tacitly accepted, let everyone save face.

Pointing out to the adults the harm and destruction of their external "authorities" would not do anything. They *already knew*, at least implicitly, and didn't want to hear it. That's why blatant dishonesty exuded from politics, yet the people, for the most part, accepted it.

Miss Annabelle succeeded because her group consisted of *children*. She succeeded because children were the only *willing parties* to discard the matrix of illusions. They were willing parties because the burden of life that begged for the stimulations of external "authorities" had not yet settled in children. So, their minds were still able to pierce through the matrix of illusions to accept *what is*. Those twelve children, in turn, grew up and created the *supersociety stimulations* that overpowered the anticivilization's spiral-of-death stimulations. It was their supersociety stimulations — Daniel's get-the-people-rich political paradigm, Theodore's get-the-people-creative business paradigm, Robert's person-you-were-meant-to-be work paradigm, Jeremiah's immortality-here-on-Earth religious paradigm, Ian's Overlay Charts proving the Universe's God-Man paradigm, Natasha's true-happiness/true-love-forever relationship paradigm, Sally's we-can-live-forever medical paradigm, Reggie's super-sense-of-life music paradigm, Al's values-first media paradigm — that stimulated adults beyond the previous stimulations and pulled them free from the anticivilization. And, of course, the supersociety stimulations sent people on to becoming value creators filled with exhilaration and supreme love ´for conscious life. Indeed, it was far better to create than to stagnate! Project Life and Project Sustain Life brought those God-Men the greatest supersociety stimulation: the chance of becoming immortals.

Jake shook his head and thought, thank goodness Miss Annabelle was a third-grade school teacher...the best there ever was.

Jake got up, still in a daze, and stumbled out of the editing room. He plunked himself down on the couch in his office, too consumed with thoughts to work. He let his mind do what it wanted as it rummaged through the condition of this Twelve-Visions World of near-immortals. The new world was a spectacular place. There were almost no more human deaths. Catastrophic, fatal accidents were the sole remaining culprits that could wipe out the supreme value. The standard of living was phenomenal. People were wealthy. Immortals were rich and happy, just as Daniel had predicted. Immortals were deeply in love, just as Natasha had predicted. The power structures created from external "authorities" that once ruled the world were gone. They had fallen one after the other like dominos. Those false power structures existed for the stimulation they brought society, albeit destructive stimulation like the stimulation from a cigarette. Their illusions of being something good for the people actually *saved face* for everyone. Human beings needed stimulation, and the external "authorities" gave it to them. In the end, the external "authorities" ruled over the people for easy money and power. They were the structures of politicians, regulatory bureaucrats, ego-justice judges, politically dependent businessmen, government-sponsored academe, the politically invested media, and organized religions.

Through Neothink, supersociety stimulations surpassed the spiral-of-death stimulations. With superior, more prosperous stimulation available to them, the adults *let themselves* see through the illusions to *what is*. The adults *let themselves* finally see what Miss Annabelle's students saw thirty-five years ago as eight-year-olds.

Jake was deep in thought as Jasmine walked into their office. She immediately knew what that distant stare on his face meant and why his body seemed paralyzed.

"Can you share some of those thoughts?" she said softly.

Without breaking his stare, barely moving a muscle, Jake said, "By the time people let themselves see through the illusions to *the essence* of the power structures that once ruled the world, the false power vanished as a nightmare vanishes when the light is turned on. The support system of those power structures vanished with the illusions, and the structures collapsed. Governments and their regulatory bureaucracies, political legal systems, politically dependent big businesses, state universities, the politically driven media machine...in short, the Establishment collapsed around the world."

"But there was no chaos," Jasmine added.

"None," said Jake. "The garage and in-house entrepreneurs stepped in immediately to create a new support structure never seen before. The garage and in-house entrepreneurs created the greatest efficiencies, safety, justice, and prosperity ever known

Beholding the Puzzle-Picture

to mankind."

"Yes, the superpuzzles," Jasmine said.

Jake nodded. "It was their super prosperous stimulations that lifted the world to new levels," he said. "Remember how Mr. Melbourne predicted *the supersociety* way back when Daniel was running for President?"

"I remember," Jasmine said. She remembered the story in *The First Immortals.* "It's amazing he wrote that novel seven years ago."

"Can you believe that? Way back then, Mr. Melbourne described the Operation and how a year later death would be cured around the world."

"And he predicted the Church of God-Man would be the only religion on Earth."

"He must've known," said Jake, "what it would mean when external authorities no longer existed, not in religions, not in governments. He must've known what it would mean when Daniel's Prime Law of Protection (page 426) would, in essence, become the Constitution of Earth as it is of the Universe. With no initiatory force from any source on Earth, no ruling class could exist by *forcing* society to pay taxes. Without a ruling class, progress took off."

Jake paused. "But, even the Prime Law is symbolic now," he said. "We now know, in this world of supersociety stimulations, no crime, war, abuse, or force ever exists. They couldn't. Dishonesty and force, even for stimulation, just are no longer needed. *Love* born out of self-interest and magnificent value exchange dominates the world."

Jake knew the supreme love that filled the supersociety was eternal because value creation drove human beings. The source of supreme love — value creation — never stopped generating pride, happiness and love for life. The *source* put man in natural harmony with himself and the Universe. Indeed, the supersociety unlocked Nature's Quintessential Secret — man is *the creator*...the God-Man. Mankind would now live with love and happiness forever and eventually join his cousins in the Civilization of the Universe. Humanity was now safe from self-destruction, from dishonesty and its symbiotic weapons of destruction: nuclear wars, chemical, biological, and nuclear

921

terrorism. Man was now free from anxieties and depression. Man was free from aging and death.

"People everywhere are living their Friday-Night essences," he continued. "They're the persons they were meant to be, living the creative lives they were meant to live. And they pursue their deepest motivational roots in their open-ended entrepreneurial jobs of the mind. People love their work, for their work is *them*, who they are. Distractions that once took them away from who they are such as sports, hobbies, vacations have shifted from being escapes from the burden of life to being ways to spend time with loved ones during their exhilarating lives. Children love to talk with their parents about their parents' creations and goals. Just look at Daniel's son, or look at Rico's children, and look at Reggie's children. They can't wait to start creating values themselves. They love to listen and learn from their parents the thrill of value creation — the thrill of life. On the grand scale, people are what conscious beings were meant to be: *creators*. Immortal creators."

Jake sank back into his chair and resumed his distant stare. Material things, he realized, became so abundant and so affordable that children and adults were no longer motivated by material things. Now, people easily acquired whatever they wanted. People were motivated by their *creations*. Jake silently nodded. They were motivated to bring who they were inside — their essences — to the world outside through their value creations and the marketing of their creations to the masses. In the new division-of-essence business paradigm, Jake concluded, people's work, their value creations, brought stimulation, pride and happiness into their lives and into their families, which was the meaning of life.

Jasmine's pleasing voice intercepted Jake's thoughts. "As families grow closer and share ambitions," she said, "family love and romantic love seem to fill every precious moment; and although most people will now live forever, they *cherish every moment*."

Jake, the writer and observer, was astounded by a revelation prompted by Jasmine's comment: people's longevity was multiplying as, simultaneously, their *moment by moment* exhilaration, happiness, and love were multiplying...almost as though extending the length of one's life had a proportionate effect on the depth of one's moment-by-moment happiness. Similarly, Jake noticed that the faster knowledge advanced, the slower time passed as people soaked in the preciousness and pleasure within every moment. Those phenomena at first seemed like contradictions to Jake, like a line or an object moving in two directions at once, but then he realized they were not contradictions at all. They were merely the new properties of a supersociety, properties that could never exist before in an anticivilization.

In understanding those new properties, he easily answered the question: Would immortals experience growth and happiness, forever? *Yes*, he realized, for this is how our God-Man and Zon cousins throughout the Civilization of the Universe continually enjoy eternal life. People are *so happy*.

"In the midst of all that's new and changing around us," Jake said, "with the great prosperity coming to even the most unfortunate among us, I sometimes find myself remembering in disbelief the way it used to be. Remember the *fear* everyone used to feel about biological and nuclear terrorism?"

"It's so weird, isn't it?" Jasmine said. "Governments and theocracies actually had the power to destroy civilization, and they were driven by irrationality and dishonesty! We sure were fortunate to survive our nuclear-power threshold and make it into the peaceful Civilization of the Universe."

"It all changed when the supersociety stimulations took over," Jake said, "They obsoleted the need for the spiral-of-death stimulations. The rationalizations and the compulsive need for external authorities vanished. That's when war, crime, and violence vanished. No one needed them anymore."

Jake was quiet for awhile, still thinking. After a long minute, he continued, "You know, at times I remember things like the old jobs of labor or the old religions in the way one might remember a tragic accident...or a painful disease. People were so stagnant and sinking in miserable stagnation at work, year after year; they succumbed to unbearable boredom and resignation. Not creating values...then sports, entertainment, hobbies, even religions and politics were actually more exciting than their work! Imagine...*conscious* life being bored and stagnant! That really seems bizarre now."

Jake stopped talking and became distant again. Used to the Twelve-Visions World now, he could hardly believe his bizarre memories of the old world. Living in this new world of peace and Friday-Night essences, he thought, people build who they really are into the world around them; it's like making love to the world. They're exhilarated by their creations and full of hope and anticipation for their next creation. But when I look back at the anticivilization, he pondered, everything about the violent and boring old world seems weird and archaic. In the old world, hope eventually became suppressed and *forgotten!* He shook his head. Suppressed hope would manifest itself in a belief, a mystical hope, for a better existence in the afterlife...a place where there would be no more burden. Heaven represented relief from the burden of life and was an invigorating thought, even if people knew down deep it wasn't real. Jake sighed. People now live the exciting lives they were meant to live; gone is suppressed hope and pathetic, wishful religious beliefs for some payoff *after you die!* Jake shook his head and muttered, "Geez, what a mess it was."

"What was?" Jasmine said, reminding Jake she was there.

"Oh...that old world," he said, still with a distant look, "that world ruled by external authorities. Trying to see into this world from that world just a few years ago was impossible. No one, except for Miss Annabelle and her twelve students, could have emotionally felt what it would be like...no one until the burden of living was gone...no one until man became the value *creator.*"

CHAPTER
NINETY-SEVEN

"Wow, the weather's really nice out here!" said Al. He hung up his cell phone and stepped from the balcony back into his penthouse overlooking New York City. He looked up and noticed Debra sitting on the couch, staring straight ahead.

"Hey, hey, what's the matter?" he said. He knelt down before her. Nowadays, there was very little that could potentially trouble someone.

Al took Debra's hand in his and, again, softly said, "What's wrong?" Debra looked down. Al bent down and tilted his head up to look into his fiance's eyes. He saw sadness there. Sadness was nearly extinct now.

"Al...you're so special to me that sometimes my fear of losing you consumes me."

"You mean...to a tragic accident of some kind?"

Debra nodded.

"But *why*? The odds are so remote!" Al was momentarily flattered, but he wanted to cure Debra of her sadness.

She shook her head.

"Deb," Al said. He put his index finger under her chin and lifted her face so she could see straight into his eyes. "What is it?"

Looking into Al's loving eyes, seeing her eternal soul mate

before her, allowed her to share her dark secret.

"I get bouts of anxiety and, sometimes, I have panic attacks. I'm afraid of losing those I love."

"Panic attacks...why?"

"I never told anyone. I mentioned something to Jake and Jasmine about a month ago when they visited me at my house. But I couldn't talk about it."

Al felt his body and soul being drawn toward Debra to help insulate and protect her from pain. "Go on, my love," he said.

"I can't talk about the details," Debra pleaded. She shook her head. She looked frightened.

"Darling—" Al paused. He looked into her eyes and said, "There's only one experience that can cause such sadness. You lost a loved one."

Debra winced, then she nodded, "Two," she barely whispered.

Al didn't say anymore. He wrapped his loving arms around her. "We'll talk about it when you're ready," he whispered.

Debra closed her eyes. In Al's arms, she felt secure and began to talk. "I stayed with my parents on the farm often," she whispered. She mustered all her courage to continue. "We were very close. Remember, I worked with them in the first two Kirkland Burger restaurants while growing up in Cheektowaga. Now, they ran a successful farm outside the city. It was what they loved doing. About three years ago, I went there for what turned out to be my last visit." She paused a long time before saying, "My mom and I watched my dad die in a horrible farming accident. I can't think about it...oh, it was so horrible...we could do nothing, nothing but watch."

Debra desperately pulled herself tighter against Al, absorbing his strength and love to help anesthetize the painful memory. She squeezed her eyes closed. "I really needed my mom," she said. Al sat back a little to look into her eyes, but her eyes remained closed. Helpless to the world around her, she timbered forward, inside Al's arms, burying her face into Al's shoulder. Al held her. About three years ago, he pondered. That means her parents died just a few months before the unsuccessful Operation on Martin Castlebury, and just a few more months before the successful Operation II on Andy Konosovic.

"I thought there could be nothing in the world worse than

what happened that day," Debra said. "But then…when I woke up the next morning, I found my poor mom. She just couldn't take it; she loved Dad so much. During the night, she took her own life."

"Oh, my darling," Al said. He hugged Debra with every bit of love that existed within his soul. After several moments rocking her in his arms, he said, "You've always had such control over life, until the day your father and your mother died. You had no control over that. For the first time in your life, you had no control when it mattered most." Al knew he had struck a nerve when Debra hugged him very tightly. He continued, "That's why you feel helpless at times…helpless you might lose those you love." Debra nodded, and she cried in his arms.

"I just want to know one thing," he whispered. He leaned back to look into his fiance's eyes. "Do you feel certain we'll end that one remaining horror of catastrophic death?" Debra sniffled and nodded. "I want you to remember that feeling of certainty whenever you feel the fear coming on. We're in a supersociety now, and catastrophic death is on its deathbed."

*

The Group stood in the viewing room, looking through the clear glass at Ian. He was preparing his second experiment on transferring the human I-ness through a quantum computer, just a month after his first experiment with George.

Ian sat down on the chair next to the bed and smiled at his volunteer. "Hi Christine," he said.

"Hi, Dr. Scott."

"As we discussed before, you'll be awake and aware at the crucial time. You won't feel anything physically. But we know you'll experience things psychologically no one else has ever experienced. You're a mentally strong person, Christine. That's why we selected you for this historic experiment."

Christine nodded and said, "I'm excited to do this. I don't feel afraid; I feel…determined."

"That's exactly what we need. Now, it's going to be a long day. You should close your eyes and try to sleep for the next few hours. We'll wake you when we begin to transfer your brain's electrical activity that is your I-ness. Instead of uploading and momentarily storing that electrical charge as we did in a previous experiment, we're going to send it directly from your brain through the computer and to your clone's brain that will already have your memory banks, your knowledge, and your emotions downloaded. At that point, what you sense and perceive is unknown territory."

"I'm ready," Christine said.

"All right, dear. We'll give you a sedative to help you sleep until we're ready to send your I-ness."

Christine fell asleep with a calm look upon her face.

"Alright, check all connections please," Ian said to his assistants. "Now, let's review the procedure. First we upload her memory banks, then her left brain, then her right brain. We'll download in that order into the tabula rasa brain. When that's complete, we'll wake the patient. Then, the excitement begins. Instead of mapping her electrical impulses — her charge of I-ness — we'll send it directly to her clone, into a brain that has the exact same memories, experiences, knowledge, and emotions. As I said, before the transfer begins, we'll awaken Christine. During the transfer itself, we'll awaken her clone when the charge of I-ness reaches the critical point.

A little over three hours later, Ian sat next to Christine and gently rocked her shoulder. "Christine," he said gently, "it's time to wake up."

She opened her eyes. Ian watched her and noticed she looked steady and determined.

"In a few minutes," Ian said, leaning a little closer to his patient, "we're going to send your charge of I-ness to your clone." He patted her on the shoulder then stood up and walked back to the large terminal and looked at the screen.

"Phil, what are her vitals?" he asked his assistant.

"Christine's at a normal waking state and her clone's at a normal resting state."

"Good," Ian said. Then he looked at Christine and said, "Are you ready, sweetheart?"

"I'm ready."

Ian turned to his two assistants at the terminal controls and said, "Map her brain's electrical impulses and stream them directly through the computer, into her clone. Also, download those electrical impulses into her brain download on the computer."

"So, send the charge of I-ness to two places — directly into her clone's brain and onto the computer model of her brain?" his assistant Melisa said.

"Yes...yes," said Ian as his eyes studied the images on the terminal screen.

Thirty minutes later, his assistant Phil said, "We have our initial map of her charge of I-ness. Of course, a couple hours would give us a more complete—"

"That's okay," Ian said, "let's send the initial map to the clone and onto the computer, and then let's keep sending the electrical impulses of the I-ness for awhile...as long as she's handling it."

"When do we wake up Christine II?" Melisa asked.

Ian looked directly at Melisa and Phil, and he said, "As soon as that initial charge of I-ness loads into Christine II, let me know."

"Will do," Phil said.

Ian looked at the anesthesiologist standing at the head of the clone's bed. "At that point, I'll have you bring Christine II to consciousness."

The doctor nodded.

Twenty minutes later, Phil said, "The initial charge of I-ness is now loaded in Christine's clone."

"Doctor, bring Christine II to consciousness," Ian said. Then Ian snapped his head around toward Phil and Melisa. "Keep streaming to Christine II, the clone, Christine's ongoing electrical charge of I-ness. You two run the controls while I observe."

"We got it."

Ian pulled his chair to the foot of the beds and watched Christine and Christine II as Christine II opened her eyes.

Although Christine was aware and could see Ian, she did not seem to perceive his presence. After studying her eyes, he said to himself: I know that expression — she's in deep concentration.

929

Best not to talk to her...I can learn everything from her later.

Then Ian shifted his eyes to Christine II. Look at that, he said to himself, her eyes have the identical expression...that deep concentration.

"Do you have the charge of I-ness streaming from Christine to Christine II?" Ian asked his assistants.

"Yes."

"How are her vitals?"

"Everything's good."

Ian refocused on Christine and Christine II, shifting his eyes back and forth like watching a ping pong competition. "Would you look at that," he barely whispered. Then he finished the thought in his head: when Christine's eyes move to the left or right, Christine II's eyes do too. Their eyes move in synchronization. God, I want to talk to them...but look at them. They're in very deep concentration. I don't know what's going on inside their heads, but I'd better stay out of it right now.

After several minutes passed, their eyes started moving around quite rapidly.

"Vitals?" Ian said.

"Slightly accelerated heartbeat," his assistant said.

Christine's and Christine II's eyes stopped moving around, and they both knitted their eyebrows at exactly the same time. ...Fascinating, Ian thought.

"Heart rate is rising," Melisa said. "Breaths per second are increasing."

Ian noticed his patients were breathing faster than normal. "How long have we been streaming the charge of I-ness?" Ian asked.

"About eighteen minutes of continuous streaming now beyond the initial thirty-minute map downloaded into Christine II," Phil said.

Ian thought a moment, then decided to speak to Christine. "Are you feeling okay?" he asked her.

To his amazement, both Christine and Christine II looked at him at identically the same time, and both said, "yes" at identically the same moment.

"I'm going to ask you some questions," Ian said. "Can you carry on a conversation?"

"Yes, I can," both Christine and Christine II said in unison. Ian was fascinated at how they both talked so perfectly together as though the two were controlled by one mind, not two. "I was just trying to figure out what was happening to me."

Ian was very excited about the two talking simultaneously and, while doing so, using the references "I" and "me"...as though one mind was at work, one I-ness, although it communicated through the two mouths of two bodies. "Have you figured out what's happening to you?" he said, following up on Christine's first comments.

"It's so weird...it's like I'm in two places at once...in me and in my clone. I can perceive sight from my eyes or from my clone's eyes, but I have to really concentrate from which set of eyes I want to see...and my awareness goes there. It sort of reminds me of something my brother once told me. He has a condition called a lazy eye. Once he told me if he really concentrates, he can without moving his eyes, switch his awareness of sight from one eye to the other, which sees a different set of things because it looks away from the front at about a forty-five degree angle or more toward the side. When he really concentrates, he sees what the drifting eye is looking at, then he really concentrates again and that view fades out as the view from his other eye comes into focus. That's sort of how it's like between my two bodies. When I really concentrate, I'm aware of seeing through my clone's eyes...then I concentrate and I'm aware of seeing through my own eyes."

"Who's eyes are you seeing through right now?"

"My clone's eyes."

"Fascinating, Christine..."

"We just hit 135 BPM, and it's rising," Melisa said. Ian noticed Christine was breathing rapidly.

"Do you feel winded?" he asked her.

"I...I do."

"Okay, stop streaming the charge of I-ness," Ian said to Phil and Melisa.

"Done," Phil said a second later.

"Oh...wow..." Christine II said, looking over at Christine and at Ian, "I...I ended up in my clone's body."

"I know I was in my clone's body for awhile," Christine then said, "but I ended up back here in my body."

They were no longer talking together.

"I don't believe it," Ian said. He looked at Christine II. "What do you remember?"

"I started the experiment in my original body, then while really concentrating, my awareness came into my clone's body. ...I went back and forth through sheer concentration. I ended up here after the experiment ended."

"Fascinating," Ian said. He then looked at the original Christine and said, "What do you remember?"

"I started the experiment here in my body, then while really concentrating, my awareness went into my clone's body. ...I went back and forth through sheer concentration. I ended up back here after the experiment ended."

"Absolutely fascinating," Ian said. After a moment, he called out, "Vitals?"

"Everything's dropping back to normal."

"How are you feeling?" he said, looking at Christine.

"I feel winded, but okay."

Ian smiled and nodded. "And how are you feeling, dear?" he said, looking at Christine II.

"A little tired," she said.

"Alright, I'm going to tell you my initial conclusion, and then let you two rest for awhile. ...It's a fascinating thing, but while we had the continuous stream going from Christine's original brain directly to Christine's cloned brain, I believe one I-ness existed. You both talk about awareness. I believe the I-ness is tied into this *realm of awareness* I'll call it. There was one I-ness, but two bodies, two brains. So the realm of awareness that contains the I-ness travelled back and forth, as controlled by your concentration. The moment we shut off the continuous stream and your two brains were no longer interconnected, supporting one realm of awareness, the two separated physical entities created two realms of awareness...and two different people now with uniquely developing I-nesses. You're both Christine...but now there are two, and you're both unique."

Ian saw excitement in their expressions, but he also saw weariness. "I want you both to rest for a couple of hours," he said. "I'll be back in a little while to talk more. Christine, you did a wonderful job here today." He nodded at both ladies and got up to leave.

"Oh, by the way," Christine II said, "I don't know if this was real or not, but at some point I felt almost as though I was aware of being in the computer."

"Me too," Christine said without hesitation. "I couldn't see or hear or feel anything...but I seemed to somehow sense it."

"Exactly," Christine II said.

"Hmmm. An awareness on the computer," Ian said as he left the room.

*

An hour later The Group, which had watched the entire experiment from the time Ian awakened Christine and sent her charge of I-ness in a continuous stream to her Body II, met in the conference room with Ian.

"This experiment opened up an area of thought that may bring back hope to cure catastrophic death this way," Ian said.

"What's that?" Mr. Melbourne asked.

"The realm of awareness," Ian said. "There's something about it — some key there — that could reopen hope that I'll be able to eradicate catastrophic death this way."

"And," said Theodore, "that our lost loved ones could still exist."

CHAPTER
NINETY-EIGHT

Jake could feel thick emotions that could make a strong man laugh one moment, cry the next. He knew they needed him to make the announcements and introductions because he could keep his composure. But as he sat there looking at Miss Annabelle and her former students, he wondered if he could keep his composure.

Afterall, he thought, I listened to all their tapes from third grade. I know the history, the love, the struggles. To go from then to now...what a journey.

All those emotions, from the first day of school thirty-five years ago until now, filled the air. Jake could feel those emotions all around him and through him, like an ether of love. Those emotions of love and perseverance were wonderful emotions, but the kind that can bring the most worldly man whose seen everything...helplessly to tears.

Jake stood up from the white folding chair and walked to the outdoor podium. The wedding scene was just outside the gourmet restaurant that sat on the hilltop, overlooking the entire grounds. He looked at the gathering of people sitting on white folding chairs spread across the green September grass, and he gazed out over the rolling green hills and clumps of trees. The air was so comfortable that no perception of temperature, no warm or cool, registered upon him. In the distance, he could see the Pacific Ocean.

Jake took a moment before opening the ceremony; he took in a deep breath of the rich air, and he watched the children play. Three of Rico's children, Rosa, Rico Jr., and Tony, chased each other across the sloping grass in a game of tag. A moment later Danny, Daniel's son, joined them. Look at Tony, Jake thought; he's so tall now! He's already ten years old! Let's see, that makes Rico Jr. about twelve and Rosa about fourteen. And look at Monica, now seventeen! She's a beautiful young woman now; my how time passes so fast, Jake pondered. Monica sat with her mom and dad, Olivia and Rico. My how quickly the kids have grown, Jake thought. He remembered his first visit with Rico over seven years before. Jake remembered Rico lamenting how fast his children's childhoods pass by. Little Tony, Jake thought, is as old as Monica was when I first visited, and that seems like yesterday.

Jake looked over at his own son, little fourteen-month-old Jakey sleeping in his stroller next to Jasmine, and he thought more about what Rico told him several times before: absorb the precious time together with your child, for when the stages pass by, you can *never* get them back. Jake saw Reggie's wife, Naomi, and realized the teenagers sitting next to her must be Reginald and Alexis, son and daughter. Jake spotted one-month-old Dillan lying on Jessie's arm in a football hold. Wrapped around his other arm was a beautiful young woman, Angie, who had gone through the Operation and had her young body back. Their first son, Dillan, was among the first wave of babies developed in man-made "placentas."

Jake's view expanded from the children to the adults sitting in their chairs. Today, Jake thought, *half* of Miss Annabelle's original twelve students are getting married. Only Rico, Daniel, and Reggie of those original students have children now. Jake remembered Debra's words on her private beach of why she had no serious relationship, before her beloved soul mate, Alan. These superachievers, Jake pondered, while accomplishing the superpuzzle of immortality, were so totally absorbed in their all-out sprint to achieve immortal life that they simply did not have the opportunity to either fall in love or take the next step of

935

having children. Oh, what happiness they have before them, Jake thought. Oh, what precious happiness, he thought as he looked at little Jakey.

Jake cleared his throat and leaned into the mic. "Good evening, my dear friends," he said. "We gather here today for three precious marriages." People began clapping. "I can't think of a more exciting way to begin the ceremonies than turning the next twenty minutes over to the renowned Reginald Tucker and his music. He composed this piece for the occasion. So, I give you the man who needs no introduction and his music...his gift to his beloved soul mates who wed today. Ladies and gentlemen, Reggie Tucker!"

A few yards behind Jake, Reggie's face appeared, rising upward from beneath the ground; then his shoulders rose. Then, behind Reggie, many faces appeared, rising upward; then their shoulders rose, then their instruments...an entire 100-piece symphony orchestra appeared before the crowd. When they rose to ground level, Reggie bowed to the crowd, then turned around, faced his orchestra, raised his hands. A moment of perfect stillness passed. Everyone seemed to be paralyzed with anticipation; then something wonderful happened as Reggie's gift began: a single note was held steadily on nearly every string instrument in the orchestra, at three different octaves. The sound was so soothing it seemed as though the hush that preceded the music was the first note and the next note, actually the first, was a dominant chord. The single note in three octaves rang out for an extended moment, carrying forth the anticipation. Suddenly, gently, each different octave of the same note broke into a beautiful song...each octave playing its own beautiful song...three different beautiful songs, blending so perfectly into *one* harmonious symphony that one could amazingly listen to the piece *as one* or *as three*. Jake and the others at once realized in amazement that the three songs were symbolic of three weddings — each beautifully different, yet each in perfect harmony with the others...three soul-mate couples playing the same song, each in their own way. The symphony was the superpuzzle, and the three songs were the puzzle pieces. When the crowd recognized the awesome metaphor, people wanted to clap in sheer amazement, yet not a soul stirred. No one dared

936

move; no one wanted to miss a single note of the unprecedented beauty enveloping their senses. The captivated silence from this special group of people was one of the most meaningful compliments Reggie ever experienced.

As the symphony continued, it reached into the listener's soul with the sense of life of the original twelve children of the Civilization of the Universe. Jake felt surges of exhilaration filling his soul. The feeling was overwhelming. He looked around at the onlookers' faces and knew they, too, felt overcome as each different song came crashing into the same dominant chord, symbolically reflecting The Group's concerted efforts to achieve their superpuzzle of biological immortality. Oh, Jake thought, the beauty of it all!

Then, in a most unexpected surge of glorious energy, the music tripled in volume and sailed over the hilltops and swept all who heard it into tears of joy. Oh, Reggie's music! Jake screamed inside his head as it swept him away.

Jake's lips were trembling as he looked up from the seated musicians to Reggie. What a sight! Jake's eyes were drawn like a magnet to Reggie's loose, white sleeves flapping with his exertion like victory flags. Such confidence, Jake thought as Reggie's powerful arms swooped up and down, back and forth conducting the 100-piece orchestra performing three different songs simultaneously, blending together into one overwhelming symphony.

When Jake thought there was nothing left in his own emotions for Reggie to reach, the music aroused the most powerful feelings within Jake. Unmistakably, one of the three songs broke away from the other two and played the saddest melody. All who heard knew at once this was Sally and Jeremiah's song of mourning for the loved ones they could not save — the song for our lost loved ones. The other two songs continued the euphoric exhilaration of those who made it into the Civilization of the Universe, and the one song played the sad, sad loss of those who did not make it. The three songs played on, blending beautifully with exhilarating joy, touched by unbearable sorrow.

The people had never heard anything like this before; the combination was overwhelming. Jake looked over at Reggie's wife, Naomi, a beautiful woman with a gentle, childlike face.

Her soft, brown cheeks were streaked with tears. Miss Annabelle, who sat next to Naomi, was dabbing the tears from her own cheeks. Jake had to blink to clear his own eyes as he glanced at Jasmine and the others. They were watching Reggie, caught in his beautiful spell; their faces, too, streaked with tears.

When the music ended, no one could move, stunned and silent. No applause whatsoever was the most moving reflection Reggie could receive for his creation. He turned and bowed as the platform silently sank beneath the ground. The performance ended as it began — with perfect stillness.

After a few moments, Miss Annabelle turned and hugged Naomi. Neither could talk. In her silent hug, Miss Annabelle was congratulating Naomi, the woman who made Miss Annabelle's "little" Reggie, who had grown so big, a very happy man.

*

"My girls will all soon be married to my boys," Miss Annabelle quietly said to herself as the couples approached the large arch made of summer flowers. She thought about how Theodore and Cathy had been married for nearly twenty years, and she wished, for a fleeting instant, that today's ceremony also had occurred two decades sooner.

As would a mother, Miss Annabelle reflected on her four other married boys: Rico, Ian, Daniel, and Reggie. She saw each of their spouses in her mind's eye — Olivia, Diana, Marcy, Naomi — and Miss Annabelle knew how special those four women were, each perfect for her boys.

When Sally and Jeremiah, Debra and Al, Natasha and Robert reached the arch of flowers and turned to face Miss Annabelle, she quietly sighed. Tender emotions ran up and down her neck. *Ah, look at those faces*, she thought. *They're a little bit nervous...oh my, I can see their little eight-year-old faces on that first day of third grade, looking at me like this, a little nervous, a little shy. God, I love them!*

Jake could see the motherly love radiating from Miss Annabelle as she, in her 20-year-old Body II, gazed upon her former students.

Beholding the Puzzle-Picture

"My dearest loved ones," she said, "my dear Natasha and Robert, my dear Sally and Jeremiah, my dear Debra and Alan...you belong together. You have each travelled extraordinary journeys and experienced exhilarating happiness. That is what I had hoped for you when you were my little eight-year-olds. I still remember your precious faces the first day of school as I told you it was my dream that you grow up to live extraordinary lives, to achieve your dreams. Here you are, achieving super dreams. Now, you will add to your extraordinary journeys and exhilarating happiness. You will add *everlasting romantic love*. I smile with wondrous anticipation for you, having shared that path with my husband for thirty-five years. The best years of your life will come to you now that you've found your eternal romantic soul mates.

"Now that you've finally come together, I must tell you a little secret I've kept for thirty-five years: When I was your third-grade teacher, something started to happen that year. We started becoming a world of our own. As that special world of pure honesty formed and strengthened, a time came when I knew you twelve children were different than other children your age and would be for life. My husband-to-be and I watched with excitement and joy as your minds jumped into the Neothink mentality. We marveled over you. Halfway through that year, we began to suspect that my four girls would someday be married to four of the boys in the class. We grew to believe it because you were already in the Civilization of the Universe, the C of U, in the third grade! And since a woman must have a man she can look up to and admire to be deeply, permanently happy in romantic love, I knew when my girls grew up, they could only find such a man — a man who never entered the anticivilization — among their classmates.

"I never told you that, for you were too young and needed to develop on your own. ...Needless to say, today is one of the most wonderful days of my life."

Jake knew Miss Annabelle well, and he could see that she was talking easily. In emotional occasions such as this, in the past, Miss Annabelle would be shivering with emotions...but not now. Her former students had asked her to preside over the wedding ceremony and to announce them husband and wife. Jake

939

was surprised Miss Annabelle was so calm and collected.

As each of the couples read their vows aloud to each other, everyone smiled freely, easily. Tears did not seem to sneak up on anyone; tears were mysteriously absent from student, from teacher, from onlooker. Jake realized that he, too, did not feel any tears welling up. Yet, he was aware he was overwhelmed by emotions.

The beautiful vows ended. Miss Annabelle announced each couple husband and wife. As she did, the words she spoke made Jake suddenly know why tears were not part of this emotional wedding ceremony:

"My beloved Jeremiah and Sally, I pronounce you husband and wife, *for eternity*. My beloved Robert and Natasha, I pronounce you husband and wife, *for eternity*. My beloved Alan and Debra, I pronounce you husband and wife, *for eternity*."

Yes, Jake thought, no more tears were necessary, for all this beauty, love, and happiness does not someday end, does not vanish behind the burden of life and permanently end with human death. No, now this beauty, love, and happiness will last *forever*.

CHAPTER
NINETY-NINE

Olivia walked into Rico's home office. It was late.

"Darling," she whispered as she gently placed her hand on his shoulder. He appeared to have fallen asleep on his desk. Rico slowly lifted his head. For the first time in her life, she saw Rico's eyes were crying. "Oh, my darling, what's happened?" She was terrified that some catastrophe had struck.

"Nothing bad has happened. It's just...the past year, I've been working on this project. It's consumed me. It's finally coming together now. I didn't want to show you or The Group until it all came together." He turned around and reached behind his bookcase and pulled out a long, rolled-up paper. He slid off the rubberband, unrolled it, and put paperweights on each corner. "Here she is," he said while flattening the paper across his desk.

Olivia's mouth dropped in astonishment as she looked at an artist's rendition of *Rodriguezway*.

"At first, I called it Rodriguez's Way," he said softly as she studied it, "but I shortened the name to Rodriguezway."

"Darling, this is *incredible!* When...what got you started on this project?"

"Our family," Rico answered.

"Rico, it's beautiful...it's...it's...beautiful!" She bent over the drawing and studied it further. Rico enjoyed watching his wife's reaction.

"Remember," he said, "how we always wished there were more ways to spend time with the kids, beginning with Monica? We created so many enjoyable things to do together, which we also did with Rosa, Rico, and Tony when they came along. Remember?"

Olivia looked at him and nodded. She looked down again at the drawing. After a long moment, she said, "Oh my...Rico. You recreated our past." She looked up at Rico. "You recreated our past!"

"I see people, really good people," he said, "who love their children more than anything in the world. But...they just don't know how to get in there and get that love out of their one-and-only, very brief experience of their children's childhood. Before they know it, it's too late, and they forever missed out — both parent and child. That's so unbelievably tragic. They want to get closer to their children, but don't really know how. Well, I aggressively got in there and discovered how to get close and experience our love. And I'm eternally grateful that I did, and I'm at peace. I want to help other parents get close to their children and experience fully that special childhood-love that one day, before we're ready for it, ceases to be a childhood-love."

Olivia's face seemed to melt. She looked back at the rendition. "I didn't just design an amusement park," Rico continued, "although there are superb rides and amusement-park attractions all throughout Rodriguezway. Some of the most enjoyable memories we've had with the kids were at Disney World, so I designated a lot of expense toward creating a superb amusement park environment. But that's just one of our many loving times with the kids. Rodriguezway recreates all our special experiences with our children. Look at the beautiful Rodriguezway fishing pond or the cozy Rodriguezway campsite where families may stay overnight, camping inside the park. My love for our family was my downstream focus while designing it. Over this past year, I relived our precious moments, moment by moment. Those memories are so special to me. Rodriguezway will create precious moments and eternal memories for others, for every phase of their children's lives, just as those experiences did for us." Olivia lifted her eyes. She and Rico looked lovingly into each other's eyes. He said, "Every section of the park brought tears to my eyes as I designed them. I'd imagine our times together, our times with the kids. Every section of Rodriguezway is filled with *our love*. The whole thing is built on love. Every visitor will feel the love with his family."

"Ohhh...Rico." Overwhelmed and drawn like a magnet to Rico, she leaned forward and kissed him tenderly. When their lips parted, she softly said, "I'm so *in love* with you. I'm just so touched and so proud of you." She kissed him again. With her lips still touching his, she whispered, "But when I walked in here, darling, you looked...*sad*."

Rico sat up straight. With a faraway look on his face, he said, "You know, it's funny, now that we have immortality, I thought the only thing that could ever make me sad again were those rare catastrophic deaths, and we all know even catastrophic death will be eradicated soon. But as I design my park, I get all choked up over the precious moments we've spent with the kids. I remember their phases, and as I develop my park, I relive the memories in my thoughts as if we're right there. Then, after stirring up those feelings again, it hits me: that whole phase of their lives is over. Those special feelings are in the past, forever. We have wonderful new phases and new feelings to experience, but those very precious feelings from earlier phases of their lives can never be experienced again. ...Remember when we taught Monica to swim? Remember the look of trust on her face and the precious closeness we all felt? Remember when she looked at me after you let go of her for a second, and she said in an exhausted little voice, 'Daddy...*clap*.'"

Olivia laughed. "Oh, honey, I do remember that," she said.

"Or remember the first time we took the kids horseback riding...both Rosa and Rico sitting on the saddle with me. They giggled and laughed the whole time!"

Olivia smiled. "Ahhh...they were so cute," she lamented.

"Remember the time we took the kids to watch the monster trucks. Tony's eyes were so big. He kept looking at me and shouting, 'Did you see that, Dad? Was that cool or what!' ...Ah, Olivia, we'll never see those expressions or hear those ecstatic voices again. I know even better things are ahead, but when I relive those memories, I really miss them. ...I want to make my park so parents and children get their fill of those precious phases that tend to pass right by us. Once they pass, they're gone forever. I want families to be able to always look back with nothing but satisfaction. To miss out on those precious phases is an irreparable tragedy. One unforgiving day, we all wake up and know those precious moments are gone, forever."

Olivia nodded and looked down, sadly. She took a deep breath as though her breath had been taken away for a moment. Then she looked up again, directly at her husband. She slowly shook her head. "You are so special," she whispered. "What a gift Rodriguezway will be to the world."

*

"Robert's worked for over seven years, ever since the reunion, quietly building a new puzzle," Natasha told Jake at a gathering of The Group. Mr. Melbourne walked by, and Natasha took him by the arm and stopped him. She knew he would want to hear this conversation. "When Robert showed me his work," Natasha continued, "I devoted myself to the project. He knew all along that society's leap into the Civilization of the Universe and the individual's leap into the God-Man would create an entirely different perspective to life beyond anything anyone, even the members of The Group, could know while still surrounded by the anticivilization. To gain that perspective in the anticivilization required years of insights."

Mr. Melbourne was nodding. Robert had consulted with Mr. Melbourne several times during the seven-year study. Mr. Melbourne said, "Robert anticipated perhaps the single most common-denominator need once civilization took the leap out of the anticivilization. He projected that people would want an orientation, of sorts. The leap into the God-Man changes everything, from one's livelihood to one's moment-by-moment emotions. An orientation course would help people get their bearings. Robert's course helps them understand their changing perspectives. His program makes everything suddenly clear."

Robert and Natasha quietly began testing the Civilization-of-the-Universe orientation course in the new Paradise City near Chicago. It had been less than a year since Daniel started building Paradise Cities following the first Paradise City near Laguna, but the breakthrough construction technologies nearly cut construction start-to-finish by over sixty percent.

Robert used the large clubhouse beneath the five-star restaurant to house the weekend events. The demand for the course was immediately overwhelming.

Cathy and Theodore called Robert and Natasha after the fourth consecutive weekend. "The national message center for Paradise Cities is going berserk," Cathy said. "Residents in our other Paradise Cities are asking for your orientation course to come to their Paradise Cities, too. I'm not even sure how they know about it. How quickly can you and Natasha replicate your course to be delivered all week long in all our Paradise Cities?"

"How many Paradise Cities exist now?" Robert asked.

"Seventeen with residents, fifty-two being started or built now."

"We can get my program in those with residents in three weeks," Robert said. Natasha looked surprised. "And we'll be ready when the others become occupied."

Five weeks later, Cathy called Robert. "Just about everyone in our Paradise Cities wants to go through your C-of-U orientation!"

"By the way," Robert interrupted, "I've named the course: *Thank God-Man...It's the Civilization of the Universe* — TGIC for short."

"I like that," Cathy said. She nodded and smiled. "In just the first two weeks, the word-of-mouth spread so fast that the residents *and* the visitors in the Paradise Hotels want to attend. The numbers tell us those in the hotels talk about your TGIC course to their families, friends, and neighbors when they return home. Now, people from cities all over the world are calling the Paradise City Hotels, specifically to come and attend the TGIC course. Our hotels are booked for months. The demand has exploded and the number of people calling and emailing us is growing out of control. We need to at least triple the TGIC courses in our Paradise Cities. Can you do it?"

Robert was quiet. He suddenly realized his TGIC course was more than a superb value; it was something most living people would attend. Two days later, Jake and Jasmine published a front-page article in all Patterson Papers titled, *Robert Chapman's TGIC: The Greatest Life-Lifting Force on Earth.* The article unleashed the most powerful buzz around the world since Operation II.

Robert didn't even notice the giant 8-foot snowman Rico and Olivia helped their children build. Robert walked right past it on the way into Rico's mansion. *I have to ask the members of The Group for help,* he repeated in his mind, over and over. Once inside, he did not see the enormous twenty-foot Christmas tree in the family room. People still celebrated Christmas, for the historical Jesus was one of the early God-Men on Earth. But Robert did not see the Christmas decorations or anything in his path. He walked right past them all.

"Let me show you the growth chart of TGIC," Robert said to open the meeting, holding up an impressive chart. "As you can see, the demand is expanding exponentially. It's become obvious to me that this is a common-denominator that just about everyone wants and will attend. I really do think nearly every person alive will go through the course. It's too valuable and too affordable not to do it. I've thought about this and can see only one way to begin to put a dent into the demand." Robert then looked at Jeremiah and said, "During the weekdays, if we could lease your churches around the world, we could make a small dent into this demand, especially if most of your church leaders — your thousands of in-house entrepreneurs — take on the delivery of the program. They'd be the best people in the world to do this. It'd be a perfect fit."

"It'd be an honor," Jeremiah answered without hesitation. He knew this had to happen. "But it's only a beginning; you're going to need a lot more than my churches and my in-house entrepreneurs."

Jake's thoughts drifted from the conversation as he pondered an interesting fact: the Church of God-Man was the only religion on Earth. The dynamic process of acting on fully integrated honesty to see *what is* had become easy and natural to human beings. The dynamic process of using honesty obsoleted static codes of living. Philosophy and religious belief systems vanished because their static codes of living were no longer needed in a civilization where everyone easily acted on fully integrated honesty in every situation. How elegantly simple, Jake thought. Who needs philosophy or religious idea systems anymore? Acting on honesty instead of doctrines has taken over.

Jake lost touch with the conversation around him.

So, without religions, Jake wondered, why does the Church of God-Man still exist? After some thought, he realized it congregated weekly for the advantages and pleasures that come with networking and socializing. Of course, he thought, that's why the Business Alliance Discussion Board on the Internet still functioned — for its networking value — even though the Pact for Eternal Life was now part of history.

But religion for religion's sake was over. The Bible, which reflected humanity's leap from bicameral man into human consciousness when read in its original context, was now obsolete. It's static codes of living had no meaning in the Civilization of the Universe.

The three-volume Heirloom Packages published by the Church of God-Man replaced the Bible in nearly every home. The Heirloom Packages captured humanity's leap into Neothink. Jeremiah determined the canon of the Heirloom Packages, bringing together eight books written by the world's most knowledgeable people on man's leap into Neothink.

Jake returned to the present discussion around him. The members of The Group were tackling the problem of getting the supply of TGIC to meet the demand.

What a wonderful problem, Jake thought.

*

"You know what, dear?" Jake said to Jasmine while sitting in their office in the Patterson Building, "I've noticed that a lot of Civilization-of-the-Universe values seem to originate in the Paradise Cities and then grow into other cities around the world, such as the TGIC phenomenon." Jake paused and raised an eyebrow. "And I know why. The Paradise Cities are the first pure concretization of the Civilization of the Universe on Earth. They were born and built in the Civilization of the Universe. The rest of the cities around the world were born and built in the anticivilization. They're now, in a sense, evolving into Paradise Cities themselves through absorbing unique C-of-U values that originate in the Paradise Cities."

After thinking about Jake's insight for a moment, Jasmine nodded and said, "I think we'll see that happen when Rico opens Rodriguezway."

CHAPTER
ONE HUNDRED

"Merry Christmas," Olivia said as Jake and Jasmine entered her mansion for the meeting. Christmas was a few days away. The Group decided on having this end-of-the-year meeting, for the members wanted to see each other during the holidays.

"The home looks so beautiful," Jasmine said. "It's like a Christmas house right out of a children's book."

"Thank you, honey," Olivia said. "After the meeting, I'll take everyone out back to the glass edifice for a Christmas dinner and party. You'll love how it's been decorated."

*

"I want to build Rodriguezway," Daniel said after studying the artist's rendition at the monthly meeting of The Group.

"And I want it built in our largest Paradise City," said Cathy.

Miss Annabelle was remembering the time she came to Rico's home over Christmas Break when he was just eight years old. She remembered how Rico tried to send her away because he wanted to save her from a confrontation with his father. My precious Rico, she thought, you went from a relationship with your father that was filled with hate and violence to a relationship with your children that is filled with a love so strong you literally

949

dove in front of a bullet to protect them.

"I'm so proud of you," Miss Annabelle said. Rico looked at her. The look on his face reminded Miss Annabelle of the proud look on his face thirty-five years ago after he opened his Christmas present from her...the three books still in his library today.

As Jake witnessed the closeness between Miss Annabelle and her beloved Rico, Jake realized the special love she always felt for her twelve students was the same special love that now filled Rico for his four children. Indeed, the special love Rico felt from and for Miss Annabelle during the Miracle Year overcame the hatred he felt from and for his father during Rico's entire childhood. Yes, Jake pondered, that special love is a powerful, beautiful thing. Rodriguezway is the manifestation of that special love.

"How long until the grand opening?" Cathy asked Daniel.

"In the new world of super rapidly advancing technologies, construction takes a fraction of the time it used to," Daniel answered. His eyes were still studying the artist's rendition. "The first Rodriguezway could be ready for its grand opening as early as six months after construction begins."

After the brief meeting, The Group went out the back to the glass edifice where the reunion had been held. One after the other, they gasped upon entering the edifice.

"Oh, Olivia," said Miss Annabelle, "this is a Winter Wonderland." She stared at the life-size figures of children playing in snow-covered hills meandering throughout the glass edifice. Suddenly, a feeling of urgency rushed through her: *when will John and I have our own children?*

*

"You know, sweetheart, the more the Civilization of the Universe unfolds on Earth, the more it matches the vision you had a couple of years ago," said Jasmine. She curled up next to him on the couch in their New York brownstone. She handed Jake a cup of hot chocolate and wrapped both her hands around her own cup. "It's so cold outside," she said. Jake looked out the window and saw Christmas snow falling and piling up on the windowsill outside.

Jake looked at Jasmine curiously. He smiled and said, "You remember my vision?"

Jasmine nodded. He continued, "You know, I was going to lay out my vision in a meeting of The Group two years ago — the same meeting when Sally revealed that Charlene Clement's computerized, robotic hands would accelerate Project Life like an assembly-line. In the excitement, though, I held off, and after that, I got so caught up in Project Sustain Life that I never wrote the article."

"But your vision holds up more than ever."

"It does. I mean, think about it: two years ago, after the success of Operation II, the unthinkable consequence of a person dying and losing *eternity* thrust people and their businesses behind Project Sustain Life at all costs — even at the costs of profits, even life fortunes. Their supreme love for conscious life overrode every other consideration.

"Now, as the human race safely enters the world of immortals, other considerations of business have returned. But, not at all like before the Operation. As I projected, the entire motivation of the business world shifted from money for profits...to love for the supreme value. Similarly, the motivation of the individual shifted from personal wealth...to pride and happiness. Anticivilization stimulations such as money, profits, and wealth have been superseded by supersociety stimulations such as love, pride, and happiness. The shift came after society's buying power soared during the Technology Revolution. People are wealthy. They no longer desperately depend on their incomes; they could live very well for a long time on a small savings. The forces of nature driving them to instant financial gratification have been replaced with the forces of the supersociety driving them into their deepest motivational roots — their Friday-Night essences — and onto value creation. They live with Nature's Quintessential Secret as exhilarated value creators, which fills them with supreme love for conscious life. Driving on their Friday-Night essences, they assert their creativity to provide humanity with powerful values that often snap into immensely important life-lifting superpuzzles, just as Charlene

Clement has done with her breakthrough computer program that accelerated Project Life.

"Profits per se aren't the dominant motivating force of business or of the Civilization of the Universe, although profits provide an important indicator of a product's value to society. The properties of business have changed. Everything's different in the Civilization of the Universe.

"Head-to-head competition is less and less a driving force in the supersociety. People's neothinking sends them on unique, creative vectors. The more creative people become through Neothink, the more head-to-head competition becomes coincidental, like two combination locks coincidentally having the same combination. Instead, businesses and entrepreneurs function in harmony through brilliant creation and coordination as they create and snap their unique pieces into the superpuzzles born out of love for the supreme value. Now all this is much easier to see than it was two years ago."

Jasmine stared at Jake, admiring his ability to pull together the big picture.

"The supersociety of the Twelve-Visions World," Jake was saying, "is driven not by profits and competition per se, but by people's deepest motivational roots driven to create values for the love of conscious life. As with Charlene, the greater the value they can create for mankind, the more motivated to accomplish it and the more proud and happy they become upon accomplishing it. The supersociety gives us more and more people such as Charlene, driven by love for conscious life, creating invaluable pieces to life-and-love-giving superpuzzles."

True to Jake's projection, Jasmine thought, the new world had become a beautiful, beautiful place physically and emotionally, and it became more beautiful with each new superpuzzle. ...The only threat still to be removed was the possibility of a catastrophic accident that would snatch eternity away from a conscious immortal. That was a big problem. People felt on edge about their health and safety. When taking into consideration eternity, the value of human life multiplied infinitely. The loss of life from a catastrophic event was immeasurably more tragic than before in the mortal anticivilization. The loss of a loved one's eternal life and eternal love was almost beyond the surviving loved ones' human limits of coping. Both the "garage" and in-house entrepreneurs world wide were swarming all over the health and safety superpuzzle to rapidly reduce catastrophic deaths.

"Love, pride, and happiness," Jake mumbled, grasping for concepts, "have replaced profits and personal wealth as the driving forces of business and the individual. Love, pride, and happiness drive the supersociety. Love, pride, and happiness are the driving forces of the Civilization of the Universe." He paused to think, then added, "That love comes from our supreme love for conscious life. That pride and happiness come from our value creation."

"Supreme love and value creation..." Jasmine repeated softly, "supreme love and value creation."

"Now, I have a prediction that I didn't have two years ago," Jake said with fresh vigor. "Money itself seems to be getting less and less relevant. Material things have become so affordable now, people's standards of living are about the same — very high — regardless of how much money they make. The cost of living is dropping so low, because of the Technological Revolution, that the amount of money in a person's bank account seems more and more irrelevant now, doesn't it? Most material things are affordable now to almost whoever wants them. After awhile, how necessary will money — in the form of currency — be anyway? Can you see the trend?"

Jasmine's eyes widened. "I never even thought about that. Mankind has used money since the beginning of time. But...you're right. It truly is becoming less and less relevant."

"Money in the form of currency seems like a tool of the past that'll eventually become obsolete in the Civilization of the Universe," Jake continued. "My prediction is that wealth in the future will not be in the form of tangible currency. I predict that 'money' will be replaced by *pride*, based on the measurable benefit one's particular value creation is to mankind. The measurement of that value will be based on things such as how many people use it and how often and what they gain from it. The higher those variables go, the more pride one will reap from his value creation. His wealth will be measured in accumulated pride, which will be measured by his accrued value to mankind.

And civilization's wealth will be measured by the *creative energy* value creators put into society."

Jasmine uttered, "From tangible money...to emotional wealth. Pride will replace money, measured by the benefit of the value creation to mankind. And society's wealth will be measured by the creative energy pouring into society. ...Jake," she said, "that's the ultimate expression of love — creating values for the sole purpose of benefiting mankind."

"Not just creating values," said Jake, "but creating the maximum values one can conceive. I know it's hard to imagine it — no more money as we know it. Money has always been an accounting tool and metaphor needed for effectively exchanging values, even emotional values. That fundamental nature of money won't and can't change. But, can the glowing feeling within oneself, that feeling of bringing values to mankind, of advancing society — *can pride itself* replace money as the driving force behind advancing civilization, especially as the price of goods continues to drop to negligible levels? The idea of not paying for values is mind-boggling, especially when I think in terms of *balance*. For example, my value creations to society might only indirectly benefit the builder of my house from whom I'd receive a major direct value. How could money not come in and balance the gap? Yet, the role of money in society steadily grows irrelevant. In the end, I think love of mankind and pride in oneself will create all the wealth."

Jasmine leaned into Jake and kissed him lovingly on the lips. "Merry Christmas, darling," she whispered. Little Jakey slept cozily in his crib.

CHAPTER
ONE HUNDRED ONE

"The Grand Opening of Rodriguezway in the Paradise City near Philadelphia took people aback," began Jake and Jasmine's article the morning of Rodriguezway's debut. "People have never seen a park like it. The outstanding feature is the breadth and depth of activities. Families cannot begin to get through even one-fifth of the activities during an average three-day stay. On the other hand, a family could comfortably come in, say, after school or after work for a couple of hours and devote themselves to one activity, such as visiting a section of the 900 exotic-animal zoo, or enjoying the most advanced, completely safe waterpark, or just to relax and enjoy dinner in the festive environment and perhaps stay to see a movie. Rodriguezway is done in such a way that will always be remembered; the fishing pond, for example, is not just a pond of water stocked with fish. It seems to come right off the canvas of a painting with its deep-in-the-forest look and aroma under large shade trees surrounded by moss-covered rocks and ferns and softly flowing man-made brooks feeding the pond. Colorful wildflowers fill the air with the sweet scent of honeysuckles. The banks are made of soft green grass. Crawling bugs and critters are pleasingly absent. The new, odorless exterminatory agent is harmless to humans. A person could put his infant on the soft green grass to sleep.

955

Everywhere you go in Rodriguezway, the atmosphere deposits pleasing impressions on the human senses so that the precious moments will always be remembered. The beautiful summer weather that arrived here this week has been a special, welcoming salute to the opening of Rodriguezway."

*

"Rodriguezway is quickly becoming the place to go," Curtis, the ambitious in-house entrepreneur running Rodriguezway, told Rico during a meeting a month after the Grand Opening. "Whenever families want to be together, or even when the older kids want somewhere to go, they go to Rodriguezway. Customers become routine visitors. The nature of Rodriguezway is for families to visit frequently, if not routinely. Similar to the stories I've heard about Mr. Chapman's TGIC courses, people from all over want Rodriguezway to come to their neighborhoods. I think we should meet with Mr. and Mrs. Winters. A Rodriguezway should be in every Paradise City."

The next morning, Daniel called Rico.

"My numbers-man — you remember him, Sam — he called me yesterday. What do you think about a Rodriguezway in every Paradise City?" Daniel asked Rico. "Sam insisted the numbers demand it. I called Cathy and Theodore about it. They're with me on this. We want to go back to all the Paradise Cities and replicate a Rodriguezway in each. Cathy and Ted also want to make Rodriguezway an integral part of each new Paradise City we build."

"Curtis called me yesterday with the exact same conclusion," Rico said. "By all means, Danny, let's do it. The only thing I'll need is a few days with the plans for each Rodriguezway. I'll have to make some slight adjustments unique to each Paradise City. I'll study its mother Paradise City first in order to make my parks best fit into their given environments. ...How long will it take to build all those parks?"

"Not much longer than building one park. Now I can build these, in essence, on a production line."

"Hey, Daniel, what if, as with TGIC, we need to bring

Rodriguezway to cities around the world, even beyond Paradise Cities? Curtis tells me that tourists return home from Paradise City, and both the kids and parents talk so enthusiastically about Rodriguezway to their neighbors and friends that a demand is growing in cities worldwide. And since Rodriguezway is not specialized such as, say, an amusement park...since Rodriguezway is for parents to be with children and to be close in every imaginable way, Rodriguezway could actually come to most cities successfully because of the weekly, even daily, repeat customers. Parents and children, when looking for something to do together, can go to Rodriguezway, over and over again. All the activities a child and parent can do together are in one place — in Rodriguezway."

"I'll build 'em for you, Rico. I'll build all of them. I agree that Rodriguezway can and will go in nearly every city around the world. I know your park was born from your love and experiences with your children. You're right, everyone wants that now."

*

"What's in here?" Danny, who was now thirteen years old, asked his mom and dad. Daniel looked around inside the large room that reminded him of the garden inside Olivia's glass house at Rico's mansion. The aroma of flowers, the sound of fountains, and the sight of colorful lighting filled the room.

On this day, Daniel and Marcy had taken their boy, Danny, to the first Rodriguezway.

"Let me look at the map," Daniel said, opening a colorful map of attractions. "Let's see...this is the Garden of Love. It says here, 'In this beautiful garden, designed after Olivia Rodriguez's personal gardens, amid the fountains and flowers, you will find a collection of expressions handpicked by Rico Rodriguez himself. Look on the walls and on the free-standing plaques. There you will find poetic expressions of love written not by professionals, but by ordinary people like you and me. Rico Rodriguez captured those expressions of love he feels speaks to most of us, and he immortalized them here for us to enjoy.'"

Daniel finished reading the description and looked up, but

Superpuzzle

Danny was no longer standing there. Marcy was a few feet away reading a plaque on a stand, surrounded by roses.

"Listen to this, honey," she said, and then she read from the plaque out loud:

"Last Day of Second Grade"
Dear Mrs. Bonner,
Did you know how much I loved being with you every day?
Did you know how much I loved working hard for you?
I loved doing my homework after school because I wanted to do well for you.

After holidays, I loved coming back to class
My heart was happy when I'd see
you walk into our room, always smiling
I asked a lot of questions because
I wanted to do things right, for you
You were always *so nice,*
I wish you could be my teacher every year

I learned a lot from you
I also learned I love to learn
I loved all the little notes you wrote to me on my papers and in my journal
I wanted to come back today to tell you all this, but I couldn't stop crying
This was the first time I was not happy the last day of school.
I was so, so sad.

After being with you every weekday
It's hard to believe it's all over now
I know I'll have other nice teachers
But no one ever made me as happy as you.

My daddy told me: in life, we must move on
But I will always miss the mornings
When you'd smile and look at us and say, "Good morning, everyone!"
And we'd all smile and answer,

"Good-morning, Mrs. Bonner!"
I'll really miss you and my happy, second-grade school days.
Love forever,
Kelly

After Marcy finished reading, she said, "You know, a child who loves her teacher really would feel a major loss because she's too young to carry on a relationship with a teacher after the school year's over. I could feel the loss in this little girl's heart."

Daniel was remembering his last day of third grade. Soon thereafter, he lost all contact with his beloved Miss Annabelle for twenty-six years. He understood Kelly's sense of loss.

As he reminisced, Daniel saw his son a few feet away, reading a long plaque hanging on the wall. Daniel walked over, next to his son, and noticed his boy's face seemed flush. ...Must be the lighting, Daniel figured as he put his hand on his son's shoulder.

But his son immediately said, "Oh, man...dad, I...I'll always..." but he just turned and hugged his dad, and then went to find his mom. Daniel turned to the plaque and curiously began to read what had made his son so loving:

Mother's Silent Message To Her Best Friend

I run and push you on your bike
I cheer for you as you wobble forward on your own
Yesterday I took the training wheels off
Now, as I watch your tense little shoulders, my little boy, I sigh with love. And I laugh.

I laugh most when I play with you
I feel most when I care for you
Little as you are, you are my best friend.
I am now your whole world — I'm your best friend, too.

Two years later...

I sent you off to summer camp this morning

Superpuzzle

I really miss you.
You see, you're my best friend
You wanted to stay home,
and you cried as you did the first day of pre-K
You wanted to be with me
And I wanted you, too
'Cause I know I'm still your best friend

But I know I must gently push you
to expand your horizons
Even if I must let go of your hand
And stand by and watch as you meet new friends...and maybe
a new best friend.
I laugh on the outside as you steady your course
That is my goal, you see.

But I cry on the inside, knowing our time together will
someday dwindle
What an irony to push you out there and cheer for you as
you wobble forward on your own
That I must do, although I dread the day I'm not your best
friend
I must do that because you will always be my best friend

I could keep you all to myself, make you my little mamma's
boy
You would fill my heart with warmth and joy till my dying
day...or for eternity
But I love you too much to keep you from the world
I must send you out there, on your way.

My deepest mission by my own design
Is to let you grow, expand, and find
Your own life with many layers of important things
With me fading from being the most important thing in your
life
Fading in importance to an occasional visit or call

Years later...

Beholding the Puzzle-Picture

Our time as soul mates soon will end
And although I'm no longer first on your list,
After all these years, you still are the most important thing
in the world to me
You are and always will be *my best friend*

I still remember each social moment of pushing you along
"Can I sit with you?" You asked sheepishly.
"No...go sit with the other kids!" I answered with a painful
throb in my heart
I still remember your face at that moment — so full of your
love for me, reluctant to leave my side.

"Go, go..." I cried as my heart throbbed harder.
And I watched your tense little shoulders walk away from
me, toward the other kids...as you wobbled forward on your
own.

Oh, how I'd love to go back to that day and instead wrap
my arms tightly around you and say,
"Yes darling, sit here with me."
I wish every day we could be together again. *Best friends*
— you and me.

Every day I remember times we spent together
I remember your face at different ages; your emotions at
different stages.
I relive them and smile, sometimes sick with nostalgia, yet
all the while
I know I did the best for you
And to that end I was always true.

You probably don't remember the time we set out one
morning before preschool for pancakes
And I told you the story of Henry Ford.
Or when I held you up and helped you ride your first pair
of roller skates in our garage.
"*Thank you*," you said breathlessly when we were done,
having had so much fun.

961

Superpuzzle

How I panicked when you went on your first date!
Remember when we'd just sit up and talk late?
I do remember, over and over
And sometimes I cry alone that our time is gone.
I smile at each vivid memory
and then a sadness reminds me...it's all over.

I could have convinced you to stay and attend the local
community college
We could still to this day spend a lot of time together
And that would be *so nice*
But it would also be *so sad,*
For you'd be hanging onto the past...a has-been world on
the decline
Instead of moving into your future...*your world* on the rise

Most important of all, I want you to know...
I get filled with bursts of happiness and lasting peace and
pride
As I watch you move ahead on your own, so strong and
successful.
Your shoulders steady and set, I nod and then smile.
You never wobble now.

Love always,
Mom

Daniel sighed. Wow..., he thought, that will leave an impression with parents and children that'll never be forgotten. Rico is giving us gifts here, gifts that help us appreciate *now* the preciousness of what we have so nothing slips by. He's amplifying the love of parent and child.

Daniel found Danny hugging his mom, something he had not done in nearly two years. Daniel thought, my Danny, Marcy, and I will now feel how special each year is that we still have left together with Danny still at home.

That night, Daniel called Rico. "My wife, my son, and I thank you for bringing this priceless value into our lives," Daniel said. His voice was deep with feelings. "We can't wait to build the Rodriguezway in Paradise City near San Diego."

Rico could tell by Daniel's voice he had visited Rodriguezway, specifically the Garden of Love. Rico said, "My friend, we've sure come a long way since the days of the Fearsome Four, haven't we?"

CHAPTER
ONE HUNDRED TWO

"As eternity opens up to us, our perspective of time has changed," read Jake and Jasmine's article commemorating the third anniversary of Operation II. "Suddenly, the realization mercilessly came into focus of how *close* our lost loved ones had come, without making it. The painful realization hits us unexpectedly, without warning, at any moment. The more wonderful our Twelve-Visions World becomes, the more we miss our loved ones who did not make it. It is one of only two debilitating feelings left in the Civilization of the Universe. The other, of course, is the fear of losing oneself or a loved one to a catastrophic accident.

"Three years after Operation II, 'garage' and in-house entrepreneurs have eliminated most risks in transportation. Technology has conquered catastrophic weather conditions and natural disasters. Medicine and genetic engineering have eradicated nearly every disease and infection. Once or twice a year an unforeseen catastrophe happens that causes a person to die. News of a human death now sends the entire world into a gripping depression.

"Dr. Ian Scott works day and night on his attempts to capture the I-ness onto a quantum computer. He hopes that the I-ness can remain dormant until activated by the Ian-Scott Charge. In the event of a catastrophe that wipes out a human life, he hopes to activate that person's I-ness by downloading his stored mind activity into a cloned Body II with a blank brain. Upon activating the I-ness through the Ian-Scott Charge, that person would be back, Dr. Scott hopes, minus the experiences since his or her last download, but with the original I-ness."

During this drive to end catastrophic death, the Patterson Paper in Ft. Lauderdale got a phone call from a local hospital. They were going to lose a 12-year-old boy who had drowned, was revived by his father, but the brain damage was overwhelming. The boy had been in a coma for two months.

Jake and Jasmine were assigned to the story, for a human death was now world news. Even more tragic, many experts believed that this poor boy would be the last person on Earth to die.

Jake and Jasmine got on the company rocket plane and were at the hospital in Florida in thirty minutes for the sad scene.

Jake felt his heart pounding as he and Jasmine talked to the doctor in charge.

"I'm not able to do anything," the doctor said in a hoarse voice laced with pain. "Total brain damage occurred from lack of oxygen. I'm just waiting now for his family to tell me to turn off the life support. I ran several series of tests over the past two months to be absolutely certain of the degree of brain damage. The tests were conclusive."

"Why was he swimming without an MLS bracelet?" Jasmine asked. Swimming was an activity people abandoned until the garage entrepreneurs moved in and essentially removed all risks. The MyLifeSaver bracelets at life-guard rated pools, as started at Paradise Cities, removed the risks. Even the waterparks at the Rodriguezways, which had several water slides and tubing rides, were rated completely safe.

"He wasn't swimming," the doctor replied softly. "It was a fluke accident no one could foresee. The young lad slipped in the rain and hit his head on a curb. He somehow landed, unconscious, next to a sidewalk drain that was backed up. His father discovered him lying in the gutter, his head submerged under the drainage."

Superpuzzle

A shaken, saddened nurse stepped in the doorway. "It's time," she told the doctor.

Jake saw a flash of fear blind the doctor's eyes for an instant. Jake felt his own heart pound with fear.

"Okay," the doctor said, distantly.

Jake and Jasmine stayed by the door of the boy's room. The doctor entered the room where the boy lay. Without saying a word, he walked over and shut down the respirator, took the tube out of the boy's mouth, and gently dabbed the boy's supple lips with a tissue. Jake could see the boy's lips respond to the doctor's touch. Jake slowly widened his view from the boy's lips to see his innocent face with soft brown bangs neatly trimmed just above his closed, peacefully sleeping eyes. Although across the room, Jake could see the boy's long eyelashes touching his cheeks. The boy's face looked so sweet, like an angel, lying so still on the puffy white pillow. Jake was aware that tears were falling from his own eyes. He looked at the boy's mother holding her son's small hand with both of her hands. Jake looked at the boy's father kneeling on the floor, his head right before his son's closed eyes with his arm wrapped over and around his boy's waist as if letting his son know he was right there with him, and his son was not alone — they would go through this together, father and son.

Then, it happened. The boy's body began to twitch and then jerk as his body fought for oxygen, but could not breathe. Then, his body jerked much harder. His mother cried out, "No! Oh, my baby...*my baby*. Nooo!" His father stayed quiet and tried to soothe his son. Dad's face started twitching too and turned dark red under the enormous pressure of watching his near-immortal — *his son* — losing eternity.

His son kicked his legs, one last time, in the way a child kicks off his covers in his sleep. His father moved his arm up along his boy's side as though he were about to sit him up and hug him, and he cried, "It's okay, precious...it's okay."

As if he heard his dad, all at once, the boy lay still. His eyes stayed closed; his face looked peaceful as though he were just napping. The final struggle was over, and everything suddenly became so still and silent. The reality hit the boy's dad: his son was now gone — gone *forever*.

"Oh, DONNIE!" his father cried. He scooped his boy up and hugged him tightly. The boy's arms dangled lifelessly by his side. How small he looked in his father's arms.

"MY BEAUTIFUL SON!" his father cried, and the devastated dad buried his face into his son's small shoulder. Dad's large body shook over and over as he cried so hard he didn't make a sound, rocking his lifeless son in his arms.

When the father caught his breath, he screamed, "I can't stand losing you!" He lifted his head off his son's shoulder and cupped the back of his son's head in his large hand to look at his boy's gentle face.

"Oh, Donnie, where are you?" The father's lips were pulled down at the sides as though they were carrying large weights as he cried, "Oh, my Donnie. My baby boy! *Where are you? Where are you!*"

*

Five weeks later, sidewalk drains around the world were being removed. Garage entrepreneurs swooped down on that risk and devised a new technology of tiny suction holes that immediately removed all flooding from streets, no matter how severe.

Ian was getting only a few hours of sleep a day, desperately trying to succeed at capturing the I-ness and realm of awareness onto a quantum computer. That way, everyone could have their minds and I-nesses stored in case of such unforeseeable catastrophes.

Entering the world of immortals, Jake could not stop seeing in his mind the boy's father begging for an answer to his desperate question:

"Oh, Donnie, where are you? Oh, my Donnie. My baby boy! *Where are you? Where are you!*"

*

Jake decided he wanted to talk to Donnie's father. Jake and Jasmine flew to Ft. Lauderdale, after arranging a meeting. The boy's father, after five weeks, looked hopelessly devastated.

As Jake and Jasmine entered his house, they both walked over and hugged the broken man. They had not planned it, but they could not stop themselves.

"I'm Donald," he said wearily.

"We're just *so sorry*," Jasmine said. She started wiping her eyes with her fingers.

"The whole human race is," Donald said. "Do you know my Donnie just might be the last human being on Earth to die?"

Jasmine broke down and cried. She knew how close her own father had come to immortality. She knew how much losing him hurt every day. And she just could not imagine how this loving father, slouched in the chair before her, felt...losing his son *after* civilization essentially had immortality, his boy perhaps the last person to die. Looking at the depleted man before her, Jasmine could not stop crying.

Before they came to see Donald, Jake had questioned whether Jasmine should come along. He knew how hard this would be on her. And he was right. She could not take it. She had to go into another room.

"I'm sorry...I'm sorry," she cried as she and Donnie's mom went to another room. Jake could hear them both crying as Donald started talking.

"I keep reliving a memory of my boy. Do you want to hear it?"

Jake took a deep breath and nodded.

"Donnie was only three years old at the time. He sometimes said things that sounded so mature coming out of this little handsome guy with a squeaky voice and chubby cheeks. Women thought he was so cute they'd often stop in public to chat with him. Preschool teachers loved to hug him or pet his thick blond hair. He didn't mind. At three, he was a little conversationalist. An adult would ask him something, and he'd give a long, detailed explanation in his squeaky three-year-old voice. He was always so energetic and animated. Even when he got in trouble and cried, he was full of energy. He was a bundle of joy, so full of life. When my wife was on the phone and started laughing, my little Donnie would start laughing, too, even though he had no idea what his mom was laughing about. He just loved to laugh. I loved to just watch him." Donald paused. Jake could see in Donald's eyes, as he imagined his boy, for a brief moment

Donald was at peace. Donald sighed and then continued, "As I said, even when he got in trouble, I got a kick out of his expressions and comments. He'd get so upset at himself when he spilled something because his mother would get so upset. He didn't realize she was upset with *him*, and he'd get so upset with himself that his mom ended up saying, 'It's okay, Donnie, it's really okay.'" Donald stopped talking and pressed his hand over his face. His moment of peace had passed, his precious memories of Donnie shattered by reality. Donnie was gone now. Gone forever. Jake put his hand on Donald's shoulder.

Donald dropped his hand to his lap. Without looking up, he continued, "The day the family dog died was the first time I saw Donnie without energy; he was so lifeless. He was still three, and it was the first time he dealt with death. I picked him up myself from preschool and took him to the park. He loved being surprised by me when, on occasions, I'd pick him up from school. He loved even more going to the park with me. My heart was breaking on the drive to the park, seeing how excited he was. I knew this was the first time his innocent world would be crushed.

"We got to the park and Donnie said, 'I have a great idea, Daddy. After we play, let's pick up Freddy from the dog doctor on the way home.' I knelt down to look eye to eye with Donnie. 'Sweetie, Freddy's not coming home.' Donnie blinked a few times, then said, 'Oh, then we'll visit him. ...Can we, please?' It broke my heart, watching his face as I said, 'Freddy was very sick. The doggy doctor...he couldn't fix Freddy this time.' I felt a tear roll down my cheek, and I'll never forget the transition on Donnie's face from happy innocence to a cruel anticivilization reality when I said, 'Freddy died.'

"Donnie cried so hard; he just couldn't believe he would never play with Freddy again. He had to see his dog once more. So we went to the vet. Freddy was laid out in a shallow box. When Donnie saw him, he said some of the most touching words I've ever heard. 'I don't know why you had to die, Freddy, because I love you so much.' Donnie cried and reached down into the box and hugged his dog. 'I would've always taken care of you,' Donnie whispered, 'even when I grow up.' Then Donnie sat up and pet his dog over and over, so caringly. It was as if he wanted his dog to know how much he meant to him. 'You're my very best friend, and now I won't be able to play with you.'

"When it was time to go, Donnie looked up at me in a panic and asked, 'Will I see Freddy again?' I could only shake my head. It was very hard for Donnie to leave Freddy. 'Daddy, this'll be the last time I'll ever see Freddy?' His face was suspended in fear of the inevitable answer. 'Yes, sweetheart, this will be the last time,' I answered, and his face collapsed.

"When we walked out of the animal hospital to the car, Donnie was crying and said he really missed Freddy. He asked if we could go back in to see Freddy one more time. I sighed and said, 'Sure, big guy.'

"For two weeks, Donnie was so lifeless at home and in school. I worried about him. His spark was gone. I later realized he was quietly pondering death, what it was, and what it meant.

"At three years old, he was forced to grasp the concept of death. One day after preschool, about two weeks after Freddie died, Donnie walked up to his mother in the kitchen and nervously asked her, 'Mommy, will you ever die?'

"My wife looked at the little fellow standing about three feet tall, looking up at her with big, worried eyes. She didn't want to tell him she would die someday, as we all thought we would nine years ago, but she knew she needed to be honest. She almost cried as she said, 'Darling, someday, *a long time from now*, I'll be very old. I'll get sick, and I'll die.'

"Little Donnie was so crushed. 'But mommy,' he said; he blinked and three big tears rushed down his red cheeks, 'I'm going to *really miss you.*'

"My wife dropped what she was doing, knelt down and scooped Donnie against her. 'Oh, sweetheart,' she said. She hugged his little frame. His head went against her shoulder, and he was really crying. That's when I came home and saw him. While he was crying, the little guy said in short spurts, 'Mommy...I don't want...you to die! I'm going to be *so sad.*' Donnie was crying and begging his mommy to never die—" Donald's hand suddenly covered his face again, and this time he burst out crying.

Jake did all he could to keep from crying as he said, "Little

Donnie felt the supreme value of conscious life and was expressing every child's natural mission in life to preserve that supreme value."

"And *he* lost..." Donald wailed, his hand pressed over his face, "and *he* lost."

Jake sat there doing everything he could to keep his composure while staring at a wall of pictures of Donnie as his father wept. A coldness made Jake shiver. He looked at Donnie's father weeping in agony and sadly wondered, was your beautiful boy *the last one to die?*

CHAPTER
ONE HUNDRED THREE

"There'll be no more Donnies," Ian said. Sally watched her close friend turn bright red. *"I'm responsible,"* a devastated Ian said to The Group. "I let catastrophe take Donnie's life."

Sally knew this feeling well, which she used to shoulder. The color in Ian's face deepened.

"I'M RESPONSIBLE!" he said again. There was no relief.

"Oh, Ian," Sally whispered to herself, seeing the torture he felt...a torture she knew only too well during the SSL period, "it's not your fault." Later, she talked to him.

"I know that nothing I say can give you relief over Donnie's death. I felt this way after losing Kelsie and Eric. But it's important not to feel blame, because feeling blame will paralyze your progress." She knew, however, none of that talk would do him any good right now. She knew that, in many ways, he was all alone. She knew that, alone in his lab, he drove himself beyond human capacity.

*

"Ian," Diana said softly, "you come to bed now and get some rest."

"I can't..."

972

"*Why*, my love?"

"Because I must save the next Donnie." Ian stopped working for a moment and looked at his wife. "Because I must save *eternity* for the next Donnie."

"But, darling, you're working too strenuously for too long. You haven't come to bed for days. You just sleep at your terminal whenever you can't hold your head up. Honey, *I'm scared*. I'm scared of a catastrophe happening to you!"

Ian looked up, eyes glazed over, and as if he did not hear Diana's plea, he said, "The key is in the realm of awareness. It travels."

"What?"

"It travels — the realm of awareness. And the I-ness is inextricably linked to this realm of awareness. When we map and then move the charge of I-ness, we must do so in concert with the realm of awareness. Then, the person we are trying to save travels with the I-ness and continues to be."

Diana, who observed both the George and the Christine experiments, said, "I follow that. The original George never himself left his body to enter his clone, whereas the original Christine actually did leave her body and enter her clone."

"*Exactly*," Ian said, his eyes no longer glazed over, suddenly bulging with excitement. "It's as though a person's spirit is his I-ness *interlocked* with his realm of awareness. I'm beginning to know how to move a person's spirit around, so to speak." He was quiet for a moment, then sighed and said, "But how do I *preserve* that spirit? That's the only way to eradicate catastrophic death — by preserving the spirit."

"You've come so far," Diana said, shaking her head.

"I'll tell you what I've been so crazily driven on in here," Ian said. He leaned toward Diana. "Christine and Christine II said they had a sense of themselves, maybe a fraction of an awareness, of passing through the quantum computer."

Diana nodded. She remembered the comment.

"A realm of awareness — what is that, really? Part of our awareness comes from the brain interfacing with the world around it, which happens through the five senses. The other part of our realm of awareness comes from the act of thinking, which can be done even when all senses shut down. Well, I've been studying this thing I call a realm of awareness, and I'm approaching the conclusion that I can actually store the realm of awareness with the I-ness on the quantum computer. The capacity is great enough to simulate the senses and connect those senses to the stored brain activity."

"So it could see, hear, feel?"

"Yes! That's what I've been working on."

"That's amazing. ...But, how could that stored brain activity actually *think*?"

"It'd have to be able to fire off its own electrical activity at its own will in order to think. I can give it a special source of power, a sort of static-electrical field, which the stored brain could use as it wants, which is *thinking*."

"If you could do that, you'd truly capture a living mind on the computer."

"I'd capture a person's realm of awareness and his I-ness. I'd capture his spirit."

"Oh, my darling...I had no idea. Now I know why you're driving like superman in here. This is...it's phenomenal what you do!"

"Well, it's not just that," Ian said. His expression returned to harsh reality. He dropped his head down in pain. "I can't get over Donnie. It drives me...it drives me insane with desire to eradicate catastrophic death."

Ian looked dazed as his thoughts returned to Donnie. Then Diana said, "I talked to Sally. She told me she knows you're not sleeping. She told me to tell you she knows because she went through the same thing with Project Life and Project Sustain Life. But she said she swears to you she discovered that a short night on a bed — about five hours — made her more effective at work than just taking cat naps in her lab and not lying down."

Ian was quiet, weighing the advice. "Well, I respect Sally's opinion on this," he finally said to Diana's delight. "What time is it, anyway?"

"A little after two o'clock in the morning."

Ian stood up and walked over to Diana and wrapped his arm around her back. "Let's set the alarm for seven."

*

Ian sat up in bed the next morning a half hour before the alarm. "I feel so down," he whispered to himself when he got out of bed, "so, so down." He walked to the bathroom saying, "Donnie didn't have to die — not if I could've stored his I-ness and realm of awareness on the computer. Damn, Donnie didn't have to die..."

Diana got up and followed Ian into the master bathroom. "Honey," she said, "you have to let him go. There's nothing you could've done to save that poor boy. Right now, you need to put that out of your mind so you can move ahead."

"I know, *I know*, but *I can't*." Ian shook his head and said, "I just can't."

"Can you try?"

Ian hesitated. *Can I try.* After a moment of self-examination he said, "Honey, I'll try not to let the pain paralyze my thoughts so much."

*

"You won't believe who's in our living room, waiting to see you," Diana said. She walked into Ian's computer room.

Ian stopped his work. "Jake and Jasmine?"

Diana shook her head. "I hope you're ready to handle this," she said. "It's Donnie's father, Donald senior."

Ian dropped his pencil onto the desk before him. "Oh," he said. "He's here?"

"Yes."

Although Ian thought he would introduce himself in a professional manner, the moment he saw Donald's expression trapped in a tomb of eternal loss, Ian was overwhelmed with emotion.

"I'm so, so sorry," Ian said the moment Donald saw him. "I can't tell you how many times I've tried to see if somehow I could've broken through sooner — in time to have saved your son. But as of now, I'm still far from storing a person's I-ness, his spirit, on a quantum computer."

Donald nodded. He seemed to call upon all his strength to pull together his thoughts deep within and talk. His face turned red as he said, "Dr. Scott, you once believed our lost loved ones

975

were saved by advanced conscious beings, and that someday we'd be able to get them back or be with them again." Suddenly, Donald grimaced. His lips trembled.

Ian looked down. *God, I wish I could have the same discussion with Donald that I had with Jasmine after her father died*, Ian thought; *this poor man needs to hear his son didn't perish, but I'm not so sure of my theory right now.* Ian looked up again; Donald was wiping his eyes.

"Donald, I've done two experiments recently, trying to store a person's spirit," Ian said. "Both experiments yielded two independent I-nesses. I couldn't store the original I-ness itself. Those results cast doubts on my theory. ...I'm sorry."

Donald looked away and nodded. His face turned very red. He said, "Is there any hope?" He looked back at Ian. "I mean...*I really miss my boy*." He buried his face into his large hand, unable to remain composed any longer. In a distorted voice, Donald cried, "I really miss my boy!"

"I know..." Ian said hoarsely. He hesitated, then added, "There is hope."

Donald lifted his devastated face from his hand to look at Ian.

"There's a realm of awareness that can't be separated from the I-ness, and I can move the realm of awareness around. If I find that I can store the realm of awareness on the computer, then it seems there's hope that storing one's I-ness could be scientifically sound. If it is, then you and I know there's a good chance Donnie was saved."

Donald smiled, nodded, and cried.

*

Ian went back to work with a drive only Sally understood. *There's not going to be another Donnie*, he kept telling himself. Instead of the pain paralyzing his thoughts, seeing Donnie's devastated father now drove Ian with superhuman effort. *I've got to get his boy back*, he kept thinking. He was back to little or no sleep.

"The realm of awareness," Diana overheard him saying as she was leaving his work area after dropping off some food and water, "I must understand it. If there's hope, that's where I'll find it."

CHAPTER
ONE HUNDRED FOUR

"I have a scheduled meeting with Christine here, this afternoon," Ian said during the next meeting of The Group at his compound just outside Olean, New York, consisting of his large country home, his famous observatory with the most powerful telescopes in the Eastern United States, a rare quantum-computer lab, a well-equipped medical lab, a full-scale surgical center, and three guest houses on thirty acres of undisturbed land.

"Why don't we bring her in here so we can all listen?" Mr. Melbourne said.

"I thought you'd like that," Ian said. "She'll be here soon."

*

During the lunchbreak, Ian sat outside. He loved the cool October air and the colorful change of leaves. He walked out the back door onto his wide wooden porch that ran the full width of his house. He placed his food on one of the round white porch tables and sat down. He looked into his large back yard at the children of the members of The Group.

Ah, I love that sound, he thought as the children laughed and played.

"There you are, honey," said Diana. She walked over and

sat down with him. "You know, I've noticed something. At our monthly meetings, whether here or at Rico's mansion, you seem to slip out the back a lot during our breaks."

"I guess I should tell you why." He paused. Diana looked at him curiously. "I really love the sound of the children playing. It's so quiet all month, until the monthly meetings."

"And you always end up playing with the little ones." Diana said. Suddenly, she smiled. "Ian, do you want to have children now? You know I can barely wait to start our own family."

"Yes, I want to very much. But...honey...I don't want to miss out on those irretrievable childhood phases that Rico so eloquently describes. I'm so looking forward to having those precious times with our children. So, I can't have them right now." Ian took a deep breath. "But that's okay, because with immortality, there's no rush. Once I cure catastrophic death, we'll have our children, and I'll be able to share their childhood with them."

Diana looked at Ian. Her face was serious.

"What is it?" Ian asked her.

"Darling, I agree with everything you just said. But please get some rest while you're driving day and night on the cure. Everything will come crashing down if a catastrophe happens to you, my love." She put her hand on his. He looked at her, and he nodded.

"Unc I'n! Unc I'n!" yelled two-year-old little Jakey. He spotted Ian and ran for the porch as fast as his bitty legs could go. As he ran, his head bounced up and down and his cheeks flapped.

Diana burst out laughing. "He's so cute!" she said.

"Unc I'n, Unc I'n!" Little Jakey yelled. He climbed the porch stairs with his nanny's help and ran straight into Ian's arms.

"C'mere little guy!" Ian said. He hoisted Jakey onto his lap, and together, he and little Jakey started singing, "Old MacDonald had a farm, E-I-E-I-O!"

*

After Christine arrived, Ian brought her into the meeting with

979

The Group.

"Remember last time how you told me you seemed to sense yourself pass through the computer?" Ian asked her.

"Yes...yes I mostly was aware of being in my clone, but, for a moment there, I seemed to sense myself in the computer. It was weird."

"Well, next we're going to attempt to explicitly bring your realm of awareness and your I-ness — your spirit, so to speak — into the computer. I put sensors on the computer that'll act as computerized sense organs, which'll let you see and hear, and I put a sort of static field that'll let you think. You'll be able to interface with the world. As you well know, Christine, I must learn how to preserve one's spirit in order to, hopefully soon, eradicate catastrophic death."

"I volunteer," Christine said enthusiastically.

"No fears?"

"None."

"Good. I was hoping you'd say that. I asked you 'cause you've done this before, and I was impressed during that experiment how you handled yourself. Your psychological makeup and motivation is perfect for this."

"Thank you. The whole thing you're doing fascinates me. It's the greatest possible value to mankind, and I'm honored to be part of it."

"Thank you, Christine. The most important goal of this experiment is for you to concentrate on bringing your realm of awareness onto the computer, *completely*. Only by being able to do that can I store people's spirits on computer to eradicate catastrophic death."

"I'll do it, Dr. Scott. I'll give it my all, you know that."

"That I do," Ian said, happy and relieved Christine was his volunteer again. "By the way, how are you and Christine II getting along?"

"She's my closest friend in the world. Now, I honestly can't imagine life without her. I really can't. I was going to tell you, this is something you might want to commercialize."

Sally's eyes suddenly looked down. She was, out of the blue, remembering Eric's final, dying moments in his mother's arms when fear kicked in as he was losing himself forever. After some painful reflection, Sally looked up. Her face glowed with a new light of knowledge.

"People don't realize it, but they're closest to themselves," she said. She had seen several people, including Eric, at their final moments when they were losing themselves. "They'd love to have someone with the same original I-ness as a friend or working partner. ...I would've loved to have had a few people with my I-ness, especially during those years I worked alone." She looked at Ian. He nodded and smiled.

Jeremiah found himself thinking about the painful period when he made the decision to leave Maria for Sally, wishing Ian's amazing technology was available then.

"Wouldn't that be something," Cathy said. "The ultimate friend. I know it sounds weird, but what a wonderful thing."

After a moment of silence, Christine said, "When do we do the experiment?"

"Next week is the earliest I can go."

"Then next week?"

*

"You're becoming an old pro at this," Ian said while gently touching and looking over the thin fibers running from Christine's head to the quantum computer.

"I can't think of anything I'd rather contribute to," Christine said.

"Everything looks good," Ian said to his assistants. "Let's get busy."

"We're ready to go," Melisa said.

"You ready?" Ian said. He looked back at Christine.

"Ready."

"Okay Phil, okay Melisa, you know what to do."

"Download all information first, map the initial charge of I-ness next, then send it over to Christine III," Phil said. He pointed to the quantum computer they named Christine III.

"Then send a continuous stream of the electrical charges of I-ness," Melisa added.

Ian nodded and turned to observe Christine. In about thirty minutes, he thought, she's going to be seeing and hearing and thinking from inside a computer. If I can do this, then I can preserve a person's spirit. There'll be no more losses like poor Donnie.

"Doctor..." Phil said after several minutes, breaking Ian's thoughts.

"Yes?"

"We've sent her cerebral information to the computer, we're about to send the map of her charge of I-ness over, and in a moment we'll begin to stream."

Without saying a word, Ian leaned forward in his chair to observe Christine closely. Her eyes, he silently said in his mind, have that exact same look of intense concentration, just as they did last time.

"Doctor," said Phil, "you might want to come look at this."

Ian turned around to look at the screen showing the activity in Christine's brain and in Christine III, the computer.

"There's electrical activity in Christine III," Phil said.

"I don't believe it," Ian whispered too softly for his assistants to hear.

"The computer's *thinking*, sir," Melisa said.

Ian turned back around. "Christine," he said.

At precisely the same instance, Christine and the computer said, "Yes, I hear you."

"Christine, can you concentrate real hard and take your awareness into the computer?" Ian said. He was breathing quickly from the excitement.

"I'm already there," Christine and the computer said.

"More, Christine...get every bit of your awareness there. Don't hang onto your body...go into the computer...*completely*."

She's really concentrating, Ian silently said to himself as he studied her face. A few minutes later the computer spoke, "I'm completely in here," Christine III said.

Christine's lips moved, Ian noticed, but no voice spoke the words. Only the computer spoke. "Great work!" Ian said. "Describe what's going on."

"I see you. Things look two-dimensional and blurry like I need glasses, but I see you. It's a little strange, but I'm here. I'm right here, all right."

"Yes!" Ian shouted.

"Ouch," the computer said.

"What? What happened?"

"When you yelled, it was too loud. It didn't exactly hurt, but I perceived it as unpleasant."

"Amazing," Ian said, "just amazing. ...Christine, we're going to carry on a conversation as long as you can, all right?"

"Okay."

An hour and twenty minutes later, Christine's heart rate and breathing accelerated. Ian gave the command, "Cut off the continuous streaming." His assistants stopped sending the ongoing charge of I-ness from Christine's brain to the computer's "brain". He stood, staring at Christine. *What's it going to be?* he wondered. *Is her realm of awareness back...or is it still in the computer?* He couldn't stand the suspense, but he was not going to say anything. *I don't want to disorient her*, he thought. Bursting with anticipation, he stared at Christine.

"Over here," the computer said.

Ian snapped his head 45 degrees to his right and stared straight at the computer. His heart pounded so hard in his chest he could hear it. *Have I done it?* he wondered; *have I captured her spirit?* "Christine?" he said timidly.

"Yes," the computer said, "I'm here."

"Ah haaaa!" Ian shouted. "Ya haaaaaa!"

"Oh...please stop. I'm sorry, but my head's pounding."

Ian jerked his head back to his left. Christine had said that. He rushed to the side of her bed. "Christine?" he said.

"Uh hu," she said, obviously not feeling right.

Ian quickly knelt down by her side, "What's the matter?" His heart was pounding again...with fear.

"My head...it really hurts."

Ian looked through the window to the viewing room to call in Sally, but she was already rushing through the door. She stopped at the monitor that scanned Christine's brain. She was looking for any sign of blood leaking into the brain. After a moment, Sally said, "Everything looks okay there."

She went by the bed and knelt next to Ian. "Christine, I'm Doctor Salberg."

"I know," Christine said, smiling slightly as Sally put her

hands against the patient's head. "Does this hurt when I squeeze?"

"No."

Sally moved her hands around again and then squeezed again, this time holding her grip around Christine's hatline.

"How does that feel?" Sally said.

"Better. ...Yeah, that feels good."

Sally took a deep breath and smiled. "She's okay," she told Ian, "she's got an intense stress-related headache."

"Is...is she going to be okay?" Sally looked around; the computer had asked the question.

"Yes...she's going to be just fine," Sally said.

*

What happened? Ian asked himself after he knew Christine was fine. This time we moved Christine's I-ness and awareness — her spirit — successfully to the computer but could not keep it there. We ended up with Christine and Christine III — a computer with a thinking mind and Christine's original I-ness, but not her awareness — not her spirit. ...Why did the computer lose Christine's spirit after having it?

"You gave us quite a scare," Ian said to Christine after she was feeling better.

"I'm sorry, Doctor," she said. "You know, I think I jeopardized the experiment. I feel really bad."

"How do you mean, you think you jeopardized the experiment?"

"I was in the computer, but when Melisa told you my heart rate and breathing were going up, I knew you were going to cut off the continuous stream. I suddenly got really scared that I wouldn't be able to get back to my body. So, right before you cut the continuous stream, my realm of awareness rushed back to my original body."

"I'm relieved to hear that," Ian said.

"You're not upset?"

"You couldn't help that natural impulse, but I now know I'm close with this approach. ...Let me ask you this: If your body were dying, would you get scared and go back?"

Christine thought for a moment, then said, "No...I'd stay in the computer."

"I'm going to need to do another experiment right away."

"Now that I know how I'm going to react, I promise you I'll stay in the computer this time, as long as you'll send me back to my body sometime within a week. ...What will my body and brain be like, anyway, when I'm away — inside the computer?"

Ian hesitated to answer and looked up at the Christine III computer. Finally, he shook his head. "I don't know," he said. "I don't know. No, we can't proceed." He was quiet for awhile, thinking, weighing things in his head. "First I have to be sure I can successfully get the spirit from a computer into a human," he finally said. "When I know I can do that, then we'll do the next experiment. And, yes, I'd like to use you again, Christine. But I can't guarantee you I can get you back into your original body and brain because I don't know what'll happen. I may need to anesthetize your body and brain when your realm of awareness leaves to the computer. That way, your brain stays unconscious, which prevents the possibility of yet another unique I-ness forming. In any case, I at least need to be sure I can get you back into a clone of your body and brain. That I'll be sure of before we proceed."

*

"Please get me out of here!" Christine III screamed again. Ian had kept Christine III's active, thinking mind on the computer to study it and to understand the bigger possibilities of storing one's spirit on the quantum computer. But over the past forty-eight hours, Christine III started, calmly at first, saying she needed to get out of the computer and into a clone. Now, she seemed to panic.

"Christine," Ian said, "You need to remain calm. Otherwise you risk causing the procedure to malfunction. I'm going to get a generic clone in here, and we'll do the transfer."

"Thank you," Christine III said. "It's just that I feel trapped in here. I must get out. I need my arms and legs. I need to move around."

I wasn't able to get the original spirits of George and Christine to leave their original hosts — their bodies — for a substantial length of time, Ian pondered. Now, how am I going to get Christine III to leave her host — the computer? Won't I just end up with a Christine IV in the clone, and Christine III in the computer'll still be there?

The next day, Ian nervously proceeded with the experiment of attempting to transfer the spirit on the computer into a generic clone.

"Christine III," he said while looking at the quantum computer, "when I wake her, just after I send over the initial map of your I-ness," he said while gesturing his head toward the pretty generic clone lying on the bed, "I want you to concentrate on sending your realm of awareness to her. It's crucial for you to fully and completely plant all your realm of awareness in her. If you don't, you'll remain trapped inside that computer. Is that clear?"

"Yes it is. Believe me, *I want out of here!*"

"Okay, we all know what to do," Ian said to his crew, "Let's get to it."

A half hour later, Ian said, "Cut off the continuous stream." The room became very quiet as he looked at the clone on the bed and then at the quantum computer named Christine III.

"Christine III?" he said in nervous anticipation.

"I'm here," the pretty female clone on the bed said. Ian nodded, then walked over to the computer and said, "Christine III, are you in here?" The room was quiet. Not looking away, Ian said again, "Is any part of you still in here?" No answer, just silence.

"There's no activity on the terminal," Melisa said. "The computer's no longer thinking."

Ian studied the screen. All the information in Christine III's brain still existed in the quantum computer, but there was no interfacing with the world and no thinking. It's like, the data's there, Ian thought, but no operating system. The sensors were not active — no seeing, no hearing, no sensory experience, no interfacing, no thinking...no awareness. With the sensors and thinking down like this, Ian thought, Christine III on the computer — her "brain" — is not conscious...perhaps similar to how a biological brain would be if put under anesthesia immediately after transferring its realm of awareness to a computer or clone. But if I brought that unconscious brain up to consciousness, wouldn't that realm of awareness instantly bring about another unique person?

The thoughts that began to bombard Ian were broken by a gentle voice: "I did what you said," the clone said. "I put every bit of my realm of awareness over here. I didn't want to stay inside the computer. I *really wanted* a body."

That's when it hit him: *Desire*, Ian thought, moves the realm of awareness effectively. Christine did *not* desire to leave her body for a computer, whereas Christine III *did* desire to leave the computer for a body. Eureka! Ian felt the significance of that discovery.

"I began to freak out in the computer. I'm so sorry you had to do this emergency experiment, but I just couldn't take it any longer. I was getting frightened in there." Christine III was well aware of how Ian was hoping to preserve the human spirit in a quantum computer for a much longer period of time to eradicate catastrophic death. "I'm sorry."

"Don't be sorry," Ian said quickly. "You just gave me a key missing piece to the puzzle."

CHAPTER
ONE HUNDRED FIVE

"In a couple of years, we'll move here," Jake said. He stopped and absorbed the sights and smells of autumn in Paradise: rolling green hills painted with freshly fallen red and orange leaves, some still dancing in the air before landing like a drop of paint on the ground. Jake took a deep breath of the crisp air. He filled his lungs again with the fresh air and looked at his wrist computer. Jake, Jasmine, and Jakey were in the new Paradise City in New Jersey awaiting *The Great Moment*, which would happen on this day.

Jake and Jasmine continued their leisurely stroll along the walkway next to the river. Little Jakey, now two years and three months old, was running up the grassy knolls and running back down as fast as his tiny legs would carry him, laughing and yelling, "Woaoaoa!"

"Try this!" Jasmine said. She ran up a hill, and then, to Little Jakey's amazement, she lay down and rolled down the hill as fast as she could go. Wow, Jakey had discovered a new adventure in life. Big Jake stopped walking to let his son roll down the same hill over and over again. Jake stood there, filled with love, watching his boy's childhood fun.

As he stood there, his mind went back in time a few days and replayed Daniel's last Thursday-Night announcement: "Good evening, near-immortals. Tonight, we've come to the end of an era. Let me show you something: Do you remember these?" Jake remembered Daniel holding up a piece of paper that looked like a chart of some kind, with over half of its boxes filled in with X's. "This is my Life Chart that I started in the Third Grade." Jake remembered thinking at that moment that Miss Annabelle and her former students must have felt a burst of nostalgia. "Well, those of you who still fill out a Life Chart, as I still do, will never have to do that again, starting next week. Estimated time between a human death on Earth — calculated by a quantum computer passing millions of pieces of information — has been steadily expanding. Garage and in-house entrepreneurs relentlessly remove potential risks everywhere, even risks we do not realize exist. Risks vanish so quickly, we can see permanent, physical changes occurring around us from one day to the next, such as the worldwide elimination of curbside storm drains, replaced almost overnight with curbside microsuction holes. Garage and in-house entrepreneurs, snapping vital pieces one after another into the superpuzzles, helped conquer threatening weather conditions and natural disasters...from hurricanes to earthquakes. The quantum computers almost assure society no one will die from weather conditions or natural disasters again. Superpuzzles involving both large companies and garage entrepreneurs essentially removed the risks even in cars, rocket planes, and supertrains that travel at high speeds. The value of life is the supreme value in the Universe, and many millions of garage and in-house entrepreneurs for the past three-and-a-half years have driven on removing risks. Immortal conscious life is too valuable to accept any potentially deadly risks, no matter how remote the risk. Children, teenagers, and young adults can no longer get seriously hurt in active sports.

"Over the following week, the era of living when near-immortals concern themselves about losing a human life to catastrophe, will end. Merciless eternal pain such as losing Donnie — the last little soldier to die on Earth in the war against death — will end. The estimated length of time before another human loss will become equal to the estimated length of time before catastrophic death is eradicated. Next Thursday, I'll greet you not as near-immortals, but as immortals, as our new era

989

begins. My friends, finally, the human race is going home.

"Before I end this Thursday-Night Announcement, I must deliver this postscript out of respect for a fellow member of The Group and an eternal friend of mine, the great Dr. Ian Scott. He opposes acknowledging The Great Moment. In fact, he calls it The Great Tragedy because he thinks it can cause a sense of relief; the garage entrepreneurs could subconsciously let up just enough...and we end up losing one more Donnie. ...Good-night, near-immortals."

As Jake stood there watching his beautiful wife and beloved little mini-me Jakey rolling down the grass hill, feeling overwhelming love in his heart for his wife and little boy, Jake found himself thinking: All of us harbor an unforgiving fear of a catastrophic accident that could snatch the life of an immortal...of a loved one. Jake winced at the thought as he watched his boy and wife playing. Even though the odds are so minute, he thought, the value is so extreme. The human I-ness, the spirit, needs to somehow become indestructible. Jake subconsciously nodded. The world's pressure certainly has shifted from Sally to Ian as he pursues his theory of preserving the I-ness. Will another person die? Millions of entrepreneurs are working day and night to answer that question with a: NO. But, in the end, it may all come down to Ian and whether or not he can preserve the I-ness. Jake sighed. *What value these twelve students of Miss Annabelle have been to mankind.*

People all around them suddenly huddled into family groups, drawing Jake's attention back to the occasion. At 3:25 p.m. EST on this day, November 3rd, quantum computer #1 estimated statistically that the next catastrophic human loss would occur in slightly more than seventeen months if the definitive cure to catastrophic death were not developed.

Quantum computer #2, at 3:25 p.m. EST, estimated the definitive cure to catastrophic conscious death would be developed in slightly less than eleven months, and its world-wide implementation would extend the estimated next catastrophic human loss beyond what it would take for the definitive cure to reach all segments of the population. In other words, from this point forward, by the odds, no one would die again.

Jake looked at his watch. It was 3:20 p.m. Everyone became silent. Jakey and Jasmine ran to his side. Not a sound. At precisely 3:25 p.m., a chorus of poof sounds filled the air all around them. Suddenly, golden spheres that looked like miniature Suns rose up from the grounds all around Paradise City. There were thousands of those mini-Suns rising up one after the other, filling the sky with more and more mini-suns until a solid cluster of gold formed above them, casting a brilliant golden glow over Paradise City to commemorate The Golden Moment — *The Great Moment.*

"Daddy...LOOK!" Jakey shouted, pointing at the golden sky. Ever since he turned two, he loved to show his dad everything the little fellow thought his dad would find exciting.

"Yes, Jakey...I see that!" Jake answered with great enthusiasm. Jakey proudly smiled. He knew he had shown his father something that pleased him.

The people in Paradise City celebrated The Great Moment. Many of the residents were overcome with emotion. This moment meant that their loved ones and they themselves, by the odds, would not be stolen away by catastrophic death. People were overcome...crying and cheering in the same breath.

Ian, locked in his office in his home, did not go outside. He did not take his eyes off his computer screen. He refused to let The Great Moment slow him down for even a second — just as the quantum computers had calculated.

Jasmine dropped her gaze from the sky...onto Jake. Jake dropped his eyes onto hers and involuntarily gasped; her hair, face, lips, radiated with a golden glow. Her eyes danced with golden sparkles. "Beautiful woman," he whispered, "you're mine, *forever.*"

Jasmine wrapped her arms around Jake and cried, "And you're mine, *forever.*"

Their lips met in their first kiss as immortals. Jake could feel the love inside him flowing through their embrace, into Jasmine, and he could feel Jasmine's love flowing through the embrace deep into his soul...down into his pounding heart. As they stood interlocked in eternal love, a giggling little body pressed itself between their legs. They opened their eyes and looked down at Jakey who had squeezed between them, looking up at them, laughing, blinking his big eyes.

Superpuzzle

"He's ours, *forever*," Jake whispered.

"And in a few days, little Ameena will be with us — our immortal baby girl!" Jasmine said.

"We'll have our daughter *forever*."

"And I didn't have to go through pregnancy and delivery! I still can't get over it!"

"I still can't get over you!" Jake said, and he kissed her glowing, golden lips again.

This golden moment, The Great Moment, meant the odds favored that not another conscious death would occur on Earth. That good news from the computer caused people to celebrate around the world, for that meant citizens of Earth now *formally* lived in the Civilization of the Universe in which no one dies.

Jake threw his head back and shouted victoriously, "The garage and in-house entrepreneurs have done it!"

"Daddy!" scolded Jakey. His dad and mom laughed and kissed again. November 3rd, the day the odds favored no one else would ever die, would become Earth's eternal celebration day for her freedom from conscious death. After their lips pulled apart, Jake looked into his beautiful wife's eyes and calmly added, "Now, it's up to Ian to come through and take us home for good."

Jake then looked around. People were laughing. People were crying. Jake looked back down at his son and smiled at his boy's chubby cheeks glowing in this golden moment like two harvest moons. Jake shook his head at the joy he felt inside. Barely able to stand it, he looked deep into Jasmine's eyes and took a deep breath.

"Darling," he said, "look at him." He gestured his head down toward Jakey. All of a sudden, Jake couldn't talk. He was overwhelmed. But Jasmine knew what was going through his mind.

"It's so wonderful," she whispered. "We're *Earth's first immortals*."

II.

The
Reach Beyond

CHAPTER
ONE HUNDRED SIX

"Darling, it's Al on the phone," Diana said. She walked up the stairs into Ian's work area.

Ian pushed a button on his keyboard.

"Hi, Al," Ian said, talking through his computer.

"Happy New Year, Ian!"

"Oh, Happy New Year to you, Al! Well, I hope this'll be the year I cure catastrophic death."

"You still upset about The Great Moment?"

"The Great Moment drives me crazy; it risks another Donnie. I've seen how the garage entrepreneurs have relaxed a little. I feel more pressure than ever—"

Ian stopped talking. A thought flashed through his mind: I wonder if the quantum computers calculated my reaction to The Great Moment. Did they calculate that I'd intensify my work as others relaxed a bit? After all, only I can do this. In the big picture, could it be for the best, for I'm driven more than ever before to do this?

"Hey Ian," Al said. He broke Ian out of his moment of contemplation. "There's a situation I need to talk to you about. I got a call today from a 52-year-old man. He has a massive aneurysm deep in his brain."

"Well, nowadays the blood flow can be rerouted with

essentially no risk," Ian said.

"I guess this one's different. They can fix it, but apparently, they can't tell for sure which vein to reroute, and there's not enough time to be wrong. There's a good chance of losing him."

"Even with the latest nanotechnologies, they can't tell?"

"Apparently not."

"Wow," said Ian. He shook his head. "I can move his I-ness and spirit to a clone quickly and without risk."

"That's essentially what I told him."

"Do we have time to clone his body?"

"No, we need to move immediately. His aneurysm could burst at any moment."

"Then we'll use a generic clone," Ian said. He punched some data into his computer. "I've got a male clone ready to go immediately."

*

"Hi, I'm Nick's doctor, Michael Marley."

"Glad to meet you, Dr. Marley. I'm Ian Scott, and this is Christine. She's gone through the procedure twice and will be a great help to Nick. How's his condition?"

The three of them looked through the viewing window into the procedure room where Ian's assistants were prepping Nick.

"Not good," said Dr. Marley. "Oh, he feels fine, he feels nothing wrong. But the situation inside his brain is really bad; he might go tonight. The aneurysm could burst at any moment, and the damage to the brain would be instant and irreparable. He'd quickly die."

Ian nodded and said, "Let's go in and see him." The three walked into the procedure room. "Hello Nick. I'm Dr. Ian Scott, and this is Christine. She's gone through this experiment twice and has some important first-hand knowledge that'll assure your transfer is a success."

Nick was sitting in the "up" position of the bed. His body was prepped with tiny fiber-optic wires attached to his shaved head. He sighed and nodded.

"You nervous?" Christine asked him.

"Yes, I'm really, really nervous."

"Nick, you must understand where things can go wrong," said Ian. "If you don't go 100% into this transfer, you'll stay in your body, and you could die because of the timing of this thing."

"Oh, I'll do this with all my desire," said Nick quickly. "The reason I'm nervous isn't what you think. I'm scared to death my aneurysm could go at any moment as I sit here. I'm so scared of losing my eternity. I just want to get safely in that clone." Nick gestured his head toward the generic clone in the bed next to him that was breathing with the help of a respirator.

Ian took a deep breath of relief. *Perfect*, he thought. He said, "Thank goodness. That's why I brought Christine here to help inspire that attitude."

Christine was nodding. "It's so important to want it badly. I got scared and the transfer of my I-ness and spirit didn't happen. But then again, I wasn't dying. Just be prepared, though, things seem weird and confusing. You have to push your realm of awareness into the clone. You have to push your perception of the world into the clone. You have to look through the clone's eyes, smell through its nose, and most important, think within its head. Once you're there, you'll know it. Then concentrate on those perceptions — seeing, hearing, smelling, tasting...and thinking from the clone's head. Don't let your realm of awareness slip back to your current body. Don't get scared."

Nick listened to every word. When he realized Christine was done, he said, "Okay...I'm ready. Thank you. Believe me, I won't go back."

*

After the procedure was underway, Christine stood close to Ian and said, "This is a rare and beautiful occasion. You're saving a person's life here."

"Isn't it exciting?" Ian said. Then he glanced away from the computer screen to Christine for a second and said, "You know, after I transferred Christine III from the quantum computer to the generic clone, I knew the transfer of the I-ness and realm of awareness would be successful from human to human. I planned to call you soon to consider the experiment." He looked back at the computer screen. "But I'll get my answers today."

"I would've done it, you know."

"I know," Ian said. He looked away from the computer screen for a longer moment this time to study Christine's eyes. He thought he caught a glimpse of sadness there. "You know," he said, "I'll always feel a deep gratitude to you for being my volunteer through these critical experiments."

Christine smiled. She looked at Nick lying on the bed and said, "I just want to do whatever I can to help bring mankind a definitive cure to death. When you're ready to try this from human to computer and back again, I'm ready."

Ian smiled and nodded. "How's his vitals?" he called out.

"Everything's great," Phil said.

Ian studied Nick. He looked relaxed. He's at peace with this, Ian thought, this'll work. Ian studied Nick's expressions. What a handsome man, Ian thought; those powerful brown eyes unmistakably speak for the man, the power to create radiates from those eyes. I wonder what he's created. He's so frighteningly close to a sudden death.

But there's more than power alone radiating from those eyes, Ian pondered. There's compassion. I know that with the power to create values comes the passion to solve problems. I can see into those eyes...they tell Nick's story: creating values and solving problems for civilization fills those eyes with the love and compassion found in the new God-Man. He feels the supreme value of life, he feels supreme love for mankind.

And then, suddenly, the warm loving glow vanished from Nick's eyes. It was gone. Ian blinked several times and looked closer at Nick's eyes; they were frozen in a dead cold stare, fixed on nothing...nothing at all. A moment ago existed the supreme value in the universe burning with love and compassion, now existed a dull meaningless stare.

Oh my...his soul has left its body, Ian thought, his eyes are no longer Nick's. They're just eyes — eyes of a wax figure — lifeless, empty, a manufactured art form, void of the glow of life. The soul is gone.

Ian looked at the generic clone. His eyes were open and looking around. Then the clone stopped looking around and looked straight ahead. Ian could see that those eyes were concentrating. Ian studied those eyes. Every second that passed,

998

Ian saw more and more familiarity there until, all at once, he saw Nick...the powerful, compassionate man. *That is Nick*, unmistakably Nick. Ian looked back at Nick...his eyes were vacant; he was forever gone. His soul had traveled into the clone.

Without even looking at the computer screen, Ian said, "Shut it off."

"The continuous streaming...is now off," Phil said. "We show full thinking activity in the clone's brain, zero thinking activity in Nick's brain...just life-sustaining reflexes."

Ian looked at the clone and gently said, "Nick, you're safe now."

Nick, now in the generic clone, turned his head sideways to look at Ian, then past Ian, at his body left behind. He stared at his body and face left behind. He rolled off the bed and slowly approached his body given to him at conception, serving him for over half a century. He walked over and gently rubbed his fingers across the forehead. His former eyes reflexively blinked and then stared ahead helplessly. Nick sighed. He knew his handsome face was now a vegetable.

"Ahhh, look at you," he said. He rubbed the palm of his hand lovingly along the side of the nonresponsive face before him. The body was breathing and warm, but the face was empty.

Nick sat down on the bed next to his old body. He sadly looked at his old self. There before him was himself for all his life until now, breathing and alive but without his spirit to serve. There before him sat himself — soulless, helpless. Nick leaned over and hugged his old body.

"You've been such a wonderful companion," Nick said. Suddenly, Nick's old body twitched in Nick's new arms. "Are you okay?" Nick said. He pulled back his head to look at his old face — the face he had seen all his life in the mirror. The eyes of that handsome face before him blinked several times. The whites of those eyes reddened with each blink until they were, all at once, severely bloodshot. Nick held his former body in his arms as the muscles went limp and the head fell forward against Nick's new body.

"Look at the computer imaging," Phil called out to Ian.

Ian looked at the brain scan on the computer screen and saw

a massive hemorrhage killing Nick's body. When Nick realized what was going on — the aneurysm had burst — he broke down and cried as he watched his beloved body dying before him. He hugged his warm body tightly as it died.

"Good-bye," he whispered, "I'll miss you."

*

"I freely move the human spirit around now. The breakthrough came by understanding the three inseparable components to the human spirit, which are the *charge of I-ness,* the *realm of awareness,* and its mover — the *person's desire* to move to another body."

Jake looked around the room at the members of The Group as Ian talked. Those mighty achievers looked like children listening to a fascinating tale.

"But there's a problem...a big problem. One of those inseparable components to the human spirit — the realm of awareness — can be only one place at a time, not two. Two bodies or a body and a quantum computer can initially have the same I-ness, but because both have their own realms of awareness, they're instantly two different people. When the original body dies, that original realm of awareness — that human spirit — is lost forever even though we've duplicated his original I-ness. And that means I can't preserve his spirit as a backup in case of catastrophic death. His realm of awareness, *who he is*, dies with the catastrophe. So..." Ian took a deep breath, "that's bad news. I'm not able to eradicate catastrophic death. There can be only *one* realm of awareness that *moves* to another place, never losing that original realm of awareness of the original person. In other words, I can move the human spirit around, BUT I CAN'T PRESERVE IT." Ian stopped. His voiced dropped. He said, "I'm beginning to think the idea of preserving the spirit is fundamentally flawed."

Jake looked around and saw terror in the former classmates' eyes, for that statement reached beyond to even wider implications: If the human spirit could not be preserved...that placed a heavy doubt on whether it was even possible within the laws of science. If not, Jake thought, Zons could *not* have saved our lost loved ones.

Jake rubbed his hand across the back of his neck and ran those thoughts through his head again: We've actually achieved capturing the human spirit; we can actually move it around from one physical carrier to another, but we can't *preserve it*, which we somehow need to do to wipe out catastrophic death...and to hope our lost loved ones didn't perish with death.

"I've nearly conceded," said Ian, continuing his terrifying findings toward a horrific conclusion. "It may be fundamentally impossible to do. I know how this hurts the possibilities that we'll ever again see our lost loved ones. I feel sick about my findings." He shook his head. "Either a realm of awareness is there, in *one* physical place, or it is gone, dead. I have confidence this procedure could obsolete the Operation as a better way to move a person's mind and spirit to a younger clone, but the eighteen-again serum that reverses aging would probably win that battle. My objective, of course, has been to preserve the human spirit in order to prevent the catastrophic loss of another Donnie. I'm still upset about The Great Moment, because now I'm completely stuck. I guess the garage and in-house entrepreneurs could continue to effectively eradicate catastrophic death. But I won't try to hide the fact that my failure casts a dark shadow over our hopes to see our lost loved ones again." Ian sighed bitterly. "I'm not giving up yet, but I'm really stuck. In fact, I've decided I have to turn away from this for awhile. I'm going to turn outward, toward the cosmos, and bury myself in the Space Library. Sometimes I need to do this — expand outward in order to get an insight inward...*something* to break this stalemate."

Jake took a deep breath and looked around. Ian had voiced what The Group dreaded most. The anxiety of the anticivilization was back.

CHAPTER
ONE HUNDRED SEVEN

That evening, the monthly celebration among the Group's families in Ian's compound seemed empty. Anxieties from the anticivilization bothered the superachievers. But, Jake thought, you can't tell anything's wrong by looking at the children. Tonight, besides 19-year-old Monica, the children wanted to sit together at their own table in the large buffet-style banquet room. Two-year-old Jakey wanted to sit with the "big" kids. So Reginald, Alexis, Rosa, Rico Jr., Danny, now teenagers, and eleven-year-old Tony, sat at a large round table with little Jakey. Rosa and Rico Jr. sat on both sides of Jakey and helped him with his dinner.

Jake listened in delight to the conversations and the carefree laughter from that table behind him. He particularly enjoyed hearing his two-and-a-half-year-old Jakey joining into the conversation and laughter. Ah, listen to him, Jake said to himself, he's in heaven. Jake turned around to see his talkative two-year-old son at the table where the "big kids" sat. Ah, look at him, Jake said to himself, he believes he's a big boy of the world now. Jake watched his son talking and laughing, just socializing effortlessly. Jake was filled with pride.

"He's the next generation," Jasmine whispered.

Jake was quiet for a moment, then he said, "If something ever happened to us, we'd likely never see him again." He was reflecting the somber sentiments of Ian in the meeting earlier that day.

Jasmine sighed. "I hope Ian finds a way; I hope our lost ones are waiting for us. I hope one day daddy sees our little Jakey and Ameena." Jasmine had just expressed what the members of The Group had been feeling since the meeting.

Jake put his arm around Jasmine. Some other members of The Group heard Jasmine's comments.

"I'm not giving up, honey," Ian said paternally. "I'm just shifting my focus out into the cosmos. I actually feel I'll get my answers faster that way."

Jasmine smiled and said, "I know, Ian."

*

Jake looked at his beautiful wife sleeping, and he took the quiet moment to simply enjoy watching her. The more he watched her, the more she looked different, younger. What a woman I have, he thought. What's this? She's smiling in her sleep?

"That's so beautiful," Jake whispered.

At that moment, Jasmine opened her eyes. She looked at Jake, then her eyes quickly glanced around the room. "I was dreaming. I was with Daddy again, and I was so *happy*." She lay still, trying to absorb the happy remnants of her dream.

"This was how I felt when I woke up every morning as a little girl, after spending three beautiful hours with daddy the evening before." Her thoughts were racing back to her childhood. "Oh, yeah...I used to always wake up with a smile on my face."

After searching her memory, she said, "It's almost as if daddy visited me last night." Her smile slowly faded as she remembered the last meeting of The Group and Ian's findings.

A sound interrupted her thoughts. "I'll get her," Jasmine said, slowly getting off the bed.

A moment later, she returned, nursing their eleven-week-old daughter, Ameena. Many new moms took the nursing pill to still nurse, even though they now bypassed pregnancy and delivery. "Jakey's still sleeping," Jasmine said. Ameena stopped nursing and strained her happy eyes back to see her daddy. Jake laughed; he felt like laughing a lot when he was with his infant daughter and toddler son. Hearing her daddy laugh, Ameena wriggled in delight. Jake knew he had discovered the preciousness he witnessed between Rico and his children.

It was Saturday, their family day together. They really enjoyed their Saturday activities together — not because of the activities per se, but for the feeling of being *together*. Together, as a family, Jake and Jasmine would *feel* the happiness they built and earned through their value creations.

But today, as Jasmine sat on the bed with the baby, Jake noticed an unusual look on her face.

"What is it, my love?" he asked.

"When I picked up Ameena, I all of a sudden felt there was something we must do. ...I'm not sure why, but something is telling me to get to the Space Library."

The Space Library was Ian's creation as president of Beyond. It was similar in concept to the privatized Library of Congress for books, but for data collected from space. Most data collected from space was sent to the Space Library. Some "garage" entrepreneurs and some large companies on a rapidly progressing, specific commercial course did not feed their data to the Space Library, for all data there was for anyone's beneficial use, which was different in nature than entrepreneurs' web sites where data was intellectual property that others did not touch unless directly reaching an agreement with its owner. Data at the Space Library could be tapped and used by anyone, unilaterally, although Ian established a very attractive incentive for scientist-entrepreneurs to contribute data captured from space: he set up a generous sliding scale of *puzzle-piece royalties* as he called them. Any entrepreneur or business that used data from the Space Library as a piece toward a commercial product was obliged to pay the puzzle-piece royalty to the original scientist-entrepreneur who contributed the data to the Space Library. This was extremely conducive to feeding data to Ian's Space Library, for he had several hundred full-time scientists working around the clock examining the massive accumulation of data, always driving toward Neothink puzzle building to create commercial values.

Ian had moved his work on capturing a person's I-ness with

1004

a quantum computer to a section within the Space Library. Ian found, as is often the nature of science, that he gained crucial understandings for his work on the definitive cure to catastrophic death by going out to the broadest reaches of the cosmos through the Space Library and, at the same time, going in to the most specific focus on the mind through the quantum computers. Ian worked an enormous workload and long hours, integrating and coordinating this dual, outward-into-the-cosmos work with his inward-into-the-mind work. In an earlier article, Jake and Jasmine expressed how much Ian's split schedule and long work hours in his Space Library reminded them of Sally in her lab during the frantic SSL period with her split schedule on both Project Life and Project Sustain Life.

"Can we start tomorrow?" Jake asked, looking at Jasmine curiously. "You know Ian's in the Space Library on Sundays."

But something was driving Jasmine to get to the Space Library immediately. "I can't wait, darling," she said, almost in a panic.

"Great! Let's get with it!" Jake said, doing a western roll off the bed. He loved a mystery. He loved making discoveries and creating new values that did not exist before. And when Jasmine could not wait one day more to go, he figured her widely integrating, creative right brain might be on the verge of a big-puzzle breakthrough that her logical left brain could not quite snap together yet.

The two of them rushed to get ready as though they were late for catching a plane. Ian's Space Library, however, was just a few blocks away.

*

Ian saw them come in, Ameena dangling against Jake's stomach in a baby wrap. Whenever Jake walked in the Space Library, he thought how inappropriate the term *Library* seemed. Inside the "Library" seemed nothing at all like a library. This "Library" was stuffed with hundreds of computers and hundreds of men and women intensely working on them. The inside of the Space Library seemed more like the inside of a software company.

1005

Superpuzzle

"You guys are really behind!" Ian yelled from the loft overseeing the large computer-stuffed front room upon seeing Jake and Jasmine. And Ian meant it. "Two weeks is just too long to be away from this place. This is the epicenter of almost everything reaching out into the Civilization of the Universe. We find it first here. So much has been found this past week!"

Jake looked at Jasmine. Her sense of urgency proved to be right. They needed to be here. Jakey had already run into the child-care play area. He and the other children loved the large indoor playground and activity center, packed with mazes of tunnels to crawl through, arcade and video games, singing karaokes, arts and crafts, a learning room, and the newest virtual reality stations for the kids to explore.

"Ian," Jake said, looking at the great scientist, "can the Patterson Group set up a small office here. Jasmine and I will track progress day by day."

"An office? You need more than that — you need twenty-four/seven coverage from now on. You'll see what I mean, come on." Ian nearly ran down the stairs, and led them into another room filled with what seemed to be hundreds more computer terminals. Some were manned, some were not. But all had a series of charts on them.

"What's all this?" Jasmine asked, not remembering all those computers here a week ago.

"That's what I'm telling you. Every computer in here contains several Overlay Charts revealing Zons at work out there. We've uncovered hundreds the past week alone."

"Why all of a sudden?" Jake asked.

"Lots of reasons...from my data, my physicists, my techniques, my computers. But let me tell you, next week when I get my new telescopes operating, we'll see perhaps thousands of demonstrations of Zons."

Jake knew now that the Space Library was the place to be.

"But Jake, here's what *I must* show you. We found it last night." Ian led Jake and Jasmine to a computer that had several physicists around it.

"Can you men step back for a minute?" Ian asked. As they did, Ian said, "Anything new you can tell me?"

"We've determined the date of the event," said a young man

who looked to be about eighteen years old. "It happened eleven years ago. If a temporary or continuous beam were sent, our guys will find it either in the archives or on a dish before today's over." Jake knew the young physicist was a Body II. Jake could now spot Body IIs by the wisdom encased in such young bodies.

Ian's eyes opened wide. "Good work."

Jake looked at Jasmine, then back at Ian. Jasmine pulled out her pad and automatic pencil. Little Ameena was smiling at everybody, sensing the excitement in the air.

"What's going on?" Jasmine asked.

"It's not happy news," Ian answered, "but it's very important. Look here." He pointed at two charts on the computer screen. "The first chart shows the nonconscious course of mass and energy in a specific planetary system in a nearby star system only ten light years away. The second chart shows the actual course of mass and energy that took place. Now..." Ian leaned over and pushed a few buttons on the keyboard, "let's superimpose them. ...There!"

Jake and Jasmine saw one chart consisting of many irregular squiggles.

"As you know," said Ian, "those squiggles represent conscious interference altering the nonconscious course of mass and energy. Now, I'll bring up several superimposed Overlay Charts from other planetary systems about the same age as this one." Ian leaned over the keyboard. Suddenly, the chart they had been looking at reduced in size right in the middle of the screen as eight other charts appeared around it.

"Look!" Ian said, pointing at the nine charts.

Jake and Jasmine leaned close to the screen to study the charts. The other eight had squiggles that looked very consistent to each other whereas the one in the middle looked quite different.

"What does it mean?" Jasmine asked.

"We have, in total, over two thousand Overlay Charts of planetary systems with conscious control," Ian said. "They all have a correlation to the eight consistent charts here. Over two thousand Overlay Charts with this correlation demonstrate the peaceful, borderless, business dynamics of the Civilization of the Universe with open-ended value creation. ...I believe this chart here demonstrates an unbelievably tragic event: the culmination of the anticivilization ending in nuclear holocaust. Our spectrographic analysis of this planet confirms this unbelievable tragedy."

Jake and Jasmine both gasped and sat down. The thought of conscious death now seemed bizarre and barbaric, from a quickly forgotten, distant past. But the idea of *mass death*...they could not fathom it and had to think about it in disbelief for awhile before talking. Little Ameena, sensing the horror in her parents' expression, started crying loudly.

"Was the entire conscious race obliterated?" Jake finally said, hoarsely.

"We don't know," one of the competent-looking scientists answered. "We're searching through our data gathered over the past year for a beam, and we have every dish we own aggressively trying to locate a beam."

Jake nodded, and his eyes glazed over.

"Thank you, guys," Ian said. That was the scientists' cue, and they swarmed back to the computer.

"Come with me," he said to Jake and Jasmine.

They followed Ian, in a daze, through the massive Space Library building into another room with just as many computers, and all were manned.

"I'm directly feeding my archives and all my dishes into these computers," Ian said. "If anyone survived and sent a beam in our direction within the first year after the nuclear destruction, then it would've reached us by now, and we'll find it soon."

Jake knew that he must jump all over this story and feed it through Patterson's cable TV channel and get a full-scale article in the next morning's paper. But, he and Jasmine never faced death like this. Even though they did not know the people who were obliterated, they could not come to grips with the notion of conscious life — an entire conscious civilization — being eliminated from existence.

"In order to approach this story right, I need a half hour to cope," Jake told Ian. Jasmine nodded in agreement. Little Ameena was sucking her thumb for comfort. "Then Jasmine and I and the whole might of the Patterson Media Group will give this full coverage."

Beholding the Puzzle-Picture

Ian expected Jake's reaction, for Ian had gone through the same thing upon the grisly discovery.

*

Al Patterson put his cable TV station on full, 24-hour coverage at the Space Library. Jake and Jasmine were intensely at work trying to pull together the full story and the enormous number of details for their front-page story to go Sunday morning in all Patterson Papers. Ian set up a large room at the Space Library for the Patterson Group, including a sleepover room for Jake and Jasmine.

A little after 10:15 p.m., Ian announced over the PA system for everyone in the Space Library to gather in the large front room. When Jake entered, hundreds of scientists already stood waiting; all were talking to one another. A moment later, Ian addressed them from the loft area so they could all see him.

"When I announced for you to gather here, less than ten people knew. By my quick calculations on how fast people can talk, I figure that by now, five minutes later, about half of you know." Several people in the crowd chuckled.

Then, Ian shouted, "A beam was isolated!"

A great cheer exploded from those who did not know as well as from those who did, for a beam meant *conscious life.* Someone survived!

CHAPTER
ONE HUNDRED EIGHT

"It's a simple radio beam with a brief message that repeats over and over," Ian explained. "The syntax is strikingly close to English and is now being decoded by our language decryption computers."

At noon the next day, East Coast time, Ian addressed the crowd again. The decryption experts were able to crack the message's meaning. Ian would now read it over the PA system to his scientists and the Patterson Group, which was sending his presentation live.

Much of the world tuned in. A new rating service gave a color code to TV programming in regards to newsworthiness, historical importance, intellectual importance, and entertainment value. The highest color rating of purple had never shown up before.

Since Patterson's cable TV coverage began the previous afternoon at the Space Library, however, the color glowing next to the Patterson Channel, for the first time since the rating service began, was purple. Thus, nearly every person around the world who turned on his TV turned to the Patterson Channel. Nearly two billion people around the world were eagerly waiting for this moment. ...Ian began his announcement:

"Ladies and gentlemen around the world: it seems so hard to believe that an entire civilization eliminated itself from existence. Although our civilization once came very close to the same end, now it seems impossible, as though it could have never happened.

"I have over two thousand Overlay Charts here at the Space Library that show the Civilization of the Universe exists in pure peace, pure honesty, pure business, pure love. Yesterday, we discovered one anomaly. That civilization was destroyed by violence, dishonesty, government. The nuclear destruction of an entire civilization occurred on a planet ten light years away. The nuclear holocaust occurred eleven years ago."

Ian paused to let viewers recall the nearly forgotten concepts of violence, dishonesty, government.

"We have received a radio beam sent from that planet a few months after the event that killed its civilization.

"The language spoken was close to English, and we have decoded it. ...I will now read to you the decoded message."

The Patterson Channel had been covering the discovery for nearly 24 hours now, so the viewers had time to brace themselves and grasp the magnitude of the loss. They were able to listen now, and concentrate. Ian picked up a piece of paper and read the decoded message. Jake got goose bumps listening to the message of a conscious being from another planet:

"They did it. The master neocheaters let the nuclear bombs fly, and I believe everyone died, but me. Yeah, those humanoids — those leaders — thought they would be safe in their bunkers built by their own scientists. Ha!

"My name is Beorapparaus Rasaraus. I'm 29 years old."
Ian paused and explained his astronomers had calculated his age in Earth years and that his name was *not* translated — he was actually called Beorapparaus on his planet. Then, Ian continued reading the decoded message of Beorapparaus:

"I'm sending this message after a personal epiphany. I was a wealthy geologist, and for years I used my wealth to build a large underground bunker that would survive the predictable holocaust. I could see it coming and refused to let those humanoids destroy me.

Superpuzzle

"*But here is where my plan went wrong: I built a bunker large enough and stocked enough to hold 300 people. This post-war civilization would be the rise of the honest civilization on our planet.*

"*Of course, the carefully selected 300 people lived normal lives. They were to arrive at any serious warning signs of a confrontation. …But there were none. One night during a week when I was in the bunker running pressure tests on the caliche walls, the bombs flew. Every government that controlled nuclear bombs launched them all in the most unbelievable yet predictable act of our dishonest anticivilization: total self-annihilation.*

"*For a few months in my bunker, I could not comprehend what it must be like outside. Not until I emerged did I realize the horror. I cannot go near the cities again and see the deceased. By my measurements, no one else survived unless some others built bunkers of my caliber. However, sending radio messages around my planet has not drawn any indication of life. I think the radiation killed all survivors.*

"*I've gone through something far beyond what psychologists called clinical depression. With everyone dead, I can't even feel right about feeling bad about myself or my emotional needs. For months, I asked myself: What difference does anything I do now make? What difference do I make? What difference could I make? None!*

"*A few nights ago, I lay in my bed, suffering from the loss, every moment of every day, yet I could not even acknowledge my emotional suffering because of the magnitude of the loss around me — all the little children are dead!*"

Ian put down the paper from which he was reading Beorapparaus's decoded message to gather himself. That last comment nearly broke Ian's heart. To continue, he had to stop thinking about what he was reading. He took a deep breath and said, "The next several lines did not resemble English or any language known on Earth. Its tonality sounded like a mix between a sad, sad emotional cry and an outburst for vengeance of some sort. Our language decryption experts speculate that Beorapparaus emotionally broke down at this point, thinking about all the death, especially the innocent children destroyed by the forces of the anticivilization—" Ian's voice broke and he stood blinking helplessly at the cameras for a moment; but he took a deep breath and was able to regroup and continue, "and Beorapparaus yelled out a cry of sorrow for the victims followed by a cry of damnation against the leaders."

Not one of Ian's former classmates had seen him emotionally break down since the day he was not allowed to see Miss Annabelle upon her release from prison nearly thirty-three years before. They thought he might break down now from this enormous loss of innocent life, especially when Beorapparaus referred to the lost children. Ian braced himself and said, steadily, "Now, I'll continue with the rest of Beorapparaus's decoded message." Ian looked down and continued reading:

"Although I didn't allow myself the luxury to contemplate my feelings or my fate, I was far, far beyond clinical depression. The horror, the magnitude of the loss caused me to vomit continuously. Although I never let myself think about myself, on this particular evening, I quickly knew I would end my life. There was no physical or psychological sense to continue suffering.

"During my final moments, I felt relief that my suffering would soon be over. For the first time, I didn't feel nauseated.

"As I carefully mixed my fatal drink, I felt my first state of physical equilibrium since the event. I started thinking clearly for the first time. I was the last of civilization. When I go, I thought, there'll be nothing more. While thinking about the end, I started wondering, how did it all begin...how did we get here in the first place? I started thinking about the massive Universe. One thought led to another, when suddenly a picture formed in my mind: I envisioned conscious life not just on my devastated planet, but all throughout the vast Universe. Of course!

"As that picture formed in my mind, I felt some relief. Then I started to see color in that mental picture. Of course...those civilizations even a little older than mine would have had to leap past their evil ones. Their growing power could only exist in pure rationality, pure honesty...as my civilization proved at the cost of hundreds of millions of children..." Ian dropped his head and squeezed the tear ducts in his eyes between his thumb and index finger. Every time Beorapparaus spoke of the children, Ian felt it deeply. This was Donnie, millions of times over. He

1013

dare not let himself think about it or ponder why, lest he break down right there and then. He sniffed his tears back and looked up.

"The same nondecodable cry of sorrow and damnation occurred again here," he said in a whisper. Then, after another pause, Ian continued Beorapparaus's message:

"That means, civilization not only still exists, but exists all around me. I now have a reason for living, for I think I can, somehow, make a difference. I can be productive again. I just don't know how to put values into the civilization that surrounds me. To learn how to do that has given me reason to live."

Ian put the paper down and looked at his audience, and somberly said, "That's it. Apparently, just one man survived the unimaginable event. His beam reached Earth just a couple of months ago. Of course, we'll continue feeding it into our computers in case he started using his beam to communicate his progress. Also, we'll continue searching in the event he's sending a separate beam reflecting his progress.

"If we can determine that he has discovered Nature's Quintessential Secret and is on a vector of open-ended value creation, then the odds are very high that Beorapparaus is happy and, therefore, alive today, ten years later. He would be just 39 years old now. If we can demonstrate he has learned, in his situation, how to become a value creator, then he has reason to live on, and I believe we should send him a beam to let him know we're coming to get him."

The somber crowd burst into applause for Ian's intentions.

*

"Do you know where Ian went?" Diana asked Jake moments after Ian's announcement to the world.

Jake looked up from the video replay. "No, didn't notice," he said.

Diana checked Ian's office in the Space Library. He was not there. With no sign of him in the crowded rooms, she went back to their living quarters in the Space Library.

She opened the door to their Space Library suite.

"Ian!" she said. There before her was her husband sitting on the sofa, slouched over, his head buried in his arms folded across his knees.

"I...I've got to find a way to electronically store a person's spirit," he said, "'cause if I don't...if it's fundamentally flawed...then Donnie's gone forever."

"But, Ian—"

"Then all those billions of people are gone forever!" He lifted his head off his arms and looked at Diana. His face radiated terror.

"Oh, my darling," Diana said. She rushed over to him and got on her knees and hugged him.

"I just can't prove anything, Diana! I just can't prove anything right now!"

CHAPTER
ONE HUNDRED NINE

"Thank you so much for coming; I knew you would," Ian said to The Group. He looked around at his closest friends. They stood in the conference room in the Space Library late that night. Travelling across the country took just a couple of hours in the rocket planes that exited and re-entered the atmosphere. Miss Annabelle had to teach the next morning, but pulling all-nighters was no problem now with her 23-year-old body. Ian continued, "About four hours ago, we found another beam. My computer experts on translations and encryption are working on it right now. I looked at what they have, so far, just before this meeting. I'm excited to announce that Beorapparaus has discovered Nature's Quintessential Secret — he has become an aggressive value creator and is moving in an open-ended vector of value creation. He's sending all his progress through the second beam we found. That means, to me, the odds are that he is now, ten years later, alive and happy. ...Ladies and gentlemen, let's go get him!"

"Let's go get him!" The Group, like a group of third-graders, yelled back with a burst of sheer glee. Jake yelled it too and felt that burst of glee. Wow, he thought, to save one life, *one* life, is *everything* to that conscious being. Beorapparaus needs *us* to bring him to civilization, Jake pondered; we are *his* Zons.

Suddenly, Jake grasped the big picture: there are many, perhaps infinite levels of Zons. Then Jake remembered Jeremiah's Church of God-Man definition of a Zon: the God-Man who *creates* new realms of consciousness, through creating new realms of existence. This is our initiation into Zonhood, Jake thought, chuckling to himself at the idea of *Zonhood*. We aren't creating a new realm of consciousness, but we are reaching into another realm beyond our own to save consciousness. Doing this, he thought with great satisfaction, lifts us from God-Man to the first-level Zon. ...Now Jake finally knew what the *second* puzzle was, recalling the night before the Operation four years before when Mr. Melbourne had said The Group was putting together the final pieces of the *first* puzzle, biological immortality. *Ah ha*, Jake thought, whereas the first puzzle was saving our own consciousness from death, our second puzzle is saving consciousness beyond our own from death. Hmmm, he thought, what does that mean with all the Zons out there?

Before he could pursue that thought, Jake became aware that The Group was talking quickly, passionately, putting together their next great superpuzzle since curing death on Earth. This reminds me, Jake thought, of the morning after the reunion in the morning room when these great people started their first superpuzzle. Jake sat back in awe, watching The Group, working together again, their extraordinary Neothinking in high gear, building their first great *Zon* superpuzzle.

As Jake listened to them talk about saving Beorapparaus's life, he felt polar feelings yanking back and forth within him, fighting for dominance: the overwhelming sadness of the destruction of an entire civilization of billions of people, including hundreds of millions of young children...versus the joy of saving life beyond our realm of consciousness, leaping into Zonhood.

"What time frames are we dealing with?" Jasmine asked The Group, digging for details for the article she and Jake would be writing until 2:00 a.m. — the latest time the Patterson Papers could hold its presses. Of course, she and Jake would continue expanding this article through the night and into the next day because the Internet edition was updated continually around the clock.

"Our company *Beyond* has just opened up the capacity for

multi-decade, manned deep-space missions, largely because of recent breakthroughs in controlled nuclear fusion and matter/antimatter energy sources," Ian said. "We're still in need of several technological breakthroughs before we can launch, but technology is advancing so fast now, we can begin planning immediately and start production of portions of the ship immediately. Let's see...it's early February now...hummn...I'd say we can look for a launching date before Thanksgiving. Yeah, I'd say we can launch her in nine or ten months."

"Nine or ten months!" Jake could not help himself, "Yes!" he shouted. He thought Ian would say something like two-and-a-half years. "And you're calculating into that time those several needed technological breakthroughs?" he asked.

Ian nodded confidently.

"Oh man, *I love the supersociety*!" Jake said with an incredible grin. He thought about how knowledge, technology, values advanced so quickly each day, each *hour*, bringing forth thrilling news every day, throughout the day.

"The nature of technological breakthroughs has completely changed in the supersociety," Ian said. "In the anticivilization, a technological breakthrough came first, then entrepreneurs would need months or years to figure out how to apply it commercially and create a demand for it. In the supersociety, by contrast, superpuzzles form quickly, and during their formation, several technological breakthroughs are often needed to complete the superpuzzles. Therefore, such Neothink superpuzzle formations of advanced, commercial products put forth great marketing pressures to make the necessary technological breakthroughs. The specific breakthroughs needed are known *before* they're made. They are, in essence, made 'on schedule', quickly and efficiently—"

A rapid, urgent knock on the glass door cut off Ian and momentarily stopped the meeting. Ian waved in the attractive woman.

"Sorry to interrupt, but I thought you needed to know this right away. Sir, tens of millions of people from all over the world are electronically filling our cash accounts." Her voice was throttled with emotions, feeling the *compassion* of the human race. "They say it's to go toward Project-Save-Beorapparaus.

Sir," she gasped with tension, for she was so proud and so moved, "we've already surpassed a trillion dollars and the money just doesn't stop coming in." She put her hand over her mouth; tears filled her eyes. "I'm sorry," the young woman said; some tears escaped and bounced off her cheeks, "it's all just so much to take in. I'm just so sorry for those who perished, and just so proud of our people."

Everyone stopped for a moment. In the midst of absorbing the horrible loss, they felt the compassion, the *love* of the human race. In the heat of the unraveling discovery, everyone was brought to a stop because they were so moved.

Jake glanced around the room; everyone seemed to be searching within. As those great people sat in silence, Jake could see the love among them. They looked so young and innocent — like children. They looked so beautiful.

This magical moment happened once before, Jake thought. In the third grade, Sally lifted her head off Miss Annabelle's shoulder and looked at her classmates silently, one by one, the morning after she learned her mother had terminal cancer. Jake remembered Angie and Jessie telling him the story. The silent visual exchange with her classmates on that morning thirty-seven years ago gave her strength when she needed it. Today, Sally looked at her former classmates, one by one, her eyes sparkling with excitement. She seemed to fill them with peace of mind, although not a word was spoken. This is the mirror image of that magical moment in Third Grade, Jake thought. He glanced at Miss Annabelle. The overhead lights were reflecting off her glassy lavender eyes, and she was smiling...watching her students, overflowing with pride and love for them. She, too, remembered.

Sally looked at Jake, and he, too, was filled with peace of mind. In fact, her eyes answered the question he started to ponder a few minutes before about the second puzzle of saving those beyond our own. Her eyes explained it: this phenomenon, this unrestrained, worldwide outpouring of energy in the form of money spent toward saving a conscious life beyond our own realm of existence was *proof* of how God-Man behaves in the Civilization of the Universe. And that outpouring gave us reason to hope that our loved ones — Sally's mother, Jasmine's father,

Debra's parents, Martin, Kelsie, Eric, Donnie, and all the precious loved ones lost to the anticivilization — were saved by Zons.

The room remained silent. We're learning, Jake thought, we're already learning what might have happened to our lost loved ones...by taking the first steps of the journey to save Beorapparaus. We're going to discover where our lost loved ones are — if they are — through this journey.

Jasmine broke the silence. "This is our opportunity!" she said. "This project is our opportunity to put our most advanced nuclear power toward freeing and *saving life* as opposed to ruling over and *destroying life*. Going outside our realm of consciousness to save conscious life is our opportunity to *add* value to Zon's creation — to our Universe. Don't you see? This is our test. Once we launch the rescue ship, proving our ability to control the cosmos through pure love and compassion for conscious life, then we'll have earned the title of Zon. Perhaps as Zons, we'll find a way to..." she stopped short, unable to say maybe she would see her father again someday.

She's right, Jake thought. Zon is an advanced conscious being who controls the cosmos through love and compassion for conscious life. When we do that, too, we become Zons and contribute important values to his creation...our Universe.

Although the expenditures and efforts of an entire planet to save one conscious being may seem like acts of selfless sacrifice, Jake pondered, they certainly were not. The efforts were made out of each person's *love* for values, and human consciousness was the supreme value. No material effort was too great to save that supreme value.

Jake pondered the pure love he felt within versus the fools-love of the leaders in the nearly forgotten anticivilization, which was brought back to his memory because of the horrors expressed in Beorapparaus's message. I can remember the momentous change on Earth, he thought, when pure love drove out fools-love. Jake buried his head between his hands, which he often did when creating an image in his thoughts. Pure love, he thought, was the precursor to supreme love. When I come home to Jakey or hold my baby girl in my arms, I feel pure love for them with all of love's protective feelings. Even if Jakey and Ameena were born back in those anticivilization days, I could never let any dishonesty, rationalization, laziness or external authority affect my mind in any way that would have harmed my precious Jakey or Ameena. My pure love for them is too great. Even back in those ancient days, my pure love for Jakey and Ameena would have overpowered everything harmful, from the most intimidating external authority to the most subtle self-imposed rationalization. Jake's mind suddenly skipped back to the miracle year thirty-seven years before when Miss Annabelle's heart was filled with pure love for her twelve students. That pure love that filled her heart, and the protective passions that filled her soul, drove out the dishonesties around her and filled her mind with self-thinking, pure honesty, which brought her the immense power that shocked the school board...particularly Hammerschmidt. Now, the human race followed in her footsteps of love.

Jake thought further about pure love in one's heart, protective feelings and passions in one's soul, permanently driving out dishonesties and external authorities and bringing pure honesty to one's mind. The leap into the Neothink mentality, he knew, required fully integrated honesty — a state of the mind that thinks through things on its own and thinks honestly to see past complicated illusions and subtle rationalizations to the essence of things. Once at the essence of things, any ordinary person holds the puzzle pieces to build Neothink puzzles and *create* values. That fully honest state of mind in the anticivilization, however, was difficult if not impossible to sustain, even if using enormous discipline. Just too many illusions and vested interests and stimulations in the anticivilization created the subtlest rationalizations that held people as helpless as prisoners to external authorities and other destructive forces of nature. Those subtle rationalizations, Jake realized, prevented the state of mind that was fully honest at the deepest level, blocking the essences of things, blocking the puzzle pieces to Neothink. Only from the fully honest state of mind — seeing through illusions and rationalizations to the *essences* of things — sprang forth puzzle-building Neothink, then value *creation*, then the transformation to God-Man. Like removing the final impurities in a nuclear power reactor to enable a chain reaction of explosive power, removing those final traces of rationalizations and dishonesties in the human psyche *through supreme love and passionate protective feelings for precious conscious life* enabled humanity's Neothink explosion of power. Jake remembered explicitly when pure love really began to rise in America about seven years earlier after the mid-term elections during Daniel's term as the last U.S. President. Jake remembered when pure love really kicked in world-wide about five years ago during the drive for Project Life.

Looking back, pure love was the human condition that exorcised and forever buried the anticivilization-man who was retarded by illusions, dishonesties, external authorities. Pure love — *supreme love for conscious life* — was the human condition that set in motion the leap into God-Man. Now, Jake thought, pure love — supreme love for conscious life — fills me and fills every heart and soul around the world as it did Miss Annabelle and her students that Miracle Year so long ago. Dishonesty and external authorities never stood another chance to control the human race, not once pure love...supreme love...for conscious life kicked in and filled the human race. For, that's when Anchor #3 — expectation of our deaths — broke and Project Sustain Life took off. ...Project Sustain Life, Jake pondered, the Sustain-and-Save-Life period on Earth...are we engaging in SSL now *beyond Earth?*

Jake's thoughts drifted back to what Jasmine had just said about controlling the cosmos through pure love and compassion for conscious life...and then becoming Zons. A big-picture understanding of the Universe suddenly filled Jake's mind, pushing everything else out. The Neothink puzzle that filled his mind at that moment had to be shared with The Group before moving on.

"Jasmine's right," he said. "And when you understand what she's saying, that the ultimate test of Zonhood is controlling the cosmos through compassion and supreme love for conscious life, then something wonderful happens. ...Ian," Jake said, looking at the great astrophysicist who, along with the others, was smiling after hearing the term *Zonhood* for the first time, "first we must add the final piece to your predictive description of Farmer Zons creating new realms or 'fields' of existence. You say, like a Farmer John on Earth, Farmer Zon 'seeds the field' with existence, then lets the forces of nature take their course as life springs up and evolves toward human consciousness in those new realms or 'fields' of existence. The rising conscious civilizations eventually become 'ripe' and join the Civilization of the Universe and contribute advanced value creation...as our civilization on Earth is about to do. The Universe then 'harvests' those magnificent value creations. Now, the final piece to complete your description is to realize that the ends for Farmer John are the collective, maximum crop output for minimal outlay. But, the ends for Farmer Zon go beyond — go to the individual — because the individual is the supreme value in the Universe. Whereas a Farmer John doesn't feel compassion and love for his crop, Farmer Zon feels compassion and love for his individual conscious beings, more compassion and love for that supreme value than for anything else. Therefore, the Zons of the Universe — their actions — will always be directed by *love* and *compassion* for conscious life."

Mr. Melbourne looked at Jake and nodded.

"In fact, their actions, directed by supreme love for conscious life," said Ian, "should be provable by Overlay Charts, especially now that we know to look for it."

"When you realize that," said Jake, "then a wonderful understanding evolves about Beorapparaus's lost civilization: wouldn't Zons at higher levels than us who function through love and compassion for conscious life, wouldn't they have saved the spirits of those billions of obliterated people just as we — Zons at the first level — will save Beorapparaus?"

"Wouldn't *our* lost loved ones be safe?" Sally added.

"I honestly don't know," said Ian. His mood changed; he looked away. "The whole idea of electronically storing the conscious spirit seems to be fundamentally flawed. We're *physically* saving Beorapparaus. It's another thing to store one's spirit, which is what Zons would have to do." Ian looked back at Jake. "In any case, soon we won't have to speculate. *We'll know.* I've put nearly two hundred astrophysicists searching for overlay data to find a way to get the answers. And I don't think it'll take long."

Jake quietly predicted that Ian and his teams of astrophysicists would soon discover the answers. Somehow, Jake felt, the

1023

acquisition of knowledge required to build and launch the rescue ship would unveil what happened to our lost loved ones who died during the anticivilization. *If* they still exist, he thought, I bet we'll discover how to be with them, again.

Jake pondered a little longer about the idea of Zons saving us. What about those leaders responsible for killing millions of people, such as the leaders on Beorapparaus's planet? Would they have been left behind to die, like pulling out weeds from the crop? Is that the ultimate, universal justice? ...Jake had so many questions, and he knew Ian would soon get the answers. As he looked at the intense scientist before him, Jake smiled and was glad that Ian worked seven days a week with just a few hours of sleep each night. ...I can't wait, Jake thought, to get the answers! But then again, what if those answers are the unthinkable?

Refocusing on the meeting, Jake realized The Group, like himself, was a bit stunned from the meeting's discussion. They resumed the most advanced superpuzzle ever undertaken on Earth with feelings of happiness and pride bursting within them. They were entering the realm of Zons. Ah, how wonderful life was in the Civilization of the Universe!

CHAPTER
ONE HUNDRED TEN

When The Group gathered again two days later at the Space Library, Jake overheard Ian and Theodore talking.

"I've adjusted to four hours of sleep at night," Ian was saying to Theodore when Jake walked in. "And now, some of my scientists have adjusted to just a handful of hours of sleep, too. I have to make my scientists go home to sleep. They're all so excited about the discovery and the initiation of Project-Save-Beorapparaus that they don't want to leave the Space Library or the hangar."

"You know...you've just identified perhaps the supersociety's greatest common-denominator need next to biological immortality itself: a sleep-reduction technology," Theodore said. He crinkled his forehead and thought about it some more, then said, "That timesaving invention would be the most in-demand product today because you're gaining conscious life. Everyone's so excited by his Friday-Night essence and by building his own competitive creations and spending time with his loved ones that everyone would love to eliminate sleep or at least cut it back by 80% or more."

"When my work on saving Beorapparaus and eliminating catastrophic death is done," Ian said, "I'd like to work on that project with you."

Superpuzzle

Jake listened to the conversation between the Nobel-Prize-winning businessman and Nobel-Prize-winning scientist and thought: they make such a great team because Ian drives on the science to make the discovery or breakthrough, and Theodore brings the breakthrough directly into the mass marketplace.

"Well, you know full well the growing demands Beyond will bring on you next," Theodore replied.

Recalculating his future work on the ether project, Ian said, "You're right, but if I can't create it, I want to be the first customer!" They chuckled, and then Ian began the meeting.

"I have some interesting information for you about the second beam," he said, looking around at his soul mates, then resting his eyes on Natasha, "Beorapparaus can envision the supersociety. Moreover, he ingeniously predicted the phenomenon that we discovered in the supersociety: the superpuzzles. From that, he realizes that without being able to snap his Neothink creations into larger superpuzzles, he can't move forward fast enough to bring competitive, meaningful values to his Zons. So, interestingly, he decided to turn to *art*. He has devoted himself to capturing the contrast between the dark, everyone-dies anticivilization and the bright, everyone-lives Civilization of the Universe, which he knows is 'out there waiting for me'."

Oh yes, that would be a wonderful value Jake thought, remembering his own thoughts about how he and Jasmine, coming out of the anticivilization, would always have an added shine of appreciation for the Civilization of the Universe that Jakey and Ameena never would. But with Beorapparaus's art, if done successfully, Jakey and Ameena and every generation thereafter, forever into the future, could also have that added shine of appreciation for their world of pure good, free from purposeful *bad*. Yes, Jake reflected, that would be a powerful, eternal value to Zons everywhere. In fact, Jake realized, Beorapparaus may have come upon one of the most unique values in existence: it would be the *only* value in which the higher the level of the Zon, then the more valuable the art becomes, for it would give that advanced Zon a unique experience, a unique appreciation of the beauty around him. No second-generation Zon could create this value — only a survivor of the anticivilization.

"I want to deviate for a moment," continued Ian, "to something I find amazing." Ian looked again at Natasha. "Natasha's story in our Third-Grade *Breakthrough News* really affected me back then. Last night, I went back and read her story called *Sole Survivor* about Sergio, the great scientist. Natasha, it's amazing how your story written when you were just a child so parallels this unfolding discovery of Beorapparaus, especially your identification that Sergio turned to the arts...in your story, he turned to classical music."

The meeting continued. The Neothink puzzle pieces to the superpuzzle Project-Save-Beorapparaus were snapped into place. The former students were going to create the future, again. Jake, now 30 years old, felt eruptions of happiness going off inside him. What will the next nine months bring? Will Project-Save-Beorapparaus lead us to our lost loved ones? *They've just got to still exist!*

*

A week passed, and The Group gathered at the Space Library for the latest progress. Ian slowly entered the meeting room.

"We learned that some of those who were supposed to go to Beorapparaus's bunker were connected on line by video streaming to his sophisticated Internet server in his bunker," said Ian slowly. "He was randomly downloading some video streaming from a few locations the morning the nuclear attacks unexpectedly occurred. I couldn't begin to tell you what we just decoded on the second beam...what Beorapparaus so painfully relayed to us. I wouldn't be able to get through it, so I'm going to play this CD of my decoding expert as he decodes Beorapparaus's story."

Ian pushed the play button on his CD player.

"My brother and his family were among those who would join me in my bunker," the decoding expert said, decoding Beorapparaus verbatim. "When the land above me was destroyed and I was separated from the world, I desperately searched through the video streaming I had downloaded over the past twelve hours. I raced through the data straight to my brother's location. His video streaming equipment was on at the time and streaming to my server. I watched what was downloaded in desperate hope for good news. Here's what I saw:

"The outside backyard camera was streaming at the time. My brother was playing tag in his backyard with his three children, his two-year-old baby girl and his five and his seven-year-old boys. He loved his children more than any father I ever knew. He'd use all his spare time playing with them, just as he was on this day. His three treasures were *so happy*; their Daddy was IT, pretending he was an old man who could not catch them. They were all laughing so hard, they could barely run. All three were screaming, 'Daddy! Daddy! Daddy!' to get him to chase them. …Suddenly, I saw it in the sky directly behind them. My brother saw it, too. He stopped and looked up. Slowly falling through the sky was a missile…a large nuclear missile. The look on his face…oh, he knew. There was no escape. It was too close. The initial blast would incinerate them. No basement, no local fallout shelter could save them. In about three minutes, he and his three little children and his precious wife would have each other no more. My brother turned his head and looked directly into the webcam, knowing I'd later see this, and he frowned and shook his head. The devastation in my brother's eyes…he…I…oh my god. Let me move on: Knowing these seconds were the last he and his family would ever have, he turned away from the camera and changed his horror-filled frown into a love-filled grin and started chasing his three little treasures again, hobbling after them like an old man, lunging for them and just missing them with each try. Of course, they had no idea. Zoraus, his five-year-old boy, was laughing so hard he couldn't stand up. He fell to the ground laughing. His daddy put his arms up and walked toward Zoraus to tag him. Zoraus was laughing too hard to get up, so he was rolling away from Daddy as fast as he could go, his tiny sister cheering and laughing and his big brother encouraging him to 'roll faster, roll faster!' The missile had now passed over the house where it could not be seen. Daddy called Mommy outside to see their hilarious kids. She stepped outside, not knowing this was their last moment together. Everyone was laughing. My brother stopped and took two deep breaths filled with the love of his family, absorbing their happiness, the preciousness of that moment, the ultimate reason for living. The kids saw that look of love as he absorbed their happy images and relished the love that had grown so powerful for them. Through the camera, I could see what he saw...his three children side by side, looking at him, so happy and so in love with their daddy. He filled his eyes with them and watched their happy faces. Then, I saw the last thing he saw: in the blinding flash of light that took their lives, in that final instance, he could still see three little sets of smiling teeth. ...Pure, infinite happiness."

Ian pushed the stop button on the CD player and silently left the room without looking at anyone. The members of The Group could not talk or look at one another. One by one, they got up and silently left the meeting room. That night they hugged their children and spouses, feeling more tenderness and love for them, *appreciating them* more than ever before. The glimpse back at the supreme loss in the anticivilization allowed them to more intensely appreciate the supreme value of the Civilization of the Universe.

CHAPTER
ONE HUNDRED ELEVEN

"Knock, knock," Diana said as she entered Ian's private office. Ian spent most of his day now with a team of fourteen astrophysicists in a makeshift, computer-jammed office in a corner of a massive hangar in a huge fenced-off field in New Jersey. He spent most of his night alone with his quantum computer in another makeshift private office next to his sleeping room where he and Diana slept. He worked furiously every night on how to store the I-ness.

"Before you get too deep into your work tonight," Diana said, "I have today's update from the Space Library."

"Oh, perfect," he said. Ian needed to be on site to oversee Beyond's building of the rescue ship. But he closely tracked the findings of the Space Library and directed its work from the hangar. The Group officially gathered there in the hangar, in Ian's temporary office, once a week.

"Today, we got more decoded material from the second beam..." Diana stopped. "Honey, something's wrong."

"No...no..."

"You always look at me like a starving puppy at feeding time when I have the update; you jump up and pull the papers from my hands when we get decoded information from the second beam. But look at you. Just now you weren't even looking at me."

"I'm sorry..." Ian dropped his head onto his arms, folded on his desk.

"Ian?" Diana hurried across the room. She wrapped her arm around Ian's shoulders and knelt next to him. She dropped her head slightly, trying to see under his downturned face to his eyes. "Ian, honey, what's wrong?"

"I can't stop seeing Zoraus and his brother and sister in my head. I can't stop seeing Donnie in my head. Then I imagine the hundreds of millions of Donnies and Zorauses obliterated — just goddamn obliterated! Diana..." Ian lifted his head to look at his wife, but his eyes were so filled with tears and his face so strained, he looked lost and barely able to see.

"Oh honey!" cried Diana. She pulled his head against hers and kissed the side of his head as a mother does to her baby.

"I just can't take anymore of this," Ian cried. "I just can't figure out how to store the realm of awareness with the I-ness. And if I can't store that human spirit, that means Donnie and Zoraus and all those blessed children are gone for eternity!"

Diana held her wretched husband, comforted him, soothed him. There's so much pressure on him, she thought, *so much pressure to succeed*; the fate of our lost loved ones — of Beorapparaus's entire civilization — erroneously falls on Ian's shoulders. I must help him shift his perspective.

*

After one week designing parts of the ship, they began initial construction phases. Six weeks later, deep into building the ship, Ian asked The Group to stay over an extra half a day. The next morning, he told them:

"Something came through the second beam yesterday that I found fascinating. I'm going to give all of you a decoded transcript before you go. Right now, I'll try to summarize what Beorapparaus sent. Beorapparaus, you must understand, spent all day, every day after the nuclear holocaust, in turmoil, digging deeper and deeper into his planet's equivalent of the human psyche to get down, as he put it, past the *why* and *what* in the human psyche that caused the nuclear holocaust to happen...down to *how* the human psyche got in such a state that caused the anticivilization to form and its holocaust to obliterate it—"

"Could you stop just a moment?" Mr. Melbourne interrupted. Everyone looked at him. "Damn, I can't wait to hear what comes next," he said. Jake smiled at seeing this man in his seventies sound and act like a man in his twenties. "But I've got to stop you for a second, Ian."

He paused to pull together his thoughts. Jake noticed Miss Annabelle, stunningly sexy with her renewed 23-year-old body, staring at her husband. Jake saw admiration and even schoolgirl infatuation sparkling in her eyes.

"I spent my life in the anticivilization uncovering the *why* and *what* in the human psyche caused the anticivilization," Mr. Melbourne said after gathering himself. *"What* caused it? External authorities. *Why?* Because of our bicameral mutations, our primitive need to follow 'the voices,' namely religions and governments. Those are specifics. But now, the much more general question of *how* did the human psyche formulate such an anticivilization opens an entire new realm of thought. I have to admit, I've never reached down that deep...I've never considered the question of *how*. Perhaps the only way to be pushed so deep to find that out would be...to have lost your civilization to the conclusion of the anticivilization — its nuclear destruction — as did Beorapparaus. ...Sorry Ian, go ahead and tell us *how*."

"You just touched upon the point Beorapparaus made about being psychologically tormented to find out *how* his civilization let this happen," Ian said. "Beorapparaus explained that the annihilation of his world drove him deeper and deeper to dig up *how* the conscious psyche got into the state that enabled its physical destruction."

Jake shivered; the conclusion of the anticivilization is the physical destruction of all conscious life, he thought, and *how close we came!* What a grand gap between the conclusion of the Civilization of the Universe and the purpose of this gathering of The Group — the preservation of *every* conscious life. Jake pondered the unbridgeable nature of that gap between the anticivilization and the Civilization of the Universe. That unbridgeable gap made it essentially impossible for an

1032

anticivilization to change into a Civilization of the Universe. *If not for Miss Annabelle and her students*, he thought, *we would've all perished just as they did on Beorapparaus' planet!*

Mr. Melbourne's voice cracked through Jake's thoughts: "What'd he say? Just how did the conscious psyche get to the point that it destroyed itself?" He shifted forward on his chair. "*How* did the anticivilization form?"

"Beorapparaus said the answer to *how* the anticivilization formed is found in the planet's first major epic or epics when consciousness was first developing."

"That'd be Homer's *Iliad* and *Odyssey* on our planet," Mr. Melbourne said quickly.

"Beorapparaus said in the first epic or epics came the models for what it meant to be *human*...I mean, his planet's equivalent of human. He said that those first epics shaped the early psyche of man that forms the civilization. If the human psyche is molded one way, civilization will go into an anticivilization. If the human psyche is molded another way, civilization will go into the Civilization of the Universe. He accurately used the analogy of the Universe and how the earliest subatomic matter/energy reactions in the earliest moments of the formation of the Universe, fractions of a second out of the big-bang birth of the Universe, formed the properties, the Laws of Nature of the Universe. If those matter/energy reactions occurred differently, then the Universe would have completely different Laws of Nature, completely different properties."

Jake listened closely. The last comment about different properties of different universes clicked with Jake. He had noticed different properties in the Civilization of the Universe that broke the laws of logic from the previous anticivilization. On his own, Jake had realized the world he lived in today had completely different properties than the world he lived in a few years ago. ...Before he started thinking about this further, Jake forced himself to put his thoughts on hold to continue listening to Ian.

"Beorapparaus went back to the first epics of his civilization, an anticivilization, and found that those initial epics instilled the idea that to survive and achieve success — to be human, so to speak — was to collect *honor* and *glory*...at all costs. Honor and glory was the mortal human's way to achieve immortality — to be remembered after his death. Honor and glory, irregardless of right or wrong, morality or immorality, was the way for the 'human' to make a name for himself...once again, to achieve immortality, which he sought. The more honor and glory, the longer one would be remembered after his death."

Mr. Melbourne sank back in his chair, his mind too occupied to perform the automatic function of sitting up straight. A moment later, he raised his finger. *"Timê and kleos,"* he said. He lurched forward in his chair, overcome with excitement. *"Timê and kleos...honor* and *glory*! Achilles and Ulysses...they lived for *timê and kleos*, and had no concern for morality. Heroic characters in the *Iliad* and the *Odyssey* plundered cities, slaughtered their citizens, raped women, and even killed children for honor and glory — for timê and kleos. They conquered all — murdered even innocent little children — without regard to morality...for honor and glory. ...My oh my, that does explain *how* the human psyche allowed the anticivilization to exist...those bizarre properties of the anticivilization and all its external authorities, from Achilles to the Kings, Popes, Ayatollahs, Prime Ministers, and Presidents. Man lived to collect honor and glory without regard for honesty. The bizarre properties of the anticivilization based on honor and glory, not on fully integrated honesty, explain why we once had those strange phenomena called governments and religions."

"Now I can better understand why our task to lift civilization out of the anticivilization into the Civilization of the Universe was so difficult," Ian said. "Using Beorapparaus's analogy to the Laws of Nature: the Laws of Nature can't be changed once those Laws of Nature — Laws of Science — are established in the first milliseconds of the Universes's big-bang birth. Not even the highest level Zon can change or defy the Laws of Nature within the Universe. To change to new Laws of Nature, we'd have to transport people to another universe altogether. Similarly, the laws of logic within the anticivilization could not be changed, not even by God-Man. To change to new laws of logic, we had to transport the people, so to speak, to another civilization altogether — to the Civilization of the Universe."

"You did just that!" shouted Jake. Jasmine looked up from

her note-taking and smiled. She knew her Jake, and she knew emotions overtook him as he said, "The people in this room — in The Group — created the supersociety stimulations that outcompeted the spiral-of-death stimulations. You transported the people from one civilization to the other. Your awe-inspiring work transported civilization piece by competitive piece out of one universe that ended in misery and death...into another universe that gives eternal life and happiness. You saved me, my wife, and my beautiful children from death. You...you're all just so breathtaking."

Jake felt emotions from deep inside rushing to the surface. Grasping the magnitude of what The Group had pulled off sent overpowering memories to the surface, one after the next. He couldn't stop those memories from overflowing.

"I remember the day I first called you, Rico. When I asked you if you remembered Miss Annabelle, there was *that pause*. I dreaded you'd forgotten Miss Annabelle and all the values she'd given you. I squeezed my eyes shut in agony when you didn't answer. And then, I'll never forget it, you said with the emotional embrace of a son who'd lost his mother, *'I loved that woman.'* Man, I'll never forget how, at that moment, I knew you lived in another world — a world where values don't fade and die."

Rico and Miss Annabelle looked at each other; their eyes filled with loving emotions. She never knew about that until now.

Seeing their reactions made Jake's throat swell. He continued, "When I met all of you at the reunion, I was in awe, beyond belief. As I sit here and listen to you today, ten years later, I'm still in awe, still beyond belief. When I listened to the tapes of Miss Annabelle's lectures delivered to you twelve little Zons thirty-seven years ago, hearing your comments *as children* made my skin crawl in awe. I could hear that you were in another world that I'd never known. When I watched Jeremiah run into that burning inferno for the love of life to save Maria, I was overcome with awe. When I watched Rico save his wife and daughter and *all of us* from those insane gunmen, I was overcome with awe. When I saw Daniel lying in the hospital, nearly assassinated, telling us, for the love of life, the violence would not stop him, I was in awe of that man. When I watched Sally give life back to Andy Konosovic, my lungs hurt from breathing so hard...I was in complete awe. When I saw Miss Annabelle step into her old room as a young woman again, and I heard each one of you givers of life gasp, I was awestruck and overwhelmed." Jake's cheeks started twitching. "The love...*the love*...the..." he sighed. "Ah, sorry," he said hoarsely, "I can't go on here." He swallowed through his swollen throat. "I've just felt so honored to be part of your superpuzzles..."

Jake couldn't say another word. His face turned red, and he looked down. Everyone in there knew he wanted to express his love for them but couldn't put together or get out the words. Jasmine walked over and wrapped her arms around him.

A deep, gentle voice broke the silence. "That's beautiful, what you said there, Jake." It was Jessie. In that same soothing voice and nourishing wisdom that helped Miss Annabelle get through her year teaching at Duncan Elementary thirty-six years earlier, he continued, "When you and I talked at Duncan Elementary nine years ago, I knew you were different, Jake. And that's why I told you the story of Miss Annabelle and her students. While you were staying with us, Angie and I would go to bed at night and talk about you like you were our own son. There was something about you, something different, something about how concerned you were for Miss Annabelle right from the start. I still remember you asking me 'What happened to her?' over and over, before I could tell you." Jake smiled, remembering how he felt back then, and he looked over at Angie and saw her smiling at him. "I wouldn't have told you the story, son, but you were so caring and protective of Miss Annabelle and her students. So, I told you *everything*." Jake nodded. He sighed and smiled as Jessie continued, "Miss Annabelle was the Sun. She filled the world with warmth and light." Jessie looked at Miss Annabelle...and then at her former students. "Her students grew in her light into the twelve trees of honesty — never part of the forests that grew for honor and glory. Mr. Melbourne nourished those trees of honesty. Bruce Salinski left the forests of honor and glory, and he joined the trees of honesty. Jake...you and Jasmine were the wind that came along and spread their seeds of honesty across the land.

...Through your articles, you've expressed your love for these people, and expressed it well."

Jake bit his bottom lip and looked down. Angie walked over and hugged Jake and Jasmine. They were the youngsters of The Group.

After a moment, Jake looked up at Jessie and said, "And you and Angie were the reservoir of strength Miss Annabelle needed to get through the Miracle Year."

Miss Annabelle looked at her dearest friends, Jessie and Angie. "Yes you were," Miss Annabelle said. "Whenever the stress got too much for me as Hammerschmidt dishonestly drove for his honor and glory, his timê and kleos, you two were always there to rescue me with strength and refuge. You'd always remind me of what was important — teaching my students. And that was what I needed to continue — focus on my students...my children—" She stopped; nostalgia gripped her. In her mind, she could see those little eight-year-old students thirty-six years ago. She looked around the room at them now, and although she now looked half their age, the same maternal love radiated from her lavender eyes that radiated from her eyes thirty-six years ago when looking at her students...a motherly love that never left.

As Jake studied her eyes, he suddenly realized why she did not, as yet, have any children of her own. *I see it in her eyes,* he thought. *She so loves teaching, she so loves her eight-year-old students...yet, she missed teaching for thirty-two years! She never got to know hundreds of children who would have loved her in the same way her original students love her to this day. She can't give up teaching right now; she's only in her third year back. And there are no worries,* Jake thought, *for now she has eternity to have her own children.*

Miss Annabelle suddenly turned toward Jake. She had always felt deeply grateful for Jake's drive nine years before to bring her out of obscurity and reunite her with her students. "*Thank you*, Jake, for caring about me and my students and bringing this beautiful group together again. That's meant more to me than anything in the world." ...Jake felt the immense love that filled this woman fall upon him and cover him with warmth as though the Sun had just shined upon him. It was one of the most wonderful moments in his life. As he basked in her love, he was silently saying in his mind, "No, Miss Annabelle, thank *you*."

As the memories and the history of the formation of the anticivilization and the Civilization of the Universe continued, Jake could not get over the irony: whereas the entire world had quickly forgotten the meaningless anticivilization, here gathered the group of people who formed the Civilization of the Universe on Earth and pulled the world out of the anticivilization...here they were passionately discussing and remembering the anticivilization. It was the responsible thing to do, Jake realized, like the father of a murdered child in those horror-filled anticivilization days, attending the trial of his child's murderer, even long after everyone else had forgotten about the crime, and seeing the trial through to the end, to closure...attending and viewing, out of restitution for his poor child, the viewing of the execution chamber and death of his child's murderer. Here together sat The Group — the parents of the new world on Earth that gave happiness and life — responsibly seeing to the very end, out of restitution for all the poor children who died in the anticivilization, the final understanding...the last breath of the anticivilization. After today, honor and glory void of honesty would never exist again, not even as a fleeting thought in someone's mind. After this final understanding today, the last breath of the anticivilization would be spent.

*

"Before you go, I have a treat for you," Ian announced toward the end of the day-and-a-half meeting. "Beorapparaus also sent, in the second beam, a description of the art he plans to develop. And, the concept of the art is breathtaking.

"He properly identified the role of consciousness in the Universe — value creation, which occurs through business. He identified Nature's Quintessential Secret — controlling mass and energy through value creation, which occurs through business. He identified that in the natural Civilization of the Universe, to be a conscious being is to be an immortal being, which occurs not through timê and kleos, but through business.

"*Business*, he identified, is synonymous with value creation and consciousness and Nature's Quintessential Secret. Indeed, the nature of the Civilization of the Universe is *business*...value creation. And, surely enough, when he looked in every possible area of life, from love to safety, business cleaned out the anticivilization...cleaned out value destruction.

"For instance, take the seemingly most unlikely connection to business: *love*. He explained: husbands and wives sitting around on weekends or after work — sitting couch potatoes watching TV. However, help them discover their Friday-Night essences, and their lives light up and their love heats up. Business makes love and sex hot. Business also cleans up crime. Go into any crime-ridden neighborhood and fill it with business: malls, office buildings, restaurants. The crime nearly vanishes. Bring business into any poverty-stricken country and the standard of living soars. Bring business into medicine, and disease after disease gets eradicated. Bring business to science and theories get advanced into valuable applications. Bring business to art, and the art is elevated from a drawing to Disneyland." Ian explained that his language decoders made a hypothetical guess that Beorapparaus was referring to a place on his planet similar to Disneyland on ours.

"Beorapparaus goes on," said Ian, "business turns ideas into cars, airplanes, computers, and turns inventions into lighted homes filled with music and television. Business eliminates disease, hunger, crime. Business, if left unhampered, eliminates death. Business eliminates problems and creates never-before-known values, conveniences, fun and happiness.

"No one on his planet, explained Beorapparaus, ever knew the real beauty of business. If they had seen the beauty of business, the ugliness of the anticivilization would have vanished. ...Had they seen the beauty, all the little children would still be alive.

"So, his art will show that beauty. Every ugly niche of the anticivilization will be found and painted, and next to the ugliness will be the beauty of business as it comes in and cleans out the ugliness. The painting will be beautiful despite its beauty's contrast to ugliness, says Beorapparaus, for the ugliness amplifies the beauty...and, the beauty seems to surround and dissolve the ugly in a kaleidoscopic, swirling metamorphosis from the anticivilization to the Civilization of the Universe. The beauty is in unstoppable motion. One more fraction of a turn, and there'll be no more ugly…no more anticivilization. Beauty cleans out the ugly."

"Wow!" Daniel yelled, trying to imagine the painting.

"Beorapparaus passionately believes," Ian continued, "that this piece of art, when he's done with it, would flip good people trapped in the anticivilization perspective of life…into the Civilization of the Universe perspective. With this art, he says, his civilization would've never allowed the holocaust. His equivalent of Homeric Man living for timê and kleos would've no longer existed. For, legitimate honor and glory and *real* immortality would've come so much more easily and effectively and *honestly* through business. The inferior *how* behind the anticivilization — timê and kleos — would've been forever replaced with the superior *how* behind the Civilization of the Universe, *business*.

"And, this fluid piece of art is the last-moment, one-fraction-of-a-second last visual of the anticivilization — one last, powerful contrast to the Civilization of the Universe — before that kaleidoscope moves another fraction of a turn when the anticivilization will be gone forever. It's that one bizarre moment when Homeric Man and God-Man meet. After that one instant of contact, Homeric Man then vanishes forever.

"Zons at every level will be able to look at that art and feel a special feeling, available to them no other way. They'll absorb a special appreciation of the beauty that surrounds them, an appreciation multigenerational Zons could otherwise never get, never knowing of the anticivilization."

"Damn, that's brilliant," Mr. Melbourne said. He shook his head, and added, "It'll be a one-of-a-kind memorial. What I mean is: to fully know the beauty of the Civilization of the Universe, one must know the ugliness of the anticivilization." He was moved; everyone in the room was moved. One-sentence comments, said in awe of the proposed art, filled the room. Jake, the reporter, drifted off into a new tangent of thought that had never entered his head before.

I think I can somewhat *experience* Beorapparaus's brilliant Neothink Art proposal in order to more successfully capture its feeling in a headline article, he thought; just before the human race graduates into Zonhood, I'll give everyone a final look back to forever capture that added shine of appreciation for what's ahead. I need to go where Homeric Man and that small, remaining ugly place, the anticivilization, still exists on Earth before that last fraction of a turn when it's gone forever. I must go to the last remains of the anticivilization on Earth, soon to vanish from Earth. I must go...to the ostracism wastelands.

CHAPTER
ONE HUNDRED TWELVE

During his two weeks preparing to go to the ostracism wastelands, Jake published a preview to his adventure, for most people had forgotten about the wastelands. "After the leap into the Civilization of the Universe," his preview explained, "almost everyone was swept along, eventually making the natural jump from value producer to value creator, which is the natural role of consciousness in our Universe. Even criminals of the anticivilization made the jump into the Civilization of the Universe, into beloved value creators.

"Society ostracized, however, a very small percentage of people who were responsible, through design, for the deaths of innocent people. Those people had gone beyond the point of no return. Now, they had nowhere to go besides designated canyons or islands called *ostracism wastelands*.

"Two weeks after receiving Beorapparaus's proposed painting, I will venture into the ostracism wastelands. Beorapparaus's painting will butt the political anticivilization against the business-driven Civilization of the Universe. The painting will show that the anticivilization got cleaned up and cleared out by business. Inspired by the painting's concept, I decided to see first-hand the contrast one last time, before it becomes extinct. This will give me valuable research for my future article elaborating on the nature of Beorapparaus's art design.

"I will enter the largest ostracism wasteland in North America — the Florida Keys. The ostracized inhabitants were not forced to live there, but the wastelands are the only places where they can survive for a few brutal years before death.

"I will go to the Florida Keys without my wife and writing partner, Jasmine Catchings. I will go with twenty bodyguards. This trip exposes us to some slight risks, which caused me to struggle over whether or not to do this. In the wastelands, none of the products that remove the risks of living are in place. But our advanced technology should overwhelm any danger.

"I'll also be accompanied by a historian who is an expert at recognizing faces. The wastelands consist of murderers and politicians from the upper echelons of former governments around the world. The ostriches — the name given to those caught in the ostracism matrix — migrated thousands of miles in some cases to reach the warmer ostracism wastelands, for there the chances of survival are better.

"We will take a boat to the wastelands. We will all be armed with electronic belts. One press of the button is powerful enough to knock down an attacking tiger thirty feet away. We will wear light, comfortable metal meshes that cover our heads, necks, and bodies. The meshes will stop any stone, arrow, or bullet. We will stay for only a few hours. The bodyguards going with me were former President Daniel Ward's *Fearsome Four* bodyguards from their Street-Fight-In-D.C. days. Another sixteen bodyguards will accompany us. My task-force leader is the legendary Ralley Sanders who was Daniel Ward's top secret-service agent back in the days when Daniel Ward was President and bodyguards were still needed. Today, their old bodyguard skills are needed only because we are heading back into the anticivilization."

When Jake and his team landed on the beach, what Jake saw made him cringe in disbelief. He spoke softly into his CD recorder: "Men are scattered about. The place looks like an eerie mixture between an insane asylum where insane people haplessly care for themselves…and a zoo of gorillas."

Jake kept at a distance and observed. Overcome by the wasted human life, he asked himself, *why am I here?* After a mental struggle, he remembered: *I'm gaining emotional insight into the powerful contrast that Beorapparaus's art will bring to Earth. By going back into the anticivilization from the Civilization of the Universe, I'm going through the emotional trauma of the anticivilization and gaining an exquisite appreciation of the Civilization of the Universe.*

"It appears that when the sun goes down," Jake said into his hand-recorder, "the ostriches gather in the Big Center — my name for a flat, cleared area that serves as their gathering place — to eat the food they acquire during the day, which is mostly fish and fruits. ...Although I'd planned to leave before dusk, I consulted with my team, and we've decided to stay to observe this daily eating ritual.

At dusk, men started slowly walking toward a single destination...some carrying food, some not.

As the outcasts entered the Big Center, Jake described the scene, speaking softly into his hand-recorder so as not to startle or upset the outcasts: "It's bizarre how slowly they walk — like zombies from old horror movies. When men have no purpose, they move at a fraction of the speed of men with purpose. Over the past half-hour, several hundred men have gathered here in the Big Center. No one talks. They just walk in line and drop their food in the center and others begin preparing it, cooking the catch on large open bonfires. God, this is unreal. The men just sit and say nothing, nothing at all, as they wait for their food. I wonder if they've forgotten how to talk! Their only purpose, it appears, is to eat and then return tomorrow to eat again." Jake turned off the recorder.

"They look like someone lobotomized them," he whispered to the historian.

"I was thinking they really do look like orangutans in a zoo," the historian replied. Both descriptions fit.

"I'm going to enter the Big Center," Jake said. "Then, we all go in," said Ralley.

As Jake and his men walked into the Big Center, dozens of heads slowly turned and looked at them, but did nothing more. These animal-like men had seen God-Men before and knew the God-Men could easily, effortlessly cause them great physical pain. So they did nothing but look...and look away.

As Jake and his team walked toward the middle of the Big Center, Jake did not see any females. After these ostracized people die, he thought, there'll be no more; these people are the living dead. This here is the physical end of the anticivilization. He started wondering, what if a woman were here who bore a child? What about that child? Suddenly, a voice cracked the silence. It sounded like an explosion, startling everyone in the Big Center.

"Cerdos capitalistas – ¡asesinos!" screamed an old man, who stood up and charged at Jake. The old man had his hands spread wide with grey fingernails an inch long, all pointed toward Jake's face. The old man drew back his lips and opened his diseased mouth half filled with rotting teeth targeting Jake's neck. When the old man ran harder and faster straight toward Jake, the young man had no choice. He pressed the button on his belt, and the old man fell to the ground in shock.

The historian rushed over to study the old man's face.

"Do you know what he yelled?" Jake asked.

"It was Spanish," the historian answered while rolling the old man over. "He yelled. 'Capitalist pigs — murderers!'" The historian then laughed when he saw the old man's face, and added, "I should've guessed."

"Do you recognize him?" Jake asked.

"Yes. He's Fidel Castro."

*

After the attempted attack, Jake looked at the other faces. They were blank. None of the others seemed to be excited by the action. One large male sitting near the fire caught Jake's eye. He had badly matted grey hair, dust-caked skin showing through the large holes in his dirt-soaked clothes, and a large, sun-damaged nose and red, sunburned face. After Fidel Castro's attempted attack, that large male watched, but his beady, empty eyes looked away unaffected when Jake looked at him. No emotions existed in him anymore. He was emotionally empty like a gorilla in the zoo.

The historian saw Jake looking at the large male next to the fire.

1045

"I recognize him, too," the historian whispered.

"Yeah, he looks familiar — who is he?"

"That's Bill Clinton."

*

The wasteland was a bizarre sight at night. The houses, hotels, and other buildings still stood on the island, but there was no electricity. Jake wondered if the buildings were even used anymore, for the males all seemed to lie down to sleep right where they finished eating.

Jake and his men set up camp on the beach. They had brought along, as a precaution, a lightweight, portable "house" that was covered with the bulletproof mesh and reinforced with a lightweight, extremely strong alloy. The portable house was, in essence, more secure than a fort.

Sitting in the portable home, Jake thought how these ostracized people potentially could build for themselves a thriving little civilization. But their laziness took over, he realized; their laziness made them exist at bare sustenance. He knew if these ostracized people were welcomed into the Civilization of the Universe, they would live as wealthy people...*even if they remained lazy!* But these ostracized people would not be welcomed into the Civilization of the Universe, at least not until the day it was proven that Zons saved our dying loved ones, whom these people were directly responsible for killing.

After Jake talked to Jasmine on his satellite-feed phone/computer, he jumped off his air bed.

"Men," he called to the others in their eight-hundred-square-foot fortified home. "Will you pull an all-nighter with me? As long as we're here, I want to observe some more."

The twenty bodyguards, who had worked with Jake frequently in Washington, were smiling at him. Then Jake noticed not one of them had taken off his gear.

"I guess you knew I'd ask you that, huh?" Jake said sheepishly.

They laughed and nodded.

"We knew when you asked us to stay the night," Ralley said.

Jake put his gear back on, and they went outside. Men were

1046

sleeping anywhere — in the open with no shelter. They either dropped down to sleep wherever they finished eating or stumbled a few yards away before sleeping. Most bodies were lined side by side in the Big Center.

It's all *so eerie*, Jake kept thinking. Seeing the men lined up, lying on the dirt ground in the Big Center reminded him of grotesque finds in the anticivilization of those mass suicides of religious cults. ...Seeing this small, last place of horrible ugliness on Earth gave Jake an overwhelming appreciation of the beauty all over Earth. Timê and kleos without regard to honesty led to this ugly nightmare. Business led to the rest of the world — a world of beautiful dreams come true.

As Jake pondered that contrast between the two worlds, a pungent smell filled the air around him. The task-force leader immediately registered the odor.

"Someone died," Ralley said. He then pushed through the brush. "There!" he shouted, pointing to an open, mass grave filled with dozens of dead bodies. Yes, Jake pondered upon seeing the grisly sight, people still die here — the anticivilization of certain death still exists.

Despite the stench, Jake could not take his eyes off the dead bodies. He stared at them, almost expecting them to move, to get up and walk away. *They're dead*, he told himself in disbelief, human beings...*dead!* But then, as he felt great sorrow rising within, he realized, those people were not really human beings, for they were responsible for killing people. Human consciousness does not do that, not even in an anticivilization, except in self-defense. "No," Jake mumbled, "they weren't human beings; they were some kind of mentally demented humanoids." With that insight, suddenly Jake's inherent love and compassion and sorrow for those people vanished and the stench and shocking sight of their decomposing carcasses caused him to quickly turn away and hurry out of there.

As Jake and his team explored the island, he eventually thought maybe they would go back to their fort and either leave or get a few hours of sleep, for everything was lifeless and dark and everyone was asleep. Before he called the exploration to a halt, he asked for the portable air lift, which would lift him above tree level for a good look around.

Above tree level, Jake saw something he figured could not be true. He figured what he saw was a reflection of some kind that caused an illusion. But it sure looked like a house with lights on inside. In any case, he and his team hiked the couple of miles to check it out.

When they reached their destination, they were amazed. Seeing the little house with lights was like finding a bright radiating diamond in a pile of dark coal.

Jake walked over and knocked on the door.

The door opened quickly and an older yet handsome face full of life — the only such face Jake had seen in the wasteland — cried, "God-Man! Oh...please come in!"

Jake looked behind him at his team. They shared a look of bewilderment and entered the house.

"I recognize you!" the mystery man said. He was bursting with excitement. "You're Jake Catchings — the greatest reporter who ever lived! You helped kill that monster I once was. You don't know how deeply grateful I am to you...and how sorry I am."

"Who are you?" Jake asked him.

"That's so unimportant," the man replied. Jake looked at the historian who looked back at Jake, shrugged his shoulders, and shook his head. He could not identify this man.

Jake studied the mystery man before him. He stood in complete contrast to the others on the island. First and foremost, his face was full of life, purpose, and emotions. Physically, although an older man, his skin was supple, and his body seemed to be in excellent shape.

Jake looked around the house. He saw what looked like manuscript printouts everywhere on many topics from medicine to farming to boat building to a classic by Victor Hugo. Jake looked at an open doorway to a bedroom and noticed a glow.

"Can it be?" he muttered as he walked to the doorway and looked inside. "It is...a working computer!" He walked over and looked at the screen. This man was on the Internet!

"It's my lifeline," the man said. "Afterall, was it not the Internet that gave The Group the leverage to catapult the people out of the anticivilization into the Civilization of the Universe?"

"Yes, you're right," Jake said. His writer's mind was trying to evaluate this mystery man. He was at least a generation older than Jake, probably more, with healthy good looks and a fit body. The mystery man, though, started answering questions before Jake asked them:

"I repaired a generator to bring myself electricity. They would've robbed me of everything by now, probably would've killed me, but I build and repair the boats that bring them their fish. And I manage the orchards and crops that bring them their fruits and vegetables. They need me, so they leave me alone."

Jake asked again, "Who are you?"

"You mean, who *was* I?" the mystery man said, seriously. "Who I was...is now dead. I'm not that person anymore. I'm so ashamed, so sickened by that person I can't even say his name. I love your world and visit it whenever I can...through the Internet. I spend my nights in the virtual world. My computer logs on directly through a satellite connection. I'm on a rapid learning curve. I'm no value creator yet, but I will be someday. ...Jake, Mr. Catchings, I want to go with you into the Civilization of the Universe."

"But—" Jake started to say, but was cut off by the mystery man.

"I can't be a value creator there yet," the mystery man said desperately, "but I can be a good value producer. I have tremendous energy and can produce values. I already know what I can do out there for The Group."

"But, I can't stop—" Jake started to say, but was cut off again. The mystery man was obviously afraid of being rejected.

"I must tell you a little story to show you *how much I want to be* in the Civilization of the Universe and to demonstrate my potential to someday be a great value creator.

"When I came here, I was like all of them out there. For the longest time, I felt relentless depression. After that, I felt *nothing*. It's worse than death to *feel nothing*. One day, while I still had my memory — which was, by the way, quickly fading — I remembered my childhood love for boats. Then I thought...what if I *build* a boat? It was the most daring thought I'd had on the island. No one here builds anything; the thought doesn't even enter their heads. Well, I built a crude little boat, and for the first time in the two years I had been here, I *felt*

1049

something — something good. I realized that good feeling came from *building* something. So, I built another boat...and another. I used them to fish. People were starving and dropping dead like flies...until I built a small fleet of boats and began the systematized daily fishing program.

"Then I started building other things...and feeling better. I found a generator in a former hotel and restored it, which gave me electricity. I found a computer in a former doctor's office, which gave me access to the Internet. Every time I built something or restored something, I felt good. With the Internet, I started learning rapidly about farming, medicine, fishing. It's me who's kept these zombies alive — not because I give a damn about them...I sometimes get physically sick looking at them. But I like to learn and build, and my knowledge and programs have kept them from starving. I'm the reason this wasteland has become the most populated one in the world.

"I was willing to live the rest of my life as the island's only significant producer...until two weeks ago when I saw *it*." The man stopped and looked away.

"Saw what?" Jake asked.

When the man looked back, his eyes were filled with tears. "The soul of the God-Man. My soul when I was five years old. The soul of Dr. Sally Salberg Jones, Jeremiah Jones, Dr. Ian Scott, Theodore Winters, Cathy Winters, Daniel Ward, Robert Chapman, Natasha Stokov Chapman, Rico Rodriguez, Reggie Tucker, Al Patterson, and Debra Kirkland Patterson. The business soul — the soul that exists to create values — I *want* that soul. I *want* to build values so badly, Mr. Catchings. I want to someday build values for the God-Man! Jake..." he started choking up and clearing his throat.

"What did you see two weeks ago that made you feel this way?" Jake asked.

"I saw on the Internet...Beorapparaus's proposed art design. When I studied the plans for his design, I was swept away...into another dimension. I suddenly saw the *beauty* of *business*. Business is value creation, which is what I want to do. Business makes everything wonderful. Business rids the world of places like this. Although I've been somewhat productive here, seeing

Beorapparaus's projection of his art made me want to enter the beautiful world of business and, eventually, become a value creator. His projected art changed me forever. It let me see and feel life from the beautiful perspective of the Civilization of the Universe. ...Mr. Catchings, please sir, take me with you into the Civilization of the Universe!"

CHAPTER
ONE HUNDRED THIRTEEN

"But society ostracized you," Jake said. "It won't do any good to take you with me. You'll perish there. I mean...no one's stopping you from going back, but you'll be ostracized, just like before. At least here you can survive."

"I'm asking to be a value producer for one of the persons in The Group — to live with that person until I can raise my value rating out of the ostracism range."

"But isn't your value rating irrevocable? Aren't you here because you're responsible for ending innocent life?"

"Never directly, Mr. Catchings. I was an evil person, and my actions indirectly led to innocent death. But never, *never* did I directly end life. There's no question I would have killed thousands, millions for my false sense of importance if given the power to. But I never had that kind of power."

"If your value rating comes to sub-100, then I must leave you here, you know."

"I know that, and I accept that."

"The value scanner is back at my camp," Jake said. "You'll have to come with us, and we must leave now."

"I'm ready. There's nothing I need from this world."

Value scanners read several aspects of a person's physical presence, both exterior and interior, to make an absolutely certain

1052

identification that was more accurate than fingerprints. The value scanners were inexpensive and easy to install. They were equipped with a database that held nearly every living person and his or her past. After identifying the person, the value scanners then matched the identity with the person's past accomplishments (or crimes). A person walked through the inexpensive value scanners, and within five seconds, a value rating was displayed on the screen.

Every store, every business had a value scanner on the front door. At first they were used to ostracize the value destroyers left over from the dying anticivilization. A reading of sub-100 meant a person directly and intentionally caused the death of one or more innocent persons. Those people with a value rating of sub-100 were not able to access any values in the Civilization of the Universe, which drove those people, on their own accord, to the wastelands where at least they could eat.

The value scanners did not disappear, however, even after the ostracism was complete...after society's cleansing of the destroyers of life. For, everyone discovered a value in knowing from the first handshake, the value rating of the person one was dealing with. So the value scanners were kept in place, no longer as tools for removing the negative, but as tools for embracing the positive. Knowing a person's value rating immediately oriented a business to most efficiently service that person's needs.

"So, you're taking me?" the man asked; his lips were tense and quivering. Jake could see the child in the man's face and felt sorry for him...and close to him.

"I'm taking you as far as our camp," Jake answered. "If you're sub-100, you go no further." The man smiled as a tear escaped from his eye. Jake smiled back, and he hoped this man's rating would not be sub-100.

Suddenly Jake felt a strong urge to get back to camp and to get off the island.

"We must go *now*," he instructed everyone. Without even glancing back one last time at his home, the man walked toward the door. Jake, however, stepped in the bedroom to see what was on the computer screen. He leaned close to the screen to see what the text said.

"I'll be darned," Jake muttered as he read the mystery man's comments to be posted on a discussion board dedicated to Beorapparaus's art project.

"Jake!" Ralley yelled. Jake did not like the tension in that voice. He took a deep breath and ran outside; he confronted a frightening sight. His men had already formed a semi-circle, their shoulders pressed against each other. The bodyguard closest to the door yanked Jake, then the historian, and then the mystery man into the middle of their huddle, and then they closed the circle, their backs facing each other.

Dozens if not hundreds of large males surrounded them. Their faces looked desperate.

"What do they want?" Jake asked the mystery man. Before he could answer, a giant black man the height of a professional basketball star, the thickness of a professional linebacker, bellowed at Jake:

"We can still speak!"

"What?" Jake asked.

"We can *still* speak! So hear me out. Eddie ain't leavin' us!" He was pointing at the stranger next to Jake.

Jake looked at the sagging bloodshot eyes of the convict eight yards before him. Those eyes were not filled with hatred or bitterness. His voice was not filled with anger. In fact, the more Jake looked at him, the more the big man's eyes seemed to be begging Jake, and his voice seemed to be on the verge of crying like a desperate child who had just gotten lost from his parents. The weather-beaten, worn body and soul before Jake did not want a confrontation, but he and the dozens of males around him had no choice but to fight to the death to keep their main supplier of food in their community.

"Don't feel for him," the man they called Eddie said softly to Jake. "He murdered every member of an innocent family, including three little children! And the man next to him tortured to death farmers in Mexico who spoke out against the government, and he starved their families. These people deserve to be dead...and I've kept them alive. It's time to let justice be served!"

Jake nodded.

"Can we fry our way through·'em?" one of the bodyguards asked Ralley Sanders, the task-force leader.

"No...too many. We're going to battle, men."

Jake and his team pulled their mesh protection over their heads. The males around them began snarling and shaking their heads.

"Wait!" Eddie whispered. "Listen...just behind me there's a shed. We'll have to get through some of them. But once inside, the door locks, and I've dug out a tunnel toward the beach, which'll get us past them and on our way."

"Let's move!" shouted Ralley.

Like a sand crab, the team quickly moved in unison toward the shed. The frightened males charged them. Many were carrying sticks and clubs over their heads. How bizarrely primitive they looked, Jake thought.

As the large males rushed the task force, swinging clubs and throwing stones, Jake's team sent out battle-strength, fatal electrical currents that electrocuted the perpetrators. Jake could swear he saw in their faces relief at the moment they were zapped to their deaths. The most inconceivable event that would be met with sheer horror in the Civilization of the Universe — one's death — was met with relief, even gratitude, in the anticivilization.

The bizarre horror of seeing death — people *welcoming* death — constricted Jake's breathing. He was struggling for air as he experienced his first asthma attack of his life. He kept moving, though, keeping pace with the team. But his breathing was mercilessly closing up. In strange coincidence, Eddie, the man next to Jake, pulled out of his pocket a small spray bottle and put it in Jake's mouth and squeezed it.

Almost immediately, Jake's breath came easier as the battle continued around them.

"My medical studies paid off!" the man mumbled.

The twenty bodyguards, protecting Jake, the historian, and the man called Eddie, reached the front of the shed.

"Break!" Ralley commanded. Those facing the shed opened its door and pulled Jake, the historian, and Eddie in with them. Then the others turned and jumped inside. Ralley entered last and two men threw down the four-by-six board onto the brackets to lock the door.

"Under there!" Eddie yelled, pointing to a large, iron plate on the ground.

The bodyguards threw the 300-pound plate aside as if it were cardboard. Inside was a tunnel that went twenty yards straight West.

"It'll get us past them," the man called Eddie said. "They don't think. They have no organized plan. We'll get a clear run to your boat once we're past them."

"Let's move!" Ralley yelled. Two men dropped into the black hole. Suddenly, a hand reached up and grabbed Jake's leg. It was Manny Franks.

"C'mon!"

Jake jumped in, followed by Eddie and the rest.

As the team was exiting the other end of the tunnel, they could hear the walls to the wooden shed crashing down. Then came a loud cry, unmistakably from the large black man. After that, Jake heard the loud wailing of the other males. They knew they could not get back their food supplier. They knew they would soon starve.

God, that's pathetic, Jake thought. As he and his team were running for their boat, he felt very sad for those left behind, doomed to die; yet, he thought he shouldn't feel sad for them. I don't understand, he admitted. Maybe Jasmine can help me understand.

Having seen those primitive figures swinging sticks, throwing stones, being electrocuted, screaming and dying reminded Jake why they were unable to survive in the supersociety, not even as street criminals after the value scanners were installed. In those early days of the Civilization of the Universe when weapons manufacturing companies still existed and private police forces still patrolled the streets, people with negative value ratings, meaning they were value destroyers, were unable to purchase weapons. Moreover, the private police forces around the world swiftly and efficiently removed weapons from every person with a negative value rating. Against the value scanners, the worst of the value destroyers — the sub-100s — could not acquire even the minimum food to live on, for society ostracized them. And against the hi-tech stun belts, those value destroyers had no way to steal food or anything else. Outmatched, the sub-100 value destroyers had no choice but to migrate to the ostracism wastelands.

As the team raced along, Jake could feel the gulf between this island where danger and death was rampant versus the new Paradise Cities springing up across the rest of the world where danger and death were extinct. It's the gulf between business-free and business-driven, he thought, between ugly and beauty. Jake knew this final confrontation with danger gave him the emotional depth needed to write an article that would do justice to describing Beorapparaus's proposed painting.

During the three-mile run back to the boat, Jake was amazed at how this older man Eddie kept up. Eddie noticed the looks of astonishment he got from Jake.

"I'm the only one here who jogs and lifts weights," he huffed as they ran at a tiring pace across the dark terrain.

When they got back to camp, Jake rushed Eddie into the fortified house and attached the value scanner. Jake was aware that he strongly hoped this man would not be sub-100.

Eddie walked through the scanner. Three seconds later his value rating was displayed on the screen.

"Sub-97!" Jake shouted. Whereas a sub-97 is the rating of an evil value destroyer, which is why Eddie was ostracized by businesses to the point of being driven to the wastelands, he was still redeemable. At sub-97, he was not directly responsible for killing someone.

A sub-97 meant he was once a grotesque human being, as evil as one can get without actually directing people to their deaths. Jake surprised himself with his internal leap of joy when he knew he could take a sub-97 back with him.

"You're coming with us!" Jake said with a broad smile. He gave Eddie a congratulatory slap on the back. Jake saw every muscle in Eddie's face twitching and knew what this meant to him.

Although the value rating gave a complete history of the person scanned, Jake had no time to read it. He only had time to see "Sub-97" before his team cleared the island, leaving the portable home with the value scanner behind.

As their boat whisked Jake and his team away, they suddenly heard the loud moans of the doomed-to-die. Jake looked back and saw the males filling the beach. Their life-giver, Eddie, had left them. As the males moaned and dropped to their knees, Daniel thought of the ugliness he was witnessing — the anticivilization. He thought of Beorapparaus's art projection: one more instant on the human time-line, and that ugliness will be gone forever...replaced by the beauty of the business-driven Civilization of the Universe.

CHAPTER
ONE HUNDRED FOURTEEN

Safely on their way, Jake sat down next to his new passenger. "With a sub-97, they'll ostracize you out there, you know."

"I know. But I was hoping I could be a value producer for someone in The Group until I can, eventually, get my value rating well into the positive."

"What values can you produce that computerized robots don't already do better?"

"Probably none. But I can do as well. Mr. Catchings, I've robbed, lied, deceived, and hurt a lot of people in my former dishonest, lazy life. First, I must grow. I must be a value producer now. And given some time, my learning curve will enable me to jump to a value creator. I'd be an investment. Ownership of my first great value creation will go to the person who takes me in. Ownership of my following, many value creations will go to those whom I've hurt in my past. I'll work for decades or longer, whatever it takes, to pay restitution to my victims."

Jake was really starting to like this man.

*

By the first week of summer, just five months remained

before the projected launch date of the rescue ship. Ian had asked The Group if they could meet at Rico's mansion just outside of Philadelphia this week because of the number of computer technicians in his office running tests.

Driving down Rico's long driveway, each member of The Group was shocked to see *a man* manually trimming the hedges. People had not cared for Rico's lawns and gardens for nearly four years now.

Manual labor was very, very rare as people easily and naturally flowed into value creators as Jessie had done in the Civilization of the Universe. Indeed, Jessie was now a flourishing "garage" entrepreneur, a multimillionaire who designed revolutionary systems for automated, self-cleaning rooms. His new self-cleaning-room technologies were being installed in existing homes and becoming a fixture in most new homes including all new Paradise City Homes. His technology was currently being installed in every one of Miss Annabelle's Schools of Geniuses across the nation and was being considered for the rescue ship.

When ordinary people naturally flowed into value creators, very little supply of manual-labor employees remained. Thus, businesses developed computerized robots to fill the void caused by the great exodus of humans from jobs of labor to jobs of the mind. ...Now, after the successful transition, manual labor would be very inefficient compared to the perfected computerized robots.

For four years, Rico's bushes were trimmed by computer programmed trimmers moving on flexible nylon arms. Once a week, the trimmers rose from their one-foot, hidden green holding pipes, implanted in the ground, and the trimmers extended on retractable nylon stems, moving around the bushes like arms as each one followed its own computer-memory program and trimmed the bushes. The bushes were always perfectly trimmed, perfectly shaped. The grass was cut weekly by three little dome-shaped computerized mowers.

Caring for Rico's lawns and gardens had been fully computerized and automated for nearly four years. All over the world, manual labor was handled by computerized robots, and people were soaring on value-creation vectors of the mind.

So, it was a surprise of antiquity as the members of The Group arrived at Rico's mansion to find *a man* hard at work caring for the lawns and gardens. Jake and Rico had told them about Eddie. He had been working at Rico's for two months now. But it still shocked them to see manual labor.

It was the ongoing, first topic of discussion that came into the large meeting room as each person entered. The unusual sight brought the questions flowing from their mouths.

"Did you disengage your computerized system?" Sally asked Rico.

"Yes I did. I know that system costs me nothing now and is perfect every time, but this fellow needs to work hard for awhile to learn about the world of values. And I love watching his transition into a value producer. I'll tell you what: he's keeping up to what my lawn-care system did for me. It'll be special watching him making the leap, down the road, into the value creator. He'll need your help, Robert."

"Just think about it," Robert pondered aloud, "he'll be the last person on Earth to make the leap."

They all walked over to the window to watch him.

"I used to have a crew of eight men to do what he alone does," Rico said, admiring the manual laborer. "I told him we could have two-thirds or at least half the lawns and gardens cared for by the computer system, but he insisted he wanted to do it all himself. He's out there from sunrise 'til sundown, seven days a week. Then he goes into his room and spends hours reading or surfing the net. He must only get four or five hours of sleep."

They watched him carrying large bags of fertilizer, placing them around the lawn. Although the temperature was unusually comfortable for mid-June, he was sweating heavily from the pace at which he pushed himself.

"He's driven," Jeremiah said. Seeing the man grinning wider the harder he toiled, Jeremiah added, "Yeah, he wants to feel the hurt."

"It's the first time in his life he's produced values," Rico explained. "It's his first taste, and he loves it."

"He looks like he's rushing," Cathy said.

"He is," Rico responded. "He told me he wants to repay everyone he hurt as quickly as possible."

The harder he toiled, the more he grinned.

"Blood, sweat, and joy," Jeremiah said. "I understand perfectly."

The man, with his back to the window, unaware he was being watched, grabbed a jug of water and took a long drink, and then he poured some of the water on his hair and neck. Overheated from his punishing pace, he stripped off his shirt.

Jake was impressed at just how in shape Eddie was. His back was lined with striations of lean muscles. His shoulders were large and rounded. Even as an older man, his body was the perfect combination of a slim body and muscle mass.

Eddie stretched, threw his shirt on the ground, picked up the hedge cutters, and turned around.

"Oh, my," Miss Annabelle gasped.

"Look at that," Sally said.

"It can't be!" Daniel shouted. "No, I don't believe it!"

"It is!" Jake said in disbelief.

No one but Daniel and Jake, whom Daniel had previously confided in, knew what was happening as Daniel raced out the door and ran toward the man with the strange scar on his stomach...shaped like...a peace sign.

Eddie looked up and saw Daniel running toward him. Eddie dropped the clippers. For a moment, he was paralyzed. Then he stood straight, at attention, and conducted a salute that was radiating with admiration.

"Thank you, sir!" Eddie shouted as Daniel approached him.

"Bullfrog?" Daniel said, still in disbelief.

"He's dead, sir," the gardener replied. "I killed that evil man and replaced him with me, a good person. I'm Eddie." Then he looked in Daniel's eyes and said, "Thank you, *so much*, Mr. Ward. You're my greatest hero of all time."

The other members of The Group were outside, rushing toward Daniel and Eddie. Jake was in the lead.

"*Oh my god*," he said, as he got closer.

"What's going on?" Jasmine asked.

"Darling, Eddie's the former Senator from Massachusetts."

Eddie overheard him; Jasmine stopped walking.

"Jasmine...Mrs. Catchings...I'm so sorry," Eddie said with feelings so deep that everyone could feel his sincerity. His shoulders and arms seemed to wither. "I will find and make restitution to people I've hurt. I will repay your father and you."

"My father's dead."

Eddie blinked several times and looked lost.

"I...I'm so sorry..." Eddie said, his voice dropping off. Knowing how much he had hurt her and her father by driving his development company into bankruptcy through environmental legislation, knowing how much love and happiness he had stolen from their lives, Eddie looked at the ground.

"I feel so much *pain* for those I've hurt...*beautiful people* like you and your father." Eddie's head hung low on his shoulders. He looked as though his body were sinking. He shook his head. Then, his big bare shoulders started shaking up and down. Jake bent over a little to look at Eddie's face. He was crying quietly, but hard; the emotional dam holding back his reservoirs of regrets had cracked. He rubbed both cheeks with the palms of his hands and looked up at The Group. Tears and dirt were smeared across his devastated face.

"Please don't hate me!" he pleaded. "I love all of you more than you can know." Then a powerful fit of crying overwhelmed him. It was a deep, genuine cry of a good man who had badly hurt someone but had no way to correct the harm. He was letting out pain that had built up for years, and he could not hold it inside anymore.

A long, long minute passed, filled only with the sounds of Eddie crying. Jasmine then spoke in a voice so precious that one could almost hear the little girl who loved her daddy more than anything in the world still within her. "I'll always hate the monster you once were. But I won't hate the person you are now, Eddie. ...Neither would my father."

Eddie cried even harder upon witnessing to her forgiving, innocent soul. Knowing he could never repay them for the life and love he had stolen from them, yet hearing her tender forgiveness, just tore him up inside.

Jasmine, who suddenly felt that her father and Eddie could have become close friends now, if her father were still alive, walked over and hugged Eddie. He dropped his head on her shoulder and cried like a baby.

This man has lived in turmoil for his wrongdoings, Jake

realized. He suffers every day. Seeing the depth of Eddie's agony, Jake knew the need to repay his victims tortured him, every day. And now, Eddie would never be able to repay Jasmine and her father.

When Eddie regained some control, each member of The Group welcomed him with a handshake.

When Daniel walked over to shake Eddie's hand, the distraught gardener looked at Daniel's face. His old nemesis was now his hero. The world around them seemed to stop. Overcome with emotions, Eddie suddenly hugged his old nemesis and said, "Thanks to you, *my hero*, I'm in the Civilization of the Universe today."

*

That night, Rico knocked on Eddie's opened door. Eddie was on the Internet concentrating on an article written by Jake and Jasmine.

"Good evening, Eddie," Rico said.

Eddie stood up and turned around.

"Good evening, sir."

"Eddie, you've been here for two months now. I want you to call me Rico and relax around me...okay?"

"But you're one of my greatest heroes, sir. I respect the members of The Group more than any people in this world."

"Even so, call me Rico...okay?"

"Okay...Rico."

"How are things going so far?"

"I can't get enough. Producing values — there's nothing like it! Making a difference — a *real* difference — *feels* so, so good! I love it here, Rico. ...I love life!"

"Ah, Eddie, just you wait," said the wise Rico. "You have yet another whole dimension of happiness coming to you...when you leap to *creating* values. There's nothing, I mean *nothing*, like THAT!"

Rico smiled and said good night to his employee and turned to leave.

"Wait!" Eddie pleaded. Rico turned back around; Eddie looked away. He became very somber and, still not looking at

Rico, Eddie said, "Do you think...umm...could Jasmine's father...you know, his spirit...still be alive?"

Eddie couldn't look at Rico; Eddie couldn't even move. His whole body was bound up in tension, and Rico saw immense agony in Eddie's profile. Eddie could not accept that he had badly hurt a man to whom he could not make restitution, not now. Rico sighed. He realized Eddie was actually hoping to still, someday, repay Jasmine's father, if Ian's original theory still proved out.

Rico studied Eddie, sitting there unable to move, and realized Eddie lived to repay those whose lives he destroyed. That quest gave him passion and direction...gave him joy. Now, the idea of not being able to repay one of those persons, one whom he hurt very badly, Jasmine's father, haunted Eddie. Rico could see that Eddie was now a prisoner of eternal remorse. As Eddie sat stiff and motionless, waiting for Rico's answer to his question, Rico felt compassion for him. Rico thought for a moment, then in a voice that had spoken with pure honesty for thirty-seven years, ever since the third grade, Rico replied, "Soon, *we'll know*."

CHAPTER
ONE HUNDRED FIFTEEN

Ian looked around his office at his team of leaders on building the great ship. It's been a long meeting, Ian thought, but they all look fresh and eager to get back to work.

"So," he said, "are we all in agreement?"

He looked around at his team again. Every person in his office was nodding.

"So, we move the launch date forward from mid-November to the first week in September?"

"The Neothink breakthroughs in construction and computer technologies are accelerating so quickly, I think we'd all have to agree," said Ian's technology-alert expert. Ian looked around the room. The others were nodding.

"He's right," someone said.

"Yes, I'll be ready," someone else said.

"Anyone disagree?" Ian asked.

No one answered.

*

"Could I use Eddie for the last few weeks before the launch?" Ian asked Rico. "I feel Eddie could be a value in the hangar."

"I was going to suggest it to you in this week's meeting,"

Rico replied. "Eddie's beginning to show little spurts of value creation, and it's something I'd like for all of us to watch...and enjoy."

That week, Rico turned on his computerized lawn-care system and brought Eddie to the hangar.

"It's such a thrill that Ian *asked for me*," Eddie said on the supertrain from Philadelphia to New Jersey. "It's such an honor to live in the hangar!"

"Ian has a small room prepared for you with a bed, a desk, and a computer. There's bathrooms and showers in the hangar." Rico said. "Ian and Diana live there as well as several scientists and engineers and their families. The Group meets there once a week. You'll be in the middle of it all, Eddie!"

Eddie quickly proved himself to be a special value there. He was an endless fountain of energy, making himself valuable in every way he could. Moreover, Ian noticed those spurts of creativity beginning to bubble over. Robert Chapman started working with Eddie to help him locate his deepest motivational root, which was shriveled and lost after all those years with no nourishment. Robert would help Eddie find and nourish that motivational root, which would eventually send him on a vector of value creation. He would then become the value creator, the God-Man he was meant to be.

*

With seven weeks to go to the launch of the great rescue ship, Ian brought Eddie to his first meeting with The Group. Ian felt The Group would appreciate Eddie's value reflection. Eddie was beside himself when invited to join the meeting with his all-time heroes. Upon Ian's request, Eddie opened the meeting.

"That island," Eddie said, a little nervously while looking at Jake, "is the same world *everyone* lived in before; it's just that now there's no illusions left and no support structure to camouflage the horrid nature of that world. Jeremiah took down the support structure with his Business Alliance. Daniel took down the illusions by depoliticizing America. Nothing was left once The Group created the supersociety stimulations, and everyone jumped over to the new world — everyone except for us on the island. We had to live in the world we created; a world that reflects our true nature. ...To think that in the anticivilization, everyone's mind was conditioned from his first conscious moments to believe *that world* was his 'natural' world! Not long ago, everyone went into that horrid world. I've become physically sick while on the island thinking about my world there, myself, my past!

"The wastelands covered our entire planet before. I mean, everyone was living in the wastelands before — *everyone*...except twelve children: Miss Annabelle's students. You saved us all — you saved the world!

"I know now, you twelve former students were the only people who never perceived that other world as the 'natural' world. You were just never part of that world. You were always part of this world. I remember coming into the Oval Office, Daniel, wanting to kill you. Now, monsters as I once was have that 'natural' world — back on the island."

Eddie cleared his throat and continued, "Every conditioned response before was for that anticivilization. So it became the 'natural' world to everybody; it became hard-wired into people's minds. The evil generated by monsters such as me was merely accepted by nearly everyone, *as natural,* year after year." Eddie shook his head, disgusted with himself. "The people couldn't break from our spiral-of-death stimulations...until The Group came along and provided spectacular new supersociety stimulations. That's when everyone jumped over, and we external authorities were left with the hell we created."

Eddie was obviously upset with himself and looked out Ian's glass wall at the rescue ship, nearly completed now. Eddie stopped talking.

"A completely bogus 'natural' world," Natasha said, thinking about Eddie's repeated use of the expression "natural" world to explain the nearly inescapable trap of the anticivilization. She and Robert had spent some time with Eddie lately uncovering his Friday-Night essence. "You know, perhaps people's lockdown in the anticivilization actually went down to their earliest learned, automatic reactions, *mimicked* reactions, maybe even down to their nervous systems. A lion's learned, automatic reactions and nervous system, for example, will encourage it to attack and kill an approaching human. But take a lion cub from its natural environment — raise it as a pet around people — and its learned, automatic reactions and its stimulus-response nervous system will be completely different as that lion accepts an approaching human. Going down to stimulus-response and learned, automatic reactions...people's lockdown in the anticivilization was final."

"Miss Annabelle took the twelve of us out of that perceived 'natural' world, as in your analogy of the lion cub," Sally said. "Like the lion cub in that movie *Born Free* I saw while growing up, we perceived our world completely differently than all others in their 'natural' environment."

"They had no idea that, underneath it all, life should *not* be a subtle burden," Eddie added. "They had no idea people like me made the average person's life that stagnant burden. No one knew life could be permanently exhilarating and euphoric. People just had no idea. But you twelve former students did know it — you saw and felt everything differently...the way we do today. You brought that better life to civilization."

Daniel smiled at Eddie as the former politician tried to cope with who he once was and who he was now.

"Your emotional essence has changed in this world, Eddie," Daniel said, reassuringly. "That's why you have a hard time believing who you once were."

"Talking about emotional essences," said Reggie, "I grew up around very poor people. Some were hard-working, like my mom. Some were lazy; they hated work, so they did as little as they could to get by. One day, about a year after starting Grassroots Music, I was in an unfamiliar neighborhood after visiting a location for shooting a show. It was around noon. I was on a high after a full morning of exciting value creation, seeing Grassroots grabbing more and more ratings. But I got lost. As I drove through that old neighborhood, a disheveled man about my age stumbled out of one very sloppy-looking shack. He'd obviously just rolled out of bed and was still in his dirty sleepwear; it gave me the creeps. It was the middle of the day, and his day had just started! Looking at him during my moment of great exhilaration sent a surge of pity through me. His life was rotting away. Yet there's so much more to life. I pulled over for directions and got to talking with him. I felt sorry for him, but in tragic irony, he didn't feel sorry for himself. He actually thought he had it 'made in the shade', as he put it, since he got government entitlement money and didn't have to work! He had no clue how pathetic he was. Whereas I felt sorry for him, he didn't even know better to feel sorry for himself!"

"Exactly!" Eddie cried. "The people in the anticivilization had no idea at all what they were missing! They didn't even know to feel bad for themselves because they didn't know what they didn't have!"

"With external authorities controlling the anticivilization and everyone's mind," Mr. Melbourne said, "it was almost impossible to go into the Neothink mentality and discover value creation." Mr. Melbourne paused. Then, looking adoringly at his wife, he said, "In all the work I've done on the human mind, Eddie is right about the helplessness of the people breaking free from that anticivilization. For over a hundred generations, the bicameral mutation in the conscious mind, which I called mysticism, was passed down from adult minds to children's minds, sort of like those computer viruses we used to get. Like those old computer viruses that were so tough to stop, mysticism was nearly impossible to stop. But my wife broke through the external authorities' matrix of illusions and stopped the virus from entering your young minds, well before you were old enough to get hopelessly pulled into their spiral-of-death stimulations. She showed you, at eight years of age, how to integrate and guide yourselves *before* you got trapped in their world. You naturally grew into the Neothink mind of the God-Man, the value creator."

"You're so right," Jeremiah said. "Miss Annabelle did two major things differently to us that made us different than everyone else. First, she filled us with the Civilization of the Universe's perspective of the *supreme value* of conscious life when we were just eight years old. So, while growing up, our whole emotional perception of life and our reactions and actions in the world around us were outside of the 'natural' world for everyone else. We were always in this world. With so much emotional grasp of the value of our lives and the eternal tragedy of death, we discovered the supreme LOVE felt only in the

Civilization of the Universe.

"Second, she enabled our minds to go into Neothink. She did this by breaking through boundaries and illusions all around us; she showed us how to see *what is*, how to go to the essence of things, see common denominators, and pull together puzzle pieces that let us build puzzles that go beyond what already exists...into *value creation*. As young children, we felt the exhilaration and inspiration that came with discovering Nature's Quintessential Secret — conscious life is *the creator;* its role is *value creation*.

"Those two unique things, in particular — showing us the *supreme value* of our lives and showing us how to *neothink* — let us grow up in a different world than everyone else...in the Civilization of the Universe."

Jake looked at Miss Annabelle. She was so physically young and striking, yet at that moment her fiery eyes seemed to be filled with melted ice cubes, filled with puddles of loving memories of her students. Those twelve would always be her babies.

"You know," said Eddie, "your love for life never faded. You continued to feel that *supreme love for life* all your life after that year with Miss Annabelle. But no one else did, not like you. You were twelve little lion cubs, so to speak, removed from the so-called 'natural' world. Way back then, you were in *this* world of today, which was really the natural world all along. Only you twelve, initially. Then you went on, through Neothink, to create the supersociety stimulations that overwhelmed the stimulus-response of the people trapped in that old world of value destruction and certain death. Analogous to that poor guy during Reggie's trip, people never knew such a beautiful life existed. By seeing and feeling what we all do now in this new world, you twelve were beyond everyone else. As I said, you were able to overpower people's stimulus-response in the old world and bring us into the beautiful life. *Thank you.* You lifted us to the beautiful life — you saved us all — by bringing us the superior stimulus and response of this new world, which pulled us out of the old world. ...I read Jake's article about Homeric Man with his honor and glory through violence and force. Now, God-Man lives for legitimate honor and glory — through business, value creation, and love. Beorapparaus's art projection let me flip up from my two-dimensional honor and glory viewpoint on that business-free island, into the three-dimensional viewpoint of this world — the beautiful dimensions of business, of values, of love."

Wow, Jake thought, seeing in his memory for an instance, a flash — The Magician — the fat and violent Senator from Massachusetts driven by honor and glory who orchestrated the failed assassination on Daniel. Had that assassination succeeded, Eddie would be sub-100 and not here today. Eddie certainly is no longer part of the mindless forces of nature, Jake thought, which exuded external authorities. No, the forces of Neothink prevailed.

Jake suddenly smiled as he realized that Eddie reminded him of a child just learning how to talk and then excitedly yapping nonstop. Eddie's on the verge of *creating* values, Jake realized, and he's so excited he can't stop talking like a beautiful child. Jake quietly chuckled.

Jake was aware he was really enjoying watching Eddie. A few years ago, though, Eddie's face was so full of evil. Now, his face was...so full of innocence. As Eddie talked and his eyes sparkled with excitement, Jake noticed the former evil politician now really looked like an exuberant child. Jake realized he was witnessing a mind in the process of making the leap from the Homeric Man to the God-Man...perhaps the last person to make the leap on planet Earth.

Jake sat back and let himself take in what he was witnessing before him. Eddie was like a child with a new discovery. Yes, Jake thought, Rico was right about the joy of watching Eddie's leap into value creation. All at once, Jake could not hold it in any longer and his joy spilled over, once again, in a delightful chuckle.

Jasmine whispered to Jake, "It's something to watch a person making the leap from a value producer to a value creator."

Ian, who heard Jake chuckle and heard Jasmine's comment, smiled and said, "Eddie, you're closing in on Nature's Quintessential Secret, my friend. You've got a little taste of it since arriving here. Your inspiration will continue to soar higher and higher. One fine day, your value creation *will add value to Zon's creation — to our Universe,* just as The Group has done."

Ian then looked at the rescue ship. One by one, the others in the room turned their heads to embrace the beauty they created on the other side of the glass wall. They gazed at their first great offering to Zon's creation. Ian described the feeling of creating a value for the Civilization of the Universe.

Jake looked back at the individuals in the room, the God-Men around him, and felt a sense of awe again. He shook his head and thought: from *Breakthrough News* to biological immortality to controlling the cosmos.

Jake then noticed another person not looking at the rescue ship, but at those in Ian's office. That person was Miss Annabelle. Jake quietly moved next to her.

"Will you tell me what you're thinking about?" he whispered.

She smiled, and without moving her eyes, she quietly said, "I was just remembering a Christmas Day, over half my life ago. I was alone, trying to imagine the world we live in now. I believed my students could get us into this world, and I was trying back then to imagine how they would do it."

Slowly Miss Annabelle turned her lavender eyes to look at Jake. She said, "Now that I know, I was standing here savoring my students and what they've done."

He smiled and nodded. He remembered Angie and Jessie telling him about that Christmas Day when he first visited them over nine years before. I guess they knew Miss Annabelle's thoughts from her diary, Jake thought.

Miss Annabelle sighed. She seemed to be thinking out loud as she softly said, "It was supreme love in their hearts and Neothink in their minds that led to the superpuzzles..."

CHAPTER
ONE HUNDRED SIXTEEN

With five weeks to go until lift-off, The Group spent a lot of time now in the hangar in New Jersey, witnessing the construction of the mammoth rescue ship. On this day, the beautiful Cathy Winters had been quietly gazing from Ian's office through the glass wall at the construction of the rescue ship.

"Let's call her *Justice*," she finally said in a distant voice.

The Group still had not named the rescue ship, and from time to time, someone would suggest a name. When someone made a suggestion, silence usually ensued as the members of The Group drifted into deep thought over the proposed name.

Justice, Jake thought. That word took his thoughts back eight-and-a-half years to a weekend just before he and Jasmine moved to Washington, D.C. They went for a weekend visit to Jessie and Angie's house. It was a Saturday afternoon, and Angie and Jasmine had left in the car to get some things from the grocery store.

Jake and Jessie were in the garage, with the door open. It had been a mild winter so far that year, and this day was an unusually warm afternoon. The fresh outdoor air felt good. Jessie was repairing the brackets to the bottom of a file drawer for the school, working efficiently at his work bench as he talked.

Then, out of nowhere, he asked Jake an unrelated question.

"Do you take justice seriously?"

Jake answered, "Yeah, I do."

"Just how seriously?"

"What do you mean?"

"Seriously enough to *serve justice* if need be?"

Jake looked at Jessie. He was leading up to something. When Jake did not answer immediately, Jessie continued.

"I believe justice must be in control, or mankind would perish," he said. "If you don't have justice, then you have chaos...especially where I came from."

Jake noticed Jessie seemed to drift off to another place.

"I'll tell you something about me that no one knows. You mustn't tell anyone — not even Angie," Jessie said.

Jake looked at the gentle man before him and sensed he wanted to confide in him...perhaps a dark secret. "Okay, I won't tell anyone," Jake promised.

"When I was a young man, a year after coming to Cheektowaga, I went back down to Philly, alone. I told Angie I needed to do some things to take care of my folks, which I did. But when I was there, I took care of justice, too. I took the law into my own hands...man, did I ever. You know, it's an awful feeling being a predator. You don't feel strong; you feel like...a cockroach, scurrying out of the light, hiding in the shadows."

Jake saw pain in Jessie's face.

"But I was there to deliver justice. I was on a mission. I had to do what I had to do."

"Tell me what happened."

Jessie's face grimaced as he went to his dark and distant past to tell the story...

*

The return to Philly was eerie for the young janitor. He stepped off the bus and filled his lungs with the damp, pungent air of the bus station.

"Philly," he mumbled, unpleasantly.

He walked fourteen blocks to his parents' home. He walked

up the steps, took another deep breath, and opened the front door with the key his mom had given him when he left home.

"Oh, my baby!" his mother cried upon seeing Jessie. She rushed over and embraced him. "Oh, my baby."

"Ma, how's everything here?" Jessie asked, hugging his mother. He did not realize, until now, how much he had missed her.

She put her head against his chest; he was touched by how excited she got over seeing him, and he was saddened that he saw her so seldom now.

"Wonderful, now that you're here," she said. Jessie suddenly knew he must see her more often, maybe on major holidays.

"Honey, your dad can't wait to be here, too."

His father was still making pizzas at La Rizza.

*

After a wonderful evening and dinner, his mom and dad went to bed. Jessie went to his room. He spent several minutes looking around nostalgically at his room filled with childhood memories. Then he got down to business and opened his suitcase. He pulled out six full sheets of paper. Each sheet had the name of one of the six men who had beaten Angie into submission and mercilessly raped her and maimed her when she was just a 17-year-old virgin.

Each sheet contained a lot of information, including a picture of the culprit taped to it, his likely location at different times of the day, his home address, his work address (if he worked), and identifying body marks. Jessie had spent every dime he had saved to get this information.

There were probably as many as nine of them who had beaten and raped Angie, but Jessie, try as he did, could be absolutely sure only of these six. He knew for certain these six were guilty.

Jessie learned that these six continued their criminal gang activities, and the word on the streets was these six continued to rape other innocent teenagers. The other three had left behind their gang days, and Jessie could not be one-hundred percent sure if they raped Angie or were passive gang members caught in an activity they never intended to be in.

Lucky for them, Jessie thought.

*

At half past ten that night, Jessie sat on a stool in a dingy bar.

"Hey, buddy, I need a Schlitz over here!" Jessie snapped.

"Yeah, yeah..." the big bartender mumbled. He filled the glass with the beer on tap and put it in front of Jessie.

Jessie stared at the tattoo of a scorpion on the bartender's right forearm.

"Thanks, *Cory*," Jessie said.

"Do I know you, *boy*?" the burly white bartender snarled.

Jessie's eyes narrowed into little slits. "Yeah, MUTHA FUCKA!" he shouted. Then, he sprang over the bar.

The bartender was *not* caught off guard, for he'd spent his life fighting in the streets and in bars. He hit Jessie hard, square on the jaw with a blow that would flatten the toughest man. But Jessie was a man possessed with rage. He had suppressed his rage for seven years. Now that rage rushed to the surface and transformed him into an unstoppable dark force. So much adrenaline filled his system that even a two-by-four could not stop him now.

Bleeding from his mouth, Jessie yelled, "I'm gonna *rape you*, bitch!"

Jessie let loose the street-tough beast within. With enormous speed, Jessie's extended arm scooped a large bottle of whiskey off the bar and, in a full, one-handed swing, smashed it across the bartender's head. The bottom of the bottle broke off and whiskey sprayed everywhere. The dazed bartender fell on his back. Jessie dropped to the ground, spread apart the big, semiconscious man's legs, and then thrust the broken bottle, jagged side first, with full force backed by seven years of rage, up into the man's opened crotch. Jessie pulled it out and thrust it up into the bleeding crotch again and again, over and over again.

The pain rushed from the big man's lungs like a woman screaming, like a woman being raped. After eight deep stabs, Jessie finally relented, unable to bear the mutilation any longer.

He let go of the bottle, which stuck straight out from the bartender's blood-soaked crotch, buried two inches deep. Jessie stood up and turned to the four petrified patrons at the bar.

"Justice served!" he screamed, blood spraying from his mouth. "Do you hear me? JUSTICE SERVED!"

That night of justice, Jessie visited the other five criminals. He served justice on them with no witnesses present. He maimed the private parts of all six men. Just as he and Angie, these six young men, if they weren't already, would now never be biological parents...not until the supersociety made it physically and morally possible again.

As Jessie planned, enough witnesses saw him at the bar to give the press and the police Jessie's description...his personal message to the gang members to stay the hell away from his family. For, dealing with this man would always yield *justice*.

*

"Angie never knew?" Jake asked, pulling Jessie's mind out of that nasty memory in Philly, back to Jessie's pleasant garage in Cheektowaga.

"We never talked about it. But I brought back from Philadelphia the morning's newspaper that reported the attacks. The headline quoted me shouting at the bar; in fact, the headline read *Justice Served!* and the article had pictures of the six criminals and a police sketch of me. I left the paper, opened to the article, on the kitchen table the following Sunday morning, and I went outside to cut the lawn. Fifteen minutes later, Angie came outside. Her eyes were red; she'd been crying. She walked over and hugged me. She held on to me so tight, I'll never forget the love in that embrace, not as long as I live. Nothing was said, but everything was communicated. No, I'll never forget that embrace, not ever."

*

"*Justice*," Jake heard, in a deep voice, pulling him back to the present in Ian's office in the hangar. It was Jessie; he and Angie now attended the meetings of The Group. Perhaps, Jake

1078

thought, Jessie had just relived the same memory.

"I like the name, *Justice*," Jessie said. "Justice makes things right."

*

Later that evening, Jake and Jasmine went for a long walk inside the hangar, around the rescue ship, strolling their eight-month-old Ameena in the baby carriage while Jakey, who would be three-years-old in two days, asked his dad a barrage of questions about the spaceship: Where was it going, why was it going there, what was space, how far, how fast, what was a planet, who was Beorapparaus, and so on. Each answer spawned several more questions causing Jake to smile at the nature of a Zon radiating through his son — his thirst for knowledge. Suddenly, Jakey spotted the holes under the ship where the release upon liftoff would pass, and the toddler took off running toward the ship.

"It's okay," Jake said when he saw Jasmine's instant concern, "they're working only inside the ship. Nothing there could hurt him."

Jasmine took advantage of the break from Jakey's unending barrage of questions. "I know why Cathy likes the name *Justice*," Jasmine said. She craned her neck back and looked up at the grand ship. "It's because of the unthinkable *injustice* that occurred on Beorapparaus's planet. You really don't need the concept of justice unless you have injustice."

Jake realized the concept of *justice* actually seemed a little odd to Jasmine...and to the others in The Group. Jasmine had just pinpointed *why*: You must have *injustice* to need the concept of justice, and injustice had been extinct on Earth for a few years, so the concept of justice had become moot. Jake had just been to the wastelands less than three months earlier, and his exposure again to the anticivilization made the concept of justice a little more fresh to him. But without that recent trip to the wastelands, and without the exposure to the reminder — the horror of what happened to Beorapparaus's civilization — the concept of justice would nearly be forgotten by now.

"You're right," Jake said. "Our world is now a paradise,

filling up with Paradise Cities." Jake paused, enlightened by a new thought. "And you know what? Before long, children will ask their parents, 'Mommy, Daddy, what does *paradise* mean?' And, you know what their parents will answer? They'll say, 'I don't know...it's just a name.' Similar to injustice and justice, you need something less, something negative, to comprehend paradise. But anything negative — things such as dishonesty and irrationality — are extinct on Earth, except in the ostracism wastelands. Before long, our paradise on Earth will become, simply, *what is*."

"Eternal bliss in the Civilization of the Universe," Jasmine reflected, "becomes, simply, *life*."

Jessie had stayed after the day's discussion to think, and he was quietly sitting against the wall, in the shadows.

Overhearing Jake and Jasmine's discussion, Jessie asked, ever so gently so as not to startle them, "We know what happened to the likes of those who raped my wife, but what about those who murdered the billions of innocent beings on Beorapparaus' planet? Somewhere, there must always be justice."

Jake had wondered that himself, too. He sensed the answer might be one of the new properties of the Civilization of the Universe that he would not know until he witnessed it. But at the rate *Beyond* absorbed new knowledge about the Universe, Jake knew that wouldn't be long.

Jake empathized with Jessie's need for justice. Jake remained quiet for a moment, pondering the need for justice and feeling compassion for Jessie. Then, Jake started nodding. He inadvertently mumbled, "Soon, *we'll know*." He looked toward Jessie; an air of relief blew through both of them.

Jessie stood up and walked out of the shadows. What had been troubling him tonight seemed to have vanished with Jake's simple comment: *soon, we'll know*. He walked over and, for the first time, he hugged Jake. Jasmine felt the impact of the paternal love Jessie held for her husband. When Jessie let go, he braced his hands on Jake's shoulders and looked lovingly into his eyes.

"You've always *cared*. Thank you, *son*."

And then, Jessie left the hangar, in peace.

CHAPTER
ONE HUNDRED SEVENTEEN

With three weeks to go to the launch, Eddie was now a regular visitor to the weekly meetings in the hangar. The members of The Group found his insights to be increasingly valuable.

"While I was on the island of the living dead," said Eddie during The Group's meeting in the hangar, "I often though about Daniel and the other eleven students of Miss Annabelle. What made them so different than everyone else? I'd ask myself that question. What made them our saviors from the anticivilization? Gradually, I came to realize you twelve perceived life differently. Shortly before Jake arrived and took me off the island, I saw Beorapparaus's projection of his art piece on the Internet. For the first time, I believed I could *feel* what you twelve students of Miss Annabelle felt all your lives. I could *really feel* the apex of beauty — *real beauty* was business. *Beautiful business!* Beautiful, beautiful business makes everything wonderful and cleans out anything miserable, cleans out the wastelands. Business is the opposite of that ugly *business-free* island!"

Eddie's eyes filled up with tears. "*Inspiration* for me now is the same as it's always been for you. Those little bursts of value creation you've noticed happening to me lately — *that's inspiration!* Everything else is nice, but value creation is *pure inspiration!* This, I know, is how you twelve students of Miss Annabelle *naturally* felt growing up, starting with your value creations such as *Breakthrough News* in third grade. You perceived business as pure beauty...and value creation as pure inspiration. I like to say: value creation is the inspiration; business is its beautiful manifestation."

Eddie's face glowed as would a child telling his parents a newly discovered treasure of knowledge. "And now, I know I'm probably the last person on Earth to discover this — knowing that no one in the wastelands will discover it — but I now know what is most *important*. It's *love*...the love you felt for each other and for your teacher thirty-six years ago, the love Sally felt for her mother, the love Jasmine felt for her father, the love Miss Annabelle felt for you, the love Rico feels for his children, the love we all felt for Martin, the love we feel for ourselves, our families, and for our fellowman for the wonderful life-enhancing values we bring to each other. My love for you people is indescribable. I can feel it...I can't find the words to adequately describe it, though."

He shook his head as he searched for words to express his love. Suddenly, he looked at his former boss, Rico, whom he had lived with for three months before coming to the hangar. He said, "But I think you can all understand what I'm trying to describe. I saw this love whenever Rico looked at his children and wife. The *love* in that man's eyes — *that's what is important!*" Eddie paused and looked around the room. His eyes were filled with tears of love.

"That *love* Rico feels comes from feeling the supreme value of our lives," Jeremiah said. "Feeling the supreme value of our lives actually comes from discovering Nature's Quintessential Secret and our exhilarating internal feeling each and every day as value creators. And as you said, Eddie, we manifest our value creation through business. Love, value creation, business...the three are inseparable. They're the Trinity of the Church of God-Man. That's why our Church naturally evolved into the Business Alliance that took down the support structure of the anticivilization."

Jake thought about what he felt at the Church of God-Man congregations: the love, the value creation, the business. Indeed, that's what's important, inspiring, and beautiful in life! That's my perception of life now. That Trinity of the Church of God-Man was actually the way of life everywhere now, for everyone, especially in the new Paradise Cities that were explicitly structured to maximize love, value creation, and business. There was no such thing as the Business Alliance any longer, for it was simply everywhere now. There was no anticivilization to collapse. The Church of God-Man ceased to be as it once was, for biological immortality was routine now. People did not die; citizens of Earth had joined the Civilization of the Universe. The Church successfully obsoleted itself as a force bringing immortality and the Civilization of Universe to Earth. Now, the Church was a weekly social and learning experience, a weekly congregation with keynote speakers giving fascinating talks on different Neothink puzzles and superpuzzles. Those talks were wonderful to listen to and learn from. Afterwards, the congregation turned into a socializing and networking hour full of value reflection, love, and valuable connections of all sorts.

Jake's thoughts drifted off to Jeremiah and his Church of God-Man...and how he and his church had joined forces with Daniel, Cathy, and Theodore in the growing phenomenon of Paradise Cities. Jake imagined the Paradise Cities he and Jasmine visited. They each consisted of a few thousand residences nestled in the plush, green environment built around the business club with its Entrepreneur Center, subsequently renamed the CEO Center because the lone entrepreneurs functioned through Theodore's Division-of-Friday-Night-essence internet software *Business* as the Chief Executive Officers of their businesses. Jeremiah built a beautiful, large Church within each Paradise City. The weekly congregation and talks tightened the community. Each week, a different member from the community would be the keynote speaker and talk about his or her value creation and business.

Keynote speakers in the Paradise Cities' Churches who were extraordinarily advanced value creators involved in major superpuzzles, such as a Theodore Winters, were considered special treats. Jeremiah would arrange special presentations of such keynote speakers and deliver them to all his churches throughout the country or throughout the world — depending on the level of the value creator — through holograms, which seemed almost lifelike now.

"The Trinity of the Church of God-Man," Jake muttered, sitting in the corner of Ian's office, quietly thinking aloud. "Business, value creation, love...beauty, inspiration, importance. They're three separate entities, yet they're one."

Mr. Melbourne who was sitting next to Jake, overheard his thoughts and raised an eyebrow.

Still quietly sorting his thoughts, Jake continued, slowly and deliberately, "You can't have *love* like we have now without value creation and business; you can't have *business* without love and value creation; you can't have *value creation* without business and love. They're all one, and they bring God-Man eternal happiness."

Jake looked around Ian's office. The people in there were soul mates. Eddie was right — the twelve former students felt these things as children. Beauty, inspiration, importance: business, value creation, love. This is how I feel now, too, Jake thought.

Then, he remembered his day on the road with Jeremiah nine years earlier during the campaign for Daniel's presidential run. Jake remembered Jeremiah telling him about the three anchors that had to be broken to free society from the anticivilization in order to take the leap into the Civilization of the Universe. And Jake remembered how Jeremiah opened Jake's eyes to how the twelve former students perceived the world differently than everyone else. Indeed, those twelve really were the saviors of the world, Jake realized, literally of everyone's life. Those twelve created the supersociety stimulations, Jake thought, so the rest of us could finally feel these God-Man feelings, too...these exhilarating feelings of beautiful business, inspired value creation, and supreme love. Miss Annabelle's students broke the three anchors: they broke Anchor #1 *politicization*...and then business became free and beautiful; their superpuzzle broke Anchor #2 *stagnation*...and then people became inspired value creators; they broke Anchor #3 *accepting death*...and then people discovered the supreme love for their lives. Then, humanity was free to make *the leap*.

"I'm listening to the tapes of the Miracle Year," Eddie was saying. "I'm so moved by the beauty you saw in Teddy building a national business, the inspiration you felt in creating *Breakthrough News*, and the importance you put on your love for your teacher and the importance she put on her love for you."

"That *love* for life emotionally drove us to achieve biological immortality," Jeremiah said. "Our neothinking into new levels of value creation and business enabled us to achieve it."

During the meeting, Debra seemed to be deep in thought. She had teamed together with Rico to successfully snap into the rescue-ship superpuzzle the vital puzzle piece of food capacity, storage, and food generation for the 30-year journey, including a bona fide Debbie's French Fry City right on board for a right-at-home feel. While the others looked back at Ian, she continued gazing at the rescue ship. Her eyes were focussed on the mouth of the great ship where Beorapparaus would enter the world of immortals in fifteen years.

"The Trinity will save Beorapparaus," she uttered when the others stopped talking. Nodding her head at the ship, she added, "She's a product of the Trinity — beautiful business, inspired value creation, and supreme love."

She paused as The Group absorbed that profound fact. Then, she voiced the thoughts of every member of The Group: "Did the Trinity save our loved ones who didn't make it?" she said. "Did beautiful business, inspired value creation, and supreme love set in place the greatest of all superpuzzles for those who didn't survive the anticivilization?"

When she asked that question, something unexpectedly filled Jake's thoughts, something Theodore had said to Jake nearly three years before while dining at the Paradise City near Laguna. Jake let himself look back at that evening. He and Jasmine sat with Theodore and Cathy in the gourmet restaurant of the first Paradise City, when it was still known as just *Paradise*, listening to Theodore discussing the progress of mankind and how that progress all snapped together into a simple three-piece puzzle. Complicated human life, Theodore explained, snapped together into a simple *one*. While recalling the conversation in *Paradise* three years prior, Jake suddenly saw a stunning connection to the conversation in the hangar on this day. Under his breath, he exclaimed, "But that's it! Without realizing it, Theodore had been talking about *the Trinity*!" Jake paused. A moment later he quietly exclaimed, "Not only that, Theodore had unwittingly taken the Trinity a step further and made it very specific, very tangible. Theodore *defined* business, value creation, and love — the Trinity — of the Civilization of the Universe." Jake stopped talking. He knew he was getting louder. But his mind was on fire: business, Jake remembered Theodore saying, worked through Theodore's supersociety software *Business;* value creation came from the "garage" and in-house entrepreneurs who repopulated the workforce after Theodore's division-of-essence business paradigm spread throughout the world, and love for mankind created the superpuzzles. Whoa! The *Trinity Tangibles*, Jake thought. In the Civilization of the Universe, the superpuzzles, the "garage" and in-house entrepreneurs, and the software *Business* were the *Trinity Tangibles*.

Jake's thoughts drifted. What would the Trinity Tangibles be out there, he wondered, beyond our world, throughout the Universe? Just what would the superpuzzles of supreme love be out there? Would they, perhaps, include saving all conscious life...including our lost loved ones? After all, what could be of greater love and importance?

Of course, the value creators, the "garage" and in-house entrepreneurs, would be Zons...but to what levels? And *their* business — that dynamic process that connects the Zons' value creations with their vast superpuzzles — what would it be? Could it be found in...the ether? Just imagine it, Jake pondered, could it be the super quantum computer that contains the Zons' versions of *Business* and *EssenceTalk*? I know Theodore thinks so. "The Trinity Tangibles," Jake muttered under his breath, "what a concept." But, he knew Ian still did not think our loved ones survived their deaths.

A cold whisper blew apart Jake's thoughts. Debra, as though she did not realize she was talking, let the deepest feeling harbored in her heart erupt and escape her lips. *"God, I hope Mom and Dad are out there."*

It was hard, so hard, Jake knew, just so unforgiving for immortals, who now included Earthlings, to have lost loved ones to the mortal anticivilization. Eternal life for the immortals...eternal death for the mortals. The gap between eternal life versus eternal nothingness was almost too overwhelming to comprehend and too unbearable to cope with when involving lost loved ones.

Jake felt stronger than ever, however, that if the supreme superpuzzle were set in place by Zons, then the journey to save Beorapparaus would somehow lead Earthlings to their lost loved ones. That thought had been filling Jake with a growing excitement lately. Indeed, the immense knowledge necessary to do this rescue, he knew, would open the shutters to the greatest secrets of the Universe.

In a voice that had changed from positing theory to stating authoritative fact, Ian said to Debra with an air of finality, regarding her parents: "Debra, when we become Zons, *we'll know*. Soon, *we'll know*."

III.

Becoming Zons

CHAPTER
ONE HUNDRED EIGHTEEN

The inside of the massive hangar in New Jersey was dark, except for the lighted bleachers. A little over two hundred VIP guests sat or stood on the bleachers. Some were just too excited to sit down. They would be the first, outside of the creators, to witness on site the grand creation that the whole world threw itself behind, financially and emotionally, for the past six-and-a-half months.

Beautiful classical music suddenly filled the air; a moment later the lights clicked on. People gasped, people swayed. The ship was so large, towering over the bleachers, it threw off the onlookers' equilibrium. Anyone standing sat down in awe.

No one spoke. They just let the music play, and they looked. The creators decided to keep quiet too. They were the only people who could talk, because they had seen the great ship grow during its creation. The others could only look and breathe.

After three minutes of music and no spoken words, Theodore and Ian walked onto the stage at the mouth of the great ship. They would address the silent crowd.

Theodore and Ian looked like two tiny mice while standing before the giant ship. The ship was round and covered the ground of ten football fields. But what made the onlookers speechless was how high that massive dome rose from the ground. The ship was built in forty layers — it was forty stories high!

Wrapping around the front of the pewter-colored ship in giant white letters was the ship's name. The VIP crowd knew what the big white letters spelled, only because of the twenty-foot model of the great ship next to the stage, which proudly displayed her name: *Trinity*.

"Thank you citizens of Earth for contributing the funds to make *Trinity* possible," Theodore began. The Patterson Channel brought the presentation to the world. "We named her *Trinity* because, well, just look at her and witness the beauty of business, feel the inspiration of value creators, and savor the manifestation of pure love!" Theodore swept his arm up toward the grand creation.

The crowd stood up and roared for a full two minutes. They had recovered from their initial shock upon seeing the massive ship, and they were now releasing their appreciation of mankind's grand accomplishment.

"Beautiful business, inspired value creation, and a superpuzzle of supreme love created her," Theodore continued. "The Trinity of the Civilization of the Universe brought together The Group and the entire human race to accomplish our first Zon Superpuzzle!"

The crowd roared again.

"*Trinity* is a powerful expression of supreme love from humankind. She makes me, and should make all of you, very proud of the human race."

When the crowd quieted down, he continued.

"She's our next-level Operation after Operation II with the same goal to save a conscious life from the everyone-dies anticivilization. During the first Operation, we lost Martin Castlebury. Operation II saved Andy Konosovic. Operation III, so to speak, will save Beorapparaus Rasaraus!"

Yes, Jake thought while sitting on the bleachers next to the other members of The Group, *Trinity* was a good name. The other two names in the final analysis were: *Justice* and *Supreme Love*. The Group decided against *Justice* because there was no more need to make a point about justice, for everything in the Civilization of the Universe was, simply, *just*. The final decision between *Trinity* versus *Supreme Love* was more difficult. *Supreme Love* for conscious life was the human condition from which this superpuzzle sprang forth. *Trinity* included the complete set of dynamics — beautiful business, inspired value creation, and supreme love — that drove this project to completion.

"Monitoring the second beam," Ian said when the crowd quieted down, "reveals that *Trinity* will bring back with Beorapparaus an eternal value to citizens of Earth...priceless expressions of art, especially for the generations to come, not as reminders of the horrors...but as appreciations of the beauty."

Everyone there had read Jake's gripping article titled *A Final Look Back* about his venture into the wastelands, which were about to be poofed away, forever. The business-free wastelands were the final few dots of ugliness on Earth. The Trinity — business, value creation, love — now filled the beautiful business-driven world. The Trinity was absent in the wastelands. Without the Trinity, there could be no beauty, no better-and-better phenomenon.

A Final Look Back enlightened the human race to the value of Beorapparaus's proposed art. In fact, every population among the Civilization of the Universe would benefit, Jake's article explained. Their citizens would forever feel, through juxtaposition, the *full* beauty of what they had.

"Beorapparaus will know we're coming to get him about five Earth years before *Trinity* arrives," Ian continued. "We've sent a beam that'll reach him in ten Earth years. *Trinity* will reach him in about fifteen Earth years."

"One-hundred families will make the journey," Theodore said. "Those one-hundred families have been carefully selected and trained. They're ready to go."

The crowd clapped. As the people around Jake clapped, his thoughts zoomed in on the word *family*. Children now became so integrated with their parents' exhilarating value creations that children became part of that value creation at very young ages, for it was the most exciting thing to do! The new world confirmed it: *man was made to create.* Family units created values together and were inseparable now. The love among parent and child grew more powerful with each passing year.

"Two surgical teams are going," Theodore continued. "They'll perform the Operation if needed during the 30-year round-trip journey and are equipped with the proper medical equipment. However, the Operation may not be necessary."

"Instead," Ian said proudly, "an ample supply of the eighteen-again serum is on board."

The crowd clapped. The eighteen-again serum was known around the world as the next great biomedical breakthrough. Sally and Ian had teamed up with Dr. Rudy Costello two years earlier. They tested his age-reversing, reproductive stem cells derivative on lizards and then on chimpanzees. Sally and Rudy had just begun testing their formula — given the popular nickname: the eighteen-again serum — on humans. The tests were successful and the serum was about to permanently replace the Operation. Soon, Theodore would take the ultimate consumer product — the eighteen-again serum — to the marketplace. Sally's original medical masterpiece — the Operation — would still be valuable for accident victims.

We've beamed Cathy Winter's health programs to help Beorapparaus stay in optimum physical shape. In ten years, he'll receive those health instructions. If he discovers our beam, he'll know we'll be there in five more years to rescue him."

Ian is, Jake reflected, essentially talking about keeping Beorapparaus healthy and alive until we reach him. "But, of course," Jake suddenly muttered under his breath, "Beorapparaus is trapped in a mortal anticivilization, and he will die there if not for us." Jake's eyes widened; he was hit with an insight. He tried to keep his voice down as he said to himself, "I'll be goddamned, Beorapparaus is part of Project Sustain Life! Project Save Beorapparaus and this huge space craft are part of Project Sustain Life! *This*," he said while leaning back to see as much of *Trinity* as he could, "is one giant life-support machine!"

He quieted down when he noticed others glancing at him. The human race, he thought, gave its all to save Beorapparaus as it did during the SSL period. As Beorapparaus's Zons, nearly everyone on Earth contributed. What, Jake wondered, would *our Zons'* Project Sustain Life be? Would it have captured our lost loved ones?

"Our travelers in *Trinity* will enjoy going to the beach with real, beach-like atmospheric conditions, including sunny days with blue skies, overcast days, and even rainy days," Theodore said after the applause subsided. "The ocean will have calm days and stormy days with large waves just as the beaches on Earth. Those aboard will enjoy a large Nature Center that contains a balanced ecosystem of plants and food for several safe, pleasing-to-look-at wild animals. I've personally enjoyed going aboard and taking my morning runs through the Nature Center."

The crowd laughed. They would love to go on board for a tour, but the ship was too large, and it would launch in twelve days. There were still three major breakthroughs needed before the launch, but knowledge advanced so fast now, the breakthroughs would easily be made and in place in time.

"The tour will start soon," Ian said. "The inside of the ship, room by room, will be shown directly before your eyes, as a three-dimensional, true-to-life hologram."

As the hologram tour began, Jake felt himself filling with pride, witnessing the apex of human achievement. Love, inspiration, and beauty filled the human soul now, for eternity. Disease, death, depression, anxiety, apathy had nearly faded from the human memory.

The second major achievement to have risen from the supreme love of the human race stood majestically before Jake as though it were aware and confident of its mission.

"Nothing will stop me," the great ship seemed to say to the crowd. "I will succeed. Fifteen years from now, Beorapparaus *will* join the immortals."

Jake admired and paid homage to the mighty ship before him. A distinguished-looking man in a long white labcoat walked inconspicuously from its mouth and onto the long escalator down.

"Let me have the binoculars!" Robert said in a rush to Natasha. He placed them against his eyes and whispered, "I know that scientist from somewhere."

Jake, who had done an article on all the scientists involved in Project Save Beorapparaus, leaned over and quietly said, "He's the scientist who first spotted the anomaly on Beorapparaus's planet, the best researcher at Beyond with the best eye for detail. That's why Ian brought him here from the Space Library to go over every square inch of *Trinity*."

"What's his name?" Robert whispered.

Jake smiled and said, "That's Saul Tannenbaum."

"Saul!" Robert said. Then he laughed. The wide grin stayed on his face as he put the binoculars back against his eyes to watch the handsome scientist. Robert remembered the broken postal worker who came to TGIF nine years ago. He had attempted to take his own life, helplessly wasting away until Robert got him on the path he was meant to travel in life. Robert remembered Saul asking him how he could ever repay him for saving his life. Binoculars still against his eyes, grin still on his face, Robert nodded and whispered to himself, "Now look at you, Saul. Oh, my friend, you have repaid me and the world many times over. I'm *so proud* of you."

*

The night before the launch, Jake could not sleep. He knew he was excited, but he was able to sleep before the Operation and Operation II when he was this excited. After two restless hours, he got out of bed, careful not to wake Jasmine, and went into his living room. Why, he wondered, can't I sleep?

He stood in his living room, recalling the meetings in the hangar when Eddie was making the leap to the God-Man. Jake smiled as he saw Eddie's face in his mind's eye.

In those meetings, Jake thought, I witnessed supreme love filling that man's heart. I saw that supreme love for conscious life pushing out all dishonesties and rationalizations from Eddie's mind, transforming him right before my eyes into a man who was fully honest, a God-Man.

What exactly is supreme love? Jake asked himself. As a journalist, he often made himself put words to what he thought he already understood. The closest comparison in the anticivilization, he thought, would have been a mother's love for her baby. Remembering back to Mr. Melbourne's speech on the forces of nature, Jake realized the most powerful of all forces of nature would be a mother's protective love for her baby. Even the most meek mother, who all her life obediently followed authority, would stand up to any male who tried to harm her baby, no matter how popular or handsome he was; she would go against the group or peer pressure for her baby; she would combat any external authority that tried to harm her baby, no matter how powerful or intimidating. She would also blast past her own weaknesses and oftentimes her own destructive habits, dishonesties, and subtle rationalizations to get down to what was best — down past appearances to the real essences of what was best for her baby. That love of a mother for her baby brought her, in the specific task of taking care of her baby, close to the state of mind of fully honest God-Man. In the anticivilization, a mother's protective love for her baby was almost a microcosm of supreme love for conscious life.

Jake sat back into his living-room chair. "Supreme love for conscious life," he said quietly, "is a dimension beyond the love of a mother for her baby. Supreme love for conscious life takes those protective passions beyond mother and baby. Supreme love for conscious life drives out the destructive forces of nature and one's own dishonesties to get past appearances to what is best — *really best* — for oneself, one's loved ones, and for all human beings."

Supreme love on Earth started rising at the worldwide level, Jake figured, sometime after the mid-term elections during Daniel's presidency, rising with the supersociety that followed. Supreme love filled the human race, Jake remembered, when the world watched Martin Castlebury not make it during The Operation. Supreme love filled people's hearts and immediately set off Project Sustain Life, which, Jake realized, would continue the next morning with the effort to save Beorapparaus from his mortal civilization.

"Yes," he softly said, "that supreme love throughout the human race culminates tomorrow, with the launching of *Trinity*."

Jake leaned back in his chair and smiled. Then he exclaimed, "We're going to bring Beorapparaus into the world of immortals!" That thought made him feel *so good* inside that the rush of happiness — the "happiness attack" — actually took him by surprise.

He pulled back the lever to lift the footrest, and he continued reflecting. He remembered other moments from the recent meetings with Eddie. He remembered some things Jeremiah said about supreme love and value creation causing the leap. Jake remembered Miss Annabelle saying that her students got into this world through supreme love in their hearts and Neothink in their minds. Of course, he thought, puzzle-building Neothink is what enables us to advance into value creation. And becoming a value creator lets us discover the supreme value of our lives. And discovering the supreme value of conscious life fills us with supreme love for conscious life. Jake thought about Eddie, about Robert's work with Eddie to help him discover his Friday-Night essence, which led to Eddie's recent spurts of Neothink and value creation and growing supreme love.

Then a mystery began to fill Jake's mind. Now he knew why he could not sleep. His mind always wanted to solve a good mystery. After all, solving a mystery was what brought him to Duncan Elementary School in Cheektowaga nearly a decade ago to begin his journey to the "other" world in which only Miss Annabelle and her students lived. And tonight, the night before the launching of *Trinity*, Jake's mind wanted to solve another mystery to conclude his journey into that "other" world in which everyone now lived...that Twelve-Visions World.

Jake pondered the mystery: He knew that the God-Man Group created the supersociety stimulations that pulled people away from the spiral-of-death anticivilization stimulations, including their external authorities. Through the supersociety stimulations, people were able to make the leap into supreme love and value creation. But which one came first, supreme love or value creation? That was the mystery. Jake knew that one led to the other — supreme love for one's life led to value creation and value creation led to supreme love for one's life.

But which one was the cause, and which one was the effect?

"Which one came first," he asked himself again, "supreme love or value creation?"

When he asked that question, he realized the question had actually been on his mind a lot since witnessing Eddie the past couple of weeks in the hangar, making the leap. The more Jake thought about it, the more it seemed like the chicken-or-the-egg dilemma. On one hand, it would seem supreme love for conscious life with its protective feelings and passions had to come first to drive out dishonesties, rationalizations, laziness, and the influences from external authorities at the deepest levels of one's mind so as not to harm that precious conscious life...like a mother overriding all harmful influences while protecting the best interests of her small child. Only with the resulting pure honesty could the mind see through illusions and rationalizations down to the bare essences to get to the puzzle pieces, build Neothink puzzles, and advance into value creation.

Yet, on the other hand, how could one feel the supreme love for conscious life without first knowing the exhilaration of *creating* values for the world? Jake was stuck on this dilemma for the longest time. *How* exactly did it happen, he wanted to know; how and when did *supreme* love get inside a person and the ability to *create* values get started?

Jake sat in his chair, switching back and forth between supreme love and value creation, wondering which one came first. Which one was the cause?

"But, of course," he said after a restless hour, "I've got a rare, hands-on experiment going on right before my eyes for the past seven weeks in Eddie. Eddie is probably the last person on Earth to make the leap, and I see him several times a week!"

Jake started recalling Eddie's progress since living in the hangar: As Eddie gets more and more into the *business* of Beyond, Jake thought, his spurts of value creation and feelings of supreme love seem to rise. Hmmm.

All at once, it hit Jake: I've been looking at it all wrong, he thought. I've been looking at this in a static way, asking which one came first. But the leap into God-Man comes from a dynamic *process*: some early spurts of value creation bring on greater love and its protective passions for conscious life, which in turn drives out pervasive, deep dishonesties and rationalizations and lets one see through more layers of illusions down to more essences, and thus access more puzzle pieces and build bigger puzzles and *create* more values, which in turn increases one's value of himself and love for life, which in turn inspires his value creation, and so on, back and forth.

When understanding it was a *dynamic process*, not a one-shot cause and effect, Jake suddenly realized that *business* was that dynamic process!

"Of course!" he said, mystery solved, "That's how Eddie is progressing — through *the business* of Beyond. *Business* is the ongoing vehicle through which spurts of value creation develop and one's love for life grows, back and forth. *Business is the process!* And anyone can start the process at any time in any business, just as Eddie did!"

And now, Jake fully understood why The Trinity was inseparable, was one. All three working together as a process, as one, took Earth's Homeric man through the leap into God-Man.

Jake went back to bed, the mystery finally solved. Neither value creation nor supreme love came first; they came hand-in-hand through business. He quickly relaxed and immediately started falling asleep. As his eyes were closing, he thought: I can't believe it...in five hours, I'll watch the launching of *Trinity*.

And then, in that moment between consciousness and unconsciousness, that point of no return that will be forgotten upon awakening, Jake knew there was one more mystery to be solved...the mystery of our lost loved ones.

CHAPTER
ONE HUNDRED NINETEEN

"Good-bye, my good friend," said Ian. He walked out of the *Trinity* and turned to look at her up close for the last time before her journey. He placed his hand against her smooth pewter-like surface and rubbed her side one last time. Then he turned and sadly walked away, across the platform toward the elevator that would take him down to where the rest of The Group was waiting. "The families are ready and very excited," he called out to his soul mates. "My control team says everything's a go. The launch time shouldn't change now."

It was six o'clock in the morning Eastern Standard Time, day zero. *Trinity* would launch in two hours. Ian came out of the platform elevator, head down, running through a checklist of details in his mind.

"Ian," said Mr. Melbourne. Ian looked up. "Congratulations...and *thank you*. You've been absolutely brilliant in bringing *Trinity* from conception to launch."

The members of The Group began clapping. It was a moment that stopped time.

Ian took a deep breath and said, "Thank *you*, *all of you* for your efforts and puzzle pieces that brought together this great superpuzzle. It's all so fantastic!"

"Jake witnessed Ian's eyes at that moment, swept with

emotion. Jake then looked at Mr. Melbourne, Miss Annabelle, and the other members. In all their eyes lay that inseparable love and admiration for each other.

With the clock ticking, and no time to spare, Ian smiled and said, "Come with me to my office one last time."

In Ian's office, jammed with computers, Jasmine asked, "Aren't you going to clear out these computers before the launch?"

"No need to, dear," said Ian. "The controlled fusion liftoff is unlike anything we've ever seen. The efficiency is mind-boggling. There'll be no heat and only a soft light that escapes."

With Ian's comments, Jake's heart started pounding wildly with excitement. *Oh man*, he thought, *it's really going to happen*. He sat down, looked through the glass, and stared at *Trinity*. He'd seen her grow from its tiny infancy. Today, she looked large, strong, and ready to go out on her own.

Twenty minutes later, Ian let out a long sigh, looked up from his computer through the glass at *Trinity*. He looked at her for a long, emotional moment. Then, he quietly said, "I'll see you in thirty years."

Ian turned to The Group. "Time to go," he said. Without looking back at *Trinity*, he walked out of his office and out of the hangar. The Group left with him, different members glancing back over their shoulders at *Trinity*. Just outside the hangar, The Group climbed aboard a bus.

"To the observation tower," Ian told the bus driver. It was a short drive, but the field around the tower was filled with hundreds of in-house entrepreneurs, scientists, engineers from Beyond and invited guests. Ian had the observation tower built at the last moment because he felt he needed an unobstructed, bird's-eye view of the launch for the best scientific study of the planet's first controlled fusion liftoff.

The bus drove them onto the viewing field, along a roped-off pathway to the observation tower. The driver drove slowly due to the many spectators on both sides of the rope.

When they reached the tower, The Group stepped out of the bus. The crowd cheered them. The members of The Group waived to the crowd of mostly scientists, engineers, and entrepreneurs who were all part of the team, and some of their personally invited guests. After a few moments, the members of The Group turned and walked into the large elevator that would take them up to the glass viewing room above. The door slid shut, and the elevator rose quickly. *God, I'm nervous*, Jake suddenly noticed. A shiver rushed through him. *This is our culmination — will everything go as planned?*

When the elevator door slid open, The Group walked into a large glass booth. No one spoke. The roof of the hangar had been removed two days before. They could see, for the first time, the top of *Trinity's* head.

"Ah, my baby," Ian muttered. Patterson had a small camera crew there, as agreed upon by The Group. The camera crew was sending every reaction and utterance of the members — the creators — live throughout the world over the Patterson Channel.

"I hear humming," Jake said. Indeed, Jake heard a gentle hum and then saw a soft light suddenly escaping through the cracks and hinges of the massive hangar. Moments later, the creators in the glass booth let out sounds of awe as the top of the huge dome slowly rose out of the hangar, like a giant conscious being coming up for a look around. Their creation had come to life!

Then the body rose, very slowly, growing bigger and bigger. It seemed to rise forever, as though the giant ship were stretching longer and longer as it rose out of the hangar, revealing its unbelievable size. The great ship now blocked the Sun and cast a humbling shadow over the glass booth, dwarfing everything beneath it. Yet these people, who looked like tiny people from the Land of Lilliput next to the giant ship, created it.

While looking up, Jake could feel his mouth drop open. The bottom of the ship finally appeared. Beneath it was a beautiful, bluish-white pillar of light. The huge ship seemed to rest on that beautiful pillar of light as it slowly, steadily lifted the ship. Jake's breathing now came in jerks as he felt overwhelmed. His body twitched as shiver after shiver rushed through him. He watched in awe.

The emerging pillar of light filled then quickly eliminated the shadow with an unusual, cool light. Jake glanced around the room at the awestruck faces, some overwhelmed to tears: Sally, Jeremiah, Theodore, Cathy, Ian, Diana, Miss Annabelle, Mr.

Superpuzzle

Melbourne, Rico, Olivia, Reggie, Naomi, Natasha, Robert, Al, Debra, Daniel, Marcy, Bruce Salinski and his wife. This phenomenon was *their* creation...and ours too, Jake thought as he wrapped his arm around Jasmine. He never felt such immense pride before in his life.

As the gentle light glowed upon the creators' faces through the glass, Jake saw, for the first time, *not* the faces of the innocent child, not the faces of God-Men...he saw the faces of *Zons*.

Jake looked back at their creation. It seemed surreal, something so big, levitating...and in such total control, so slowly and steadily rising. Citizens of Earth had never seen a controlled fusion lift off. It was beautiful: a quiet hum, a soft, cool pillar of light beneath the great ship.

Every facing window of every office building and skyscraper, nearly every yard of every house, every playground of every school for hundreds of miles was occupied by citizens of Earth to witness their launch into Zonhood.

The great pillar of light lifted the ship toward the cosmos, as though it were citizens of Earth's first great offering to the Civilization of the Universe. This was our first contribution of love and compassion beyond our realm of consciousness, our first contribution to the creator's house — our Universe. Indeed, thought Jake while bursting with pride, Zon's house of values will now harvest this first universal value creation from citizens of Earth...the newest citizens to the Civilization of the Universe. This is what it takes to become a first-level Zon, he thought...to create and inject a value of love and compassion beyond our realm into Zon's house. We're really doing that! We're really *earning* our place in the Civilization of the Universe. And that makes me *feel good*.

In the presence of the overwhelming size of the ship and the enormous energy needed to lift it, Jake could barely believe he heard only a gentle, soft hum and saw only a gentle, soft light. Jake realized this was energy captured in gorgeously efficient use. Nothing was wasted. It was the ultimate demonstration of man's mind, his bigger-than-life creations, his complete control over mass and energy.

As *Trinity* rose from Earth to begin her journey beyond our realm of consciousness, those adults he loved most, standing shoulder to shoulder next to him, changed before his eyes…from citizens of Earth to *controllers of the cosmos*. As the great ship slowly rose higher, Jake did not know what he wanted to view more — the creation or the creators. His eyes swept back and forth, back and forth, back and forth, and all he could think of was the *beauty* that filled his sight.

As the great sphere rose and its pillar of light left the Earth, the gentle light bent into the shape of a beautiful cone causing onlookers to coo. The pewter-color saucer atop the bluish-white cone rose faster and farther and faster until it looked like a little coffee saucer in the sky…and then a speck…a speckle…gone. Jake knew that he and his soul mates started the day as God-Men, but now they were Zons. Together, they reached out to control the cosmos through pure love and compassion for conscious life.

"Beorapparaus, your Zons are coming to get you," Jake whispered. "Your *Zons*."

Sally, still looking at the sky, her face radiating with beauty and power, a beautiful Zon, said, "We did it. We put our minds to the supreme test: to save the supreme value beyond our realm."

Ian, adrenaline flowing though his veins, said, "Now, we must find our lost loved ones." His impulsive comment surprised even himself with unexplainable new hope.

"I'll do *whatever* it takes," Theodore whispered.

Goosebumps broke out all over Jake's arms and back. Patterson was feeding those Zons' comments, *live* around the globe. People on every corner of the Earth felt a surge of exhilaration, and then they shuddered in anticipation of what tomorrow would bring.

*

The Group left the glass viewing tower in quiet awe, all fitting into the large elevator. Moments after the elevator door closed, euphoria overwhelmed them. "What a beautiful liftoff!" exclaimed Ian. Reggie then yelled, "Yaaa Hooooa!" in an unbelievable falsetto. Jake burst out laughing as The Group erupted into cheers and accolades around him. By the time the elevator reached the bottom, the members were congratulating and hugging each other. The elevator door opened directly to a larger celebration. *Beyond's* scientists, engineers, in-house entrepreneurs and their invited guests laughed, hugged, cheered, for the passage had occurred: *they had become Zons*.

Two figures, however, stood still. They came into focus as The Group stepped from the elevator, just a few feet away. The ecstatic group suddenly got very quiet.

Miss Annabelle turned toward Jeremiah and Sally and whispered, "I hope I did the right thing. I invited them." Those in front of Jeremiah and Sally stepped to the side, clearing a view. Then, Jeremiah saw her.

"Maria..." he said in a gust of love. A day did not pass when he did not wonder if Maria was happy; sometimes the unanswered question haunted him. The feeling in his voice brought tears to Sally's eyes, not tears of hurt or insecurity having heard the love still in his voice, rather tears of sadness for what this other woman had once meant to him, their special preciousness gone forever from his life. Although it was the right decision, Sally knew that right decisions sometimes came with tragic pain.

Maria gasped when she heard Jeremiah say her name. She spoke his name with a gust of love and sorrow, "Jeremiah." She knew him well, and she knew the gift she would give him on this day. She drew in a shaky breath and said, "I want you to meet my fiancé, Ruiz."

For the first time, Jeremiah noticed someone standing beside Maria. He was a handsome man with strong eyes, average height, Puerto Rican. He was slightly nervous, which showed a sensitive side behind those strong eyes.

Miss Annabelle had planned this moment. She knew the launch was the most important achievement in Jeremiah's life since Project Life. She and Maria wanted Jeremiah to be free...completely free to feel the happiness he so deserved. Miss Annabelle smiled and excused herself. The other members of The Group followed her lead and politely excused themselves to give the two couples privacy.

"We'll see you inside the hangar," Ian said to Jeremiah and Sally. The Group decided to walk with the hundreds of in-house entrepreneurs, scientists, engineers from Beyond back to the roofless hangar for the great celebration.

"Mr. and Mrs. Jones," Ruiz said, "I'm still stunned from the launch. The values The Group continues to bring civilization blows my mind. I'm just so honored to meet you...and a little nervous. But I always knew what I wanted to say to you when I met you. So, I'll just say it now, if it's okay with you."

Jeremiah, still stunned, barely nodded.

"Please tell us," Sally said.

"Alright, then," Ruiz said. He nervously looked down at the ground for a moment. He collected his courage, then looked back up at Sally and Jeremiah. He squinted into the sun. "When I was growing up in New Jersey, a boy and his parents moved into the neighborhood one summer, just down the street. He didn't come out to play until afternoon. At first, I thought he was sickly because his bedroom window was covered with drapes until one o'clock in the afternoon or later. I kind of avoided him. Then, when school started, he rode the school bus and waited at the same bus stop as me. I was in fourth grade, and so was he. He turned out to be a normal, nice guy. As I got to know him, I grew to like him. But on weekends, his drapes would be drawn till one o'clock in the afternoon. He wouldn't come out until two or three. One Saturday, I really wanted to play with him. But at two o'clock, he hadn't come out and his drapes were still drawn. I didn't want to knock because his parents were very creepy people who kind of scared me. But by three o'clock, I got up the nerve and knocked. His dad answered in his nightwear. His hair was messy. I asked if Matt were home. The man stepped back to let me in and pointed to Matt's closed door. Matt's dad never said a word. He just cleared his throat and walked back into the house. I opened Matt's bedroom door. It was pretty dark inside. But what was so strange was that it sounded like it was raining outside. I heard rain, lots of it. It sounded like it was pouring and splattering on the window sill. And the little bit of filtered light coming through the drapes added to the effect. It seemed as though the sky outside was covered with a thick layer of gray clouds with strong showers that would last all day. On the dresser was a cassette player playing a continuous two-way tape of a rain shower. Matt was fast asleep on his bed. I shook my head and thought, *what the hell is this?* I was a little freaked out and left. Monday at school, I asked Matt about it, and he told me his story: Ever since he was a baby, his parents played that tape in his room at night. His parents did not work, and they slept late every day. They found that if they played that tape and darkened Matt's room when he was little, he would sleep a lot longer so they could, too. When he was two or three, he figured out the illusion that kept him in bed a couple of hours longer. So, as a toddler, he'd get out of bed and peek out his drapes every time he woke up during the night. As soon as he saw that it was daytime, he would get up. But, his parents would yell at him to go back to bed and his father started hitting him. Little three-year-old Matt would still peek outside to see if it was day. When it was light out, he would get up and play around in his room. But his dad would hear him, come in and beat him for waking up his parents. Finally, the little three-year-old would just lie in bed, awake, until afternoon. He'd still get up and check to see if it was a beautiful day outside. If his dad heard him, he'd beat him. For a three-year-old to lie in bed, awake, for hours was torture.

"Eventually, it became a lot less painful to stop checking and give in and sleep. By the time Matt was old enough to get up quietly, dress himself and go outside, he no longer wanted to. Sleeping late had become part of his lifestyle. He had long, long ago stopped fighting it; he learned to accept it, and now he wanted it. He himself closed his drapes and turned on the cassette at night. Six years before I knew him, his parents had broken the toddler's spirit. Eventually, he accepted and eventually entered their world. When Matt told me this story, I felt *so sad* and *so mad*. My brother was five-years-old at the time, and I couldn't imagine him lying in bed for hours...or else that big man with messy hair would come in and beat him — I just couldn't imagine it! A few weeks went by, and I'd feel sick seeing the drapes over Matt's window until afternoon on the weekends. One day, I couldn't get out of my head that my good friend Matt would end up like his god-awful father. I felt that I had to save Matt, and I began to get very upset. I walked into my room and got my savings together, about fifty dollars.

Beholding the Puzzle-Picture

I put it in an envelope and went to Matt's window. I taped the envelope with the money to a big rock that I could barely lift. Luckily his window was downstairs. I heaved the small boulder through the window. Glass shattered everywhere, and to my delight, the rock was so heavy it pulled the drapes right off the wall! I ran away as fast as I could go and hid behind the parked cars. When I looked back, I could see Matt reading the note I had put in the envelope with the money: *The money is to pay for the window. The rock is to shatter your fake rain shower and knock you upside the head. C'mon, man, get your butt out of bed!*

"Matt's dad came in and kept yelling and looking outside the window. Matt never showed him the note. When he left, Matt pulled out my note and read it again and again. He just stood there reading my note.

"The window was fixed, but the drapes were never put back up. Matt came out every morning, except for when it was really raining, and he was often outside *waiting for me* in the morning. I never told him I threw the rock through his window, but he knew. One day, a year or so later, he told me I saved his life. I said I was sure glad I did. Thirty years later, he's a deep friend."

Ruiz stopped talking for a moment. Maria was holding Ruiz's arm. He took a deep breath and looked into Jeremiah's eyes and then into Sally's eyes. He stood up straight as though standing at attention. Then he said in a tone of voice so full of reverence that it was unmistakably a salute: "You and The Group threw the big rock through civilization's window and took down the drapes. You woke everyone up and saved *everyone's* life. You have an eternal friend in me — in everyone."

When Ruiz finished, he still stood straight as though holding at attention, waiting for Jeremiah and Sally to put him at ease. Jeremiah studied Ruiz and could see the spirit of that nine-year-old still in his eyes. Jeremiah realized Ruiz was a special person, someone extraordinarily caring and sensitive who could not let a friend, no less a loved one, succumb to something harmful. He freed his friend, Matt; and today, Ruiz would, in a sense, free Jeremiah. Jeremiah looked at Maria who was hugging Ruiz's arm. Jeremiah remembered, for a moment, when she used to hug his arm that way. He saw happiness in her eyes, and like a father who sees happiness in his daughter's eyes, that happiness in her eyes was all Jeremiah ever wanted for Maria. He could feel emotions rushing up from deep inside, bouncing around inside his body like a big pinball machine. However, the moment of silence had grown to several moments. Just before the rush of emotions reached Jeremiah's face and expression, Ruiz said, "I'm sorry. This was not the place or time to have told you all that. Please forgive me." Embarrassed, Ruiz turned to leave.

"No!" said Jeremiah. Ruiz looked back around just as the emotions hit Jeremiah's expression — welcoming, wonderful emotions! Ruiz's face lit up as Jeremiah walked over to him, placed his hands on Ruiz's shoulders, and spoke his first words to him, "Ruiz, I say to you from the bottom of my heart what Maria once said to my wife in a very special letter: I love you. *I love you, man!*"

Then Jeremiah robustly hugged Ruiz, slapped him on the back three times, then stepped back with his hands still on Ruiz's shoulders, looking into Ruiz's eyes. Jeremiah felt so, so grateful for the good man Ruiz was.

During the entire encounter, Sally felt as though she were going to burst with her feelings for Maria. When Jeremiah hugged Ruiz, Sally could not hold back her feelings any longer. She stepped forward and hugged Maria, crying new tears of joy for Maria and shedding old tears of sorrow for Maria. Sally had a strong urge to say "congratulations" as well as "I'm so sorry for what happened before." But neither comment seemed right, nor did they capture the joy and relief Sally felt for Maria. So, Sally said nothing as she hugged Maria. Sally was aware she felt an incredible bond that seemed to have a long history. Maybe, she thought, this is how it feels to have a sister.

"Oh, Maria," Sally finally said, "ever since your letter, there was so much I wanted to say to you. Right now, I don't know what to say. But I know how I feel...*I love you.*"

"Thank you," Maria whispered. She hugged Sally back.

Jeremiah turned his eyes to Maria and Sally. Again, Jeremiah saw the deep and permanent happiness in Maria's face. A moment later, her eyes met his. At that moment, the unspoken message passed between them: *Maria had found her beautiful new sunrise.*

"Come with us to celebrate!" Jeremiah said to Ruiz and Maria.

"Please," said Sally. She was looking at Maria.

Ruiz looked at Maria with hopeful eyes, but he left that decision up to her.

"We'd love to," she said. Sally hugged her new friend again while Jeremiah wrapped his arm around Ruiz's shoulders. Jeremiah wanted to know all about Ruiz's Friday-Night essence, and Sally wanted to get close to Maria.

"Ah, look at that," Jasmine said to Jake, watching the two couples walking toward the hangar. She had asked Jake to wait with her outside the hangar for Jeremiah and Sally. As the couples approached the hangar, Jake could hear their conversation:

"Understanding the exact physical and mental functions of sleep," Ruiz was saying, "is the first major step in being able to reduce sleep. We've inductively and deductively achieved that understanding. To our knowledge, we're the first. Now, Matt and I have found crucial pieces to our puzzle through EssenceTalk and are working in coordination with a microbiologist, a quantum computer programmer, and a neurosurgeon. We're picking up momentum."

"This would be a value *everyone* would want," Jeremiah said. He imagined his own possibilities.

"It'll bring Matt and me enormous pride. Ever since I woke him up with that big rock when we were kids, he and I used to talk about someday making an invention so that people never have to waste time sleeping. It looks like our childhood dream will come true."

"You've made profound progress," Sally said. They joined Jake and Jasmine. "Let's go inside and talk with Ian and Theodore. They'll be very interested in what you've done."

"I overheard Theodore, a few months ago, telling Ian he'd love to pursue a sleep-reduction machine," Jake injected into the conversation.

Walking inside to meet the great Theodore Winters and Dr. Ian Scott, moments after walking with the legendary Jeremiah Jones and Dr. Sally Salberg Jones was, to Ruiz, like being swept up into a dream.

Seeing his little Maria deeply happy again was, to Jeremiah, like removing a bullet lodged in his heart. Seeing Maria happy again released the pain that had been trapped in his heart, just as Maria knew it would.

They entered the spectacular party inside the hangar. They instantly saw television cameras labeled *Patterson Channel* sending the party live around the world. Just after they took their first few steps into the hangar, they came upon, to Ruiz's delight, Robert Chapman talking with some of the Beyond scientists. Before Jeremiah could introduce Ruiz, Robert spotted Saul talking with Ian. Robert quickly excused himself from his group.

"Saul!" Robert shouted over the noise. "Saul Tannenbaum!" Saul looked up. When he saw Robert for the first time since his visits to TGIF, Saul felt his heart pounding. Robert quickly moved through the crowd straight toward Saul and Ian. Jeremiah, Sally, Ruiz, Maria, Jake, and Jasmine followed.

"I'm very proud of you," Robert said, putting his hand on Saul's shoulder. Robert carried a sort of paternal love and protectiveness for his former "patients", for he knew them at their weakest moments. He helped Saul when Saul was more vulnerable than a small child. And it was that part of Saul, that vulnerable human being, Robert would always remember not unlike a father will always remember the days when his grown children were young and vulnerable...and needed him. And as a father feels proud of his vulnerable little boy who grows up to achieve wonderful things, Robert felt proud of his Saul. "I knew you'd someday be a scientist. Look at you now!"

Robert's opinion of him was so important to Saul — a man who once tried to take his own life — that he could not think at that moment; he could not think of what to say. For a moment, he was frozen.

"He's among my best scientists," Ian said when he realized Saul was not able to respond. "He'll be part of the team working with me on the ether project."

Robert nodded in admiration. "I'll run into you a lot now," he said. He patted Saul on his shoulder. "I'm glad our paths crossed again."

Beholding the Puzzle-Picture

In a shaky voice overcome with emotion, Saul said, "I'll really like that." Saul saw admiration in Robert's eyes, and Saul felt in his soul he was proven worthy of the time Robert had spent with him to save his life. Saul had created a major value for civilization with his irreplaceable contributions to Project Save Beorapparaus.

Jeremiah, Sally, Ruiz, Maria, Jake, and Jasmine walked over to join Saul, Robert, and Ian. Jake and Jasmine had talked with Saul twice before, over nine years earlier when they interviewed him in his house and a couple of months before the launch when they met with the top scientists working on Project Save Beorapparaus. They felt as though he were an old friend. When Saul saw them approaching, he suddenly said, "Last time we met, I didn't have a chance to thank you, Jasmine. Your advice was perfect." He smiled as a beautiful woman came to him from the side, slipped under his arm, and slid up against him. "Let me introduce to you my wife. We got back together again. As you can see, she now has her Body II...a beautiful Body II!" Jake and Jasmine smiled as Saul proudly introduced his wife to everyone.

The party went on all around them. Jake would glance up from time to time at the television monitors along the upper walls. They showed the celebrations going on both in the dozens of Paradise Cities that sprang up in less than three years and in the other cities, suburbs, and villages around the world. *They're magnificent celebrations*, he thought. He looked across a row of monitors and smiled. *It reminds me of New Year's Eve at the turn of the millennium. But now, we're at the turning point of civilization.* He took a deep breath after looking at a dozen monitors and nodded. "People everywhere," he said quietly, "people everywhere on Earth, except in the ostracism wastelands, are dancing in the streets."

CHAPTER
ONE HUNDRED TWENTY

"I've got it!" Ian yelled. "Hell yeah...I've got it!"

The morning after the launch, in sheer euphoria, he ran out of his living quarters and into the massive roofless hangar where *Trinity* was now absent. For a moment, he felt a sad throb pass through him for not seeing his giant "friend" that he had become so close to the past seven months, gone now on its own path. But the next moment, his new creation overcame him with joy. "I've got it...I've got it!" he yelled in the huge open space that was filled with thousands of geniuses the day before in perhaps the greatest party of all time. Ian gleefully released months of tension, knowing he alone, all along, had to definitively conquer catastrophic death. Now, he had done it.

"Ahhh Haaaaaaaa!" he yelled, releasing months of stress. He threw punches into the air to KO the ghosts of death. "We won!" he shouted, and he burst into victorious laughter.

Diana ran into the massive arena straight into the arms of her gladiator.

"I've got it, my love," he said.

"Tell me everything."

"I know how to eradicate catastrophic death! The approach I was taking before really was fundamentally flawed. A person's spirit could never be in two places at once. So it could never be preserved in a computer and retrieved after someone's death. His realm of awareness could never be split away from itself — that's a fundamental contradiction.

"You know," Diana said, "how could a realm of awareness not be aware of itself...unless it's not itself."

"Exactly," said Ian. "Understanding a person's realm of awareness can be only in one place at a time, not two — that was the key. It would've never worked. But now I've got it! Those latest technological breakthroughs needed to launch *Trinity* gave me the answer. Yes! I knew I had to turn away from my old approach and turn outward to the cosmos. Now look at me — I'm getting it done! Let's see, it's been ten months since The Great Moment. The quantum computer said the definitive cure to catastrophic death would happen in slightly less than eleven months. Boy, that's right on, isn't it? I'll get this done in about three weeks. Then, I must get with Ted and Sally to get this definitive cure to everyone, everywhere. Yeah!"

"C'mere, you!" Diana said. She hugged him with all her might. "Now, would you kindly tell me your creation? I'm dying to know!"

"Okay, you already know I'm able to move the realm of awareness and I-ness — the human spirit — to another physical carrier. Christine's spirit actually travelled to the quantum computer outside her own body. But that would do no good during a catastrophic event that threatens to take someone's body, someone's life, quickly. Now, one of the technological breakthroughs on *Trinity* was the quantum computer circuitry. Of course, the circuitry is made of subatomic particles. We were able to house the quantum computers in tiny, tiny diamond chips that were molecularly altered so they can't burn. They're essentially indestructible. No phenomena on Earth could harm those tiny, molecularly altered chips. Even a direct hit from a burning meteor could not destroy one of those subatomic quantum computers injected through lasers into those tiny molecularly altered diamond chips."

Ian was savoring his story, telling his wife *not* his breakthrough, but the steps leading up to his breakthrough. "Now, what if we had taken the quantum computer that Christine's spirit had travelled into...and put it inside Christine's very own head?"

"What!"

"I'm not kidding. Just substitute the quantum computer we used with one of those indestructible tiny, tiny diamond-chip quantum computers."

The light of knowledge suddenly seemed to shine on Diana's eyes; her pupils seemed to contract. "Go on, Ian," she said in a hush. "You're beginning to make sense to me."

"I'm going to connect the diamond-chip quantum computer to the brain the way I did with Christine. But this time, I'm going to implant the diamond-chip quantum computer into the head, perhaps just under the skin, perhaps anchored in the skull. In any case, to make a long story short, one's realm of awareness will shift from its nature-made physical carrier, the fragile human brain, into our man-made physical carrier — the indestructible diamond-chip quantum computer. And when the nature-made physical carrier dies, the awareness and I-ness — the spirit — continues, fully aware its host has died. It'll send out a signal letting us at Beyond know a body has passed. The signal will lead us directly to that body. We remove the diamond-chip computer that contains the human spirit and replace it in a clone of the person who died. The person's realm of awareness never died, however. It merely moved to another body, safe and sound inside an indestructible quantum computer."

"Oh, Ian." Diana buried her head in Ian's chest. Her body was trembling. *You've done it*, she thought. *Now, you'll be mine, forever, my hero.*

*

"It's good to be home," Ian said to his favorite volunteer. He was back at his compound in Olean, New York. "I was looking at it all wrong, Christine. I was trying to store the spirit in such a way that the realm of awareness and I-ness would have to exist in two places at once, which they couldn't — it's a fundamentally flawed approach. But I can store the spirit in such a way that the realm of awareness and I-ness continue to exist in one place only."

"How can you possibly do that?" Christine said. She thought

1116

for a moment, then added, "How can you possibly store the realm of awareness somewhere, yet say it exists in one place? Isn't that an impossible contradiction?"

Ian smiled and said, "I'll insert the same diamond-chip quantum computer that we used in *Trinity* right into one's head. His charge of I-ness and realm of awareness will continuously flow through that tiny quantum computer planted inside his head." Ian's smile grew as he witnessed Christine's look of astonishment. He nodded as if to convey, *this is really going to happen,* and he said, "The quantum computer can handle the information, thinking, and sensory interface with the world in concert with the circuitry of the brain. In fact, it'll become part of that circuitry. Think of it as the next step beyond Christine III, but unlike Christine III, now you can drop the III. The quantum computer in your head that becomes part of the circuitry of your brain is, simply, Christine. And now, Christine is indestructible."

"So, if I got killed in a sudden catastrophe?"

Ian was unable to hide his pride as a boyish grin overwhelmed his face. With the grin stuck on his face, he said, "Your breathing and heart stop. Your cells begin rapidly dying. Your brain cells die at an enormous rate. Rigor mortis sets in. Your body begins to decompose." Ian giggled. "Your thoughts, though, keep on thinking. You won't see through biological eyes, but you remain fully aware. In fact, I'm going to design some highly sensitive sensors that'll give the computer some perception of sight and sound after the biological eyes and ears shut down. That dead body lying on the ground still has his realm of awareness, his I-ness, *his spirit* inside his head — in my tiny quantum computer. His awareness never shuts down, not even for a moment. It never pauses or breaks. He simply becomes aware of the fact his physical carrier, his body, has died. In that state of awareness, a signal is sent to Beyond's tracking system. We immediately retrieve the body, remove the quantum computer, clone the passed body, then transfer the awareness by implanting the tiny quantum computer into the tabula rasa — the blank brain in his Body II. His realm of awareness never shuts down, never extinguishes, not for a second. His spirit lives on in Body II."

"Ian, it's like a vaccine against catastrophic death!"

"Better than a vaccine."

Christine studied Ian's face. It glowed with contagious childlike glee. Her mouth sprang into a big smile. "When do we get started?" she asked.

"How about two weeks from today?"

*

Christine lay on the table. She slept under light anesthesia; a small portion of her head was shaved.

"The connections are all the same, but this nanotube fiber is incredible," Sally said. She performed the medical procedure of implanting the fiber and computer chip. She studied a computer screen and slowly keyed in the movements for the robotic fingers. The robotic fingers were the next big tech development — the next wave of technology beyond the robotic hands responsible for mass marketing The Operation. Sally carefully manipulated the invisible fiber with the robotic fingers' special nanotechnological tools, guided by her computer commands. The movements were traced and magnified on the screen. Sally and Ian were essentially looking at an analog model of the actual procedure. They concentrated on the screen before their eyes.

"These fibers are extremely sensitive to the brain activity," Ian said without taking his eyes from the screen.

"I can't believe this new wave of technology," Sally said. "We only need to place these under the skin. We don't even have to connect them anywhere, right?"

Ian nodded and said, "That's right. Yet, those fibers register all brain activity, so the quantum computer becomes one with the biological brain!"

"Unbelievable," Sally said. "Now, where should I attach the quantum computer?"

"Drill a tiny notch in the skull right here, in this region," Ian said. He reached toward the screen and pointed. "Here, right above the right chamber of the brain. Bury the computer under a small pool of my specially-tailored glue that adheres to bone with greater strength than the bone itself."

A few minutes later Sally said, "We're just about done here." Ian stared at the screen. "Beautiful," he said.

"You ready for me to close her?"

"No, not yet," Ian said. "Let me just get in here a minute." He put his hands on the command keys. "I need to check the sensors on the quantum computer first. It's all wired."

Ian pressed a few command keys and said, "They're just temporary sensors, but without them, I'd have a hard time knowing whether the realm of awareness permeates the quantum computer as planned through the fiber connections. The sensors will prove to us the quantum computer becomes one with the brain. As she wakes up, if she starts using the sensors, if she starts to see and hear through them, we'll know her awareness permeates the computer. I'll put these sensors in the dormant mode soon after we demonstrate Christine's realm of awareness flows through her implanted computer. The sensors will reactivate temporarily if her body is ever killed by a catastrophe."

"Genius," Mr. Melbourne muttered as The Group watched the procedure from the viewing room.

"Just one last look around," Ian said after testing the sensors. "Okay. Close her up."

"It'll just take a butterfly stitch or two."

"Beautiful."

"There, Ian. We're done." For the first moment since the procedure began, Sally and Ian looked away from the analog model displayed on the screen. They looked at Christine, sleeping on the operating table.

"In a few minutes," said Ian, "she'll be an indestructible immortal, out of the clutches of catastrophic accidents." He sighed, then he looked at Sally; her eyes were bursting with hope. He could feel the hope bursting from his own eyes. He looked back at his favorite patient and said, "Christine, the anesthesia should be wearing off now. Time to wake up, Christine."

"Uh, yes," Christine said groggily, coming out of her sleep. "What do you want me to do?" she mumbled, then fell back to sleep.

"Nothing, Christine," Ian said. "You need to do nothing but wake up for us."

She opened her eyes slightly. "Okay," she said. "Okay."

"How do you feel?" Ian said.

"Good," she said, trying to keep her eyes open. "Just sleepy, but I feel good."

Ian watched her for a few moments then said, "Christine, you remember my assistants Melissa and Phil; I'm going to have Melissa carry on a conversation with you while Dr. Salberg and I study your brain activity on the screen. ...Are you feeling okay?"

"Yes."

Melissa and Christine talked. Ian and Sally studied the readings of the biological brain-activity and the computer brain-activity. The other members of The Group stood transfixed, staring through the viewing glass.

"Slowly but surely," Ian said, "the quantum computer is filling up with the charge of I-ness." A few moments later, he said, "The realm of awareness is going there. Look! Look at the sensors — they're becoming activated! Look!" Ian pointed to the screen, which displayed brain activity. "Those are the sensory fibers!"

Ian, Sally, and Phil watched those fibers spring to life with activity like a bursting storm of lightning.

"Unbelievable," Sally said. She shook her head in disbelief. Three words filled her thoughts: *You did it.* Although the operating room was soundproof, Ian and Sally and their assistants could hear muffled cheers coming from the viewing area.

"The sensors are inferior, so I'm going to desensitize them in a minute or so...but there's our proof."

...but there's our proof. Those words echoed in Sally's head. She looked at Ian's profile and said, "It seems like so long ago since you'd all but given up on trying to preserve the human spirit in a quantum computer...almost eleven months ago. You had turned to the cosmos and Project Save Beorapparaus."

"The realm of awareness couldn't be preserved in a quantum computer, as I told you." He looked at Sally. "The approach was fundamentally flawed. The realm of awareness could be only one place at a time." He looked back at the screen. "Here we've done it. We have that elusive I-ness and its realm of awareness in one place — in an *indestructible* place that'll keep going when the destructible body dies."

1120

Beholding the Puzzle-Picture

"No more catastrophic death," Sally mumbled, "the person's spirit'll get removed from its deceased body and placed into a new body, its new physical carrier, its new tool for living. Ian, just think of what you've done here, of what you've accomplished with your amazing invention."

Sally slipped into deep thought: *Our human spirit, our realm of awareness and I-ness, was trapped in a nature-developed, perishable biological brain. Given an unforeseen, catastrophic moment, our spirit could be suddenly, unforgivingly extinguished forever. But now our human spirit, our realm of awareness and I-ness, resides not in a destructible nature-developed biological brain, but in an indestructible man-developed quantum computer.* Sally looked at Ian the creator, then back at the image of his creation. She put her hands against her head in disbelief. *We've just overcome the final force of nature*, she thought. *We've just eradicated catastrophic death.*

Without taking his eyes off the computer screen, Ian said, "Yes, Sally, we've just made the leap from near-immortals to immortals."

*

The Group met at Rico's mansion two days later for its monthly meeting and a beautiful celebration.

"The sense of relief," Natasha said on her radio show that morning, "such carefree happiness fills my every waking moment."

When Jake and Jasmine arrived at Rico's mansion with Jakey and Ameena, they heard a familiar sound when getting out of their car. It was laughter. It was the celebratory laughter of Jessie and Angie and their two-year-old son, Dillan. *Oh yes!* Jake felt a rush of joy upon hearing their voices.

At the top of the steps, he saw Jessie and Angie, Mr. Melbourne and the lovely Miss Annabelle, and several of her original students surrounding Sally and Jeremiah. Sally was holding their first newborn.

"Oh, my goodness!" said Jasmine. She rushed over and hugged Sally and Jeremiah. Ah, look at Sally, Jake thought as she laughed and celebrated. Finally, she's so happy. Finally, she's a *mom.*

Jake knew that losing her mother as a child made her keenly aware of the preciousness of life. Being with Miss Annabelle for a full school year sent Sally on an amazing drive to stop precious human life from dying, a drive that lasted over thirty years until she succeeded. The demands on her, Jake realized, forced her to wait until now to become the loving mom she was meant to be. Life meant everything to Sally; she would not accept the loss of human life. And now that she stopped the loss of human life and Ian stopped catastrophic loss of human life, she could finally let herself experience creating new life.

Oh what a wonderful adventure she's beginning, Jake thought. The love in Sally...wow, what a mother she'll be. ...A sad thought passed through him, however: Sally's mom was not here to hold and love Sally's baby. It was a feeling Jake knew only too well as Jasmine's father never held or loved little Jakey and Ameena.

Family, Jake thought. He looked around at the children. He saw his little Jakey through an arched doorway in the morning room. Jakey was playing with Rico's little Tony, who was not so little anymore. Twelve-year-old Tony was patiently teaching three-year-old Jakey that gravity pulled the toy train down the hill. When the train crashed, the boys burst out laughing. *Look at them*, Jake thought. *I wonder what those guys will create someday. Will they be working together on a superpuzzle as their parents did? Will they be working with us?*

Jake took a deep breath. Ah, it's so wonderful here. These people. Their history. Our history together! We can never break up. We'll always build superpuzzles together. Jake thought about lost loved ones. Imagine...if someday we'll have our monthly get-together here, but with Jasmine's dad, Sally's mom, Debra's parents. They'd be here, laughing with us.

Jake looked around and remembered how it all began with the Miracle Year. Sally's mom being diagnosed with terminal cancer; Sally persevering. Rico battling his overbearing home life, his father a hardened criminal; Rico overcoming. Cathy battling her home life, her parents and siblings compulsive eaters; Cathy succeeding. Teddy breaking through the brink of poverty and soaring with his own national business at nine years of age.

Debbie reviving her parents' fast-food business. Danny fighting for what's right, standing up to the school bully. Alan orchestrating *Breakthrough News*. Ian fascinated with the cosmos. Reggie living in poverty with his hard-working, honest mom. Jeremiah suffocated by his fanatically religious mom. Nattie wanting a better, more loving relationship for her parents. Robert wanting exhilarating jobs for his parents so they could be happy again.

Miss Annabelle's Miracle Year launched them. Now here they stood. They landed beyond the edge of the irrational anticivilization in the purely rational Civilization of the Universe; their lives *and mine*, Jake pondered, locked together in huge superpuzzles — creation and creators, business lives and personal lives blending seamlessly together bringing superpuzzles of supreme love to the world and eternal happiness to ourselves.

Then Jake looked around at the next generation spread about in the large foyer and family room. Of course, there was little Jakey and Tony. He looked around some more, specifically looking at the children. He smiled then muttered under his breath, "Would you look at the babies...they're getting ready to walk!" Of course, he saw his own little 10-month-old Ameena holding onto the couch while feebly standing for a few moments before collapsing onto her bottom. Jasmine helped Ameena up and leaned her against the couch, facing Robert's and Natasha's year-old baby Nella. Ameena and Nella started playing a little game. They both stood steady while holding the couch with one hand and slapping it with the other hand. Each time one of the babies slapped the couch she yelled "Ahhhh!" as loud as she could, and then they would both laugh. Jake smiled and shook his head; how cute they looked! Alan and Debra saw the commotion and carried their one-year-old, Elizabeth, over. She watched Ameena and Nella and laughed with delight.

Suddenly, Jake felt something tapping his leg. He looked down. He saw two-year-old Dillan staring up at him.

"Where's Jakey?" he asked.

"Hi buddy," said Jake. He knelt down and pointed through the arched doorway to the morning room. "Look through there. Do you see over there?"

"Yes."

"Keep looking through there."

Dillan looked hard in the direction Jake was pointing. Suddenly, Dillan burst into a smile. "Hi Jakey!" he yelled. He started running toward the morning room.

"Wait honey," said Jake. "Go tell your mommy where you're going."

"I'm right behind you, Jake," said Angie.

Dillan pointed toward the morning room, and said, "Jakey's in there! Can I go?"

"Of course, honey," Angie said. She was carrying her eight-month-old.

Ah, the house is full of new life, Jake thought. He looked around. He saw Jessie and Angie and their two children, Dillan who was now two and Devon who was just eight months. Jake recalled Jessie telling him that he almost elected to get the Operation as did Angie, but had now decided to wait and take the eighteen-again serum when it went into widespread distribution. With a third child in the works, Jake thought, he'll need his energetic young body back for sure.

Jake looked around the large rooms at the children and took in the beauty of the next generation. He watched and wondered *how many Miracle Years are yet to come?*

Jake looked at all the happy new life in Rico's mansion and at the proud, happy parents. He realized that with Sally's and Jeremiah's new baby, only Ian and Diana...and Theodore and Cathy had not yet had children. Obviously, Jake thought, they were waiting to get the superpuzzle completed that eradicates catastrophic death. They still had a big job in front of them, too. Theodore would have to manufacture and distribute billions of the diamond-chip quantum computers. And Ian would be in charge, with Sally's help, of coordinating doctors to physically implant the quantum chips.

Jake studied Ian and Diana, and Jake studied Theodore and Cathy, the two original childhood sweethearts. Jake smiled and thought: what an emotional leap they'll feel when they have their own children!

Suddenly, Rosa, Rico Jr., and Tony rushed from the morning room, across the large family room, out the back door. Ah, Jake thought, that brings back a memory of the first time I was here almost ten years ago when I saw those three burst through the house when their daddy got home from work.

Jasmine had been quietly watching Jake; she picked up Ameena and walked over to him. "Darling, what are you thinking about?" she finally asked.

Jake looked at her. She was smiling, so lovely, so carefree. He smiled and said, "What am I thinking about?" With an air of happy finality, he nodded and answered, "The meaning of life, my love."

CHAPTER
ONE HUNDRED TWENTY-ONE

Jasmine lay awake in bed before the morning twilight. It had been three weeks since the launch, almost a week since curing catastrophic death, and she was too excited to sleep. She knew that Earthlings were closing in fast on the deepest secrets of the Universe, and it would not be long now before they knew about their lost loved ones.

She lay in the dark remembering a card game she used to play with her father as a little girl. They would place all the cards face down and try to turn up matches. At first, the game was unbearably slow as everything was guesswork. But at the end, the game flew by as they remembered the cards and snapped up the matches.

Remembering that game made her realize Earthlings were at the end of a game of match. They now had the knowledge and were rapidly, daily...hourly...turning over the matches. Very soon, she thought, *we'll know*.

When the twilight arrived, she looked at her little Ameena sleeping in front of her, between herself and Jake. Jasmine scooted forward, against Ameena and was surprised to see Jakey curled up there, too. He must have climbed in here during the night, she thought, chuckling at how small and precious her three-year-old and her 10-month-old looked, peacefully sleeping. She reached her arm across her treasures and onto Jake's chest.

"God, I love you guys," she whispered very quietly, enjoying the view of her precious family sound asleep next to her. After a few minutes of quiet reflection, she very softly added, "And I cannot forget you, Daddy. I love you so much, too, and I really, really miss you."

Jasmine did not know Jake was now awake. Before he could tell her, the phone rang, startling them both.

"Hello." Jake said without getting out of bed. Phones now worked by voice command anywhere in the house and could transmit and amplify voices while blocking out other frequencies to carry on clear conversations while standing, sitting, lying, or walking around, anywhere in the house.

"Jake!" Ian shouted, oblivious to the time of day.

"Hi Ian."

"Hi Jake. Jasmine...you there too?"

"I'm here," she said.

"You must come and see this. The Overlay Charts...they're revealing all the answers! Through the Overlay Charts, we've cracked a code of activities by conscious minds...a code of consciousness you might say. Essentially, what conscious beings have done, and what we will do can be charted and predicted. It's like discovering the Periodic Table for consciousness. It's just amazing...we're getting all the answers! Jasmine, we can figure out what happened to our loved ones after they died."

Jake and Jasmine were already out of bed running around, getting dressed, occasionally shouting a command like "Red sneakers!" into a voice activated transmitter. Nearly everything purchased now came with a small installed transistor. Items easily misplaced were programmed with a unique frequency and matched to a voice command. So when Jasmine said, "Red sneakers!" her red sneakers beeped. She found them quickly. Everything in the Civilization of the Universe moved toward time-saving efficiencies.

While Ian was talking, Jakey and Ameena woke up, and Jasmine stopped to help her baby girl sit up on the bed. Jakey went to his room to get his clothes that were laid out the night before at the foot of his bed.

"This is beyond description...beyond beauty," Ian cried out.

1127

Superpuzzle

"Everything has rhythm and rhyme and harmony. It's the music of Zons!"

"You're at your compound?" Jake called out.

"Oh, no, no...I'm here at the Space Library."

"Okay, great!" Jake said. Jasmine was too preoccupied to talk. She was wondering what Ian had uncovered about her dad.

"See you soon, guys!" Ian hung up.

Jake and Jasmine raced about, opening and shutting drawers and closets, putting clothes on. Little ten-month-old Ameena sat in the middle of the bed with pillows all around her, watching them, laughing and laughing as though they were putting on a show for her.

That sound, Jake thought, that amazing sound! He stopped and looked at his Little Ameena. Her brown eyes were wide and her chubby cheeks were rosy. The corners of her mouth were curved up high, a smile so full of glee that it was crooked and out of coordination. She looked back at her father and cocked her head, looking almost as if she knew something and was wondering if her father was figuring it out. Ameena laughed again.

That sound, Jake thought again, the antithesis of the anticivilization, the antithesis of the moans I heard when leaving the wastelands, the epitome of pure good...the ultimate sound, like some kind of comforting music. The small child's laugh, Jake realized, was the most soothing sound to a conscious being...the music of Zons? Yes, the music of Zons.

A small child...a million-year-old Zon — they're the same...the same innocence. Jake looked into his daughter's eyes again, deeper this time. Suddenly, Jake's skin began to fill with goose bumps. The answers are *right here,* he realized.

When he looked deep into his daughter's eyes, so full of love for her daddy, Jake experienced *eureka;* he suddenly knew the Unified Field — the single source that every event in the Civilization of the Universe linked back to: it was LOVE. Supreme love for conscious life was the state of consciousness from which value creation and business sprang forth, just exactly as humanity's supreme love for Beorapparaus was the state of consciousness from which the rescue ship and the business journey sprang forth.

In the Civilization of the Universe, Jake realized, conscious beings did not have to go through *the leap* — the process to acquire supreme love for conscious life. From the moment they were born, they were already in that world of supreme love for conscious life, like Little Ameena. Supreme love was the human condition from which flowed one's value creation and business. Supreme love was the cornucopia from which flowed all values in the Universe.

"Zons are the omnipresent love that fills the Universe, forever watching over us, forever protecting us...forever saving us," Jake whispered. Then he paused for a moment, and added, "And now, *we* are Zon rookies on our first mission to save conscious life out there. *We* are watching over Beorapparaus; *we* are saving him. *We* are Zons; *we* are part of the omnipresent love!"

With that realization, an unprecedented feeling flooded Jake's arms, legs, torso, and head. He stopped and stood still. Jasmine looked at him; he looked stunned.

"What is it?" Jasmine asked him.

"A new feeling," he said, "beyond anything I've felt before. Jassy, it's like electricity going through me...but it feels *good!* ...You know the exhilaration we wake up to every morning as God-Man?"

"Yes," she said. "That feeling's what drove our civilization to eradicate death."

"Darling...this feeling goes beyond God-Man," Jake said. "I think this is the feeling we'll wake up to every morning as Zons."

Jasmine stopped moving about. "As Zons..." she echoed. "As Zons we're saving the supreme value in the Universe, everywhere we can." Her eyes opened wide. "I think I feel it too. It's like...currents of energy!"

Ameena laughed at them again. Jake and Jasmine looked at their baby and suddenly knew that *she* felt it, too. In fact, she had felt it all along.

That's what she's been trying to tell me, Jake realized.

This early September morning was beautiful in New York City. The air was fresh. The population had been falling the past couple of years as residents moved to the lush Paradise Cities. But many people still walked the streets of New York, and the Twin Towers project led the way in bringing Paradise

Cities right into New York City.

Jake and Jasmine planned to move to one of the Paradise Cities in New Jersey early the next year. Because of the advancement of communication with face-to-face meetings anywhere in the world through realistic holograms and because of the speed of travel that shrank the world, they could live anywhere in the world and be just as effective as they were in New York City.

Knowing they would not be in New York City much longer made them acutely aware of the city and its beauty. The streets of New York were clean and the concept of crime had been forgotten other than as a historical fact.

Although Jake and Jasmine were in a hurry to get to the Space Library, when they stepped outside their renovated brownstone, Jasmine told Jake she wanted to walk. Suddenly, she felt butterflies in her stomach and needed time to brace herself for what she might find out about her father, one way or the other, once she entered the doors of the Space Library. Three-year-old Jakey perceived his mother's fear and put his arm around her leg. She looked down at her little boy. He was so full of energy he could easily make the walk without a stroller. Ameena was happily in her daddy's arms and very excited about the early venture outside.

As they started their walk, Jake was aware how the city had changed. Transparent, nano-fiber reinforced acrylic road-coverings over the city streets ended the catastrophic event of pedestrians getting struck and killed by cars. The tunnel-like coverings removed the traffic noise of the city and eliminated the traffic exhaust. Entire buildings — mostly those left vacant as people moved out of the city — were converted into parking garages. The tunnel-like streets had safe, frequent exits into those large parking garages. Cars no longer parked on the streets.

Deep in their thoughts of what lay ahead in the Space Library, Jake and Jasmine stepped onto one of the many conveyor belts along the streets. It gave them a quick yet pleasant ride over the plexiglass road-cover to the other side of the street. They continued their walk along the once-noisy city sidewalk, which now was more like a walk through the park.

But what was most beautiful about New York was the love

of life, the *happiness* on the faces of every passerby. Everyone was the person he or she was meant to be, living his or her Friday-Night essence as a value creator. The faces of passersby were filled with expressions of bliss or passion, depending upon whether their thoughts were reflecting or creating. Jake loved seeing an occasional Body II walk by. He could spot them now because of the power and wisdom that radiated from their young faces. He loved to observe them, for they were the quintessence of man conquering nature. In the anticivilization, the forces of nature conquered man. Every Body II that walked by confirmed man was now in charge.

Jake and Jasmine walked past the five-star patio restaurants serving healthy, appetizing breakfasts. The supersociety had become very service oriented for both convenience and luxury. As the little family walked along, Jake remembered a few years ago when he was closer still to the anticivilization, he felt as though New York City was becoming a vacation resort with so much service and luxury. Back then, he was not yet used to the service, luxury, and safety of the supersociety. Now, it seemed natural to him. Why would it be any other way?

They walked past a man entering a program into a floating contraption that would clean the windows of skyscrapers. They walked past a fleet of little dome-shaped computerized robots busily cleaning the sidewalks. Then they turned a corner onto the street of the Space Library. As they got closer to the Space Library, Jake noticed Jasmine was slowing down. Moreover, Ameena was trying to get her mom's attention, and Jasmine did not notice her.

"I'm a little nervous," she finally said to Jake, and then she stopped walking.

Little Jakey looked at his mother then at his father, and then at his mother again. Jake nodded and ran his hand down Jasmine's long black hair. He waited patiently, until she was ready to walk again.

When they resumed their walk, a shiver rushed through Jake. He knew that the mysteries of the story told to him by Jessie and Angie nearly ten years ago about the miracle year had all been answered...but one. The mysteries about how Miss Annabelle's students would bring mankind into the world of *what is,* beyond the matrix of illusions and rationalizations in order to end human death, had all been answered. One and only one mystery from that miracle year remained unsolved: what happened to Sally's mother after she died? That mystery had grown to become everyone's mystery once civilization went through the leap into the immortal Civilization of the Universe. That mystery enveloped his wife. Jake took a deep breath to calm his nerves. Inside the Space Library, the final mystery would be solved.

As they walked along the last block before reaching the Space Library, Jasmine looked frightened. She could hear her pulse beating in her head. She did not hear the sounds of the city. Everything seemed to move in slow motion. She turned her head to look at Jake. Is her father alive or isn't he? That was the question beating in her head, over and over, with every beat of her heart. She feared the odds. Whereas after one's physical death, the spirit could continue in a quantum computer hardwired to one's brain, the spirit could not be preserved somewhere else in some other location. That was for sure, and Jasmine was aware of a frightful fact forming in her head. She started shivering. Jake took her ice-cold hand into his free hand. They stopped again and gazed into each other's eyes. She nervously voiced what was forming in her head: "To still be alive, Daddy's spirit would've had to been preserved somewhere else."

"What do you mean?" Jake said.

"Never mind," she said, her voice shaking, too nervous to draw that fact to its conclusion.

Very gently, Jake said, "Soon, *we'll know.*"

At that moment, Jake realized that those three words — *soon, we'll know* — captured the nature of the Civilization of the Universe. Indeed, for every question, for every new knowledge sought in the Civilization of the Universe, it could be said: *Soon, we'll know.*

When they approached the entrance to the Space Library, Jasmine had no idea what the charts she was about to face would reveal about her father. She did not know if she would be eternally reunited or eternally devastated. She shuddered at the thought. The stakes were so high.

At the door, she stopped. Inside there, *they knew.* She looked down at her son, her little Zon, who looked up at her with every bit of love his little body could muster. He was normally so rambunctious, but today he stood somberly by her side. He wanted with all his might for her to be happy. She picked up her little Zon and hugged him. He let his mom carry him this time. Jasmine then looked at her daughter in Jake's arms. Little Ameena had been trying to get her mother's attention and looked so happy when her mommy noticed her. Seeing Ameena's unconditional love, Jasmine gasped, for she suddenly knew what her father saw and felt twenty-nine years ago...when he looked at her.

She reached out to rub Ameena's hair. Jasmine's hand was trembling. Little Ameena burst into one of her uncoordinated smiles of glee, which filled Jasmine with beautiful happiness.

She then realized why her daddy loved her so much...she filled him with beautiful happiness.

And now, while looking at Little Ameena, Jasmine knew Jake was right: her father's last moment, while looking up at her, was filled with beautiful happiness. He really did say, "Being with you is beautiful."

She took a deep breath and put her free hand against the door and then stopped. Sensing her hesitation, Jake reassuringly put his free arm around her. He wanted her to take this step at her own pace.

She looked into Jake's eyes and softly said, "Only someone emotionally in the Civilization of the Universe could have felt the kind of connection with a child that my dad felt with me. He was really special."

"He really was," Jake said. He remembered the look on her father's face every time he saw Jasmine. ...In this tender moment, Jake held her tighter. She took another deep breath, looked at Little Ameena and Jakey, and smiled.

"Your granddaddy belonged in the Civilization of the Universe," she told them. Seeing her mother was addressing them, Ameena took charge of the moment and started noisily blowing bubbles to reciprocate and attempt to please her mother. Jasmine started laughing at her baby's commotion while, at the same instant, Jasmine started crying, knowing her father once looked at her this way.

Encouraged by her mother's big reaction, Little Ameena

flapped her arms and legs wildly and put her entire might behind her foaming bubbles. Jasmine shook her head and smiled. She realized, now, that every joy Ameena and Jakey brought to her, she had brought to her father.

She leaned over and kissed her little girl on her cheek, which was flush from her gallant bubble-blowing efforts.

"I love you, *sugar pie*," Jasmine whispered in her baby's ear. "*You too*," she added, hugging her little passenger again.

Then she wrapped one arm more tightly around Jakey, put her other arm around Jake, and together, the little family walked through the doors, into the Space Library.

CHAPTER
ONE HUNDRED TWENTY-TWO

"I wish this train could go faster," Miss Annabelle said. She nervously looked out the window at the scenery flashing by in a blur. She and her husband were rushing to the Space Library after receiving the same phone call from Ian as Jake and Jasmine and the other members of The Group. "Jasmine and Jake are probably already there, and maybe Sally and Jeremiah are there by now, too." She winced and added, "Oh, I hope...*I really hope* Sally and Jasmine are okay."

The hi-speed supertrain was traveling at 320 miles per hour, but this morning, that seemed slow. The question of the lost loved ones, the question immortals asked themselves every day, would now be answered.

Miss Annabelle looked at her husband and calmed down some. She sighed and said, "The concluding chapter to your novel will now be written, you know." She was referring to his novel released nine years previously and now a classic entitled *The First Immortals*. His factual novel told the story of the miracle year Miss Annabelle spent with her students in the third grade, their separation, the reunion twenty-six years later, and the run for the presidency. He wrote *The First Immortals* when Daniel was running for president to help get Daniel elected. He released the factual novel for free over the Internet that summer because he wanted millions of people to see what a beautiful world awaited them if they elected Daniel. Indeed, *The First Immortals* not only told the story from the third-grade miracle year to Daniel's run for the Oval Office, but the novel then laid out a story of what would happen after Daniel were elected, climaxing with Project Life and the race for biological immortality. The novel never answered, however, whether our lost loved ones were or were not saved by Zons.

"You're right," Mr. Melbourne answered, "now we'll know the conclusion to *The First Immortals*."

"Why, darling, did you leave the question of our lost loved ones unanswered in your book?" She never felt the need to ask him before, because she implicitly knew why; but now that the answer would be known, she felt the urge to ask him.

"Time and time again, my readers wrote me to ask that question: what happened to the lost loved ones in *The First Immortals*? Were their spirits still alive after they died? In the deepest reaches of my readers' minds, I think they really wanted to know what happened to their own, real-life lost loved ones. And, that was precisely the reason why I couldn't provide the answer. To have reached for the answer in my novel would've been science fiction, which wouldn't have been satisfying and wasn't the purpose of *The First Immortals*. The purpose of *The First Immortals* was to accurately show my readers what was going to happen if Daniel were elected — what actually would come our way. The only satisfying answer about the lost loved ones in *The First Immortals*...and about *our own* lost loved ones...would be an answer that's *real*. Therefore, the final chapter had to be written by science, not science fiction. As you said, Ian's Overlay Charts have finally written the final chapter."

Miss Annabelle shuddered, knowing the train was racing them toward the final chapter. She nodded at the love of her life. "Everything you wrote about the Twelve-Visions World in your novel came true," she said, "as though you had a perfect picture of the new world. You perfectly described it."

"I did have a picture, a Neothink puzzle-picture, that is. I saw the puzzle-picture of the superpuzzle we created at the reunion. Those were perfectly fitting puzzle pieces to snap together into a clear puzzle-picture of the Civilization of the Universe on Earth. As long as Daniel won the election, the rest of the novel would come to pass."

Mr. Melbourne paused. Something jogged his memory. "Do you remember that tape you sent me in prison of your students projecting the future?" he asked. "Do you remember that tape?"

Miss Annabelle smiled and nodded. "I remember that discussion between Teddy, Danny, and Sally. They were projecting the future of computers, the economy, and medicine." ...Whoa, that was so long ago, she thought, but it seems as though I listened to it a month or two ago.

"You know, they accurately projected the future," Mr. Melbourne continued. "Your nine-year-old students actually saw the future by snapping together enough puzzle pieces to know what the completed puzzle-picture would look like, even before all the pieces were in place. That demonstration of Neothink had a major impact on me that never left me. I wrote *The First Immortals* using that puzzle-building Neothink. I had enough puzzle pieces to snap together what the Twelve-Visions World — the Civilization of the Universe on Earth — would look like. That's why everything in *The First Immortals* came true. ...But I didn't have enough puzzle pieces to answer the question of what happened to our loved ones after they died."

Miss Annabelle sighed and nodded. She leaned her head back in the soft leather chair. After a moment, she said, "You remember Beorapparaus explaining that the earliest epics formed the anticivilization?"

"Oh, yes. The first epics established what it meant to be man, which in *The Iliad* and *The Odyssey* was capturing honor and glory through plunder and war, regardless of honesty. Man achieved his immortality through this sort of legacy."

Miss Annabelle was nodding and said, "Your novel, darling, is the first epic, so to speak, of the Civilization of the Universe here on Earth. It establishes what it means to be God-Man, which in *The First Immortals* is achieving eternal happiness and love through value creation. Of course, dishonesty doesn't even enter the equation. God-Man lives with happiness and love for eternity. His supreme love for life becomes his pass into immortality." She paused. Her eyes seemed busy, as though she were sorting out her thoughts. "You snapped together the pieces to see the future," she said. "But you also created in your novel the missing pieces to complete the picture. Your novel showed humanity what a world built on pure honesty, supreme love, value creation, and business would be like. You created the way. You, my love, created the blueprints from which this world was built."

Mr. Melbourne, a modest man, quietly said, "Thank you." He leaned over and hugged his wife. She kissed this man who wrote the treasure-map into the beautiful world in which everyone now lived. Then, they both looked out the window, wondering what lay beyond this world, anxious for that final chapter. His eyes gazed into the distance. Her eyes were fixed on the ground without perceiving it, lost in her anxious thoughts. What happened to our lost loved ones? What if it's bad news? How will Sally and Jasmine and others handle it? And, oh, what if it's good news!

The ground just outside her window, speeding by in a blur, slowly came into her visual perception. A pleasing metaphor went through her thoughts as she saw the ground speeding by: that's how fast knowledge is advancing today — *in a blur.*

She tilted her head back against her seat and closed her eyes. To calm her nerves, she started humming *The Impossible Dream.* After a minute, she stopped abruptly. She lifted her head and sat up straight.

"The lyrics don't make any sense," she said.

"What?" her husband said.

"The lyrics to *The Impossible Dream...*they make no sense! They're the most hope-inspiring lyrics ever written in the anticivilization, but they make no sense in the Civilization of the Universe. No, the concept of battles against evil can't be sustained any longer in the world of pure love and honesty." She started saying the lyrics slowly, and after another verse, she stopped again. "No, they don't make any sense at all."

"Not anymore," Mr. Melbourne concurred.

She leaned her head back again and closed her eyes. She did not need an explanation. Many things once needed in the unnatural anticivilization were no longer needed in the Civilization of the Universe.

She disengaged from the world again, engrossed in her anxious thoughts. Did the Trinity of the Universe save our lost loved ones? Or is that truly the unreachable star? Or is the unreachable star no longer part of the Civilization of the Universe?

Mr. Melbourne watched his wife toss and turn with her eyes shut in her chair. He knew she was worried about the pain her students would endure if their lost loved ones were gone forever.

The anxiety is incredible, he thought, but soon this tension that I couldn't relieve in my novel will be over, for better or for worse. He put his hand on her lap. She opened her eyes and smiled. She took his hand and put it against her, hugging it just above her young breasts. He felt her heart pounding. He wrapped his other arm around her shoulders and pulled her tightly against him. The train raced them without pause toward the Space Library.

His chin rested against her soft dark hair. "Just remember, you and I, your students, the members of The Group...*we* made it into the world of immortals," he said. His thoughts turned inward. "And for that I'm so, *so* grateful. Whether or not our lost loved ones made it into the world of immortals, well, soon *we'll know*."

Miss Annabelle smiled and nodded. She laid her head against his chest, and whispered, like a distant echo, "Soon, *we'll know*." Then she closed her eyes and felt her compassion bursting painfully throughout her soul.

After a few moments in her husband's arms, she relaxed a little. When she did, the glorious launching of *Trinity* the week before flashed through her mind. The knowledge that Earthling Zons were bringing a mortal into the world of immortals filled her with happiness, even though she might never personally know him. *Happiness*, she thought, *is the purpose of conscious life.*

Out of the blue, the memory of Sally's ninth birthday party suddenly entered Miss Annabelle's thoughts. Images of Sally and her wonderful mother, weak from her medication but sitting right beside Sally, both laughing, flashed through Miss Annabelle's mind. Love filled the air that day. Sally's mother saw Sally's other world — the world of pure love, pure honesty — when she was with her classmates and teacher. Sally's mother loved and belonged in that world. And she was. Every moment she and Sally were together, they lived in the world of pure love, pure honesty. Miss Annabelle saw, in her memory, Sally turning around again and again, giving her mother hugs throughout the happy birthday party, just to hug her, just to hold her and to have her while she was still there.

The sad day Sally's mother was no longer there, did the glorious Zons, Miss Annabelle wondered, save her...that woman with pure love in her soul? If it were possible within the Laws of Science, then they must have, *they must have*, Miss Annabelle thought. ...And then, *she knew*: if it were possible within the Laws of Science, the Zons *would have* saved our lost loved ones. For, she knew from the week before, the act of bringing a mortal into the world of immortals filled the soul of pure love, the soul of Zons, with *happiness*, the very purpose of conscious life. Emotionally, nothing could stop them from putting forth the energy and expense, just as Earthlings did for Beorapparaus. Maybe something could physically stop them, but nothing could emotionally stop them. And it was that sound answer — *if it were possible within the Laws of Physics, Zons would have saved our lost loved ones* — that enabled her to endure the rest of the ride to the Space Library.

Mr. Melbourne, buried in his own thoughts, felt her entire body relax in his arms, and he overheard her whisper to herself, "With biological immortality, I don't think there's an unreachable star. ...I think it's physically possible."

* * *

Miss Annabelle and Mr. Melbourne threw open the doors to the Space Library and heard Ian talking upstairs in the loft.

"Wait until you see how this all locks together with our Overlay Charts," Ian's voice boomed throughout the Space Library. Miss Annabelle's heart was racing. She and her husband ran up the stairs as they heard Ian say, "Look here! The Code of Consciousness."

They made it to the top of the stairs to see him pointing at the theater-size screen behind him filled with what looked sort of like a Periodic Table. She looked more closely. The blocks on the chart were filled with information acquired through Overlay Charts. In those blocks, she saw many familiar things as well as things she did not understand. In a glance, she saw in one of the many boxes "Project Sustain Life — Everyone, Strangers, Every Conscious Life, Saved At Any and All Costs". She saw in another box "Project Sustain Life — Beorapparaus, One Man, Complete Stranger, Largest Expenditure of Energy and Money In History of Our Civilization".

Ian did not see Miss Annabelle or Mr. Melbourne standing off to his side at the top of the stairs as he continued, "Now I'm going to plug into the Code of Consciousness my most recent breakthrough that we just accomplished: curing catastrophic death with, as I'll call it, the continuous conscious flow." A slide then filled the next open bottom-right box with "The Continuous Conscious Flow."

"As you'll see — that was the key element to predict what's in the next empty box. But I'll let you figure it out. Do you know how predictive Periodic Tables work?" he asked his small audience of Jake and Jasmine, Sally and Jeremiah, still not seeing Miss Annabelle or Mr. Melbourne who were too busy staring at the screen to say anything.

The couples nodded, but their eyes, too, were stuck to the big chart filling the screen before them.

"Okay, then. Study this chart and see if you can tell me what goes in *right here*," he said. He turned and pointed to the next open box on the bottom right corner, next to the box he just filled in.

Miss Annabelle started shivering. But she made herself focus. As she studied the boxes, she heard her husband mutter under his breath, "Would you look at that..."

"What?" she whispered.

"Look, do you see the pattern?" Mr. Melbourne paused, and then he told her: "For every event here on Earth, there is a parallel event, a counterpart, out there in the cosmos that Ian found through Overlay Charts. That pattern begins when mankind leapt beyond the illusions of the anticivilization, ever since humanity lived through fully integrated honesty. For instance," he said while pointing toward the chart, "see how after the illusions vanished, violence dried up and disappeared here.

Now notice how Ian's Overlay Charts show no violence exists out there. Ever since the illusions vanished, there's that pattern. That's because we're now in the same Civilization of the Universe here as they are out there. Supreme love shapes society. Whatever happens here on Earth happens out there in the cosmos. And that pattern is evidence of a *code of consciousness*. Now that you see the pattern, and you realize that when something major happens here, Ian will find it happening out there...what do you see?"

"Honey," Miss Annabelle said softly.

"Yes?" he said with excitement swelling in his voice.

"The Continuous Conscious Flow just happened here—" Just then, she stopped talking. Her eyes widened. "Oh my God..." she started to say.

But at the exact moment that Miss Annabelle gasped and knew what filled the next box, Sally screamed, "Oh, God! OH MY GOD!"

Jasmine screamed. She turned and buried her face into Jake's chest. She pulled little Jakey against her and wrapped her other arm around Ameena, and she wept on Jake's chest. Little Ameena got startled. She looked up at her father's face and saw tears on his cheeks.

"Here and there," Jake uttered, "here and there. Cure death with a continuous conscious flow here, cure it with the continuous flow there."

"Like a game of match," Jasmine cried.

Miss Annabelle ran across the room and wrapped her arms around Sally and Jeremiah and held them both.

"Oh, my darling," Miss Annabelle said. She felt Sally shaking uncontrollably, "My sweet darling."

Sally turned and hugged Miss Annabelle with all her might.

"My mom's okay," Sally cried in a broken voice. "After all these years, my mom's okay!"

Seeing his beloved teacher there and seeing the reaction of those he loved caused a few large tears to roll down from Ian's large logical eyes. It was the first time anyone beyond his wife had seen him cry since Miss Annabelle had been sentenced to prison when he was nine years old. Just then, Debbie and Alan walked up the stairs into the commotion. Debbie saw the tears, and she immediately got scared. Ian saw her and smiled.

"Your mom and dad's spirits," he said gently, "are out there, presumably in the super quantum computer, waiting for us to bring them back here and give them their bodies back. They're there, waiting for us."

"Oh Daddy, we're going to get you back," Jasmine cried. Jake hugged Jasmine tightly, and Little Ameena tugged nervously on her ear.

CHAPTER
ONE HUNDRED TWENTY-THREE

"Why...why didn't you tell us this before?" Mr. Melbourne asked Ian that afternoon after the celebration settled down.

"Actually, I didn't see it, even though it was right under my nose. I saw the parallels all along, but it didn't click that I was witnessing an axiomatic code of consciousness." Ian swept his hand across the big chart behind him. "Believe it or not, as obvious as it is now, it wasn't until after I put the Continuous Conscious Flow into the Master Table late last night that I saw the significance of the pattern for the first time. As I studied the chart last night, a thought flashed through my mind: Whereas human death following The Operation was quickly reduced to catastrophic death only, in all actuality, every human death for the past three thousand years, long before The Operation, was a catastrophic death, for human death should've been cured shortly after man's leap from the bicameral mentality to human consciousness. Mankind should've naturally flowed into a supersociety. The formulation of the anticivilization was the overarching catastrophe that ultimately caused every person's death.

"Upon realizing that every human death for the past 3000 years was a catastrophic death and that I had just cured catastrophic death, I suddenly and all at once saw the fate of our lost loved ones and the code of consciousness staring me straight in the face. It was an epiphanous moment, to say the least. Of course, the moment I saw the meaning behind the pattern, I realized that...since we can now cure catastrophic death on Earth with the Continuous Conscious Flow, then Zons would have cured all catastrophic death throughout the Universe, including our lost loved ones. Our lost loved ones all died here on Earth from catastrophic death, and they were saved — each and every one."

"But...Ian," Jasmine said, overwhelmed and apparently distraught, "since I saw the Master Chart this morning, I've grown afraid this doesn't apply to our lost loved ones because the procedure needs hardware; it needs to be hardwired into the brain, which we know didn't exist in our lost loved ones."

"I know, dear," Ian said. His voice flowed with compassion. "My work here merely proves it can be done, and done rather simply, which is why this box here on the Master Table can be filled in now, with certainty: the continuous conscious flow occurred for our lost loved ones. You see the pattern, Jasmine; it's the Code of Consciousness. Whatever we do here on Earth after having gone from anticivilization man to God-Man and now Zons, they axiomatically do the same out there. It's the Code of Consciousness. In the anticivilization, we could never know the Code of Consciousness. The bicameral mutations — the mind disease — had to end first. Now, we live with no mind disease crippling our consciousness. Therefore, the Code of Consciousness becomes clear. What we do here is rational and possible within the Laws of Science. So, they do the same beyond Earth, just as we see proven over and over on the Overlay Charts. The Code of Consciousness on the Master Table now shows not only that the continuous conscious flow can be done, but that it *is* done. With hindsight, we can see the Code of Consciousness working at mankind's immortal beginnings as we achieved immortality and then dried up all ways of catastrophic death here on Earth until we eradicated catastrophic death with the continuous conscious flow. That was the Code of Consciousness kicking in during our beginnings in the Civilization of the Universe. And soon thereafter, we saw the Code of Consciousness almost immediately reaching out beyond our civilization to save Beorapparaus' life. When you combine that Code of Consciousness with the relatively simple technology to perpetuate one's consciousness, well, there's no more doubt our lost loved ones' consciousness continued after their physical deaths."

"But what about the hardware — the diamond-chip quantum computer — that's hardwired into Christine's brain?" Jasmine asked. "My dad didn't have that."

"This brings up something very interesting," Ian said. "When you stop to think about it, the continuous conscious flow through the diamond-chip quantum computer is essentially the same thing as the continuous conscious flow through the head-transfer in The Operation. It's the same thing — the transfer of the uninterrupted realm of awareness and the I-ness — except the diamond-chip quantum computer is using the next major wave of technology. It's now very evident the one-and-only way to preserve conscious life is through the continuous conscious flow. That simple fact simplifies everything for us, for now we know our Zons had to save us from catastrophic death through the continuous conscious flow. We know we went from the crude head-transfer to the noninvasive diamond-chip transfer...to what? We merely must ask ourselves: What is the next major wave of technology? When we answer that, we answer *how* they saved us.

"We know from the Code of Consciousness that Zons saved our lost loved ones. We just don't know *how* they saved us. To our knowledge, nothing was hardwired into your father, Jasmine, so they must have some kind of 'wireless' technology...maybe it has something to do with people 'seeing the light'. Remember I proved, over ten years ago, an ether of quantum gravity units exists. That ether exists everywhere — not just around you, above you, and below you, but *throughout* you. That ether exists inside your brain and just might be our Zon's diamond-chip quantum computer, so to speak, through which your realm of awareness continuously flows without ever blowing out. The frequency of capturing the I-ness would be constant, and the realm of awareness would continuously flow at one's death into the Universal Computer. ...I'm betting the technology ends up being the ether, which exists throughout the Universe and throughout our bodies and minds. I bet it's our 'implanted computer' that captures the I-ness and realm of awareness in a continuous flow. From the head transfer, down to a microscopic computer chip, down to subatomic gravity units...each being the next major wave of more sophisticated, less invasive nanotechnology to capture and transfer the continuous conscious flow. In any case, this predictive chart shows us that Zons prevented the deaths of your father's spirit, Jasmine...and your mother's spirit, Sally...and your parents' spirits, Debra."

Jasmine, Sally, Debra were fighting back tears and nodding.

"Are they aware?" Debra asked.

"Yes," Ian said. Jasmine gasped, Debra's mouth twitched, Sally sighed. Ian continued, "Just as if someone has died here, his mind, his I-ness remains aware on his diamond-chip quantum computer, aware that his body, his life-tool, has given out, quietly waiting to be found and given another body. Your parents are most likely quietly waiting to be found and given another body. We must now put our energies into a new superpuzzle to find our lost loved ones."

A new supperpuzzle, Jake thought, *oh, what a superpuzzle!*

"Where are they?" Debra asked.

"In the Universal Computer," said Ian, "just as Christine's awareness would wait in her diamond-chip quantum computer upon her catastrophic death here on Earth. Your parents must be downloaded into a physical tool — a body, a brain."

"How long until we can do that?" Sally asked.

"At the rate of progress in the supersociety, I'd say in less than ten years."

Jasmine smiled.

"What do you think the circuitry is made of?" Mr. Melbourne asked.

"I suspect this," Ian said, "the Universal Computer runs on O's and 1's—"

"O's and 1's?" Mr. Melbourne interrupted. "Wouldn't that technology be ancient?"

"Yes, it would." Ian said, "But then, every civilization would know it. The key would be the smallness of the circuitry. The computer would run on O's and 1's, but structured in the most unbelievably smallest subatomic particles — smaller than photons, light particles…maybe much smaller. Our energy and nanotechnology may not get down to that level for several years. But if we organize another superpuzzle, we could possibly develop the technology to bring back our loved ones in ten years or less."

"On what could the data possibly be stored, and how can we interface with it?" Theodore asked.

"I think it's all done on something much smaller than quantized photons, even smaller than Planck's length where the known laws of physics break down. I think it's all stored on gravity units — the 'ether'…quantized space. The data's got to be stored in gravity units. Now, how do we interface with it to download the minds of our lost loved ones into a clone and transfer their realms of awareness?" Ian shook his head. "In the supersociety with our superpuzzle, I feel we're about three to five years away from learning in theory how to interface with such a computer, and perhaps six or seven years from actually starting experimental work on this because deeper laws of physics must be discovered."

Another supreme-love-driven, grand superpuzzle, Jake thought.

"Ten years from now, I'll look into Daddy's loving eyes again," Jasmine thought out loud.

A wide grin spread across Ian's face. Diana, who was sitting on a chair behind him, stood up and walked over and held his arm. This would be Ian's next great goal after curing catastrophic death.

"The box we just revealed *does exist,*" he continued. "The contents of the minds of our lost loved ones are stored on the super quantum computer, which again I think is programmed in gravity units, the smallest possible quantum in the Universe. That conclusion," emphasized Ian, looking at Jasmine, "you can feel certain of and wonderful from and relieved by. Within ten years in this supersociety, we should be able to get our loved ones back. Jasmine, you'll have your dad back, and to him, it may seem as though he never died."

Jasmine's face was flush with emotions as she smiled and nodded.

"But what about all those conscious beings who died 100, 200, 300 years ago?" Ian looked around the room. "There are no loved ones to bring them back, right? Well, the next empty box here, when we study this Master Table and the Code of Consciousness it reveals, in theory says that those conscious beings were sent into some other body or other physical tool so the spirit could interface with the physical world. Then, the conscious being could continue creating values...continue living and experiencing happiness. What that means, I'm not sure. We'll bring back our lost loved ones, but some could have moved on and be living somewhere else now."

"Not my daddy," Jasmine whispered, "he's waiting to come back to me."

"So, if my parents have existed out there for years, why wouldn't they have contacted me?" Debra asked.

"I don't know; I can't answer that. Maybe it has something to do with physics...or maybe it has something to do with psychology, perhaps with us needing to advance and go to them — we just don't know, not yet. Soon, we will. But, I see no reason why we can't bring back our lost loved ones, aware and waiting in the super quantum computer."

Jake suddenly had an insight: Zons did save our spirits when we died in the days before biological immortality, but they wouldn't want us to know or even consider that they saved us...not before we achieved the Civilization of the Universe on Earth. No, they wouldn't have told us they saved us because that knowledge would've taken the edge off of our motivation and determination to drive our civilization into making the leap to the Civilization of the Universe. Just as parents, with their vast range of experiences beyond their children, properly keep certain knowledge from their children, Zons would've kept the saving of our spirits from Earthlings. They wouldn't have come to us, no indeed. We'd have to go to them.

"But now," Jake muttered under his breath, "we *have* achieved the Civilization of the Universe on Earth; we have achieved Zonhood." Jake's whole body shook in awe of the new superpuzzle. Yes, The Group was moving on to another grand superpuzzle. And, oh, what a superpuzzle it was.

"Damn, Ian," Mr. Melbourne said, "you amaze me more and more and more. You amazed me when you were a boy. You just blow me away as an adult."

Superpuzzle

Jake was aware of himself thinking: what Zons are doing "out there" throughout the cosmos and what we are doing "down here" on Earth seems to be blending into one.

"I mean," continued Mr. Melbourne, "you're talking about bringing back our deceased loved ones here!" He drew in a long breath, raised his eyebrows, then exhaled a long breath of sheer amazement, and he said, "Wow." He shook his head and started laughing. He waived his finger at Ian and said, "Ok Ian, you're good...you're the best there ever was." Mr. Melbourne laughed some more, and soon Sally and Debbie and Jasmine joined in. They just felt *so good* now, finally knowing their precious loved ones were safe. Then Miss Annabelle laughed. She felt *so good* for Sally, Debbie, and Jasmine. Then Jake and Ian himself started laughing. Then everyone in the room burst out laughing in sheer glee. Ah, the relief, Jake thought, the relief we feel now that the anticivilization and all its pain and destruction is forever finished.

Jake suddenly stopped laughing and sat still. *Listen to that*, he thought as the others cackled, it's the same laugh of Little Ameena early this morning. It's music to my ears. It's...it's the music of Zons.

"You ready for me to commercialize your work?" Theodore finally asked Ian when The Group settled down. "I really feel the pressure now to get the implant into everyone."

"Oh, I'm ready, Ted," Ian answered. "Just imagine, with the quantum-computer implant, a person can never perish for any reason. Everyone wants one *right now*. Yes, I'm ready."

"As we implant the quantum-computer chip into larger and larger segments of the population," said Sally, "the possibility of a catastrophic death extends further and further out into the future. We must make sure we change near-immortals to immortals very rapidly...at a rate that pushes the possibility of a catastrophic death further out into the future, more than the time it takes us to cure everyone."

"We have our work cut out for us!" Daniel blurted in an unexplainable blast of laughter. "We're no longer talking millions of operations...we're talking billions!"

And the superachievers, in sheer amazement of their own superpuzzles, burst out laughing again, with uncoordinated smiles of glee taking over their faces.

Jake looked around and saw Sally laughing and all the former students laughing as he could only imagine them doing as children. Jake looked at Miss Annabelle. She was laughing, not as a mother laughs. She was laughing as a child laughs. And that's when Jake knew: with the last threats of death essentially gone, the carefree happiness from our early childhood was back. Ameena-like happiness, back *forever*.

"But let's not stop there Dan," Al cried out in laughter. "Let's bring back our deceased loved ones!"

"Project Resurrection!" Daniel blurted. Another blast of laughter, over the incredible reaches of it all, filled the room.

CHAPTER
ONE HUNDRED TWENTY-FOUR

"Good evening, *immortals*."

Viewers around the world broke into cheers upon hearing Daniel's first-ever greeting not as near-immortals, but as *immortals*. After the Great Moment eleven months earlier, upon Ian's insistence, Daniel continued greeting his viewing audience as 'near-immortals' until the cure to catastrophic death was found.

"I'm coming to you live from the Space Library. My deep friend and miracle-year classmate, world-renowned Dr. Ian Scott, has done it: he has learned how to eradicate catastrophic death on Earth."

Daniel paused for several moments to let the magnitude of what he said to sink in.

Then, he continued, "That's stunning news; what I'm about to say next just might top it: Dr. Scott has discovered, through his Overlay Charts, a predictive Master Table. His Master Table shows that events from Zons run parallel to every major event of Earthlings since we jumped to the God-Man, when everything we did was based on pure rationality, revealing a predictable Code of Consciousness. Two recent events, when added together, present us with a magnificent discovery. The first event was our launch of *Trinity* to preserve every known conscious life in jeopardy beyond Earth. The second event is our accomplishment of capturing a continuous conscious flow, even when the body undergoes a sudden catastrophic death, capturing the spirit on a quantum computer. Add those two events together, and here's what you get: the spirits of our lost loved ones have been stored on our Zon's Universal Computer. They're just waiting for us to bring them back! Bringing them back, Dr. Scott says on behalf of Beyond, is his next major project!

"Now, ladies and gentlemen, I have a treat for you: here is the man himself, the one-and-only Dr. Ian Scott, to tell you his procedure of capturing our spirits on a quantum computer to eradicate catastrophic death. He will also unveil his Master Table and explain what it will take to get our loved ones back. Dr. Scott, let me start by thanking you for bringing us fully into the world of immortals—"

"It's the greatest joy in my life..." Ian began. He went on to describe the momentous achievements.

*

The next day, the entire world celebrated.

People filled the streets of New York; they filled the streets of every city and town around the world. It was not yet a month after the launch of *Trinity,* and they learned that their lost loved ones were coming back. This celebration of celebrations, just a month after the last great celebration, had something no celebration quite had before. Upon opening the window to his brownstone, Jake realized: *it was the laughter.*

Jake and Jasmine picked up their kids and skipped down the stairs of their brownstone. Ameena was bouncing on Mom's hip, and Jakey was bouncing on Dad's shoulders. The little guy grabbed onto Dad's cheeks. They plunged into the street party. *Who's organizing these festivities?* wondered Jake.

Jumping off his last step, into the party, Jake accidently bumped rather hard into an older gentleman. "Excuse me. I'm sorry!" Jake said. He put his hands on the old man's shoulders to steady him and to see if he was okay. "Are you hurt?"

"Oh, I'm fine!" said the older fellow. "I'm wonderful!" he added and started laughing again.

Everywhere Jake looked, people were laughing just as The

Superpuzzle

Group had been laughing a few days before at the Space Library. It was, he realized, total release from anticivilization bondage. They just kept laughing, as though the new knowledge of Project Resurrection was all over them and through them, tickling them, inside and out.

Jake took advantage of the moment to ask the old fellow what it meant to him that he could recover lost loved ones. The old man cuffed his hand over his mouth to control his laughter. Then, with a smile still on his face, he told Jake a sobering story.

"I was older when my son was born — in my fifties," he began. "I always wanted a child. I'm very paternal and have a lot of love to give. Growing up, I was very close to my younger brother, was kind of a father figure to him after my parents got divorced. My son reminds me a lot of my younger brother. As I raised my boy, I recognized in him the similar phases that my younger brother went through. Sometimes it seemed almost as if my brother just went through the same phases a few months before. I gave my son some of the same advice that I gave my younger brother, and sometimes it really felt as though I had just told that same advice to my brother only a few months before! When my brother died, my boy was seventeen years old. I remember standing there at my little brother's funeral, just standing there in disbelief that it was already all over. What really got to me was that, after all those talks I had with my little brother, which seemed like just a few months before, those same talks that I was now having with my son, well, what difference did they really make? There my little brother was before me. His life was over. Yes, he had a nice normal life, but now it was all over. ...Over so soon. All that time and thought put into preparing him for a grand life...what was it all for? In what seemed like a few short years, it was all over.

"Then, the crushing blow hit me when I looked up from my brother's closed eyes and into my son's eyes. What good were all the talks and advice I was giving *him?* He'll have a nice normal life like my brother, but in a jiffy, it'll be all over, just like my brother. I just couldn't reconcile it, for I realized there was really no meaning to life. When we were young, it seemed like life had meaning, but not as we grew older. The

1154

irreconcilable nature of my brother's death and my son's inevitable death started me on a downward spiral that was driving me insane. I forced myself to be up, to be 'happy' around my boy, but as he became more and more independent, I was sinking...I was losing it. Then I discovered The Church of God-Man and The Group's drive to end death, which saved my sanity."

The old fellow paused, and then he broke into a chuckle and said, "Now, my son won't ever die. And all that work and thought to prepare him for a grand life...well, he's not having a nice 'normal' life as a value producer but a spectacularly happy life forever as a value creator on his Friday-Night essence. And today, I learn I'm getting my brother back!" The older man burst out laughing. "It's just beautiful!" he blurted with a smile as full and uncoordinated with glee as Little Ameena's.

"Man, that's moving," Jake said to the old fellow. Jake could feel the old man's sense of relief as the old fellow laughed and laughed, which caused Jake to laugh and Jasmine and Jakey to laugh, too.

The joy Jake heard and the energy he felt in the old man's laugh was like taking his previous downward spiral toward insanity after he lost his little brother...and turning it inside out — from inescapable misery to inescapable joy and carefree happiness. His laughter would not stop...and never needed to stop again.

"Life finally has meaning!" the old man shouted triumphantly.

Jake reached out and hugged the old man, and said into his ear, "You just inspired my next article. Look for it in tomorrow's Patterson Paper. I'm Jake Catchings."

The old man pulled back to look at Jake's face, surprised he was just hugging the most renowned journalist in the world today. That phenomenon happened frequently in the supersociety. Casual encounters with people often turned out to be encounters with famous value creators.

"Oh..." the old fellow managed to say through his laughter, pointing his finger at Jake, calming himself down to talk. "I'm so honored! You...you bet I'll look for it! And *thank you* for all you've done for the world! Man, I can't wait to tell my son...*and my brother!*"

1155

Jake and the old man burst out laughing again. They just felt *so good!* As they laughed, Jake was aware how good it felt when the old man thanked him for all Jake had done for the world. I *really have* done a lot, he thought.

He and the old man nodded at each other, a sort of farewell salute of respect, and then they moved on, never to see each other again. As they parted, Jake knew the old man's life would be beautiful, forever. Jake really liked him. They had touched each other's lives, and now moved on. At the moment of departing, Jake experienced a déjà vu. He remembered, for just an instant, his farewell moment when he left his job at Steaks & Wines back in his college days. He and the manager had touched each other's lives, too, and then parted ways forever. Wherever he is, Jake thought, his life is beautiful, and today he's laughing.

Everyone was filled with the new Zon sensation that Jake had described to Jasmine a few days before. Everyone was overflowing with a new energy. Jake knew this sensation was the new feeling beyond the God-Man — the feeling of being Zon. Immense joy and happiness just flowed from people's Neothink minds. They were now Zons and, as with Jakey and Ameena and all young children, happiness overflowed from Zons, and so they *loved to laugh!*

"Oh," Jake managed to shout during one fit of laughter, "we'd better get our stomachs in better shape...because..." he could barely get the words out as spurts of laughter fought to take over, "I think this kind of laughter is a new property of the C of U!" Jake and everyone in earshot burst into laughter. Bright red faces looked at him, nodding in agreement while laughing too hard to speak.

Jake felt light-headed from laughing so hard. He realized he could not laugh like *this* in the anticivilization, no matter how wonderful or funny something was. He watched his beautiful wife and daughter laughing and looked up over his head to see his son laughing. That's when it hit Jake: the latest superpuzzle — Resurrection — removed the final emotional impurities from our lives causing this explosion of happiness and all this wonderful laughter. Man is finally...*limitless.* He is physically and emotionally limitless.

Jake took a deep breath and continued watching his son,

daughter, and wife laughing with carefree and limitless joy. In the distance, he saw the beautiful Twin Towers glistening in the sunshine, now twice as tall, disappearing into the blue sky. Jake felt his own stomach starting to quiver again, then shake, then shake hard as he heard his own laughter fill the air around him.

He became aware of how the laughter of his wife and children beautifully blended with his own laughter, and how the laughter of the hundreds of people around him supported and lifted his own laughter like an entire symphony orchestra backing up his laughter...his solo.

As the symphony of laughter filled the streets, for one fleeting moment Jake remembered the ghostly moans as he fled the ostracism wasteland with Eddie just five months earlier, and Jake realized, for one short instant, that those people were now starving or dead.

But the next instant, the thought was gone as the laughter filled the world from the ground to the sky. And that's when Jake knew for sure...the human race was filled with the *feeling* of Zon. This amazing laughter was *the proof* of mankind's leap into Zonhood. Jake let himself soak in the images of carefree happiness all around him, and he let himself soak in the sound of the laughter...the most beautiful sound in the Universe...the music of Zons. As Jake listened to the laughter, the old man's last comment echoed through Jake's mind and seemed to sing along with the laughter, over and over, like the chorus to the music of Zons...

"Life finally has meaning!"
"Life finally has meaning!"
"Life finally has meaning!"

The End

The End

EPILOGUE

Nine years later...

He wrestled his eyes open. She couldn't say anything. She just watched in disbelief.

"*Being with you is beautiful*," he whispered. Her heart jumped. That *was* the last thought on his mind, the last utterance on his lips...when he died. It was still on his mind, on his lips...now.

She suddenly leaned into him and hugged him. She felt the special celebration rush through her that she always felt around him as a little girl. This time, his arms wrapped back around her. She pulled her head back to look at his face. She could see, in his eyes, the celebration fill his soul; *his soul!* He was physically weak, but she saw pure happiness there. She shook her head and smiled as she witnessed the look of amazement on his face. She could just imagine his sensations; she could almost read his thoughts as his arms and eyes behaved differently. His eyes weren't involuntarily closing in a losing fight to absorb the last light of his life — his daughter — for every moment he had left. Instead, his eyes stayed open more and more easily until they, simply, stayed open. And he was able to move his arms and fingers and was rubbing his hand up and down Jasmine's back.

"You're going to be okay, *Daddy*," Jasmine said gently. She was clobbered by emotions as she said "Daddy" for the first time in fourteen years. She flung herself against him, tighter this time. Again, his strong arms instinctively wrapped around her and hugged her. He glanced around and noticed Jake standing behind Jasmine. There were tears in Jake's eyes, but was he…smiling?

"Oh Daddy," Jasmine said lifting her head off his chest and brushing the hair off her tear-soaked face.

"Jassy, am I dying?" he asked her.

Jake watched his beautiful wife shake her head and smile. And then her smile collapsed, her eyes closed, and she cried. She was releasing the pain of having once watched him die. She cried so hard she could not answer.

"Mozar," Jake said gently. He stepped closer to the bed and spoke from his father-in-law's perspective, as though it were fourteen years in the past: "You're going to be okay. We're certain of that, and here's why: You know how we've prepared for the Operation?"

"Yes," Jasmine's father said. He looked at Jake Jr. and Ameena, still not knowing they were his grandchildren, and smiled. Jasmine opened her eyes and listened. "The Operation is going to be successful; I know it will," Mozar said. He looked back up at Jake.

"Technology's really soaring, isn't it?" Jake asked.

"It's amazing. I love the supersociety." Mozar seemed surprised by his sudden energy.

"Mozar…the supersociety has been racing forward at accelerating speeds for nearly a decade-and-a-half since you were dying."

"What?"

"The first Operation was a tragedy just a few months after you died."

"What!"

"Operation II was a success a few months later. Mozar, it's now fourteen years after you died, and the supersociety has brought you back. Ian's theory about the Universal Computer saving us…it was right."

Jasmine's father looked at Jasmine. She was crying and nodding. That's all he had to see — her nod — to believe and accept everything.

"Oh...*oh my*...oh, my sugar pie!" He hugged his Jasmine. They cried and laughed. The celebration filled their hearts again. "I...I'm remembering something," he cried. "It's vague...like a dream. I remember...I was aware of something...a choice...*a choice* to either move on or to wait for my loved ones...to go into a sort of sleep...a sleep-and-wait mode. That way, I wouldn't get too far advanced beyond my loved ones." He pulled his head back to look at Jasmine. His eyes were drenched in tears as he said, "I wanted for us to stay together." He looked at Jake and back at his daughter. "I always want to be with my precious girl, my precious family."

Jake could not stop his tears from coming. Jake Jr., now twelve, looked up at his dad and then at his mom...and then at his grandfather. He could feel how much his grandfather loved his mom and how much she loved him. Ameena, now nine, was closely watching her mom and her grandfather the whole time. She sensed this moment was the greatest gift her mom and her grandfather could ever receive. The little girl was giggling at her mom's reactions.

"Daddy," Jasmine whispered. Then, sitting up straight, radiating with the greatest pride she ever felt in her life, she said the words she thought she would never have the chance to say: "There's two very special people here who would like to meet you."

She reached out with both arms and took her son's hand and her daughter's hand. "Daddy, these are your grandchildren, Jake Mozar Catchings and your little Ameena."

Jasmine saw her father gasp from the impact. She could not stop her tears as she saw how much this moment meant to her father. He tried to prop himself up on his elbow, fell back onto the bed, then without any hesitation he fought his way right back onto his elbow and reached out and hugged both of his grandchildren with his free arm. Jasmine gently wrapped her arm around her father's shoulders and her other arm around her children.

Jake watched the love flow from Mozar to his grandson and granddaughter. Jake watched the love flowing through his wife, his son, his daughter, and his father-in-law. And Jake felt all

1163

their love flowing through him and his love flowing through them. *Family*, he thought...*family.*

As he watched his family, Jake was aware he had never seen or felt anything so wonderful in his life. Without realizing it, he said his feelings out loud, "All that preciousness brought back, all that love, all that value...it's the most beautiful thing I've ever seen."

"Oh Jake," Jasmine responded, tilting her tear-covered face up and reaching out with her arm toward Jake, "come here..."

Jake knelt by the side of the bed and wrapped his long arms around his family, around his wife, his daughter, his son, and his father-in-law.

Jasmine wept and said, "I just want to hug you guys, forever."

Just outside the room sat Sally, Ian, and Theodore who were conducting and observing the return of Jasmine's father.

"You will, darling," Sally whispered. Then she stood up and walked to the side of the viewing room where a fourth observer was standing.

"*Forever*," Sally sighed while reaching out and hugging her mom.

Closing Word From The Author

Superpuzzle came together in my mind over a period of several months. I first told its story to a small gathering of family and friends on Thanksgiving Day, 1997. That evening, after my guests went home, I began writing *Superpuzzle*.

When the year 1999 changed to 2000, I was about a third of the way through writing *Superpuzzle,* and I put that early partial draft on my web site, which was an early draft of the first of three books. A few days later, my email inbox was filled with testimonials, some of which I put here, starting on the next page (plus a couple of post-9/11 testimonials). Those initial turn-of-the-century raw reactions to *Superpuzzle* represent the beginnings of the real-life SOS journey to a world few have ever seen.

The literary style of *Superpuzzle* is perceptively different than most novels. For instance, my words do not zoom in on a close-up, blow-by-blow description of actions and thoughts. I had to "zoom out" to broader strokes in order to paint the complete picture of tomorrow's Twelve-Visions World. The vocabulary, the scenes, the structure and style are simple and clear. But the journey is complex, filled with turbulence, anxiety, tension, failure and victory. The characters are complicated, tested and pulled to their limits, internally tormented, faced with succumbing or overcoming. The message is multilayered; five readings will bring you five layers deeper.

I always found that well-done internal conflict adds dramatic tension to a major character. After finishing *Superpuzzle* in 2006, nearly nine years after I started, I was beyond surprised when I realized not one of my main characters had significant internal conflict. They had internal struggles and challenges, but no long-term internal conflict. I studied my characters further to see if I had missed something...if I should have developed at least one main character with stirring internal conflict, but nothing about it was right for any of the characters. They had major conflicts with the people around them, but no overriding conflicts within themselves. (Jeremiah did wrestle with a very specific, self-resolving internal conflict regarding his love-life, but neither Jeremiah nor any other character fought ongoing, unresolved internal conflict.) Soon, the reason why came to me: once one psychologically and emotionally evolves into the new world as do my main characters (and as you, the reader, will too), then no sustaining internal conflicts remain, only internal harmony.

So, continue your real-life journey into entirely new dimensions of love, desire, and vision within the Society of Secrets. Your emotions, your actions, and *your creations* will never be the same, for you are part of the Society of Secrets — a microcosm of the Twelve-Visions World, the C of U on Earth. The initial, turn-of-the-century testimonials below reflect the souls of those in the Society of Secrets...your soul mates.

Testimonials

I love the *Superpuzzle*. I could not put the book down.

— Tonia W.

Wow! It sends chills up the spine. Once you get into it, and get to know the characters, the message is very powerful on an emotional level.

— Jeremiah G.

Mr. Hamilton: *Superpuzzle* is fantastic!!! I haven't finished all of it yet. So far it has taken me on an incredible emotional roller-coaster ride. I have never had this kind of reaction to a story, not even *Braveheart*, which is my all time favorite movie, the only movie that I ever shed tears to.

— Richard S.

Mark,

I'm sitting here with tears on my face trying to type. I have just finished reading Chapter 36. It only took me 8 hours, I could not stop reading...I ignored my housework and most everything around me except my child.

I believe that Chapter 36 pulled it together. I was pulled emotionally so many times by *Superpuzzle*. The cheaters, the liars, the manipulators...scary stuff...reminds me of today's world. Slowly it is changing. How wonderful it would be to live in a world where the values created are not torn down or ridiculed.

Every chapter I read had something else of value to add to my life. It was like turning on the light switches. AMAZING!!!

Thank you for your story...but one question...is it a story or perhaps a vision of what will be?? I sense some characters are stronger than others. I feel that they are actual persons today or have been influences in your life.

— Barbara S.

Superpuzzle is the most stunning novel I have ever read. Mark Hamilton deserves the "Booker Prize" for creating a modern masterpiece. Literature has the power to change society for good or bad. *Superpuzzle* has the power to dig deep into individuals' psyches and help us progress upward into a better and happier world. The one emotion that I think I took away from *Superpuzzle* above all others is love...a love for man's mind and what it can rise to, when freed from the constraints.

— J. Hawk

Just like to say that Mark Hamilton is a genius. I'm reading *Superpuzzle*, which I'm loving. I never want to finish reading this book although eventually I will. This book is the key to becoming not only your potential but is also the key to all knowledge. This book continues to amaze me and the pieces of the puzzle are snapping together like clock work. Mark is one of the best authors I have ever read and knows how to make his points clear. Thanks again Mark for showing me the way.

— Jason

Riveting. I haven't enjoyed reading something so much as *Superpuzzle*. It is now 3:20 a.m. and it is only out of sheer exhaustion that I stop. I would like to personally thank you for this story. My only wish is that everyone could get their hands on this information. Please continue spreading the truth (honesty)!

— David K.

Beholding the Puzzle-Picture

I am in awe over *Superpuzzle*. I had constant tears of joy, frustration and empathy throughout this eloquent account of the anticivilization and the Civilization of the Universe. Thank you, Mark Hamilton. You have written the ultimate epiphany. I hope this is what will transpire.

— Killairne J.

Superpuzzle is one of the most powerful creations yet. I've NEVER read anything like it. I couldn't stop reading it. I was moved by the characters and their thoughts. This story made me think about so many things, my childhood, my family, my future. I would give almost anything to have had a teacher like Miss Annabelle. I could have avoided so much pain if I had known then what I know now. It's like learning to speak a new language, it's so much easier to pick up as a child than it is as an adult. But it can be done. The same holds true for neothink. I want to thank you for sharing this great value.

— Jason D.

Has anyone out there read Mark Hamilton's incredible new work, the work that eclipses all previous works....*Superpuzzle?*

Now I liked *Atlas Shrugged*, but this thing just blows it away from an excitement and emotional perspective, as well as the broad scope of it. It is not only one of the most highly integrated works ever, but in my opinion, the most emotionally profound. It is also the most easily accessible product for the hard-working man in the street. It's something that down-to-earth people can really relate to. I predict that this publication will not only be the big crossover product that captures the general public, but I also predict it could be the most financially profitable from the standpoint of people voluntarily GIVING whatever they can afford to pay for the product. I know that I feel compelled to give the author something, if for no other reason than he brought out special feelings I hadn't felt in years.

I suspect that others may feel the same.

— Mike

Mark Hamilton's *Superpuzzle* is phenomenal. It is the best work of art I have ever come across. I was excited and emotional throughout my reading, and my mind couldn't stop wandering off with ideas and integrating new concepts.

Superpuzzle

Superpuzzle has got me excited all over again. Thank you, Mark Hamilton, for the renewed motivation and confidence injected into my being.

— Chris M.

I've already submitted my comments on *Superpuzzle* a few days ago. I was on chapter 6 then, and now I'm on chapter 30. At this point I feel compelled to say that I think that it is the most brilliant thing I have ever read. As a long time reader, I didn't think there was anything one could write that would shock me, but I was wrong. This thing will shake the guts out of anyone who thought of themselves as good hardworking people. It was incredible how Mark Hamilton has seamlessly integrated every important concept and advantage into a highly enjoyable and readable narrative. Don't expect this to be the last you hear of me about this incredible work, for the more I read the more I feel like shouting out how great it is! Thanks again, Mike "the Rev" C.

— Mike C.

I am reading, perhaps, the best book that I have ever read. It's in the same category of *Gone With The Wind*, *Sea Wolf*, and another 101 of the World's Best Books. I am surely enjoying *Superpuzzle*.

— Peter A.

Dear Mark, to give you insight on the supremacy of *Superpuzzle*, allow me to tell you that in my four years in Saudi Arabia, more than two decades ago, I read all the English books in Abqaiq, Radhwa, Juaimah, three libraries! Not one of the best sellers can come close to the intimacy I had with the characters in *Superpuzzle*. *Superpuzzle* burns my heart, even now; it's been two weeks since I finished reading *Superpuzzle*. The eloquence of *Superpuzzle* was its simplicity, honesty, and its mirror of real life today. I would be surprised if it is not a real story! Fiction cannot even approximate the reality from beginning to end. This is the story that is meant for a movie.

— Paul D.

This is so amazing! *Superpuzzle* is changing my life as I read it. I can now feel positive about my life and my children's lives. *Superpuzzle* is so powerful and so true I have seen it happen in my life and others around me, it is so exciting and invigorating to see.

I feel so lucky, because I am a 21-year-old mom and my oldest is 6 and my youngest is 4. I made my way through high school and I started college this year. What a gift you have given, and will continue to give! I am behind you 100%!

If you make a movie, I would love to play Miss Annabelle, I think her character is so great, and I would love to be a Miss Annabelle for my children and many other children because to spread the truth like she did is what I have been doing, only on a much smaller scale with my daughter and her friends!

The truth has finally been set free, and it makes me so happy! I no longer have to live the anticivilization lie! I love You!

— Raquel F.

This is the best story I have ever read. Thank You; Rufus, age 73.

— Rufus John W.

I'm done reading *Superpuzzle*. What a wonderful book. I must admit it's better than *The Matrix*. Reading *Superpuzzle* allowed me to see the big picture of the New World.

This book is made for the movies. My conclusion: this is the most positive prediction of the future I've ever read.

— BJ

What can I say? Mark Hamilton's *Superpuzzle* is spot on.

I like the analogy of equaling the roller coaster emotional tide felt in *Braveheart* with that battle cry of FREEEEEEEEEEDOM.

Superpuzzle gave me more satisfaction than Ayn Rand's *Fountainhead*. And that's saying something. Rand's works were very powerful, riveting messages and Mark Hamilton went beyond that.

Mind blowing stuff.

All I can say is, when is the movie coming out? It will surpass *Titanic*, *Ben Hur*, and *The Matrix* by far.

— Howie H.

Mark, I have read most of everything you have written in the last ten years, and have always been supremely happy with the values delivered, but you have struck "pure gold" with this book, and have made it not only easy but enjoyable to warm one's attention of

1171

involvement with Neothink.

Well done, kudos, kudos, KUDOS.

— Garwin E. R.

Mark, this is a very powerful story. It reached me emotionally in a way that no other literature has done. I found myself in tears at points in *Superpuzzle*. It seemed that certain emotional blocks in my life were being broken through. I find myself valuing life and hating death at more of an emotional level as a result of your story. Thanks, Rob.

— Robert K.

This is my second time reading *Superpuzzle* and it has renewed a passion within me that I had thought was lost. Since the events of September 11th, I have felt a void in my life. Happiness seemed unattainable anymore due to the chaotic reality of life. It was not until I reread Ms. Annabelle's encounter with the school board that I realized that life can only cause you pain as long as you inflict it upon yourself. Sure, there are maniacal people with hate in their hearts in the world, but there are also beautiful souls who love and continue to produce and create values even when the world looks bleak.

I long to live purposefully by adding and creating values for others. I would love to become a teacher; to be able to enrich young lives and minds with logic and fully-integrated honesty.

— Elizabeth R.

Mr. Hamilton,

First, let me say that everything I've read from you is nothing but great.

Due to my busy schedule, I have never taken the time to write to you about the value of your books until now. I was refraining from writing a positive testimonial because the testimonial isn't even close to being finished. But, your latest creation *Superpuzzle* has really changed me in many ways. *Superpuzzle* has given me what I believe is the needed boost that will catapult me into the highest level.

I never had the mentor I needed. I always sought those who were above me, who knew more since they were the fastest way to the highest level. Now, I feel the characters in *Superpuzzle* are my mentors.

I want to thank you tremendously for that valuable book. I definitely look forward to reading many more of your books. Thank you is not enough.

— Mathieu G.

Beholding the Puzzle-Picture

In my 54 plus years of reading, this has been the most profound, eye-opening literature I've ever read. A positive step for humankind. I wish I had had a teacher like Miss Annabelle instead of one like Ms. Minner!!

— Alan L.

Superpuzzle is the most powerful thing I've read on the Web — a big "Hell Yeah!!"

— J.P.

Thank you Mr. Hamilton for the life rendering artwork called *Superpuzzle*. It has moved and touched my heartstrings of life.

— Willie S.

This story gave me tingling sensations throughout my nervous system. It taught me the fundamentals of common denominators and how they get to the essence of happiness.

— Ladar

Mark, *Superpuzzle* is majestic. All the while my mind was elevated. I kept seeing a reflection of myself just as I was 25 years ago. I felt as though that child in me was being resurrected! *Superpuzzle* is sincerely a masterpiece contribution to the world.

— Jacqueline S.

Your novel *Superpuzzle* was the most incredible book I have ever read. I am a 23-year-old male, and I have to admit that there were several parts in the book that brought tears to my eyes — tears of joy!!! This novel helped me to realize that so many incredible things are possible.
Thanks again for writing this unbelievable novel.

— Chris W.

Right now I am in Chapter 25 of *Superpuzzle*, still being amazed by the story. So far this book is simply amazing how it is written and how it makes one think. It makes you believe more in the way philosophers think versus the way life is. Thank you so much for writing this book.

— Fred L.

Superpuzzle

After reading *Superpuzzle*...all I could do for the next few minutes was...sit in front of this computer screen and quietly & happily...clap...clap...clap...clap...clap...clap...clap...clap... clap...clap...clap...honestly...I couldn't stop as I reflected on the last thoughts & words of Miss Annabelle.

— Mark S.

I feel burdens falling away. I've just read *Superpuzzle*, this comes after starting to pursue my real essence years ago and then losing hope and enthusiasm. I feel the false burdens falling away and my motivation burning once again.

— C.N.

An excellent moving, heart warming and emotional format to convey to the world populace honesty and advantages.

— Gordon B.

This is so good. How do I get a hold of *Superpuzzle* autographed!
— R.D. Skinner

Mr. Hamilton,
I've only completed two chapters of your story so far, but it's already touched something deep inside me. I know this because a swell of emotions come up and makes me cry. I remember reading somewhere that crying because of happiness comes from years of repressed emotions...well, I'm not sure if that's true or not, but it has touched me so far. You're awesome.

— David C.

Dear Mr. Hamilton,
Your *Superpuzzle* is the most incredible, powerful thing I've ever read. I'm sharing it with my 12-year old and am seeing with a visual and mental clarity how I need to be HIS Miss Annabelle...and to my other two children as they begin their education beyond infancy.
Words of thanks are hardly enough for what you have brought out for mankind. I simply cannot articulate the explosion of hope in so many areas of my life going on inside of me now. I have a whole new outlook on life, and I know where I belong.
Heartfelt thanks and gratitude.

— Carey Y.

Beholding the Puzzle-Picture

Mr. Mark Hamilton,

I have only read through the second chapter of your story, but I had to write you now! The feelings *Superpuzzle* gives me... are... just for the lack of a better word WONDERFUL!! I can't wait to continue to read the rest of *Superpuzzle,* and I thank you for such a wonderful piece of literature.

Thank You.

— Terry

I can't wait to come home from work ever since I started reading *Superpuzzle* from your website, until I am done.

I can see through my mind's eye the events unfolding before me, as if I am there present and observing what is happening, which touched me emotionally and moved me to tears as I read every chapter!

It's great, unique, prophetic, and enlightening! Well done!

— Pedro M.

Dear Mark,

Many sincere wonderful words have been told about *Superpuzzle* by others. I am not going to repeat them. Instead of words, you have my standing ovation.

— Marek J., Australia

Hello Mark,

Thank you for the story that I have just read. The ideas have given me results in all areas of my life. *Superpuzzle* has helped me. It touched me deeply & I cried many times as I read it (both tears of joy & sorrow).

— Spencer H.

I am so excited! I'm on Chapter 13 and I fear I may be shrugging off my regular duties in light of *Superpuzzle*.

To the future!

— Lynn H.

Superpuzzle is filling me with enormous emotions that are the kind I feel happy about — I feel I'm not alone any more. *Superpuzzle* fills my being with happiness so great tears fill my eyes and make it difficult to read further. I don't know what else to say. I'm wrung out.

— Wayne H. K.

Superpuzzle

Upon finishing *Superpuzzle*, I have realized that among the many emotions experienced during the course of the reading, one emotion stands above the rest: hope. Fighting the battle of disillusionment with our current world, while witnessing the injustices, the robberies, and the murders by society's "leaders" is a constant source of pain and struggle. Yet the hope in me was revamped and amplified in my reading of *Superpuzzle*. I feel reenergized and ready to create.

— Daniel C.

There must be so much psychology integrated into *Superpuzzle* that the emotional feelings will be felt differently and peak at different places for any reader depending on their own minds.

— Gavriel S.

Superpuzzle is very moving and emotional. Its story form helps the reader to learn the ideas presented very quickly. I can't wait to finish it and begin rereading!

— Mike

I am not a very emotional person, but in the reading of *Superpuzzle* I was overcome with emotion several times.

I have come to the conclusion that this story will be the breakthrough that we have been seeking. The writing style of Mark Hamilton is beyond my imaginings.

Ed.........the old man from the Tenn Mts.

— E. Geoffrey S.

Superpuzzle is the best tool you have to show people the possibilities behind neothink and all the advantages within this information. I can't wait to get to the next chapter. I'm trying to read as much information as I can. Thanks for a great story.

— Josue R.

Dear Mr. Hamilton,

WORDS CANNOT DESCRIBE. I hold a great respect for your writing. My concentration was always focused 150% when I read your masterful work. I cancelled my plans for last Friday and Saturday, just so I could read *Superpuzzle*. I finished the entire work in two days. *Superpuzzle* comes to life. When I read it, I almost knew what you were going to say each chapter before I even read it.

I wish I could express my feelings right now, but I haven't developed that writing skill yet! Thank you Mark Hamilton...I hope to meet you in the New World!

— Jason

This book is an excellent novel which integrates the outline of the future. It wonderfully inspires and evokes emotions to work toward fulfilling *Superpuzzle*. I found it hard to keep from reading end to end. Great work!!! Thanks.

— Dave P.

I have the child of the past within me. I enjoy *Superpuzzle* very much. I am still reading it. I am on Chapter Eighteen. I am beginning to feel emotional.

— Jerry B.

I'll be able to shove *Superpuzzle* in the hands of girls and say, "Get back to me when you're a woman". It is such an emotional book.

I cried many times reading it. Only very short periods of crying. The suddenness of some of my outbursts reminded me of doing the same thing sometimes when I watch a neocheater on TV. Mark Hamilton is quite some writer; he uses a style of writing and depiction that seems very different.

I thought whilst reading Ch33/34 Mark Hamilton was setting me up to cry on reading the end of 35. He did. Brilliant.

— Gav

Superpuzzle has moved me more than any other story I've read. Sometimes you piss me off and sometimes you sadden me and at times I resent you for making me see through the pretty illusions woven by "them". Sometimes I wish I didn't know anything and lived in a state of blissful ignorance. But I love you. You have probably saved my life.

— Avajo G.

My Dear Mr. Hamilton,

I haven't finished your story yet, I'm on Chapter 18, but I am very impressed. If I could wish one thing for the world, it would be that all the students studying to be teachers read your story. I am so taken by what you have to say. Your story not only touched my heart, but my brain. Your story showed me that I am on the right path, I have a long way to go, but I will get there. Thank you for reminding me of all the good things to come, as I continue on my journey.

— Peggy C.

Jolted Awake! *Superpuzzle* is one of the most compelling pieces of literature I've ever read.

— Tim

Reading *Superpuzzle* is having some sort of effect, and I'm not sure exactly what kind, but I've gotten up at 3:00 a.m. to continue the reading, and even started reading it to my children.

— Charles

The joy and love I feel. It must be the next level of emotions.

— Albert C.

Superpuzzle blew me away.

— Gary R.

Speechless. To Mark Hamilton and his *Superpuzzle*: All I can say is that I'm "Speechless in Seattle." You've outdone yourself (again!) Thanks so much for such a wonderful story. I can't seem to get it out of my mind.

— Mike W.

Dear Mr. Hamilton, congratulations from France!
I like very much your *Superpuzzle*, and I hope it will be soon available in French.

— Nicolas R.

Dear Mr. Hamilton,
I woke up at 4am and had to get back to reading your story. I saw your e-mail address at the bottom of the chapter (has it always been there?) and I fought a battle with myself trying to decide whether

to write you. I thought maybe I should first read and study all your writings I could find so that I would not seem a complete idiot...but my emotions overcame my fear. (As usual.)

I just wanted to tell you how much your story means to me. It's been like a coming home. Like "Wow, there are actually people out there who think like I do...I've just never been able to put my finger on it and categorize it into a neat, simple, honest, easy to understand way of life.

Maybe now that I am starting to see things a little clearer I can begin a real life, a happy life...just tell me that there are things like described in *Superpuzzle* that are actually happening. I need that Hope.

— Susan C.

I love what I read so far in *Superpuzzle*. It connects emotionally with the reader.

— Marcel D.

Enormous emotions. From where I sit I think the writer has demonstrated an uncanny ability to write/express/convey with a high degree of accuracy while pushing the envelope of charting new frontiers. Anyone can use this work to push their own envelope to greater knowledge and penetrate deeper and wider into new and existing markets.
Warmly, Steven.

— Steve

YOWZA! I could not stop reading *Superpuzzle*. It is very well written and I think even young children could understand much of the content. Thanks for your fabulous work.

— Mark C.

I had to take a break after reading Chapter Three of *Superpuzzle*. So many thoughts, what an experience.

— G.S.

I have just been reading *Superpuzzle*, which is a very powerful revelation into life.

— J.M.

Superpuzzle

The tremendous value/benefit to the reader would warrant paying well over $1000 for *Superpuzzle*.

— Steve

Wow! I really think you have hit the nail on the head Mark! I have only finished the first three chapters, but I am eager to read the rest. It's getting late, and I must get up early and sell cars. I will continue reading Monday evening.

This is very eloquent. I look forward to finishing *Superpuzzle*!

Keep up the awesome work Mark!

— Alan

I commend your publishing of *Superpuzzle* as a BEAUTIFUL move that I did not expect! I'm shaking with excitement. Let's GET IT GOING.

If things work out the way I expect them to, I will be in a position to help with the mass exposure to these concepts, the first of which may indeed be a TV series of *Superpuzzle*.

— John S.

Hi Mark. I'm reading *Superpuzzle* now and it's truly amazing how these children were changed the way they were. I really wish I would have had a teacher just like Miss Annabelle cause I'd probably have solved all my problems by now. Just reading your published work makes me more amazed by the minute. You truly are an amazing author, and I'm looking forward to reading the entire book. Thanks again for changing my life. I can already tell things are getting better every day. It's totally amazing. Excellent work.

— J.K.

I'm reading *Superpuzzle* and am so engrossed I've just realized it's 3:40 a.m.! Fantastic stuff and so logical.

— David

I just finished reading *Superpuzzle*. Wow! Is about all I can say for now. I'm a much changed person. Which I would never have believed could happen just by reading anything.

— Floyd

Beholding the Puzzle-Picture

I am astonished at your masterpiece, *Superpuzzle*. ...I have been held captive at my computer for the past 7 hours! I want to thank you for your insight and elegantly articulated culmination of ideas expressed in your story. What a beauty. This truly is the American Beauty. Thank you for restoring my vision...I know what my *Friday Night Essence* is, and I will not be taken from that path until my goal is reached. From one value-producer to another, thank you again. "When you're smiling, the whole world smiles with you..."

— Beth, Future Recording Engineer/
Producer/Studio Manager

Hi Mark....I just read *Superpuzzle* for the first time. ...This was the best description of woman/man romantic love I've ever heard and I was impressed with your characters and the thought that went into this work......thanks!

— Terry K.

I often find myself thinking, how would so and so of the initial group of twelve handle this or that particular situation I am experiencing at work, at home with the kids or with my spouse. I love to transpose *Superpuzzle* into my daily life...

— Charles

Just finished reading your novel. I'm a little addle-brained as I just finished and it's 2:00 in the morning. I purchased and started reading your early-release manuscript some time ago, then lost it on the way back from a construction job in Lexington Va. I found it on the web site and was captivated by the concepts in it, confused and scared. Even though the "matrix" hasn't snapped for me yet on many levels, I see the truth of what you are saying. This was really clarified while reading the novel, bringing forth a clearer mental picture of what you are trying to get across. I hope to be among you one day, the top of my field, enjoying life, wealthy with romantic love. My greatest dream is to one day organize and fund research to help end the horror of disease. Thanks, you have really lifted my spirits and given me hope during this really dark time.

— Anne

Superpuzzle was the best book I've ever read so far...Really! Its concepts should be taught to everyone. Young or Old. Everyone!

It made me cry...it made me think.

My understanding of *Superpuzzle* had changed my life...made me love life in a sense never experienced.

Thank you!

— "Generation X"

I haven't taken time to read anything not related to my business in years. The other day, I clicked into Mark Hamilton's web site and casually began reading *Superpuzzle*. While skeptical at first, knowing what a tremendous effort is required to write effective, coherent fiction...I was surprised, amazed, and finally, delighted. Mark Hamilton's work is, I believe, the most powerful publication to date. It is mind-boggling, the mass of integrations he managed to squeeze into this attention-grabbing (and holding) drama. I hope this is just a taste of what's to come.

— Richard

I really got caught up in *Superpuzzle* and at times forgot that it was fiction. Thank you for opening my eyes to a new beginning for me and for the entire world.

— Fred

I am at page 391 of *Superpuzzle*. Every time I begin to think, "how can this happen, with all that is against it," *Superpuzzle* answers my question. Limitless...

— Dick H.

Hello Mr. Mark Hamilton, I wish I had a teacher like Miss Annabelle when I was in the 3rd grade. I think this story about Miss Annabelle should be required reading in the schools, both religious and secular. At 68 years, looking back over my life, I find that I never really knew what true love meant. Many of my generation equated the physical "act" as being "in love". Restroom "graffiti" were often our guide to sexual pleasure. As grown men, we did not know "what to do" in ways of pleasing our wives. I am just a "layman" with no degrees etc., but I hope with all of my being, that society will keep on "evolving" so that there will be "happiness in the male/female relationships." Thanks for opening my mind to other views about life!!!! and where mankind is headed.

— Earl

Hi Mark, wow that sure was a very interesting subject for *Superpuzzle*. I really wanted to read it because I was glued to the screen. Usually I don't like to read in-depth things on the computer, but I had no trouble reading your book. That was just amazing!!!!!! Sure makes you think about life itself.

— A.

I think that this is an excellent work! With it, I am turning open the spigot of riches.

I really have found a great value in this book, and it makes it a little easier for me (and I'm sure many others) to conceptualize what is happening. *Superpuzzle* hits home. I have to thank you very much for affecting my thinking for the rest of my life.

— David

Mark, *Superpuzzle* has really fired me up. *Superpuzzle* has changed everything. I've searched for, found, and am starting to implement my Friday-Night Essence. Your book really has given me the impetus. Cheers.

— Rob E.

I have read *Superpuzzle* on the web site and want to inform you that even on the first reading, it has changed my life! And yes, I am going to read it even more deeply the second time.

Superpuzzle has ignited the dream within of being able to overcome obstacles such as those experienced by Ms. Annabelle. Your work in *Superpuzzle* invokes the desire to obtain invincibility through full honesty, striking down those who would destroy if given the permission.

I admire your work in *Superpuzzle,* and I know it is something everyone in the world needs. Please keep *Superpuzzle* available! Without it, those stuck in the rut of the anticivilization will continue to sink, never discovering and entering the elusive world of happiness and wealth.

— Kurt

Superpuzzle

Inspirational fiction!

— Ken

Dear Mark, *Superpuzzle* is a wonderful story. I can identify with it because I've taught High School and resigned after seeing the atrocities.

Superpuzzle should be packaged as a pocket book with a beautiful cover and sold through all the bookstores in the United States. I think that this is the only thing that will insure that a new civilization will begin in the early 21st century.

Something BIG is going to happen. *Superpuzzle* will become a best seller. I don't see how it can't.

— Gil

I had no idea where this story would lead. I even thought it would be simple. I can see that it is going much further than I believed, and that it is not simple. It is simply written so that anyone can understand it, and it is a fascinating story.

— A. Writes

After many years of living the quasi–life, I am back. Being half here and half there showed in my world. I am back. Changes are in the works. Thanks for *Superpuzzle*. It was a refreshing refresher!

— Spizzchiro

This story has opened my eyes to things I have missed out on as a child and as a grownup. If I had someone as remarkable as Miss Annabelle in my life, I would have been a better educated man and human being. THANK YOU. I now see things I've been missing in my life.

— Dan

A great inspiration. The changes have been immense. I find that I am currently able to do a whole lot more with my time as well as spending time developing my new business venture. It only takes *Superpuzzle* to make me feel young and inspired. I believe that I am now taking control and hope to be FREE soon!!!!!!!!!!!!!!!!! I have a dream and know what I want.

— Roland

Beholding the Puzzle-Picture

I just wanted to say that *Superpuzzle* was perhaps the cleanest, purest breath of fresh air I have ever had. I was inspired by your book. I have tried to soak up as much knowledge as I possibly can. Since reading your book I have become more positive, better rested, and my relationship with my wonderful girlfriend has improved. I am striving for the ultimate happiness and riches. Give me time and I think I will make it. Sincerely, John.

— John

Superpuzzle is a very special and wonderful masterpiece of modern literature. It shows us how we, by choosing to cut through the matrix of illusions to see *what is*, can start building mental puzzles of Neothink to evolve into superachievers. How, if we can find our Friday-Night essences and become the persons that we were meant to be, we can live in complete happiness because then we will be value creators and value producers. I thank you Mr. Hamilton because I used to be severely trapped in the matrix of illusions, I was blind. You opened my eyes, and my heart. I am forever in your debt. I am on my way to finding my Friday-Night essence and discovering happiness by becoming a value creator. I can't wait to see where my personal renaissance will take me.

— Norman

I discovered *Superpuzzle* today on the website — and have spent the entire day immersed in it. I am now on Chapter 27, and am quite excited by what I have read!

This sounds like the solution for which I have been searching for so long...to transcend the limitations of the "ordinary" and become a "God-Man." It strikes me that, in order to present this information so clearly, you must have already attained this level yourself. How exhilarating it must be!

Neothink looks and "feels" like the answer for me — to not only provide wealth, but also lasting peace and happiness for myself and my family. Warmly yours.

— Troy H.

Thank you Mark Hamilton. The most wonderful story I have ever read. Inspirational, almost overwhelming. This story of what your society will do for the human race must reach everyone. I can feel the genuine love that you have for each member of this human race. I know a mind could not produce such a beautiful and powerful story of what we can be, of where we can go, of where we are going, of what we will become. No words can explain my appreciation, only my actions. Every time I read your literature, which is almost daily now, I become armed with it's power, I thirst for more, I become more. The value of my life and all human life increases, to the point that nothing else is more important than preserving and improving all human life. What a simple concept, yet impossible task in this upside down civilization. Until now. Thank you Mark Hamilton for starting the revolution that says no to death and yes to life. What a simple but wonderful concept. I return the love and passion for life that you so consistently give.

— Stewart R.

Unbelievable. I am exhausted and elated at the same time. It's as though I've glimpsed a parallel world, like sitting on a stationary train and seeing a beautiful girl on a train parallel to mine, but on a different track. She smiles fleetingly, her train begins to pull away from mine, and she is off to a destination unknown to me. Her image will continue to haunt me.

I wonder whether I have the emotional strength to return to my job this afternoon. Mr. Hamilton, you have brought upon yourself a weighty mantle of responsibility to take humanity out of a long Dark Age. The world must sense its need to evolve in the strongest possible emotional terms. I will pass *Superpuzzle* along. The task ahead of you is Herculean. But you MUST succeed.

— Stephen B.

I am reading the story of Miss Annabelle, and it is very interesting and also sad in some parts. I have not finished reading it, but I plan to finish. To tell you the truth, since I went to school I have never sat down and read a book, but this one is so interesting that I cannot put it down.

— Janie R.

I am not normally much of a reader, but I find *Superpuzzle* hard to put down. I find it to be the most emotional thing I have ever read.

— Lindon L.

Beholding the Puzzle-Picture

Mark, that is the most touching story I have ever read and I wish with all of my heart that I could have had the privilege of that kind of informed explanation when I was growing up. Love has always been such a wonderful gift for me, but I just have not had the experience of sharing with anyone the way I thought it should be. It is never too late to learn, and I have learned so much from *Superpuzzle*. I have gained much power.

— D.D.

I have just finished chapter 5, and I am relishing every word. It is so beautifully executed.

— Anne

Superpuzzle captivated me and I could not stop reading. Many of my questions about life have been answered and it has opened my mind to creativity and power.

— Ralph G.

Hi, my name is Jesal, I am a 15 yr. old boy from England. My brother introduced me to *Superpuzzle*, and I am hooked! With the nine chapters that I have read, I have been able to pierce through some of the illusions that I see. I found answers to the questions that I have been asking myself about life.

I now can look at life, and give all I have to offer, and then take what is rightfully mine. I feel I can make a different set of values for the world! It's emotional stuff!!! The way of thinking that I have now, is top! It's like I have a way of seeing life before I go to live it!!! It's weird, but that's what goes on, and it has really helped me.

I am using this story to develop my way of thinking. When I have finished reading this story, I will be able to go out into the world and do all my stuff properly, because of what you have shown me, it is just sooo right!!!

I swear, I am gonna be a millionaire within 15 years time, thanks to you. Peace out man, thanx for the new ways!!!

— Jesal P.

Superpuzzle is emotionally powerful and has helped me to regain my confidence. I feel empowered with the possibilities ahead of me.

— Dwain B.

Superpuzzle

I just read *Superpuzzle* for the zillionth time. Excellent!!! Just exactly what is needed. As I read this, the ideas of achieving my dreams just flowed.

Thank you. Thank you. And Thank you.

— Frank W.

I enjoyed reading *Superpuzzle* more than anything I ever read. And I bet it would bring someone great pleasure as described in *Superpuzzle* to be among all those benevolent people creating an extraordinarily wondrous atmosphere such as that. Perhaps it could really become an actuality within my lifetime. Hopefully, one day.

— Joe

Superpuzzle is so powerful I know my life is changing. I have affirmed that I shall live a life of total honesty with complete responsibility for self with integrity. It surely would be great if a movie was made of *Superpuzzle*.

— Jimmy R.

This is the best fictional story I've ever read. I've been an avid reader for about five years now, and read almost every book available. But nothing could have prepared me for what I was about to read during *Superpuzzle*. I'm not completely finished with the book yet, but, when I got to the end of the twenty-ninth chapter, I felt compelled to write to you and tell you how great a value this book is to humanity. Keep up the excellent work on creating a civilization that everybody will eventually prosper from.

— Robert

I just finished reading *Superpuzzle*. It was excellent. It put life into the proper perspective for me. My favorite sections were the interactions between Miss Annabelle and her young students, much like the interactions between Robin Williams and his students in *The Dead Poets Society*, only much more meaningful. By the end of the second chapter, I had formed in my mind what Miss Annabelle would look like, including hair color, eye color, skin tone, height, body structure, everything. When we finally got a description of her, I couldn't believe it because, except for the shade (I got the color right) of her eyes, which were darker than I imagined, I was dead on in every aspect. I was in love with Miss Annabelle, and I longed to be in her class. Her world was built on a foundation of honesty, truth, fairness, integrity, and justice. Her world is one that I would gladly embrace and fight for.

— Robert A.

I have read through *Superpuzzle* (MAKE IT A MOVIE, MAN!!!) When I began reading *Superpuzzle*, I was trying to loose weight, but was unlucky at all the temptations out there. Well, I have now lost a total of 17 pounds since then and it has stayed off. After reading *Superpuzzle*, I found out what I want to do. I really wanted to become a writer and inventor. I already have one book almost complete, two others in the making, and about six inventions on the drawing board. And add on top of that, I have begun reading books about quantum physics! A year ago, I would not even dream of touching the complexity of it, but now, I already have a hypothesis in the works. And to top off the Sundae, I am only 21 and am working full time and going to class full time. Now that is something that I am still amazed about.

— Mike G.

Mr. Hamilton: *Superpuzzle* was brilliant. If I had had a teacher like Miss Annabelle, I wouldn't be 37 years old getting ready to get ready. I wouldn't be a loser!!!

I want to thank you for helping me find my "Friday-Night Essence." I had never even heard of such a thing, let alone find it within myself. Since reading your material, I have nearly finished two manuscripts, and I am formulating several business ventures. I'm still working on my procrastination and my flab, but I now have a clearer vision of where my life is to go. Thank you very, very much. Finding my Friday-Night Essence alone was worth the price of *Superpuzzle*.

— Robert

Although I am still reading *Superpuzzle*, I find it very refreshing, and I can actually see through illusions as I continue to read the rest of the story. I was once like those third graders, yet there were adults who didn't give me the road map I needed, and they meant well. But their ways closed me down for a long time. Thank you for *Superpuzzle*.

— Pamela

Superpuzzle

First I'd just like to say that in terms of influential, positive, powerful, and clearly written books, your *Superpuzzle* (the fictional counterpart to your nonfiction — *Secrets, Visions, Powers*) has only one peer in history — that being Rand's *Atlas Shrugged*. *Superpuzzle* however, is wider-scope and (although easier for the general public to digest) more profound at the deepest levels of fully integrated honesty — the level that as you rightly say "pulls the 'child of the past' out from its hiding place." Through 36 chapters, there wasn't one that didn't bring tears to my eyes. In contrast, *Atlas Shrugged* brought tears to my eyes in only two spots. I could go on and on about the incomparable value of creating a story of that magnitude and with that positive view of the future, but I'd better close for now.

— Chris T.

Mr. Hamilton,
After reading your novel, I wanted to take a moment to tell you how wonderful it is. I've read it through and have just started again for the second time. This is simple, fresh, and, well, awesome.

— June

First of all I have to say I have really enjoyed S*uperpuzzle*. I've found myself not wanting to put it down and found myself rushing to get back to it. My 11-year-old son has also started reading S*uperpuzzle*, but I would like to introduce the whole idea to my 4-year-old and 14-year-old (who doesn't like to read unless he has to).

— Perci P.

I read Mark Hamilton's *Superpuzzle*. It's beautifully written. I was smiling one moment and choking on my tears the next — all through the novel.

— Alex A.

Wonderful novel. This is fabulous. Finding and building one's dream gets lost in the shuffle and scuffle. *Superpuzzle* is a wonderful way to point out the forest despite the trees. I feel a reawakening happening.

— Stephen

Remarkably well written. Truly excellent. I have a M.S. and read a lot. I feel qualified to say this is a wonderfully easy-to-read, clear and insightful narrative. Yes. Wonderfully insightful. Remarkable. I do not now feel a need to finish my morning coffee. My brain has already just been pleasantly awakened.

— Steph

I am so excited about *Superpuzzle*, I am in a rush to gain as much information as quickly as possible, and can't do it quickly enough. The thinking is so profound at such a deep level that I am shaken to the very core of my being. All my life I have been on a journey to discover, no indeed to create Who I Am and Who I Want To Be and to do it with integrity, honesty and with value to mankind. Though I am still in the early stages of reading, I am beginning to notice a change in my thinking and the way in which I view the world. I have this profound feeling that this work will provide the shift that I have so long been searching for. It is with profound gratitude that this work has found it's way into my hands. Thank You, Mark Hamilton.

— Steven

I love *Superpuzzle*. I just finished reading through it for the second time. I find it interesting how it seems to be a lot like a good movie seen over again. I am inspired.

— Dwain B.

Superpuzzle MUST be published on its own in hardback and/or paperback. Get it into the hands of the general populace, and word-of-mouth will spread like wildfire! Everyone who reads this will want to CHERISH their own personal copy and re-read it often. It will be the treasure that changes their lives forever!

— Jim P.

Superpuzzle was the most touching and enlightening piece of work I've ever read.

— Darlene T.

Superpuzzle on the internet is mind blowing!!

— Andrew A.

The turning point for me came when I read *Superpuzzle*. After devouring that, I was so emotionally stirred and intellectually stimulated. Thank you!

— Eric

Magnificent! I simply couldn't stop reading, chapter by chapter, even when my eyes started to tire. I'll go back and read it again. I want to say that *Superpuzzle* told the tale so powerfully that I was captivated beyond anything I've ever read before. I loved it. I have had many similar experiences (on a less dramatic scale).

I must admit that I was beginning to lose hope that I would ever find another human being who knew what I knew (although I have never articulated it so eloquently as *Superpuzzle*). I am beyond ecstatic at this moment. I am eagerly awaiting the opportunity to meet other people who feel "just like me." Glorious!

Superpuzzle is great, really great. Thank you so much.

— Jansett

BRAVO, BRAVO, BRAVO. A Job Well Done.

— Horus

When I was a teenager about 25 years ago someone once asked me "What is Love". At that time love was a warm feeling I felt, but I didn't know how to explain it. Over the years, that question would come to mind occasionally, yet I could never put that feeling into words. Until I read this story! W0W.

— Kiehn

I am the 51-year-old home-school teacher of a six-year-old girl. This is the best, most informative story for children I have ever read! It explains my thoughts, exactly, in a way much better than I could ever have done. You are a wonderful person.

— Kozy

The touching parts show the great strength of Mark Hamilton's writing style.

Very heartwarming stuff. I liked many parts of *Superpuzzle*. I liked Miss Annabelle's cellmate telling about her life. The part where Hamilton describes Grassroots Charts and how it worked was pretty cool too. It was also kind of exciting when Jake was running around getting the group together. I guess those parts would be my favorites.

— Marquis de S.

Superpuzzle knocked my socks off. It seems to crystallize through simplicity and clarity the very ideals that we all look for but are too distracted or ignorant to access. *Superpuzzle* has definitely got my motor running. Many Thanks.

— Jake

Just got done reading *Superpuzzle*, so powerful. Is there any way that it will be made into a movie format? By the end of the story, I didn't want to leave that world. Thank you for sharing the picture with me, it has changed my life forever.

— Jack D. O.

I am in the middle of reading *Superpuzzle*. It's brilliant. I feel that this story should be made into a movie. In my opinion, this story is perfect.

By coincidence, I happen to be a twenty-two year old college student and would be interested in playing the part of Jake. A long shot, but worth a try.

— Tim A.

You should make *Superpuzzle* into a movie, it would be a sure hit, and think of all the lives it could touch and change.

— Brad C.

I just had to send you another compliment on this publication. This story is awesome. This is really something new, different, and exciting. It really gets down to practical application. Well, I believe that you have really done that with this story.

I have been speed reading with a vengeance for the past three evenings, and I am totally into this story! This is great work. Please publish this gem. I want to own a bound volume of this publication. I cannot wait to sit down with my son and read this with him. Now, back to my reading!!

— J.G.M.

Thank you so much for *Superpuzzle*. First of all, the book is outstanding. That's actually an understatement. It's uplifting, inspirational, educating and a very easy, captivating read. Everyone from age 9-90 should have a copy. It could simply change the world.

— David A. K.

Dear Mr. Hamilton, I read *Superpuzzle* and found it to be every bit as enlightening, provocative and effective as Ayn Rand's *Atlas Shrugged*. Congratulations on a well crafted story.

— Andy D.

Superpuzzle would make a good movie, even an old-fashioned radio drama.

— Mark W.

Mark, fantastic stuff. Can't wait until the next one, and how soon until the movie? Steven Speilberg as director.

— Howard

Goddamn *Superpuzzle* is awesome! It kicks extreme ass! I've read through about six chapters and it's rekindled feelings I had not felt for years... The pure radiant innocence of this is incredible! I think this could be the big crossover point that gets the Twelve-Visions concepts to the masses in a digestible form. I'm getting thoughts like "is this for real?" and "don't worry — happiness in the Universe is inescapable." I realize that this "civilization" is a pretext for slavery; not obvious slavery, but a slow, piecemeal, debilitating slavery where the "authorities" keep the forces of production at just enough to sustain the masses, neither completely killing the populace nor allowing full blown prosperity. Man, those people are incredible bastards.

My heart went out to Miss Annabelle and those kids. I had feelings of wanting to beat up those idiots on the school board. She and those children should have been protected at all costs. Unlike Ayn Rand, this story while retaining the same positive sense of life as that book had, if not more so, was written from a male perspective, and thus sir, you have created one of the most intensely sexually attractive characters I've ever seen in Miss Annabelle.

— Mike C. T.

These people in *Superpuzzle* DO represent what is available to us

NOW! They too started off in the anticivilization, yet they started injecting their natural creativity in society. *Superpuzzle* gave me hope and showed me the way things SHOULD be in society.

— Mike M.

Chapter 11, that's where I am so far; the book is certainly attractive and sure seems to wake that sleeping child in me.

A feeling of satisfaction and passion for life passed through me. Yeah, that's HAPPINESS!

— B.A.J.

I am enjoying reading *Superpuzzle* immensely; I have felt myself brought almost to tears in parts. I think *Superpuzzle* will switch a lot of brains on!!

— Lee H.

I'm on chapter 24 of *Superpuzzle*, and I can't stop. I have read most of your books and really like them, but this one helps me put the basics into other members of my family in an easier way.

— Ricardo L.

With the "honesty" formula as presented in *Superpuzzle*, the world must become a better place...without it there will be certain destruction.

— Michael M.

What is *Superpuzzle* all about?

Removing negatives. In a nutshell, it's all about love and passion with a little anxiety woven in. It's the first novel written from the Twelve-Visions World.

— Steven

Superpuzzle is exciting and enlightening. In fact, I have realized we have wasted the juicy part of our lives. We were just schooled into the bicameral-values and just fell to all their directions. We were cowed into submission. Our creativity vent was entirely blocked. This is a masterpiece. Mark Hamilton is just awesome. He is excellent. It is liberating.

— Alexandre

Superpuzzle

Dear Mr. Hamilton,

Thank you for a wonderful story.

What a society it would be where doing nothing actually improves my ability to do a task!

Thank you again for a beautiful vision of the future.

— Bob S.

Many thanks to the author of *Superpuzzle*. *Superpuzzle* is like a map, and you can follow that map to the future.

— Perry

I wish I could leave where I am and go to this kind of community that has this kind of teaching, I would do it.

— Aurie

A breakthrough — the inner child. The past few days I have been reading *Superpuzzle* in what little spare time I have. Ummm...everything is starting to click together now. The inner-child thing really got me. I have rediscovered my inner child and brought back that ability to think creatively to put the pieces together. It would be an absolute travesty if I ever let that ability fade in my daughter. As I make other breakthroughs, it will help me keep those alive in her as well.

I have taken small steps; this is my first leap. Cheers to many more to come!

— Lynn

Dear Mark,

Happiness is here to stay and your story made me feel so Great. Thanks.

— Mr. Keyman

Mark Hamilton's most recent endeavor comes across to this reader as most evidently a real labor of love. It is heart warming.

— John Mac

After reading *Superpuzzle* several times, I realized that I was never going to be the same person again. I was so overwhelmed by its content that I ordered a further three copies to give to friends. I feel

1196

that *Superpuzzle* has encapsulated the essence of life in such a way that I no longer feel alone, after having cast aside the indoctrinated beliefs of my past.

— Stephen W.

Hello Mr. Hamilton; I feel a little strange knowing that I'm actually addressing you; someone I've, up 'till now, have only read and read about. Great story!

— Jason M.

Superpuzzle. Completely understood. I love it. Thank You again Mark Hamilton, it looks as though the light at the end of the tunnel is very near.

— Rick G.

Dear Mr. Hamilton,
Superpuzzle is, in a word, "brilliant".

— A.L.

Awesome. I find myself laughing and cheering out loud. This story is a powerful tool I can use to influence family & friends, THANK YOU! My brothers and I have been following your business model and will be replicating it across the country perhaps as soon as next year.

— Michael S.

Superpuzzle really makes sense. It was written on my level so that I have a better understanding. Mark you've done an outstanding job. Keep up the GREAT WORK YOU'RE DOING.

— Paul G. L.

Dear Mr. Hamilton,
I am currently on Chapter Twelve and can't seem to get enough of *Superpuzzle*. During Chapter Eleven, Jake and Jessie talk about Daniel Ward (the Presidential candidate). My question is, do we have such a candidate? Is it possible that You are that person? If not, who is? I'd like to give my support in any way possible!

Thank you for enlightening me and helping me turn my life around for the better! I truly mean that from the bottom of my heart!

1197

Superpuzzle

Sincerely yours.

— John J.

Mr. Hamilton, I think *Superpuzzle* teaches the essence of happiness in a neat way. Congratulations!

— Ramon

What I like about *Superpuzzle* was the people's heart and the love they had. I can't wait until we see this. I would love to see more stories like this from Mark.

— Paul

I'm reading *Superpuzzle*. I'm fascinated! It seems I've been searching for this all my life. I want to be involved in any way I can.

— Floyd

Wow, I'm just starting Chapter Four. I've definitely gained a ton of value already from the three previous chapters. Great job.

— Brian G.

A very solid story about happiness and true dreams, not those dreams that are cookie cutter capitalist crap.

— Jason B.

I think this is a tremendous insight. This story is very simple and straight forward. We often forget about what makes us truly happy. We get so wrapped up as adults into our day to day living that we miss the true reason for living.

I am glad I read this story today. Now I hope I can put it back into practice.

— Mark F.

This will really open eyes. I was in a chat group and someone told me to get a copy of *Superpuzzle*. I'm so happy I did, I have been struggling with issues like this my whole life. It really opened my eyes.

— Laurel

I just finished reading *Superpuzzle*, and I realized one thing — there will be no limit for the advancements of the supersociety; life will be a never ending story that gets better and better. There's a very interesting point in *Superpuzzle* when Jake reflects about the biggest problem that prevented people from discovering Nature's Quintessential Secret, and finds out that the change of mentality started with an emotional change, which then triggered the people's motivation. It simply comes down to that…a matter of having the positive emotions to start one's motivational drive in order to make a start in creating values. After that one critical starting point, one will never stop integrating and creating values. *Superpuzzle* triggers the reader's motivation!

— M.M.

I liked *Superpuzzle* very much. At times it brought tears of joy and excitement like I had not felt in years.

— Miranda

Superpuzzle should be in every grade-school classroom and library.

— Mary

Mark, your story is amazing and I'm only on the third chapter. Very inspiring. You really inspired me to continue the fight.

— Iva M.

I find its concepts mind-opening and fascinating. I am keen to embrace many of the concepts and in particular those of educating my young children (4 and 1) in the methods of integrated-honesty thinking as brilliantly portrayed in *Superpuzzle*. Many thanks.

— Mark F.

I will recommend *Superpuzzle* to my friends as it has touched a deep emotional chord with me and so it will with others.

— Dwain B.

I really liked *Superpuzzle*. There should have been more teachers like Ms. Annabelle while I was growing up. Thanks for setting me on to something that makes sense in this weird, confusing world.

— John H.

Having read *Superpuzzle* and digested its message, I have come to a greater understanding of what has been an obsession of mine since birth, that is the meaning of our existence and the purpose for which we serve in the Universe. I am only 21 years old, but I feel like I have aged a lifetime with the new ideas and methods of perception that have been hinted at and portrayed.

— James T.

Wow, I thought we had lost *Superpuzzle* from the web site. What mega values come with this story. Maybe missing it from the web site for a few days makes for more appreciation of these values when they are returned. Thanks Mark.

— Andy P.

Hi! My name is Crystal, I have read *Superpuzzle* and I think you truly have a gift for bringing about an awareness through narrative means. I'm a Canadian, 22-year-old studying Psychology and Biotechnology at the University of Saskatchewan. For years I have been confused about religion and why there are so many different perspectives. I felt lost. But after reading your story, I have begun to grasp the concept of the irrational forces at work in the world. I want to uncloud others like you have, but I don't know how.
Take care, Yours honestly, Crystal.

— Crystal W.

I must say *Superpuzzle* amazes me. As closed-minded as some people are today about letting go of old beliefs that no longer serve them, can you imagine what a challenge it was for Miss Annabelle at that time? If all people had her courage, love of life, and the determination to live the truth, just imagine how wonderful the world would be. I applaud Miss Annabelle for her courage, integrity, honesty, and most of all, her love.

— Kathy

Mr. Hamilton: I believe you're conveying a very special and important message through your writings. I hope that you will always continue, even in the face of criticism from skeptics and those who would benefit from society's mindset.

— Terrance

Superpuzzle has helped me answer certain questions. I like to call it survival of the truly honest.

— Ramon C.

Superpuzzle clearly explains and demonstrates value-producing ideas. BEAUTIFUL!!! I would be honored to contribute funds for a movie.

— Danny T.

I am busy reading *Superpuzzle* and find that it helps me to live with a happy frame of mind, knowing that so much of what goes on in the world is merely an illusion created by government and media.

— John M.

You are a fine writer, very good.

— Tod S.

Hello Mark, *Superpuzzle* was fabulous; it should be read by everyone.

— Lance

The beautiful values created by all of the positive characters! At the same time the outrage I felt for the abhorrent behavior of those who destroyed values. The contrast took me on an emotional roller coaster ride.

The producers/creators created a kind of snowball effect of the values created. The determination to do the right thing by these characters is enlightening, based on the scope of values generated. All the different levels of actions from small to big, such as Belle giving hugs to those she loved all the way to Sally's achievements, was impressive.

The artists seem to be coming out and creating values for the public to get with the program. I believe it was Ayn Rand who said she had fled Communist Russia when she saw the artists bow down to that regime. Today the artists are singing a different tune and the world is getting better every day. May you achieve the happiness that you have worked for. Kind Regards, Leon

— Leon K.

Superpuzzle blows apart illusions.

— Lee H.

Superpuzzle

Superpuzzle instills a hard-driving determination towards a better, happier place for all.

— L. K.

Superpuzzle inspired me to someday have a dream house like Rico's. It also showed so much love for kids and family, it was touching. I really liked the reunion. It was wonderful that the twelve students finally got together. Made me teary eyed.

— Patrick

My favorite part of *Superpuzzle*, I think it's when Hammerschmidt, or whatever his name was, decides to take on Melbourne during his insane attempt to rape Annabelle. The crazy buffoon makes like a bull and charges with his head down to try to take out Melbourne, but only succeeds in killing himself. Poetic Justice.

— Ed

Dear Mr. Hamilton, I love your characters in *Superpuzzle*. Miss Annabelle is wonderful and so are her 12 children. Many have asked you to make this into a movie? Please let me know.

— Laurie B.

I would like to see *Superpuzzle* made into a movie or even a mini-series followed by a weekly TV show.

— R. Michael

I have no skills in the movie-making process, but I would happily be an investor to the right producing company endorsed by Mark. Someone email me if this comes about so I can contribute my capital to this venture. One of hundreds...maybe thousands.

— L. Proit

Hi Mark; absolutely brilliant, when can we expect to see the film? Every success to you.

— Andy

I am still interested in the investment of $$$, and more valuable, *time* for a project of bringing *Superpuzzle* to a worldwide marketable movie. I am sincere and passionate. Please join me in promoting this as a worldwide HIT in the cinematic spectrum. Again, thanks Mr. Hamilton for your epiphany. My honestly warm regards.

— Killairne

Just a thought on the movie version: Michelle Pfeiffer as Miss Annabelle, Louis Gossett Jr. as the janitor, Oprah Winfrey as the janitor's wife (she'll slim down for the part), Matthew Broderick as the college student (he can still pass for one), Kevin Spacey as the pip squeak guidance counselor, cameos Howard Stern as the abusive husband (flashback scene) seriously, he could play an evil version of himself.

Maybe instead of a movie, it could become a TV serial, like how they converted Stephen King's *Golden Years* into one hour-a-week episodes.

With the flashbacks and the time span dealt with in *Superpuzzle*, it reminds me of the story of Reuben Hurricane Carter. That movie is a must see.

— A Fan

I really enjoyed the story and have spent the past two days reading it. What a beautiful world. I think it would make a great movie.

— A.A.

Superpuzzle could be a great movie.

I think that I'd be delighted if a film was made from Mr. Hamilton's book. I think, too, that I'm not the only one who thinks so.

— Nicolas

You have hit on a good idea with *Superpuzzle*. I am through Chapter 12, I hope that you are planning on publishing this. I would like to be able to savor this as well as read it with my 16-year-old son. It is a great read that embodies your philosophy in a manner that can be understood by many.

— J. M.

I thoroughly enjoyed *Superpuzzle* about Miss Annabelle. I applaud you.

— Delores S.

Superpuzzle

Dear Mark Hamilton,
  I just read *Superpuzzle*. I am amazed.
  — Lazarus L.

  You know, after reading *Superpuzzle*, the more I see what is going on.
  — Mike C.

  Superpuzzle: I see ways of honestly dealing with the dishonest people, and some good ideas on how to help educate my own children. A little simpler than it seems sometimes.
  — Willy

  I was amazed at how so many of the things that Miss Annabelle was teaching the students were already integral to my thinking, but I'd never felt they would be welcomed by others.
  — Darna M.

  I Loved *Superpuzzle*; it has wonderful insight into our future.
  — Sandi S.

  Superpuzzle is Brilliant!! I have been reading your books for ten years but *Superpuzzle* makes it all clear.
  — Bill P.

  I enjoy the spiritually uplifting qualities of *Superpuzzle*.
  — David Wayne C.

  I'm in the process of reading *Superpuzzle*, and I feel everyone who reads it can benefit from it.
  — Gloria M.

  I am impressed by the content of *Superpuzzle*. I'm finding it inspirational.
  — Jim B.

  Superpuzzle is worth reading, Mark Hamilton proves to be a good storyteller. He makes good use of his ideas in his story. Only wish I had the book instead of having to read it off my computer screen.
  — Ed

1204

Beholding the Puzzle-Picture

Thank you so much for making *Superpuzzle* available on the Internet. I did have good teachers, but none like Miss Annabelle. I'm now 79 years old.

— Joy

I've just completed the second chapter of *Superpuzzle*, superb!

— C. E.

Mark — I thoroughly enjoyed Chapter One of *Superpuzzle* and look forward to reading the rest. Is it best to order from Borders? I love kids and I self-publish books for kids. Your subject matter was of special interest.

— Sue L.

I ENJOYED *SUPERPUZZLE*!!!!!!!!!!!!!!!!!!

— Herb C.

Superpuzzle is very well written and quite insightful.

— Vince G.

I like reading *Superpuzzle* as it helps to put the puzzle together. You have shown the way!

— Craig D.

Brilliant story.

— Red

I note the polite tact and extreme good manners of the main character. Too many people forget this sort of outward behavior. It can be very effective in dealing with those of poor character—a sort of political guerrilla people-handling tool.

— Steve R.

You should make *Superpuzzle* into a movie.

— A.P.

I love your story. I always knew reality was the key. Thanks for your great story.

— Julia R.

Superpuzzle

Did you like the New Civilization as described in *Superpuzzle*? Did you like that new life? Would you like for *Superpuzzle* to become real in this life? Would you like to experience happiness as described in *Superpuzzle*? Would you like to have more friends that understand *Superpuzzle* the way you do? Solution: Introduce more and more people you know to *Superpuzzle*. Get them *Superpuzzle*. Results will come. *Superpuzzle* is understood by people. Introduce *Superpuzzle*. It will work. I know.

— Jenny

Superpuzzle seems to reflect some very misunderstood notions regarding everyday life as we live it. The understanding of these differences could lead many to a new existence in their life. Very interesting and powerful!

— R. K.

I discovered *Superpuzzle* by Mark Hamilton. The story helped me into a better society.

— M. H.

I'm in the process of reading *Superpuzzle*, and I feel everyone who reads it can benefit from it.

— G. M.

I am in the middle of *Superpuzzle* right now, and I am thinking, this is what I have been searching for. I have explored almost everything else.

— C. W.

Superpuzzle is the best mind-opening experience. I thank you for all the valuable information.

— J. S.

Superpuzzle is needed by so many wonderful people. Read *Superpuzzle*, you will love it!

— R. J.

Superpuzzle is a sweet story and is reminiscent of realities we humans have suffered far too long with.

— M. D.

Beholding the Puzzle-Picture

Superpuzzle motivates me to think more responsibly about the Child within me. I find it invigorating. It was a warm reception of "childhood". ...Imagine what could be accomplished if we stopped beating our kids and started treating our kids as the special people they will soon become.

— P.

Somebody at work told me about this web site and told me to read *Superpuzzle*. What interested me at first was the concepts the teacher used to teach her children. I have a two-year old, and I want to help him. I purchased *Superpuzzle* and have found my calling.

— B. E.

I am now reading *Superpuzzle*...NOTHING LIKE IT!!!!!!!

— R. L.

Superpuzzle is really making sense. It was written on my level so that I can have a better understanding. Mark, you've done an outstanding job.

— P. L.

I have just been reading *Superpuzzle* which is a very powerful revelation into life.

— J. M.

Superpuzzle is brilliant. It has made life much more clear to me.

— B. P.

I've just read *Superpuzzle* and I've enjoyed it very much. Nevertheless, I wish it were available in a book instead of on line, so that it could be bought and offered to friends. Thanks very much for your integrated masterpiece.

— N. R.

Wow, *Superpuzzle* is *it*; where are these teachers? This ranks right up there with *The Fountainhead* and *Anthem*. I am honored to be reading it. Thank you.

— J. B.

Superpuzzle

Superpuzzle on the internet is mind-blowing!!

— A. A.

Two days ago I found *Superpuzzle* and have not been able to put it down. I only stopped today to send a note of thanks. *Thank you* for allowing me to see that my feelings were *not* wrong, as you have provided proof to the questions I have had all my 40 years.

— S. F.

After reading *Superpuzzle*, I was emotionally moved beyond words. If only all teachers could be like Miss Annabelle — what a world it would be.

— A. Z.

The story of Miss Annabelle had me glued to every word and made me cry.

— L. A.

Superpuzzle is so powerful I know my life is changing. I have affirmed that I shall live a life of total honesty with complete responsibility for self with integrity. It surely would be great if a movie was made of *Superpuzzle*.

— J. R.

Nothing has ever inspired me like this writing.

— P. J.

I'm reading *Superpuzzle* about Miss Annabelle's children. I'm fascinated! It seems I've been searching for this all my life.

— F. E.

This is one of the Greatest Books I have ever read; it's hard to put it down.

— C. P.

I find *Superpuzzle* very exciting and positive reading; only time stops me at the end of a chapter from finishing the entire book straight away.

— R. B.

Beholding the Puzzle-Picture

I absolutely love *Superpuzzle*. Truer words have never been spoken. I have challenged the school systems myself because of insecurities and power and control issues of principals, teachers, and, yes, guidance counselors. I have always known that the most valuable was the encouragement of children and to expand the minds of these little people who, without the blockers and blinders on, can make leaps and bounds in our future society. Thank you! You made my heart and soul soar like I was on the wings of an eagle!!!!

— D. S.

Mr. Hamilton, I am amazed by your work. It has opened my eyes and changed my life in so many ways. I am 17 years old and you have given me something to live for when before there was nothing. Thank you for your inspiration.

— T. W.

I found *Superpuzzle* very interesting to read, and you are really offering the "world" to people.

— E. R.

Thank you for your gift to mankind with your powerful and enlightening writing style in *Superpuzzle*. You are very intelligent and you write books better than Stephen King!

— Gerald M.

I love *Superpuzzle*: it is the most amazing, inspiring, and motivating piece of art I have ever encountered. It made me laugh, it made me cry, and it gave me a whole new perspective on life. I am a completely different person since I read *Superpuzzle* and I just want to say "thank you".

— B. J.

Hello. I just felt the strong need to write to you and tell you what an absolutely WONDERFUL experience I am having reading *Superpuzzle*! I must say it is the best reading that I have had the privilege to experience in a very long time. I am not even half way through it, but I became so excited that I HAD to write! I was sent this story from a man whom I love and respect deeply and very much, and he will never know how grateful I am that he was gracious enough

1209

Superpuzzle

to share this with me. He said that it moved him to tears several times. (That's when you KNOW it is good stuff!) I have to say that for me it is wonderful and frustrating at the same time, and I am sure I am going to experience a lot more of these feelings as I continue to read on. I just wanted to say Thank You, in advance, for such an absolutely fascinating and awesome story! It's the best!

— Cathy

Reading *Superpuzzle* last night and thinking it over, it reminds me of a delicate glass figurine arrested in a poise of clear-cut beauty and integrity.

When I think of it, it evokes a feeling of admiration and pleasure in me (and don't let Burke break it!)

Superpuzzle is an abstraction of basic life principles written in a simple language with a rhythm that has an immediate emotional effect on the reader summed up in a few sentences: This is good. This is right. I like it. This is how children must be treated. They must be drawn by beauty and example and directed to a purposeful life of value creation and happiness.

— E. F.

I have never been more excited than after reading *Superpuzzle*. I have my wife and sons reading it now. I introduced it to my mother who is introducing it to several of her friends and so on. I can now, for the first time, see.

— Phil

* * *